THE HISTORY OF FOUR-FOOTED BEASTS, SERPENTS, AND INSECTS

DESCRIBING AT LARGE THEIR TRUE AND LIVELY
FIGURE, THEIR SEVERAL NAMES, CONDITIONS, KINDS,
VIRTUES (BOTH NATURAL AND MEDICINAL),
COUNTRIES OF THEIR BREED, THEIR LOVE AND HATRED
TO MANKIND, AND THE WONDERFUL WORK OF GOD IN
THEIR CREATION, PRESERVATION, AND DESTRUCTION

EDWARD TOPSELL

VOLUME I OF III

Published by Left of Brain Books

Copyright © 2021 Left of Brain Books

ISBN 978-1-396-32075-0

First Edition

Table of Contents

TO THE RIGHT HONOURABLE THE LORD MARQUESSE OF DORCHESTER

EARL OF KINGSTONE, VICOUNT NEW ARKE, &C.

My very Noble LORD,

Your Lordship well knows that Honour attends upon Virtue, as the shadow doth upon the substance; there is such a magnetick force in Goodness, that it draws the hearts of men after it. The world observes that Your Honour is a great Lover of the works of Learned Writers, which is an infallible argument of an excellent mind residing in You. Wherefore I here humbly offer unto Your Noble Patronage the most Famous and Incomparable History of *CONRADUS GESNER*, a great Philosopher and Physitian, who by his vast expences, and indefatigable pains, Collected and Digested into two Volums, what ever he found scattered here and there in almost infinite Authors, concerning Fourfooted-Beasts and Serpents, adding also what he could possibly attain to by his own experience, and correspondence held with other famous Scholars every where. After him Mr. *Edward Topsel* a Learned Divine, Revised and Augmented the same History; as it is not altogether so difficult to add something to what is first begun, and to build upon such a foundation which was before so artificially laid. He hath deserved well of our English Nation in so doing; and the more, that he doth with so much modesty attribute the praise of the whole work to the Master-workman to whom it was chiefly due. The same *Gesner*, after Mr. *Edward Wotton* had begun, undertook to compose the History of Insects; which as it is a business of more curiosity and difficulty to write exactly of; so all things considered, they serve as much to set forth the Wisdom and Power of God as the greatest Creatures he hath made, and are as beneficial to Mankind, not only for dainty Food, but for the many Physical uses that arise from them. *John* Baptist fed upon Locusts and wilde Honey, and we read that our Saviour eat a piece of a Honey comb. These little *Insects* are not so contemptible as the World generally thinks they are, for they can do as much by their multitudes, as the other can by their magnitude, when as one Hornet shall be able suddenly to kill a Horse, and Gnats, Ants and Wasps to bid resistance to Bears, Lions and Elephants, and to depopulate whole

1

Countries. The Frogs, Locusts, and Lice, were none of the least Judgements in the Land of *Egypt*. Mr. *Thomas Pennius*, another Physitian, lighting his Candle by the former lights, succeeded them in this great undertaking. But all these vigilant and painful Men never could bring it to perfection, being every one of them prevented by death. And indeed, things of deep search, and high concernment, are very seldom begun and ended by the same persons. *Hippocrates* gives the reason for it, that Art is long, Life short, Experience difficult, occasion precipitate, Judgement uncertain. I may say farther, which he also comprehends in the close of that Aphorism, that all must perform their several offices; which is not often done, but ingenious men frequently labour under the want of means, and find small encouragement to proceed in their great designs, especially in this latter age of the World. *Gesner* makes a sad complaint in behalf of himself, and *Topsel* doth the like, and so do all the rest who spent their Estates, and wasted their Spirits for the common good. Which is sufficient proof to convince many rich men of blindness and ingratitude, and confirms that truth the Poet speaks;

> *Haud facilè emerguunt, quorum virtutibus obstat*
> *Res angusta domi* ——— ———

> *Good and well meaning men cannot proceed,*
> *Virtue is crusht by want, opprest by need.*

After the death of the forementioned four Worthies of their times, Mr. *Thomas Muffet* a noted *English* Physitian undertook the same task, and compleated it; whose Encomium is excellently well penned by the late Honourable Doctor of Physick Sir *Theodore Mayerne*, in his Epistle to Doctor *William Paddy* of famous memory, premised to this Book; wherein to his own immortal praise, he hath so Anatomically dissected many of the chiefest *Insects*, even to admiration, that he hath let the World understand by it, that he was a deep Philosopher, and a most accurate searcher into the secrets of Nature, and worthy of those places of Honour he enjoyed in Great Princes Courts. This large History is not, nor could possibly be the production of one Age; both able Divines, and Physitians contributed what they had, and employed their Talents, and greatest studies, for many years in their severall generations, to bring it forth; whereby it may appear how necessary this Work is for the souls and bodies of Men, to teach them to know the Wisdom and Omnipotence of God in the Creation of these Creatures, and Goodness to bestow them upon Man, both for profit and delight; and though many of them be Dangerous and

Venomous, yet they were not so when God first made them. For the *Wiseman* saith, *That God made not death, neither takes he pleasure in the destruction of the living, for he created all things that they mighe have their being, and the Generations of the World were healthful, and there was no poison of destruction in them, no Kingdom of death upon the earth, but ungodly men by their wicked works and words, called it to them.* This Book will plentifully furnish us with Remedies against most of these inconveniences, which is no small occasion to put us in mind how much we stand obliged to the memories of the learned Authours of it; who spared no cost nor pains that they might prove beneficial to the then present, and to succeeding Ages. And the same reason is very strong in behalf of those who now have been at this vast charge to Reprint and to perfect the same, that it never should be lost by time or casualties, which consume all things; and to supply the whole Work with a double Physical Index, to ease the Readers labour, that he might not wander up and down, and lose himself in this great wilderness of Beasts and Insects, searching after that he stands in need of, but may in an instant be provided with all those known remedies these several Creatures can afford him. Should such a Fabrique as this decay and come to ruine, the dammage were unspeakable and irreparable; the *Mausolean Sepulchre*, the Colossus of *Rhodes*, or the *Pyramids* of *Egypt* might sooner be renewed and built again. Wherefore Men are bound in conscience, by the Laws of God, of Nature, and of Nations, to consider of the great Expence and Pains now taken in it, and to promote the Work to the best advantage of the present undertakers for the publick good, who have now brought it to this perfection, that they may say of it, what *Ovid* did of his *Metamorphosis*;

> *Jamque opus exegi, quod nec Jovis ira, nec ignis,*
> *Nec poterit ferrum, nec edax abolere vetustas.*

> *The Work is ended, which can envies fume,*
> *Nor Sword, nor Fire, nor wasting time consume.*

Never was there so compleate a History of the Creatures as this is since the daies of *Solomon*, who writ the story of Beasts and Creeping things: and indeed it requires a Kingly Treasure and Understanding to accomplish it. And *Petrus Gillius* writes, that in former Ages, all the Histories of Creatures were compiled by Kings, or Dedicated to them; who are best able to bear the charge of it, and most fit be honoured with it. What would the World now give for that Book of *Solomons*, which by the negligence of ungrateful men and length of time is

3

utterly lost? How highly then ought we to esteem of this History of *Gesner* and *Muffet*, which is inferiour to none but that? For what *Aristotle* set forth upon this subject at the appointment of *Alexander* the Great, and for which he received from him 400 Talents as a Kingly reward, is all comprehended in this, with the addition of many hundreds more that have travelled in the same way. *Orpheus*, whom the Poets so much magnifie for drawing the Beasts after him, could do no more with all his melodious harmony, then these famous and ingenious Men have done. And because I cannot but think, what the Poets fancied concerning him, was but an Hieroglyphical representation (according to the dim light they had) of all the Creatures coming to *Noah* into the Ark, this History seems to me to be like another Ark of *Noah*, wherein the several kinds of beasts are once again met together, for their better preservation in the understanding of Man; & however there were multitudes of Birds in the Ark which are not here (it may be because *Aldrovandus* and others have written largely to that purpose) yet here are abundance of Insects that never were in *Noahs* Ark, and whereof we never had, or we can find extant, any compleate History untill this was made; which is like to another Paradise, where the Beasts, as they were brought to *Adam*, are again described by their Natures, and named in most Languages; which serves to make some reparation for the great loss of that excellent knowledge of the Creature, which our first Parents brought upon their posterity when they fell from God. We read in the *10th* of the *Acts*, that when a vessel was let down from heaven, wherein there were all manner of Fourfooted-Beasts and Creeping things, that St. *Peter* wondered at it: who then can choose but admire to see so many living Creatures that Nature hath divided and scattered in Woods, Mountains and Vallies, over the face of the whole earth, to come all together to a general muster, and to act their several parts in order upon the same Theater? I confess there are many Men so barbarous, that they make no account of this kind of learning, but think all charge and pains fruitless that is imployed this way; shewing themselves herein more unreasonable and brutish then the irrational Beasts. For next unto Man are these Creatures rankt in dignity, and they were ordained by God to live upon the same earth, and to be Fellow-commoners with Man; having all the Plants and Vegetables appointed them for their food as well as Man had; and have obtained one priviledge beyond us, in that they were created before Man was; and ever since they are obnoxious to the same casualties, and have the same coming into the World, and going out that we have; *For that which befals the Sons of Men befals Beasts, even one thing befals them both, as the one dyeth, so dyeth the other; so that Man hath no preeminence above the Beasts. All go unto one place, all are of the dust, and all return to dust again:* Eccles. *3, 19, 20.* And

4

the Prophet *David* doubts not to compare Man being in honour, and having no understanding, unto the Beasts that perish. As for Minerals, they are yet another degree below Beasts, all the Gold, Jewels, and Diamonds in the World, are not comparable to any one of the meanest Creatures that hath within it the breath of life. God hath bountifully bestowed them all on Man, whom he hath advanced above them all, for food, and raiment, and other necessary uses; also for his pleasure and recreation: and so long as we use them with Sobriety and Thankfulness, we shall finde an infinite benefit and advantage by them; but when we prove ungratefull unto God, they become so many Instruments of his vengeance against sinners, to make up that fourfold Judgement, with the Sword, Famine, and Pestilence, the Prophet threatens the Jews with. I fear to be tedious, therefore I beseech Your Honour to accept this History in good part from him who humbly prayeth for Your Lordships temporal and eternal happiness, and who is

Your Honours most affectionately
humble Servant
JOHN ROWLAND.

TO THE REVEREND AND RIGHT WORSHIPFUL *RICHARD NEILE*, D. OF DIVINITY

DEAN OF WESTMINSTER, MASTER OF THE SAVOY, AND CLERK OF THE KING HIS MOST EXCELLENT MAJESTIES CLOSET; ALL FELICITY TEMPORAL, SPIRITUAL, AND ETERNAL.

The Library of *English* Books, and Catalogue of Writers, (Right Worthy and Learned DEAN, my most respected PATRON) have grown to the height, not only of a just number, but almost innumerable: and no marvel, for God himself hath in all ages preserved Learning in the next place to Life; for as Life is the Ministerial Governor and Mover in this World, so is Learning the Ministerial Governor and Mover in Life: As an Interpreter in a strange Countrey is necessary for a Traveller that is ignorant of Languages (or else he should perish,) so is Knowledge and Learning to us poor Pilgrims in this our Perigrination, out of Paradise unto Paradise; whereby confused BABELS tongues are again reduced to their significant Dialects, not in the builders of BABEL to further and finish an earthly Tower, but in the builders of JERUSALEM, to bring them all to their own Countrey *which they seek*, and to the desired rest of souls. *Literæ obstetrices artium, quarum beneficio ab interitu vindicantur.* As Life is different and divers, according to the Spirit wherein it is seated, and by which it is nourished as with a current; so also is Learning, according to the tast, use, and practise of Rules, Canons, and Authors, from whom as from a Fountain it taketh both beginning and encrease: even as the spirit of a Serpent is much quicker then the spirit of an Ox; and the Learning of *Aristotle* and *Pliny* more lively and lightsome then the knowledge of other obscure Philosophers, unworthy to be named, which either through Envy or *Non-proficiencie* durst never write. *Si cum hac exceptione detur sapientia, ut illam inclusam teneam, nec enuntiem, rejiciam. Nullius boni sine socio jucunda est possessio.* And therefore I say with *Petrus Blesen: Scientiarum generosa possessio in plures dispersa, non perditur, & distributa per partes, minorationis detrimentum non sentit: sed eo diuturntus perpetuata senescit, quo publicata fœcundius se diffundit.*

The greatest men stored with all helps of Learning, Nature and Fortune, were the first Writers, who as they did excell other men in Possessions and

Worldly dignity, so they manifested their Virtues and Worth in the edition of excellent parts of knowledge, either for the delight or profit of the World, according to the Poets profession:

Aut prodesse volunt, aut delectare Poetæ,
Aut simul & jucunda & idonea dicere vitæ.
Omne tulit punctum, qui miscuit utile dulci,
Lectorem delectando, pariterque monendo.

Yet now of late daies this custom hath been almost discontinued to the infinite prejudice of sacred inviolable Learning and Science, for *Turpis sæpe fama datur minoribus,* (as *Ausonius* wrote in his time) for indeed the reason is pregnant:

Haud facile emergunt, quorum virtutibus obstat
Res angusta domi. ——— ———

But yet the great Rector and Chancellor of all the Academies in the World *Jesus Christ, in whom are hid all the treasures of wisdom and knowledge,* the Master of that Colledge wherein he was but a Servant or Steward, *that was learned in all the learning of the* Egyptians, (I mean *Moses*) the first writer, the first Author, the first commender of knowledge, and the first ordainer of a lawful Commonwealth, and Ruler of Church and State, hath not left our age without some monuments of great Princes, Earls, Lords, Knights, for the ornament and honour of Learning, who for general and particular causes and benefits have added their Names to the society of Writers, and divulged their works in Print, which are likely to be remembred till the Worlds end. Such are our most Temperate, Just, Wise, and Learned King and Soveraign. The Right Noble, and Honourable Earl of *Surry*, long ago departed out of this earthly *Horizon*. The now living Earls of *Dorset, Northampton, Salisbury*; and many Knights, Sir *Philip Sidney*, Sir *George Moore*, Sir *Richard Bartlet*, Sir *Francis Hastings*, and others. But of *Aarons*, and such as sit at the Helme of the Church, or are worthily advanced for their knowledge in Learning and State, I mean both Bishops and Doctors, almost innumerable, of all whom I can say no more, if I were worthy to say any thing, then apply unto them particularly that which was said of one of the greatest Scholars and Divines that ever *England* had:

——— ——— *Dic obsecro sancta*
Posteritas, nec enim mihi fas est dicere: tantum
De tantis tacitum, aut tantos audire juvabit.

7

Then why should I presume, being every way the least and meanest of all other, now the third time to publish any part of my conceived studies for the age present and succeeding, and so to have my Name inrolled amongst the benefactors and Authors of Learning?

——— ——— *Non omnia grandior ætas*
Quæ fugiamus habet; seris venit usus ab annis.

Alas Sir, I have never abounded in any thing, except want and labour, and I thank God that one of these hath been prepared to feed the other, therefore I will not stand upon any mans objections, who like Horses as it is in the Fable being led empty, well fed, and without burden, do scorn the laden Asse, adding misery to his load, till his back was broke, and then was all laid upon the pampred disdainful Horse: even so these proud displeasing spirits are eased by the labors of us that bear the burthens, and if they content not themselves with ease, but will also sit in the seat of the scornful, let them remember, that when our backs be broak, they must take up the carriage. But pardon me (I beseech you) if by way of Preface I open my heart unto your Worship, who is better able then ten thousand of the *Momus's,* and more charitably generous in receiving such gifts with the right hand (as these are) although they were given with the left; for seeing I have chosen you the Patron of this Work, I will briefly declare and open my mind unto you concerning the whole Volum, sparing any other praises of your demerits then those which by *Martial* are ascribed to *Regulus,* which I will without flattery or fear of the envious thus apply unto you:

Cum sit Sophiæ par fama & cura deorum,   [SSS. Trinitatis]
Ingenio pietas nec minor ipsa tuo.
Ignorat meritis dare munera, qui tibi librum
Et qui maratur [Neiile] Thura dari.

So then leaving these perorations, I will endevor to prove unto you that this Work which I now publish and divulge unto the world, under the Patronage of your Name, is Divine, and necessary for all men to know; True, and therefore without slander or suspicious scandall to be received; and that no man ought rather to publish this unto the World, then a Divine or Preacher. For the first, that the knowledge of Boasts, like as the knowledge of the other creatures and works of God, is Divine, I see no cause why any man should doubt thereof, seeing that at the first they were created and brought to man as we may read *Gen.* I. 24, 25. and all by the Lord himself, so that their Life and Creation is Divine in respect of their Maker; their naming Divine, in respect that *Adam* out of the plenty of his own divine wisdom, gave them their several appellations, as it were out of a fountain of Prophesie, foreshewing the nature of every kind in one elegant and significant denomination, which to the great losse of all his children was taken away, lost and confounded at *Babel*. When I affirm that the knowledge of Beasts is Divine, I do mean no other then the right and perfect description of their Names, Figures; and Natures, and this is in the Creator himself most Divine, and therefore such as is the Fountain, such are the streams issuing from the same into the minds of men. Now it is most clear in *Genesis* how the Holy Ghost remembreth the creation of all living creatures, and the Fourfooted next before the creation of Man, as though they alone were appointed the Ushers, going immediately before the race of Men. And therefore all the Divines observe both in the *Hebrew*, in the *Greek* and *Latin*, that they were created of three several sorts or kinds. The first *Jumentum*, as Oxen, Horse, Asses and such like, *Quia hominum juvamenta.* The second, *Reptile, quia hominum medicina.* The third, *Bestia, i. à vastando,* for that they were wilde and depopulators of other their associates, rising also against Man, after that by his fall he had lost his first image and integrity. Now were it not a knowledge Divine, why should the holy Scriptures relate it, and divide the kinds? Yea, why should all holy Men take examples from the natures of Beast, Birds, *&c.* and apply them to heavenly things, except by the ordinance of God they were both allowed and commanded so to do? and therefore in admiration of them the Prophet *David* cryeth our, *Quam magnifica sunt opera tua Domine! omnia in sapientia fecisti.* The old *Manichees* among other blasphemies accused the creation of hurtful, venomous, ravening, and destroying Beasts, affirming them to be made by an evil God, and also they accused the creation of Mice and other unprofitable creatures, because their dulness was no kinder to the Lord, but like cruel and covetous Misers, made no account of those Beasts, which brought not profit to their purse. You know (Right Learned Dean) how that grave Father answered that calumny, first affirming that the same thing which seemed idle to Men, was profitable to God; and the same that appeared ugly to them, was beautiful to him, *Qui omnibus utitur ad gubernationem universi.* He therefore wisely compareth a fool that knows not the use of the creatures in this world, to one ignorant that cometh into the workhouse of a cunning Man, viewing a number of strange tools, and having no cunning but in an Axe or a Rake, thinketh, that all those rare inventions of a wise workman are idle toies: and whilst thus he thinketh, wandring to and fro, not looking to his feet, suddenly falleth into some furnace in the same Work-house, or chance to take up some sharp tool whereby he is wounded, then he also thinketh that the same are hurtful and dangerous. *Quorum tamen usum quia novit artifex, insipientiam ejus irridet, & verba inepta non curans officinam suam constanter exercet*. But we that are ashamed to deny the use of instruments in the shops of rare Artisans, but rather admire their invention, yet are not afraid to condemn in Gods storehouse sundry of his creatures, which are rare inventions, although through folly we be wounded or harmed by them, and therefore he concludeth that all Beasts are either *utilia*, and against them we dare not speak; or *perniciosa*, whereby we are terrified that we should not love this perilous life; or else they are *superflua*, which to affirm were most ridiculous: for as in a great house all things are not for use, but some for ornament, so is it in this World, the inferiour Palace of God. *Thus far Austin*.

Therefore I will conclude this first part, that not only the knowledge of the profitable creature is divine, and was first of all taught by God, but also of the hurtful: *For a wise Man*, saith *Solomon, seeth the Plague* (by the revelation of God) *and hideth himself from it.* And *John Baptist, Quis ves docuit ab ira ventura fugere?* These things have I principally laboured in this Treatise, to shew unto Men what Beasts are their friends, and what their enemies, which to trust, and which avoid, in which to find nourishment, and which to shun as poison. Another thing that perswadeth me in the necessary use of this History, that it was divine, was the preservation of all creatures living, which are ingendred by copulation (except Fishes) in the Ark of *Noah*, unto whom it pleased the Creator at that time to insuse an instinct, and bring them home to man as to a fold: surely it was for that a man might gain out of them much Divine knowledge, such as is imprinted in them by nature, as a type or spark of that great wisdom whereby they were created. In Mice and Serpents a foreknowledge of things to come, in the Ant and Pismire a providence against old age: in the Bear the love of young; in the Lion his stately pace; in the Cock and Sheep, change of weather; as S. *Basil* in his *Hexameron, Etiam in Brutis quidem futuri sensus est, ut nos praesenti vitæ non addicti simus, sed de futuro saculo omne studium habemus.*

For this cause there were of beasts in holy Scripture three holy uses, one for Sacrifice, another in Vision, and a third for Reproof and Instruction.

In Sacrifices were the clean beasts, which Men were bound first to know, and then to offer; for it is unreasonable that those things should be sacred at the Lords altar, which are refused worthily at private mens Tables. Now although we have no use of Sacrificing of Beasts, *Nam sicut bruta pro peccatis immolabantur, ita jam vitia pro corporibus*; yet we have use of clean Beasts for food and nourishment, and therefore for the inriching of the minds and tables of men, it is necessary to know not only the liberty that we have to eat, but also the quality and nutriment of the Beast we eat, not for any Religion, but for health and corporal necessity. This point is also opened in this story, and the other of Sacrifice, wherein I have not omitted to speak of the Divine use of every Beast, both among the *Jews* and among the prophane *Gentiles*.

Now for the second holy use of Beasts in Visions, the Prophet *Daniels* Visions, and *Ezekiels*, and S. *Johns* in the *Revelation* do testifie of them, whereby the most Divines have observed how great Princes and Kingdoms after they have shaken off the practise of Justice and Piety, turn Tyrants and ravening Beasts. For so Man being in honour understandeth not, but becometh like the Beasts that perish, and so as *Dionysius* saith by Visions of Beasts, *Infima reducuntur pur media in suprema.* Now there were, as S. *Augustine* saith, three kinds of visions, *Sensibiles, intellectuales, & imaginariæ*: the first were most pregnant, because to the understanding and conceiving, a Man never lost his senses, and therefore God did suddenly create savage Beasts both of natural and extraordinary shapes, whereby he shewed to his servants the Prophets, the ruine or uprising of beastly States and Kingdoms. And not only thus, but also in heaven (as St. *John* saith) there are 4 Beasts ful of eyes before the throne of God; both which must needs magnifie the knowledge of these *Quadrupedes*; for seeing God hath used them as Sacraments or Mysteries to contain his will, (not only in monstrous treble-headed, or seven-horned shapes, but also) in pure, ordinary, natural limbs and members; how shall we be able to ghesse at the meaning in the secret, that do not understand the revealed? And what use can we make of the invisible part of that Sacrament, where we know not the meaning of the visible? Doth the Lord compare the Devil to a Lion; evill Judges to Bears; false Prophets to Wolves; secret and crafty persecutors to Foxes; open enemies in hostility to wilde Boars; Hereticks and false Preachers to Scorpions; good men to the Fowles of heaven, and Martyrs to Sheep, and yet we have no knowledge of the natures of Lions, Wolves, Bears, Foxes, wilde Boars, or Scorpions? Surely when *Solomon* saith to the sluggard, Go to the Pismire, he willeth him to learn the nature of the Pismire, and then according thereto reform his manners: And so all the World are bid to learn the natures of all Beasts, for there is alway something to be learned in them, according to this saying of St. *Basil, A deo nibil non providum in natura rebus est, neque quicquam pertinentis ad secura expert, & si ipsas animalium partes consideraveris, inventes quod ineque superstuum quid conditor opposuit, neque necessaria detraxit.* Then it being clear that every Beast is a natural Vision, which we ought to see and understand, for the more clear apprehension of the

11

invisible Majesty of God, I will conclude that I have not omitted this part of the use of Beasts, but have collected, expressed, and declared, what the Writers of all ages have herein observed.

Now the third and last holy use that is made of Beasts in Scripture, is for Reproof and Instruction; so the Lord in *Job* 38, & 39. mentioneth the Lion, the Raven, the wilde Goats, the Hinds, the Hind-Calves, the wilde Asses, the Unicorn, the Ostrich, the Stork, the puissant Horse, the Hawke, the Eagle, the Vulture, the Whale, and the Dragon, that is, the Fowles, Fishes, Serpents, and Four-footed Beasts: All which he reckoneth as known things to *Job*, and discourseth of as strange things in their natures as any we have inserted for truth in our History, as may appear to any man whatsoever, that will look studiously into them.

Shall I add hereunto how *Moses*, and all the Prophets, St. *John Baptist*, our most blessed Saviour, St. *Paul*, and all the Writers since his time (both ancient and later) have made profession of this part of Divinity; so that he was an unskilful Divine and not apt to teach, which could not at his fingers speak of these things: for (saith our Saviour) *If I tell you earthly things and ye believe not, how shall ye believe when I tell you heavenly things*?

Solomon, as it is witnessed in holy Scripture, wrote of Plants, of Birds, of Fishes, and Beasts, and even then when he stood in good favour with God, therefore it is an exercise of the highest Wisdom to travel in, and the Noblest minds to study in: for in it as I will shew you (with your good patience, for I have no other Preface) there is both the knowledge of God and Man. If any man object, *Multa multi de musca, de apicula, de vermiculo, pauca de Deo*: I will answer with the words of *Theodorus Gaza*, *Permulta enim de Deo is tractat, qui doctrina rerum conditarum exquisitissima, conditorem ipsum declarat, neque musca, neque vermiculus omittendus est ubi de mira solertia agitur*. Whereunto St. *Austin* agreeth when he saith, *Majestatem divinam æque in formicæ membris atque magno jamento tranante fluvium*. And for the knowledge of man, many and most excellent rules for publick and private affaires, both for preserving a good conscience, and avoiding an evill danger, are gathered from Beasts: It were too long to run over all, let me (I beseech you) be bold to reckon a few which descend from Nature our common parent, and therefore are neither strained, counterfeit, inconstant, or deceitful; but free, full of power to perswade, true, having the seal of the Highest for their evidence; constant and never altred in any age; faithful, such as have been tryed at fire and touch-stone.

Were not this a good perswasion against murder, to see all Beasts so to maintain their natures, that they kill not their own kind? Who is so unnatural and unthankful to his Parents, but by reading how the young *Storkes* and *Wood-peckers* do in their parents old age feed and nourish them, will not repent, amend his folly, and be more natural? What man is so void of compassion, that hearing the bounty of the *Bone-breaker Bird* to the young *Eagles*, will not become more liberal? Where is there such a sluggard and drone, that considereth the labours, pains, and travels of the Emmet, little Bee, Field-mouse, Squirrel, and such other that will not learn for shame to be more industrious, and set his fingers to work? Why should any man living fall to do evill against his Conscience, or at the temptation of the Devill, seeing a Lion will never yeeld? *Mori scit, vinci nescit*; and seeing the little *Wren* doth fight with an *Eagle*, contending for Soveraingty? Would it not make all men to reverence a good King set over them by God, seeing the Bees seek out their King if he lose himself, and by a most sagacious smelling sense, never cease till he be found out, and then bear him upon their bodies if he be not able to flie, but if he die they all forsake him? And what King is not invited to clemency, and dehorted from tyranny, seeing the King of Bees hath a sting, but never useth the same?

How great is the love & faithfulness of Dogs, the meekness of Elephants, the modesty or shamefastness of the adulterous Lioness, the neatness and politure of the Cat and Peacock, the justice of the Bee, which gathereth from all flowers that which serveth their turn, and yet destroyeth not the flower; the care of the Nightingale to make her voice pleasant, the chastity of a Turtle, the canonical voice and watchfulness of a Cock, and to conclude, the utility of a Sheep? All these and ten thousand more I could recite, to shew what the knowledge of the nature of brutish creatures doth work or teach the minds of men; but I will conclude this part with the words of S. *Jerom* against *Jovinian*. *Ad Herodem dicitur propter malitiam, Ite & dicite vulpi huic*, Luk. 13. *ad Scribas & Pharisæos genimina viperarum*, Mat. 23. *ad libidinosos equi hinmentes in proximorum faminas*, Jer. 5. *de voluptuoso, Nolite mittere margaritas vestras ante porcos. De impudentibus, neque sanctum date canibus*, Mat. 7. *de infidelibus, Ephesi cum bestiis pugnavi in similitudine hominum*. And thus far S. *Jerom*. Whereby we may boldly aver by way of induction, that wherein the knowledge of God, the knowledge of Man, the precepts of Virtue, the means to avoid evill are to be learned, that Science is Divine and ought of all men to be inquired and sought after: and such have I manifested in this History following.

Now again the necessity of this History is to be preferred before the Chronicles and Records of all ages made by Men, because the events and accidents of the time past, are peradventure such things as shall never again come in use; but this sheweth that Chronicle which was made by God himself, every living Beast being a word, every Kind being a sentence, and all of them together a large History, containing admirable knowledge and learning, which was, which is, which shall continue, (if not for ever) yet to the Worlds end.

Et patris, & nostras, nonumque prematur in annum,
Membranis intus positis delere licebit
Quod non edideris —— ——

The second thing in this discourse which I have promised to affirm, is the truth of the History of Creatures, for the mark of a good Writer is to follow truth and not deceivable Fables. And in this kind I have passed the straightest passage, because the relation of most things in this Book are taken out of Heathen writers, such as peradventure are many times superstitiously credulous, and have added of their own very many rash inventions, without reason, authority, or probability, as if they had been hired to sell such Fables: For, *Non bene conducti vendunt perjuria testes.* I would not have the Reader of these Histories to imagine that I have inserted or related all that ever is said of these Beasts, but only so much as is said by many, *For in the mouth of two or three witnesses standeth every word*: and if at any time I have set down a single Testimony, it was because the matter was clear and needeth not farther probation, or else I have laid it upon the Author with special words, not giving the Reader any warrant from me to believe it.

Besides, I have taken regard to imitate the best Writers, which was easie for me to do, because *Gesner* relateth every mans opinion (like a common place or *Dictionary*, as he professeth;) and if at any time he seemed obscure, I turned to the Books which I had at hand to ghesse their meaning, putting in that which he had left out of many good Authors, and leaving out many magical devises. Now although I have used no small diligence or care in collecting those things which were most essential to every Beast, most true without exception, and most evident by the Testimony of many good Authors; yet I have delivered in this Treatise many strange and rare things, not as Fictions, but Miracles of nature, for wisemen to behold and observe to their singular comfort, if they love the power, glory, and praise of their maker, not withholding their consent to the things expressed, because they intreat of living things made by God himself. *Si ergo quærimus quis fecerit, Deus est: Si per quod, dixit, Fiat, & facta sunt: Si quare fiat, quia bonus est. Nec enim autor est excellentior Deo, nec ars efficacior Dei verbo, nec causa melior, quam ut bonum crearetur a Deo beno*; and this *Plato* said was the only cause of the worlds creation, *ut a Deo bono opera bona fierent.*

Now I do in a sort challenge a consent unto the probability of these things to wise and learned men, although no belief. For *Fides*, is *credere invisibilia*; but *consensus* is a cleaving or yeelding to a relation untill the manifestation of another truth; and when any man shall justly reprove any thing I have written for false and erroneous, I will not stick to release the Readers consent, but make satisfact on for usurpation. But for the rude and vulgar sort (who being utterly ignorant of the operation of Learning, do presently condemn all strange things wch are not ingraven in the palms of their own hands, or evident in their own herds and flocks) I care not, for my ears have heard some of them speak against the History of *Sampson*, where he tied fire-brands to the tails of Foxes, and many of them against the miracles of Christ. I may remember you (*R. W.*) of a Countrey tale of an old Masse-Priest in the daies of *Henry* the eight, who reading in *English* after the translation of the Bible, the miracles of the five Loaves and two Fishes, and when he came to the verse that reckoneth the number of the ghests or eaters of the banquet, he paused a little, and at last said, they were about five hundred: The *Clerk*, that was a little wiser, whispered into the Priests ears that it was *five thousand*, but the Priest turned back and replyed with indignation, *Hold your peace sirrah, we shall never make them believe they were five hundred.*

Such Priests, such People, such persons I shall draw upon my back, and although I do not challenge a power of not erring, yet because I speak of the power of God, that is unlimitable, I will be bold to aver that for truth in the Book of Creatures (although first observed by Heathen men) which is not contrary to the book of Scriptures.

Lastly, that it is the proper office of a Preacher or Divine to set forth these works of God, I think no wiseman will make question, for so did *Moses*, and *David*, and *Solomon*, and *Christ*, and S. *Paul*, and S. *John*, and S. *Ireney*, S. *Gregory*, S. *Basil*, S. *Austin*, S. *Jerom*, S. *Bernard* in his enarrations or Sermons upon the Canticles, and of latter daies *Isidorus*; The Monks of *Messuen*, *Geminianus*, and to conclude, that ornament of our time *Jeronimus Zanchius*. For how shall we be able to speak the whole Counsel of God unto his people, if we read unto them but one of his books, when he hath another in the world, which we never study past the title or outside; although the great God have made them an Epistle Dedicatory to the whole race of Mankind?

This is my indevour and pains in this Book, that I might profit and delight the Reader, whereinto he may look on the Holiest daies, (not omitting prayer and the publick service of God) and passe away the Sabbaths in heavenly meditations upon earthly creatures. I have followed *D. Gesner* as neer as I could, I do profess him my Author in most of my Stories, yet I have gathered up that which he let fall, and added many Pictures and Stories as may appear by Conference of both together. In the names of the Beasts, and the Physick I have not swarved from him at all. He was a Protestant Physician, (a rare thing to finde any Religion in a Physitian) although St. *Luke* a Physician were a writer of the Gospell. His praises therefore shall remain, and all living Creatures shall witnesse for him at the last day. This my labor whatsoever it be, I consecrate to the benefit of all our *English* Nation under your Name and Patronage, a publick Professor, a learned and reverend Divine, a famous Preacher, observed in Court and Countrey; if you will vouchsafe to allow of my Labors, I stand not upon others, and if it have your commendation, it shall incourage me to proceed to the residue, wherein I fear no impediment but ability to carry out the charge, my case so standing that I have not any accesse of maintenance, but by voluntary benevolence for personal pains, receiving no more but a laborious wages, and but for you, that had also been taken from me: Therefore I conclude with the words of St. *Gregory* to *Leontius, Et nos bona quæ de vobis multipliciter praedicantur addiscentes, assidue pro gloria vestræ incolumitate omnipotentem valeamus Dominum deprecari.*

Your Chaplain in the Church of
St. *Botolph Aldersgate*,
EDWARD TOPSELL.

THE HISTORY OF FOUR-FOOTED BEASTS

THE ANTALOPE.

THE *Antalope* called in Latin *Calopus*, and of the Grecians *Analopos*, or *Aptolos*: of this beast there is no mention made among the Ancient Writers, except *Suidas*, and the Epistle of *Alexander* to *Aristotle*, interpreted by *Cornelius Nepotius*. They are bred in *India* and *Syria*, neer the River *Euphrates*, and delight much to drink of the cold water thereof: Their body is like the body of a *Roe*, and they have horns growing forth of the crown of their head, which are very long and sharp; so that *Alexander* affirmed they pierced through the shields of his Souldiers, and fought with them very irefully: at which time his company slew as he travelled to *India*, eight thousand five hundred and fifty; which great slaughter may be the occasion why they are so rare, and seldom seen to this day, because thereby the breeders and means of their continuance (which consisted in their multitude) were weakned and destroyed. Their horns are great and made like a saw, and they with them can cut asunder the branches of Osier or small trees, whereby it cometh to passe that many times their necks are taken in the twists of the falling boughs, whereat the Beast with repining cry, bewrayeth himself to the Hunters, and so is taken. The virtues of this Beast is unknown, and therefore *Suidas* saith, an *Antalope* is but good in part.

OF THE APE.

AN *Ape* called in Latin *Simia*, and sometimes *Simius* and *Simiolus*; of the Greek word *Simos* (*viz.*) signifying the flatnesse of the Nostrils: for so are an Apes: and called of the Hebrews *Koph*, and plurally *Kophim*; as it is by S. *Jerom* translated, 1 King. 10. 22. From whence it may be probably conjectured, came the Latin words *Cepi* and *Cephi*, for Apes that have tails. Sometimes they are called of the Hebrews *Boglah*, and of the *Chaldees Kokin*. The *Italians Saniada Majonio*, and *Bertuccia*, and a Munkey *Gatto Maimone*. The ancient Grecians *Pithecos* and the later

Mimon, and *Ark bizanes*, by reason of his imitation. The Moors *Bugia*, the Spaniards *Mona*, or *Ximio*, the French *Singe*, the Germanes *Aff*, the Flemish *Simme* or *Schimmekell*, the Illyrians *Opicze*, and generally they are held for a subtill, ironicall, ridiculous and unprofitable Beast, whose flesh is not good for meat, as a sheep, neither his back for burden, as an Asses; nor yet commodious to keep a house, like a Dog; but of the Grecians termed *Gelotopoios*, made for laughter.

[1]*Anacharsis* the Philosopher, being at a banquet wherein divers Jesters were brought in to make them merry, yet never laughed, among the residue; at length was brought in an Ape, at the sight whereof he laughed heartily; and being demanded the cause why he laughed not before, answered, that men do but faign merriments, whereas Apes are naturally made for that purpose. Moreover Apes are much given to imitation and derision, and they are called *Cercopes*, because of their wicked wasts, deceits, impostures and flatteries: wherefore of the Poets it is faigned, that there were two brethren most wicked fellows, that were turned into Apes, and from their seat or habitation came the *Pithecusan* Islands, which *Virgil* calleth *Inarime*: for *Arime* was an old *Hetrurian* word for an Ape, and those Islands being the seats of the[2] Giants (who being by God overthrown for their wickedness) in derision of them, Apes were planted in their rooms. Apes have been taught to leap, sing, drive Wagons, reigning and whipping the horses very artificially, and are very capable of all humane actions, having an excellent memory either to shew love to his friends, or hateful revenge to them that have harmed him, but the saying is good, that the threatning of a flatterer, and the anger of an Ape, are both alike regarded. It delighteth much in the company of Dogs and young Children, yet it will strangle young Children if they be not well looked unto. A certain Ape seeing a Woman washing her Child in a bason of warm water, observed her diligently, and getting into the house when the Nurse was gone, took the Child out of the cradle, and setting water on the fire, when it was hot, stripped the Child naked, and washed the Child therewith untill it killed it.

---

[1] *Athenæus.*

[2] *Varinus.*

19

The Countreys where Apes are found, are *Lybia* and all that desert Woods betwixt *Egypt*, *Æthiopia* and *Lybia*, and that part of *Caucasus* which reacheth to the red Sea. In *India* they are most abundant, both red, black, green, dust-colour, and white ones, which they use to bring into Cities (except red ones, who are so venereous that they will ravish their Women) and present to their Kings, which grow so tame, that they go up and down the streets so boldly and civilly, as if they were Children, frequenting the Market places without any offence: whereof so many shewed themselves to *Alexander* standing upright, that he deemed them at first to be an Army of enemies, and commanded to joyn battel with them, untill he was certified by *Taxilus* a King of that Countrey then in his Campe, they were but Apes.

In *Caucasus* there are trees of Pepper and Spices whereof Apes are the gatherers, living among those trees: for the Inhabitants come, and under the trees make plain a plat of ground, and afterward cast thereupon boughs and branches of Pepper, and other fruits, as it were carelesly; which the Apes secretly observing, in the night season, they gather together in great abundance all the branches loaden with Pepper, and lay them on heaps upon that plat of ground, and so in the morning come the *Indians* and gather the Pepper from those boughs in great measure, reaping no small advantage by the labor of Apes, who gather their fruits for them whiles they sleep: for which cause they love them and defend them from Lions, Dogs, and other wild Beasts. In the region of *Basman*, subject to the great *Cham* of *Tartaria*, are many and divers sorts of Apes, very like mankind, which when the Hunters take, they pull of their hairs all but the beard and the hole behind, and afterward dry them with hot spices, and poudering them, sell them to Merchants, who carry them about the world, perswading simple people that there are men in Islands of no greater stature. To conclude, there are Apes in *Troglodytæ* which are maned about the neck like Lions, as big as great Bel-weathers. So are some called *Cercopitheci*, *Munkies*, *Chæropitheci*, *Hog Apes*, *Cepi*, *Callitriches*, *Marmosits*, *Cynocephali*, of a Dog and an Ape, *Satyres*, and *Sphinges*, of which we will speak in order, for they are not all alike, but some resemble men one way, and some another: as for a *Chymæra*, which *Albertus* maketh an Ape, it is but a figment of the Poets. The same man maketh *Pigmeys* a kind of Apes, and not men, but *Niphus* proveth that they are not men, because they have no perfect use of Reason, no modesty, no honesty, nor justice of government, and although they speak, yet is their language imperfect; and above all they cannot be men, because they have no Religion, which (*Plato* saith truly) is proper to every man. Besides, their stature being not past three, four, or five spans long, their life not above eight years, and their imitation of man, do plainly prove them rather to be Apes then Men: and also the flatness of their Noses, their combats with Cranes and Partridges for their egges, and other circumstances I will not stand upon, but follow the description of Apes in general. Apes do outwardly resemble men very much, and *Vesalius* sheweth, that their proportion differeth from mans in more things then *Galen* observed, as in the muscles of the breast, and those that move the armes, the elbow and the ham, likewise in the inward frame of the hand, in the muscles moving the toes of the feet, and the feet and shoulders, and in the instrument moving in the sole of the foot, also in the fundament and mesentery, the lap of the liver, and the hollow vein holding it up, which men have not; yet in their face, nostrils, ears, eye-lids, breasts, armes, thumbes, fingers and nails, they agree very much. Their hair is very harsh and short, and therefore hairy in the upper part like men, and in the neather part like beasts: they have teeth before and behind like men, having a round face, and eye-lids above and beneath, which other *Quadrupedes* have not. *Politianus* saith, that the face of a Bull or Lion is more comely then the face of an Ape, which is like a mans. They have two Dugs, their breasts and armes like men, but rougher, such as they use to bend, as a man doth his foot. So their hands, fingers and nails, are like a mans, but ruder and nimbler; and nature having placed their Dugs in their breast, gave them armes to lift their young ones up to suck them. Their feet are proper, and not like mans, having the middle one longest, for they are like great hands, and consist of fingers like hands, but they are alike in bigness, except that which is least to a man, is greatest to an Ape, whose sole is like the hand but that it is longer, and in the hinder part it is more fleshy, somewhat resembling a heel, but put backward it is like a fist.

21

They use their feet both for going and handling; the neather parts of their armes, and their thighes are shorter then the proportion of their elbows and shins: they have no Navel, but there is a hard thing in that place; the upper part of their body is far greater then the neather, like other *Quadrupedes*, consisting of a *proportion between five and three*: by reason wereof they grow out of kind, having feet like hands and feet. They live more downward then upward, like other four-footed Beasts, and they want Buttocks, (although *Albertus* saith they have large ones) they have no tail, like two legged creatures, or a very small signe thereof. The genitall or privy place of the female is like a Womans, but the Males is like a Dogs: their nourishment goeth more forward then backward, like the best Horses, and the *Arabian Seraph*, which are higher before then behind; and that Ape whose meat goeth forward by reason of the heat of heart and liver, is most like to a man, in standing upright: their eyes are hollow, and that thing in men is accounted for a signe of a malicious mind, as little eyes are a token of a base and abject spirit. Men that have low and flat Nostrils are Libidinous as Apes that attempt women, and having thick lips, the upper hanging over the neather, they are deemed fools, like the lips of Asses and Apes. *Albertus* saith, he saw the heart of a Male Ape, having two tops or sharpe ends, which I know not whether to term a wonder or a Monster. An Ape and a Cat have a small back, and so hath a weak hearted man, a broad and strong back signifieth a valiant and magnanimous mind. The Apes nails are half round, and when they are in copulation, they bend their Elbowes before them, the sinews of their hinder joynts being turned clean about, but with a man it is clean otherwise. The veins of their armes are no otherwise dissected then a mans, having a very small and ridiculous crooked thumb, by reason of the Muscles which come out of the hinder part of the leg, into the middle of the shin, and the fore muscles drawing the leg backward, they cannot exactly stand upright, and therefore they run and stand, like a man that counterfeits a lame mans halting.

And as the body of an Ape is ridiculous, by reason of an indecent likeness and imitation of man, so is his soul or spirit; for they are kept only in rich mens houses to sport withall, being for that cause easily tamed, following every action he seeth done, even to his own harme without discretion. A certain Ape after a shipwrack swimming to land, was seen by a Countrey-man, and thinking him to be a man in the water, gave him his hand to save him, yet in the mean time asked him what Countreyman he was, who answered, he was an *Athenian*: well, said the man, dost thou know *Piræus*? (which was a port in *Athens*) very well said the Ape, and his wife, friends, and children, whereat the man being moved, did what he could to drown him. They keep for the most part in Caves and hollow places of hils, in rocks and trees, feeding upon Apples and Nuts, but if they find any bitterness in the shell, they cast all away. They eat Lice, and pick them out of heads and garments. They will drink wine till they be drunk, but if they drink it oft, they grow not great, specially they lose their nails, as other *Quadrupedes* do. They are best contented to sit aloft, although tied with chains. They are taken by laying for them shoos and other things, for they which hunt them will anoint their eyes with water in their presence, and so departing, leave a pot of lime or hony in stead of the water, which the Ape espying, cometh and anointeth her eyes therewith, and so being not able to see, doth the hunter take her. If they lay shoos, they are leaden ones, too heavy for them to wear, wherein are made such devises of gins, that when once the Ape hath put them on, they cannot be gotten off without the help of man: So likewise for little bags made like breeches, wherewithal they are deceived and taken. They bring forth young ones for the most part by twins, whereof they love the one and hate the other; that which they love they bear in their armes, the other hangeth at the damns back, and for the most part she killeth that which she loveth, by pressing it too hard; afterward she setteth her whole delight upon the other.

The *Egyptians* when they describe a Father leaving his inheritance to his Son that he loveth not picture an Ape with her young one upon her back. The male and female abide with the young one, and if it want any thing, the male with fist, and ireful aspect punisheth the female. When the Moon is in the wane, they are heavie and sorrowful, which in that kind have tails; but they leap and rejoyce at the change: for as other Beasts, so do these, fear the defect of the Stars and Planets. They are full of dissimulation, and imitation of man, they readilyer follow the evill then the good they see. They are very fierce by nature, and yet tamed forget it, but still remain subject to madness. They love Conies very tenderly, for in *England* an old Ape (scarse able to go) did defend tame Conies from the Weasel, as Sir *Thomas More* reported. They fear a shell fish and a Snail very greatly, as appeareth by this History.

In *Rome*, a certain Boy put a Snail in his hat and came to an Ape, who as he was accustomed, leaps upon his shoulder and took off his hat to kill Lice in his head, but espying the Snail, it was a wonder to see with what haste the Ape leaped from the Boys shoulder, and in trembling manner looked back to see if the Snail followed him. Also when a Snail was tied to the one end of another Apes chain, so that he could not chuse but continually look upon it, one cannot imagine how the Ape was tormented therewith, finding no means to get from it, cast up whatsoever was in his stomach, and fell into a grievous Fever till it was removed from the Snail, and refreshed with wine and water. *Cardane* reporteth, that it was an ancient custom in former time when a Parricide was executed, he was (after he was whipped with bloudy stripes) put into a sack, with a live Serpent, a Dog, an Ape and a Cock: by the Serpent was signified his extreme malice to mankind in killing his Father, by the Ape that in the likeness of man he was a Beast, by the Dog how like a Dog he spared none, no not his own Father, and by a Cock his hateful pride, and then were they all together hurl'd headlong into the Sea. That he might be deemed unworthy of all the Elements of life, and other blessings of nature.

A Lion ruleth the Beasts of the Earth, and a Dolphin the Beasts of the Sea; when the Dolphin is in age and sickness, she recovereth by eating a Sea-ape: and so the Lion by eating an Ape of the earth, and therefore the *Egyptians* paint a Lion eating an Ape, to signifie a sick man curing himself. The heart of an Ape sod and dryed, whereof the weight of a groat drunk in a draught of stale Hony, sod in water, called *Melicraton*, strengthneth the heart, emboldneth it, and driveth away the pulse and pusillanimity thereof: sharpeneth ones understanding, and is soveraign against the falling evill.

THE MUNKEY.

THE *Munkey* called in Greek *Cercopithecos*, and so in Latin *Cercopithecus*, that is, a tailed Ape: not to distinguish it from all other Apes, but from other vulgar and common Apes, for there be Apes with tails besides a Munkey, but not so often seen. It is thought of some that the Hebrew *Ziim*, signifieth a Munkey, other *Ochim*. Isa. 13. *Babel shal be destroyed, and the fearful beast Ziim shal lie there, and Ochim shal fill their houses.* Which *Ochim*, is interpreted Munkeys, but not generally; wherefore there is an opinion that this kind of Ape is generated of a wild Cat very like an Ape, and an Ape having two black spots on the cheeks, a long tail, and black at the end thereof, it is called of the Italians *Gatto maimone*, of the French *Marmot* of *Marmona*, that is, the Ape of a male, for *Mona* signifieth an Ape, of the Germans *Meerkatz*, that is the Cat of the Sea, of the Illyrian, *Morska*, and *Koczka*; as for *Mammonet*, it is a beast lesse then an Ape; of the Celts it is called *Abranas*. They are very sportful, and given to imitate the actions of men like Apes, it being a question, whether Dogs, Elephants, or Munkeys, have the most understanding among Brutes, and as was said before, when the Moon waneth, it is heavie and dull, but in the new Moon joccond and pleasant.

Betwixt the *Mammonets* and Apes is continuall war, and the *Mammonet* being the weaker, yet the wiser and craftier creature, is much more couragious in fight then an Ape. These Munkeys of all things most abhor a *Crocodile*, for at the sight of the skin afar off, it hath been seen how the creature hath run through fire and water, crying and trembling for the naturall dread thereof.

They are bred in the hils of *Constance*, in the woods of *Bugia* and *Mauritania*. In *Æthiopia*, they have black heads, hair like Asses, and voices like to other. In *India* they report that the Munkeys will clime the most steep and high rocks, and fling stones at them that prosecute to take them. When the King of *Ioga* in *India* for Religion goeth on Pilgrimage, he carryeth with him very many Munkeys. In like sort, Munkeys are brought from the new found Lands, from *Calechut* and *Prusia*; and not far from *Aden* a City of *Arabia*, is a most high hill abounding in these beasts, who are a great hinderance to the poor vintagers of the Countrey of *Calechut*, for they will climb into the high Palm trees, and breaking the vessels set to receive the Wine, pour forth that liquor they find in them: they will eat hearbs and grain, and ears of grasse, going together in great flocks, whereof one ever watcheth at the utmost bounds of their camp, that he may cry out when the husbandman cometh, and then all flying and leaping into the next trees escape away: the females carry their young ones about with them on their shoulders, and with that burden leap from tree to tree.

There be of this kind of Munkeys two sorts, one greater, the other lesser, as is accounted in *England*, and Munkeys are in like sort so divided, that there be in all four kinds differing in bigness, whereof the least is little bigger then a Squirrel, and because of their marvellous and divers mowings, movings, voices and gestures, the Englishmen call any man using such Histrionical Actours a Munkey.

The only difference betwixt these and other Apes aforesaid, is their tail; they differ from men in their nerves, in the joints of their loynes, and their processes, and they want the third muscle moving the fingers of their hands. *Mammonets* are lesse then an Ape, brown on the back, and white on the belly, having a long and hairy tail, his neck almost so big as his body, for which cause they are tied by the hips that they slip not collar. They have a round head, a face like a man, but black and bald on the crown, his nose in a reasonable distance from his mouth like a mans, and not continued like an Apes, his stones greenish blew, like a Turkey stone. They are caught after the manner of Apes, and being tamed and taught, they conceive and work very admirable feats, and their skins pulled off them being dead are dressed for garments. The foolish *Arabians* dedicated *Memnonius cercopithecus* unto heaven, and in all afflictions implored his aid. There is one other kind of Munkeys, whose tail is only hairy at the tip, called *Cercolipis*.

THE CEPUS, OR MARTINE MUNKEY.

THE *Martin* called *Cepus* of the Greek word, *Kepos*, which *Aristotle* writeth *Kebos*, and some translate *Cæbus*, some *Cephus* or *Cepphus* or more barbarously *Celphus*, the Latines sometimes *Ortus*, for indeed this kind of Ape in his best estate is like[3] a garden set with divers flowers, and therefore the best kind of them is discerned and known by the sweetest

---

[3] *Dioderus Siculus.*

27

favour, such being alwayes the most ingenious imitators of men. It is very probable that this name *Cepus* is derived of the *Hebrew Koph* and *Kophin* signifying Apes in general, as is before said, but yet this kind is distinguished from other by *Strabo*, *Ælianus* and *Pliny*, although *Aristotle* doth make no difference betwixt this and another ordinary Munkey.

The games of great *Pompey* first of all brought these *Martines* to the sight of the *Romans*, and afterward *Rome* saw no more; they are the same which are brought out of *Æthiopia* and the farthest *Arabia*; their feet and knees being like a mans, and their forefeet like hands, their inward parts like a mans, so that some have doubted what kind of creature this should be, which is in part a man, and yet a Four-footed beast: it having a face like a Lion, and some part of the body like a Panther, being as big as a wilde Goat or Roe-buck, or as one of the Dogs of *Erithrea*, and a long tail, the which such of them as have tasted flesh wil eat from their own bodies. Concerning their colour, howsoever they are not all alike, for some are black with white spots, having a greater voice then others, some yellow, some Lion-tauny, some golden-yellow, and some cole-black: yet for the most part, the head and back parts to the tail, are of a fiery colour, with some golden hair aspersed among the residue, a white snowt, and certain golden strakes like a collar going about the neck, the inferiour parts of the neck down to the breast, and the forefeet are white, their two dugs as big as a mans hand can gripe, are of a blewish colour, and their belly white, their hinder legs black, and the shape of their snout like a *Cynochephale*: which may be the difference betwixt *Ælianus* and *Strabo* their *Cepus*, and *Aristotles Cebus*, for nature many times bringeth forth-like beasts which are not of the same kind. In *England* there was a *Martine* that had his back and sides of a green colour, having here and there white hair, the belly, chin and beard (which was round) white, the face and shins black, and the nose white, being of the lesser kind, for in bigness it exceeded not a Coney. Some of them in *Æthiopia* have a face like a Satyre, and other members in part resembling a Bear, and in part a Dog, so are the *Prasian* Apes. This *Martine* did the *Babylonians*, inhabiting neer *Memphis*, for the stangeness, the colour, and shape thereof, worship for a God. They are of evill disposition like Apes, and therefore we will spare both their pictures and further description, finding very little of them in Histories worth commemoration.

THE APE CALITRICH.

THE *Calitrich*, so called by reason of his beard, and may be termed in English a bearded Ape, will live no other where then in *Ethiopia* and *India*, which are easie to take, but very hard to bring away alive into these Countrys. They differ in appearance from all other Apes, having a long beard and a large tail, hairy at the end, being in *India* all white, which the *Indians* hunt with darts, and being tamed, they are so apt to play, that a man would think they were created for no other purpose; whereupon the *Grecians* use in proverbe, an Ape having a beard, for a ridiculous and foolish jesting man.

OF THE PRASYAN APES.

MEGASTHENES (saith *Ælianus* and *Strabo*) writeth of Apes in *Prasia* a Region in *India*, which are no lesse then great Dogs, and five cubits high, having hair like a Man coming forth of their forehead and beards, being altogether white except their tails, which are two cubits and a half long, very like a Lions; and unto a simple man it might seem, that their tufts of hair were artificially trimmed, thought it grow naturally. Their beard is much like a Satyres, and although their body be white, yet is their head and tip of their tail yellow, so that the *Martins* before mentioned, seem to be affianced to these. These *Prasyan* Apes live in Mountains and Woods, and yet are they not wilde, but so tame that oftentimes in great multitudes they come down to the Gates and Suburbs of *Latagis*, where the King commandeth them dayly sodden Rice for their food, which they eat, and being filled return again to their home and usuall places of harbour in great moderation, doing no harme to any thing.

Peter Martyr telleth this story of one of these, that he being like to a great Munkey, but having a longer tail, by rowling over and over three or four times together taketh such strength, that he leapeth from bough to bough, and tree to tree, as if he flew. An archer of that Sea-voyage hurt one of them with an arrow, the wounded beast presently leapeth to the ground, and setteth upon the archer, as fiercely as a mad Dog; he drew his sword and struck off one of his armes, and so at last with much ado took the maimed beast, who being brought to the Navy, and accustomed to the society of men, began by little and little to waxe tame.

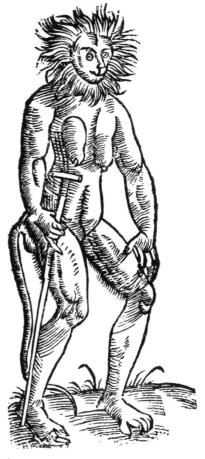

While he was in the ship bound with chains, other of the company having been on land to forrage, brought out of the Marishes a Bore, which Bore was shewed to the Munkey; at the first sight either of other set up their bristles, the raging Munkey leapeth upon the Bore, and windeth his tail round about the Bore, and with the one arme which he had left, caught him, and held him so fast by the throat, that he stifled him.

There is another kind of Munkey, for stature, bignesse and shape like a Man, for by his knees, secret parts and face, you would judge him a wilde man, such as inhabit *Numidia*, and the *Lapones*, for he is altogether overgrown with hair; no creature, except a man can stand so long as he; he loveth women and children dearly, like other of his own kind, and is so venereous that he will attempt to ravish women, whose Image is here described, as it was taken forth of the book of the description of the holy Land.

OF THE CYNOCEPALE OR BABOUN.

CYNOCEPHALES, are a kind of Apes, whose heads are like Dogs, and their other parts like a mans; wherefore *Gaza* translateth them *Canicipites,* (to wit) dog-heads. In the *French, German,* and *Illyrian* tongues, they are called of some *Babion,* and *Babuino* in *Italian,* is a small kind of Ape; but *Aristotle* saith, that a *Cynocephale* is bigger then an Ape. In *English* they are called *Babouns.*

There are many kinds of *Baboons,* whereof some are much given to fishing, so that they will tarry a whole day in the deep hunting for fish, and at length come forth with a great multitude. Again, there are some which abhor fishes, (as *Orus* saith) which kind the *Egyptians* Emblematically use to paint, when they will decipher a sacrifice. Some there are which are able to write, and naturally to discern letters; which kind the old *Egyptian* Priests bring into their Temples, and at their first entrance the Priest bringeth him a writing Table, a pencil and inke, that so by seeing him write, he may make tryall whether he be of the right kind and the beast quickly sheweth his skill: wherefore in ancient time, they were dedicated to *Mercury,* the fained god of learning.

The reason why the *Egyptians* do nourish them among their hallowed things is, that by them they may know the time of the conjunction betwixt the Sun and Moon; because the nature of this beast is, to have a kind of feeling of that conjunction, for after that these two signs meet, the male *Baboun* neither will look up nor eat, but cast his eyes to the ground, as it were lamenting the ravishment of the Moon with disdainful passion: In like manner the female, who moreover, at that time sendeth forth bloud out of her womb of conception: whereupon the *Egyptians* signifie by a *Baboun* the Moon, the rising of the Moon, by his standing upright holding his hands up toward heaven, and wearing a crown on his head, because with such gestures doth that Beast congratulate her first appearance.

Another cause why they bring them into their Temples is, because of the holyness of circumcision, for it is most true (though strange) that they are brought forth circumcised, at the least wise in some appearance; whereunto the Priests give great heed to accomplish and finish the work begun. The *Egyptians* also paint a *Baboun* sitting to signifie the *Equinoctium*, for in every *Equinoctium* they bark or howl twelve times in one day, and so many times make water: wherefore the *Egyptians* also upon their *Hydrologies* or Conduits did grave a *Baboun*, out of whose yard or privy part issued forth water; and they also say that this beast so nourished among their holy things, dyeth not at once like other beasts, but every day one part by the space of 72 days (the other parts remaining in perfection of nature) which the Priests take and put in the earth day by day, till all perish and be consumed.

The West region of *Lybia* and *Æthiopia* have great store of *Cynocephals*, *Babouns*, and *Acephals*, beasts without a head whose eyes and mouth are in their breasts. In like sort in *Arabia*, from *Dira* Southward in a Promontory, there are many *Babouns*, and in the Continent called *Dachinabades* beyond *Barygaza*, and the Eastern Mountains of the *Mediterranean* region; and those which *Apollonius* saw betwixt the rivers *Ganges* and *Hyphasis*, seem to be of this sort, in that he describeth them to be black haird, Dog-faced, and like little men; wherewithall *Ælianus* seemeth to be deceived, in saying, that there are men *Cynoprosopoi*, Dog-faced, whereas it is the error of vulgar people, to think that *Babouns* are men, differing only in the face or visage.

Concerning their members or parts in several, they are black and hairy, rough skinned, red and bright eyes, a long Dogs face, and teeth stronger and longer then Dogs: the face of a Lion must not be attributed to this beast, nor yet a Satyres, though it be more like. It hath a grim and fearful face, and the female hath naturally her womb cast out of her body, and so she beareth it about all her life long: their voice is a shrill whizing, for they cannot speak, and yet they understand the *Indian* language; under their beard they have a chin growing like a Serpents, and bearding about the lips like a Dragon; their hands are armed with most strong nails, and sharp; they are very swift of foot, and hard to be taken, wherefore they will run to the waters when they are hunted, being not ignorant that among waters they are most hardly taken; they are very fierce and active in leaping, biting deep and eagerly where they lay hold, neither do they ever grow so tame, but that they remain furious also. They love and nourish sheep and Goats, and drink their milk; they know how to take the kernels out of Almonds, Walnuts and Nuts, as well as men, finding the meat within, though the shell be unprofitable: they will also drink wine and eat flesh, sod, rosted, or deliciously dressed, and they will eat Venison, which they by reason of their swiftness take easily, and having taken it tear it in pieces and rost it in the Sun; they can swim safely over any waters, and therefore among the *Egyptians* they signifie swimming.

They are evill mannered and natured, wherefore also they are pictured to signifie wrath, they are so unappeasable. The Latins use them adjectively to signifie any angry, stubborn, froward, or ravening man. They will imitate all humane actions, loving wonderfully to wear garments, and of their own accord they clothe themselves in the skins of wilde beasts they have killed, they are as lustful and venereous as Goats, attempting to defile all sorts of women, and yet they love little children, and their females will suffer them to suck their breasts if they be held to them, and some say they will suck womens breasts like little children. There was such a beast brought to the French King, his head being like a Dogs, and his other parts like a mans, having legs, hands and armes naked like a mans, and a white neck; he did eat sod flesh so mannerly and modestly, taking his meat in his hands, and putting it to his mouth, that any man would think he had understood humane conditions: he stood upright like a man, and sat down like a man. He discerned men and women asunder, and above all loved the company of women, and young maidens; his genital member was greater then might match the quantity of his other parts: he being moved to wrath, would rage and set upon men, but being pacified, behaved himself as meekly and gently as a man, and was overcome with fair words: shewing himself well pleased with those that sported with him. The *Nomades* people of *Æthiopia*, and the Nations of *Menitimori* live upon the milk of *Cynocephales*, keeping great herds of them, and killing all the males, except some few preserved for procreation.

A TARTARINE.

THERE was at *Paris* another beast called a *Tartarine*, and in some places a *Magot* (much like a *Baboun*, as appeareth by his natural circumcision) being as great as a Gray-hound, and walketh for the most part upon two legs, being cloathed with a Souldiers coat, and a sword girded to his side, so that the most part thought him to be some Monster-little-man, for being commanded to his kennel, he would go and tarry there all night, and in the day time walk abroad to be seen of every man, it was doubtful whether he were of the *Munkey* kind or the *Baboun*, his voice was like the squeeking of a Mouse, but his aspect and countenance was fierce, truculent and fearful, as his image is here deciphered.

THE SATYRE.

As the *Cynocephal* or *Baboun* Apes have given occasion to some to imagine (though falsely) there were such men, so the Satyres a most rare and seldom seen beast, hath occasioned other to think it was a Devil; and the Poets with their Apes, the Painters, Limmers, and Carvers, to encrease that superstition, have therefore described him with horns on his head, and feet like Goats, whereas Satyres have neither of both. And it may be that Devils have at some time appeared to men in this likeness, as they have done in the likenesse of the *Onocentaure* and wild Asse, and other shapes; it being also probable, that Devils take not any denomination or shape from Satyres, but rather the Apes themselves from Devils whom they resemble, for there are many things common to the Satyre-Apes and Devilish-Satyres, as their humane shape, their abode in solitary places, their rough hair, and lust to women, wherewithall other Apes are naturally infected: but especially Satyres. Wherefore the Ancient Grecians conjecture their name to be derived as it were of *Stathes*, signifying the yard or virile member: and it is certain that the Devils have exercised their prestigious lust, or rather their imagination of lust upon mankind, whereof cometh that distinction of *Fauni*, that some are *Incubi* defilers of Women, and some *Succubi* defiled by men. Peradventure the name of Satyre is more fitly derived from the Hebrew *Sair*, Isa. 34. whereof the plural is *Seirim*, Isa. 13. which is interpreted monsters of the Desert, or rough hairy Fawnes; and when *issim* is put to *seir*, it signifieth Goats.

The *Chaldeans* for *Seirim*, render *Schedin*; that is, evill Devils: and the *Arabians*, *Leseiathin*; that is, *Satanas*: the *Persians*, *Devan*; the *Illyrians*, *Devadai* and *Dewas*; the *Germans*, *Teusel*. They which passed through the world and exercised dauncing and other sports, for *Dionysius*, were called *Satyres*, and sometimes *Tytiri*, because of their

36

wanton songs; sometimes *Sileni* (although the difference is, that the smaller and younger beasts are called *Satyri*, the elder and greater *Sileni*). Also *Bacche* and *Nymphæ*, whereof *Bacchus* is pictured riding in a Chariot of Vinebranches, *Silenus* riding beside him on an Asse, and the *Bacchæ* or *Satyres* shaking together their stalkie Javelines and Paulmers. By reason of their leaping they are called *Scirti*, and the antick or Satyrical dancing *Sicinnis*, and they also sometimes *Sicinnistæ*; sometimes *Ægipanæ*: wherefore *Pliny* reporteth, that among the Western *Ethiopians*, there are certain little hils of the *Satyrique Ægipanæ*, and that in the night time they use great fires, piping and dancing, with a wonderful noise of Timbrels and Cymbals: and so also in *Atlas* amongst the *Moores*, whereof there was no footing, remnant, or appearance to be found in the day time.

The *Satyres* are in the Islands *Satyridæ*, which are three in number, standing right over against *India* on the farther side of *Ganges*; of which *Euphemas Car* rehearseth this History, That when he sailed into *Italy*, by the rage of wind and evill weather, they were driven to a Coast unnavigable, where were many desert Islands inhabited of wilde men, and the Mariners refused to land upon some Islands, having heretofore had trial of the inhumane and uncivil behaviour of the inhabitants; so that they brought us to the *Satyrian Islands*, where we saw the inhabitants red, and had tails joyned to their back, not much less then horses. These being perceived by the Mariners to run to the ships and lay hold on the women that were in them, the ship-men for fear took one of the Barbarian women and set her on the land among them, whom in most odious and filthy manner they abused, not only in that part that nature hath ordained, but over the whole body most libidinously, whereby they found them to be very brute beasts.

There are also *Satyres* in the Eastern mountains of *India*, in the Countrey of the *Cartaduli*, and in the Province of the *Cumari* and *Corudæ*, but the *Cebi* spoken of before bred in *Ethiopia*, are not Satyres (though faced like them:) nor the *Prasyan* Apes, which resemble Satyres in short beards. There are many kinds of these Satyres better distinguished by names then any properties natural known unto us. Such are the *Ægipanæ* before declared, *Nymphes* of the Poets, *Fawnes*, *Pan*, & *Sileni*, which in the time of the Gentiles were worshipped for gods; and it was one part of their Religion, to set up the picture of a Satyre at their doors and gates, for a remedy against the bewitching of envious persons; and the statue of *Priapus* in the *Agalma* of a Satyre in their Gardens: for which cause we read of many pictures made of Satyres. *Antiphalus* made a very noble one in a *Panthers* skin, calling it *Apuscopon*, that is, *Wry-faced*. Another Painter of *Aristides*, painted it crowned with a drinking cup, signifying thereby the beastlinesse of drunkards. *Miron* had one painted hearing and admiring pipes, and another called *Periboetos* at *Athens*, as is reported, & that *Praxiteles* was wonderfully in love therewith; whereupon being at supper with *Phryne* the noble harlot, who had begged of him the best piece of work he had, consented with this condition, that he would not tel her which he loved best; whereupon she to satisfie herself, privately suborned one of his slaves, to come in at supper time, and tell him his house and most of his goods were burned; whereat being amazed, demanded if *Cupid*, and the

Satyre were safe; by which she knew the best piece, and asked *Cupid*, refusing the Satyre. *Protogenes* had one painted holding pipes in his hand, and was called *Anapauomenos & Timanthes* had painted *Cyclops* sleeping in a little tabler, with Satyrs standing beside him, measuring with a javelin the length of his thumb.

Satyres have no humane conditions in them, nor other resemblance of men beside their outward shape: though *Solinus* speak of them like as of men. They cary their meat under their chin as in a storehouse, and from thence being hungry they take it forth to eat, making it ordinary with them every day which is but annual in the *Formicæ* Lions; being of very unquiet motions above other Apes. They are hardly taken, except sick, great with young, old, or asleep; for *Sylla* had a Satyre brought aim which was taken asleep neer *Apollonia*, in the holy place *Nymphæum*, of whom he (by divers interpreters) demanded many questions, but received no answer, save only a voice much like the neying of a horse, whereof he being afraid, sent him away alive. *Philostratus* telleth another history, how that *Apollonius* and his colleagues supping in a village of Ethiopia, beyond the fall of *Nilus*, they heard a sudden outcry of women calling to one another; some saying, *Take him*, others, *Follow him*: likewise provoking their husbands to help them: the men presently took clubs, stones, or what came first to hand, complaining of an injury done unto their wives. Now some ten moneths before there had appeared a fearful shew of a Satyre, raging upon their women, and had slain two of them, with whom he was in love: the companions of *Apollonius* quaked at the hearing hereof, and *Nilus* one of them sware (by *Jove*) that they being naked and unarmed, could not be able to resist him in his outragious lust, but that he would accomplish his wantonness as before: yet said *Apollonius*, there is a remedy to quail these wanton leaping beasts, which men say *Midas* used (for *Midas* was of kindred to Satyres, as appeared by his ears.) This *Midas* heard his mother say, that Satyres loved to be drunk with wine, and then sleep soundly, and after that be so moderate, mild and gentle, that a man would think they had lost their first nature.

Whereupon he put wine into a fountain neer the high-way, whereof when the Satyre had tasted he waxed meek suddenly, and was overcome. Now, that we think not this a fable (saith *Apollonius*) let us go to the governor of the Town, and inquire of him whether there be any wine to be had that we may offer it to the Satyre: whereunto all consented, and they filled four great *Egyptian* earthen vessels with wine, and put it into the fountain where their cattel were watered; this done, *Apollonius* called the Satyre, secretly threatning him, and the Satyre inraged with the savour of the wine came; after he had drunk thereof, Now said *Apollonius*, let us sacrifice to the Satyre, for he sleepeth, and so led the inhabitants to the dens of the *Nymphes*, distant a furlong from the Town, and shewed them the Satyre, saying, Neither beat, curse, or provoke him henceforth, and he shall never harme you. It is certain, that the Devils do many wayes delude men in the likeness of Satyres, for when the drunken feasts of *Bacchus* were yearly celebrated in *Parnassus*, there were many sights of Satyres, and voices, and sounding of Cymbals heard; yet is it likely that there are Men also like Satyres inhabiting in some desert places; for S. *Jerom* in the life of *Paul* the *Eremite*, reporteth there appeared to S. *Antony* an *Hippocentaure*, such as the Poets describe, and presently he saw in a rocky valley adjoyning, a little man having crooked nostrils, hornes growing out of his forehead, and the neather part of his body had Goats feet: the holy man not dismayed, taking the shield of Faith, and the breastplate of Righteousness, like a good Souldier of Christ, pressed toward him, which brought him some fruits of palms as pledges of his peace, upon which he fed in the journey; which St. *Antony* perceiving, he asked him who he was, and received this answer, I am a mortall creature, one of the inhabitants of this Desert, whom the Gentiles (deceived with error) do worship and call *Fauni*, Satyres, and *Incubi*: I am come in ambassage from our flock, intreating that thou wouldst pray for us unto the common GOD, who came to save the world; the which words were no sooner ended, but he ran away as fast as any fowl could flie. And lest this should seem false, under *Constantine* at *Alexandria*, there was such a man to be seen alive, and was a publick spectacle to all the World; the carcass whereof after his death was kept from corruption by heat, through salt, and was carried to *ANTIOCHIA* that the Emperor himself might see it.

Satyres are very seldom seen, and taken with great difficulty, as is before said: for there were two of those sound in the Woods of *Saxony* towards *Dacia*, in a Desert, the female whereof was killed by the darts of the hunters, and the biting Dogs, but the male was taken alive, being in the upper parts like a Man, and in the neather part like a Goat, but all hairy throughout; he was brought to be tame, and learned to go upright, and also to speak some words, but with a voice like a Goat, and without all reason: he was exceeding lustful to women, attempting to ravish many of what condition soever they were, and of this kind there are store in *Ethiopia*.

THE FIGURE OF ANOTHER MONSTER.

THE famous learned man *George Fabricus*, shewed me this shape of a monstrous beast that is fit to be joyned to the story of Satyres. There was (said he) in the Territory of the Bishop of *Saltzburgh*, in a forrest called *Fammesburgh*, a certain four-footed beast, of a yellowish-carnation colour, but so wild that he would never be drawn to look upon any Colour and man, hiding himself in the darkest places, and being watched diligently, would not be provoked to come forth so much as to eat his meat, so that in a very short time it was famished. The hinder legs were much unlike the former, and also much longer. It was taken about the year of the Lord, One thousand five hundred thirty, whose image being here so lively described, may save us further labour in discoursing of his main and different parts and proportion.

OF THE NORWEGIAN MONSTERS.

WHEN as certain Ambassadors were sent from *James* the fourth of that name, King of *Scotland*, among whom was *James Ogill* that famous Scholar of the University of *Aberdene*, they no sooner took shipping and hoisted sail, but there sudainly arose such a tempestuous storm, that they were driven to the coasts of *Norway*: and there going on shoar, they were very strangely affrighted, to see (as to them it appeared) certain wild, monstrous men, running on the tops of the mountains. Afterward they were told by the inhabitants that they were beasts (and not men) which did bear mortal hatred to mankind, although they could not abide the presence of a mans countenance, yet in dark nights, when the reverend visage of humane creatures are covered, they will come down by troops upon the Villages, and except the barking of Dogs drive them back, they break open doors, and enter houses, killing and devouring whosoever they find; for their strength is so unresistible and great, that they can pull up by the roots a tree of mean stature, and tearing the boughs from the body, with the stock or stem thereof they fight one with another. Which when the Ambassa|dors heard, they caused a sure watch to be kept all night, and withall made exceeding great fires, and when the light appeared, they took their farewel of those Monster-breeding-shores, recovering with joy, the course which before they had lost by tempest.

OF THE ÆGOPITHECUS.

UNDER the *Equinoctial* toward the East and South, there is a kind of Ape called *Ægopithecus*, an Ape like a Goat. For there are Apes like Bears, called *Arctopitheci*, and some like Lions, called *Leontopitheci*, and some

42

like Dogs, called *Cynocephali*, as is before expressed; and many other which have a mixt resemblance of other creatures in their members.

Amongst the rest is there a beast called *PAN*; who in his head, face, horns, legs, and from the loins downwards resembleth a Goat; but in his belly, breast, and armes, an Ape: such a one was sent by the King of *Indians* to *Constantine*, which being shut up in a Cave or close place, by reason of the wildness thereof, lived there but a season, and when it was dead and bowelled, they pouldred it with spices, and carried it to be seen at *Constantinople*: the which having been seen of the ancient *Grecians*, were so amazed at the strangeness thereof, that they received it for a god, as they did a Satyre and other strange beasts.

43

OF THE SPHINGA OR SPHINX.

THE *Sphinx* or *Sphinga* is of the kind of Apes, having his body rough like Apes, but his breast up to his neck, pilde and smooth without hair: the face is very round yet sharp and piked, having the breasts of women, and their favour or visage much like them: In that part of then body which is bare without hair, there is a certain red thing rising in a round circle like Millet seed, which giveth great grace and comliness to their colour, which in the middle part is humane. Their voice is very like a mans but not articulate, founding as if one did speak hastily with indignation or sorrow. Their hair brown or swarthy colour. They are bred in *India* and *Ethiopia*. In the Promontory of the farthest *Arabia* neer *Dira*, are *Sphinges*, and certain Lions called *Formicæ*, so likewise they are to be found amongst the *Troglodytæ*. As the *Babouns* and *Cynocephales* are more wild then other Apes, so the Satyres and *Sphinges* are more meek and gentle, for they are

not so wilde that they will not be tamed, nor yet so tame but they will revenge their own harms; as appeared by that which was slain in a publick spectacle among the *Thebanes*. They carry their meat in the storehouses of their own chaps or cheeks, taking it forth when they are hungry, and so eat it: not being like the *Formicæ*, for that which is annual in them, is dayly and hourly amongst these.

The name of this *Sphinx* is taken from binding, as appeareth by the Greek notation, or else of delicacie and dainty nice loosness, (wherefore there were certain common strumpets called *Sphinctæ*, and the *Megarian Sphingas,* was a very popular phrase for notorious harlots)

hath given occasion to the Poets, to saign a certain monster called *Sphinx*, which they say was thus derived. *Hydra* brought forth the *Chymæra*, *Chymæra* by *Orthus* the *Sphinx*, and the *Nemean* Lion: now this *Orthus* was one of the *Geryons* Dogs. This *Sphinx* they make a treble formed monster, a Maidens face, a Lions legs, and the wings of a Fowl; or as *Ausonius* and *Varinus* say, the face and hand of a Maid, the body of a Dog, the wings of a Bird, the voice of a man, the claws of a Lion, and the tail of a Dragon: and that she kept continually in the *Sphincian* mountain; propounding to all travellers that came that way, an *Ænigma* or Riddle, which was this, *What was the creature that first of all goeth on four legs, afterwards on two, and lastly on three*: and all of them that could not dissolve that Riddle, she presently flew, by taking them and throwing them down headlong from the top of the Rock. At last *Oedipus* came that way and declared the secret, that it was *(a Man) who in his infancy creepeth on all four, afterward in youth, goeth upright upon two legs, and last of all in old age, taketh unto him a staffe which maketh him to go as it were on three legs*; which the monster hearing, she presently threw down her self from the former rock, and so she ended. Whereupon *Oedipus* is taken for a subtle and wise opener of mysteries.

But the truth is, that when *Cadmus* had maried an Amazonian woman, called *Sphinx*, and with her came to *Thebes*, and there slew *Draco* their King, and possessed his Kingdom; afterward there was a sister unto *Draco* called *Harmona*, whom *Cadmus* maried, *Sphinx* being yet alive: She in revenge (being assisted by many followers) departed with great store of wealth into the Mountain *SPHINCIUS*, taking with her a great Dog which *Cadmus* held in great account, and there made daily incursions or spoils upon his people: Now *Ænigma* in the *Theban* language, signifieth an inrode or warlike incursion, wherefore the people complained in this sort, *This* Grecian Sphinx *robbeth us, in setting upon with an* Ænigma, *but no man knoweth after what manner she maketh this* Ænigma.

Cadmus hereupon made Proclamation, that he would give a very bountiful reward unto him that would kill *Sphinx*, upon which occasion the *CORINTHIAN Oedipus* came unto her, being mounted on a swift Courser, and accompanied with some *Thebans* in the night season, slew her. Others say, that *Oedipus* by counterfeiting friendship, slew her, making shew to be of her faction; and *Pausanias* saith, that the former Riddle was not a Riddle, but an Oracle of *Apollo*, which *Cadmus* had received, whereby his posterity should be inheritors of the *Theban* Kingdom; and whereas *Oedipus*, being the Son of *Laius* a former King of that Countrey, was taught the Oracle in his sleep, he recovered the Kingdom usurped by *Sphinx* his Sister, and afterward unknown, maried his own Mother *Jocasta*. But the true moral of this Poetical fiction, is by that learned *Alciatus* in one of his emblems deciphered, that her monstrous treble-formed-shape, signified her lustful pleasure under a Virgins face, her cruel pride under the Lions claws, her winde-driven levity under the Eagles or Birds feathers, and I will conclude with the words of *Suidas* concerning such Monsters, that the *Tritons, Sphinges*, and *Centaures*, are the images of those things, which are not to be found within the compasse of the whole world.

The true *Sphinx* first described, is of a fierce though a tameable nature, and if a man do first of all perceive or discern these natural *Sphinges*, before the beast discern or perceive the man, he shall be safe; but if the beast first descry the man, then is it mortal to the man. These *Sphinges* were of great account for their strangeness: with their image did *Augustus* sign all his Grants, Libels, and Epistles: afterward he left that, and signed with the image of *Alexander* the great, and last of all with his own. *Syclis* the King in the City of the *Boristhenites*, had a fair house, about which there were *Sphinges* and *Gryphins* wrought out of white stone. At *Athens*, in the Temple *Parthenona*, there is described the contention betwixt *Pallas* and *Neptune*, about the earth, and the image of *Pallas* made of Ivory and gold, hath in the midst of her shield the picture of a *Sphinx*. *Amasis* the King of *Egypt*, built in the porch of *Pallas*, an admirable work called *Sai*: where he placed such great *Colosses* and *Andro-Sphinges*, that it was afterward supposed he was buried therein, and was lively to be seen imputrible. To conclude, the *Egyptians* in the porches of their Temples painted a *Sphinx*, whereby they insinuated that their divine wisdom was but dark and uncertain, and so covered with fables, that there scarce appeared in it any sparkles or footsteps of verity.

OF THE SAGOIN, CALLED GALEOPITHECUS.

THIS figure of the *Sagoin*, I received of *Peter Cordenberg*, a very learned Apothecary at *Antwerpe*, wch is three times as big as my picture, and *John Cay* that famous *English* Doctor hath advertised me, that it no way resembleth the *Sagoin* it self, which is not much greater then a Rat, a little Conny, or a young Hedghog: for he had seen several ones of that bigness, of a grisseld colour, a neat beard, and somewhat ash-coloured, a tail like a Rat, but hairy; the feet of a Squirrel, and the face almost like a Martine, or Satyre, a round ear, but very short and open, the hair black at the root, and white at the end, and in other conditions like a Munkey. They are much set, by among women, and by the *Brasilians* where they are bred and called *Sagoins*, it being very probable that they are conceived by a small Ape and Weasell, for in that Countrey, by reason of the heat thereof, there are many such unnatural commixtions. It is a nimble, lively, and quick spirited beast, but fearful; it will eat white-bread, Apples, Sweet-grapes, dryed in the Sun, Figs or Pears. There was one of them at *Antwerpe* sold for fifty Crowns. In France they call a *Sagoin* a little beast not much bigger then a Squirrel, and not able to endure any cold. Some other affirme that a *Sagoin* is a bearded creature, but without a tail, of an ash-colour, not much bigger then a fist; but of this beast there is not any author writeth more then is already rehearsed.

OF THE BEAR-APE ARCTOPITHECUS.

THERE is in *America* a very deformed beast which the inhabitants call *Haut* or *Hauti*, and the *Frenchmen, Guenon*, as big as a great *African* Munkey. His belly hangeth very low; his head and face like unto a childs, as may be seen by this lively picture, and being taken it will sigh like a young child. His skin is of an ash-colour, and hairy like a Bear; he hath but three claws on a foot, as long as four fingers, and like the thornes of Privet, whereby he climeth up into the highest trees, and for the most part liveth of the leaves of a certain tree being of an exceeding height, which the *Americans* call *Amahut*, and thereof this beast is called *Haut*. Their tail is about three fingers long, having very little hair thereon; it hath been often tried, that though it suffer any famine, it will not eat the flesh of a living man; and one of them was given me by a *Frenchman*, which I kept alive six and twenty dayes, and at the last it was killed by Dogs, and in that time when I had set it abroad in the open aire, I observed, that although it often rained, yet was that beast never wet. When it is tame it is very loving to a man, and desirous to climb up to his shoulders, which those naked *Americans* cannot endure, by reason of the sharpeness of his claws.

48

OF THE SIMIVULPA, OR APISH-FOX.

THOSE which have travelled the Countrey of *Payran*, do affirme, that they have seen a four-footed beast, called in *Latin, Simivulpa*, in *Greek, Alopecopithecos*, and in *German, Fuchssaffe*: in the forepatt like a Fox, and in the hinder part like an Ape, except that it had mans feet, and ears like a Bat, and underneath the common belly, there was a skin like a bag or scrip, wherein she keepeth, lodgeth, and carryeth her young ones, untill they are able to provide for themselves, without the help of their dam; neither do they come forth of that receptacle, except it be to suck milk, or sport themselves, so that the same under-belly is her best remedy against the furious Hunters, and other ravening beasts, to preserve her young ones, for she is incredibly swift, running with that carriage as if she had no burthen. It hath a tail like a Munkey: there was one of them with three young Whelpes taken and brought into a ship, but the Whelps died quickly: the old one living longer was brought to *Sivill*, and afterward to *Granado*, where the King of *Spain* saw it, which soon after by reason of the change of aire and incertainty of diet, did also pine away and die. The like things doth *Cardan* report of a beast called *Chiurca*, in *Hispania Nova*, and *Stadinius* of a *Suruvoy* in *America*: but I conjecture that the former is this *Fox-Ape* called in *Greek, Alopecopithecos*, and of the *Germans Fuschsaffe*, the latter the

49

Female *Cynocephal*, which carryeth her womb wherein lie her young ones without her belly. There is a fish called *Glaucus*, whereof the male swalloweth up all the young ones when they are indangered by other, and afterward yeeldeth them forth again safe and sound.

OF THE ASSE.

THE *Asse*, is called in *Latin*, *Asinus*, in *Greek*, *Onos* and *Killos*, be reason of his labour in bearing burdens, and of some *Megamucos*, because of his unpleasant voice: Of others *Cochutous*, or *Canthon*, from whence cometh *Cantharus*, that is, a *Scarabee* or Flie, bred of the dung of Asses. The *Hebrew* call it *Chamor*, Deut. 5. and the *Persians*, *Care*, the latter *Hebrews* do indifferently take *Gajedor*, *Tartak*, and *Caar* for an Asse; the *Italians*, *L'asino*, the *Spaniards*, *Asno*, the *French*, *Ung asne*, the *Germans*, *Esel, Mul, Mulle-resel*, and the *Illyrians, Osel*; the which Beast is intituled or phrased with many Epithets among Poets; as slow, burthen-bearing, back-bearing, vile, cart-drawing, mill-labouring, sluggish, crooked, vulgar, slow-paced, long-eared, blockish, braying, idle, devil-haired, filthy, saddle-bearer, four-foot, unsavoury, and a beast of miserable condition; besides many other such titles in the Greek. Yet this silly beast hath among the Astronomers found more favour, for in the sign *Cancer* there are two Stars called the two Asses, placed there as some say, by *Bacchus*, who in his fury which *Juno* laid upon him, travelled to the *Dodanæan* Temple of *Apollo* to recover his wits, by the counsel of the Oracle, came to a certain lake of water, over which he could not passe, and meeting there two Asses, took one of them, upon whose back he was safely carried over drie foot. Afterward, when he had recovered his wits, in thankfulness for that good turn, he placed the two Asses amongst the stars.

Howsoever this may be a fabulous commendation of this beast, yet holy Writ teacheth us, that an Asse saw an Angel, and opened his mouth in reproof of his master *Balaam*: and our most blessed Saviour rode on an Asse to *Jerusalem* to shew his humility: and *Sampson* out of the jaw-bone of an Asse, quenched his thirst. *Apuleius* in his eleven books of his golden Asse, taketh that beast for an Emblem, to note the manners of mankind; how some by youthful pleasures become beasts, and afterward by timely repentant old-age, are reformed men again: Some are in their lives Wolves; some Foxes, some Swine, some Asses, and so other may be compared to other beasts: and as *Origen* saith, only by pleasure is a man a horse or Mule, when a beastly soul liveth in a humane shape. This world is unto them as an inchanted cup of *Circes*, wherein they drink up a portion of oblivion, error and ignorance; afterwards brutizing in their whole life, till they taste the Roses of true science and grace inlightning their minds, which is their new recovery of humane wit, life, and understanding.

Asses are bred in *Arcadia*, wherefore proverbially, the best Asses are signified by the *Arcadian* Asse, and the greatest Asses by the *Arcarnican* Asse. In *Timochain* in *Persia*, are very beautiful Asses, whereof one hath been sold for thirty pounds of silver. Likewise in *Rea*, in *Italy*, in *Illyria*, *Thracia*, and *Epirus*, there are Asses but very small ones, although all other Cattel there are very large. In *India* among the *Psilians*, they are no greater then Rams, and generally all their Cattel are of a very small growth. In *Scythia*, *Pontus*, *Celta*, and the regions confining them, are no Asses bred, by reason of extremity of cold, for Asses are very impatient of cold. In *Mysia* there are also asses; but their flanks are crooked, and indented as if they were broken; whereupon a proverbial common speech ariseth (one having a broken flanke) for a *Mysian* Asse.

Asses are ingendred both by their own kind, and also by horses, for they chose stallions and put them to their Asses, who have large bodies, well-set legs, strong necks, broad and strong ribs, brawny and high creasts, thighes full of sinews, and of black or flea-bitten colour (for a Mouse-colour is not approved) wherefore he that will have a good flock of Asses, must look that the male and female be sound, and of a good age, that they may breed long time, and out of a good Seminary, as of *Arcadia* or *Rea*: for as the best Lampreyes are in *Sicilia*, and the delicate fish *Helops* in *Rhodes* and not elsewhere; so are best Asses in those forenamed places. When they make choise of a Stallion, they look principally that he have a great head. An Asse is more desirous of copulation then an Horse, and both male and female do couple at thirty moneths, although it prove not untill three years, or three and a half. Men say that *Anna* the father in law of *Esau*, did first invent the copulation of Horses and Asses together; for as a Horse doth cover a she Asse, so an Asse will cover a Mare, and an Asse will sooner fill the lust of a Mare then a Horse.

If a Horse cover a female Asse which hath been entred by a male Asse, he cannot alter the seed of the Asse: but if an Asse cover a Mare which a Horse hath formerly entred, he will destroy the seed of the Horse, so that the Mare shall suffer abortment, by reason that the seed genital of an Asse is more frigid, then an Horses. The Mares of *Elis* cannot at all conceive by Asses copulation, and there is more abortments falleth out by commixtion of Horses with Asses, or Asses with Mares, then when every kind mingleth amongst themselves. It is but a superstition of some, which affirme that an Asse cannot conceive for so many years, as she hath eaten grains of Barly corn defiled with womens purgation; but this is certain, that if an Asse conceive not at the first losing of her teeth, she remaineth barren. They are not coupled in generation in the Spring *Æquinoctium*, like Mares and other beasts; but in the Summer *Solstice*, by reason of their cold natures, that they may bring forth their young ones about the same time, for in the twelfe moneth after their copulation, they render their Foles. If the males be kept from labour they are the worse for generation, wherefore they are not to be suffered idle at that time; but it is not so with the female, she must rest, that the Fole may be the stronger: but presently after she is covered, she must be coursed and driven to and fro, or else she will cast forth again the received seed.

The time that she goeth with young, is according to the male kind by which she is covered, for so long as the male lay in the belly of his dam, so long will the Asse carry her young before deliverance: but in the stature of body, strength, and beauty, the young one taketh more after the female then the male. The best kind of Asses are the Foles of a wild Asse and a tame female Asse. They use when an Asse is foaled, to take it from the dam, and put it to suck a Mare, that it may be the greater, which Fole is callid *Hippothela*, that is, a Horse suckling; and Mares will not be covered by Asses, except by such a one as was a horse-suckling. A she Asse will engender till she be thirty years old, which is her whole life long, but if she conceive often, she will quickly be barren; whereof their keepers must take such care, that they cause them to be kept from often copulation.

They will not Fole in the sight of man, or in the light, but in darkness; they bring forth but one a time, for it hath not been heard of in the life of man, that an Asse hath ever brought forth twins. As soon as they are conceived they have milk in their udders, but some hold not untill the tenth moneth. They love their young ones very tenderly for they will run through fire to come at them, but if there be any water betwixt them, it cooleth their affections; for of all things they love not to wet their feet. They will drive their young ones from sucking at the sixth moneth, because of the pain in their udders, but their keepers wean them not till a whole year after their foaling, Their milk is so thick that it is used in stead of sodder: a Mares is more thin, and a Camels is thinnest of all. It is mortal to their young ones to tast the dams milk for two dayes after their foaling, for the food is so fat that it breedeth in their mouthes the *Colostracion* or *Beestings*.

Touching their several parts, they have teeth on either chap like a Man and a Horse, an Asse and a Mule have 36 teeth, and joyned neer together: the bloud of Asses and Buls is the thickest of all other, as the bloud of man is the thinnest: His head is great and his ears long and broad: both male and female lose their fore-teeth in the thirtieth moneth of their age, and the second to the first, in the sixt moneth; their third and fourth teeth are called *Gnomons*, that is, *Regulars*, because by them there is a tryed rule to know their age; and those teeth also they lose in the sixt moneth. The heart of an Asse is great, as all other fearful beasts have. The belly is uniform as in other beasts that have a solid or whole hoof. It wanteth a gall, and hath two udders betwixt the thighes, the forepart of the back neer the shoulder is weakest, and there appeareth the figure of a Crosse, and the hinder part neer the loins is stronger. The hoofs are whole and not parted: the *Stygian* water is so cold that nothing can hold it, except the hoof of an Asse or Mule; although *Ælianus* affirme, that it cannot be contained but in the horns of *Scythian* Asses. Their tails are longer by one joint then a horses (though not so hairy). They are purged with monethly courses more then Sheep or Goats, and the urine of the female is more thin then the males. If an Asse was hindered by any disease from making water, certain superstitious persons for the ease of the beast, muttered this charm:

> *Gallus bibit & non meiit, Myoxus meiit & non bibit: that is,*
> *The Cock drinketh and maketh not water,*
> *The Dormouse maketh water and never drinketh.*

They will eat Canes or Reeds, which to other beasts is almost poison: wherefore in the old time an Asse was dedicated to *Bacchus* as the Canes were sacred unto him: and at the time of their copulation they give them herb *Basill* to stir up their lust: They will be satisfied with any never so base food, as chaffe, whereof there is abundance in every Countrey, young thornes and fruits of trees, twiges of Osier, or a bundle of boughs to browse upon: in so much as *Q. Hortentius* was wont to say, that he had more care that his Barbels should not hunger in his fish-pools, then his Asses in *Rosea*: but the young ones newly weaned must be more tendered, for they must be fed with hay, chaffe or Barley, green corn, or barley bran. Asses will hardly drink but at watering places in their folds, or such as they have been accustomed withall, and where they may drink without wetting their feet; and that which is more strange, they cannot be brought to go over hollow bridges, through which the water appeareth in the chinks of the planks; and when in travail they are very thirsty, they must be unladen and constrained to drink; yea, *Herodotus* reporteth, that there are certain Asses among the *African* shepherds, which never drink. When they sleep they lie at length, and in their sleep conceive many forceable dreams, as appeareth by their often beating back their hinder legs, which if they strike not against the vain aire but against some harder substance, they are for ever utterly lamed.

When the Asses of *Thuscia* have eaten Hemlock, or an herb much like unto it, they sleep so long and strangely, that oftentimes the Countrey men begin to flea them, and on the suddain their skins half taken off and the other half on, they awake, braying in such horrible manner, that the poor men are most dreadfully affrighted therewith. Their voice is very rude and fearful, as the Poet said;

Quirritat verres, tardus rudit, uncat assellus.

And therefore the *Grecians* to express the same, haved faigned many new words, and call it *Ogkethmos*, as the *Latins*, *Rudere*; that is, to utter forth a voice in a base and rude manner. The Poets feign, that at that time when *Jupiter* came to war with the Gyants, *Bacchus* and *Vulcan*, the *Satyres* and *Sileni* assisted and attended him, being carryed upon Asses. When the time came that the battell began the Asses for very fear brayed most horribly, whereat the Gyants not being acquainted with such strange and unknown voices and cries, took them to their heels and so were overcome.

In the sacrifice of the Godesse *Vacuna*, an Asse was feasted with bread, and crowned with flowers, hung with rich Jewels and Peytrels, because (as they say) when *Priapus* would have ravished *Vesta* being asleep, she was suddenly awaked by the braying of an Asse, and so escaped that infamy. And the *Lampsaceni* in the disgrace of *Priapus* did offer him an Asse. But this is accounted certain, that among the *Scythians* by reason of cold, an Asse is never heard or seen; and therefore when the *Scythians* set upon the *Persians*, their Horses will not abide the braying of Asses, wondring both at the strangeness of an Asses shape, and rudeness of his cry: wherefore there are certain birds, resembling in their chattering the braying of Asses, and are therefore termed *Onacratuli*.

When an Asse dyeth, out of his body are ingendred certain Flies, called *Scurabees*. They are infested with the same diseases that Horses be, and also cured by the same meanes (except in letting of bloud) for by reason their veins be small and their bodies cold, in no case must any bloud be taken from them.

Asses are subject to madness when they have tasted to certain herbs growing neer *Potnias*; as are Bears, Horses, Leopards and Wolves: they only among all other hairy beasts are not troubled with either tikes or lice, but principally they perish by a swelling about the crown of their pasterne, or by a *Catarrhe* called *Malis*, which falling down upon their liver they die, but if it purge out of their nostrils they shall be safe: and *Columella* writeth, that if sheep be stabled where Mules or Asses have been housed, they will incur the scab. There is great use made of the skins of Asses, for the *Germanes* do make thereof a substance to paint and write upon, which is called *Eselshut*. The *Arabians* have a cloth called *Mesha*, made of Asses and Goates hair, whereof the inhabitants of their deserts make them tents and sacks. It is reported that *Empedocles* was called *Colysancmas*, because when the *Agrigentines* were troubled with winds by hanging about their City innumerable Asse skins, he safe-guarded them from the winds: whereupon some have thought (but falsly) that there was some secret in Asses skins, against outragious Tempestes.

The bones of Asses have been used for pipes, the Artificers made more reckoning of them then of the bones of Hartes, and therefore *Esop* in *Plutarch* wondereth that so grosse and dull a creature, should have such shrill and musical bones; and the *Busirites* called the Philosophers *Naucratites*, because they played musick upon Asses bones, for they cannot abide the sound of a trumpet, because it resembleth the voice of an Asse, who is very hateful to them for *Typhons* sake.

Mæcenus allowed the flesh of young Asses to be eaten, preferring it before the flesh of wilde Asses, and this custome also prevailed at *Athens*, where they did eat the flesh of old Asses, which hurteth the stomach, having in it no good juice or sweetness, and is very hard to be digested. In like sort about the coasts of *Alexandria*, men use to eat the flesh of Asses, which begetting in their body much melancholick and adusted humor, causeth them to fall into the *Elephantia* or spotted leprosie.

Asses are tamed at three years old, and taught for those businesses which they must be applied unto; some for the mill, some for husbandry and the plough, some for burthens and carriage, some for the wars, and some for draught. Merchants use Asses to carry their wine, oil, corn, and other things to the sea-side; wherefore the Countrey man maketh principal account of this beast for his carriage to and fro, being fit to carry both on his neck and on his back: with them they go to market with their wares, and upon them bring home their houshold necessaries.

> ——— *Tardè costas agitator, aselli,*
> *Vilibus aut onerat pomis, lapidemq; revertens,*
> *Incussum, aut atrae massam picis urbe reportat.*

They grind in their mils and fetch home their corn, they plough their land, as in *Campania, Lybia,* and Bœtia, where the ground is soft, and in *Byzantium* that fruitful Countrey, which repayeth the husbandmans labor with increase of an hundred and fifty times more then the seed, and where in drie weather their ground is not arable with the whole strength of Buls, yet after a little rain, one Asse in one end of a yoak, and an old woman at the other end, do easily draw the plough, and open the earth to sow their seed: wherefore *Cato* said merrily, that Mules, Horses and Asses, keep no holy-dayes, except they be such Asses as keep within doors. In like sort they draw from place to place the carts of Bakers, or Carts laden with any other carriage, if it be not over great.

The people *Carmani* (by reason they want Horses) use Asses in their wars, so also do the *Scaracori,* who never use them in mils or any such base works, but upon them undertake all their martial perils. There was a custome amongst the *Cumani,* that when a Woman was taken in Adultery, she was led to the Market, and there set upon a bare stone, afterwards she was set upon a bare Asses back, and so carryed throughout the City, then brought back again to the former stone for a publick spectacle to all the City, whereby she remained infamous all her life after, and was called *Onobatis,* that is, one that had ridden an Asse; and the stone whereupon she stood, was accounted an unlucky, and an odious place for all posterity. In like sort among the *Parthians,* it was held a disgraceful thing to ride or be carryed upon a bare Asses back. The dung of Asses is pretious for a garden, especially for Cabages; and if an Apple tree be dying, it may be recovered by washing it in Asses dung by the space of six dayes; and some have used to put into Gardens the skull of a Mare or she Asse that hath been covered in copulation, with perswasion that the Gardens will be the more fruitful.

Asses are of very foolish conditions and slender capacity, but yet very tame, not refusing any manner of burthen although it break his back: being loaded, it will not out of the way for any man or beast, and it only understandeth the voice of that man, with whom it is laboured, knowing also the way whereunto it is accustomed. *Ammonianus* was in such love with an Asse, and holdding him of so great a capacity, that he had one continually to hear his Lectures of Philosophie. *Galen* affirmeth, that an Asse understandeth *genus, species & individuum*, because if you shew him a Camell that never saw one before, he is terrified and cannot indure his sight: but if he have been accustomed to such a sight, if you shew him never so many, he is not moved at them. In like sort, he knoweth men in general, being not affraid of them, but if he see or hear his keeper, he knoweth him for his keeper or master.

There was a cunning player in *Africa*, in a City called *Alcair*, who taught an Asse divers strange tricks or feats; for in a publick spectacle, turning to his Asse (being on a scaffold to shew sport) said, The great *Sultan* purposeth to build him an house, and shall need all the Asses of *Alcair* to fetch and carry wood, stones, lime, and other necessaries for that business; presently the Asse falleth down turneth up his heals into the air, groneth, and shutteth his eyes fast, as if he had been dead: while he lay thus, the Player desired the beholders to consider his estate, for his Asse was dead; he was a poor man, and therefore moved them to give him money to buy another Asse. In the mean time having gotten as much money as he could, he told the people he was not dead, but knowing his masters poverty, counterfeited in that manner, whereby he might get money to buy him provender, and therefore he turned again to his Asse and bid him arise, but he stirred not at all. Then did he strike and beat him sore (as it seemed) to make him arise, but all in vain, the Asse lay still.

Then said the player again, our *Sultan* hath commanded that to morrow there be a great triumph without the City, and that all the noble women shall ride thither upon the fairest Asses, and this night they must be fed with Oates, and have the best water of *Nilus* to drink. At the hearing whereof, up started the Asse, snorting and leaping for joy: then said the Player, the Governor of this Town hath desired me to lend him this my Asse for his old deformed wife to ride upon; at which words the Asse hangeth down his ears, and understanding like a reasonable creature, began to halt as if his leg had been out of joint; why, but said the Player, had thou lifer carry a fair young Woman? The Asse wagged his head in token of consent to that bargain, go then (said the player) and among all these fair Women, chuse one that thou mayest carry; then the Asse looketh round about the Assembly, and at last went to a sober woman and touched her with his nose, whereat the residue wondered and laughed, shutting up the sport, with crying out, *An Asses Woman, An Asses Woman,* and so the Player went unto another Town.

Such things do serve to teach us that Asses are not altogether indocible, besides in their own nature they know how to refresh themselves in their weariness, by wallowing on the ground, and being overcome with melancholy humor, they naturally look for the hearb *Ceterach* or *Finger-fearne* to cure them. When the Asses of *Maurusium* are bound to a journey, they set forward so fast, that a man would think they rather flew then ran; but being overwearyed they are so abased, that they send forth tears, and then are they drawn at Horses tails to their journeys end.

The Asse is never at peace with the Crow, because it longeth for the Asses eyes, likewise the bird *Salem,* for when the Asse cometh to the thornes, to rub himself where the said bird buildeth her nest, the Asse spoileth it, wherefore the said bird maketh continual assault upon him. In like sort the *Colota* or *Stellio,* for it sleepeth in the managers, and creepeth up into the Asses nose to hinder him from eating.

The Wolf is also an enemy to the Asse, for he loveth his flesh, and with small force doth he compasse the destruction of an Asse, for the blockish Asse when he seeth a Wolf, layeth his head on his side, that so he might not see, thinking that because he seeth not the Wolfe, the Wolfe cannot see him; but the Wolfe upon this advantage setteth upon the beast on the blind side, and easily destroyeth the courageless Asse. Another argument of an Asses stupidity, is that he careth not for his own life, but will with quietness starve, if meat be not laid before him. Wherefore it is apparent that when a dull Scholar not apt to learn, is bid to sell an Asse to signifie his blockishness, is no vain sentence; therefore they which resemble Asses in their head, round forehead, or great face, are said to be blockish; in their fleshie face, fearful; in broad or great eyes, simple; and like to be mad in thick lips, and the upper hanging over the neather, Fools; and in their voice, contumelious and disdainful. To conclude, the ancients have made many significations of Asses and their shapes, making a man with an Asses head to signifie; First, one ignorant of manners, histories, and Countryes. Secondly, immoderate riot of stubborn persons in Scripture is deciphered in an Asse. Thirdly, impudency and shamelesness, because an Asse will not for any stripes forsake his own wayes. Fourthly, the *Jewish* people, who like Asses could not understand the evident truth of Christ in the plain text of Scripture, wherefore our Saviour secretly upbraided their dulness, when he rode upon an Asse. Fistly, the *Egyptians* by an Asse, noted a man without all divine knowledge; wherefore they used to take an Asse and follow him with all despight, beating him from place to place till he brake his own neck; for they believed that an Asse was possessed of a Devil. Sixtly, Indocibility, by an Asse bridled. Seventhly, the snares of flatterers; for their Priests set an Asse between flowers and ointments, neither of both partaining to an Asses skill; teaching thereby how mighty men fall by treachery of flatterers. Eightly, a Woman dissembling her Pregnancy. Ninthly, by a man weaving a cord, and an Asse behind him biting it asunder; they signifie, a painful husband and a prodigal wife. Tenthly, a good Vine-dresser, for when an Asse did bite of the branch of a vine, it was observed that the next year the Vine was more fruitful. Finally, base servisity, trifling sluggishness, good fortune, Tyrants, and fools, are Hierogliphically comprized under the discourse of Asses.

Touching such medicinal vertues as have been tried and found to be in the several parts of Asses, by learned and approved writers, now in the conclusion of this History they shall be briefly remembred, and so this Narration be finished.

A draught or two of the same water whereof an Asse or an Oxe hath drunk, will ease the head-ache, the forehead of an Asse tied to the flesh of one that hath the falling evill, cureth him; and the brain of an Asse steeped in sweet water and infumed in leaves, whereof taken for certain days, half an ounce, easeth the falling evill: the number of which dayes cannot be less then thirty, but this is very ridiculous, that if a man hurt by a Scorpion, do whisper his harme in the ear of an Asse, presently the hurt ceaseth. When one is vexed with a Quotidian Fever, with three drops of bloud out of the vein of an Asses ear, put into eighteen ounces of water and drunk by the patient, easeth that pain.

The liver of an Asse burnt, driveth away venomed things, and the same dried and beat to powder, helpeth the Cough and shortness of breath, and rosted to be eaten, if it be eaten fasting it is against the falling evill. Other say, if it be mixed with *Opponax*, and instilled into the mouth forty days together, defendeth infants from the aforesaid sickness. Also the heart of a male black Asse, eaten with bread at the evening, in the first or second day of the Moon, is good against the falling evill. The liver dried with Parsely, and three Walnuts clensed from the pill and put into hony, is marvellous good for one that is liver sick; the ashes of it mixt with oil, taketh away Wens; and the ashes of the liver and the flesh is good against the chapping, clefts, or slisters in the body, which come by cold: but *Dioscorides*; whom I rather follow, attributeth both these virtues to the ashes of the hoof. He that is sick of the milt, may be holpt with the old milt of an Asse, if he eat thereof every day dryed and fasting, he shall find ease by it within three days. The same first dryed and then steeped in water, maketh the dugs full of milk, so also doth the Spleen, and the Spleen with sewet of a Bear, and oil made as thick as hony, by anointing the eye-lids therewith restoreth the hairs which are wanting. The reins exenterated, bruised and put into new pure wine, do help the bladder, and stay the incontinency of the Urine. The same dried, burned, and beaten into very small powder, whereof a nut shell full put into two cups of pure wine and drunk off, cureth the Strangury.

It is thought, that with the powder of the Asses genital, the hair may be made grow thicker: and the same beaten with lead and oil, and annointing the head where gray hairs are shaven off, keepeth from more gray hairs. The stones of an Asse kept in salt and sprinkled in a potion of Asses milk or Water, helpeth the falling evill. The Gall of an Asse or a Bull, either of them, severally broke into Water, taketh away the spots in the face, if after the patients skin be pilled, he must keep himself from sun and wind.

61

The bloud of an Asse stayeth the flux of bloud coming from the skin or films of the brain; and two or three drops of the same drunk with wine, cureth the Quotidian Fever: the self same thing is reported of the bloud let out of the vein in the ear. The bloud of the Fole of an Asse with wine, cureth the Kings evil. The sroath or scum of *Nitre* with the fat of an Asse or the fat of a Sow; cureth the bitings of Dogs: and if there be any scars in the body, the fat maketh them of the same colour with the residue of the body. And if one vexed with the Falling evill, be annointed with the suet or fat of an Asse, it will ease them very much; likewise the marrow of Asses helpeth the Scabs from a man, and with the suet the places infected with Catarrhs, Leprosies, or Scars, receive their former colour; and the skin laid upon young Infants, maketh them without fear. And if the bill of a *Heron* wrapped in an Asses skin, be bound to ones forehead, it provoketh sleep.

A Palsie man will fall down if he taste of the perfume made of the hairs of an Asse or Mule. The ashes of the hairs of Asses, stayeth bleeding; and the same hath the more force if they be of a male, and be mixed with Vinegar and laid in wooll to the issue bleeding. The bones of an Asse broken and sod, are very soveraign against the venom of a Sea-hair-fish. The powder of an Asses hoof drunk a moneth together, two spoonfuls at a time, helpeth the Falling evill very greatly: and the same mixed with oil, helpeth the Kings evill; and being put upon Kibes or Chil-blanes, cureth them. The hoofs of Asses burned and beaten to powder, given to them that have the Falling evill in drink, helpeth them speedily; also a burned hoof is mingled with many medicines, to cure the swelling of the Navel in children; and the hoofs perfumed procure speedy deliverance in travel of young, that the dead thing may come forth, otherwise it is not used, for it will kill the living young ones.

The dust thereof with the milk of an Asse, by annointing cureth the Scars and Webs of the eyes, and as *Marcellus* saith, only the parings of an Asses hoof scraped and mingled with a womans milk; and they say, that if an *Epileptick* man wear a ring made of an Asses hoof wherein is no blackness, it will preserve him from falling. The powder of an Asses hoof burned and beaten, laid in Vinegar and made in little bals, and one of them put into the mouth and there held, helpeth the looseness and pain in the teeth. There is a collection of certain hard matter about an Asses legs, called *Lichen*, which if it be burned and beaten, and put into old oil, will cause hairs to grow out of baldness, and it is of such force, that if it be applyed to a womans cheek, it will produce the same effect, and mingled with Vinegar it raiseth up the *Lethargike* man.

And if a man take the Ring-wormes growing naturally on Asses legs, and shredding them into powder put them in Vinegar, it stayeth all pain in the head, which maketh one sleepy. The flesh of Asses sod in pottage helpeth them that have the *Phthisis* or disease of the Lungs, and there are some which prescribe the taking of Asses flesh, or the bloud, of Asses mingled with Vinegar, to be taken forty days together against the falling evill. The milk of an Asse mingled with hony and drunk, loosneth the belly, and therefore *Hippocrates* gave it for a gentle purgation, being moister then any other kind of milk, and fitter to take down the belly. It will also ease the tooth-ach, if the teeth be washed in it, and fasten them that are loose, being very good to wash the teeth withal. *Galen* gave Asses milk mixt with hony, to one in a Consumption when he came newly from a bath, and therefore it is given in Fevers *Hecticks*, and all consuming diseases, because the substance of it is fitter for detersion then nutriment: when the brests, are in pain, by drinking Asses milk they be holpt; and the same mingled with hony, causeth Womens purgation; by drinking Asses milk, an exulcerate stomach is relieved: likewise all other pains in the stomach, which come of sadness or sorrow, sighing, and desperation: and *Heraclides* gave Asses milk with Anniseed to one that had his lights stopped, and it is likewise commended against the Cough, extenuation, spitting of bloud, Dropsie, and hardness of the Spleen, but it is not good for a weak head troubled with giddiness or noise, yet will it loosen the hardness of the belly in a Fever.

It is also privately used against eating of Morture, White-lead, Sulphur, and Quicksilver; and when a mans meat doth not neither nourish nor digest, let him drink Asses milk safely: and it is also good to gargarize in sore chaps or throats. Likewise in a Fever when there is no head-ache. The ancient in old time gave Asses milk to children before meat, and for want thereof Goats milk; for sore mouthes it must be gargarized. It is very profitable against the Colick and Blondy-flux, if hony be put thereto; loosness or desire of stool is taken away by drinking Asses milk: the whay or milk of an Asse did *Hippocrates* prescribe against the Consumption of the reins or back; and the same with the root of a pomgranat against the looseness and other diseases of the belly to be drunk.

Also there are examples where the whay of Asses milk have helped the Gowt, both in hand and foot: sweet water with Asses milk is wholesome against poison of Hen-bane, and other poisons, but it must be used new, or else soon after warmed: This milk will make womens skins whiter; wherefore *Poppea*, the wife of *Demitius Nero* carryed about with her in her progress fifty milch Asses, wherewith she did use to bath her self.

The Urine with the own dung, healeth straight shooing, scabs in a man, and the roughness of the nails. It taketh away the scurffe of Oxen. It is given in drink, to cure them that have ache in their reins, and with *Pepper-wort* it is profitable against Suppurations and Apostems in the flesh. If any be hurt by the Stars, wash them in Asses stale, mingled with *Spiknard*: the same force hath it against cornes and all hardness or thickness of skin. The dung of Asses new with oil of Roses, distilled warme into the ears, helpeth deafness; and pushes or suddain boils of the head, are cured with the juice of Asses dung, and of Sea-onions beat to powder, and the fat of beef, layed to the boils like a plaister: both the dung of Asses and Horses either raw or burnt mingled with Vinegar, restraineth bleeding both in Fluxes and Wounds, used like a plaister, being new and mingled with Vinegar; and for the bleeding at the nose, snuffe in the ashes of Asses dung burnt to powder. The dung of Asses cureth the Piles, and the same dried and moistened in wine being drunk of Cattel which are stung with Scorpions, cureth them if it be at grasse; and it is found true by long experience, that the dung of an Asse rubbed, in quantity two spoonfuls, and taken every day, delivereth one from the falling evill.

mitis prodest ex ubere succus asellæ,
Si tepido vino infundas ac mella piperque.

This is good against the gall and running over thereof, if it be mingled with warm wine, pepper, and hony. The *Syrians* call the dung of a young

Fole which it first castest up after the foling, *Polean*; and give it against the sickness of the milt.

In sapa decoctum colo magnopere prodest.

The same is good against the Colick and the Bloudy-flux. The juice of Asses dung, Asses milk, and sweet wine, anointed on the sick member, cureth the Gowt: and the same stayeth the flowres of women with child; the juice hereof cureth the closing up of the eyes in the night. The skin wherein the young Fole lyeth in the dams belly being smelled unto by him that hath the Falling evill, it easeth him. *Anaxilaus* hath reported, that if the excrements of a Mares copulation be burned, there will appear monstrous shapes of Horses heads. If a Horse have a web in his eye, mingle together the milk of an Asse, the bloud of a Dove, and the dew of Cabages, and anoint him therewith: and there be some which take of the dirt where an Asse hath made water in the way, and therewith anoint the Scabs of sheep for their recovery: but when one is strucken with a Scorpion, the Asses dung must be presently applyed, or else it profiteth nothing in that malady.

OF THE HINNUS, INNUS, AND GINNUS, MANNUS, MANNULUS, BEFI & BURDENES, &C.

THERE is no language besides the *Greek* that have any words to express these Beasts, and the *Latins* have derived these termes from them. These are beasts of a small size, as dwarfes among men, and therefore seldom seen in these parts of the world. They which are called *Hinni*, are conceived of a Horse, and a she Asse, who although they take their denomination from the male, yet do they more resemble the female. In ancient time, the males which were conceived of a Horse and a she Asse, were called *Hinnuli*, and likewise of an Asse and a Mare, *Muli*; so are the young ones of little Goats, Deer, Hares, and other like: although some take *Innuli* for the young Harts, and the *Hinni* and *Hinnuli* for the breed of a Horse and an Asse; so that there appeareth two kinds, and both of them transplanted out of other.

65

The *Hinnus* is lesse then the Mule, but more ruddy, having ears like a Horse, and a mane and tail like an Asse, lying in the womb before the foling twelve moneths like a Horse, and are brought up like little Horses, whose age is discerned by their teeth, and they are sometimes procreated of a Horse and a Mule, and because of their aptness to beare, they are called *Burdones*, or else of *Bardus* by reason of their folly and slowness.

Manni and *Mannuli* are very little low horses, being very gentle and easie to be handled, being called also among the *Civilians, Burdi*. There is in *France*, not far from *Grationopolis*, a kind of *Mules* which in the Countrey speech are called *Iumar*, being bred of an Asse and a Bull, and in the *Helvetian* Alpes beyond *Curia*, about the Town *Speluga*, I have been sincerely informed, that there was a Horse conceived of a Bull and a Mare, and therefore *Scaliger* saith, that such a fole is called *Hinnulus*, whereof he reporteth he had seen many, and he himself had two of them, and at that instant had only one female, betwixt whose ears there were two bony bunches about the bigness of half a Wal-nut, giving evident testimony by the forehead, that her father or *Syre* was a Bull: and some say that this kind want their upper teeth: and their underchap doth in a deformed manner stretch forth it self beyond the upper, as it is in many fishes, being called of the *Gabala* and *Arverni, Befi*: And at this day there is in the Court of *France* a certain beast which in the former part is like an Asse, and in the hinder a Sheep. In *Ferraria* among other strange beasts, they nourish dwarvish Asses, of whom *Martial* made a *Distichon* to this effect, that they are not so high as a man, when he sitteth on the ground.

His tibi de mulis non est metuenda ruina:
Altius in terris pene sedere soles.

For the *Innus*, and *Ginnus*, or *Hinnus*, they are conceived by a *Mule* and a *Mare*, which are very small by reason of some disease the dam that beareth them hath in her belly: the word *Lass* signifying a young or new born Nephew, and is attributed to this kind of beasts, because they never exceed the quantity of a young fole. Both the *Mule* and the *Burdo* remain barren and never conceive, these neigh like a Horse, and that brayeth like an Asse. A *Musimon* is a short Horse, Asse, or Mule.

OF THE WILD ASSE.

A Wild Asse, called of the *Latins, Onager*; of the *Hebrews, Arod* and *Ere*, and as *Sebastian Munster* affirmeth, *Meroda* and *Arda*; in the *German* tongue it may be termed *Ein Waldesell*, and the young ones are called *Lalisions*.

Dum tener est Onager, solaque lalisio matre
Pascitur: hoc infans, sed breve nomen habet.

These wild Asses are not *Elks*, as some have reported of *Elks*, nor that *Oryx* which the ancient writers do constantly affirm to live in a continual thirst, as for the most part wild Asses do. Of these Asses are great store in *Phrygia, Lycaonia*, and *Africa*, and it is said, that the *Saracen* King of *Tunis* in *Africk*, sent unto *Ferdinand* King of *Naples*, a goodly great wild Asse, such an one as hath not been seen in this part of the world.

Apollonius affirmeth, that he saw wild Asses in great plenty beyond *Catadupa* in *Egypt*; so are there many in *Cauda*, an Island neer *Creit*: in *Persis*, in *Asia*, in *Madera*, and *Abasia, Arabia* desert, *Mauritania*, and *Armenia. Callisius* reporteth that there are such wild Asses in that region under the *Equinoctial* towards the East and South, of wonderful stature, their skins (beside the usual manner) being of divers colours, interlined variably with white and black, and the Zones and strakes descending from the top of the back unto the sides, and there divided by their winding and turning, make the foles appear of admirable variety.

These Asses love the highest Mountains and rocks, as holy Scripture teacheth, Jer. 14. *The Asses stood in the high places and drew in the wind like Dragons:* which words gave occasion to some to imagine, that wild Asses would quench their thirst with the wind without water; whereas it is the manner of all wild beasts, in extremity of thirst, to gape wide and greedily draw in the cold refreshing air, and they will not drink but of pure fountain water. They live in flocks and great companies together, but in desolate places: the males going before the females, and commonly one male will lead and rule the whole flock of females, being exceeding swift, and fearful, and therefore do they often change their places of abode; and yet it is observed, that the wild Asses of *Licia* never go over the mountain that divideth them from *Cappadocia*.

They engender among themselves, their females being much more lustfull then the males, and therefore do the males observe and watch them with a jealous eye toward their own foles, especially after they have conceived; and the female as warily avoideth the sight of the male, espcially at the time of her foling; for if she bring forth a female, the male receiveth it with all love, joy, and welcome; but if a male, then doth he with angry and envious countenance look upon it, taking it heavily that another male is bred, which in time may in the fathers place possess his dam; wherefore in a raging madness he falleth upon the fole, seeking by all his power to bite off his stones; the poor female although weakned with pain of delivery, yet helpeth her young one against the fathers rage, and like a Mother who seeing her Son slain in war, embraceth his bleeding corps, and cryeth out with doleful voice, tearing her cheeks and bleeding betwixt her brests: so would you think this silly female Asse, to mourn for her fole, now ready to die by the Sires cruelty; saying, *O my husband why is thy aspect so ireful? Why are thy eyes now become so bloudy, which even now were as white as light? Dost thou look upon the face of that monster Medusa? which turneth men into stones; or dost thou look upon some new hatched horrible Dragon, or the whelp of some Lion lately littered? Why wilt thou geld this our young one which nature hath given unto us both by procreation? O wretched beast that I am, which have conceived an unhappy fole by the fathers wickedness! O my poor and unhappy son, which for a jealous fear art deprived of thy natural parts, not by the claws of Lions (for that I would endure) but by the unnatural and more then hostile teeth of thy own father.*

These wild Asses have good and strong hoofs, their swiftness is compared to the wind, and in the time that they are hunted, they cast backward with their heels stones with such violence, as they pierce the brests of them that prosecute them if they be not very wary. They are of a large, broad, tall and beautiful body; long ears, and a silver colour, (that is as I ghesse) a bright cloud-colour, for it is but vain to imagine, that an Asse can be all white, for then were all the ancients deceived, which with one voice affirm, that he hath a black list on the back, at either side whereof are two white lines.

68

Their food is only grasse and herbs of the earth, whereby they grow very fat, their heart being the fattest part of their body, and they will not abide any flesh-eating beast, especially the Lion whom he feareth very much, for all these strong beasts devour and eat them. These Asses are very fit for civil uses, as for plowing and sowing, for being tamed they never grow wild again, as other beasts will, and they easily grow tame. It is observed, that the same being tamed, is most tame which before time was most wild. They love figs and meal above all things, wherefore the *Armenians* use to take a certain black fish bred in their waters which is poison, and covering it with meal the wild Asses come and lick thereof, and so are destroyed. The best of them are generated of a Mare and a wild Asse tamed, for they are the swiftest in course, of hardest hoof, a lean body, but of a generous and untireable stomach. The *Indian* wild Asses have one horn in their forehead, and their body all white, but their head is red: So is there another beast in *India* very like a wild Asse, which the Inhabitants eat (as we have read) about the straights of *Magellana*: When these Asses are hunted with Dogs, they cast forth their time or dung, with the favour whereof the Dogs are stayed while it is hot, and by that means the beast escapeth danger: but the Asses of *Mauritania* are very short winded, and subject to weariness and stumbling, for which cause they are more easily taken, and the best of all are not so swift as a *Barbary* horse; besides their nature is, when they see a man to stand stone still, crying, braying, and kicking, till you come at them, and when one is ready to take them, they take their heels and run away. The Inhabitants of *Arabia* Desert, by many gins and other deceitful devises take them, and on horseback follow them till they tyre, or can strike them with their darts. Their flesh being hot, doth stink and taste like an other Asses, but boyled and kept two dayes hath a pleasant taste; yet doth it not breed good bloud, because it is viscous and hard to be concocted, although there be many which eat that, as also the flesh of Panthers and other such beasts.

Pliny teacheth that there is more vertue in the wild Asses milk and bones against venome and poison, then in the tame. Likewise, in the heel of an Asse, is a principal remedy against Apostemations and bunches in the flesh, if it be applyed to the inner part of the thigh. The gall draweth out botches, and must be anointed upon impostumate scars. It is used also in Emplasters against Saint *Antonies* fire, the leprosie, and swelling in the legs and guts. The fat with oil of herbe *Mary* by anointing the reins of the back, helpeth and easeth that pain which was engendred by wind. The spleen dryed to powder and drunk in wine or drink, is good against the sickness of the spleen. The flesh is good against the pain in the ridge and hip-bones: and *Galen* affirmeth, that the urine breaketh and dissolveth the stone in the bladder. The ashes of the hoof helpeth the falling evill, and mingled with oil, cureth the kings evill, and the looseness of the hair. The marrow easeth the Gowt, and the dung mixed with the yolk of an egge and applyed to the forehead, stayeth bleeding: also the same curleth the hair if it be mingled with an Oxes gall and dryed: put into wine and drunk, cureth the sting of a Scorpion: and *Zor* an *Hebrew* affirmeth very constantly, that if a man look into an Asse; eye, it preserveth the sight, and hindereth the water that descendeth into the eye.

OF THE SCYTHIAN ASSES.

THE Asses of *Scythia* have horns wherein it is reported that the *Stygian* water of *Arcadia* may be contained, although it will eat through all other vessels be they never so hard. *Sosipater* brought of them to *Alexander* the great, who admiring the rareness, would not put them to any private use, but sent them to *Delphos*, to be offered to *Pythias*; but that these can be properly called Asses, no man can defend, although *Herodotus* also affirm, that among the *Africans* called *Aratours*, there be Asses with horns.

OF THE INDIAN ASSES.

IT is questionable whether the *Monoceros*, commonly called a *Unicorne*, the *Rhinoceros*, the *Oryx*, and the *Indian* Asse be all one beast or divers; for the *Unicorn* and *Rhinoceros* have the same things attributed to them in stories, and differ in very few reports: but for the Asses of *India*, both *Aristotle*, *Pliny* and *Ælianus*, joyntly agree, that they differ from all other whole-footed beasts, because they have one horn in the forehead, and so also have the *Rhinoceros*, *Monoceros*, and *Oryx*, but the *Indians* call a *Unicorne*, *Cartazono*; and the horn so highly prized at this day, is thought to be of the *Rhinoceros*; but *Ælianus* and *Philes* acknowledge no other *Unicorne* then the *Indian* Asse, who in bigness equalleth a Horse among the *Indians*, being all white on the body, but purple headed or red (as some say) black eyes, but *Volateranus* saith blew, having one horn in the forehead a cubit and a half long, whose upper part is red or bay, the middle black, and the neather part white, wherein the Kings and mighty men of *India* use to drink, adorning it for that purpose with sundry bracelets, pretious stones, and works of gold, holding for truth that all those which drink in those horns, shall be freed from annoyance of incurable diseases, as Convulsions, the Falling evill, and deadly poysons.

These wilde Asses exceed all other, both in stature of body, and also swiftness of foot, for at the first, they set forth very gently, and afterward speed their journey with better pace, so that it is very hard for any to follow them, but impossible to overgo them. The males take great pains in keeping their young ones, whom they continually watch and hide in the most remote and desert places they can finde. When they are hunted, they keep their weak young ones behind them, and fight for them very furiously, neither fear they to encounter horsemen. They are so strong, that no beast may stand before them, for they will receive the charge of Horses with such violence, that in their encounter they bite out their sides and tear their guts out of their belly: for which cause they are dreadful to Horses, who are most unwilling to joyn with them, for they never meet but they both perish.

They fight with their heels, but their teeth are most dangerous, for what they apprehend in them they bring it clean away: and because of this rage, those which are of any years, can never be tamed. The great King of *India* doth once every year appoint all manner of fights both men and beasts, wherein are wilde Buls, tame Rams, these wild Asses with one horn, *Hyaenaes* and Elephants. To conclude, it is but a fable of *Volaterranus*, that saith, these Asses want a gall, for they have the bladder of the gall, a portion whereof drunk, cureth the falling evill.

71

OF THE ALBORACH AND AXIS.

THERE are two other beasts to be added to the end of this rank, namely the *Alborach* among the Turks, being a fair white beast like an Asse, whereupon the Turkish Priests blasphemous idolaters, perswade the silly Pilgrims of *Mecha*, that *Mahomet* was carryed up to heaven. The *Axis*, of which *Pliny* speaketh, is a wilde beast, having a skin like the *Hinnulus* aforesaid, but spred over with whiter spots, which is bred in *India*. *Bellonius* affirmeth, that he saw two of them in the Castle of *Cair*, a male and a female, and either sex wanted horns, having long tails down to their mid-legs like Deer, and differ very little from Deer, saving in their large white spots and yellow colour, yeelding a much more clear and sounding voice then a Deer, and the female thereof is smaller then the male. This beast is by idolatrous people, dedicated to their drunken god *Bacchus*.

OF THE BADGER, OTHERWISE CALLED A BROCKE, A GRAY, OR A BAUSON.

THE *Badger* could never find a *Greek name*, although some through ignorance have foisted into a *Greek* Dictionary *Melis*, whereas in truth that is his *Latin* word, *Mele* or *Meles*, and so called, because above all other things, he loveth hony, and some later writers call him *Taxus*, *Tassus*, *Taxo*, and *Albertus Magnus*, *Daxus*. But whereas in the Scripture some translate *Tesson*, *Tahas*, or *Tachasch*, and plurally *Techaseim*,

Badgers, yet is not the matter so clear, for there is no such beauty in a Badgers skin, as to cover the Arke, or to make Princes shooes thereof: therefore some *Hebrews* say, that it signifieth an Oxe of an exceeding hard skin. *Onkelus* translateth it *Sasgona*, that is, a beast skin of divers colours; *Symmachus* and *Aquila* a jacinct colour, which cannot be; but the *Arabians, Darasch*, and the *Persians, Asthak*; yet it may be rather said, that those skins spoken of Exod. 25. Numb. 4. Ezek. 26. be of the *Lynx*, or some such other beast: for *Tachasch* cometh neer *Thos*, signifying a kind of Wolf not hurtful to men, being rough and hairy in Winter, but smooth in Summer.

The *Italians* call a Badger *Tasso*, the *Rhetians, Tasch*; the *French, Tausson, Taixin, Tasson, Tesson*, and sometime *Grisart*, for her colour: sometime *Blareau*, and at *Paris, Bedevo*. The *Spaniards, Tasugo, Texon*; the *Germans, Tachs*, or *Daxs*; the *Illyrians, Gezwecz*.

Badgers are plentiful in *Naples, Sicily, Lucane*, and in the *Alpine* and *Helvetian* coasts, so are they also in *England*. In *Lucane* there is a certain wilde beast, resembling both a Bear and a Hog, not in quantity, but in form and proportion of body; which therefore may fitly be called in *Greek, Suarctos*, for a *Gray*, in short legs, ears and feet, is like a Bear, but in fatness like a Swine. Therefore it is observed, that there be two kinds of this beast, one resembling a Dog in his feet, which is cald *Canine*; the other a Hog in his cloven hoof, and is cald *Swinish*: also these differ in the fashion of their snowt, one resembling the snowt of a Dog, the other of a Swine: and in their meat, the one eating flesh and carrion like a Dog, the other roots and fruits like a Hog, as both kinds have been found in *Normandy* and other parts of *France* and *Sicilie*. This beast diggeth her a den or cave in the earth, and there liveth; never coming forth but for meat and easement, which it maketh out of his den: when they dig their den, after they have entred a good depth for avoiding the earth out, one of them falleth on the back, and the other layeth all the earth on his belly, and so taking his hinder feet in his mouth, draweth the belly-laden Badger out of the cave, which disburdeneth her cariage, and goeth in for more till all be finished and emptied. The wily Fox never makth a Den for himself, but finding a Badgers cave, in her absence, layeth his excrements at the hole of the Den, the which when the *Gray* returneth, if she smell (as the savour is strong) she forbeareth to enter as noisome, and so leaveth her elaborate house to the Fox. These Badgers are very sleepy, especially in the day time, and stir not abroad but in the night, for which cause they are called *Lucifugæ*; that is, *avoiders of the light*. They eat hony, and wormes, and hornets, and such like things, because they are not very swift of foot to take other creatures. They love Orchards, Vines, and places of fruits also, and in the autumn they grow therewith very fat.

They are in quantity as big as a Fox, but of a shorter and thicker body; their skin is hard, but rough and rugged, their hair harsh and stubborn, of an intermingled grisard colour, sometime white, sometime black, his back covered with black, and his belly with white, his head from the top thereof to the ridge of his shoulder, is adorned with strakes of white and black, being black in the middle, and white at each side. He hath very sharp teeth, and is therefore accounted a deep-biting beast. His back is broad, his legs (as some say) longer on the right side then on the left, and therefore he runneth best when he getteth to the side of a hill, or a cart-road-way. His tail is short but hairy, and of divers colours, having a long face or snowt like the *Zibethus*: his forelegs being a full span long, and the hinder legs shorter, short ears and little eyes, a great bladder of gall, a body very fat betwixt the skin and the flesh, and about the heart; and it is held that this fat increaseth with the Moon, and decreaseth with the same, being none at all at the change: his forelegs have very sharp nails, bare and apt to dig withall, being five both before and behind, but the hinder very short ones and covered with hair. His savour is strong, and is much troubled with lice about his secrets; the length of his body from the nose which hangeth out like a Hogs nose, to the tail or rump, is some thirty inches and a little more, the hair of his back three fingers long; his neck is short and like a Dogs: both male and female have under their hole another outwardly, but not inwardly in the male. If she be hunted out of her Den with Hounds, she biteth them grievously if she lay hold on them, wherefore they avoid her carefully, and the Hunters put great broad collars made of a Grayes skin about their Dogs neck, to keep them the safer from the Badgers teeth: her manner is to fight on her back, using

74

thereby both her teeth and her nails, and by blowing up her skin above measure after an unknown manner, she defendeth her self against the strokes of men, and the teeth of Dogs: wherefore she is hardly taken, but by devises and gins for that purpose invented; with their skins they make quivers for arrows, and some shepheards in *Italy* use thereof to make sacks, wherein they wrap themselves from the injury of rain.

In *Italy* and *Germany* they eat Grays flesh, and boil with it pears, which maketh the flesh taste like the flesh of a Porcupine. The flesh is best in *September* if it be fat, and of the two kinds, the Swinish Badger is better flesh then the other. There are sundry vertues confected out of this beast; for it is affirmed, that if the fat of a Badger mingled with crude hony, and anointed upon a bare place of a horse, where the former hairs are pulled off, it will make new white hairs grow in that place: and it is certain (although the *Grecians* make no reckoning of Badgers grease, yet) it is a very soveraign thing to soften, and therefore *Serenus* prescribeth it to anoint them that have Fevers or Inflamations of the body,

Nec spernendus adeps dederit, quem bestia melis.

And not to be despised for other cures: as for example, the easing of the pain of the reins if it be given in a glyster, and likewise the fat of a Dog and a Badger mingled together, do loosen contracted sinews.

The ashes of a Badger is found to help the bleeding of the stomach, and the same sod and drunk, preventeth danger by the biting of a mad Dog: and *Brunfelsius* affirmeth, that if the bloud of a Badger be instilled into the horns of Cattel with salt, it keepeth them from the murrain, and the same dryed and beat to powder doth wonderfully help the Leprosie. The brain sod with oil easeth all aches; the liver taken out of water, helpeth swellings in the mouth; and some affirm, that if one wear soles made of Badgers skins in their shooes, it giveth great ease unto the Gowt. The biting of this beast is venemous, because it feedeth upon all venemous meats which creep upon the earth, although *Arnoldus* be of a contrary judgement; and of this beast I can report no other thing worth the noting, save that the Noble family of the *Taxons* in *Ferraria*, took their name from this creature.

OF THE BEAR.

A Bear is called in the *Hebrew, Dob,* and plurally *Dubim*; of the *Arabians, Dubbe*; of the *Chaldeans, Duba, Aldub* and *Daboube*; of the *Grecians, Arctos*; of some *Dasyllis*, because of the roughness of his hair; of other *Beiros*, and *Monios*, signifying a solitary Bear. The *Latins* call him *Ursur*, which some conjecture to be *tanquam orsus*, signifying that it is but begun to be framed in the dams belly, and perfected after the littering thereof. The *Italians* call it *Orso*, so also the *Spaniards*; the *French, Ours*; the *Germans, Bear*, and *Beer*; the *Bohemians, Nedwed*; the *Polonians, Vuluver*: and the attributes of this beast are many among Authors, both *Greek* and *Latin*; as *Æmonian* Bears, armed, filthy, deformed, cruel, dreadful, fierce, greedy, *Calydonian, Erymanthean*, bloudy, heavy, night ranging, *Lybican*, menacing, *Numidian, Ossean*, head-long, ravening, rigid and terrible Bear; all which serve to set forth the nature hereof, as shall be afterward in particular discoursed.

First, therefore concerning several kinds of Bears, it is observed, that there is in general two; a greater, and a lesser; and these lesser are more apt to clime trees then the other, neither do they ever grow to so great a stature as the other. Besides there are Bears which are called *Amphibia*, because they live both on the Land and in the Sea, hunting and catching fish like an *Otter* or *Beaver*, and these are white coloured. In the Ocean Islands towards the North, there are Bears of a great stature, fierce and cruel, who with their fore-feet do break up the hardest congealed Ice on the Sea, or other great Waters, and draw out of those holes great abundance of fishes: and so in other frozen Seas are many such like, having black claws, living for the most part upon the Seas, except tempestuous weather drive them to the Land.

In the Eastern parts of *India*, there is a beast in proportion of body very like a Bear, yet indued with no other quality of that kind, (being neither so wild, nor ravenous, nor strong) and it is called a *Formicarian* Bear; for God hath so provided, that whereas that Countrey is abundantly annoyed with the Emmets or Ants, that beast doth so prey and feed upon them, that by the strength and vertuous humor of his tongue, the silly poor Inhabitans are exceedingly relieved from their grievous and dangerous numbers.

Bears are bred in many Countreys, as in the *Helvetian* Alpine region, where they are so strong and full of courage, that they can tear in pieces both Oxen and Horses, for which cause the Inhabitants study by all means to take them. Likewise there are Bears in *Persia*, which do raven beyond all measure, and all other; so also the Bears of *Numidia*, which are of a more elegant form and composition then the residue;

Profuit ergo nihil misero, quod cominus ursos
Figebat Numidas, Albena nudus arena.

And whereas *Pliny* affirmeth, that there are no Bears in *Africk*, he mistook that Countrey for *Creet*, and so some say, that in that Island be no Wolves, Vipers, or other such venemous creatures; whereof the Poets give a vain reason, because *Jupiter* was born there: but we know also, that there be no Bears bred in *England*.

In the Countrey of *Arabia*, from the Promontory *Dira* to the South, are Bears which live upon eating of flesh, being of a yellowish colour, which do far excel all other Bears, both in activity or swiftness, and in quantity of body. Among the *Roxolani* and *Lituanians*, are Bears, which being tamed are presents for Princes. *Aristotle* in his wonders reporteth, that there are white Bears in *Misia*, which being eagerly hunted, do send forth such a breath, that putrifieth immediately the flesh of the Dogs, and whatsoever other beast cometh within the favour thereof, it maketh the flesh of them not fit to be eaten: but if either men or dogs approach or come nigh them, they vomit forth such abundance of phlegm, that either the hunters are thereby choked or blinded.

Thracta also breedeth white Bears, and the King of *Æthiopia* in his *Hebrew* Epistle which he wrote to the Bishop of *Rome*, affirmeth, that there are Bears in his Countrey: In *Muscovia* are Bears, both of a Snow white, yellow, and dusky colour, and it hath been seen that the Noble womens Chariots drawn by six Horses, have been covered with the skins of white Bears, from the pastern to the head: and as all other creatures do bring forth some white, and some black, so also do Bears, who in general do breed and bring forth their young in all cold Countreys, some of a dusky and some of a brown black colour.

A Bear is of a most venereous and lustful disposition, for night and day the females with most ardent inflamed desires, do provoke the males to copulation; and for this cause at that time they are most fierce and angry.

Philippus Cosseus of *Constance*, did most confidently tell me, that in the Mountains of *Savoy*, a Bear carryed a young maid into his den by violence, where in venereous manner he had the carnal use of her body, and while he kept her in his den, he daily went forth and brought her home the best Apples and other fruits he could get, presenting them unto her for her meat in very amorous sort; but always when he went to forrage, he rouled a huge great stone upon the mouth of his den, that the Virgin should not escape away: at length her parents with long search, found their little Daughter in the Bears den, who delivered her from that savage and beastial captivity.

The time of their copulation is in the beginning of Winter, although sometime in Summer, (but such young ones seldom live) yet most commonly in *February* or *January*. The manner of their copulation is like to a mans, the male moving himself upon the belly of the female, which lyeth on the earth flat upon the back, and either embraceth other with their fore-feet: they remain very long time in that act, inasmuch as if they were very fat at their first entrance, they disjoin not themselves again till they be made lean.

Immediately after they have conceived, they betake themselves to their dens; where they (without meat) grow very fat (especially the males) only by sucking their fore-feet. When they enter into their den, they convey themselves in backwards, that so they may put out their foot-steps from the sight of the hunters. The males give great honor to the females great with young, during the time of their secresie, so that, although they lie together in one cave, yet do they part it by a division or small ditch in the midst, neither of them touching the other. The nature of all of them is, to avoid cold, and therefore in the Winter time do they hide themselves, chusing rather to suffer famine then cold; lying for the most part three or four months together and never see the light, whereby their guts grow so empty, that they are almost closed up and stick together.

When they first enter into their den, they betake themselves to quiet and rest, sleeping without any awaking, for the first fourteen dayes, so that it is thought an easie stroke cannot awake them. But how long the females go with young is not certain, some affirm three months, others but thirty dayes, which is more probable, for wild beasts do not couple themselves being with young (except a Hare and a Linx) and the Bears being (as is already said) very lustful, to the intent that they may no longer want the company of their males, do violently cast their Whelps, and so presently after delivery, do after the manner of Conies betake themselves to their lust, and nourishing their young ones both together: and this is certain, that they never come out of their caves, till their young ones be thirty dayes old at the least; and *Pliny* precisely affirmeth, that they litter the thirtyeth day after their conception; and for this cause, a Bear bringeth forth the least whelp of all other great beasts; for their whelps at their first littering are no bigger then rats, nor longer then ones finger. And whereas it hath been believed and received, that the whelps of Bears at their first littering are without all form and fashion, and nothing but a little congealed blood like a lump of flesh, which afterwards the old one frameth with her tongue to her own likeness, as *Pliny, Solinus, Ælianus, Orus, Oppianus,* and *Ovid* have reported, yet is the truth most evidently otherwise, as by the eye-witness of *Joachimus Rheticus*, and other, is disproved: only it is littered blind without eyes, naked without hair, and the hinder legs not perfect, the fore-feet folded up like a fist, and other members deformed by reason of the immoderate humor or moystness in them, which also is one cause, why the Womb of the Bear cannot retain the seed to the perfection of her young ones.

They bring forth sometimes two, and never above five, which the old Bear daily keepeth close to her brest, so warming them with the heat of her body and the breath of her mouth, till they be thirty days old; at what time they come abroad, being in the beginning of *May*, which is the third Month from the Spring. The old ones being almost dazled with long darkness, coming into light again seem to stagger and reel to and fro, and then for the straightness of their guts, by reason of their long fasting do eat the hearb *Arum*, commonly called in English *Wake-Robbin* or *Calves-foot*, being of very sharp and tart taste, which enlargeth their guts, and so being recovered, they remain all the time their young are with them, more fierce and cruel then at other times. And concerning the same *Arum*, called also *Dracunculus* and *Oryx*, there is a pleasant vulgar tale, whereby some have conceived that Bears eat this herb before their lying secret; and by vertue thereof (without meat, or sense of cold) they pass away the whole Winter in sleep.

There was a certain Cow-herd in the Mountains of *Helvetia*, which coming down a hill with a great Caldron on his back, he saw a Bear eating of a root which he had pulled up with his feet; the Cow-herd stood still till the Bear was gone, and afterward came to the place where the beast had eaten the same, and finding more of the same root, did likewise eat it; he had no sooner tasted thereof, but he had such a desire to sleep, that he could not contain himself, but he must needs lie down in the way and their fell asleep, having covered his head with the Caldron, to keep himself from the vehemency of the cold, and their slept all the Winter time without harm, and never rose again till the Spring time: Which fable if a man will believe, then doubtless this hearb may cause the Bears to be sleepers, not for fourteen days, but for fourscore days together.

The ordinary food of Bears is fish: for the Water-bear and others will eat fruits, Apples, Grapes, Leaves, and Pease, and will break into Bee-hives sucking out the Hony; Likewise Bees, Snayls, and Emmets, and flesh if it be lean or ready to putrifie; but if a Bear do chance to kill a Swine, or a Bull, or Sheep, he eateth them presently, whereas other Beasts eat not hearbs if they eat flesh: likewise they drink water; but not like other beasts, neither sucking it or lapping it, but as it were, even biting at it.

Some affirm, that Bears do wax or grow as long as they live, that there have been seen some of them five cubits long; yea I my self saw a Bears skin of that length, and broader then an Oxes skin.

The head of a Bear is his weakest part (as the hand of a Lyon is the strongest) for by a small blow on his head he hath often been strucken dead, the bones of the head being very thin and tender: yea more tender then the beak of a Parrot. The mouth of a Bear is like a Hogs mouth, but longer; being armed with teeth on both sides, like a saw, and standing deep in his mouth, they have very thick lips, for which cause, he cannot easily or hastily with his teeth break asunder the hunters nets, except with his fore-feet.

His neck is short, like a Tygers and a Lyons, apt to bend downwards to his meat; his belly is very large, being uniform, and next to it the intrals as in a Wolf: It hath also four speans to her Paps. The genital of a Bear after his death waxeth as hard as horn, his knees and elbows are like to an Apes, for which cause they are not swift or nimble: his feet are like hands, and in them and his loins is his greatest strength, by reason whereof, he sometimes setteth himself upright upon his hinder legs: the pastern of his leg being fleshy like a Cammels, which maketh them unfit for travel; they have sharp claws, but a very small tail as all other long haired creatures have.

They are exceeding full of fat or lard-grease, which some use superstitiously beaten with Oyl, wherewith they anoynt their Grape-sickles when they go to vintage, perswading themselves that if no body know thereof, their tender Vine-branches shall never be consumed by Caterpillers.

Other attribute this to the vertue of Bears blood, and *Theophrastus* affirmeth, that if Bears grease be kept in a vessel, at such time as the Bears lie secret, it will either fill it up, or cause it to run over. The flesh of Bears is unfit for meat, yet some use to eat it, after it hath been twice sod; other eat it baked in pasties; but the truth is, it is better for medicine then for food. *Theophrastus* likewise affirmeth, that at the time when Bears lie secret, their dead flesh encreaseth which is kept in houses, but Bears fore-feet are held for a very delicate and well tasted food, full of sweetness; and much used by the *German* Princes.

The skins of Bears are used in the far Northern regions for garments in the Winter time, which they make so artificially, covering themselves with them from the crown of the head to the feet; that (as *Munster* affirmed) some men deceived with that appearance, deemed the people of *Lapponia* to be hairy all over. The souldiers of the *Moors* wear garments made of Lyons, Pardals, and Bears skins, and sleep upon them; and so it is reported of *Herodotus Megarensis* the Musitian, who in the day time wore a Lyons skin, and in the night lay in a Bears skin.

The constitution of the body of a Bear is beyond measure phlegmatique, because he fasteth in the Winter time so long without meat: His voyce is fierce and fearful in his rage, but in the night time mournful, being given much to ravening. If a Bear do eat of *Mandragoras*, he presently dyeth, except he meet with Emmets, by licking of whom he recovereth: so likewise if he be sick of a Surfeit.

A Bear is much subject to blindness of the eyes, and for that cause they desire the Hives of Bees, not only for the Hony, but by the stinging of the Bees, their eyes are cured. It hath not been seen that a female Bear was taken great with young, which cometh to pass, by reason that they go to their Dens so soon as they are conceived, and come not out thence till they have littered: And because of the fierceness of this beast, they are seldom taken alive, except they be very young: so that some are killed in the Mountains by poyson, the Countrey being so steep and rocky that Hunters cannot follow them; some taken in ditches of the earth, and other gins. *Oppianus* relateth, that near *Tygris* and *Armenia*, the Inhabitants use this stratagem to take Bears. The people go often to the Woods to find the Den of the Bear, following a Leam-hound, whose nature is so soon as he windeth the Beast, to bark, whereby his leader discovereth the prey, and so draweth off the Hound with the leam; then come the people in great multitude, and compassing him about with long nets, placing certain men at each end: then tye they a long rope to one side of the net as high from the ground as the small of a mans belly: whereunto are fastned divers plumes and feathers of Vultures, Swans, and other resplendent coloured birds, which with the wind make a noise or hissing, turning over and glistering; on the other side of the net they build four little hovels of green boughs, wherein they lay four men covered all over with green leaves, then all being prepared, they sound their Trumpets, and wind their Horns; at the noise whereof the Bear ariseth, and in his fearful rage runneth to and fro as if he saw fire: the young men armed make unto him, the Bear looking round about, taketh the plainest way toward the rope hung full of feathers, which being stirred and haled by them that hold it, maketh the Bear much affraid with the ratling and hissing thereof, and so flying from that side half mad, runneth into the nets, where the Keepers entrap him so cunningly, that he seldom escapeth.

When a Bear is set upon by an armed man, he standeth upright and taketh the man betwixt his fore-feet, but he being covered all over with iron plates can receive no harm, and then may easily with a sharp knife or dagger pierce through the heart of the beast.

If a she Bear having young ones be hunted, she driveth her whelps before her untill they be wearied, and then if she be not prevented, she climbeth upon a tree, carrying one of her young in her mouth, and the other on her back. A Bear will not willingly fight with a man, but being hurt by a man, he gnasheth his teeth, and licketh his fore-feet: and it is reported by an Ambassador of *Poland*, that when the *Sarmatians* find a Bear, they inclose the whole Wood by a multitude of people, standing not above a cubit one from another, then cut they down the outmost trees, so that they raise a wall of wood to hem in the Bears; this being effected, they raise the Bear, having certain forks in their hands made for that purpose, and when the Bear approacheth, they (with those forks) fall upon him, one keeping his head, another one leg, another his body, and so with force muzzle him and tie his legs, leading him away. The *Rhætians* use this policy to take Wolves and Bears: they raise up great posts, and cross them with a long beam laded with heavy weights, unto the which beam they fasten a cord with meat therein, whereunto the beast coming, and biting at the meat, pulleth down the beam upon her own pate.

The Inhabitants of *Helvetia* hunt them with mastiff Dogs, because they should not kill their Cattel left at large in the field in the day time; They likewise shoot them with guns, giving a good sum of money to them that can bring them a slain Bear. The *Sarmatians* use to take Bears by this sleight; under those trees wherein Bees breed, they plant a great many of sharp pointed stakes, putting one hard into the hole wherein the Bees go in and out, whereunto the Bear climbing, and coming to pull it forth, to the end that he may come to the Hony, and being angry that the stake sticketh so fast in the hole, with violence plucketh it forth with both her fore-feet, whereby she looseth her hold and falleth down upon the picked stakes, whereupon she dieth, if they that watch for her come not to take her off. There was reported by *Demetrius* Ambassador at *Rome*, from the King of *Musco*, that a neighbour of his going to seek Hony, fell into a hollow tree up to the brest in Hony, where he lay two days, being not heard by any man to complain; at length came a great Bear to this Hony; and putting his head into the tree, the poor man took hold thereof, whereat the Bear suddenly affrighted, drew the man out of that deadly danger, and so ran away for fear of a worse creature.

But if there be no tree wherein Bees do breed neer to the place where the Bear abideth, then they use to anoynt some hollow place of a tree with Hony, whereinto Bees will enter and make Hony-combes, and when the Bear findeth them she is killed as aforesaid. In *Norway* they use to saw the tree almost asunder, so that when the beast climbeth it, she falleth down upon piked stakes laid underneath to kill her: And some make a hollow place in a tree, wherein they put a great pot of water, having anoynted it with Hony, at the bottom whereof are fastened certain hooks bending downward, leaving an easie passage for the Bear to thrust in her head to get the Hony, but impossible to pull it forth again alone, because the hooks take hold on her skin: this pot they binde fast to a tree, whereby the Bear is taken alive, and blindefolded, and though her strength break the cord or chain wherewith the pot is fastened, yet can she not escape or hurt any body in the taking, by reason her head is fastened in the pot.

To conclude, other make ditches or pits under Apple-trees, laying upon their mouth rotten sticks, which they cover with earth, and strow upon it herbs, and when the Bear cometh to the Apple-tree, she falleth into the pit and is taken.

The herb Wolfeban or Libardine is poison to Foxes, Wolves, Dogs, and Bears, and to all beasts that are littered blinde, as the *Alpine*

Rhætians affirm. There is one kinde of this called *Cyclamine*, which the *Valdensians* call *Tora*, and with the juyce thereof they poyson their darts, whereof I have credibly received this story; That a certain *Valdensian*, seeing a wilde Bear, having a dart poysoned herewith, did cast it at the Bear being far from him, and lightly wounded her; it being no sooner done, but the Bear ran to and fro in a wonderful perplexity through the woods, unto a very sharp cliffe of a rock, where the man saw her draw her last breath, as soon as the poyson had entered to her heart, as he afterward found by opening of her body. The like is reported of Hen-bane, another herb: But there is a certain black fish in *Armenia*, full of poyson, with the powder whereof they poyson Figs, and cast them in those places where wilde beasts are most plentiful, which they eat, and so are killed.

Concerning the industry or natural disposition of a Bear, it is certain that they are very hardly tamed, and not to be trusted though they seem never so tame; for which cause there is a story of *Diana* in *Lysias*, that there was a certain Bear made so tame that it went up and down among men and would feed with them, taking meat at their hands, giving no occasion to fear or mistrust her cruelty: on a day, a young maid playing with the Bear lasciviously did so provoke it, that he tore her in pieces; the Virgins brethren seeing the murther, with their darts slew the Bear, whereupon followed a great pestilence through all that region: and when they consulted with the Oracle, the paynim God gave answer, that the plague could not cease, untill they dedicated some Virgins unto *Diana* for the Bears sake that was slain; which some interpreting that they should sacrifice them: *Embarus* upon condition the Priesthood might remain in his family, slew his only daughter to end the pestilence, and for this cause the Virgins were after dedicated to *Diana* before their marriage, when they were betwixt ten and fifteen year old, which was performed in the month of *January*, otherwise they could not be married: Yet Bears are tamed for labours, and especially for sports among the *Roxolani* and *Lybians*, being taught to draw water with wheels out of the deepest wels; likewise stones upon sleds to the building of walls.

A Prince of *Lituania* nourished a Bear very tenderly, feeding her from his table with his own hand, for he had used her to be familiar in his Court, and to come into his own chamber when he listed, so that she would go abroad into the fields and woods, returning home again of her own accord, and would with her hand or foot rub the Kings chamber door to have it opened, when she was hungry; it being locked: it happened that certain young Noble-men conspired the death of this Prince, and came to his chamber door, rubbing it after the custom of the Bear, the King not doubting any evill, and supposing it had been his Bear, opened the door, and they presently slew him.

There is a fable of a certain wilde Bear, of huge stature, which terrified all them that looked upon her, the which *Pythagoras* sent for, and kept to himself, very familiarly using to stroke and milk her; at the length when he was weary of her, he whispered in her ear, and bound her with an oath, that being departed she should never more harm any living thing, which saith the fable, she observed to her dying day. These Bears care not for any thing that is dead, and therefore if a man can hold his breath as if he were dead, they will not harm him; which gave occasion to *Esope*, to fable of two companions and sworn friends, who travelling together met with a Bear, whereat they being amazed, one of them ran away and gat up into a tree; the other fell down and counterfeited himself dead, unto whom the Bear came and smelt at his nostrils and ears for breath, but perceiving none, departed without hurting him: soon after the other friend came down from the tree, and merrily asked his companion what the Bear said in his ear, Marry (quoth he) she warn'd me that I should never trust such a fugitive friend as thou art, which didst forsake me in my greatest necessity: thus far *Esop*.

They will bury one another being dead, as *Tzetzes* affirmeth, and it is received in many Nations, that children have been nursed by Bears: *Paris* thrown out of the City, was nourished by a Bear. There is in *France* a Noble house of the *Ursons*, whose first founder is reported to have been certain years together nourished by a Bear, and for that cause was called *Urson*: and some affirm, that *Arcesius* was so, being deceived by the name of his mother who was called *Arctos*, a Bear: as among the *Latines* was *Ursula*. And it is reported in the year of our Lord 1274. that the Concubine of Pope *Nicholas* (being with childe as was supposed) brought forth a young Bear, which she did not by any unlawful copulation with such a beast, but only with the most holy Pope; and conceived such a creature, by strength of imagination, lying in his Palace, where she saw the pictures of many Bears; so that the holy Father being first put in good hope of a son, and afterward seeing this monster (like himself, Rev. 13.) for anger and shame defaced all his pictures of those beasts. There is a mountain called the Mountain of Bears in *Cyzicus*, betwixt *Chersonesus* and *Propontus*; so called, because as some have affirmed, *Helice* and *Cynosuta* were turned into Bears in that place, but the reason is more probable, because it was full of Bears, or else because it was so high that it seemed to touch the *Bear*-star.

There is a Constellation called the Bear in the figure of seven Stars like a Cart, whereof four stand in the place of the wheels, and three in the room of Horses. The *Septentrions* call them *Triones*, that is yoked Oxen. But there are two Bears, a greater and a lesser. The greater is called *Callisto*, after the name of *Lycaons* daughter, who reigned in *Arcadia*, whereof many give divers reasons. For they say *Callisto* was a companion of *Diana*, and used to hunt with her being very like unto her, and one day *Iupiter* came to her in the likeness of *Diana*, and deflowred her, and when she was with childe, *Diana* asked how that happened, to whom *Callisto* answered, that it happened by her fact: wherewith the Goddess being angry, turned her into a Bear, in which shape she brought forth *Arcas*, and they both wandering in the Woods, were taken and brought for a present unto *Lycaon* her father: And upon a day, the Bear being ignorant of the law, entered into the Temple of *Jupiter Lycæus*, and her son followed her, for which the *Arcadians* would have slain them both, but *Iupiter* in pity of them took them both into Heaven, and placed them among the Stars.

Other say that *Callisto* was turned into a Bear by *Iuno*, whom afterward *Diana* slew, and coming to knowledge that it was *Callisto*, she placed her for a sign in Heaven, which is called *Ursa Major*, the great Bear; which before that time was called *Hamaxa*; but the reason of these fables is rendred by *Palæphatus*, because that *Callisto* going into a Bears den, was by the Bear devoured, and so her foolish companions seeing none come forth but the Bear, fondly imagined that the Virgin was turned into a Bear.

There is another Constellation next to the great Bear, called *Arctophylax, Bootes,* or the little Bear, in whose girdle is a bright Star called *Arcturus,* and from this constellation of Bears, cometh the denomination of the *Arctique* and *Antarctique pole.* Other affirm, that the two Bears were *Helice* and *Cynosura,* the two Nurses of *Iupiter,* because sometime they are so named; the cause whereof is apparent in the *Greek* tongue, for *Helice* is a Star, having as it were a tail rowled up, and *Cynosura,* a tail at length like a Dog: They are also nourished for sport for as their bodies do in one sort resemble Apes, so do also their dispositions, being apt to sundry gestures and pastimes, lying upon their backs, and turning their hands and feet, rock themselves upon them as a woman rocketh her childe in a cradle; but principally for fight: for which occasion they were preserved of old time by the *Romans*: For when *Messala* was Consul, *Ænobarbus Domitius* presented in one ring or circle, an hundred Bears, and so many hunters with them.

> —— *Rabido nec proditus ore*
> *Fumantem nasum vivi tentaveris ursi,*
> *Sit placidus licet, & lambat digitosque manusque:*
> *Si dolor & bilis, si justa coegerit ira,*
> *Ursus erit vacua dentes in pelle fatiges.*

They will not willingly fight with a man, although men may do it without hurt, for if they annoynt or sprinkle the months of Lyons or Bears with Vitriol or Copperas, it will so bind their chaps together, that they shall not be able to bite, which caused *Martiall* to write thus:

> *Præceps sanguinea dum se rotat ursus arena,*
> *Implicitam visco perdidit ille fugam.*
> *Splendida jam tecto cessent venabula ferro:*
> *Nec volet excussa lancea torta manu.*
> *Deprendat vacuo venator in aere prædam,*
> *Si captare feras aucupis arte placet.*

Alexander had a certain *Indian* Dog given unto him, to whom was put a Bore and a Bear to fight withall, but he disdaining them, would not once regard them, but when a Lyon came, he rose up and fought with him.

Bears, they will fight with Buls, Dogs, and Horses: when they fight with Buls, they take them by their horns, and so with the weight of their body, they weary and press the beast, untill they may easily slay him: and this fight is for the most part on his pack. A *Rhinoceros* set on by a Bear in a publick spectacle at *Rome*, did easily cast him off from the hold he had on his horn. She doth not adventure on a wilde Bore, except the Bore be asleep, or not seeing her. There is also a mortal hatred betwixt a Horse and a Bear, for they know one another at the first sight; and prepare to combat, which they rather act by policy then by strength: The Bear falling flat on his back the Horse leaping on the Bear, which pulleth at his guts with her fore-feet-nails, and is by the heels of the Horse wounded to death, if he strike the Bear upon his head. Also Bears fear a Sea-calf, and will not fight with them if they can be avoided, for they know they shall be overcome.

Great is the fierceness of a Bear, as appeareth by holy Scripture, Hos. 13. *I will meet them as a Bear robbed of her whelps* (saith the Lord) *and will tear in pieces their froward heart:* And *Chusai* telleth *Absalom*, 2 Sam. 17. *Thou knowest that thy Father and the men that be with him be most valiant and fierce, like a she Bear robbed of her Whelps*: for a she Bear is more couragious then a male.

There is a filthy Nation of men called *Taifah*, who are given unto a Sodomitical buggery, to commit uncleanness man with man, and especially with young boyes; but if any of them take a wilde Bore, or kill a Bear, he shall be exempted from this kind of beastly impudicity. *Heliogabalus* was wont to shut up his drunken friends together, and suddenly in the night would put in among them Bears, Wolves, Lyons, and Leopards, muzled and disarmed, so that when they did awake, they should finde such chamber-fellows, as they could not behold (if darkness did not blind them) without singular terror; whereby many of them fell into swounds, sickness, extasie and madness.

Vitoldus King of *Lituania*, kept certain Bears of purpose, to whom he cast all persons which spoke against his tyranny, putting them first of all into Bears skins; whose cruelty was so great, that if he had commanded any of them to hang themselves, they would rather obey him then endure the terror of his indignation: In like sort did *Alexander Pheræus* deal with his subjects, as is reported by *Textor*. *Valentinianus* the Emperor nourished two Bears devourers of men, one of them called golden *Mica*, the other *Innocentia*; which he lodged neer his own Chamber: at length after many slaughters of men, he let *Innocentia* go loose in the Woods for her good deserts, in bringing so many people to their funerals.

There are many natural operations in Bears. *Pliny* reporteth, that if a woman be in sore travail of childe-birth, let a stone or arrow which hath killed a Man, a Bear or a Bore, be thrown over the house wherein the woman is, and she shall be eased of her pain. There is a small worm called *Volvox*, which eateth the Vine-branches when they are young, but if the Vine-sickles be anoynted with Bears blood, that worm will never hurt them. If the blood or grease of a Bear be set under a bed, it will draw unto it all the fleas, and so kill them by cleaving thereunto. But the vertues medicinal are very many: and the first of all, the blood cureth all manner of Bunches and Apostumes in the flesh, and bringeth hair upon the eye-lids if the bare place be anoynted therewith.

The fat of a Lyon is most hot and dry, and next to a Lyons, a Leopards; next to a Leopards, a Bears; and next to a Bears, a Buls. The later Physitians use to cure convulsed and distracted parts, spots, and tumors in the body. It also helpeth the pain in the loyns, if the sick part be anoynted therewith, and all Ulcers in the legs or shins, when a Plaister is made thereof with Bole-Armorick. Also the Ulcers of the feet, mingled with Allom. It is soveraign against the falling of the hair, compounded with wilde roses. The *Spaniards* burn the brain of Bears when they die in any publick sports, holding them venemous, because being drunk, they drive a man to be as mad as a Bear; and the like is reported of the heart of a Lyon, and the brain of a Cat. The right eye of a Bear dryed to powder, and hung about childrens necks in a little bag, driveth away the terror of dreams, and both the eyes whole, bound to a mans left arm, easeth a quartain Ague.

The Liver of a Sow, a Lamb, and a Bear put together, and trod to powder under ones shooes easeeth and defendeth Cripples from inflamation: the gall being preserved and warmed in water, delivereth the body from cold, when all other medicine falleth. Some give it mixt with water, to them that are bitten with a mad Dog, holding it for a singular remedy, if the party can fast three days before. It is also given against the Palsie, the Kings Evill, the Falling-sickness, an old Cough, the

Inflamation of the Eyes, the running of the Ears, the difficulty of Urine, and delivery in Childe-birth, the Hemorrhoides, the weakness of the Back. The stones in a Perfume are good against the Falling evill, and the Palsie; and that women may go their full time, they make Amulets of Bears nails, and cause them to wear them all the time they are with childe.

OF THE BEAVER MALE AND FEMALE.

A Beaver is called in *Greek, Castor*; in *Latine, Fiber*; in *Italian, Bivarro*, or *Bivero*, and *Ilcastoreo*; in *Spanish, Castor*; in *French, Bieure*, and sometime *Castor*; in *Illyrian, Bobr*; in *Germain, Biber*: all which words at the first sight seem to be derived from the *Latine*: There is no certain word for it in *Hebrew*: in *Arabia* it is called *Albednester*: it is also called in *Latine, Canis Ponticus*, but *Canis Fluviatilis*, is another Beast, as we shall manifest in the succeeding discourse of an Otter: and the reason why in *Latine* it is called *Fiber*, is, because (as *Varro* saith) it covereth the sides, banks, or extremities of the river, as the extremities or laps of the ear and liver are called *Fibræ*, and the skirts of garments *Fimbriæ*: but the reason why the *Græcians* call it *Castor*, is not as the *Latines* have supposed, because it biteth off his own stones, *quasi castandro seipsum*, as shall be manifested soon after, but of *Castrando*, because for the stones thereof it is hunted and killed; or rather of *Gaster*, signifying a belly, for that the body is long and almost all belly; or rather because of the colour & ill savour thereof.

This Beaver is no other then that which *Aristotle* calleth *Latax*, and it differeth from an *Otter* only in the tayl. Some compare a Beaver with a

Badger, but they attribute to him a longer body and smoother hair, but shorter and softer then a Badgers: their colour is somewhat yellow and white, aspersed with ash-colour, which stand out beyond the shorter hairs, double their length: they are neat and soft like unto an Otters, and the hairs length of the one and others colour, is not equal. Some have seen them brown declining to black, which *Albertus* preferreth, and *Silvius* affirmeth, that his long hairs are like a Dogs, and the short ones like an Otter. They are most plentiful in *Pontus*, for which cause it is called *Canis Ponticus*, they are also bred in the Rivers of *Spain*, and in the River *Marn* in *France*; *Padus*, in *Italy*; in *Savoy*, in the Rivers *Isara* and *Rhoan*, and in the Island called *Camargo*, and in *Helvetia*, neer *Arula*, *Ursa* and *Limagus*: Likewise throughout all *Germany*, *Polonia*, *Sclavonia*, *Russia* and *Prussia*: and there are Beavers in the woods of *Mosco* and *Lituania*, of excellent perfection and stature, above others, having longer white hairs which glister above other. These beasts live both in the water and on the land, for in the day time they keep the water, and in the night they keep the land, and yet without water they cannot live, for they do participate much of the nature of fishes, as may be well considered by their hinder legs and tail.

Their quantity is not much bigger then a Countrey Dog, their head short, their ears very small and round, their teeth very long, the under teeth standing out beyond their lips three fingers breadth, and the upper about half a finger, being very broad, crooked, strong and sharp, standing; or growing double very deep in their mouth, bending compass like the edge of an Axe, and their colour yellowish red, wherewith they defend themselves against beasts, take fishes as it were upon hooks, and will gnaw in sunder trees as big as a mans thigh: they have also grinding teeth very sharp, wherein are certain wrinckles or folds, so that they seem to be made for grinding some hard substance, for with them they eat the rindes or bark of trees; wherefore the biting of this beast is very deep, being able to crash asunder the hardest bones, and commonly he never loseth his hold, untill he feeleth his teeth gnash one against another. *Pliny* and *Solinus* affirm, that the person so bitten cannot be cured, except he hear the crashing of the teeth; which take to be an opinion without truth.

They have certain hairs about their mouth, which seem in their quantity or bigness to be rather horn they are so hard, but their bones are most hard of all and without marrow: Their forefeet are like a Dogs, and their hinder like a Gooses, made as it were of purpose to go on the land, and swim in the water, but the tail of this beast is most strange of all, in that it cometh nearest to the nature of fishes, being without hair, and covered over with a skin like the scales of fish, it being like a soal, and for the most part six fingers broad and half a foot long, which some have affirmed the beast never pulleth out of the water; whereas it is manifest, that when it is very cold, or the water frozen he pulleth it up to his body, although *Agricola* affirm, that his hinder legs and tail, freeze with the water; and no lesse untrue is the assertion, that they compell the Otter in time of cold and frost, to wait upon their tail, and to trouble the water so that it may not freeze round about them; but yet the Beaver holdeth the Otter in subjection, and either overcometh it in fight, or killeth it with his teeth.

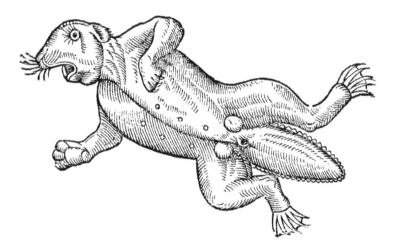

This tail he useth for a stern when he swimmeth after fish to catch them. There hath been taken of them whose tails have weighed four pound weight, and they are accounted a very delicate dish; for being dressed they eat like Barbles: they are used by the *Lotharingians* and *Savoyans* for meat allowed to be eaten on fish-dayes, although the body that beareth them be flesh and unclean for food. The manner of their dressing is, first roasting, and afterward seething in an open pot, that so the evill vapor may go away, and some in pottage made with Saffron; other with Ginger, and many with Brine; it is certain that the tail and forefeet tast very sweet, from whence came the Proverbe, *That sweet is that fish, which is not fish at all.*

These beasts use to build them Caves or Dens neer the Waters, so as the Water may come into them, or else they may quickly leap into the water, and their wit or natural invention in building of their Caves is most wonderful: for you must understand that in the night time they go to land, and there with their teeth gnaw down boughes and trees which they likewise bite very short fitting their purpose, and so being busied about this work, they will often look up to the tree when they perceive it almost asunder, thereby to discern when it is ready to fall, lest it might light upon their own pates: the tree being down and prepared, they take one of the oldest of their company, whose teeth could not be used for the cutting, (or as others say, they constrain some strange Beaver whom they meet withal) to fall flat on his back (as before you have heard the Badgers do) and upon his belly lade they all their timber, which they so ingeniously work and fasten into the compasse of his legs that it may not fall, and so the residue by the tail, draw him to the water side, where these buildings are to be framed: and this the rather seemeth to be true, because there have been some such taken, that had no hair on their backs, but were pilled; which being espied by the hunters, in pity of their slavery, or bondage, they have let them go away free.

These beasts are so constant in their purpose, that they will never change the tree that they have once chosen to build withal, how long time so ever they spend in biting down the same; it is likewise to be observed; that they never go to the same, during the time of their labour, but in one and the same path, and so in the same return to the water again. When they have thus brought their wood together, then dig they a hole or ditch in the bank side, where they underset the earth to bear it up from falling, with the aforesaid timber; and so they proceed, making two or three rooms like several chambers, one above another, to the intent that if the water rise they may go further, and if it fall they may descend unto it. And as the husbandmen of *Egypt* do observe the buildings of the Crocodile, so do the inhabitants of the Countrey where they breed, observe the Beavers, that

94

when they build high, they may expect an inundation, and sow on the Mountains; and when they build low, they look for a calm or drought, and plow the vallies. There is nothing so worthy in this beast as his stones, for they are much sought after and desired by all Merchants, so that they will give for them any great price.

There is both in male and female, certain bunches under their belly as great as great as a Gooses egge, which some have unskilfully taken for their code; & between these is the secret or privie part of both sexes; which tumours or bunches are nothing else, but a little fleshie bag within a little thin skin, in the middle whereof is a hole or passage, out of the which the beast sucketh a certain liquor, and afterward therewith anointeth every part of her body that she can reach with her tongue. Now it is very plain that these bunches are not their cods; for these reasons; Because that there is no passage either of the seed into them, or from them into the yard: Besides, their stones are found within their body; neither ought this to seem strange, seeing that Hares have the like bunches, and also the *Moschus* or *Musk-cat*: the female hath but one passage for all her excrements, and to conceive or bring forth young ones.

It hath been an opinion of some, that when a Beaver is hunted and is in danger to be taken, she biteth off her own stones, knowing that for them only her life is sought, which caused *Alciatus* to make this Emblem,

> *Et pedibus segnis, tumida & propendulus alvo;*
> *Hac tamen insidias effugit arte fiber:*
> *Mordicus ipse sibi medicata virilia vellit:*
> *Atque abjicit sese gnarus ob illa peti.*
> *Hujus ab exemplo disces non parcere rebus,*
> *Et vitam ut redimas hostibus æra dare.*

Teaching by the example of a Beaver, to give our purse to theeves, rather then our lives, and by our wealth to redeem our danger, for by this means the Beaver often escapeth. There have been many of them found that wanted stones, which gave some strength to this errour, but this was exploded in ancient time for a fable; and in this and all other honest discourses of any part of Philosophy, the only mark whereat every good student and professor ought to aime, must be verity and not tales; wherein many of the ancient have greatly offended (as is manifested by *Marcellus Virgilius*) especially *Plato*: and this poyson hath also crept into and corrupted the whole body of Religion. The *Egytians* in the opinion of the aforesaid *Castration*, when they will signifie a man that hurteth himself, they picture a Beaver biting off his own stones. But this is most false, as by *Sertius, Plinius, Dioscorides*, and *Albertus*, is manifested. First, because their stones are very small, and so placed in their body as are a Boars, and therefore impossible for them to touch or come by them. Secondly; they cleave so fast unto their back, that they cannot be taken away but the beast must of necessity lose his life; and therefore ridiculous is their relation, who likewise affirm, that when it is hunted (having formerly bitten off his stones) that he standeth upright and sheweth the hunters that he hath none for them, and therefore his death cannot profit them, by means whereof they are averted and seek for another.

These Beavers eat fish, fruits, and the bitter rindes of trees, which are unto them most delicate, especially Aldern, Poplar, and Willow; whereupon it is proverbially said, of one that serveth another for gain: *Sic me subes quotidie ut fiber salicem*; you love me as the Bever doth the Willow, which eateth the bark and destroyeth the tree.

They are taken for their skins, tails, and cods, and that many wayes; and first of all when their Calves are found, there is made a great hole or breach therein, whereinto is put a little Dog, which the beast espying, flyeth to the end of her den, and there defendeth her self by her teeth, till all her structure or building be rased, and she laid open to her enemies, who with such instruments as they have preset, beat her to death: some affirm that she rouzeth up her body, and by the strong savour of her stones she driveth away the Dogs; which may be probable, if the stones could be seen. These Dogs are the same which hunt wild fowl and Otters.

It is reported that in *Prussia* they take them in bow-nets, baited with the rinde of trees, whereinto they enter for the food, but being entrapped cannot go forth again. They cannot dive long time under water but must put up their heads for breath, which being espied by them that beset them, they kill them with gun-shot, or pierce them with Otters speares, so that one would think seeing such a one in the water, that it was some hairy kind of fish; and his nature is, if he hear any noise to put his head above water, whereby he is discovered and loseth his life. His skin is pretious in *Polonia*, either for garment, or for Gloves, but not so pretious as an Otters, yet it is used for the edging of all other fur garments, making the best shew and enduring longest; they are best that are blackest, and of the bellies which are like felt wool, they make caps and stockings against rain and foul weather.

The medicinall vertues of this beast are in the skin, the urine, the gall and the cods: and first, a garment made of the skins, is good for a Paralytick person; and the skins burned with dry Onions and liquid pitch, stayeth the bleeding of the nose, and being put into the soles of shooes easeth the Gowt. The urine preserved in the bladder, is an antidote against poyson: and the gall is profitable for many things, but especially being turned into a glew it helpeth the falling evill. The genitals of a Beaver are called by the Physitians *Castoreum*, and therefore we will in this discourse use that word for expressing the nature, qualities, remedies, and miraculous operation thereof, wherefore they must be very warily and skilfully taken forth, for there is in a little skin compassing them about a certain sweet humor (called *Humor Melleus*) and with that they must be cut out, the utter skin being cut asunder to make the more easie entrance, and the Apothecaries use to take all the fat about them, which they put into the oil of the *Castoreum*, and sell it unto fisher-men to make bait for fishes. The females have stones or *Castoreum*, as well as the males, but very small ones. Now you must take great heed to the choise of your Beaver, and then to the stones which must grow from one root conjoyned, otherwise they are not precious, and the beast must neither be a young one nor one very old, but in the mean betwixt both, being in vigor and perfection of strength.

The Beavers of *Spain* yeeld not such virtuous *Castoreum* as they of *Pontus*, and therefore if it be possible, take a *Pontique* Beaver, next one of *Gallatia*, and lastly of *Africk*. Some do corrupt them putting into their skin Gum and *Ammoniack* with blood, other take the reins of the beast, and so make the *Castoreum* very big, which in it self is but small. This beast hath two bladders, which I remember not are in any other living creature, and you must beware that none of these be joyned to the *Castoreum*. You may know if it be mingled with *Ammoniack* by the tast, for although the colour be like, yet is the savour different. *Platearius* sheweth, that some adulterate *Castoreum*, by taking off his skin, or some cod newly taken forth of another beast, filling it with bloud, sinews and the powder of *Castoreum*, that so it may not want his strong smell or favour: other fill it with earth and bloud: other with bloud, rosen, gum, sinews and pepper, to make it tast sharp: but this is a falsification discernible, and of this sort is the *Castoreum* which is sold in *Venice*, as *Brasovala* affirmeth: and the most of them sold at this day are bigger then the true *Castoreum*, for the just weight of the right stones is not above twelve ounces and a half, one of them being bigger then the other, being six fingers breadth long, and four in breadth. Now the substance contained in the bag is yellowish, solid like wax, and sticking like glew, not sharp and cracking betwixt the teeth (as the counterfeit is). These stones are of a strong and stinking savour, such as is not in any other, but not rotten and sharp, as *Grammarians* affirm; yer I have smelled of it dryed, which was not unpleasant, and things once seasoned with the savour thereof, will ever tast of it, although they have not touched it, but lie covered with it in the same box or pot; and therefore the *Castoreum* of *Persia* is counterfeit, which hath no such smell, for if a man smell to the right *Castoreum*, it will draw bloud out of his nose.

After it is taken forth from the beast, it must be hung up in some place to be dryed in the shadow, and when it is dry, it is soft and white: it will continue it strength six years, and some say seven; the *Persians* affirm, that their *Castoreum* will hold his virtue ten years, which is as false as the matter they speak of is counterfeit. *Archigenes* wrote a whole book of the virtue of this *Castoreum*, whereunto they may resort, that require an exact and full declaration of all his medicinal operations: it shall only be our purpose, to touch some general heads, and not to enter into a particular discovery thereof.

Being so dryed as is declared, it must be warily used, for it falleth out herein as in other medicinal subjects, that ignorance turneth a curing herb or substance, into a venemous and destructive quality; therefore we will first of all set down the dangers to be avoided, and afterward some particular cures that come by the right use of it. Therefore it must be understood that there is poyson in it, not naturally, but by accident, as may be in any other good and wholesome matter: and that especially in the smell or savour thereof, whereunto if a woman with childe do smell, it will kill the childe unborn and cause abortment; for a womans womb is like a creature, nourished with good favours, and destroyed with evill: therefore burning of feathers, shoo-soles, woollen clothes, pitch, *Galbanum*, gum, onions, and garlick is noysom to them. It may be corrupted not only as is before declared; but also, if it be shut up close without vent into pure aire, when it is hanged up to be dryed, or if the bag be kept moist, so that it cannot dry; and it is true (as *Avicen* saith) that if it be used being so corrupted, it killeth within a dayes space, driving one into madness, making the sick person continually to hold forth his tongue, and infecting him with a Fever by inflaming the body, loosing the continuity of the parts, through sharp vapors arising from the stomach: and for a proof that it will inflame, if you take a little of it mingled with oil, and rub upon any part of the body, or upon your nail, you shall feel it.

But there is also a remedy for it being corrupted; namely, Asses milk mingled with some sharp syrup of *Citron*, or if need require, drink a dram of *Philons* Antidote at the most; or take butter and sweet water which will cause vomit, and vomit therewith so long, as you feel the savour of the stone, and afterward take syrup of Limmons or Citrons: and some affirm upon experience, that two penny weight of *Coriander-seed,* scorched in the fire, is a present remedy for this evill. And it is most strange, that seeing it is in greatest strength, when the favour is hottest, which is very displeasing to a mans nature in outward appearance, yet doth it never harm a man taken inwardly, (being pure and rightly compounded) if the person be without a Fever, for in that case only it doth hurt inwardly, otherwise apply it to a moist body lacking refrigeration, or to a cold body wanting excalfaction, or to a cold and moist body, you shall perceive an evident commodity thereby, if there be no Fever: and yet it hath profited many where the Fever hath not been over hot, as in Extasies and Lethargies, ministred with white Pepper, and Melicrate, and with Rose cakes laid to the neck or head. The same virtues it hath being outwardly applyed and mingled with oil, if the bodies be in any heat, and purely without oil, if the body be cold, for in heating it holdeth the third degree, and in drying the second. The manner how it is to be administred is in drink, for the most part, the sweet liquor being taken from it, and the little skins appearing therein cleansed away, and so it hath among many other these operations following. Drunk with Vinegar, it is good against all venom of Serpents, and against the *Chameleon*, but with this difference, against the Scorpion with wine, against Spiders with sweet water, against the Lizzards with Myrtite, against *Dipsas* and *Cerastes*, with *Oponax*, or wine made of *Rew*, and against other Serpents with wine simply. Take of every one two drams, for a cold take it a scruple and a half in four cups of wine, used with *Ladanum*, it cureth the Fistulaes and Ulcers, provoking sneezing by smelling to it; procureth sleep, they being anointed with it; Maiden-weed and Conserve of Roses, and being drunk in water, helpeth Phrensie, and with the Roses and Maiden-weed aforesaid, easeth head-ach; being laid to the head like a plaister, it cureth all cold and windy affections therein; or if one draw in the smoak of it perfumed, though the pain be from the mothers womb, and given in three cups of sweet Vinegar fasting, it helpeth the Falling sickness, but if the person have often fits, the same given in a Glyster, giveth great ease: Then must the quantity be two drams of *Castoreum*, one sextary of honey and oil, and the like quantity of water, but in the fit it helpeth with Vinegar by smelling to it. It helpeth the Palsie, taken in Rew or wine, sod in Rew, so also all heart trembling, ach in the stomach, and quaking of the sinews. It being infused into them that lie in Lethargies with Vinegar and Conserve of Roses doth presently awake them, for it strengthneth the brain, and moveth sternutation. It helpeth oblivion coming by reason of sickness, the parry being first purged with *Hiera Ruffi, Castoreum,* with oil bound to the hinder part of the head, and afterward a dram drunk with *Melicrate,* also taken with oil, cureth all Convulsion proceeding of cold humors, if the Convulsion be full and perfect, and not temporal or in some particular member, which may come to passe in any sickness.

The same mixed with hony helpeth the clearness of the eyes, and their inflamations; likewise used with the juice of Popy, and infused to the ears, or mixed with hony, helpeth all pains in them. With the seed of Hemlocks beaten in Vinegar, it sharneth the sense of hearing, if the cause be cold, and it cureth toothach infused into that ear with oil on which side the pain resteth; for *Hippocrates* sent unto the wife of *Aspasius* (complaining of the pain in her cheek and teeth) a little *Castoreum* with Pepper, advising her to hold it in her mouth betwixt her teeth. A perfume of it drawn up into the head and stomach, easeth the pains of the lights and intrails, and given to them that sigh much with sweet Vinegar fasting, it recovereth them. It easeth the Cough, and distillations of rhume from the head to the stomach, taken with the juyce of black Popy. It is preservative against inflamations and pains in the guts or belly (although the belly be swoln with cold windy humors) being drunk with Vinegar, or *Oyxycrate*; it easeth the Colick being given with Annis beaten small, and two spoonfuls of sweet water; and it is found by experiment, that when a horse cannot make water, let him be covered over with his cloth, and then put underneath him a fire of coals, wherein make a perfume with that *Castoreum* till the Horses belly and cods smell thereof, then taking away the coals, walk the horse up and down covered, and he will presently stale.

To soften the belly they use *Castoreum* with sweet water two drams, and if it be not forcible enough, they take the root of a set Cucumber one dram, and the some of Salt Peter two drams. It is also used with the juice of Withy and decoction of Vinegar applyed to the reins and genital parts like a plaister against the *Gonorrhæan* passion. It will stir up a womans monethly courses, and cause an easie travail, two drams being drunk in water with Penny-royal. And if a Woman with childe go over a Beaver, she will suffer abortment; and *Hippocrates* affirmeth, that a perfume made with *Castoreum*, Asses dung, and Swines grease, openeth a closed womb.

There is an Antidote called *Diacostu*, made of this *Castoreum*, good against the Megrim, Falling sickness, Apoplexies, Palsies, and weakness of lims, as may be seen in *Myrepsus*: against the impotency of the tongue, trembling of the members, and other such infirmities. These vertues of a Beaver thus described, I will conclude this discourse with a History of a strange beast like unto this, related by *Dunranus Campus-bellus* (a noble Knight) who affirmed, that there are in *Arcadia*, seaven great lakes some 30 miles compass, and some lesse, whereof one is called *Garloil*, out of which in *Anno* 1510 about the midst of Summer, in a morning came a beast about the bigness of a water Dog, having feet like a Goose, who with his tail easily threw down small trees, and presently with a swift pace he made after some men that he saw, and with three strokes he likewise overthrew three of them, the residue climbing up into trees escaped, and the beast without any long tarrying, returned back again into the water, which beast hath at other times been seen, and it is observed, that this appearance of the Monster, did give warning of some strange evils upon the Land: which story is recorded by *Hector Boethius*.

OF THE BISON.

A Bison called of some *Latins*, though corruptly, *Urson*, and *Veson*; of the *Grecians*, *Bisoon*; of the *Lituanians*, *Suber*; of the *Polonians*, *Zuber*, from whence some *Latins* derived *Zubro*, for a Bison. Of the *Germans*, *Visent*, and *Væsent*, and *Wisent*: a beast very strange as may appear by his figure prefixed, which by many Authors is taken for *Urus*, some for a *Bugil*, or wilde Ox; other for *Rangifer*, and many for the beast *Tarandus* a *Buffe*. By reason whereof there are not many things, which can by infallible collection be learned of this beast among the writers; yet it is truly and generally held for a kind of wilde Ox, bred in the Northern parts of the World for the most part, and never tamed, as in *Scythia*, *Moscovia*, *Hercynia*, *Thracia*, and *Prussia*. But those tall wilde Oxen which are said to be in *Lapponia*, and the Dukedom of *Angermannia*, are more truly said to be *Uri*, as in their story shall be afterward declared.

Their name is taken from *Thracia*, which was once called *Bistonia*, and the people thereof *Bistones*, from *Bisto* the Son of *Cicas* and *Terpsichore*; and thereof came *Bistoniæ Grues*, cranes of *Thracia*, and *Bistoniæ Lacus*, for the lake or sea of *Dicæa*, near *Abdera*, where never living thing, or other of lesse weight was cast in but it presently sunk and was drowned.

This Bison is called *Taurus Pæonicus*, the *Pæonian Bull*, whereof I finde two kinds, one of greater, and another of lesser size, called the *Scotian*, or *Calydonian Bison*, whereof you shall see the picture and qualities at the foot of this History.

The greater is as big as any Bull or Oxe, being maned about the neck and back like a Lion, and hath hair hanging down under his chin or neather lip like a large beard: and a rising or little ridge down along his face, beginning at the height of his head, and continuing to his nose very hairy; his horns great and very sharp, yet turning up towards his back, and at the points hooked like the wilde Goats of the Alpes, but much greater: they are black of colour, and with them through the admirable strength of his neck can he tosse into the air, a horse and horseman both together. They are as big as the *Dextarii* which are the greatest *Stallions* of *Italy*. Their face looketh downward, and they have a strange strength in their tongue, for by licking they grate like a file any indifferent hard substance, but especially they can therewith draw unto them any man or beast of inferior condition, whom by licking they wound to death.

Their hair is red, yellow, or black, their eyes very great and terrible; they smell like a *Moschus* or *Musk-cat*, and their mane reacheth over their shoulders, shaking it irefully when he brayeth; their face or forehead very broad, especially betwixt their horns, for *Sigismond* King of *Polonia*, having kild one of them in hunting, stood betwixt his horns, with two other men not much lesser in quantity then himself, who was a goodly well proportioned and personal Prince.

There are two bunches on his back, the former near his shoulders, which is the higher, and the other near the rump, which is somewhat lower. I have seen the horns of a Bison, which was in the hands of a Goldsmith to tip with silver and gilt, that it might be fit to drink in: it did bend like the talon of an Eagle or Gryphin, or some ravenous bird. The flesh in Summer time is most fat, but it tasteth so much of wilde

Garlick, or Ramsens, that it is not pleasant to eat, being full of small veins and strings, and is accounted a noble and strong kind of flesh: the bloud is the most purest in the world, excelling in colour any purple, and yet for all that it is so hot, that being let forth when the Beast dyeth, within two houres space it putrefieth, and the flesh it self in the coldest Winter will not keep sweet many hours, by reason of the immoderate heat thereof, if the Hunter do not after the fall of the beast, separate from it the intrails: and which is most strange of all, being pierced alive with any hunting spear, dart, or sword, the weapon by the heat of the body is made so weak and soluble, that it cometh forth as flexible as lead: and to conclude, it is a most noble and fierce spirited beast, never afraid, or yeelding till breath faileth, neither can he be taken with any nets or gins, untill they be thoroughly wearyed: wherefore they which hunt him, must be very strong, nimble and skilful men, or else that sport will be their own undoing and overthrow.

Therefore when they go to hunt this Bison, they choose a place replenished with large trees, neither so great that they cannot easily wind about them; nor so little that they shall not be able to cover their bodies from the horn or tongue of the beast: behind which the hunters place themselves out of sight: and then the Dogs rouze up the beast, driving him to that place where the hunters stand; whom the beast first espyeth, to him he maketh force, who must warily keep the tree for his shield, and with his spear wound him where he can, who will not fall without many mortal strokes, but waxe more and more eager, not only with horn but with tongue, for if he can but apprehend any part of the hunters garment with his tongue, he loseth no hold but draweth him unto him, and with his horn and feet killeth him: but if the fight be long, and so the hunter wearied and out of breath, then doth he cast a red cap unto the beast, who maketh at it with head and feet, never leaving till it be all in pieces; and if another come to help him as hunters must, if they will return alive, then shall he easily draw the beast to combate, and forsake the first man, if he cry *Lu-lu-lu*.

Pausanias sheweth how these Bisons are taken alive, in this sort. The hunters (saith he) chuse out some steep and slippery down hill, whereupon they lay skins of beasts newly taken off, and if they want such, then anoint they old skins with oil, and so leave them spread upon those steeping or bending passages; then raise they the beasts, and with Dogs and other means on horseback drive them along to the places where they laid their hides, and as soon as they come upon the skins they slip and fall down, rowling headlong till they come into the valleys, from whence they constrain them back again some other way, three or four times a day, making them fall down the hils as aforesaid, and so wearying them with continual hunting, and fasting. At the last they come unto them, when they are no more able to rise for faintness, and give them Pine-apples taken out of the shels, (for with that meat are they delighted) and so while they eagerly feed and lie weary on the ground, they intoil them in bands and manacles, and lead them away alive. The medicines coming from this beast may be conjectured to be more forcible, then of common and ordinary Oxen, but because they were not known to the *Grecians* and *Arabians*, and we finde nothing recorded thereof; we will conclude the story of this great Bison, with good opinion of the virtues, though we are not able to learn or discover them to others.

OF THE WHITE SCOTIAN BISON.

IN the Woods of *Scotland*, called *Callender* or *Caldar*, and in ancient time *Calydonia*, which reacheth from *Monteth* and *Erunal*, unto

Atholia and *Loqubabria*, there are bred white Oxen, maned about the neck like a Lyon, but in other parts like ordinary and common Oxen. This wood was once full of them, but now they are all slain, except in that part which is called *Cummirnald*. This beast is so hateful and fearful of mankind, that it will not feed of that grasse or those hearbs, whereof he favoureth a man hath touched, no not for many days together; and if by art or policy they happen to be taken alive, they will die with very sullen grief. If they meet a man, presently they make force at him, fearing neither Dogs, Spears, nor other weapons. Their flesh is very pleasant, though full of sinews, and very acceptable to the greatest Nobles, for which cause they are grown to a small number; their qualities being like to the former beast, excepting their colour and beard, I will term them a white *Calydonian*, or *Scotian BISON*.

BONASUS, THE FIGURE OF THE HEAD AND HORNS.

THIS beast is called in *Greek Bonasos*, and in *Latin, Bonasus*, and is also called *Monops*, or *Monopios*, and once in *Aristotle, Bolinthus*, the *Bohemians, Loli*, now the *Germans & English* call the long hair about the neck of any beast, a *Mæne* or Mane, from whence cometh this word *Monapios*, which signifieth a maned Ox. This *Bison* is the greatest beast, Bull or Ox, though it be shorter in length, yet are the sides larger and broader then all other. They are bred in *Pæonia* in the mountain

Mesapus, not in *Lydia* and *Phrygia*, as *Solinus* and *Albertus* have delivered; being deceived, because the *Pæonians* were joyned with the *Medians* which they derive from *Madi* a people of *Asia*, whereas the *Pæonians* and *Medi* in *Pliny*, (as is observed by *Hermolaus* in his *Castigations* of *Pliny*) are a people of *Thracia* in *Europe*: so called of *Pæon* the Son of *Endymion* and brother of *Epeus*, who was seated near the river *Axius* in *Macedonia*: for it was agreed betwixt the two brethren striving for the kingdom, that he which was overrun by the other, should yeeld the kingdom in quietness to his brother.

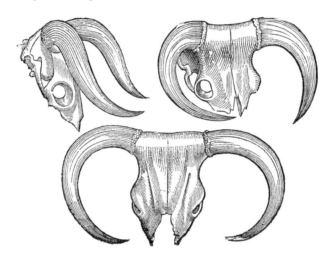

The head of this beast is like the head of an Ox or Bull, his horns bending round to the sides of the cheek, by reason whereof he hath no defence by them, neither can a man be hurt that is cast upon them. His neck is very thick with a large mane, from his eyes down to his shoulders in length like an Horses, but the hair thereof is much softer, and lyeth more smoothly, the uppermost hairs being harsher, and the undermost softer like wool. Their colour betwixt red and ash colour, but black and yellow appeareth not in them. They have no upper teeth, in this point resembling an Ox and other horned beasts; their horns being in compass about nine inches and somewhat more, are very smooth and black like varnish. Their voice is like the voice of an Ox, their legs all hairy, and their feet cloven, their tail too short for the other members of the body like a Bugles, their back stretched out at length, is as long as a seat for seaven men; their flesh is very sweet, for which cause he is much sought for in hunting; he will with his feet dig up the ground like an Ox or Bull in his rage; when he is once struck, he flyeth away, fighting with his heels backward; and whereas nature hath denied him the benefit of horns, which other beasts have, so that he is only adorned and not armed by those weapons, like a Souldier that cannot draw forth his Sword; she hath given him the secret operation of his dung, which in his chase he casteth forth of his body so plentifully upon the Dogs or other that pursue him, by the space of four paces backward, that he stayeth their course, and the heat of his dung is so admirable, that it scorcheth or burneth the hair or skin of any beasts or men that hunt him: neither hath this time such vertuous operation at any other time, but only when the beast flyeth, being hunted and pursued for life, at other times it lying quiet, there is no such virtue therein: neither ought this to seem incredible, seeing many other beasts in their chase, have the like or at the least do then eject their excrement more plentifully and noisomly then at other times: as the *Cuttell-fish*, for when in chase the intrails are heated, and the passage somewhat restrained, so that the holding in of breath breedeth more wind in the guts, it may very naturally chance, the excrement being with the inclosed wind and heat sent forth by violent eruption, that it may flie far backward, and also burn as aforesaid. These beasts Calve in the Mountains, and before that time cometh she chuseth a place, which she walleth in with the abundance of her own dung, so high as it may cover her young one, for there is no beast that is naturally so full of excrement as a *Bonasus*. Their ears are very broad as the Poet saith, *Patulæ camuris sub cornibus aures*, broad ears, under crooked winding blunt horns; the skin is so large, that it hath covered a good part of a house, the inward colour whereof is like the earth whereon the beast did use to feed. That excellent Physitian of *England John Cay*, did send me the head of this beast, with this description, in an Epistle, saying,

"I Send unto thee the head of a great wilde beast, the bare mouth and the bones supporters of the horns being very weighty, and therefore bearing up some like heavy burden, the horns are recurved and bending backward, so that they do not spire directly downward but rather forward, though in a crooked manner, which because it could not appear forward, as they do when the beast is alive, therefore they are described turning on the one side: the space betwixt the horns or breadth of the forehead, is three *Roman* palms and a half; the length of the horns, three palms one finger and a half; and their compass where they are joyned to the head, is one foot one palm and a half. In the Castle of *Warwick* where are preserved the Armor and Spear of one Earl *Guy* of *Warwick* a most valiant strong man, I have seen the head of a beast not unlike to this, saving that if the bones whereon the horns grow should be joyned together, then would the horns be longer, and of another crooked fashion. And in the same place there is also the neckbone of the same beast, the compasse thereof is at the least three *Roman* feet two palms and a half, whereunto I may also add that shoulder-blade which hangeth on the North gate of the City of *Coventry*, being in the lowest part three foot broad and two fingers, and four foot long and two palms: and the compasse of the arme hole wherein the shoulder is joyned, is three foot and one palm, and the whole compasse of them both in breadth and length is eleven foot one palm and a half.

"In the Chappel of the said great *Guy*, distant from *Warwick* about one thousand paces (or a mile) there hangeth a rib of this beast (as I suppose) the compasse whereof in the smallest place is three palms, and in length it is six foot and a half the rib is dry and rotten in the superficies thereof. The vulgar people affirm, that it is the peece of a Boar, which was slain by Earl *Guy*; other say, by tradition of their elders, that it is a piece of a wilde Cow remaining neer *Coventry*, and did much harm to many people; which latter opinion I embrace, taking it for a *Bonasus*, who in most things is like a Cow, and therefore some affirm it is an *Indian* Cow (but ignorantly) because any thing that is not common is usually attributed to some strange Countrey breed (with an addition to that it most of all resembleth.)

Thus far D. Cay."

Whereunto I assent, holding his conjectures to be very probable, untill by the diligent industry of some other, or my own eye-sight we may deliver to the world some more assured and perfect knowledge in these kind of beasts. Exhorting in the mean season all learned men, to discover more exactly their present or future knowledge herein, to the high benefit of all them that are diligent students in this part of Gods creation.

A Buffe is called in *Greek, Tarandos*; and in *Latine, Tarandus*; which some have corrupted barbarously, tearming it *Parandrus* and *Pyradus*; and I conjecture that it is the same beast, which the *Polonians* call *Tur* or *Thuro*; howsoever other confound this *Tarandus* with another beast, called *Rangifer*; and some with a kinde of *Urus*, which have many properties in common with a Buffe, yet my reason, why the *Polonian Tur* can be no other then a Buffe, is, because the head and mouth differeth from those beasts; and also because this is taken in *Sarmatia*, where the common people call it *Daran*, or *Darau*; although the later Writers call it *Duran* and *Durau*, and translate it a *Bonasus*, which can by no means agree with this beast; and the name of *Daran* is easily derived from *Tarandus*, or *Tarandos*.

Also that the *Polonian Tur* should not be a Buffe, all that can be objected, is, that the horns thereof are cragged or branched, which thing *Pliny* attributeth to a Buffe: whereunto I answer, that the Ancients did confound a Buffe with an Elk, and a *Rangifer*; for in the description of an Elk they vary, divers times mistaking one for another, by reason that they wrote altogether by report, none of them being seen in their Countries, and therefore may easily be deceived in a Buffe, as well as in an Elk. The chief Authors of this opinion have been Sir *Thomas Eliot*, and *Georgius Agricola*, with whom I will not contend, nor with any other man that can give better reason: for *Pliny* maketh a Buffe to be a beast proportioned betwixt an Hart and an Oxe, of which sort is not a *Rangifer*, as shall be manifested; and if it be, yet can it never appear that a *Rangifer* doth change colour like a Buffe, as also we will make more evident: So then distinguishing a Buffe from a Rangifer, and presuming that the *Polonian Thuro*, or *Tur*, is a Buffe; we will proceed to his description.

The head of this beast is like the head of a Hart, and his horns branched or ragged; his body for the most part like a wilde Oxes, his hair deep and harsh like a Bears, his hide is so hard and thick, that of it the *Scythians* make breast-plates, which no dart can pierce through. His colour, for the most part, like an Asses, but when he is hunted or feared, he changeth his hew into whatsoever thing he seeth; as among trees he is like them; among green boughs he seemeth green; amongst rocks of stone, he it transmuted into their colour also; as it is generally by most Writers affirmed: as *Pliny* and *Sclinus* among the Ancient; *Stephanus* and *Eustathius* among the later Writers.

This indeed is the thing that seemeth most incredible, but there are two reasons which draw me to subscribe hereunto: first, because we see that the face of men and beasts through fear, joy, anger, and other passions, do quickly change; from ruddy to white, from black to pale, and from pale to ruddy again. Now as this beast hath the head of a Hart, so also hath it the fear of a Hart, but in a higher degree; and therefore by secret operation it may easily alter the colour of their hair, as a passion in a reasonable man, may alter the colour of his face.

The same things are reported by *Pliny* of a beast in *India* called *Lycaon*, as shall be afterward declared; and besides these two, there is no other among creatures covered with hair, that changeth colour. Another reason forcing me to yeeld hereunto is, that in the Sea a *Polypus*-fish, and in the earth among creeping things, a *Chamæleon*, do also change their colour in like sort and fashion: whereunto it may be replyed, that the *Chamæleon* and *Polypus*-fish, are pilled or bare without hair, and therefore may more easily be verse-coloured; but it is a thing impossible in nature, for the hair to receive any tincture from the passions: but I answer, that the same nature can multiply and diminish her power in lesser and smaller Beasts, according to her pleasure, and reserveth an operation for the nails, and feathers of birds, and fins and scales of fishes, making one sort of divers colour from the other: and therefore may and doth as forcibly work in the hairs of a Buffe, as in the skin of a *Chamæleon*; adding so much more force to transmute them, by how much farther off they stand from the blood, like as an Archer, which setteth his arm and bow higher to shoot farther, and therefore it is worthy observation, that as this beast hath the best defence by her skin above all other, so she hath a weakest and most timerous heart above all other.

These Buffes are bred in *Scythia*, and are therefore called *Tarandi Scythici*; they are also among the *Sarmatians*, and called *Budini*, and neer *Gelonis*, and in a part of *Poland*, in the *Duchy* of *Mazavia*, betwixt *Uszezke* and *Garvolyin*. And if the *Polonian Thuro* before mentioned, have a name (whereof I am ignorant) then will I also take that beast for a kinde of *Bison*. In *Phrygia* there is a territory called *Tarandros*, and peradventure this beast had his name from that Countrey, wherein it may be he was first discovered and made known.

The quantity of this beast, exceedeth not the quantity of a wilde Ox, whereunto in all the parts of his body he is most like, except in his head, face, and horns: his legs and hoofs are also like an Oxes. The goodness of his hide is memorable, and desired in all the cold Countries in the world, wherein only these beasts and all other of strong thick hides are found, for the thinnest and most unprofitable skins of beasts, are in the hot and warmer parts of the world: and God hath provided thick, warm, most commodious, and precious covers for those beasts that live farthest from the Sun. Whereupon many take the hides of other beasts for Buffe, for being tawed and wrought artificially they make garments of them, as it is daily to be seen in *Germany*.

OF THE VULGAR BUGIL.

A Bugil is called in *Latine*, *Bubalus*; and *Buffalus*; in *French*, *Beufle*; in *Spanish*, *Bufano*; in *German*, *Buffel*; and in the *Illyrian* tongue, *Bouwol*. The *Hebrews* have no proper word for it, but comprehend it under *To*, which signifieth any kind of wilde Oxen; for neither can it be expressed by *Meriah*, which signifieth fatted Oxen; or *Bekarmi*, which signifieth Oxen properly; or *Jachmur*, which the *Persians* call *Kutzcohi*, or *Buzcohi*, and is usually translated a Wilde-Asse. For which beast the *Hebrews* have many words; neither have the *Græcians* any proper word for a vulgar Bugil, for *Boubatos* and *Boubatis*, are amongst them taken for a kinde of *Roe-buck*. So that this *Bubalus* was first of all some modern or barbarous term in *Africk*, taken up by the *Italians*, and attributed to this beast, and many other for whom they knew no proper names. For in the time of *Pliny*, they used to call strange beasts like Oxen or Bulls, *Uri*; as now a days (led with the same error, or rather ignorance) they call such *Bubali*, or *Buffali*. The true effigies of the vulgar *Bugil*, was sent unto me by *Cornelius Sittardus*, a famous Physitian in *Norimberg*; and it is pictured by a tame and familiar Bugil, such as liveth among men for labour, as it seemeth to me. For there is difference among these beasts, (as *Aristotle* hath affirmed) both in colour, mouth, horn, and strength.

This vulgar Bugil, is of a kinde of wilde Oxen, greater and taller then the ordinary Oxen, their body being thicker and stronger, and their limbs better compact together; their skin most hard, their other parts very lean, their hair short, small, and black, but little or none at all upon the tail, which is also short and small. The head hangeth downward to the earth, and is but little, being compared with the residue of his body; and his aspect or face betokeneth a tameable and simple disposition. His fore-head is broad and curled with hair, his horns more flat then round, very long, bending together at the top, as a Goats do backward: insomuch as in *Crete*, they make bows of them: and they are not for defence of the beast, but for distinction of kinde and ornament. His neck is thick and long, and his rump or neather part of his back is lower then the residue, descending to the tail. His legs are very great, broad and strong, but shorter then the quantity of his body would seem to permit. They are very fierce being tamed, but that is corrected by putting an Iron ring through his Nostrils, whereinto is also put a cord, by which he is led and ruled, as a Horse by a bridle (for which cause in *Germany* they call a simple man over-ruled by the advise of another to his own hurt, a Bugle, led with a ring in his nose.)

His feet are cloven, and with the formost he will dig the earth, and with the hindmost fight like a Horse, setting on his blows with great force, and redoubling them again if his object remove not. His voyce is like the voyce of an Oxe; when he is chased he runneth forth right, seldom winding or turning, and when he is angred, he runneth into the water; wherein he covereth himself all over, except his mouth, to cool the heat of his blood; for this beast can neither endure outward cold nor inward heat: for which cause, they breed not but in hot Countries, and being at liberty are seldom from the waters. They are very tame, so that children may ride on their backs; but on a sodain they will run into the waters, and so many times indanger the childrens lives.

Their love to their young ones is very great, they alway give milk from their copulation to their Calving; neither will they suffer a Calf of another kinde (whom they discern by their smell) to suck their milk, but beat it away if it be put unto them: wherefore their keepers do in such case, anoynt the Calf with Bugils excrement, and then she will admit her suckling.

They are very strong, and will draw more at once then two Horses; wheresore they are tamed for service, and will draw Waggons and Plows, and carry burdens also, but they are not very fit for Carts: yet when they do draw, they carry also great burthens or loads tyed to their backs with ropes and wantyghtes. At the first setting forward they bend their legs very much, but afterward they go upright, and being over-loden they will fall to the earth, from which they cannot be raised by any stripes untill their load or carriage be lessened. There is no great account made of their hides, although they be very thick: *Solinus* reporteth, that the old *Britons* made Boats of Osier twigs or reeds, covering them round with Bugils skins, and sayled in them: and the Inhabitants of the Kingdom of *Caraiani*, make them bucklers and shields of Bugils skins, which they use in Wars; the flesh is not good for meat, which caused *Baptista Fiera* to make this Poem:

> *Bubalus hine abeat, neve intret prandia nostra:*
> *Non edat hunc quisquam: sub juga semper eat.*

For they ingender melancholy, and have no good taste, being raw they are not unpleasant to behold, but sod or rosted they shew a deformed substance. The milk of this beast maketh very hard Cheese, which tasteth like earth.

114

The medicines made of this beast are not many: with the horns or hoofs they make rings to wear against the Cramp, and it hath been believed (but without reason) that if a man or woman wear rings made of the horns or hoofs of a Bugil in the time of carnal copulation, that they will naturally fly off from their fingers; whereas this secret was wont to be attributed to rings of *Chrysolytes* or, *Smaragde* stones. To conclude, some teach husbandmen to burn the horns or dung of their Bugils on the windy side of their corn and plants, to keep them from Cankers and blasting: and thus much of the vulgar Bugil, called *Bubalus Recentiorum*: whose beginning in this part of the world is unknown, although in *Italy*, and other parts of *Europe* they are now bred and fostered.

OF THE AFRICAN BUGIL.

BELLONIUS reporteth, that he saw in *Cair* a small beast, which was in al things like a little Oxe, of a beautiful body, full of flesh, well and neatly limmed, which he could take for no other then the *African* Oxe, or Bugill of the old *Græcians*, which was brought out of the Kingdom of

Asamia, unto the City *Cair*; it was old, and not so big as a *Hart*, but greater then a *Roe*; he never in all his life took more pleasure to behold a beast, then in the viewing the excellent beauty of every part in this creature. His hair was yellowish, glistering as if had been combed and trimmed by the art of a Barber, under his belly it was somewhat more red and tauny then upon his back. His feet in all things like a vulgar Bugils, his legs short and strong, the neck short and thick, whereon the two dew-laps of his crest did scarse appear. His head like an Oxes, and his horns growing out of the crown of his head, black, long, and bending like an half Moon; whereof he hath no use to defend himself, or anoy another, by reason their points turn inward. His ears like a Cows, and shoulder blades standing up a little above the ridge very strongly. His tail to the knees like a *Camelopardals*, from whence hangeth some few black hairs, twice so great as the hairs in a Horses tail. His voyce was like an Oxes, but not so strong and loud: to conclude therefore, for his description; if a man conceive in his minde a little yellow neat Oxe, with smooth hair, strong members, and high horns above his head, like a half Moon; his minde cannot erre from the true and perfect shape of this beast. There was such a one to be seen of late at *Florence*, under the name of an *Indian* Oxe, saving his head was greater and longer, his horns not high nor bending together, but standing up right, and a little wreathing into spires above their root, and the hinder part of the back much lower then the shoulders, but it may be the observer of this beast failed and took not the true description of it.

This creature of *African Bugil*, must be understood to be a wilde beast, and not of a tame kinde, although *Bellonius* expresseth not so much. *Leo* in his description of *Africk*, relateth a discourse of a certain beast called *Laut*, or *Daut*, who is less then an Oxe, but of more elegant feature in his legs, white horns, and black nails, which is so swift, that no beast can out-run it, except a *Barbary* Horse: it is taken most easily in the Summer time: with the skin whereof they make targets and shields, which cannot be pierced by any weapon, except Gunshot; for which cause they sell them very dear; which is conjectured to be the *Bugil* that *Bellonius* describeth, although it be not just of the same colour, which may vary in this beast as well as in any other, and I have a certain

Manuscript without the Authors name, that affirmeth there be *Bugils* in *Lybia*, in likeness resembling a Hart and an Oxe, but much lesser, and that these beasts are never taken asleep, which causeth an opinion that they never sleep; and that there is another Bugil beyond the *Alpes*, neer the River *Rhene*, which is very fierce and of a white colour.

There is a horn in the Town-house of *Argentine* four *Roman* cubits long, which is conjectured to be the horn of some *Urus* (or rather as I think of some *Bugil*) it hath hung there at the least two or three generations, and by scraping it I found it to be a horn, although I forgat to measure the compass thereof, yet because antiquity thought it worthy to be reserved in so honourable a place for a monument of some strange beast, I have also thought good to mention it in this discourse: as when *Philip* King of *Macedon*, did with a dart kill a wilde Bull at the foot of the Mountain *Orbelus*, and consecrated the horns thereof in the Temple of *Hercules*, which were fifteen yards or paces long, for posterity to behold.

OF THE BULL.

A Bull is the husband of a Cow, and ring-leader of the herd, (for which cause *Homer* compareth *Agamemnon* the great Emperor of the

Græcian Army to a Bull) reserved only for procreation, and is sometimes indifferently called an Oxe, as Oxen are likewise of Authors taken for Bulls, *Virg.*

> *Pingue Jolum primis extemplo mensibus anni,*
> *Fortes invertant boves. ———*

The *Hebrews* call him *Tor*, or *Taur*; which the *Chaldes* call *Abir*, for a strong Oxe: so the *Arabians, Taur*: the *Græcians, Tauros*; the *Latines, Taurus*; the *Italians, Tauro*; the *French, Taureau*; the *Germans, ein Stier, ein Vuucherstier, das Vucher, ein Mummelstier, ein Hagen,* and *ein Bollen*; the *Illyrians, Vul,* and *Iunecz*: by all which several appellations, it is evident, that the name *Taurus* in *Latine* is not derived from *Tanouros*, the stretching out the tayl; nor from *Gauros*, signifying proud; but from the *Hebrew, Tor*; which signifieth great: upon which occasion, the *Græcians* called all large, great, and violent things, by the name of *Tauroi*, and that word *Taurus* among the *Latines*, hath given denomination to Men, Stars, Mountains, Rivers, Trees, Ships, and many other things, which caused *Ioachimus Camerarius* to make thereof this ænigmatical riddle.

> *Mœchus eram regis: sed lignea membra sequebar.*
> *Et Cilicum mens sum: sed mons sum nomine solo.*
> *Et vehor in cœlo: sed in ipsis ambulo terris.*

That is in divers senses, *Taurus* was a Kings *Pander*, the root of a tree, a Mountain in *Cilicia*, a Bull, a Mountain in name, a Star or sign in heaven, and a River upon the earth: so also we read of *Statilius Taurus*, and *Pomponius Vitulus*, two *Romans*. It was the custom in those days, to give the names of beasts to their children, especially among the *Troglodytæ*, and that Adulterer which ravished *Europa*, was *Taurus* the King of *Crete*; or as some say, a King that came in a Ship, whose *Ensign* and name was the Bull; and other affirm, that it was *Iupiter* in the likeness of a Bull, because he had so defloured *Ceres* when he begat *Proserpina*, and afterward defloured *Proserpina* his daughter, in the likeness of a Dragon. It is reported that when *Achelous* did fight with *Hercules* for *Deianeira* the Daughter of *Oeneus* King of *Calydon*, finding himself to be too weak to match *Hercules*, turned himself suddenly into a Serpent, and afterward into a Bull; *Hercules* seeing him in that proportion, speedily pulled from him one of his horns, and gave it to *Copia* the companion of Fortune, whereof cometh that phrase of *Cornucopia*. Afterward, *Achelous* gave unto *Hercules* one of the Horns of *Amalthea*, and so received his own again, and being overcome by *Hercules*, hid himself in the River of *Thoas*, which after his own name bending forth into one horn or crook, was called *Achelous*. By these things the Poets had singular intentions to decipher matters of great moment under hidden and dark Narrations.

But there are four reasons given, why Rivers are called *Taurocrani*: that is, Bul-heads. First, because when they empty themselves into the Sea, they roar or bellow like Buls, with the noise of their falling water. Secondly, because they surrow the earth like a draught of Oxen with a plow, and much deeper. Thirdly, because the sweetest and deepest pastures unto which these cattel resort, are near the rivers. Fourthly, because by their crooking and winding, they imitate the fashion of a horn, and also are impetuous, violent, and unresistible.

The strength of the head and neck of a Bull is very great, and his forehead seemeth to be made for fight: having horns short, but strong and piked, upon which he can toss into the air very great and weighty beasts, which he receiveth again as they fall down, doubling their elevation with renewed strength and rage, untill they be utterly confounded. Their strength in all the parts of their body is great, and they use to strike backward with their heels: yet is it reported by *Cælius Titornus* a Neat-heard of *Ætolia*, that being in the field among the cattel, took one of the most fierce and strongest Buls in the herd by the hinder-leg, and there in despite of the Bull striving to the contrary, held him with one hand, untill another Bull came by him, whom he likewise took in his other hand, and so perforce held them both: which thing being seen by *Milo Crotoniates*, he lifted up his hands to heaven, crying out by way of Interrogation to *Jupiter*, and saying: *O* Jupiter, *hast thou sent another* Hercules *amongst us*? Whereupon came the common proverb of a strong armed man: *This is another* Hercules. The like story is reported by *Suidas* of *Polydamas*, who first of all slew a Lyon, and after held a Bull by the leg so fast, that the beast striving to get out of his hands, lest the hoof of his foot behind him.

The *Epithites* of this beast are many among Writers, as when they call him Brazen-footed, wilde, chearful, sharp, plower, warrier, horn-bearer, blockish, great, glistering, fierce, valiant, and louring, which seemeth to be natural to this beast; insomuch as the *Grammarians* derive *Torvitas*, grimness or lowring, from *Taurus*, a Bull, whose aspect carryeth wrath and hatred in it: wherefore it is Proverbially said in *Westphalia*, of a lowring and scouling countenance, *Eir sic als ein ochs der dem, fleschruwer Entlofferist*: That is, he looketh like a Bull escaped from one stroke of the Butcher. Their horns are lesser but stronger then Oxen or Kie, for all beasts that are not gelded, have smaller horns and thicker skuls then other, but the Buls of *Scythia* as is said elsewhere, have no horns. Their heart is full of nerves or sinews, their blood is full of small veins, for which cause he ingendereth with most speed, and it hardneth quickly. In the gall of a Bull there is a stone called *Gaers*, and in some places the gall is called *Mammasur*. They are plentiful in most Countries, as is said in the discourse of Oxen, but the best sort are in *Epirus*, next in *Thracia*, and then in *Italy, Syria, England, Macedonia, Phrygia*, and *Belgia*: for the Buls of *Gallia* are impaired by labour, and the Buls of *Æthiope* are the *Rhinocerotes*, as the Buls of the woods are Elephants.

They desire the Cow at eight months old, but they are not able to fill her till they be two years old, and they may remain tolerable for breeders untill they be 12 and not past. Every Bull is sufficient for ten Kie, and the Buls must not feed with the Kie, for two months before their leaping time, and then let them come together without restraint, and give them Pease, or Barley, if their pasture be not good. The best time to suffer them with their females, is the midst of the Spring, and if the Bull be heavy, take the tayl of an Hart and burn it to powder, then moisten it in Wine, and rub therewith the genitals of a Bull, and he will rise above measure into lust: wherefore, if it be more then tolerable, it must be allayed with Oyl. The violence of a Bull in the act of copulation is so great, that if he miss the females genital entrance, he woundeth or much harmeth her in any other place; sending forth his seed without any motion except touching, and a Cow being filled by him, he will never after leap her, during the time she is with Calf: wherefore the *Egyptians* decipher by a Bull in health, without the itch of lust, a temperate continent man, and *Epictetus* saying of *Sustine* and *Alstine*; that is *Bear* and *Forbear*, was emblematically described by a Bull, having his knee bound and tyed to a Cow in the hand of the Neat-herd, with this subscription. *Hard fortune is to be endured with patience, and happiness is often to be feared, for* Epictetus *said, Bear and forbear; we must suffer many things, and with-hold our fingers from forbidden fruits; for so the Bull which swayeth rule among beasts, being bound in his right knee, abstaineth from his female great with young.*

When they burn in lust, their wrath is most outragious against their companions in the same pasture, with whom they agreed in former times, and then the conquerer coupleth with the Cow: but when he is weakened with generation, the beast that was overcome, setteth upon him afresh, and oftentimes overcometh: which kinde of love-fight is elegantly described by *Oppianus*, as followeth. One that is the chiefest ruleth over all the other herd, who tremble at the sight and presence of this their eager King, and especially the Kye, knowing the insulting jealousie of their raging husband. When the herds of other places meet together, beholding one another with disdainful countenances, and with their loughing terrible voices provoke each other, puffing out their flaming rage of defiance, and dimming the glistering light with their often dust-beating-feet into the air, who presently take up the challenge, and separate themselves from the company, joyning together at the sound of their own trumpets-loughing voyce, in fearful and sharp conflicts, not sparing, not yeelding, not retiring, till one or both of them fall wounded to the earth: sometimes turning round, sometimes holding heads together, as if they were Coach-fellows: and as two mighty ships well manned, with sufficient arms and strength, by force of winds and floods violently rushing one against another, do break and split asunder, with the horrible cry of the Souldiers, and ratling of the armour: so do these Buls, with voice, legs, horns, and strength, like cunning and valiant Martialists, make the sounds of their blows to ring betwixt heaven and earth, untill one of them be vanquished and overthrown.

The poor over-comed beast, with shame retireth from the herd, and will no more appear, untill he be enabled to make his party good against his triumphant adversary: then he feedeth solitary in the Woods and

Mountains, for it is proverbially said, to signifie a single and unmarried life, *abtit Taurus in silvam*: that is, the Bull is gone to the Wood to live solitarily without his female, often exercising himself like a studious Champion against the day of a new combate, and when he findeth his strength increased, and his courage armed for the day of battel, then roareth he in the Woods and Mountains, to provoke his adversary to answer; and perceiving his own voyce to be more fierce and violent then is his enemies, forth he proceedeth like some refreshed Giant, confident in his strength, descending the lists of a second combate, where he easily overcometh the Victor, weakned with copulation, and not exercised or fitted to such a triall through fulness and venery: so the first that was vanquished becometh Conqueror.

The very same is in other words described by *Virgil*: Bulls are enemies to all beasts that live upon prey, as Bears, Lyons, and Wolves: when they fight with Wolves, they winde their tails together, and so drive them away with their horns; when the Bear fighteth with an Oxe, she falleth on her back, watching opportunity to take his horns with her fore-feet; which if she catch, with the weight of her body she wearieth the beast, who is so earnest in combate with these beasts, that they will fight their tongues hanging out of their mouths. The Crow is enemy to Bulls and Asses, for in her flight she will strike at their eyes; and it is easier for the Bull to be revenged of a Lyon, then on such a bird: Red colour stirreth up a Bull to fight, neither can the Neat-herds govern these with such facility as they do the females, for when they wander and go astray, nothing can recall them but the voice of their females for copulation, which they understand and hear, being a mile or two distant.

The voyce of a Bull is sharper and shriller then is the loughing of a Cow; they are most couragious that have short and thick necks, and in their greatest wildeness, if their right knee can be bound, they will not stir; or if they be tyed to a wilde fig-tree, which is so fearful to the nature of an Oxe or Bull, that it hath been seen, how a very few sticks of that wood have sod a great quantity of Buls flesh in shorter time, then a far greater number of other wood set on fire could perform: which caused the *Egyptians* in ancient time, to picture a Bull tyed to a wilde fig-tree, to signifie a man that changed his manners through calamity.

Out of the hides of Bulls, especially their ears, necks, and genitals, is most excellent glew confected; but for the most part it is corrupted, by seething with it old leather of shooes or boots: but that of *Rhodes* is without all fraud, fit for Physitians and Painters, and evermore the whiter the better, for that which is black is good for nothing; wherefore that which is made out of Bulls hides, is so white, that it sendeth forth a brightness, whose vertuous conjunction in conglutination is so powerful, that it is easier to break a whole piece of wood then any part so glewed together therewith: and for this invention, we are (saith *Pliny*) indebted to *Dedalus* the first author thereof. They used it in instruments of musick, and such other tender and pretious actions.

The gall of an Oxe put upon Copper or Brass, maketh it glister like Gold; for which cause it is used by Players, to colour their counterfeit Crowns. The flesh of a Bull is good for meat, but yet not so good as an Oxe or Cow; yet did the *Egyptians* abstain from eating Cows flesh, and not from the flesh of Bulls.

These beasts are used in some places to plow, in some to fight; and it is reported by *Ælianus*, that *Mythridates* King of *Pontus*, beside his guard of men, had also a guard of a Bull, a Horse, and a Hart, which he tamed with his own hands; so that when his followers were asleep, if any stranger came neer, they failed not to awake him, by one of their several voyces. It is reported also, that if the nostrils of a Bull be anoynted with Oyl of Roses, he will presently lose his eye-sight: and that in the Lake *Asphalites* there can no living creature abide, and yet many Bulls and Camels swim therein safely. It is but fabulous that there were Bulls in *Colchis*, which did breath out fire, except by that fiction the Poets understood the beastly rage of the rich Inhabitants. Touching the sacrificing of Bulls; it was also the custom of the old *Egyptians* to sacrifice a Bull unto *Epaphus*: and their manner was, first of all to try him whether it were fit for sacrifice, by laying meal before them, whereof if they refused to taste, they were adjudged not apt for the Temple.

The *Drutdæ* call a general sacrifice *Viscum*, whereby they affirm all grievances may be cured. First they prepared a banquet with sacrifice under some tree, then brought they two white Bulls fastened together by the horns, and then they gave a drink to any barren creature, woman, or brute beast, holding religiously, that by that drink they should be made fruitful, and free from all poyson: Unto so great a height did the folly of blinde people arise, to put religion in every unreasonable invention, under pretence of any good intention devised by idolatrous Priests. As often as they flew and offered a Bull, and poured Frankincense and Wine upon the hoast, they said; The Bull is increased with Frankincense and Wine: but the *Ionians* did best comfort themselves in their sacrifices, where the Bull before his death did lough at the Altar: and the *Messenians* did binde their Bull which was to be sacrificed to the ghost of *Aristomene*, unto certain Pillars in his Sepulchre: if therefore the Bull did shake the pillar while he leaped to and fro to get liberty, they took it for a good sign or *Omen*, but if it stood immoveable, they held it a mournful and lamentable thing.

It is likewise reported by *Varinus*, that when *Agamemnon* ignorantly killed one of the Harts of *Diana* in *Aulis*, she was so wroth, that she stayed the winds from blowing upon his Navy, so as they could not stir out of harbour: hereupon they went to the Oracle, where answer was given, that the goddess was to be pacified with some one of *Agamemnons* blood, therefore *Ulysses* was sent away to fetch *Iphigenia*, the daughter of *Agamemnon* from her mother *Clitemnestra*, under pretence to be marryed to *Achilles*; but when she was ready to be sacrificed, the goddess took pity on her, and accepted a Bull in her stead, which ought not to be thought incredible, seeing that in holy Scripture a Ram was substituted in the place of *Isaac*.

They were wont also to sacrifice a Bull to *Neptune*, and to all the Rivers, because of that affinity which they held a Bull hath with all waters: and to *Apollo*, according to this *Virgilian* verse, *Taurum Neptuno, Taurum tibi pulcher Apollo*. But unto *Jupiter* it was unaccustomed to be offered, perhaps because he had often shewed himself in that likeness, to ravish and deflour women. There be certain Proverbs of a Bull, which are not altogether impertinent in this place. First, it is commonly said, that he may bear a Bull that hath born a Calf; whereby is meant, that he may be more subject to filthiness in age, which was so in youth. *Quartilla* was a woman of most vile reputation for uncleanness, because she said, that when she was little, she lay with little ones like her self, and when she grew bigger, she applied her self to the pleasure of elder men, growing in filthiness as she had increased in years. Likewise they were wont to say of an absurd or impossible thing; that if a Bull could reach his head over *Taygetus*, he might drink of the river *Eurota*: and the beginning of this proverb, was taken of an *Apothegme* of *Geradas*, when his Hoast upon a time did ask him what punishment the *Lacedemonians* had appointed for adulterers, he answered: there was no adulterers in *Lacedemon*, and therefore the punishment and question were frivolous. His Hoast replyed; But if there should be an adulterer there, what punishment would they appoint for him? Marry (said *Geradas*) he should pay such a Bull as would reach over *Taygetus* to drink of the water *Eurota*; whereat the host laughed, demanding where such a Bull could be found? then said *Geradas*, and where can you finde an adulterer in *Lacedemon*? so putting off one absurdity with another. And thus much of the natures and properties of a Bull in general. In the next place before this beast be turned into the Woods, we will describe his medicinal vertues, and so let him loose.

The powder of a Bulls horn drunk in water stayeth a flux of blood, and the loosness of the belly. *Sextus* and *Esculatus* say, that if a Bulls horn be burned in a place where Serpents abide, it driveth them away. The blood of Bulls mingled with Barley flower, driveth away hardness in the flesh, and being dryed cureth Aposthumes in every part of the body. It taketh away spots in the face, and killeth Serpents: It is commended warm against the Gout, especially in Horses. It is not good for to drink, because it is easily congealed, except the little veins be taken out. It is accounted among the chiefest poysons, and therefore it is thought by *Plutarch*, that *Hannibal* poysoned himself by drinking Bulls blood, being thereunto perswaded by his servant: for so dyed *Themistocles*, and *Psammenitus* King of *Egypt*, taken by *Cambyss*, was constrained to drink the blood of a Bull; whereupon immediately he gave up the ghost. For remedy hereof, it is good to beware of vomiting, because the blood congealed in the stomach into lumps, stoppeth the throat; wherefore all those things which dissolve milk in the stomach, are also medicinable against the blood of Bulls. In these cases let the party be first of all purged by Glyster or otherwise, and then anoynt the stomach and belly with Barly meal and sweet Water, laying it unto them like a plaister: likewise

Lupines, Oxymel, and Nitre, are soveraign in this, as all Physitians know. The dry leaves of Neppe and Calamach is profitable against this Malady; so also are ashes made of the lees of Wine burned.

The fat of a Bull is profitable to many things. First therefore, it must he plucked out warm from the reins of a Bull and washed in a River or Brook of running Water, pulling out the skins and tunicles, then melt it in a new earthen pot, having cast among it a little salt, then set it in fair cold Water, and when it beginneth to congeal, rub it up and down in the hands, wringing out the water, and letting it soke in again, untill it appear well washed; then boyl it in a pot with a little sweet Wine; and being sodden, let it stand all night: if in the morning it savour strong, then pour in more Wine, seeche it again, untill that savour cease, and so all the poyson be removed: and beware of Salt in it, especially if it be to be used in diseases, whereunto Salt is an enemy, but being thus used, it looketh very white: after the same manner may be used the fat of Lions, Leopards, Panthers, Camels, Boars, and Horses.

The fat kall about the guts melted in a frying pan, and anoynted upon the genitals and breast, helpeth the *Dysenterie*. The marrow of a Bul beaten and drunk, cureth the pain in the smal of the belly: and *Rasis* saith, that if it be melted at a fire, and mingled with one fourth part of Myrrhe and Oyl of Bays, and the hands and feet be therewith anointed and rubbed, morning and evening; it helpeth the contractions of the Nerves and Sinews.

The fat of a Dormouse, of a Hen, and the marrow of a Bull, melted together, and poured warm into the ears, easeth their pain very much: and if the liver of a Bull be broyled on a soft fire, and put into ones mouth that hath the Tooth-ach, the pain will go away so soon as ever the teeth touch it. The gall of a Bull is sharper then an Oxes, and it is mingled with Hony for a Wound-plaister, and in all outward remedies against poyson. It hath also a quality to gnaw the deadness or corruption out of Wounds, and with the juyce of Leeks and the Milk of women, it is applyed against the Swine-pox, and Fistulaes; but the gall alone rubbed upon the biting of an Ape, cureth that Malady. Likewise the Ulcers in the head, both of men, women, and children. And if the wool of an Hare be burned to ashes, and mingled with oyl of Myrtles, Bulls gall, and beaten Alome, and so warmed and anoynted upon the head, it stayeth the falling away of the hair of head.

With the gall of a Bull, and the white of an Egge, they make an Eye-salve, and so anoynt therewith dissolved in water four days together; but it is thought to be better with Hony and Balsam: and instilled with sweet new Wine into the Ears; it helpeth away the pains of them especially running-mattry Ears, with Womans or Goats milk. It being taken wich Hony into the mouth, helpeth the clifts and sores therein; and taken with the Water of new *Coloquintida* and given to a woman in travel, causeth an easie childe-birth *Galen* was wont to give of a Bulls gall the quantity of an Almond, with two spoonfuls of Wine, called (*Vinum Lymphatum*) to a woman that hath her childe dead within her body, which would presently cause the dead Embryon to come forth. The genital of a red Bull, dryed to powder, and drunk of a woman, to the quantity of a golden Noble, it maketh her to loath all manner of copulation: but in men (as the later Physitians affirm) it causeth that desire of lust to increase. The dung of a Bull laid to warm, helpeth all hardness; and burnt to powder, helpeth the member that is burnt. The urine or stale of Buls with a little Nitre taketh away Scabs and Leprosie.

OF ANOTHER BEAST CALLED BUSELAPHUS.

THERE was (saith *D. Cay*) a cloven-footed beast brought out of the Deserts of *Mauritania* into *England*, of the bigness of a Hinde, in form and countenance betwixt a Hinde and a Cow, and therefore for the resemblance it beareth of both, I will call it *Buselaphus*, or *Bovicervus*, or *Moschelaphus*, or a Cow-Hart: having a long and thin head and ear, a lean and slender leg and shin, so that it may seem to be made for chase and celerity. His tail not much longer then a foot, but the form thereof very like a Cows, and the length like a Harts; as if nature seemed to doubt whether it should encline to a Cow or a Hart: his upper parts were yellowish and smooth, his neither parts black and rough; the hair of his body betwixt yellow and red, falling close to the skin, but in his fore-head standing up like a Star; and so also about the horns which were black, and at the top smooth, but downward rough with wrinkles meeting on the contrary part, and on the neerer side spreading from one another, twice or thrice their quantity. These horns are in length one foot and a hand-breadth, but three hands-breadth thick at the root, and their distance at the root was not above one fingers breadth, so arising to their middle, and a little beyond where they differ or grow asunder three hands breadth and a half; then yeeld they together again a little, and so with another crook depart asunder the second time, yet so, as the tops of the horns do not stand asunder above two hands-breadth, three fingers and a half. From the crown of the head to the nostrils, there goeth a black strake which is one foot, two palms and one finger long, in breadth above the eyes where it is broadest, it is seven fingers, in thickness one foot and three palms, it hath eight teeth, and wanteth the uppermost like a Cow, and yet cheweth the Cud, it hath two udders under the belly like a Heifer that never had a Calf, it is a gentle and pleasant beast, apt to play and sport, being not only swift to run, but light and active to leap: It will eat any thing, either bread, broth; salted or powdred beef, grass or herbs, and the use hereof being alive is for hunting, and being dead the flesh is sweet and pleasant for meat.

OF THE OXE AND COW.

WE are now to describe those beasts which are less forein and strange, and more commonly known to all Nations, then any other four-footed beast: for howsoever Bugils, Buffes, Lyons, Bears, Tigers, Beavers, Porcupines and such other, are not alway found in every Nation, yet for the most part are Oxen, Kine, Buls and Horses, by the Providence of Almighty God, disseminated in all the habitable places of the world: and to speak the truth, Oxen and Horses were the first riches, and such things wherein our Elders gat the first property, long before houses and lands: with them they rewarded men of highest desert, as *Melampus*, who opened an Oracle to *Neleus* that sought out the lost Oxen of *Iphiclus*. And *Erix* King of *Sicily*, so much loved Oxen, that *Hercules* recovered from *Geryon*, that when he was to contend with *Hercules* about these, he rather yeelded to depart from his Kingdom then from his Cattel: and *Iulius Pollux* affirmeth, that there was an ancient coin of mony, which was stamped with the figure of an Oxe, and therefore the Cryer in every publick spectacle made proclamation, that he which deserved well, should be rewarded with an Oxe, (meaning a piece of mony having that impress upon it: which was a piece of Gold compared in value to an *English* Rose-noble) and in my opinion the first name of mony among the *Latines* is derived from Cattel, for I cannot invent any more probable etymologie of *Pecunia*, then from *Pecus*, signifying all manner of Cattel: howsoever it is related by some Writers, that on the one side of their coin was the Kings face, and on the other an Oxes picture; and that *Servius* was the first that ever figured money with Sheep or Oxen. *Miron* the great painter of *Eleutheris*, and disciple of *Agelas*, made an Heifer or Cow of Brass, which all Poets of *Greece* have celebrated in sundry Epigrams, because a Calf came unto it to suck it, being deceived with the proportion, and *Ausonius* also added this following unto the said Calf and Cow, saying:

Ubera quid pulsas frigentia matris abenæ,
O vitula? & succum lactis ab ære petis?

Whereunto the brazen Cow in caused to make this answer following:

Hunc quoque præstarem, si me pro parte parasset,
Exteriore Miron, interiore Deus.

Whereby he derideth their vain labours, which endeavour to satisfie themselves upon mens devises, which are cold and comfortless without the blessing of Almighty God. To begin therefore with these beasts, it must be first of all remembred, that the name *Bos*, or an Oxe as we say in *English*, is the most vulgar and ordinary name for Bugils, Bulls, Cows, Buffes, and all great cloven-footed horned beasts; although in proper speech, it signifieth a beast gelded or libbed of his stones: and *Boas* signifieth a huge great Serpent whereof there were one found in *Italy*, that had swallowed a childe whole without breaking one of his bones, observing also in Oxen the distinction of years or age: which giveth them several names, for in their young age they are called Calves, in their second age Steeres, in their third Oxen, and the *Latines* adde also a fourth, which they call *Vetuli*, old Oxen. These are also distinguished in sex, the Male Calf is *Vitulus*, the Female *Vitula*; likewise *Iuvencus*, a Steer, and *Iuvenca*, an Heifer, *Bos*, an Oxe, and *Vacca*, a Cow; *Taurus*, a Bull; *Taura*, a barren Cow; and *Horda*, a bearing and fruitful Cow: of whom the *Romans* observed certain festival days called *Hordicalia*, wherein they sacrificed those Cattel. The *Latines* have also *Vaccula* and *Bucula* for a little Cow:

> *Vaccula non nunquam secreta cubilia captans, Virg.*
> And again,
> —— *Aut Bucula Cœlum.*

And *Bucalus* or *Bos novellus* for a little Oxe. *Schor* in the *Hebrew* signifieth a Bull or Oxe, *Bakar*, Herds, or a Cow. *Thor* in the *Chaldee* hath the same signification with *Schor*, and among the later Writers you may finde *Tora* a masculine, and *Torata* a feminine, for a Bull and a Cow, accustomed to be handled for labour. The *Grœcians* call them *Bous* and *Boes*, the *Arabians*, *Bakar*: and it is to be noted, that the holy Scriptures distinguish betwixt *Tzon*, signifying flocks of Sheep and Goats, and *Bakar* for Herds of Cattel and Neat: and *Meria* is taken for Bugils, or the greatest Oxen, or rather for fatted Oxen, for the verb *Marah* signifieth to feed fat. *Egela* is interpreted Jer. 46. for a young Cow; and the *Persians*, *Gojalais*. It is very probable that the *Latine*, *Vacca*, is derived from the *Hebrew*, *Bakar*, as the *Saracen* word, *Baccara*; so in *Hebrew*, *Para* is a Cow, and *Par*, a Steer, and *Ben Bakar*, the son of an Oxe, or Calf: and whereas the *Hebrews* take *Parim*, for Oxen in general, the *Chaldees* translate it *Tore*; the *Arabs, Bakera*; the *Persians, Nadgacah*, or *Madagaucha*; the *Italians*, call it *Bue*; the *French, Beuf*; the *Spaniards, Buey*; the *Germans, Ochs*, and *Rind*; the *Illyrians, Wull*. The *Italians* call a Cow *Vacca* at this day; the *Grœcians, Bubalis*, and *Damalis*, or *Damalai*; (for a Cow which never was covered with a Bull, or tamed with a yoke) and *Agelada*. The *French, Vache*; the *Spaniard, Vaca*; the *Germans, Ku*, or *Kuhe*; and the Citizens of *Altina, Ceva*: from which the *English* word Cow seemeth to be derived; the *Latine* word is, a young Heifer, which hath ceased to be a Calf.

There are Oxen in most part of the world, which differ in quantity, nature, and manner, one from another, and therefore do require a several Tractate. And first, their Oxen of *Italy* are most famous, for as much as some learned men have affirmed, that the name *Italia*, was first of all derived of the *Greek* word *Italous*, signifying Oxen; because of the abundance bred and nourished in those parts, and the great account the ancient *Romans* made hereof, appeareth by notable example of punishment, who banished a certain Countrey man for killing an Oxe in his rage, and denying that he eat thereof, as if he had killed a man: likewise in *Italy* their Oxen are not all alike, for they of *Campania* are for the most part white and slender, yet able to manure the Countrey wherein they are bred; they of *Umbria*, are of great bodies, yet white and red coloured. In *Hetruria* and *Latrum*, they are very compact and well set or made, strong for labour, but the most strong are those of *Apeunine*, although they appear not to the eye very beautiful.

The *Egyptians* which dwell about *Nilus* have Oxen as white as snow, and of exceeding high and great stature, (greater then the Oxen of *Grecia*) yet so meek and gentle, that they are easily ruled and governed by men. The *Aonian* Oxen are of divers colours, intermingled one within another, having a whole round hoof like a horse, and but one horn growing out of the middle of their forehead.

The domestical or tame Oxen of *Africk* are so small that one would take them for Calves of two years old; the *Africans* (saith *Strabo*) which dwell betwixt *Getulia* and our Coast or Countrey, have Oxen and Horses which have longer lips and hoofs then other, and by the *Grecians* are termed *Macrokeilateroi*.

The *Armenian* Oxen have two horns, but winding and crooking to and fro like Ivie which cleaveth to Oaks, which are of such exceeding hardness that they will blunt any sword that is stroke upon them, without receiving any impression or cut thereby. Some are of opinion, that the only excellent breed of Cattel is in *Bœnia*, neer the City *Tanagra* (called once *Pœmandra*) by reason of their famous Cattel, the which Oxen are called *Coprophaga*, by reason that they will eat the dung of man; so also do the Oxen of *Cyprus*, to ease the pains of their small guts. The *Caricians* in a part of *Asia* are not pleasant to behold, having shaggie hair, and bunches on either shoulders, reaching or swelling to their necks; but those which are either white, or black, are refused for labour.

Epirus yeeldeth also very great and large Oxen, which the inhabitants call *Pyrrici*, because that their first stock or seminary were kept by King *Pyrrhus*: howsoever other say, that they have their name of their fiery flaming colour: they are also called *Larani* of a Village *Larinum*, or of *Larinus*, a chief Neat-herd: of whom *Atheneus* maketh mention, who received this great breed of Cattel of *Hercules* when he returned from the slaughter of *Gerion*: who reigned about *Ambracia* and *Ampholochi*, where through the fatness of the earth and goodness of the Pasture they grow to so great a stature. Other call them *Cestrini*, I know not for what cause, yet it may be probable that they are called *Larini*, by reason of their broad Nostrils, for *Rines* in *Greek* signifieth Nostrils: but the true cause of their great bone and stature is, because that neither sex were suffered to couple one with another, untill they were four years old at the least, and therefore they were called *Atauri*, and *Setauri*, and they were the proper goods of the King: neither could they live in any other place but in *Epirus*, by reason that the whole Countrey is full of sweet and deep pastures.

All the Oxen in *Eulœa* are white at the time of their Calving, and for this cause the Poets call that Countrey *Argoboeon*. If that Oxen or Swine be transported or brought into *Hispaniola*, they grow so great, that the Oxen have been taken for Elephants, and their Swine for Mules, but I take this relation to be hyperbolical.

There are Oxen in *India* which will eat flesh like Wolves, and have but one horn, and whole hoofs; some also have three horns; there be other as high as Camels, and their horns four foot broad. There was a horn brought out of *India* to *Ptolemy* the second, which received three *Amphoraes* of water, amounting the least to thirty *English* gallons of wine measure; whereby it may be conjectured of how great quantity is the beast that bare it. The *Indians*, both Kings and people, make no small reckoning of these beasts, (I mean their vulgar Oxen) for they are most swift in course, and will run a race as fast as any horse, so that in their course you cannot know an Ox from a Horse, waging both gold and silver upon their heads; and the Kings themselves are so much delighted with this pastime, that they follow in their Wagons, and will with their own mouths and hands provoke the beasts to run more speedily: and herein the Ox exceedeth a Horse, because he will not accomplish his race with sufficient celerity, except his rider draw bloud from his sides with the spur, but the Oxes rider need not to lay any hands or pricks at all upon him, his only ambitious nature of overcoming (carrying him more swiftly then all the rods or spurs of the world could prevail on him). And of this game, the lowest of the people also are very greedy, laying many wagers, making many matches, and adventuring much time and price to see their event.

Among the *Indians* there are also other Oxen which are not much greater then great Goats, who likewise in their yoaks are accustomed to run many races, which they performe with as great speed as a *Getican* Horse; and all these Oxen must be understood to be wilde Oxen.

There be Oxen in *Leuctria* (which *Aristotle* affirmeth) have their ears and horns growing both together forth of one stem. The Oxen of the *Garamants*, and all other Neat among them, feed with their necks doubled backward, for by reason of their long and hanging horns, they cannot eat their meat, holding their heads directly straight. The self same is reported of the beasts of *Troglodytæ*; in other things they differ not from other Oxen, save only in the hardness of their skin, and these Oxen are called *Opisthonomi*.

In the Province of *Bangala*, are Oxen (saith *Paulus Venetus*) which equall the Elephant in height. The Oxen in *Mysia* have no horns, which other affirm also of the *Scythians*, whereof they assign this reason, because the universal bone of the skull hath no *Commissure* or joint opened, and cannot receive any humour flowing unto it, by reason of the hardness resisting, and the veins belonging to this bone are weaker and smaller then in other; for which also they are more unfit to convey nourishment to the place: and so the neck of these beasts must needs be more dry and lesse strong, because the veins are very little. The Oxen have bunches growing on their backes like Camels, and upon them do they bear their burdens, being taught by the discipline of men, to bend on their knee to receive their load.

Among the *Nomades* (which winter their Cattel about the Marishes of *Mæotis*) there are also certain Cattel without horns; whereof some are so naturally, the other have their horns sawed off, as soon as they grow forth, because of all the parts of their body, they only can endure no cold.

There be Oxen in *Phrygia* and *Erythrea* which are of a flaming red colour, of a very high and winding neck, their horns are not like any other in the world, for they are moved with their ears turning in a flexible manner sometime one way and sometime another.

The *Syrian* Oxen called *Pellet* are of great strength, having a broad forehead, strong horns, and fearful or couragious aspect, being neither too fat or too lean of their bodies; and they are used both for war and also for running.

The Oxen of the *Belgian* Provinces, especially *Friseland* and *Holland*, are also of very great stature, for it hath been found by good experience, that one of them hath weighed sixteen hundred pounds *Troy* weight: and when the Earl of *Hoochstate* was at *Michlin* in *Friseland*, there was presented unto him a great Ox, which being killed, weighed above two thousand five hundred twenty and eight pound. The which thing being so strange as the like had not been beforetime observed; to the intent that succeeding ages might not mistrust such a memorable report, the said Earl caused the full picture of the said Ox, to be set up in his Palace, with an inscription of the day and year when this Ox was delivered and killed.

OF COWES.

HAVING thus noted briefly the Countries wherein Oxen are bred and nourished, with their several forms: it must be also observed that

Kine or Cowes which are the female of this kind, are likewise found in all the places aforesaid with correspondent and semblable quantities, qualities, members, parts, and other accidents to such creatures appertaining; excepted alwayes those things which belong to their sex, which principally concern their milk. And first of all the Kine of most plentiful Milk in all *Italy*, are about *Altinas* a City of the *Venetians*, neer *Aquileia*, which Kine are of the smallest body, and yet the greatest labourers, who are not yoaked or coupled together by their necks as in other Countries, but only by their heads.

The Cowes of *Arabia* have the most beautiful horns, by reason of aboundance of humours which flow to them, feeding them continually with such generous liquor as naturally doth encrease them.

The *Pyrrhean* Kie are not admitted to the Bull till they be four year old at the least, which thing caused them to grow to a very high and tall stature: whereof there were ever four hundred kept for the Kings store.

These Kie do give at one time seaven or eight gallons of Milk, of Wine measure, and they are so tall, that the person which milketh them must stand upright, or else stoop very little: neither ought this seem incredible, for it is evident that the Cowes of the *Phœnicians* were so high, that a very tall man could not milk them except he stood upon a footstool.

The manner is in *Germany* and *Helvetia*, that about *April* some take Kie to hire, which have none of their own, and other buy Kie to farme them out to other; and the common price of a Cow for six moneths is payed in Butter, and is rated at seventy five pounds, twelve ounces to the pound; which payment is due to the owner, or money to that value. Other again, buy Kie and let them forth to farm, reserving the Calf to themselves; and if by the negligence of the Cow-herd or farmer of them, the Cow cast the Calf, then is the hirer bound to answer the value, but if it miscarry without his negligence (as oftentimes they may) then is the losse equall to the Locatour or Farmer. Yet it is noted, that the Kie of greatest bodies, are not alway best or most plentifull in Milke; for the Cowes or *Cæve* of *Altinos* in Italy, are of little bodies, but yet very full of Milk.

The principal benefit of Cowes Milk is for making of Butter, for the Milk it self, the Cheese and Whay, are not so fit for nourishment of man, as are those of Sheep; and the reason is, because the Milk of Kie is fattest of all other, and therefore the name of Butter, which is in *Greek*, *Boutyros* and *Boutyron*, and *Butyrum* in *Latin*, is derived properly from this kinde of Cattel. The Cow-herds do also for their profit, observe the pasture and food, which doth above other multiplie Milk; and therefore they give their Kie *Trifolie*, or Three-leaved grasse; and *Medica*, (which is a kinde of Claver grasse) Vetches, Pulse, and Beans, for Beans have a great virtue to multiply Milk: likewise I have seen bundles of Hemlock, or an herb much like unto it, (which we call Harts tongue) given to milch Kie.

There is an herb much like Crow-foot, called of the *Germans*, *Butterbloumen*, and in *English*, Butter-flower, which is used to colour Butter, for thereby is the whiteness thereof taken away: they will not eat Wal-wort or night-shade (commonly called Deaths herb) but if they eat herbs whereupon falleth an Hony-dew, then will their Milk be wonderful sweet and plentiful: there is no food so good for Cowes, as that which is green, if the Countrey will afford it; especially Kie love the wet and wateryplaces, although the Butter coming from the milk of such beasts, is not so wholesome as that which is made of such as are feed in dryer Pastures. The like care is had of their drink, for although they love the coldest and clearest waters, yet about their time of Calving it is much for better them to have warmer waters, and therefore the Lakes which are heated and made to some by the rain; are most wholesome to them, and do greatly help to ease their burden and pains in that business.

Pausanias reporteth a wonder in nature, of the Rivers *Milichus* and *Charadrus*, running through the City *Patræ*, that all the Kie which drink of them in the Spring time, do for the most part bring forth males, wherefore their herdmen avoid those places at that time. Kie for the most part before their Calving, are dry and without milk (especially about *Torona*). They are also purged of their menstrua in greater measure, then either Goats or Sheep, which especially come from them a little before or after they have been with the Bull; howsoever *Aristotle* saith, that they come from them after they have been five moneths with Calf, and are discerned by their urine; for the urine of a Cow is the thinnest of all other.

These beasts are very lustful, and do most eagerly desire the company of their male, which if they have not within the space of three hours after they mourn for it, their lust asswageth till another time. In a Village of *Egypt* called *Schussa* (under the government of the *Hermopolites*) they worship *Venus* under the title *Urania* in the shape of a Cow, perswading themselves that there is great affinity betwixt the Goddesse and this beast; for by her mournful voice she giveth notice of her love, who receiveth the token many times a mile or two off, and so presently runneth to accomplish the lust of nature: and for this cause do the *Egyptians* picture *Isis* with a Cows horns, and likewise a Bull to signifie hearing. The signes of their Bulling (as it is termed) are their cries, and disorderly forsaking their fellows, and resisting the government of their keeper. Likewise, their secret hangeth forth more then at other times, and they will leap upon their fellows as if they were males: besides after the manner of Mares, they oftner make water then at other times.

The most cunning heardmen have means to provoke them to desire the Bull, if they be slack, first of all they withdraw from them some part of their meat (if they be fat) for that will make them fitter to conceive; then take they the genitals or stones of a Bull, and hold it to their nose, by smelling whereof they are provoked to desire copulation; and if that prevail not, then take they the tendrest part of Shrimps, which is their fish, and beat them in water till they be an ointment, and therewith anoint the breasts of the Cow, after they have been well washed, untill it work upon her. And some affirm, that the tail of an Eel put into her hath the same virtue; other attribute much force to the wilde willow, to procure lust and conception.

They are a great while in copulation, and some have ghessed by certain signes at the time of copulation, whether the Calf prove male or female; for say they, if the Bull leap down on the right side of the Cow, it will be a male, if on the left, it will be a female: which conjecture is no longer true, then when the Cow admitteth but one Bull, and conceiveth at the first conjunction, for which cause the *Egyptians* decipher a woman bringing forth a maiden childe; by a Bull, looking to the left hand, and likewise bearing a man childe, by a Bull, looking to the right hand.

They are not to be admitted to copulation before they be two year old at the least, or if it may be four; yet it hath been seen, that a Heifer of a year old hath conceived, and that another of four moneths old hath likewise desired the Bull; but this was taken for a monster, and the other never thrived.

One Bull is sufficient for fifteen Kie, although *Varro* faith, that he had but two Buls for threescore and ten Kie; and one of them was two year old, the other one. The best time for their copulation is about the time of the Daulphins appearance, and so continueth for two or three and fourty daies, which is about *June* and *July*, for those which conceive at that time, will bring forth their young ones in a most temperate time of the year: and it hath been observed, that an Ox immediately after his gelding, before he had forgotten his former desire and inclination, his seed not dryed up, hath filled a Cow, and she proved with Calf.

They go with Calf ten moneths, except eighteen or twenty daies; but those which are Calved before that time, cannot live; and a Cow may bear every year (if the Countrey wherein she liveth be full of grasse, and the Calf taken away from her at fifteen days old).

And if a man desire that the Calf should be a male, then let him tie the right stone of the Bull at the time of copulation; and for a female bind the left. Others work this by natural observation; for when they would have a male, they let their Cattel couple when the North wind bloweth; and when a female, they put them together when the air is Southerly. They live not above fifteen years, and thereof ten times they may ingender. The best time to Calve in, is *April*, because then the

Spring bringeth on grasse, both for themselves, and to increase milk for the young ones.

They bear not but in their right side, although they have twins in their belly, which happeneth very seldom, and the beast immediately after her delivery, must be nourished with some good meat, for except she be well fed, she will forsake her young to provide for her self: therefore it is requisite to give her Vetches, Millet-seed, and milk mingled with water, and scorched Corne; and unto the Calves themselves, dryed Millet in milk, in the manner of a mash: and the Kie must also be kept up in stables, so as they may not touch their meat at the going forth, for they are quickly brought to forsake and loath that which is continually before them: and it is observed that when Kie in the Summer time do in greater number above custom go to the Bull then at other times, it betokeneth and foresheweth a wet and rainy winter, for it cannot be (saith *Albertus*) that a beast so dry as is a Cow, can be increased in moisture, which stirreth up the desire of procreation, except also there be a mutation in the air unto abundance of moisture. And to conclude this discourse of a Cow, in ancient time they were wont to call light women Heifers, Harlots, and Kine, by reason of two famous harlots of *Athens, Cuina* and *Salanachha*, and from this came the fiction of *Io*, whose fable is at large prosecuted by *Ovid*, how she being the daughter of *Iuachus*, was in a darkness brought upon her by *Jupiter*, by him ravished, which mist being espied by *Juno*, she descended to the earth, and *Jupiter* fearing his wives jealousie turned the said *Io* into a Heifer, from which shape she was afterwards delivered and maried to *Osiris* the King of *Egypt*, and after her death was worshipped by the *Egyptians* for a god, and called *Isis*, unto whom they sacrificed Geese which were called *Sacra Isiaca*.

In the choise of Kie, you must observe this direction, you must buy them in the moneth of *March*, let them be young, not past their first or second Calf, their colour black or red, seldom brown or white, bright coloured, specially red, brown legs, blackish horns smooth and beautiful, high fore-heads, great eyes and black, hairy and grisly ears, flat Nostrils like an Apes, but open and wide, their back bones bending somewhat backward, black lips, long and thick necks, most broad fair crests descending from the neck, well ribbed, a great belly, the back and shoulders very broad, the buttockes broad, with a long tail hanging down to their heels, and their neather part in many places crisped and curled, well set and compacted legs rough and short, straight knees, and their bunches hanging over; their small feet, not broad but round, standing in good distance one from other, not growing crooked or splay-footed, and their hoofs smooth and like one another every way. Finally, it were a profitable thing to prosecute natures perfection in every one of their several parts, but I spare to speak any more of the Females, and returning again to the story of Oxen from which we have digressed, leaving the readers who desire to hear more of this discourse of Kie to other Authors, who purposely describe every part more particularly.

To begin therefore with their description, because among folded beasts they are of most dignity and worth, especially in *Italy*, where the bounds of their best priviledged and flourishing Cities, were first of all declared and layed out, by the lowing together of an Ox and a Cow in one yoak. *Mago Carthaginensis* teacheth, that the time to provide or buy oxen, is best in the time of *March*, because then in their lean bodies, they which sell them cannot cover their faults so well, as if they were fatter, and also if they should be unruly and stubborn, they may be the more easily tamed, before their flesh increase their strength.

Their notes or markes must be these, let them be young, having square and great lims, a sound body, thick and short, having his muscles standing up red and round, and all his body smooth, his horns black, strong and large, without crooking or winding, after the fashion of a half moon, great and rough ears, their eyes and lips black, broad Nostrils and flat upward, a long thick and soft neck, his crest descending down to the knee, a great breast, large shoulders, big belly, long straight sides, broad loins, a straight back descending a little, and a round pair of buttocks, straight, sound and sinewy, short legs, good knees, great hoofs, and long tails rough and grisly. And it is to be noted, that the Oxen of a mans own Countrey breed, are better and to be preferred before strangers, because he is already naturally fitted to the air, food, water, and temper of the soil: for it is not good to bring them from the Mountains to the Vallies, because then they will grow lasie and fat, and so into diseases; neither from the Vallies to the

140

Mountains, because they will quickly grow out of heart through want of their first deep and fat pasture; and above all, have regard to match them equally in yoak, so as one may not overbear the other. Oxen loose their teeth at two or three year old, but not all as a Horse doth, their nerves are harder, but not so hard as a Buls; their flesh is dry and melancholick, their horns are greater and larger then are a Buls, for the same reason that Eunuchs and gelded persons can never be bald; for copulation weakneth the brain, only a Bull hath a stronger forehead then an Ox, because the humour that should grow forth into horns, is hardned under the bone: and the horns of Kie which are also bigger then a Buls; may through heat be made flexible with wax or water, and bend every way: and if when they are thus made soft, you do slit or cut them into four, that is, every horn in two, they will so grow afterward, as if every beast had four horns, and sometime through the thickness of their scull, closing up the part where the horn should grow, and the smalness of their veins in that place to feed the horns, there come no horns at all, but remain polled; And it is reported that they have a little stone in their head, which in the fear of death they breath out. Their teeth do all touch one another, and are changed twice, they chew the cud like sheep, wanting a row of their upper teeth, that is four of them, their eyes are black and broad, and their heart full of sinews, yet without any bony substance, although *Pliny* affirmeth that sometimes in the hearts of Oxen and Horses are found bones.

Their crest called *Palea* cometh of *Pilus* their hair, and it is nothing else but long strakes in their hair, whereby the generosity and stomach of the beast is apparent. A Cow hath two udders under her loins, with four speans, like a Goat and a Sheep, because the concoction and juice of their meat may better descend to the lower parts then to the upper; their navell is filled with many veins, their hair short and soft, their tail long, with harder hair then in the other parts of the body; their milt is long and not round, their reins are like the reins of a Sea-calf, and by reason of their dry bodies they grow very fat, and this fat will not easily be dissolved, but their manner of feeding maintaineth their strength, for they which eat much are slow in the chewing, and speedy in the concoction, for they do better preserve their fat which eat slowly: then those that eat hastily and with more greediness.

It hath been already shewed, that some Oxen will eat flesh, and tear wilde beasts in pieces, the people of *Prasias* give to their yoaked or working Oxen fish, and also in the Province of *Aden*, and where their Horses, Sheep, and Oxen, eat dryed fish, by reason that the abundance of heat doth dry up their pasture: neither is any thing so plentiful among them as fish: the like is reported of the people *Horotæ*, and *Gedrusti*, and of *Motynum* a City of *Thracia*, and in *Friseland*: in the Province of *Narbon*, there is an herb growing in waters, which is so much desired of their Cattel, that they will thrust their heads into the water above their ears, to bite that to the roots: and the Oxen of the Northern ocean Islands of *Germany* do grow so fat, that they are indangered to die thereby.

The most common food for Oxen, is the same that is already specified in the former discourse of Kie; namely, Three-leaved grasse, Claver grasse, all green herbs, Hay, Beans, Vetches, Chaffe, and in some places Barley and Straw. There is also a monethly diet or food given to Oxen, for in *January* and *February*, they give them Vetches, and Lupines, bruised in water among Chaffe or Pease, so bruised and mingled, and where is want of such pulse, they may give them pressings of Grapes dryed and cleansed, which is not turned into wine, and mingle them with chaffe for the Cattel to eat, but the Grapes themselves are much better before the pressing, with their small twigs or leaves, because they are both meat and drink, and will fat an Ox very speedily.

The like may be added of boughs, of Laurel, Elme, and other leaves, and also Nuts and Acornes, but if they be not wearyed and fed with Acornes till they loath them, they will fall into scabs. In *March* and *April*, give them Hay, and from *April* unto *June* give them Grasse, and such green meat as may be found abroad; Afterward all the Summer and Autumn, they may be satisfied with the leaves of Elme, Bay, Holm, and especially that kind of Oake which is without prickles, and therefore they cannot abide Juniper. In *November* and *December*, while the seed time lasteth, they must have as much given them as they can desire, either of the forenamed food, or else of some better if need require; for it must be principally regarded, that the Cattel fall not into leanness in the Winter time, for leanness is the mother of many sicknesses in Cattel, and their utter overthrow, and therefore the benefits by their full feeding are many, as may appear by that common proverbe, *Bos ad acervum*, that is, an Ox to a whole heap, to signifie such men as live in all plenty and aboundance. The like care must be had of their drink, for the Neat-herd must diligently look unto their drink, that it may be alway clear, and it is reported of the rivers *Crathis* and *Sibaris*, that the Cattel which drink of their water do turn white, whatsoever colour they had in former times.

They will live in strength and perfection twelve years, and their whole life is for the most part but twenty, Kie live not so long; the means to know their age is by their teeth and their horn, for it is observed that their teeth grow black in their age, and their horns wax more circled as they grow in years, although I dare not affirm that every circle betokeneth a years growth, (as some have writen) yet I am assured the smooth horn sheweth a young beast. Moreover, although Kie will endure much cold and heat both in Winter and Summer, yet must you have more regard to your Oxen, and therefore it is required that they in the Winter cold weather be kept dry and housed in stals, which must be of convenient quantity, so as every Ox may be lodged upon straw, the floor made higher under their forefeet then their hinder, so as their urine may passe away and not stand to hurt their hoofs: and there be also allowed for the standing and lodging of every Ox eight foot in breadth, and a length answerable. The like regard must be had to their manger and rack, whereof the slaves must not stand above one foot, or rather lesse from one another, that so they may not draw out their meat and stamp it underfoot.

But all the diet and food that the wit of man can ordain, will do them no manner of good if regard be not had to their bodily health, and preservation of strength, for which cause they must receive an ordinary medicine every quarter of the year; that is, in the end of the Spring, Summer, Autumn, and Winter; which in some places is thus made and given in potion, they take of Cypres, and Lupine leaves an equall quantity, beat them small, then set them in water in the open air a day and a night, and afterward give unto every one for three daies together warmed as much as a wine pinte.

In other places they give them to prevent sickness, a raw Egge, a handful of salt in a pinte of wine: and other put into the meat of Oxen, the foam of new oil mingled with water, first a little at once until they be accustomed unto it, and afterward more, and this they do every fourth or fifth day. *Cato* reciteth a certain vow or prayer, which the old Idolatrous *Romans* were wont to make for the health of their Cattel, to *Silvanus Mars*, which was on this manner. First, they take three pound of green wheat, and of Lard four pounds, and four pound and a half of fleshie sinews, and three pints and a half of wine, then put them into earthen pots with hony, and put in the wine by it self, and this they did yearly, but no woman might know how it is made, or be present at the time of the preparation, and it being made must be presently consumed by fire. Unto this ridiculous and superstitious idle invention, serving more to express the folly of man, then to benefit either man or beast, I may add that kind of sacrifice made for beasts, which *Pliny* calleth *Daps*, that was made in the Spring time when the Pear-tree did blossom, the manner whereof was thus, They did offer to *Jupiter Dapalis* a bowl of wine, on the same day the herd-men and herds make their sacrifice, saying in this manner, O *Jupiter Dapalis*, I offer unto thee this cup of wine, in the behalf of my self, family and Cattel, if thou wilt perform that unto them which belongeth to thee, be good to this wine beneath, be good to this my sacrifice: Afterward the party washed his hands, and then drank the wine saying, O *Jupiter Dapalis*, be good to this my sacrifice, be good to this inferiour wine, and if thou wilt, give part thereof to *Vesta*: the sacrifice being ended he took Millet-seed, Lentils, Oxipanum, and Garlick: *Thus far Cato*; wherewith if any Reader be offended, let him remember to pity such poor remedies, and commend his Cattel to the true God, that saveth man and beast. The *Druides* of the *Gauls*, called a certain herb growing in moyst places *Samolum*; which being gathered by the left hand of them that were fasting, they gave it for an Antidote to Oxen and Swine. And *Galen* telleth of another superstitious cure for Oxen, when a man took the horn of a Hart, and layed it upon the Chappel of *Pan*, and set upon it a burning Candle, which must not be forgotten, but alway thought upon in the day time, calling upon holy *Demusaris*, which foolish people have thought as it were by a witchcraft, to cure the evils of their Cattel.

But to let passe these and such like trifles, let us follow a more perfect description and rule to cure all manner of diseases in this Cattel, whose safegard and health next to a mans, is to be preferred above all other: and first of all the means whereby their sickness is discovered may be considered, as all Lassitude or wearisomeness through overmuch labour, which appeareth by forbearing their meat, or eating after another fashion then they are wont, or by their often lying down, or else by holding out their tongue, all which and many more signes of their diseases, are manifest to them that have observed them in the time of their health; and on the other side it is manifest, that the health of an Ox may be known by his agility, life and stirring, when they are lightly touched or pricked, starting, and holding their ears upright, fulness of their belly, and many other wayes.

There be also herbs which increase in Cattel divers diseases, as herbs bedewed with Hony bringeth the Murrain, the juyce of black *Chamæleon* killeth young Kie like the Chine, black *Hellebore*, *Aconitum*, or Wolf-bane, which is that grasse in *Cilicia*, which inflameth Oxen, herb Henry, and others. It is also reported by *Aristotle*, that in a piece of *Thracia*, not far from that City which is called the City of *Media*, there is a place almost thirty furlongs in length, where naturally groweth a kind of Barley, which is good for men, but pernicious for beasts. The like may be said of *Aegolothros, Orobanche* and *Aestur*, but I will hasten to the particular description of their diseases.

In the first place is the *Malis* or *Glaunders* already spoken of in the story of the Asse, which may be known by these signes, the Oxes hair will be rough and hard, his eyes and neck hang down, matter running out of the nose, his pace heavy, chewing his cud little, his backbone sharp, and his meat loathsome unto him; for remedy hereof take Sea-onions or Garlick, Lupines or Cipres, or else the foam of oil. And if a beast eat Hogs dung, they presently fall sick of the Pestilence, which infecteth the herbs and grasse they breath on, the waters whereof they drink, and the stals and lodgings wherein they lie. The humors which annoy the body of Oxen are many, the first is a moist one called Malis, issuing at the nose, the second a dry one when nothing appeareth outwardly, only the beast forsaketh his meat, the third an articular, when the fore or hinder legs of the beast halt, and yet the hoofs appear sound, the fourth is *Farciminous*, wherein the whole body breaketh forth into mattry bunches and biles, and appear healed till they break forth in other places, the fifth

145

Subtercutaneus, when under the skin there runneth a humour that breaketh forth in many places of the body; the sixth a *Subrenal*, when the hinder legs halt by reason of some pain in the loins, the seventh a Maungie or Leprosie, and lastly a madness or Phrensie, all which are contagious, and if once they enter into a herd, they will infect every beast if they be not separated from the sick, and speedy remedy obtained.

The remedies against the last seven are thus described by *Columella*. First take *Oxipanum* and seaholy roots mingled with Fennel-seed and meal of beaten wheat rath-ripe; put them in spring water warmed with hony nine spoonfuls at a time, and with that medicine anoint the breast of the beast, then take the bloud of a Sea-snail, and for want thereof a common Snail, and put it into wine, and give the beast in at his nose, and it hath been approved to work effectually. It is not good at any time to stir up Oxen to running, for chasing will either move them to looseness of the belly, or drive them into a Feaver: now the signes of a Feaver are these, an immoderate heat over the whole body, especially about the mouth, tongue and eares, tears falling out of the eyes, hollowness of their eyes, a heavy and stooping drowzie head, matter running out of his nose, a hot and difficult breath, and sometime sighing and violent beating of his veins and loathing of meat: for remedy whereof, let the beast fast one whole day, then let him be let bloud under the tail fasting, and afterward make him a drink of bole-wort stalkes sod with oil and liquor of fish sauce, and so let him drink it for five daies together before he eat meat; afterward let him eat the tops of Lentils, and young small Vine branches, then keep his nose and mouth clean with a spunge, and give him cold water to drink three times a day, for the best means of recovery are cold meats and drinks, neither must the beast be turned out of doors, till he be recovered: When an Ox is sick of a cold, give him black wine, and it will presently help him.

If an Ox in his meat tast of hens dung, his belly will presently be tormented, and swell unto death if remedy be not given; for this malady, take three ounces of parsley seed, a pinte and a half of Cummin, two pounds of honey, beat these together and put it down his throat warme, then drive the beast up and down, as long as he can stand, then let as many as can stand about him rub his belly, untill the medicine work to

146

purgation: and *Vegetius* addeth, that the ashes of Elme wood well sod in oil, and put down the beasts throat, cureth the inflamation of hen-dung. If at any time it happen, that an Ox get into his mouth and throat a horse-leech, which at the first will take fast hold, and suck the place she holds (be it mouth or throat) til she have kild the beast: if you cannot take hold on her with the hand, then put into the Oxes throat a Cane, or little hollow pipe, even to the place where the Leech sucketh, and into that pipe put warm oil, which as soon as the Leech feeleth, she presently leaveth hold.

It fortuneth sometimes that an Ox is stung or bitten with a Serpent, Adder, Viper, or other such venomous beast; for that wound take sharp Trifoly, which groweth in rockie places, strain out the juice and beat it with salt, then scarifie the wound with that ointment, till it be wrought in. If a field-mouse bite an Ox, so as the dint of her teeth appear, then take a little Cumin or soft Pitch, and with that make a plaister for the wound or if you can get another field-mouse, put her into oil, and there let it remain till the members of it be almost rotten, then bruise it and lay it to the sore; and the same body shall cure, whose nature gave the wound. Oxen are also much troubled with a disease called the Hide-bound; for remedy wereof, when the beast is taken from his work, and panteth, then let him be sprinkled over with wine and put pieces of fat into his mouth: if then you perceive no amendment, then seethe some Laurel, and therewith heat his back, and afterward with oil and wine scarifie him all over, plucking his skin up from the ribs, and this must be done in the sunshine, or else in a very warm place.

For the scabs, take the juice of Garlick, and rub the beast all over; and with this medicine may the biting of a Wolf or a mad Dog be cured: although other affirm, that the hoof of any beast with Brimstone, Oil, Water and Vinegar, is a more present remedy; but there is no better thing then Butter and stale Urine: When they are vexed with wormes, poure cold water upon them, afterward anoint them with the juice of onions mingled with Salt.

If an Ox be wrinched and strained in his sinews, in travel or labour, by stumping on any root or hard sharp thing, then let the contrary foot or leg be let bloud, if the sinews swell: If his neck swell, let him bloud, or if his neck be winding or weak (as if it were broken) then let him bloud in that ear to which side the head bendeth. When their necks be bald, grinde two tile together, a new one and an old, and when the yoak is taken off, cast the powder upon their necks, and afterward oil, and so with a little rest the hair will come again.

When an Ox hangeth down his ears and eateth not his meat, he is troubled with a *Cephalalgie*; that is, a pain in his head: for which, seethe Thyme in Wine, with Salt and Garlick, and therewith rub his tongue a good space: also raw Barly steeped in Wine, helpeth this disease. Sometime an Ox is troubled with madness, for which men burn them betwixt the horns in the forehead till they bleed: sometime there is a Flie which biting them continually, driveth them into madness; for which they are wont to cast Brimstone and bay sprigs sod in water in the Pastures where they feed, but I know not what good can come thereby. When Oxen are troubled with fleam, put a sprig of black *Hellebore* through their ears wherein let it remain till the next day at the same hour. All the evils of the eyes are for the most part cured by infusion of Hony, and some mingle therewith *Ammoniack*, *Salt*, and *Boetick*. When the palat or roof of their mouth is so swelled that the beast forsaketh meat, and bendeth on the one side, let his mouth be paired with a sharpe instrument, or else burned or abated some other way, giving them green and soft meat till the tender sore be cured: but when the cheeks swell, for remedy whereof they sell them away to the Butcher for slaughter: it falleth out very often that there grow certain bunches on their tongues, which make them forsake their meat, and for this thing they cut the tongue, and afterward rub the wound with Garlick and Salt, till all the fleamy matter issue forth.

When their veins in their cheeks and chaps swell out into ulcers, they soften and wash them with Vinegar and Lees, till they be cured. When they are liver-sick, they give them *Rubarbe*, *Mushroms*, and *Gentian*, mingled together. For the Cough and short breath, they give them twigs of Vines, or Juniper mingled with Salt; and some use Betony.

There is a certain herb called *Asplenon* or *Citteraeh*, which consumeth the milts of Oxen, found by this occasion: in *Crete* there is a River called *Protereus*, running betwixt the two Cities *Gnoson* and

Gortina, on both sides thereof there were herds of Cattel, but those which fed neer to *Gortina* had no Spleen, and the other which feed neer to *Gnoson* were full of Spleen: when the Physitians endevoured to find out the true cause hereof, they sound an herb growing on the coast of *Gortina*, which diminished their Spleen, and for that cause called it *Asplenon*. But now to come to the diseases of their breast and stomach, and first of all to begin with the Cough, which if it be new may be cured by a pinte of Barley meal with a raw Egge, and half a pinte of sod wine: and if the Cough be old, take two pounds of beaten Hysop sod in three pints of water, beaten Lentils, or the roots of Onions washed and baked with Wheat meal given fasting, do drive away the oldest Cough. For shortness of breath, their Neat-herds hang about their neck Deaths-herb and Harts-wort: but if their Livers or Lungs be corrupted, (which appeareth by a long Cough and leaness) take the root of Hasell, and put it through the Oxes ear; then a like or equall quantity of the juyce of Onions, and oil mingled, and put into a pinte of Wine, let it be given to the beast many dayes together. If the Ox be troubled with crudity, or a raw evill stomach, you shall know by these signes; he will often belch, his belly will rumble, he will forbear his meat, hanging down his eyes, and neither chew the cud or lick himself with his tongue: for remedy whereof, take two quarts of warm water, thirty stalkes of *Boleworts*, seethe them together till they be soft, and then give them to the beast with Vinegar.

But if the crudity cause his belly to stand out and swell, then pull his tail downward with all the force that you can, and binde thereunto Mother-wort, mingled with salt, or else give them a Glyster, or anoint a Womans hand with oil, and let her draw out the dung from the fundament; and afterward cut a vein in his tail with a sharp knife. When they be distempered with choler, burn their legs to the hoofs with a hot Iron, and afterward let them rest upon clean and soft straw: when their guts or intrails are pained, they are eased with the sight of a Duck or a Drake.

But when the small guts are infected, take fifteen *Cypres* Apples, and so many Gauls, mingle and beat them with their weight of old Cheese in four pints of the sharpest wine you can get, and so divide it into four parts, giving to the beast every day one quantity. The excrements of the belly do deprive the body of all strength and power to labour; wherefore when they are troubled with it, they must rest, and drink nothing for three daies together, and the first day let them forbear meat, the second day give them the tops of wilde Olives, or in defect thereof Canes or Reeds; the stalks of *Lentiske* and *Myrtill*; and a third day a little water, and unto this some add dryed Grapes in six pintes of sharp wine, given every day in like quantity. When their hinder parts are lame through congealed bloud in them, whereof there is no outward appearance, take a bunch of Nettles with their roots and put it into their mouths, by rubbing whereof the condensate bloud will remove away.

When Oxen come first of all after Winter to grasse, they fall grasse-sick, and pisse bloud; for which they seethe together in water Barly, Bread, and Lard, and so give them all together in a drink to the beast: some praise the kernels of Walnuts put into Eggeshels for this cure; and other take the bloudy water it self, and blow it into the beasts Nostrils; and herd-men by experience have found that there is no better thing then Herb-Robert, to stay the pissing of bloud; they must also be kept in a stall within doors, and be fed with dry grasse and the best hay. If their horns be anointed with wax, oil, and pitch, they feel no pain in their hoofs, except in cases where any beast treadeth and presseth anothers hoof; in which case take oil and sod wine, and then use them in a hot Barly plaister or poultess layed to the wounded place: but if the plough-share hurt the Oxes foot, then lay thereunto Stone-pitch, Grease and Brimstone, having first of all seared the wound with a hot Iron bound about with shorn wool.

Now to return to the taming and instruction of Oxen. It is said that *Busiris* King of *Egypt* was the first that ever tamed or yoaked Oxen, having his name given him for that purpose. Oxen are by nature meek, gentle, slow, and not stubborne, because being deprived of his genitals he is more tractable, and for this cause it is requisite that they be alwayes used to hand, and to be familiar with man, that he may take bread at his hand, and be tyed up to the rack, for by gentleness they are best tamed, being thereby more willing and strong for labour, then if they were roughly yoaked or suffered to run wilde without the society and sight of men. *Varro* saith, that it is best to tame them betwixt five and three year old, for before three it is too soon, because they are too tender; and after five it is too late, by reason they are too unweildy and stubborn.

But if any be taken more wilde and unruly, take this direction for their taming: First, if you have any old tamed Oxen, joyne them together, (a wilde and a tame) and if you please, you may make a yoak to hold the necks of three Oxen; so that if the beast would rage and be disobedient, then will the old one both by example and strength draw him on, keeping him from starting aside, and falling down. They must also be accustomed to draw an empty Cart, Wain, or sled through some Town or Village, where there is some concourse of people, or a plow in fallowed ground or sand, so as the beast may not be discouraged by the weight and strength of the business; their keeper must often with his own hand give them meat into their mouth, and stroke their Noses, that so they may be acquainted with the smell of a man; and likewise put his hands to their sides, and stroke them under their belly, whereby the beast may feel no displeasure by being touched. In some Countries, they wash them all over with wine for two or three daies together, and afterward in a horn give them wine to drink, which doth wonderfully tame them, although they have never been so wild. Other put their necks into engins, and tame them by substracting their meat. Other affirm, that if a wilde Ox be tyed with a halter made of wool, he will presently wax tame: but to this I leave every man to his particular inclination for this business; only let them change their Oxens sides, and set them sometime on the right side, and sometime on the left side, and beware that he avoid the Oxes heel, for if once he get the habite of kicking, he will very hardly be restrained from it again. He hath a good memory, and will not forget the man that pricked him, whereas he will not stir at another, being like a man in fetters, who dissembleth vengeance untill he be released, and then payeth the person that hath grieved him. Wherefore it is not good to use a young Oxe to a goad: but rather to awaken his dulness with a whip.

These beasts do understand their own names, and distinguish betwixt the voice of their keepers and strangers. They are also said to remember and understand numbers, for the King of *Persia* had certain

Oxen, which every day drew water to *Susis* to water his Gardens, their number was an hundred Vessels, which through custom they grew to observe, and therefore not one of them would halt or loiter in that business, till the whole was accomplished: but after the number fulfilled, there was no goad, whip, or other means, could once make them stir, to fetch another draught or burthen. They are said to love their fellows with whom they draw in yoak most tenderly, whom they seek out with mourning if he be wanting. It is likewise observed in the licking of themselves against the hair, (but as *Cicero* saith) if he bend to the right side and lick that, it presageth a storm; but if he bend to the left side, he foretelleth a calmy fair day: In like manner, when he lougheth and smelleth to the earth, or when he feedeth fuller then ordinary, it betokeneth change of weather: but in the *Autumn*, if Sheep or Oxen dig the earth with their feet, or lie down head to head, it is held for an assured token of a tempest.

They feed by companies and flocks, and their nature is to follow any one which strayeth away; for if the Neat-herd be not present to restrain them, they will all follow to their own danger. Being angred and provoked they will fight with strangers very irefully, with unappeasable contention: for it was seen in *Rhætia*, betwixt *Curia* and *Velcuria*, that when the herds of two Villages met in a certain plain together, they fought so long, that of threescore, four and twenty were slain, and all of them wounded, eight excepted, which the inhabitants took for an ill presage or mischief of some ensuing calamity, and therefore they would not suffer their bodies to be covered with earth: to avoid this contention, skilful Neat-herds give their Cattel some strong herbs, as garlick and such like, that the savour may avert that strife. They which come about Oxen, Buls, and Bugils, must not wear any red garments, because their nature riseth and is provoked to rage, if they see such a colour.

There is great enmity between Oxen and Wolves, for the Wolf (being a flesh-eating creature) lyeth in wait to destroy them; and it is said, that there is so great a natural fear in them, that if a Wolves tail be hanged in the rack or manger where an Ox feedeth, he will abstain from eating. This beast is but simple, though his aspect seem to be very grave; and thereof came the proverb of the Oxen to the yoak, which was called *Ceroma*;

wherewithal Wrastlers and Prize-players were anointed, but when a foolish and heavie man was anointed they said ironically *Bos ad ceroma*.

Again the folly of this beast appeareth by another *Greek* proverb, which saith, that *An Ox raiseth dust which blindeth his own eyes*; to signifie, that foolish and indiscreet men stir up the occasion of their own harmes. The manifold *Epithets* given this beast in *Greek* and *Latin* by sundry authors, do demonstratively shew the manifold conditions of this beast; as that it is called a Plower, Wilde, an earth-tiller, brazen-footed, by reason of his hard hoofs, *Cerebrous*, more brain then wit; horned, stubborn, horn-stiking, hard, rough, untamed, devourer of grasse, yoak-bearer, fearful, overtamed, drudges, wry-faced, flow, and ill favoured, with many other such notes of their nature, ordination, and condition.

There remain yet of this discourse of Oxen, two other necessary *Tractates*; the one natural, and the other moral. That which is natural, contains the several uses of their particular parts, and first for their flesh, which is held singular for nourishment, for which cause, after their labour which bringeth leanness, they use to put them by for sagination, or (as it is said) in *English* for feeding, which in all countries hath a several manner or custom. *Sotion* affirmeth, that if you give your Cattel when they come fresh from their pasture, Cabbage leaves beaten small with some sharp Vinegar poured among them, and afterward chaffe winowed in a sieve, and mingled with Bran for five daies together, it will much fatten and encrease their flesh, and the sixth day ground Barly, encreasing the quantity by little and little for six daies together.

Now the best time to feed them in the Winter is about the Cock crowing, and afterward in the morning twilight, and soon after that let them drink: in the Summer let them have their first meat in the morning, and their second service at noon, and then drink after that second meat or eating, and their third meat before evening again, and so let them drink the second time; It is also to be observed, that their water in Winter time be warmed, and in the Summer time colder. And while they feed, you must often wash the roof and sides of her mouth, for therein will grow certain Wormes, which will annoy the beast, and hinder his eating, and after the washing, rub his tongue well with salt: If therefore they be carefully regarded they will grow very fat, especially if they be not over aged or very young at the time of their feeding; for by reason of age their teeth grow loose and fall out, and in youth they cannot exceed in fatness, because of their growth: above all Heifers and barren Kie will exceed in fatness, for *Varro* affirmeth, that he saw a field Mouse bring forth young ones in the fat of a Cow having eaten into her body she being alive: the self same thing is reported of a Sow in *Arcadia*: Kie will also grow fat when they are with Calf, especially in the middest of that time. The *Turks* use in their greatest feasts and Mariages, to roast or seethe an Ox whole, putting in the Oxes, belly a whole Sow, and in the Sowes belly a Goose, and in the Goofes belly an Egge, to note forth their plenty in great and small things: but the best flesh is of a young Ox, and the worst of an old one, for it begetteth an ill juyce or concoction, especially if they which eat it be troubled with a Cough or rheumy fleam, or if the party be in a Consumption, or for a woman that hath ulcers in her belly, the tongue of an Ox or Cow salted and slit asunder, is accounted a very delicate dish, which the Priests of *Mercury* said did belong to them, because they were the servants of speach, and howsoever in all sacrifices the beasts tongue was refused as a profane member, yet these Priests made choise thereof, under colour of sacrifice to feed their dainty stomachs.

The horns of Oxen by art of man are made very flexible and straight, whereof are made Combes, hafts for knives, and the ancients have used them for cups to drink in, and for this cause was *Bacchus* painted with horns, and *Crater* was taken for a cup, which is derived of *Kera* a horn. In like manner the first Trumpets were made of horns, as *Virgil* alludeth unto this sentence, *Rauco strepuerunt cornua cantu*, and now adaies it is become familiar for the cariage of Gunpowder in war. It is reported by some husbandmen, that if seed be cast into the earth out of an Oxes horn (called in old time *Cerasbola*) by reason of a certain coldness, it will never spring up well out of the earth, at the least not so well as when it is sowed with the hand of man. Their skin is used for shooes, Garments, and Gum, because of a spongy matter therein contained, also to make Gunpowder, and it is used in navigation when a shot hath pierced the sides of the ship, presently they clap a raw Ox hide to the mouth of the breach, which instantly keepeth the Water from entring in: likewise they were wont to make bucklers or shieldes or hides of Oxen and Bugils, and the seven-folded or doubled shield of *Ajax*, was nothing else but a shield made of an Ox hide, so many times layed one piece upon another, which caused *Homer* to call it *Sacos heptabreton*.

Of the teeth of Oxen I know no other use but scraping and making paper smooth with them; their gall being sprinkled among seed which is to be sowen maketh it come up quickly, and killeth field-mise that tast of it, and it is the bane or poison of those creatures, so that they will not come neer to it, no not in bread if they discern it; and birds if they eat corn touched with an Oxes gall put into hot water first of all, and the lees of wine, they wax thereby astonished: likewise Emmets will not come upon those places where there remaineth any savour of this gall; and for this cause they anoint herewith the roots of trees. The dung of Oxen is beneficial to Bees if the hive be anointed therewith, for it killeth Spiders, Gnats, and drone-bees; and if good heed be not taken, it will work the like effect upon the Bees themselves: for this cause they use to smother or burn this kind of dung under the mouthes of the Hives in the spring time, which so displayeth and disperseth all the little enemy-bees in Bee-hives that they never breed again. There is a proverb of the stable of *Augea*, which *Augea* was so rich in Cattel, that he defiled the Countrey with their dung, whereupon that proverb grew: when *Hercules* came unto him he promised him a part of his Countrey to purge that stable, which was not cleansed by the yearly labour of 3000 Oxen, but *Hercules* undertaking the labour turned a River upon it, and so cleansed all. When *Augea* saw that his stable was purged by art, and not by labour, he denied the reward; and because *Phyleus* his eldest Son reproved him for not regarding a man so well deserving, he cast him out of his family for ever.

The manifold use of the members of Oxen and Kie in medicine, now remaineth to be briefly touched. The horn beaten into powder, cureth the Cough, especially the tips or point of the horn, which is also received against the Ptisick, or short breath made into pils with Honey. The powder of a Cowes horn mixed with Vinegar, helpeth the morphew, being washed or anointed therewith. The same infused into the Nostrils, stayeth the bleeding: likewise mingled with warm water and Vinegar, given to a *Splenitick* man for three daies together, it wonderfully worketh upon that passion: powder of the hoof of an Ox with water put upon the Kings evill helpeth it, and with Water and Honey it helpeth the apostemes and swelling of the body: and the same burned and put into drink, and given to a Woman that lacketh Milk, it encreaseth milk and strengtheneth her very much. Other take the tongue of a Cow, which they dry so long till it may be beaten into powder, and so give it to a woman in white wine or broath. The dust of the heel of an Ox or ancle bone, taken in wine and put to the gums or teeth do fasten them, and remove the ach away: The ribs of Oxen beaten to powder do stay the flux of bloud, and restrain the aboundance of monthly courses in women. The ancle of a white Cow laid forty daies and nights into wine, and rubbed on the face with white Linet, taketh spots and maketh the skin look very clear.

Where a man biteth any other living creature, seethe the flesh of an Ox or a Calf, and after five daies lay it to the sore, and it shall work the ease thereof. The flesh being warm layed to the swellings of the body, easeth them: so also do the warm bloud and gall of the same beast.

The broath of beef healeth the loosness of the belly, coming by reason of choler; and the broath of Cowes flesh, or the marrow of a Cow, healeth the ulcers and chinks of the mouth. The skin of a Ox (especially the leather thereof) warm in a shooe, burned and applyed to pimples in the body or face, cureth them. The skin of the feet and nose of an Ox or Sheep, sod over a soft and gentle fire, untill there arise a certain scum like to glew from it, and afterward dried in the cold, windie air, and drunk helpeth (or at least) easeth burstness very much.

The marrow of an Ox, or the sewet, helpeth the strains of sinews if they be anointed therewith. If one make a small candle of Paper and Cowes marrow, setting the same on fire, under his browes or eye-lids which are bald without hair, and often anointing the place, he shall have very decent and comely hair grow thereupon. Likewise the sewet of Oxen helpeth against all outward poison: so in all Leprosies, Botches, and Scurviness of the skin, the same mingled with Goose grease, and poured into the eares, helpeth the deafness of them. It is also good against the inflamation of the ears, the stupidity and dulness of the teeth, the running of the eyes, the ulcers and rimes of the mouth, and stifness of the neck. If ones bloud be liquid and apt to run forth of the body, it may be well thickned and retained, by drinking Ox bloud mingled with Vinegar: and the bloud of a Cow poured into a wound that bleedeth, stayeth the bloud. Likewise the bloud of Oxen cureth the scabs in Dogs.

Concerning their Milk, volumes may be written of the several and manifold virtues thereof, for the *Arcadians* refused all medicine, only in the Spring time when their beasts did eat grasse, they drank Cowes milk, being perswaded, that the virtue and vigour of all good herbs and fruits were received and digested into that liquor; for they gave it medicinally to them which were sick of the Ptisick, of Consumption, of an old Cough, of the Consumption of the reins, of the hardness of the belly, and of all manner of poisons which burn inwardly; which is also the opinion of all the *Greek* Physitians: and the shell of a Walnut sod in Cow-milk and said to the place where a Serpent hath bitteh, it cureth it, and stayeth the poison.

The same being new and warm Gargarized into the throat, helpeth the soreness of the kernels, and all pain in the Arteries, and swelling in the throat and stomach: and if any man be in danger of a short breath, let him take dayly soft pitch with the hearb *Mummie*, and Harts suet clarified in a Cup of new Milk, and it hath been proved very profitable.

Where the pains of the stomach come by sadness, Melancholy, or desperation, drink Cow-milk, Womans milk, or Asses milk, wherein a flint stone hath been sodden. When one is troubled with a desire of going often to the stool, and can egest nothing, let him drink Cow-milk and Asses-milk sod together; the same also heated with gads of Iron or steel, and mingled with one fourth part of water, helpeth the Bloudy flux; mingled with a little Hony and a Buls gall, with Cummin and gourds layed to the Navel: and some affirm, that Cow-milk doth help conception if a woman be troubled with the whiteflux so that her womb be indangered, let her drink a purgation for her upper parts, and afterward Asses milk, last of all let her drink Cow-milk and new wine (for forty daies together if need be) so mingled that the wine appear not in the milk, and it shall stay the flux. But in the use of milk, the rule of *Hippocrates* must be continually observed, that it be not used with any sharp or tartd liquor for then it curdleth in the stomach, and turneth into corruption. The whay of Cow-milk mingled with Hony and Salt, as much as the tast will permit and drunk, looseneth the hardness of the belly.

The marrow of a Cow mingled with a little meal, and with new cheese, wonderfully stayeth the Bloudyflux. It is affirmed, that there is in the head of an Ox, a certain little stone, which only in the fear of death he casteth out at his mouth, if this stone be taken from them suddenly by cutting the head, it doth make children to breed teeth easily, being soon tyed about them. If a man or woman, drink of the same water, whereof an Ox drunk a little before, it will ease the headach: and in the second venter of a Cow there is a round black *Tophus* found, being of no weight, which is accounted very profitable to Women in hard travails of child-birth. The Liver of an Ox or Cow dryed, and drunk in powder cureth the flux of boud. The gall of a Cow is more forcible in operation then all other beasts gals whatsoever. The gall of an Ox mixed with Hony, draweth out any thorn or point of a needle or other Iron thing out of the flesh where it sticketh. Likewise it being mingled with Alome and Myrrhe as thick as hony, it cureth those evils which creep and annoy the privie parts; laying upon it afterward Beets sod in wine.

It will not suffer the Kings evill to grow or spread it self if it be laid upon it at the beginning. The hands washed in an Oxes gall and water, are made white how black soever they were before time; and if purblind eyes be anointed with the gall of a black Cow, one may read any writing the more plainly: there is in the gall of an Ox a certain little stone, like a ring, which the Philosophers call *Alcheron* (and some *Guers* and *Nassatum*) which being beaten and held to ones Nose, it cleareth the eyes, and maketh that no humour do distil to annoy them: and if one take thereof the quantity of a Lintel seed, with the juice of Beets, it is profitable against the Falling evill. If one be deaf or thick of hearing, take the gall of an Ox and the urine of a Goat; or the gall of Goose: likewise, it easeth the headach in an Ague, and applyed to the temples provoketh sleep, and if the breasts of a woman be anointed therewith it keeps her milk from curdling.

The milt of an Ox is eaten in hony for easing the pains of the milt in a man, and with the skin that a Calf cast out of his dams belly, the ulcers in the face are taken away: and if twenty heads of Garlick be beaten in a

Oxes bladder, with a pinte of Vinegar, and laid to the back, it will cure the milt. It is likewise given against the Spleen, and the Colick made like a plaister, and layed to the Navel till one sweat.

The urine of an Ox causeth a cold stomach to recover, and I have seen that the urine of a Cow taken in Gargarizing, did cure intolerable ulcers in the mouth. When the Bee hath tasted of the flower of the Corn-tree, she presently dyeth by looseness of the belly, except she tast the urine of a Man or an Ox.

There are likewise many uses of the dung of Oxen made in Physick, whereof Authors are full, but especially against the Gowt, plaistering the sick member therewith hot and newly made: and against the Dropsie, making a plaister thereof with Barley meal and a little Brimstone aspersed, to cover the belly of a man. And thus much for the natural properties of this kind, now we will briefly proceed to the moral.

The moral uses of this beast, both in labour and other things, do declare the dignity and high account our forefathers made hereof, both in Vintage, Harvest, Plowing, Carriage, Drawing, Sacrificing, and making Leagues of truce and peace; in so much as that if this failed, all tillage and vintage must in many places of the world be utterly put down; and in truth, neither the fowls of the air, nor the Horse for the battle, nor the Swine and Dogs could have no sustenance but by the labor of Oxen: for although in some places they have Mules, or Camels, or Elephants, which help them in this labor, yet can there not be in any Nation a neglect of Oxen; and their reverence was so great, that in ancient time when an offender was to be fined in his Cattel (as all amerciaments were in those daies) the Judge might not name an Ox, untill he had first named a Sheep; and they fined a smal offence at two Sheep and not under, and the greatest offence criminal, at thirty Oxen and not above, which were redeemed, by giving for every Ox an hundred Asses, and ten for every Sheep.

It is some question among the ancients, who did first joyn Oxen together for plowing; some affirming that *Aristeus* first learned it of the *Nymphs*, in the Island *Co*: and *Diodorus* affirmeth, that *Dionysius* Son of *Jupiter* and *Ceres* or *Proserpina*, did first of all invent the plow. Some attribute it to *Briges* the *Athenian*; other to *Triptolemus, Osiris, Habides* a King of *Spain*; and *Virgil* affirmeth most constantly, that it was *Ceres*, as appeareth by this verse;

> *Prima Ceres ferro mortales vertere terram*
> *Instituit*, &c.

Whereunto agreeth *Servius*: but I rather incline to *Josephus, Lactantius* and *Eusebius*, who affirm, that long before *Ceres* was born, or *Osiris*, or *Hercules*, or any of the residue, their was a practise of plowing, both among the *Hebrews* and *Egyptians*; and therefore as the God of plowing called by the *Romans Jugatinus* (because of yoaking Oxen) was a fond aberration from the truth, so are the residue of their inventions about the first man that tilled with Oxen: seeing it is said of *Cain* and *Noah*, that they were husbandmen and tilled the earth. The *Athenians* had three several plow-feasts which they observed yearly, one in *Scirus*, the other in *Rharia*, and the third under *Pelintus*: and they call their mariage-feasts, plow-seasons, because then they endevoured by the seed of man to multiply the world, in procreation of children, as they did by the plow to encrease food in the earth.

The *Grecians* had a kind of writing called *Boustraphedon*, which began, turned, and ended as the Oxen do in plowing a furrow, continuing from the left hand to the right, and from the right hand to the left again, which no man could read, but he that turned the Paper or Table at every lines end. It is also certain, that in ancient time, the leagues of truce and peace were written in an Oxes hide, as appeareth by that peace which was made by *Tarquinius*, betwixt the *Romans* and the *Gabli*, the which was hanged up in the Temple of *Jupiter*, as *Dionysius* and *Pompeius Sextus* affirm (in the likeness of a buckler or shield;) and the chief heads of that peace remained legible in that hide, unto their time, and therefore the ancients called the Oxes hide a shield, in regard that by that conclusion of peace, they were defended from the wars of the *Gabii*.

And there were certain people called *Homolotti* by *Herodotus*, who were wont to strike up their leagues of peace after war and contention, by cutting an Ox into small pieces, which were divided among the people that were to be united, in token of an inseparable union. There be that affirm, that a Team or yoak of Oxen, taking six or eight to the Team, wil plow every year, or rather every season a hyde of ground; that is, as some account 20 *Mansa*, or in *English* and *Germane* account 30 Acres; which hath gotten the name *Jugera* from this occasion, as *Eustathius* and *Varinus* report. When *Sychæus* the husband of *Dido*, who was daughter of *Agenor* & sister to *Pygmalion*, wandered to and fro in the world with great store of treasure, he was slain by *Pygmalion* secretly, in hope to get his wealth: After which time, it is said, that he appeared to his wife *Dido*, bidding her to save her life from her cruell brother; who more esteemed money then nature, she fled into *Lybia*, taking with her some *Tyrians* among whom she had dwelled, and a competent sum of money; who being come thither, craved of *Iarbas* King of *Nomades*, to give her but so much land as she could compass in with an Oxes hide, which with much ado she obtained, and then did cut an Oxes skin into smal and narrow thongs or lists, wherewithall she compassed in so much as builded the large City of *Carthage*, and first of all was called the New City, and the Castle thereof *Byrsa*, which signifieth a Hide.

Eustuthius also reporteth another story to the building of this City, namely that it was called *Carthage* of one of the daughters of *Hercules*, and that when *Elisa* and the other companions of *Dido* came thither for the foundation of the City, they found an Oxes head, whereupon they were discouraged to build there any more, supposing that *Omen* betokened evill unto them, and a perpetual slavery in labour and misery, such as Oxen live in, but afterward they tryed in another corner of that ground, wherein they found a Horses head, which they accepted as a good signification of riches, honour, magnanimity, and pleasure, because Horses have all food and maintenance provided for them. Among the *Egyptians* they paint a Lion for strength, an Ox for labor, and a Horse for magnanimity and courage, and the Image of *Mithra* which among the *Persians* signifieth the Sun, is pictured in the face of a Lyon holding the horns of a striving Ox in both hands, whereby they signifie that the Moon doth receive light from the Sun, when she beginneth to be separated from her beams.

There is in the Coasts of *Babylon* a Gem or precious stone like the heart of an Ox, and there is another called *Sarcites*, which representeth the flesh of an Ox. The ancients had likewise so great regard of this beast, that they would neither sacrifice nor eat of a labouring Oxe; wherefore

161

Hercules was condemned when he had desired meat of *Theodomantis* in *Dyropia*, for his hungry companion the Son of *Hyla*, because by violence he took from him one of his Oxen and slew him. A crowned Oxe was also among the *Romans* a sign of peace; for the Souldiers which kept the Castle of *Anathon* neer the river *Euphrates* against *Julianus* and his Army, when they yeelded themselves to mercy, they descended from the Castle, driving before them a crowned Oxe: from this manifold necessity and dignity of this beast came the Idolatrous custom of the Heathens, and especially the *Egyptians*, for they worshipped him in stead of God calling him *Apis* and *Epaphus*: whose choyce was on this sort. He had on his right side an exceeding splendent white spot, and his horns crooking together like the new Moon, having a great bunch on his tongue, which they call *Cantharus*: neither do they suffer him to exceed a certain number of years, or grow very big, for these causes they give him not of the water of *Nilus* to drink, but of another consecrated well, which hindereth his growth: and also when he is come to his full age, they kill him, by drowning him in another consecrated well of the Priests: which being done, they seek with mourning another (having shaved their heads) to substitute in his place, wherein they are never very long but they finde one, and then in a holy Ship, sacred for that purpose, they transport and convey him to *Memphis*. And the *Egyptians* did account him a blessed and happy man, out of whose fold the Priest had taken that Oxe-God. He hath two Temples erected for him, which they call his Chambers, where he giveth forth his Augurisms, answering none but children and youths playing before his Temples: and refusing aged persons, especially women; and if any not sacred, happen to enter into one of his Temples, he dyeth for it, and if into the other, it fore-sheweth some monstrous cursed event, as they fondly imagine.

The manner of his answers is privately to them that give him meat, taking it at their hands; and they observe with great religion, that when *Germanicus* the Emperour came to ask counsel of him, he turned from him and would not take meat at his hand; for presently after he was slain. Once in a year they shew him a Cow, with such marks as he hath, and alway they put him to death upon the same day of the week that he was found; and in *Nilus* neer *Memphis*, there was a place called *Phiala*, where were preserved a Golden and a Silver-dish, which upon the birth or Calving days of *Apis*, they threw down into the river, and those days were seaven; wherein they affirm that never man was hurt by Crocodiles. The *Egyptians* do also consecrate an Oxe to the Moon, and a Cow to *Urania*. It is reported that *Mycerinus* King of *Egypt*, fell in love with his own Daughter: and by violence did ravish her; she not able to endure the conscience of such a fact, hanged herself: whereupon the King her impure father, did bury her in a wooden Oxe, and so placed her in a secret place or chamber, to whom daily they offer many odours; but the mother of the maiden did cut off the hands of those Virgins or Women that attended on her Daughter, and would not rescue her from so vile a contempt. There were also many other pictures of Oxen, as in *Corcyra* and *Eretria*; and most famous was that of *Perillus*, which he made and presented to *Phalaris* the Tyrant of *Agrigent*, shewing him; that if he would torment a man, he should put him into that Oxe set over a fire, and his voyce of crying should be like the loughing of a Heifer; which thing being heard of, the Tyrant to shew his detestation of more strange invented torments then he had formerly used, he caused *Perillus*, that presented it unto him, to be put into it alive, and so setting it over a fire; made experiment of the work upon the workman, who bellowed like a Cow, and was so tormented to death for that damnable and dangerous invention; which caused *Ovid* to write thus:

Et Phalaris tauro violentus membra Perilli
Torruit: infœlix imbuit author opus.

When an Oxe or Cow in ancient time did dye of themselves, (*Viz.*) if it were an Oxe, they buried him under the walls of some City, leaving his horn sticking visibly out of the earth, to signifie the place of his burial, for when his flesh was consumed, they took it up again, and buryed the bones in the Temples of *Venus* in other places: but the body of a dead Cow they cast into some great River neer adjoyning. The Poets have faigned a certain Monster called *Minotaurus*, having in part the form of a man, and in part the form of a Bull; and they say, that *Pasiphae* the Daughter of the *Sun* and wife of *Minos*, King of *Crete*, fell in love with a Bull, and by the help of *Dedalus*, she was included in a wooden Heifer, covered with a Cows

163

hide, and so had copulation with the Bull, and so came that monster *Minos* included in a labyrinth; and constrained the *Athenians*, who had slain his son *Androgeus*, to send every year seven young men, and seven maids to be given to that Monsters to feed upon, for he would eat mans flesh. At last *Theseus* son of *Ægeus* King of *Athens*, came into that labyrinth, and slew that *Minotaure*, and by the help of *Ariadne* escaped out of the labyrinth. Other relate the story in this manner; that when the *Cretenstans* would have expelled *Minos* from his Kingdom; he vowed that whatsoever likeness first appeared out of the Sea for sign of victory unto him, he would sacrifice it to the Gods, if he did enjoy his Regiment: and there-upon a goodly Bull came unto him out of the Sea, wherewithall he was delighted: But after he had recovered his Kingdom in quiet, he kept that Bull in his own hands, and sacrificed another; and that by this Bull was the *Minotaure* begotten on his wife *Pasiphae*. But the truth is; that when *Minos* was in danger to lose his Kingdom; one *Taurus*, a valiant Prince and Captain, came with a Navy of good souldiers, and established him in quiet. Afterward falling in love with *Pasiphae* King *Minos* wife, he lay with her in the house of *Dædalus*: which *Dædalus* wrought with the Queen to give him his pleasure, and that the *Minotaure* was a Monster in *Crete*, that had the face of an Oxe, and the other members like a man, such an one was seen in *Aristotles* time. Although other take it for a fiction; because the *Romans* had it pictured in their Ensigns of war, untill *Caius Marius* altered it to an Eagle, which remaineth to this day. *Alciatus* yeeldeth this reason, why the *Romans* gave such an arms, to signifie that secresie becometh a Captain, and that proud and crafty counsels do hurt the authors of them.

> *Limine quod cæco obscura & caligine monstrum*
> *Gnossiacis clausit Dædalus in latebris:*
> *Depictum Romana phalanx in prælia gestat,*
> *Semiviroque nitent signa superba bove:*
> *Nosque monent debere ducum secreta latere*
> *Consilia, authori cognita techna nocet.*

It is reported also, that when *Cadmus* went from *Delphos* to *Phocis*, an Oxe did direct him in the way, and was his guide; which Oxe was brought out of the herds of *Pelagon*, having in both his sides a white spot: it must needs be understood of the Moon, for *Cadmus* flying by night, having the Moon to shine upon him (which is Hieroglyphically deciphered by the Oxe,) gave him light and direction to another City. It were endless to prosecute the several speeches, proverbs, allusions, emblemes, plays, prizes, and hieroglyphicks made upon Oxen; whereby, men and women, Cities, Regions, and People have taken denomination from Oxen; but also some of the stars in the firmament: therefore I will not proceed to those devises, but only touch the sacrifices made with Oxen, and so conclude this story.

It cannot be denied, that the prime institution of sacrifices, was from, by, and for the Ordinance of God, to teach the world to worship him in blood for sin: which could not be expiated but by the blood of the only immaculate Son and Lamb of God; and therefore I will but remember how corruption polluted that Ordinance, which was purely without idle Ceremonies instituted by the everlasting God; and yet was by mans invention made wretched, horrible, and damnable, through abuse of the fact, that otherwise by divine constitution (as appears in holy Scripture) was heavenly, honourable and blessed.

To begin therefore with the original of that Heathenish and Paganish sacrifice, in stead of God the only true and divine Essence, to whom all sacrifice and divine worship was due, and whose creatures, both Men, Oxen, and all other living and visible things are; they offered unto all the hoasts of Heaven, the Sun, and Stars, the Heathen gods, *Jupiter, Mars, Minerva, Pandrisus*, and others: and if the Sacrifice were costly and sumptuous, it was called *Hecatombe*. Now before their Sacrifice they made Prayers, burned Incense for odours, presented *Prothymes* (as they were tearmed) certain preparations and cakes made of Barley and Salt, (called *Ulochytæ*.) After which, the Priest turned him sometimes to the right hand, and sometimes to the left, and then began to take the grisle hairs growing on the Oxes fore-head betwixt his horns, making a taste of them, and casting them in the fire to begin the Sacrifice. Then did he give into the hands of the people standing by, little pots of Wine likewise, to taste for Sacrifice, and then he which killed the beast drew his knife, or axe, or cleaver, from the head to the tayl of the beast. Now in every Sacrifice they had burning torches, which were lawful for none to carry but for men, and not women; then the Priest commanded to kill the Sacrifice, which sometime they did by knocking him on the head, if the beast were to be sacrificed to Hell, and those that were therein; for they sacrificed a barren Cow, or a black Sheep to those ghosts. But if the Sacrifice were for Heaven, and to the powers thereof, they lifted up his head and cut his throat: then put they under him their *Sphagian* vessels to receive his blood, and when the beast was faln down, they flayed off his skin.

Then did the Priest or *Flamen* divide the intrails, that so he might make his augurism (the bowels being proved at the Altar.) Having looked into the bowels, they took out of every gut, member and part, a first fruits, moulded them together in the meal of green wheat-corn, then was it given to the Priest, who put thereunto frankincense, herbmary, and fire, and so burned them all together, which was called a perfect Hoast. But if they sacrificed to the gods of the Sea, then did they first of all wave the bowels of the beast in the Sea-floods before it was burned. The best Sacrifices were fatted and white Oxen or Kine, such as had never been under yoke; for the beast used to labour was accounted unclean: they never offered in Sacrifice one under thirty days old, nor over five years by the laws of the Priests. When the *Spartanes* overcame their enemies by stratagem, they sacrificed to *Mars* an Oxe; but when by open force, they sacrificed a Cock; for they esteemed more of an unbloody then a bloody victory. When a man sacrificed a Cow to *Minerva*, he was bound to Sacrifice a Sheep and an Oxe to *Pandrysus*.

When the *Locrensians* in a publick spectacle would make a Sacrifice, they wanted an Oxe; for which cause they gathered together so many sticks of small wood, as made the Image of an Oxe artificially conjoyned together, and so setting it on fire burned it for an offering: whereupon a *Locrensian* Oxe, was an Ironical Proverb, for a Sacrifice of no weight or merit. It is also reported, that an Heifer being brought to the Altar of *Minerva* to be sacrificed, did there Calve; wherefore the Priests would not meddle with her, but let her go away free; because *Minerva* was the goddess of procreation; holding it an impious thing to kill that in Sacrifice which had brought forth a young one at the Altar: to conclude, as *Vegetius* saith, that on a time Justice was so offended with men, because they imbrewed every Altar with the blood of Oxen and Cattel, that therefore she left the Earth, and retired back again to dwell among the Stars: so will we in this discourse cease from any further prosecution of the Moral or Natural description of these Beasts, leaving their lawful use to the necessity of mankinde, and their abusive idolatrous sacrifices to him that loveth all his creatures, and will require at mans hand an account of the life and blood of brute beasts.

OF THE CALF.

A Calf, is a young or late enixed Bull or Cow, which is called in *Hebrew*, *Egel*; or *Par*: and sometimes *Ben-bakar*, the son of an Oxe. Yet *Rabbi Solomon*, and *Abraham Ezra*, expound *Egel*, for a Calf of one year old. The *Sarazens* of that word call a Calf *Hesel*. The *Græcians*, *Moschos*; whereof is derived *Moscharios*: but at this day they call him *Mouskari*, or *Moschare*. The *Italians*, *Vitello*; the *French*, *Veau*; the *Spaniards*, *Ternera* of *Teneritudo*, signifying tenderness; and sometimes *Bezeron* and *Vezerro*; the *Germans*, *Ein Kalb*, the *Flemmings*, *Kalf*; and the *Latines*, *Vitulus*, of the old word *Vitulor*, signifying to be wanton, for Calves are exceedingly given to sport and wantonness; or as other suppose from the *Greek* word *Italous*, came *Vitulus*; and therefore the *Latines* do not alway take *Vitulus* for a young or new foaled beast, but sometime for a Cow, as *Virgil Eclog.*

> ———— *Ego hano vitulam (ne forte recuses,*
> *Bis venit ad mulctram, binos alit ubere sœtus)*
> *Depono.* ———— ————

And this word (like the *Greek*, *Moschos*) signifieth male and female: whereunto by divers Authors both *Greek* and *Latine*, are added divers Epithites by way of explication, both of the condition, inclination, and use of this young beast; calling it wilde, ripe for the temples, unarmed, weak, sucklings, tender, wandring, unhorned, and such like. And because the Poets faign that *Io* was turned into a Cow, and that the violet herb was assigned by *Iupiter* for her meat; they derive *Viola*, a Violet, from *Vitula* a Calf, by a kinde of *Græcian* imitation.

167

It is also certain that the honor of this young beast have given denomination to some men, as *Pomponius Vitulus*, and *Vitulus Niger Turamius*, and *Vitellius* was derived from this stem or theam, although he were an Emperour. The like may be said of *Moschos* in *Greek*, signifying a Calf; for there was one *Moschus* a Sophist that drank nothing but water, and there was another *Moschus*, a Grammarian of *Syracuse*, whom *Athenæus* doth record, was a familiar of *Aristarchus*, and also of another, a Poet of the *Bucolicks*; and this serveth to shew us, that the love our Ancestors bare unto Cattel, appeared in taking upon them their names, and were not ashamed in those elder times, wherein wisdom and invention was most pregnable, to glory in their herds from which they received maintenance. But to the purpose, that which is said of the several parts of an Oxe and a Cow, belongeth also to a Calf; for their Anatomy differeth not, because they are conceived and generated by them, and in them: and also their birth, and other such things concerning that, must be inquired in the discourse of a Cow.

It is reported by an obscure Author, that if the hoof of a Calf be not absolved or finished in the Dams belly before the time of Calving, it will dye. And also it must be observed, that the same diseases which do infest and harm an Oxe, do also befall Calves, to their extreme perill: but they are to be cured by the same fore-named remedies. And above the residue, these young beasts are troubled with worms, which are ingendered by crudity, but their cure is to keep them fasting till they have well digested their meat, and then take lupines half sod, and half raw, beaten together, and let the juyce thereof be poured down his throat; otherwise take dry figs and fitches beaten together with *Santonica*, called Lavender-cotten, and so put it down the calves throat as aforesaid, or else the fat of a Calf and Marrube with the joyce of Leeks, will certainly kill these Evils. It is the manner to regard what Calves you will keep, and what you will make of and kill either for sacrifice, as in an ancient time, or private use, and to mark and name those that are to be reserved for breed and labour, according to these verses:

Post partum curant, vitulus traducitur omnis,
Et quos aut pecori malunt submittere habendo.

Continuoque notas & nomina gentis inurunt,
Aut aris servare sacris, aut scindere terram,
Et campum horrentem fractis invertere glebis.

And all these things are to be performed immediately after their weaning: and then in the next place you must regard to geld the males, which is to be performed in *Iune*, or as *Magus* saith, in *May*, or at the farthest let them not be above a year old; for else they will grow very deformed and small: but if you lib them after two years old, they will prove stubborn and intractable; wherefore it is better to geld them while they be young ones, which is to be performed not with any knife or iron instrument, because it will draw much blood, and indanger the beast through pain, but rather with a cloven reed or stick, pressing it together by little and little: but if it happen that one of a year or two years old be to be libbed, then you must use a sharp knife, after you have pressed the stones into the cods, and cut them out at one stroke, and for stanching of the blood, let the cod, and the ends of the veins be seared with an hot iron, and so the wound is cured as soon as it is made.

And now the time for the effecting hereof, is best in the wane of the Moon, either in the Spring or Autumn; but it is good to leave as many of the veins and nerves of the virile member untouched and whole as may be, that so he may not lose any condition of a male, except the power of generation. And if the wound be overmuch given to bleed, lay upon it ashes with the spume of silver, which is apt to stanch blood in all green wounds; and that day let him not drink, and eat but a very little meat: for three days after give him green tops or grass, soft and easie to chew, and at the third days end, anoint the wound with liquid pitch, ashes, and a little Oyl, which will soon cure the scar and keep the flies from stinging or harming it. If at any time a Cow cast her Calf, you may put unto her another Calf, that hath not suckt enough from his own Dam; and they use in some Countries to give their Calves Wheat-bran, and Barly-meal, and tender meat; especially regarding that they drink morning and evening. Let them not lye together in the night with their Dam, but asunder, untill their sucking time, and then immediately separate them again, unless the Cow be well fed when the Calf sucketh; her ordinary food will yeeld no great tribute of Milk; and for this cause you must

169

begin to give the Calf green meat betimes. Afterward being weaned, you may suffer those young ones to feed with their Dams in the Autumn, which were calved in the Spring. Then in the next place, you must regard the taming of the beast, being ready for labour, which is expressed in the former treatise of an Oxe.

The Ancients called *Victoria* by the name of the Goddess *Vitula*, because they sacrificed unto her Calves, which was tearmed a *Vitulation*: and this was usual for victory and plenty, as is to be seen at large in *Giraldus, Macrobius, Nonius, Ovid*, and *Virgil*: but the Heathens had this knowledge, that their Gods would not accept at their hands a lame Calf for a Sacrifice, although it were brought to the Altar; and if the tail of the Calf did not touch the joynts of his hinder legs, they did not receive him for Sacrifice. And it is said of *Æmilius Paulus*, when he was to go against the *Macedonians*, he sacrificed to the Moon in her declination eleven Calves. It is very strange, that a Calf being ready to be sacrificed at the Temple of *Ierusalem*, brought forth a Lamb, which was one fore-shewing sign of *Ierusalems* destruction. But *Aristotle* declareth, that in his time, there was a Calf that had the head of a childe; and in *Luceria* a Town of *Helvetia*, was there a Calf which in his hinder parts was a Hart.

When *Charles* the fifth, went with his Army into *Africk*, and arrived at *Larghera*, a Noble City of *Sardinia*, there happened an exceeding great wonder; for an Oxe brought forth a Calf with two heads; and the woman that did owe the Oxe, presented the Calf to the Emperor: and since that time I have seen the picture of a more strange beast calved at *Bonna*, in the Bishoprick of *Colen*, which had two heads; one of them in the side not bigger then a Hares head, and two bodies joyned together; whereof the hinder parts were smooth and bald, but the tail black and hairy; it had also seven feet; whereof one had three hoofs: this Monster lived a little while, and was brought forth in *Anno* 1552 the 16 day of *May*, to the wonder and admiration of all them, who either knew the truth, or had seen the picture.

Butchers are wont to buy Calves for to kill, and sell their flesh; for in all creatures, the flesh of the young ones are much better then the elder, because they are moist and soft, and therefore will digest and concoct more easily: and for this cause Kids, Lambs, and Calves, are not out of season in any time of the year; and are good from fifteen days to two months old, being ornaments to the Tables of great Noble men; which caused *Fiera* to make this *Distichon*:

Assiduos habeant vitulum tua prandia in usus,
Cui madida & sapida juncta tepore caro est.

And principally the *Germans* use the chawthern, the head, and the feet, for the beginning of their meals; and the other part either roasted, or baked, and sometime sod in broth, and then buttered, spiced and sauced, and eaten with Onyons.

The Medicines arising from this beast, are the same that come from his Sires before spoken of, and especially the flesh of a Calf doth keep the flesh of a new wound, (if it be applyed thereunto) from swelling, and being sodden, it is precious against the bitings of a mans teeth: and when a mad Dog hath bitten a man or a beast, they use to pare the wound to the quick; and having sodden Veal mingled with the sewet and heel, they lay some to the wound, and make the patient drink of the broath: and the same broath is soveraign against all the bitings of Serpents. The horns of a Calf sod soft, are good against all intoxicate poyson, and especially Hemlock. The powder of a Calves thigh drunk in Womans Milk, cureth all filthy running Ulcers; and out of the brains of a Calf they make an Oyntment, to loosen the hardness of the belly. The marrow softneth all the joynts, driveth away the bunches arising in the body; having an operation to soften, fill, dry and heat. Take Oyl, Wax, Rust, and the marrow of a Calf, against all bunches in the face: and Calves marrow with an equal quantity of Whay, Oyl, Rose-cake and an Egge, do soften the hardness of the cheeks and eye-lids, being laid to for a plaister, and the same mixed with Cummin, and infused into the ears, healeth the pains of them: and also easeth the Ulcers in the mouth.

The marrow with the sewet composed together, cureth all Ulcers and corruptions in the Secrets of Men and Women. The Fat pounded with Salt, cureth the Louzy evill, and likewise the ulcerous sores in the head. The same mixed with the fat of a Goose, and the juyce of Basil or wilde

Cummin, and infused into the ears, helpeth deafness and pains thereof. The fat taken out of the thigh of a Calf, and sod in three porringers of water, and supped up, is good for them that have the Flux: and the dung of a Calf fryed in a pan, laid to the Buttocks and Secrets, doth wonderfully cure the Bloodyflix: also laid to the reins, provoketh Urine; and sod with Rue, cureth all the inflamations in the seat of a man or woman. The Sewet of a Calf with *Nitre*, asswageth the swelling of the cods, being applyed to them like a plaister: and the Sewet alone, doth cure the peeling of the Nails. The Liver with Sage leaves cut together, and pressed to a liquor, being drunk, easeth the pain in the small of the Belly. The gall mingled with powder of a Harts-born, and the Seed of Marjoram, cureth Leprosies and Scurfs; and the gall alone anointed upon the head, driveth away nits. The milt of a Calf is good for the milt of a man, and for Ulcers in the mouth; and glew made of his stones, as thick as Hony, and anointed upon the leprous place, cureth the same, if it be suffered to dry thereupon.

With the dung of Calves they perfume the places which are hurt with Scorpions; and the ashes of this dung with Vinegar, stayeth bleeding: *Marcellus* magnifieth it above measure, for the cure of the Gout, to take the fime of a Calf which never eat grass, mixed with lees of Vinegar; and also for the deafness of the ears, (when there is pain withall) take the Urine of a Bull, Goat, or Calf, and one third part of Vinegar well sod together, with the herb *Fullonia*, then put it into a flagon with a small mouth, and let the neck of the Patient be perfumed therewith.

OF THE SUPPOSED BEAST CACUS.

THERE be some of the late Writers, which take the *Cacus* spoken of by *Virgil* in his eight Book of *Æneids*, to be a wilde beast, which *Virgil* describeth in these words:

> *Hic spelunca fuit, vasto submota recessu:*
> *Semihominis Caci: facies quam dira tegebat,*
> *Solis inaccensam radiis, semperque recenti*

172

Cæde tepebat humus, foribusque affixa superbis
Ora virum tristi pendebant pallida tabo.
Huic monstro Vulcanus erat pater: illius atros
Ore vomens ignes magna se mole ferebat.
—— *Nequeunt expleri corda tuendo:*
Pectora semiferi atque extinctos faucibus ignes;

That is, *Cacus* was half a beast and half a man, who had a cave in the earth against the Sun, his Den replenished with the heads of men, and he himself breathing out fire, so that the earth was warmed with the slaughter of men slain by him, whose slaughter he fastened upon his own doores, being supposed to be the son of *Vulcan*. And there be some that affirm this *Cacus*, to have wasted and depopulated all *Italy*; and at length when *Hercules* had slain *Geryon*, as he came out of *Spain* through *Italy* with the Oxen which he had taken from *Geryon*, *Cacus* drew divers of them into his cave by their tails: but when *Hercules* missed daily some of Cattel, and knew not which way they strayed, at last he came to the den of *Cacus*: and seeing all the steps stand forward, by reason the cattel were drawn in backward, he departed; and going away, he heard the loughing of the Oxen for their fellows, whereby he discovered the fraud of *Cacus*: whereupon he presently ran and took his club, the Monster being within his cave, closed up the mouth thereof with a wonderful great stone, and so hid himself for fear: but *Hercules* went to the top of the Mountain, and there digging down the same, untill he opened the cave, then leaped in suddenly and slew the Monster, and recovered his Oxen.

But the truth is, this forged *Cacus* was a wicked servant of *Evander*, which used great robbery in the Mountains, and by reason of his evill life was called *Cacus*; for *Cakos* in *Greek* signifieth evill. He was said to breath forth fire, because he burned up their corn growing in the fields, and at last was betrayed of his own Sister; for which cause she was deified, and the Virgins of *Vesta* made Sacrifice to her: and therefore it shall be idle to prosecute this fable any farther (as *Albertus Magnus* doth) it being like the fable of *Alcida*, which the Poets faign was a Bird of the earth, and being invincible burned up all *Phrygia*, and at last was slain by *Minerva*.

OF THE CAMEL.

ALTHOUGH there be divers sorts of Camels, according to their several Countries; yet is the name not much varied, but taken in the general sense of the denomination of every particular. The *Hebrews* call it *Gamal*; the *Chaldeans, Gamela*; and *Gamele*: the *Arabians, Gemal: Gemel Alnegeb: Algiazar.* The *Persians, Schetor*; the *Saracent, Shymel*; the *Turks* call a company of Camels traveling together, *Caravana*. The *Italians* and *Spaniards* call a Camel, *Camello*; the *French, Chameau*; the *Germans, Ramelthier*; all derived of the *Latine, Camelus*; and the *Greek, Camelos.* The *Illyrians,* call it *Vuelblud*: and the reason of the name *Camelos,* in *Greek,* is, because his burden or load is laid upon him kneeling or lying, derived (as it may seem) of *Camptein merous,* the bending of his knees, and slowness of pace; wherefore a man of a slow pace, was among the *Egyptians* deciphered by a Camel. For that cause, there is Town in *Syria* called *Gangamela*; that is, the house of a Camel, erected by *Darius* the Son of *Hystaspis,* allowing a certain provision of food therein for wearied and tyred Camels. The Epithets given to this beast are not many among Authors, for he is tearmed by them rough, deformed, and thirsting; as *Iuvenal.*

> *Deformis poterunt immania membra Cameli.*

And *Persius* in his fifth Satyre saith;

> *Tolle recens primus piper è sitiente Camelo.*

There are of them divers kindes, according to the Countries wherein they breed: as in *India,* in *Arabia,* and in *Bactria*: All those which are in *India,* are said by *Didymus* to be bred in the Mountains of the *Bactrians,* and have two bunches on their back, and one other on their breast, whereupon they lean: they have sometimes a Bore for their Sire, which feedeth with the flock of she-Camels; for as Mules and Horses will couple together in copulation, so also will Bores and Camels: and that a Camel is so ingendered sometimes, the roughness of his hair like a Bores or Swines, and the strength of his body, are sufficient evidences; and these are worthily called *Bactrians,* because they were first of all conceived among them, having two bunches on their backs; whereas the *Arabian* hath but one. The colour of this Camel is for the most part brown, or puke; yet there are herds of white ones in *India*.

Ptolemeus Lagi brought two strange things into *Egypt*, a black Camel; and a man which was the one half white, and the other half black in equal proportion; the which caused the *Egyptians* to wonder and marvail at the shape and proportion of the Camel, and to laugh at the man: whereupon it grew to a Proverb, a Camel among the *Egyptians*, for a matter fearful at the first, and ridiculous at the last.

The head and neck of this beast is different in proportion from all others; yet the *Ethiopians* have a beast called *Nabim*, which in his neck resembleth a Horse, and in his head a Camel. They have not teeth on both sides, although they want horns, (I mean both the *Arabian* and *Bactrian* Camel) whereof *Aristotle* disputeth the reason, in the third Book of the parts of creatures, and fourteenth chapter. Their necks are long and nimble, whereby the whole body is much relieved; and in their neck toward the neather part of the throat, there is a place called *Anhar*, wherein a Camel doth by spear or sword, most easily receive his mortal or deadly wound.

His belly is variable, now great, now small like an Oxes; his gall is not distinguished within him like other beasts, but only carryed in great veins, and therefore some have thought he had none, and asigned that as a cause of his long life. Betwixt his thighes he hath two udders, which have four speans depending from them like a Cow. His genital part is confected, and standeth upon a sinew, insomuch as thereof may a string be made, for the bending of the strongest bow. The tail is like the tail of an Ass, hanging down to their knees, they have knees in every leg, having in their former leg three bones, and in the hinder four. They have an ancle like an Oxes, and very small buttocks, for the proportion of their great body: their foot is cloven, but so, that in the under part it hath but two fissures or clefts, opening the breadth of a finger, and in the upper part four fissures or clefts, opening a little, and having a little thing growing in them, like as is in the foot of a Goose: The foot it self is fleshy like a Bears, and therefore they are shod with leather when they travail, lest the gauling of their feet cause them to tire.

Avicenna affirmeth, that he had seen Camels with whole feet, like a Horses, but their feet (although fleshy) are so tyed together with little lungs that they never wear; and their manner of going or pace is like a Lyons, so walking as the left foot never out-goeth the right, whereas all other beasts change the setting forward of their feet, and lean upon their left feet while they remove their right; but these alter step after step, so as the left foot behinde, followeth the right before, and the hinder foot followeth the left before. Those Camels which are conceived by Bores are the strongest, and fall not so quickly into the myre as other, although his load be twice so heavy.

Camels love grass (called *Schœnnanthi*) and especially Barley, which they eat up wonderful greedily untill all be in their stomach, and then will they chew thereupon all the night long: so that the greatness of their belly to lodge their meat in before concoction is better then the benefit of their upper teeth, because he can ruminate and chaw it so often as he pleaseth. There is a certain herb, which hath a seed like a myrtle seed, that is poyson to worms, and this seed is food for Camels; wherewith they grow fat. It is therefore called Camel-thorn, and *Astergar* in the *Arabian* tongue. In the Province of *Aden*, both Sheep, Oxen, Horses, and Camels, eat a kinde of fish, and them better being dry and stale, then new and fresh, by reason the immoderate heat in that region burneth up all pasture and fruits: neither is there any beast which is so easily fed as a Camel. They will not drink of clear or clean water, but of muddy and slimy, and therefore they stamp in it with their feet. They will endure thirst for three or four days together; but when they come to drink, they suck in above measure, recompensing their former thirst, and providing against that which is to come; and of all kindes the *Bactrians* are least troubled with thirst.

They stale from one side to another, otherwise then any other beasts do: this beast is very hot by nature, and therefore want on and full of sport and wrath; braying most fearfully when they are angred. They engender like Elephants and Tygers; that is, the female lying or sitting on the ground, which the male imbraceth like other males; and continue in copulation a whole day together. When they are to ingender, they go unto the secretest places they can finde; herein excelling in modesty the ancient *Massagetes*, who were not ashamed to lie with their wives in the open field, and publick view of one another, where as brute beasts by instinct of nature, make the procreation of their kinde to be a most secret shameful honest action.

At the time therefore of their lust, they are most unruly and fierce, yeelding to none, no not to their own keepers: the best time of their copulation is in *September*, for in *Arabia*, they begin to ingender in the third year of their age, and so within ten or eleven moneths after she is delivered of young, being never above one at a time, for twins come not in her great belly; so she goeth a year before she conceive again, although her young be separated or weaned, before which time they do not commonly. Unto their former modesty for their copulation, we may adde another divine instinct and most true observation about the same, for the male will never cover his mother, or his sister; wherefore it is sincerely reported, that when a certain Camel-keeper (desirous to try this secret) having the male, son to a female, which he also kept, he so covered the female-mother-Camel in all parts of her body, except her secrets, that nothing could be seen of her, and so brought her lustful son to cover her; which according to his present rage he performed. As soon as he had done it, his master and owner pulled away the mask or disguise from the dam, in the presence of the son; whereby he instantly perceived his keepers fraud, in making him unnaturally to have copulation with his own mother. In revenge whereof he ran upon him, and taking him in his mouth, lift him up into the air, presently letting him fall with noise and cry underneath his murdering and man-quelling feet; where, with unappeaseable wrath and blood-desiring livor, he pressed and trod to pieces the incest marriage-causer, twixt him and his dearest mother; and yet not herewith satisfied, like some reasonable creature, deprived of heavenly grace, and carryed with deadly revenge against such uncleanness, being perswaded that the guilt of such an offence could never receive sufficient expiation by the death of the first deviser, except the beguiled party suffered also some smart of penalty; adjudged himself to death, and no longer worthy to live by natures benefit, which had so violated the womb that first conceived him; and therefore running to and fro, as it were to finde out a hang-man for himself, at last found a steepy rock, from whence he leaped down to end his life; and although he could not prevent his offence, yet he thought it best to cleanse away his mothers adultery with the sacrifice of that blood which was first conceived in that wombe which he had defiled.

These Camels are kept in herds, and are as swift as Horses, according to the measure of their strength, not only because of their nimbleness, but also because their strides and reach doth gather in more ground: for which cause they are used by the *Indians* for race, when they go to fetch the gold which is said to be kept by the *Formicæ Lyons*, which are not much bigger then Foxes: yet many times do these Lyons overtake the Camels in course, and tear the riders in pieces. They have been also used for battel or war (by the *Arabians* in the *Persian* war:) but their fear is so great of an Horse, that (as *Xenophon* saith in the institution of *Cyrus*) when the Armies came to joyn, neither the Camel would approach to the Horse, or the Horse to the Camel; whereupon it is accounted a base and unprofitable thing for a man to nourish Camels for fight; yet the *Persians* for the fight of *Cyrus* in *Lydia*, ever nourished Camels and Horses together, to take away their fear one from another. Therefore they are used for carriage, which they will perform with great facility, being taught by their keepers to kneel and lye down to take up their burthens, which by reason of their height a man cannot lay on them; always provided, that he will never go beyond his ordinary lodging and baiting place, or endure more then his usual burthen; and it hath been seen that one of these *Bactrian* Camels, hath carried above ten Minars of corn, and above that a bed with five men therein. They will travel in a day above forty ordinary miles; for as *Pliny* saith, that there was from *Thomna* to *Gaza*, sixty and two lodging places for Camels, which was in length one thousand five hundred thirty and seven miles.

They are also used for the plow in *Numidia*, and for this cause are yoaked sometimes with Horses, but *Heliogabalus* like as the *Tartarians*, yoaked them together not only for private spectacles and plays; but also for drawing of Waggons and Chariots. When they desire to have them free and strong for any labour in the field, or war, they use to geld both the male and the female, the manner whereof is in this sort. The male by taking away his stones, and the female by fearing her privy parts within the brim and laps thereof with a hot iron, which being so taken away, they can never more join in copulation; and these are more patient in labour and thirst, and likewise better endure the extremity of sand in those parts, having this skill, that if the mists of rain or sand, do never so much obscure the way from the rider, yet doth she remember the same without all staggering.

The urine of this beast is excellent for the use of Fullers; of the hair called *Buber*, or Camels Wool, is cloth made for Apparel, (called *Camelotta*, or Camels hair,) and the hair of the *Caspian* Camels is so soft, that it may be therein compared with the softest *Milesian* Wool, whereof their Princes and Priests make their garments: and it is very probable, that the garments of Saint *John Baptist* was of this kinde. In the City of *Calacia*, (under the great *Cham*) and in the province of *Egrigaia*, is cloth made of the hair of Camels, and white wool (called *Zambilotti*) shewing most gloriously; but the best of this kinde are in the land of *Gog* and *Magog*.

It is forbidden in holy Scripture to eat a Camel, for although it chew the cud, yet is not the hoof altogether cloven: and besides, the flesh thereof is hard of digestion, and the juyce thereof very naught, heating the body above measure; yet many times have men of base condition and mindes eaten thereof, as in *Arabia*, and in the Kingdom of *Fezzen*; and *Atheneus* affirmeth, that the King of *Persia* was wont to have a whole Camel rosted for his own table at his royal feastings: and *Heliogabalus* likewise caused to be prepared for himself the heels of Camels, and the spurs of Cocks and Hens, pulled of alive, and whole Ostriches and Camels; saying, (though falsly) that God commanded the *Jews* to eat them. Camels milk is wholesome for meat, because it is thinnest of all other, and because thereof it breedeth fewer obstructions, and is good for softning of the belly. For the natural disposition of this beast: it is partly already related, whereby the singular use thereof may be collected: yet there are certain proverbs and stories thereof farther expressing their qualities.

It is disdainful, and a discontented creature: whereupon it is faigned of the Poets, that they besought *Iupiter* to give them Horns, with which Petition he was so offended, that he took from them their ears, and therefore in that, those are reproved, which are so far in love with other things they want, that they deserve to lose the things they have. Likewise the wantonness thereof appeareth by the proverb of a dancing Camel, when one taketh upon him more then his skill will serve to discharge: yet hath not this beast been free from ignominy; for when the Emperor *Iustinian* had found the Treason of *Arsaces* the *Armenian*, he caused him to ride through the City upon a Camel, to be shamed for his offence, although in former times it was a kinde of triumph and honor to be carryed upon a Camel, led through a City.

In the lake of *Asphaltites*, wherein all things sink that come in it, many Camels and Buls swim through without danger. The *Arabians* sacrifice a Camel to the unknown God, because Camels go into strange Countries, and likewise sacrifice their Virgins before they be marryed, because of the chastity of this beast, and the *Sagarentes* with great observance, keep the combat of Camels, in the honour of *Minerva*.

These Beasts are hated of Horses and Lyons, for when *Xerxes* travailed over the river *Chidorus*, through *Pæonia* and *Crestonia*; in the night time the Lyons descended into the camp, and touched no creatures therein, except the Camels, whom they destroyed for the most part.

A Camel will live in the soil wherein he is bred, fifty or an hundred years; and if he be translated into any other Nation, he falleth into madness or scabs, or the gowt, and then they live not above thirty years. There is a kinde of grass that groweth by the high ways in the Countrey of *Babylon*, that killeth Camels when they taste thereof.

There are also medicinal properties in Camels, for by reason he is of a hot and dry temperament: if a man infected with poyson, be put into the warm belly of a Camel newly slain, it looseneth the power of the poyson, and giveth strength to the natural parts of the body. The fat taken out of the bunch and perfumed, cureth the Hemmorhoides; and the blood of a Camel fryed, is precious against the bloodyflix, or any other looseness of the belly; the brain dryed and drunk with Vinegar, helpeth the Falling-evill; the gall drunk with Hony, helpeth the Quinzy: and if it be laid to the eye-brows and forehead, sod in three cups of the best Hony, it cureth the dimness of the eyes, and avoideth the flesh that groweth in them: and if the hairs of a Camels tail be wound together like a string, and tyed to the left arm, (*Pliny* affirmeth) they will deliver one from a quartan Ague.

The milk of Camels newly delivered of young, helpeth obstructions, and all shortness of breath; and is also good against the Dropsie and hardness of the milt. Also when one hath drunk poyson, this is a good Antidote, and amendeth the temper of the body. The fime of Camels dryed to dust with Oyl, will crispe and curl the hair, and stay bleeding at the nose; and the same hot, is good against the Gowt.

The urine is most profitable for running sores, there have been which have preserved it five years together, and used against hardness of the belly; washing also therewith sore heads: and it helpeth one to the sense of smelling, if it be held to the nose; likewise against the Dropsie, the Spleen, and the Ring-worm.

OF THE CAMEL DROMEDARY.

A Camel is called of the *Grecians*, *Dromos*, by reason of the swiftness of his race; and also an *Arabian* Camel, which hath all things common with the former *Bactrian* Camel, except, first in the shape, for she hath but one bunch on the back, and many Nations, as the *Italians*, *French*, *Germans*, and *Spaniards*, use the word *Dromedary*, only without addition; the *Græcians* never name it without the addition of a Camel. Therefore this is a kinde of Camel of less stature, but much swifter; for which cause it is derived from running. It cheweth the cud like a Sheep, and the other Camel: the *French* King had sent him from the great *Turk* two of these, white coloured; and I my self have seen one of them, being fifteen cubits high, wanting some nine inches, and about six cubits in length, having the upper lip cloven in the middle like a Hare, and two broad nails in his feet, which in the upper part appeared cloven, but underneath they were whole and fleshy without division, and round in proportion like a pewter dish: It hath also a hard bunch on its brest, whereon it leaned, sitting down and rising: and also upon either knee one: these are said to live fifty years; but the *Bactrians* an hundred: they were used for drawing of Chariots, and great presents for Princes; and when they go to war, every one carryeth two Archers, which sit upon him, back to back, shooting forth their darts, one against the front of the enemy, and the other against the prosecutors and followers.

They are able to go an hundred miles in a day, bearing a burthen of fifteen hundred weight; yea sometimes two thousand, bending upon his knee to take up his load and rider, which received, he riseth up again with great patience, being obedient and ruleable; yet kicking when he is angry, which is very seldom: and therefore *Terence* did significantly describe a good servant by the name of *Dromo*, derived from *Dromas*, a runner: And for the conclusion of the History of these two sorts of Camels, I will here adde the relation and memorable observations of *Iohannes Leo Afer*, in his ninth Book of the description of *Africk*, in his own words following.

"A Camel is a gentle and pleasant tame beast, whereof there are plenty in *Africa*, especially in the Deserts of *Lybia, Numidia*, and *Barbary*: by which *African* estimate their own wealth; for when they contend who is the richest Prince or Noble-man among them, they say he was worth, or hath so many thousand Camels, and not so many thousand Crowns. And he that hath Camels, liveth among them like a Gentleman; because he can at his pleasure travel into the Deserts, and fetch Merchandize from far, which the greatest Prince or Noble-man cannot without them, by reason of the drought of those places. And of these kinde of creatures, there are to be seen in all parts of the world, both in *Asia, Africk*, and *Europe*; for the *Tartarians, Cordians. Dalemians*, and *Turconians* use them in *Asia*; and the *Turkish* Princes convey all their carriages upon them in *Europe*:

Likewise do all the *Arabians* in *Africk*. But it must be observed, that the *African* Camels are much more worth then the *Asian*, for they can endure travel for forty and fifty days together, with very little or no meat, except sometimes in the evening, when they are unloaded, they go to the hedges, thorns, and other green places, and there eat any small thing they meet withall, as leaves and such like, wherewith they remain satisfied, whereas the *Asians* can perform no such journey, except they be kept fat and well fed: and it hath been proved by good experience, that one of the *Africans* hath travelled fifty days without meat, first wearing away the fat in their bunchy back, then about their skin and breast, and lastly, about their ribs, never giving over till it was not able to bear one hundred weight.

"But the *Asians* must alway carry provender to sustain their beasts, never travelling but they have one Camel loaden with meat, for the other loaden with carriage, and so indure a double charge: and when the *Africans* go to any Marts or Fairs being to return empty and unloaded, they take no thought for their Camels food. Of these Camels there be three kindes, one of them called *Hugiun*, (being broad and tall) and therefore apt to bear packs and burthens, but not before they be four year old, and after their ordinary load is one thousand weight of *Italian* measure, being taught by the jerking of a small rod, on the brest or knees, to lie down for their burthens, and afterward to rise up again. And the *Africans* do use to geld their Camels, reserving but one male for the covering of ten females.

"Another kinde of their Camels they call *Bechetos*, such as have two bunches, one for burthen, and the other for a man to ride upon: and the third sort are called *Ragnahil*, which are of lower stature and leaner bodies then the residue, unfit for burden and therefore are used for the saddle, by all the Noblemen of *Numidia, Arabia*, and *Lybia*: being able to run an hundred miles a day, and performing long journeys with little or no provender: for the King of *Tombuto* being to send to *Dara*, or *Selmessa*, (which is distant from his Court nine hundred miles) his messenger performeth it upon one of these *Ragnahils*, within the space of eight days.

"In the beginning of the Spring they are most frolick and unruly, because then they incline to generation: at which time, they rage and fall upon many that come unto them, and especially those from whom they have received blows, remembring at that time, and requiting their former injuries, upon such as wronged them, whom if they can take in their mouth, they lift them up into the air, and then cast them down again under their feet, and tread upon them, in which distempered venereous fury, they remain forty days.

"They can easily endure thirst, five, nine, or fifteen days in necessity; neither will their keeper give them drink at three days thirst, for fear to harm them. As these Camels are pleasant and profitable; so also they seem to participate with the nature of man: for they being wearyed, no spur or stroke can make them hasten to their journey end, therefore in *Æthiopia* and *Barbary*, they sing certain songs behinde the Beast, which so revive their decayed spirits, that they set forward so fast, forgetting their tyred limbs, to their journeys end, that their keepers can hardly follow.

"I have also seen in *Alcair*, a Camel, that could dance at the sound of a Timbrel, being thereunto taught when he was young by this means; first, he was brought into a room like a stable, the pavement whereof was made hot by a fire underneath it, and without doors stood a Musician playing on his Timbrel; the Camel, not for love of the musick, but for the heat under his feet, lifted up first one foot, and then another, as they do which dance, and so the heat increasing, he likewise did lift up faster, whereunto he was accustomed for the space of ten months; at every time one hour and a half, during which time the Timbrel still sounded; so that at last, use framed Nature to such a strain, that hearing a Timbrel, he instantly remembred the fire that was wont to punish his feet; and so presently would leap to and fro like a dancer in publick spectacle, to the admiration of all beholders."

THIS Beast is called in *Hebrew, Zamer*; Deut. 14. which the *Arabians* translate *Saraphah*, and sometime *Gyrapha, Gyraffa*, and *Zirafa*; the *Chaldeans, Deba*, and *Ana*; the *Persians, Seraphah*; and the *Septuagint Grecians, Camelopardalis*, which word is also retained by the *Latins*, whereunto *Albertus* addeth *Oraflus*, and *Orasius*. The *Ethiopians* call it *Nabin*, from whence cometh *Anabula*, and *Pausanios* translateth it an *Indian Sheep*, so indeed *Anabula* may be *English'd* a wilde Sheep.

There were ten of these seen at *Rome*, in the daies of *Gordianus* the Emperor, and before that time, *Cæsar* being Dictator. And such an one was sent by the *Sultan* of *Babylon* to the Emperor *Frederick*, so that it is without question that there is such a beast, which is engendred of a Camel and a female *Libard*, or *Panther*, as *Horace* saith;

Diversum confusa genus Panthera Camelo.

But the same which the *Latins* call *Panthera* the *Græcians* call *Pardalis*. The head thereof is like to a Camels, the neck to a Horses, the body to a Harts; and his cloven hoof is the same with a Camels; the colour of this Beast is for the most part red and white, mixed together, therefore very beautifull to behold, by reason of the variable and interchangeable skin, being full of spots: but yet they are not alway of one colour. He hath two little horns growing on his head of the colour of iron, his eyes rowling and frowing, his mouth but small like a Harts, his tongue is neer three foot long, and with that he will so speedily gather in his meat, that the eyes of a man will fail to behold his hast, and his neck diversly coloured, is fifteen foot long, which he holdeth up higher then a Camels, and far above the proportion of his other parts. His forefeet are much longer then his hinder and therefore his back declineth towards his buttocks, which are very like an Asses. The pace of this beast differeth from all other in the world, for he doth not move his right and left foot one after another, but both together, and so likewise the other, whereby his whole body is removed at every step or strain.

These beasts are plentiful in *Ethiopia, India*, and the *Georgian* region, which was once called *Media*. Likewise in the Province of *Abasia* in *India*, it is called *Surnosa*, and in *Abasia, Surnappa*, and the latter picture before set down, was truly taken by *Melchior Luorigus* at *Constantinople*, in the year of salvation 1559. by the sight of one of these, sent to the great *Turke* for a present: which picture and description, was afterward sent into *Germany*, and was imprinted at *Norimberge*. It is a solitary beast, and keepeth altogether in woods, if it be not taken when it is young: they are very tractable and easie to be handled, so that a child may lead them with a small line or cord about their head, and when any come to see them, they willingly and of their own accord turn themselves round as it were of purpose to shew their soft hairs, and beautiful colour, being as it were proud to ravish the eyes of the beholders.

The skin is of great price and estimation among Merchants and Princes, and it is said that underneath his belly, the colourable spots are wrought in fashion of a fishers net, and the whole body so admirably intercoloured with variety, that it is in vain for the wit or art of man, once to go about to endevour the emulous imitation thereof. The tail of the beast is like the tail of an Asse, and I cannot judge that it is either swift for pace or strong for labour, and therefore well tearmed a wilde Sheep, because the flesh hereof is good for meat, and was allowed to the *Jews* by God himself for a clean beast.

OF THE ALLOCAMELUS.

SCALIGER affirmeth, that in the land of the Giants, there is a beast which hath the head, neck, and ears of a Mule, but the body of a Camel; wherefore it is probable, that it is conceived by a Camel and a Mule, the picture whereof is before set down, as it was taken from the sight of the beast, and imprinted with a description at *Middleborough* in the year 1558. which was never before seen in *Germany*, nor yet spoken of by *Pliny*.

They said that it was an *Indian* Sheep, out of the region of *Peru*, and so was brought to *Antwerp*, six thousand miles distant from that nation. It was about two yards high, and five foot in length, the neck was as white as any Swan: the colour of his other parts was yellowish, and his feet like an Ostrige-Camels: and although it were a male, yet it did render his urine backward: it was afterward given to the Emperor by *Theodoric Neus*, a Citizen of the neather *Colen*. It was a most gentle and meek beast like the *Camelopardal*, not past four year old: wherefore I thought good to express it in this place, becouse of the similitude it hath with the manners of the former beast, although it want horns and differ in some other members.

OF ANOTHER BEAST CALLED CAMPE.

DIODORUS Siculus maketh relation, that when *Dionysius* with his Army travelled through the desert and dry places, annoyed with divers wilde beasts, he came to *Zambirra* a City of *Lybia*, where he slew a beast bred in those parts called *Campe*, which had before that time destroyed many men, which action did purchase him among the inhabitantes a never dying fame, and that therefore there might remain a continual remembrance to all posterity of that fact, he raised up there a monument of the slain beast to stand for evermore.

OF THE CAT.

A *Cat* is a familiar and well known beast, called of the *Hebrews, Catull,* and *Schanar,* and *Schunara*; of the *Grecians, Aeluros,* and *Kattes,* and *Katis*; of the *Saracens, Katt*; the *Italians, Gatta,* and *Gotto*; the *Spaniards*; *Gata,* and *Gato*; the *French, Chat*; the *Germans, Katz*; the *Illyrians, Kozka,* and *Furioz,* (which is used for a Cat by *Albertus Magnus*) and I conjecture, to be either the *Persian* or the *Arabian* word. The *Latins* call it *Feles,* and sometimes *Murilegus,* and *Musio,* because it catcheth Mise, but most commonly *Catus,* which is derived of *Cautus,* signifying wary. *Ovid* saith, that when the Giants warred with the Gods, the Gods put upon them the shapes of Beasts, and the sister of *Apollo* lay for a spy in the likeness of a Cat, for a Cat is a watchful and wary beast seldom overtaken, and most attendant to her sport and prey: according to that observation of *Mantuan*;

> *Non secus ac muricatus, ille invadere pernam,*
> *Nititur, hic rimas oculis observat acutis.*

And for this cause did the *Egyptians* place them for hallowed beasts, and kept them in their Temples although they alleadged the use of their skins for the cover of Shields, which was but an unreasonable shift, for the softness of a Cats skin is not fit to defend or bear a blow: It is known also, that it was capital among them, to kill an *Ibis,* an Aspe, a Crocodile, a Dog, or a Cat; in so much as, that in the dayes of King *Ptolemie*, when a peace was lately made betwixt the *Romans* and the *Egyptians*; and the *Roman* Ambassadors remaining still in *Egypt*, it fortuned that a *Roman* unawares killed a Cat, which being by the multitude of the *Egyptians* espied, they presently fell upon the Ambassadors house, to rase down the same, except the offender might be delivered unto them to suffer death: so that neither the honour of the *Roman* name, nor the necessity of peace, could have restrained them from that fury, had not the King himself and his greatest Lords come in person, not so much to deliver the *Roman* Cat-murderer, as to safegard him from the peoples violence. And not only the *Egyptians* were fools in this kind, but the *Arabians* also, who worshipped a Cat for a God; and when the Cat dyed, they mourned as much for her, as for the father of the family, shaving the hair from their eye-lids, and carrying the beast to the Temple, where the Priests salted it and gave it a holy funeral in *Bubastum*, (which was a burying place for Cats neer the Altar) wherein may appear to all men, in what miserable blindness the wisest men of the world, (forsaking, or deprived of the true knowledge of God) are more then captivated, so that their wretched estate cannot better be expressed then by the words of St. *Paul, When they thought to be wise, they became fools.*

Once Cats were all wild, but afterward they retired to houses, wherefore there are plenty of them in all Countries: *Martial* in an Epigram, celebrated a *Pannonian* Cat with this distichon;

> *I annonicas nobis nunquam dedit Umbria Cattas,*
> *Mavult hæc dominæ mittere dona pudens.*

The *Spanish* black Cats are of most price among the *Germans*, because they are nimblest, and have the softest hair fit for garment.

A Cat is in all parts like a Lioness, except in her sharp ears, wherefore the Poets seign, that when *Venus* had turned a Cat into a beautiful woman, (calling her *Aeluros*) who forgetting her good turn, contended with the Goddesse for beauty; in indignation whereof, she returned her to her first nature, only making her outward shape to resemble a Lion; which is not altogether idle, but may admonish the wisest, that fair and foul, men and beasts, hold nothing by their own worth and benefit, but by the virtue of their Creator: Wherefore if at any time they rise against their maker, let them think to lose their honour and dignity in their best part, and to return to baseness and inglorious contempt; out of which they were first taken, and howsoever their outward shape and condition please them, yet at the best are but beasts that perish, for the Lions suffer hunger.

Cats are of divers colours, but for the most part griseld, like to congealed ise, which cometh from the condition of her meat: her head is like unto the head of a Lion, except in her sharp ears: her flesh is soft and smooth: her eyes glister above measure, especially when a man cometh to see them on the suddain, and in the night they can hardly be endured, for their flaming aspect. Wherefore *Democritus* describing the *Persian Smaragde* saith that it is not transparent, but filleth the eye with pleasant brightness, such as is in the eyes of Panthers and Cats, for they cast forth beams in the shadow and darkness, but in sunshine they have no such clearness, and thereof *Alexander Aphrodise* giveth this reason, both for the sight of Cats and Bats, that they have by nature a most sharpe spirit of seeing.

Albertus compareth their eye-sight to Carbuncles in dark places, because in the night they can see perfectly to kill Rats and Mice: the root of the herb *Valerian* (commonly called *Phu*) is very like to the eye of a Cat, and wheresoever it groweth, if Cats come thereunto, they instantly dig it up, for the love thereof, as I my self have seen in mine own Garden, and not once only, but often, even then when as I had caused it to be hedged or compassed round about with thornes, for it smelleth marvellous like to a Cat.

The *Egyptians* have observed in the eyes of a Cat, the encrease of the Moon light, for with the Moon they skin more fully at the full, and more dimly in the change and wane, and the male Cat doth also vary his eyes with the Sun; for when the Sun ariseth, the apple of his eye is long; toward noon it is round, and at the evening it cannot be seen at all, but the whole eye sheweth alike.

The tongue of a Cat is very attractive and forcible like a file, attenuating by licking the flesh of a man, for which cause, when she is come neer to the bloud, so that her own spittle be mingled therewith, she falleth mad. Her teeth are like a saw, and if the long hairs growing about her mouth (which some call *Granons*) be cut away, she loseth her courage. Her nails sheathed like the nails of a Lion, striking with her forefeet, both Dogs and other things, as a man doth with his hand.

This beast is wonderful nimble, setting upon her prey like a Lion, by leaping, and therefore she hunteth both Rats, all kind of Mice, and Birds, eating not only them, but also fish, wherewithall she is best pleased. Having taken a Mouse, she first playeth with it, and then devoureth it, but her watchful eye is most strange, to see with what pace and soft steps, she taketh birds and flies; and her nature is to hide her own dung or excrement, for she knoweth that the savour and presence thereof, will drive away her sport, the little Mouse being able by that stool, to smell the presence of her mortal foe.

To keep Cats from hunting of Hens, they use to tie a little wilde Rew under their wings, and so likewise from Dove-coates, if they set it in the windowes, they dare not approach unto it for some secret in nature. Some have said that Cats will fight with Serpents, and Toads, and kill them, and perceiving that she is hurt by them; she presently drinketh water and is cured: but I cannot consent unto this opinion: it being true of the Weasell as shall be afterward declared. *Pontzettus* sheweth by experience that Cats and Serpents love one another, for there was (saith he) in a certain Monastery, a Cat nourished by the Monkes, and suddenly the most parts of the Monks which used to play with the Cat fell sick: whereof the Physitians could find no cause, but some secret poison, and all of them were assured that they never tasted any: at the last a poor labouring man came unto them, affirming that he saw the Abbey-cat playing with a Serpent, which the Physitians understanding, presently conceived that the Serpent had emptied some of her poison

191

upon the Cat, which brought the same to the Monks, and they by stroking and handling the Cat, were infected therewith; and whereas there remained one difficulty, namely, how it came to passe, the Cat her self was not poisoned thereby, it was resolved, that for as much as the Serpents poison came from him but in play and sport, and not in malice and wrath, that therefore the venom thereof being lost in play, neither harmed the Cat at all, nor much endangered the Monks: and the very like is observed of Mice that will play with Serpents.

Cats will also hunt Apes, and follow them to the woods, for in *Egypt* certain Cats set upon an Ape, who presently took himself to his heels, and climed into a tree, after whom the Cats followed with the same celerity & agility: (for they can fasten their clawes to the barke and run up very speedily:) the Ape seeing himself overmatched with number of his adversaries, leaped from branch to branch, and at last took hold of the top of a bough, whereupon he did hang so ingeniously, that the Cats durst not approach unto him for fear of falling, and so departed.

The nature of this beast is, to love the place of her breeding, neither will she tarry in any strange place, although carryed far, being never willing to forsake the house, for the love of any man, and most contrary to the nature of a Dog, who will travaile abroad with his master; and although their masters forsake their houses, yet will not these beasts bear them company, and being carryed forth in close baskets or sacks, they will yet return again or lose themselves. A Cat is much delighted to play with her image in a glasse, and if at any time she behold it in water, presently she leapeth down into the water which naturally she doth abhor, but if she be not quickly pulled forth and dryed she dyeth thereof, because she is impatient of all wet. Those which will keep their, Cats within doors, and from hunting birds abroad, must cut off their ears, for they cannot endure to have drops of rain distill into them, and therefore keep themselves in harbour. Nothing is more contrary to the nature of a Cat, then is wet and water, and for this cause came the proverb that they love not to wet their feet. It is a neat and cleanly creature, oftentimes licking her own body to keep it neat and fair, having naturally a flexible back for this purpose, and washing her face with her forefeet: but some observe, that if she put her feet beyond the crown of her head, that it is a presage of rain, and if the back of a Cat be thin the beast is of no courage or valew. They love fire and warm places, whereby it often falleth out that they often burn their Coats. They desire to lie soft, and in the time of their lust (commonly called cat-wralling) they are wilde and fierce, especially the males, who at that time (except they be gelded) will not keep the house: at which time they have a peculiar direful voice. The manner of their copulation is this, the female lyeth down, and the male standeth, and their females are above measure desirous of procreation, for which cause they provoke the male, and if he yeeld not to their lust, they beat and claw him, but it is only for love of young, and not for lust: the male is most libidinous, and therefore seeing the female will never more engender with him during the time her young ones suck, he killeth and eateth them if he meet with them, (to provoke the female to copulation with him again, for when she is deprived of her young, she seeketh out the male of her own accord) for which the female most warily keepeth them from his sight. During the time of copulation, the female continually cryeth, whereof the Writers give a double cause; one, because she is pinched with the talons or clawes of the male in the time of his lustful rage; and the other, because his seed is so fiery hot, that it almost burneth the females place of conception. When they have littered, or as we commonly say kittened, they rage against Dogs, and will suffer none to come neer their young ones. The best to keep are such as are littered in *March*; they go with young fifty daies, and the females live not above six or seven years, the males live longer, especially if they be gelt or libbed: the reason of their short life is their ravening of meat which corrupteth within them.

They cannot abide the savour of ointments, but fall mad thereby; they are sometimes infected with the falling evill, but are cured with *Gobium*. It is needless to spend any time about her loving nature to man, how she flattereth by rubbing her skin against ones Legs, she whurleth with her voice, having as many tunes as turnes, for she hath one voice to beg and to complain, another to testifie her delight and pleasure, another among her own kind by flattering, by hissing, by puffing, by spitting, in so much as some have thought that they have a peculiar intelligible language among themselves. Therefore how she beggeth, playeth, leapeth, looketh, catcheth, tosseth with her foot, riseth up to strings held over her head, sometimes creeping, sometimes lying on the back, playing with one foot, sometime on the belly, snatching now with mouth, and anon with foot, apprehending greedily any thing save the hand of a man, with divers such gestical actions, it is needless to stand upon; in so much as *Cælius* was wont to say, that being free from his Studies and more urgent weighty affaires, he was not ashamed to play and sport himself with his Cat, and verily it may well be called an idle mans pastime. As this beast hath been familiarly nourished of many, so have they payed dear for their love, being requited with the losse of their health, and sometime of their life for their friendship: and worthily, because they which love any beast in a high measure, have so much the lesse charity unto man.

Therefore it must be considered what harmes and perils come unto men by this beast. It is most certain, that the breath and savour of Cats consume the radical humour and destroy the lungs, and therefore they which keep their Cats with them in their beds have the air corrupted, and fall into severall Hecticks and Consumptions. There was a certain company of Munks much given to nourish and play with Cats, whereby they were so infected, that within a short space none of them were able either to say, read, pray, or sing, in all the Monastery; and therefore also they are dangerous in the time of Pestilence, for they are not only apt to bring home venemous infection, but to poison a man with very looking upon him; wherefore there is in some men a natural dislike and abhorring of Cats, their natures being so composed, that not only when they see them, but being neer them and unseen, and hid of purpose, they fall into passions, frettings, sweatings, pulling off their hats, and trembling fearfully, as I have known many in *Germany*; the reason whereof is, because the constellation which threatneth their bodies which is peculiar to every man, worketh by the presence and offence of these creatures: and therefore they have cryed out to take away the Cats.

The like may be said of the flesh of Cats, which can seldom be free from poison, by reason of their daily food, eating Rats and Mice, Wrens and other birds which feed on poison, and above all the brain of a Cat is most venomous, for it being above measure dry, stoppeth the animal spirits, that they cannot passe into the ventricle, by reason whereof memory faileth, and the infected person falleth into a Phrenzie. The cure whereof may be this, take of the water of sweet Marjoram with *Terra lemnia* the weight of a groat mingled together, and drink it twice in a month, putting good store of spices into all your meat to recreate the spirits withall, let him drink pure Wine, wherein put the seed of *Diamoschu*. But a Cat doth as much harm with her venemous teeth, therefore to cure her biting, they prescribe a good diet, sometime taking Hony, Turpentine, and Oil of Roses melt together and laid to the wound with *Centory*: sometime they wash the wound with the urine of a man, and lay to it the brains of some other beast and pure Wine mingled both together.

The hair also of a Cat being eaten unawares, stoppeth the Artery and causeth Suffocation: and I have heard that when a childe hath gotten the hair of a Cat into his mouth, it hath so cloven and stuck to the place that it could not be gotten off again, and hath in that place bred either the wens or the Kings evill. To conclude this point, it appeareth that this is a dangerous beast, and that therefore as for necessity we are constrained to nourish them for the suppressing of small vermine: so with a wary and discreet eye we must avoid their harms, making more account of their use then of their persons.

In *Spain* and *Gallia Narbon*, they eat Cats, but first of all take away their head and tail, and hang the prepared flesh a night or two in the open cold air, to exhale the savour and poison of it, finding the flesh thereof to be almost as sweet as a Cony. It must needs be an unclean and impure beast that liveth only upon vermin and by ravening, for it is commonly said of a man when he neeseth, that he hath eaten with Cats: likewise the familiars of Witches do most ordinarily appear in the shape of Cats, which is an argument that this beast is dangerous to soul and body. It is said that if bread be made wherein the dung of Cats is mixed, it will drive away Rats and Mice. But we conclude the story of this beast with the medicinal observations, and tarry no longer in the breath of such a creature compounded of good and evill. It is reported that the flesh of Cats salted and sweetned hath power in it to draw wens from the body, and being warmed to cure the Hemorrhoids and pains in the reins and back, according to the Verse of *Ursinus*.

Et lumbus lumbis præstat adesus opem.

Aylsius prescribeth a fat Cat sod for the Gowt, first taking the fat, and anointing therewith the sick part, and then wetting Wool or Tow in the same, and binding it to the offended place.

For the pain and blindness in the eye, by reason of any skins, webs, or nails, this is an approved medicine; Take the head of a black Cat, which hath not a spot of another colour in it, and burn it to powder in an earthen pot leaded or glazed within, then take this powder and through a quill blow it thrice a day into thy eye, and if in the night time any heat do thereby annoy thee, take two leaves of an Oke wet in cold water and bind them to the eye, and so shall all pain flie away, and blindness depart although it hath oppressed thee a whole year: and this medicine is approved by many Physicians both elder and later.

The liver of a Cat dryed and beat to powder is good against the stone: the dung of a female Cat with the claw of an Oul hanged about the neck of a man that hath had seven fits of a Quartain Ague, cureth the same: a neesing powder made of the gall of a black Cat, and the weight of a groat thereof taken and mingled with four crowns weight of Zambach, helpeth the convulsion and wryness of the mouth: and if the gall of a Cat with the black dung of the same Cat, be burned in perfume under a woman travelling with a dead childe, it will cause it presently to come forth: and *Pliny* saith that if a pin, or thorn, or fish bone, stick in ones mouth, let him rub the outside against it with a little Cats dung, and it will easily come forth. Given to a woman suffering the flux, with a little Rozen and Oil of Roses, it stayeth the humour; and for a Web in the eye of an horse, evening and morningblow in the powder of Cats dung, and it shall be cured.

OF THE WILDE CAT.

ALL Cats at the beginning were wilde, and therefore some do interpret *Iim*, Isa. 34. for wilde Cats; and the *Germans* call it *Bonumruter*, that is, a tree-rider, because she hunteth Birds and fowles from tree to tree. The *Spaniard* calleth it *Gato-montes*, and in some places of *France* it is called *Chatcarets*. There are great store of them in *Helvetia*, especially in the Woods, and sometime neer the waters, also being in colour like tame Cats but blacker, such as in *England* is called a *Poolcat*. I saw one of them, which was taken in *September*, and observed, that it was in length from the fore-head to the top of the tail, four full spans, and a black line or strake all along the back, and likewise some black upon the legs; betwixt the breast and the neck there was a large white spot, and the colour of her other parts was dusky, red, and yellow, especially about the buttocks, the heels of her feet were black, her tail longer then an ordinary house Cats, having two or three black circles about it, but toward the top all black.

They abound in *Scandivania*, where the Linxes devour them; otherwise they are hunted with Dogs, or shot with Guns, and many times the Countrey men seeing one in a tree, doth compasse it about with multitude, and when she leapeth down kill her with their cubs, according to the verse of *Neversianus*:

> ———— ———— *Felemque minacem*
> *Arboris in trunco, longis perfigere telis.*

In the province of *Malabar*, these Cats live upon trees, because they are not swift to run, but leap with such agility, that some have thought they did flie: and verily they do flie, for they have a certain skin, which when they lie in quiet, cleaveth or shrinketh up to their bellies, but being stirred, the same spreadeth from their forefeet to their hinder, like the wing of a Bat; by vertue whereof, they stay up themselves in the air, passing from tree to tree like a fowl; as also doth the *Pontique* Mouse, as shall be declared afterward.

The skins of wilde Cats are used for garments, for there is no skin warmer, as by experience appeareth in *Scythia* and *Moscovia*, where their women are clothed with the fur of Cats, but especially for buskins and sleeves with their hair turned inward, not only against cold but for medicine, against contracted sinews, or the Gowt. The fat of this beast is reserved by some for heating, softening, and displaying tumours in the flesh: and whatsoever *Rasis* or any other said of the house Cat before in the medicinal parts, that also appertaineth to this, except as in all other, so it falleth forth herein, that the virtues of the wilde kind is more effectual then the tame.

197

There are some among the *Rhœtians* and *Germans*, which eat the flesh hereof, accounting it delicate, having first cut off the head and tail; they cannot abide the sume of Rew, or of bitten Almonds; there is nothing memorable in the nature of this beast that I can learn, except that which is related by *Aetius*, that when men are bitten by Crocodils, this beast by a natural instinct hating a Crocodil, will come about the wounded persons, otherwise fearing the presence of man.

We may hereunto add the beast which is bred in *America*, called *Heyratt*, spoken of by *Theuetus*: which name signifieth a beast of Hony, and the reason is, because it desireth Hony above measure, for it will climb the trees, and coming to the caves of Bees, it will with such dexterity take out the Hony with their nails, that it neither hurteth the Bees, or receiveth harm by them. It is about the bigness of a Cat, and of a Chesse-nut colour.

OF THE COLUS.

THERE is among the *Scythians* and *Sarmatians* a four-footed wilde beast called *Colus*, and some *Sulac* in *Latin*; of the *Polonians, Soihac*, of the *Moscovites, Seigak*; of the *Tartarians, Akkitk*, and *Snak*; of the

Turkes, Acomi; being in quantity and stature betwixt a Ram and a Hart, and duskie white coloured, but the young ones yellow: of a singular swiftness and celerity in course. Her manner is to drink by the holes in her Nostrils, whereby she snuffeth up aboundance of Water, and carryeth it in her head, so that she will live in dry pastures remote from all moisture a great season, quenching her thirst by that Cistern in her head.

They are most plentiful to be found in *Tartaria*, in *Pontus*, where are so many plains, that a man can see nothing but heaven and earth; likewise they are found in *Moscovia*, in *Podocia*, and about the River *Neprus*, and *Borysthenes*: they can never be taken but by wearisomeness: wherefore if men follow them with Pipes and Timbrels, playing upon them, they so weary themselves with leaping and running to and fro, being compassed in by multitudes of men, that they fall down for weakness, and so are taken. They live in flocks together, sometimes five hundred; and after *Faster* in the Spring, two hundred in a troope: having a Snout like a Hogs, they endure much hunger, but no cold.

In *March* they dig up with their Horns a certain root, whereof they eat, and presently their lust for generation encreaseth unto rage; in so much that for satisfying thereof they continue in that act both male and female, untill they lose all strength of body, lying half dead on the earth by the space of 24 hours, not able to go or stand: during which time they are often taken alive, but when they come again to themselves, they rather die then endure to be tamed.

The flesh of them is very sweet and wholesome, they conceive and bring forth for the most part twins, or two at a time; their greatest enemy is a Wolf (for in the Winter and snow they hunt and kill them.) Their horn are about four palms in length, growing upright or bending very little and very sharp, wherewithal they can pierce the belly of a Horse or other beast that standeth over them: at the root they are about six inches compass, and so growing lesse and lesse to the top; one of them weigheth about nine ounces; the blade toward the point is transparent, being held against the light or sun, because it is white and thin, but the neather part is duskie and thicker, and therefore it is not penetrable by the eye of man.

199

There are about 14 circles like rings compassing about the horn, one above another, but the uppermost is not perfect. This horn is of great price, being a present for any Noble man, for in *Turkey* they are sold for six *Cracovian* shillings; yet I know no other use of them, but either to make hafts for knives, or else horns for Spectacles.

This beast liveth altogether in the plains except in snow, and then he runneth into the Woods; where he may be taken more easily, and killed with the stroke of a Staffe. When the *Tartarians* know in what plains they lie, their King cometh and with a multitude of men compasseth them and wearyeth them by musick as aforesaid. All this was related to me by one that had killed of them above two hundred with his own hand (saith that right honorable and most learned Gentleman *Johannes Bonarus, Baoron* of *Balszei* a *Palonian*.

OF THE CONY.

AMONG the divers kinds of Hares, Conies have the third rank, being therefore called in *Latin, Lepusculi,* (as it were little Hares) and sometime *Leberidæ,* as it were a Leveret or young Hare, as well as *Cuniculus*: whereof the reason is, that it maketh holes in the earth, for *Cuniculus* was a *Latin* word for a hole or cave in the earth, before it was taken for a Cony. *Scaphan* in the singular, and *Schephanim,* in the plural, Levit. 11. and Psal. 104. is taken in *Hebrew* for a Cony or Conies, and not for a

Hedge hog, as the *Septuagint* translate, or for a *Porcuspine*, although they live also in Caves and secret places of the earth; and therefore *Choerogrillus*, or *Choerogillius*, or *Choerogryllinus*, cannot signifie a Cony: as the *Septuagint* translate *Scaphan*, but a Hedge-hog, as the word derived from the face of a Hog doth most evidently declare, which can by no means agree with a Cony. In the 14. of Deut. the word *Scaphan* is joyned with a Hare, because it is a beast neer of kind unto it, for it is evident, that both of them chew the cud, howsoever a Cony hath not a simple cloven foot into two parts. A Cony also is called *Adapes*, because of the roughness of his feet; The *Chalde* calleth it *Thapsa*; the *Arabians, Vebar*; the *Persians, Beganzerah*; and the *Arabians*, following sometime the *Greek*, call it *Alraneb*, that is, Hares. The *Grecians* call it vulgarly *Skele* and *Dasipos, Couniclos, Scunax*, and *Lagis, Georychios* a Hare digging, living in the earth. The *Italians* call it *Conigli*; the *French, Counin*; the *Spaniards, Coneio*; the *Germans, Kinnigle*, or *Kunel*, and sometime *Kunlein*; the *Illyrians, Kralik* or *Kroliik*.

There are few Countries wherein Conies do not breed, but the most plenty of all is in *England*, they are also in an Island where are but few men neer unto *Dicæarcha*, or as it is now called *Puteoli* in *Italie*. Likewise in all *Spain*, especially in those parts neer unto *Lombardy*, whereupon *Appius* in *Varro* did write to one of his acquaintance which had tarryed long in *Spain*, that he thought he was there following or hunting of Conies, because as their multitude is great, so it would ask long time to take them. Among the *Baleares* are also great store of Conies, and once they so abounded there, that the people were constrained to entreat at the hands of *Augustus*, a military company of Pioners to destroy them; and when *Camillus* was besieging the City *Veii* in *Italy*, he learned of the Conies, which had undermined a whole City in *Spain*, likewise to take and overthrow that City by their example of undermining, whereupon *Martial* said:

Monstravit tacitas hostibus ille vias.

Vegetius saith, that the proverb *Cuniculos agere* took his beginning, when one by secret underminings, and not by open violence overthroweth a Town or Nation. There are also, saith *Albertus*, great store of wilde Conies in *Bohemia*, so like a Hare as one beast may be like another, save only they seem stronger, and are shorter and lesser, which thing caused *Baptista Fiera* to write thus:

Credideram leporem, sic forma simillima fallit,
Ambo superfœtant, dente vel aure pares.

Pet. Martyr likewise affirmeth in his *Ocæan Decades*, that in *Curiana* a region of the new found world, are Conies for colour, quantity, and hair like a Hares, which the inhabitants call *Vitias*, and there are two little Islands called *Cuniculariæ*, which seem to be denominated of Conies, standing betwixt *Corsica* and *Sardinia*. For their several parts, they are most like unto a Hare, except in their head and tail which is shorter, and their colour which is alway brighter, and lesse brown and sandy: or else sometimes Conies are white, black, griseld, tauny, blewish, yellow spotted, ash-coloured and such like. And *Alysius* saith, that in some places, they are also green, and their skins are of great use through the world, especially in all the North and East for garments, facings, and linings. The gray and yellowish are the worst, but the white and black are more pretious, especially of the *English*, if the black be aspersed with some white or silver hairs: and in their use the Bucks are most durable, yet heavier and harsher. The belly is most soft, gentle, and easie, and therefore more set by, although of lesse continuance. Their flesh is very white and sweet, especially of the young ones, being about fourteen or twenty dayes old, and some have devised a cruel delicate meat, which is to cut the young ones out of the dams belly, and so to dresse and eat them, but I trust there is no man among Christians so inhumanely gluttonous, as once to devise or approve the sweetness of so foul a dish: but the tame ones are not so good, for in *Spain* they will not eat of a tame Cony, because every creature doth partake in tast of the air wherein he liveth, and therefore tame Conies which are kept in a close and unsweet air, by reason of their own excrements, cannot tast so well, or be so wholesome as those which run wilde in the mountains and fields, free from all infection of evill air.

They love above all places the rocks, and make Dens in the earth, and whereas it is said, Psal. 104. that the stony rocks are for the Cony, it is not to be understood as if the feet of the Cony could pierce into the rock, as into the earth, and that she diggeth her hole therein as in looser ground; but that finding among the rocks holes already framed to her hand, or else some light earth mingled therewith, she more willingly entreth thereinto, as being more free from rain and floods then in lower and softer ground; for this cause they love also the hils and lower grounds and woods where are no rocks, as in *England* which is not a rocky Countrey, but wheresoever she is forced to live, there she diggeth her holes, wherein for the day time she abideth, but morning and evening cometh out from thence, and sitteth at the mouth thereof.

In their copulation they engender like Elephants, Tygres, and Linxes, that is, the male leapeth on the back of the female, their privie parts being so framed to meet one another behind, because the females do render their urine backward: their secrets and the seed of the male are very smal. They begin to breed in some Countries being but six moneths old, but in *England* at a year old, and so continue bearing every moneth, at the least seven times in one year, if they litter in *March*, but in the Winter they do not engender at all; and therefore the Authors say of these and Hares, that they abound in procreation, by reason whereof, a little store will serve to encrease a great borough. Their young being littered are blind and see not till they be nine dayes old, and their dam hath no suck for them, till she hath been six or seven hours with the male, at the least for six hours after she cannot suckle them, greatly desiring to go to the Buck, and if she be not permitted presently, she is so far displeased that she will not be so inclined again for 14 daies after.

I have been also credibly informed by one that kept tame Conies, that he had Does which littered three at a time, and within fourteen daies after, they littered four more. Their ordinary number in one litter is five, and sometimes nine, but never above: and I have seen that when a Doe hath had nine in her belly, two or three of them have perished and been oppressed in the womb by suffocation. The males will kill the young ones, if they come at them like as the Bore cats, and therefore the female doth also avoid it carefully, covering the nest or litter with gravell or earth, that so they may not be discovered: there are also some of their females very unnatural, not caring for their yong ones, but suffer them to perish, both because they never provide a warm litter or nest for them, as also because they forsake them being littered, or else devour them. For the remedy of this evill, he that loveth to keep them for his profit, must take them before they be delivered, and pull off the hair or flesh underneath their belly, and so put it upon their nest, that when the young one cometh forth, it may not perish for cold, and so the dam will be taught by experience of pain to do the like her self: *Thus far Thomas Gyplon an English Physician*. For Conies you may give them Vine-leaves, Fruits, Herbs, Grasse; Bran, Oatmel, Mallows, the parings of Apples; likewise Cabbages, Apples themselves, and Lettuce; and I my self gave to a Cony blew Wolfe-bane, which she did presently eat without hurt, but Gallingale and blind Nettle they will not eat. In the Winter they will eat Hay, Oats and Chaffe, being given to them thrice a day: when they eat Greenes they must not drink at all, for if they do, it is hazzard but they will incur the Dropsie: and at other times they must for the same cause drink but little, and that little must be alway fresh. It is also dangerous to handle their young ones, in the absence of the dam, for her jealousie will easily perceive it, which causeth her so to disdain them, that either she biteth, forsaketh, or killeth them. Foxes will of their own accord hunt both Hares and Conies, to kill and eat them.

Touching their medicinall properties, it is to be observed that the brain of Conies hath been eaten for a good Antidote against poison: so also the Hart which is hard to be digested, hath the same operation that is in treacle. There is also an approved medicine for the Squinancy or Quinsie: take a live Cony, and burn her in an earthen pot to powder, then take a spoonful of that powder in a draught of wine, and drink the most part thereof, and rub your throat with the residue, and it shall cure with speed and ease, as *Marcellus* saith. The fat is good against the stopping of the bladder and difficulty of urine being anointed at a fire upon the hairy place of the secrets, as *Alex. Benedictus* affirms. Other things I omit concerning this beast, because as it is vulgar, the benefits thereof are commonly known.

OF THE INDIAN LITTLE PIG-CONY.

I received the picture of this beast from a certain Noble-man my loving friend in *Paris*, whose parts it is not needfull to describe, seeing the image it self is perspicuous and easie to be observed. The quantity of this beast doth not exceed the quantity of a vulgar Cony, but rather the body is shorter, yet fuller, as also I observed by those two, which that noble and learned Physician *Joh. Munzingerus* sent me. It hath two little low ears, round and almost pild without hair, having also short legs, five claws upon one foot behind, and six before; teeth like a mouse, but no tail, and the colour variable. I have seen of them all white, and all yellow, and also different from both those; their voice is much like the voice of a Pig, and they eat all kinds of Herbs, Fruits, Oats, and Bread; and some give them water to drink, but I have nourished some divers moneths together, and never given them any water, but yet I gave them moist food, as Herbs, Apples, Rapes, and such like, or else they would incur the Dropsie.

Their flesh is sweet for meat, of a yellowish colour, like the Larde of Swine, and therefore not so white as is our vulgar Cony: they do not dig like other Conies, and for the farther description of their nature, I will express it in the words of *Munzingerus* aforesaid, for thus he writeth.

"One of the males is sufficient in procreation for seven or nine of the females, and by that means they are made more fruitful, but if you put them one male to one female, then will the venereous salacity of the male procure abortment. It is affirmed that they go threescore daies with young before they litter, and I saw of late one of them bear eight at one time in her womb, but three of them were stifled. They bring forth in the winter, and their whelpes are not blinde as are the Conies. They are no way so harmful as other are, either to bite or dig, but more tractable in hand; howbeit untamable. If two males be put to one female, they fight fiercely, but they will not hurt the Rabbets. As the male is most libidinous, so doth he follow the female with a little murmuring noise, bewraying his appetite for generation, without wrath, and these are also called *Spanish* Conies, by *Peter Martyr,* whose nature except in their abundant superfœtation cometh nearer to Hogs then Conies."

OF THE FALLOW DEER, COMMONLY CALLED A BUCK AND A DOE.

THERE are some beasts (saith *Pliny*) which nature hath framed, to have horns grow out of their head like fingers out of the hand, and for that cause they are called *Platicerotæ*: such is this vulgar Fallow Deer,

206

being therefore called *Cervus Palmatus*, that is a palmed Hart, by reason of the similitude the horn hath with the hand and fingers. The *Germans* call this beast *Dam*, and *Damlin*, and *Damhiriz*. The *Italians Daio* and *Danio*; the *French, Dain*, and *Daim*. The *Spaniards, Garno*, and *Cortza*; the *Cretians* vulgarly at this day *Agrimi*, and *Platogna*; and *Aristotle*, *Prox*; the *Latins, Dama*, and *Damula*, because, *de manu*, that is, it quickly flyeth from the hand of man, having no other defence but her heels; and the female *roca*, and the *Polonians, Lanis*. It is a common beast in most Countries, being as corpulent as a Hart, but in quantity resembleth more a Roe, except in colour.

The males have horns which they lose yearly, but the females none at all: their colour divers, but most commonly branded, or sandie on the back, like the furrow of a new plowed field, having a black strake down all along the back a tail almost as long as a Calves, their bellies and sides spotted with white, which spots they lose in their old age, and the females do especially vary in colour, being sometimes all white, and therefore like unto Goats, except in their hair which is shorter. The horns of this beast are carryed about every where to be seen, and therefore this is also likely to be the same beast which *Aristotle* calleth *Hippelaphus* as some would have it; yet I rather think that *Hippelaphus* was like to that rare seen horse which *Francis* the first of that name King of *France*, had presented unto him for a gift; which was engendred of a Horse and a Hart, and therefore can have no other name then *Hippelaphus*, signifying a Horse-hart.

In the bloud of these kind of Deer are not strings or *Fibres*, wherefore it doth not congeal as other doth, and this is assigned to be one cause of their fearful nature; they are also said to have no gall: in their horns they differ not much from a Harts (except in quantity) and for their other parts they much resemble a Roe-buck: their flesh is good for nourishment, but their bloud doth increase above measure melancholy, which caused *Hiera* to write thus of it, after his discourse of the Roe.

> *Damula adusta magis si matris ab ubere rapta est,*
> *Huie prior in nostro forte erit orbe locus;*

For the preparation or dressing of a Buck, we shall say more when we come to the description of a Hart. *Albertus* translateth the word *Algazel* a Fallow Deer, and sayeth that the flesh thereof is very hurtful, being cold and dry, and bringeth the Hemorhoides if it be not well seasoned with Pepper, Cinnamon, Mustard seed, and Hony, or else Garlick, which caused *Juvenal* to cry out upon the excess of rich men for their feasts and delicate fare, being compared with the Ancients which lived upon fruits, in these words following, as they are left in his eleventh Satyre.

> —— *Olim ex quavis arbore mensa fiebat,*
> *At nunc divitibus cœnandi nulla voluptas:*
> *Nil Rhombus, nil dama sapit, putere videntur*
> *Unguentum atque rosæ,* ——

The dung or fime of this beast mingled with oil of Myrtles, increaseth hair, and amendeth those which are corrupt. If the tongue hereof be perfumed under a leech or tick that sticketh in the throat of man or beast, it causeth the leech to fall off presently; and the powder of such a tongue helpeth in a Fistula; some of the late writers do prescribe the fat of a Moul, of a Deer, and of a Bear mingled together to rub the head withall for increase of memory.

OF THE SECOND KIND OF DEER THE ROE-BUCKE.

THERE is so great difference among writers about the name of this beast, that it is a difficult and hard matter to set down certainly, in the prime and original tongues, the true and perfect denomination thereof, yet I will endevour to go as neer the mark as can be, by laying together all the probabilities that I find in other, or observe by my self. To begin then with the *Hebrew* as the fountain of all the residue, they call it *Zebi*, and the feminine hereof *Zebiah*, and therefore in Deut. 14. it is permitted to the *Jewes* to eat; and the plurall of the Masculine is *Zebaim*, and of the feminine *Zebaoth*. The *Chaldee* translation calleth it *Thabia*, which in the Acts of the Apostles cap. 9. is called *Tabitha*, and is interpreted *Dorcas*, a

Roe: and sure it is probable that the *Hebrews* so call a Roe, because of the outward beauty thereof, being full of spots upon a ground or skin of another colour, shewing with great delight pleasant to the beholder, which caused *Martial* to write this Distichon;

Delicium parvo donabis dorcada nato,
Jactatis solet hanc mittere turba togis.

The representation both of male & female.

The *Persians* call this beast *Ahu*. The *Arabians, Thabiu*, which cometh neer to the *Chalde* word; the *Germans Reeh* or *Rech*, and the male *Rech-bocke*, and the female *Rech-giese*; the *Illyrians, Serna* or *Sarna*; the *French, Chireau*, and *Chevreulsauuage*. The *Spaniard, Zorito*, or *Cabronzillo-montes*; the *Italians, Capriolo*, and *Cauriolo* for the male, and *Capriola*, and *Cauriola* for the female.

The *Grecians, Dorcas*, as the *Septuagint* do every where translate, which *Strabo* termeth corruptly, *Zorces*, also *Dorx, Kemas, Nebrous*, and vulgarly as at this day *Zarkadi*; and *Dorcalis, Dorcadion*, for a little Roe. The *Latins* do also use the word *Dorcas* in common with the *Grecians*, and beside *Caprea* and *Capreolus* for a little Goat, for I do not think that any learned man can find any difference betwixt *Caprea* and *Capreolus*, except in age and quantity. The reason of these two latter names is, because of the likeness it hath with a Goat, for Goats, as we shall shew in their description, have many kindes distinguished from one another in resemblance; but in the horns a Roe doth rather resemble a Hart; for the female have no horns at all.

These beasts are most plentiful in *Africk*, beyond the Sea of *Carthage*; but they are of another kinde then those which *Aristotle* denyed to be in *Africa*: there are also in *Egypt*, and in *Germany*, and in the *Helvetian Alpes*. Likewise in *Catadupa* beyond *Nilus*, in *Arabia*, in *Spain*, and in *Lycia*: and it is to be observed, that the *Lycian* Roes do never go over the *Syrian* Mountains. *Ælianus* doth deliver these things of the *Lybian* Roes, which for the colour and parts of their body may seem to belong to all. They (saith he) are of an admirable velocity or swiftness; but yet inferiour to the *Lybian* Horses, their belly is parted with black strakes and drops, and the other parts of their body are of a red yellowish colour, they have long feet, but longer ears, their eyes black, and their horns are an ornament to their heads.

Their swiftness doth not only appear upon the earth, but also upon the waters; for with their feet they cut the waters when they swim as with Oares; and therefore they love the lakes and strong streams, breaking the floods to come by fresh pasture, as Sweet-rushes and Bul-rushes. Their horns grow only upon the males, and are set with six or seven branches, but the females have none, and therefore also they differ in horn from the Fallow-deer: so as they cannot be called *Platycerotæ*, for their horns are not palmed like a hand, and although they be branchy, yet are they shorter: they differ not much from the common Deer, but in their horn: and whereas the horns of other beasts are hollow toward the root, whereunto entereth a certain bony-substance; the horns of these (as also of the vulgar Buck and the Elk) are solid, without any such emptiness; only they are full of pores. It hath also been believed, that a Roe doth not change her horns, because they are never found; whereas in truth, they fall off yearly as doth a Harts, but they hide them, to the intent they should not be found.

It hath likewise been thought, a Roe was called in *Greek, Dorcas*; because of the quickness of her sight; and that she can see as perfectly in the night as in the day; and not only for her self, but the learned Physitians have observed a certain viscous humor about her bowels, which being taken forth, and anointed upon a mans eyes, which are dark, heavy, and neer blinde, it hath the same effect to quicken his eye-sight. It is also said of them, that they never wink, no not when they sleep, for which conceit, their blood is prescribed for them that are purblinde. The tail of this beast is shorter and lesser then is the fallow-Deers, insomuch as it is doubtful whether it be a tail or not.

They keep for the most part in the Mountains among the rocks, being very swift, and when they are pursued by Dogs, (*Martial* saith) they hang upon the rocks by their horns to deceive the Dogs, after a strange manner ready to fall and kill themselves, and yet have no harm, whither the Dogs dare not approach, as appeareth in this Epigram:

Pendentem summa capream de rupe videbis,
Casuram speres, decipit illa Canes:

Yet this doth better agree with the wilde Goat then with the Roe, as shall be manifested in due time.

Ælianus saith, that the *Cynoprosopi*, men with Dogs faces, live upon the flesh of Roes and Bugles, in the Wilderness of *Egypt*: and also it is usual to conclude them in Parks; for they will agree very naturally with

Hares and Swine: wherefore in the Lordship which *Varro* bought of *Piso*, it was seen how at the sound of a Trumpet, both Roes and Boars, would come to their usual places for meat: and although they be naturally very wilde, yet will they quickly grow tame and familiar to the hand of man; for *Blondus* did nourish many at *Rome*. Being wilde, they are hunted with Dogs, shot with Guns, taken in nets; but this falleth out seldom, because they live most among the rocks.

They are most easily taken in the Woods. When they are chased, they desire to run against the wind, because the coldness of the air refresheth them in their course; and therefore they which hunt them place their Dogs with the winde; for sometimes against the hunters mindes, do what they can to the contrary, she taketh her course that way: but Harts when they hear the barkings of Dogs, run with the wind, that the savour of their feet may pass away with them. They are often taken by the counterfeiting of their voyce, which the hunter doth by taking a leaf and hissing upon it.

They are very good meat (as *Philostratus* affirmeth) and that the *Indians* dress at their feasts whole Lyons and Roes for their ghests to eat, and the *Sophists* in their banquet, which is described by *Atheneus*, had Roes therein: and therefore *Fiera* preferreth it before the fallow-Deer, alleadging the agreement that is betwixt it and the body of man, being dressed according to Art.

Hic optata feret nobis fomenta calore
Uda levi, modicis moxque coquenda focis.

And therefore also affirmeth, that it excelleth all wilde beasts whatsoever, being not only fit for nourishment, but for the sick; as for them that have the Colick, or the Falling Evill, or the Tympany: and therefore they are best at a year old, or under. Likewise their broth with Pepper, Lovage, seed of Rue, Parsley, Honey, Mustardseed, and Oyl; and for sauce to the meat, they take Pepper, Rue, Hony melted, and an Onyon: sometime also they seethe the hanches or hips, and make Pasties of the sides and ribs. It is a beast full of fear, and therefore the flesh thereof although it be very dry, yet will it engender some melancholy; of the fear Martial saith thus:

Tam dispar aquilæ columba non est,
Ac dorcas rigido fugax leoni.

As the Dove from the Eagle, and the Roe from the Lyon, which afterward grew into a Proverb. It hath also some Epithets among Authors, which do confirm their disposition full of fear: as flying, weak, wanton, and such like; yet will they fight one with another so fiercely, that sometime they kill each other.

They fear also the Woolfs, whereof came the proverb, that first of all the Roes will be joyned to the Woolfs, to express an incredible matter. They have also been used for Sacrifice to *Diana*, for the *Saphriæ* women in *Patras*, did lay upon her great Altar whole Harts, Bores, Roes, and other beasts alive: and the *Coptitæ* did eat the males; but religiously worshipped the females, not daring to eat them, because they believed that *Isis* loved them dearly.

Of these beasts came the Islands *Capreæ* beyond *Surrentum* in *Campania*, where *Tiberius* had a famous Castle, and was ennobled by his presence; but since the decay thereof, it is now celebrated for the multitude of quails that are found therein.

The remedies or medicines coming from this beast are these: first, the flesh of them eaten, is good against all pains in the small guts, for it dryeth and stayeth the belly. *Pliny* affirmeth, that the teeth of a Dragon tyed to the sinews of a Hart in a Roes skin, and wore about ones neck, maketh a man to be gracious to his Superiors, and them to be favourable and pitiful to him in all his supplications; and if the white flesh in the brest of the *Hiæna*, & seven hairs thereof with the genital of a Hart, be tyed in a piece of Roes skin, and hanged about a Womans neck, it maketh that her womb shall suffer no abortments; but these things are trivial, and not to be believed but at pleasure. I know that the tail of a Dragon tyed to the Nerves of a Hart in a Roes skin, the suet of a Roe with Goose-grease, the marrow of a Hart, and an Onyon, with Rozen, and running Lime, do wonderfully help the falling Evill, (if it be made into a plaister.)

Sextus saith, that if one give the brain of a Roe drawn or pressed through a ring to an Infant, it will preserve him for ever from the Falling sickness and apparitions. The liver of a Roe sod in salt water, and the eyes of a purblinde man held over the fume or reek thereof, are cured of their blindeness: and some seethe it in a little cup, and anoint the eyes with the scum or froth coming from it. The same liver being burned to powder, and the dust cast on a man bleeding, stayeth the issue or flux. The gall of this beast mixed with Wine, and the Meal of Lupines the weight of a groat, and Hony, take away the spots of the face: and the same gall mixed with water, helpeth a Sun-burned-face, and freckles: The same with Hony Attick, taketh away the dimness from the eyes, and with the juyce of a gourd anointed upon the eye-brows, causeth that where the hair hath been pulled off, that it never shall grow again; and this gall is alway the better for the age thereof, and as *Hippocrates* did prescribe, it must be kept in a silver pipe or box.

For the tingling of the ears, take with this gal the Oyl of Roses, with the juyce of an Onyon beaten together, and instilled warm into the ears for a present remedy: so also, with the Oyl of Roses only, it helpeth the pain in the teeth; and with the Hony Attick, all swellings or pains in the jaws or chaps, putting thereto Myrrhe, Saffron, and Pepper. The same gall with a little Hogs-bread, and the powder of burnt Allum with Anise-seed, made into a Suppository, procureth looseness, if the party have not the Hemerrhoides.

Also the gall taken with Hony, and the juyce of Eglantine, cureth the exulceration of the virile member by anointing it. The Spleen being drunk, helpeth windiness, and the milt is commended against the Colick and biting of Serpents.

Against the Jaundise they take the dung of a Roe dryed and sifted, and drink it in Wine; the same also so drunk cureth the Ague; and because the Roe-buck doth wonderfully love his female, there be some that affirm, that if a woman eat the bladder of a Roe, it will likewise make her husband to love her exceedingly.

OF THE FIRST KINDE OF TRAGELAPHUS WHICH MAY BE CALLED A DEER-GOAT.

THERE is another kinde so like a Deer (although conceived of a Buck-Goat and a female Hart) that I cannot but express the figure and brief narration thereof (as is in the foregoing page.) It is like a Deer (except the beard and bristles growing about the shoulders) and *Pliny* affirmeth, that they are found about the river *Phasis*, in *Arabia* and *Arachotæ*, which is a City of *India* so called of *Arachotus*, a river issuing from *Caucasus* which the *Græcians* call *Tragelaphos*, and the *Germans*, *Ein Brandhirse*; and some think this beast to be mentioned by the name of *Ako*, in Deut. 14. This doubtless is the same beast which *Aristotle* calleth *Hippelaphus*, because he attributeth the self same things to it that *Pliny* ascribeth to this, both for the beard, the bristles, and deep hair about the shoulders, which hangeth down like the mane of a Horse.

The similitude both in proportion and quantity holdeth with a Hart in the feet which are cloven, and that the female thereof doth want horns. The horns of the male are like the horns of a Roe. Therefore howsoever some have imagined that there is no such beast to be found in the world, they are rather to be pitied then confuted, for it is not to be doubted, that neither the Ancients, nor other, ever have seen all the divers and marvailous shapes of Beasts, which are to be found in many remote and far distant places of the world, especially in *Arabia* and *India*, where are many Deserts; and therefore the reason why they affirm this, is, *because they never saw any such*, and so it is to be understood: for the rare pictures of these beasts called in ancient time *Canathra*, whereupon children were carried in Pageants and shews, gave them occasion to think, that these were but mens devises, and that God never ordained such creatures. *Georgius Fabritius* which sent me this picture, doth among other things write unto me very probably, that this kinde is only distinguished from other in form, name, and strength, and not in kinde: and this being more strange and less known among men, was called by the *Græcians, Tragelaphus*; being greater then the vulgar Deer, deeper haired, and blacker in colour, and this (saith he) is taken in the Ridings or Forrests of *Misena*, bordering upon *Bohemia*, and the common sort of hunters hold opinion, that by reason it loveth to lie where Coals are made, and in their dust, feeding upon such grass as groweth in those places, that therefore the *Germans* call it *Brandhirze*, and so the Foxes which resemble them in colour, are called *Brandfusche*.

It is for certain that these are greater and stronger then Harts, their upper part of the back being black, and the neather neer the belly not white (as in a Hart) but rather blackish; but about his genitals very black. I have seen the horns to have seven spires or branches, growing out of one of them, being palmed at the top. These are like to those which are called *Achæines* in *Greek*, by reason of their pain and sorrow: and *Kummerer* in *German*, because they live in continual sorrow for their young ones, while they are not able to run out of their dens, belike fearing by some instinct of nature, lest their tender and weak age, should betray them to the Hunters, before they be able to run away.

THE FIGURE OF ANOTHER TRAGELAPHUS, OR DEER-GOAT, EXPRESSED BY BELLONIUS.

THERE is another *Tragelaphus* (saith he) whereof I finde no name among the *French*: it wanteth abeard, and the hair thereof resembleth an *Ibex-Goat*, (whose description followeth afterward among Goats:) the horns hereof are like a Goats, but more crooked and bending, compassing behinde, as a Rams do, which he never loseth. His face, nose, and ears, are like a Sheeps, the skin of his cods being very thick and hanging down. His legs are white like a Sheeps: his tail white; his hairs are so long about his neck and stomach, that you would think it were bearded. His hair on the shoulders and breast black, and it hath two great spots on its flancks on either side: the nostrils are black, the beak or face white; so also is the belly beneath, but the description hereof seemeth rather to agree with a *Pygargus*, or *Musmon*, of which I shall speak afterward.

I do rather approve the relation of another of this kinde, which was sent unto me by that most learned *English* Physician *Iohn Cay*, which as he writeth unto me, was brought in the year 1561 out of the Countrey of *Mauritania*, which was cloven-footed, and liveth for the most part in the Mountain parts of that Countrey, being in quantity betwixt a fallow-Deer and a Hart, the body more like a Hart, and the side branded and hanging down: a shorter and thick neck, the colour in the Winter black, and red, set one with another; the beard like a Goat, but more divided and turned backward; his hair very long, even to his knees, a mane full of bristles, stretched out in length through his whole neck, but especially about the top of his shoulder-blades, where it standeth like bunches, being in colour darker then in other parts of the body; and the hinder legs are covered with longer and harder hairs down to the pastern, (as I think) for no other cause but to defend them from harm in his leaping: and the hoof of this beast was more strange (for being cloven, as was said before) the outward hoof in his fore-legs is longer and greater then the inward, and contrary in the hinder: and the inward clove thereof is longer and greater, and the outward smaller and shorter; so as on either side you would think one of them was the hoof of a Goat, and the other of a Hart, both of them hollow and without soals; whereof I can give no other reason, then the pleasure of nature, which hath so provided, that whereas this beast liveth among the rocks, and sharp places of the Mountains, his foot-steps are by his hollow hoofs more firm and stable, because by that means, the stones and sharp-pointed rock entreth into them to stay them up from sliding: but it is more strange in the females hoofs, for they have upon the top and upper face of them three or four pleasant impressions, (as it were of carved or imbroydered flowers, if a man mark them earnestly) which I think are given unto them only for ornament and delight.

Either sex loose every year their hoofs, and Harts do their horns, that nature may shew their resemblance in their feet to a Hart, as he doth in their head to a Goat. His ear is short like a Goats, but his eye, genital, stones, and tail, like a Harts, though somewhat shorter. The horns like a Rams, crooked and distinguished in the middle, by a black line all their length, which is two *Roman* feet and one finger, and in compass at the root, one foot, one palm and a half, standing one from another, where they differ most not above one foot, three palms, one finger and a half. The rugged circles going about them, toward the top are bunchy, and toward the bottom or root they are low, with beaten notches or impressions.

They are not at the top distant one point from another, above one foot and a palm. The length of their face, from the Crown to the tip of their nose, one foot and three fingers: the breadth in the fore-head, where it is broadest, two palms and one finger.

The height of this beast not above three foot and a half, except where his mane standeth, and the whole length hereof from the crown of the head to the tail is four feet and a half and two fingers.

It hath only teeth beneath on the neather chap, and those in number not above six, neither did I observe any defect in them. It cheweth the cud like other cloven-footed beast. The nostrils are black, from whom the upper lip is divided by a long perpendicular line. It is a gentle, pleasant & wanton beast; in the disposition rather resembling a Goat then a Hart, desiring the steepest and slipperyest places whereon it leapeth, and from whence (it is reported) that it doth cast down it self head-long upon the horns naturally, that by them it may break the violence of his fall or leap, and then stayeth his body upon the fore-knees.

It will run a pace, but it is most excellent in leaping, for by leaping it ascendeth the most highest Mountains and Rocks. The females are greater then the males, but not in horn or hair, it eateth Grass, Oats, Cheasil, Hay, and Bread, they bring forth twins every time: and this we call in *England* a *Barbary Deer*. Thus far Doctor *Cay*.

OF THE HART AND HINDE.

THE male of this beast is called in *Hebrew, Aial,* Deut. 14. and the *Arabians* do also retain that word in their translations; the *Persians* call him *Geuazen*; the *Septuagint, Elaphos*; the *Græcians* at this day *Laphe Pelaphe*; and Saint *Jerom* for the *Latines, Cervus*; the *Chaldees, Aiclah*; the *Italians, Cervo*; the *Spaniards, Ciervo*; the *French, Cerf*; the *Germans, Hirtz*, or *Hirs*, and *Hirsch*; the *Flemmings, Hert*; the *Polonians, Gelen*; the *Illyrians, Ielii, elii.* The female or Hinde likewise termed in *Hebrew, Aial*; and sometime *Alia*, and *Aielet*; the *Latines* and *Italians, Cerva*; the *Spaniards, Cierva*; the *Germans, Hinde*, and *Hindin*; and the *Germans* more specially, *Hin*, and *Wilprecht*; the *French, Biche*; and the *Polonians, Lanii.* The young Fawns or Calfs of this beast they call in *Latine, Hinnuli*; the *Græcians, Nebros*; the *Hebrews, Ofer*; the *Germans, Hindcalb.*

Also it is not to be forgotten, that they have divers other names, to distinguish their years, and Countries, as for example: when they begin to have horns, which appear in the second year of their age like bodkins without branches, which are in *Latin* called *Subulæ*, they are also called *Subulones*; for the similitude they have with Bodkins: and the *Germans* call such an one *Spirzhirtz*, which in *English* is called a *Spittard*; and the

Italians, Corbiati; but the *French* have no proper name for this beast that I can learn, untill he be a three yearing, and then they call him (*tin Gabler*) which in *Latine* are called *Furcarii*.

And indeed I was once of this opinion, that these *Subulones* were only two-yearing Harts, untill I consulted with a *Savoyan* of *Segusium*, who did assure me from the mouths of men trained up in hunting wilde Beasts from their youth; that there are a kinde of *Subulones*, which they call also *Brocardi*, with straight and unforked horns except one branch, in the Mountain of *Jura* near the lake *Lemanus*, and that these also do live among other Harts; for there was seen neer a Monastery, called the *Roman* Monastery, by certain Hunters, in the year 1553. a vulgar Hart with branched horns, and his female; and likewise with a *Subulon*, or *Brocarde*, which when in pursuit he was constrained to leap from rock to rock, to get to the water, he brake his leg and so was taken. These *Brocards* are as great in quantity as other vulgar Harts, but their bodies are leaner, and they swifter in course.

They have but one branch growing out of the stem of their horn, which is not bigger then a mans finger, and for this cause in the rutting time, when they joyn with their females, they easily overcome the vulgar

Hart, with his branched and forked horns. The Hunters call this *Brocard* the shield-bearer to the residue; for by him they are delivered being hunted: for whereas it is the nature of the vulgar Hart, to get into ditches, and hide himself in hollow places when he heareth the Hounds, this Beast never coveteth any secret place to cover himself, but runneth still in the sight of Dogs, who leave the other that hide themselves, because they keep this on foot: and so when the Hunters are passed by the lurking Harts, they return back again, being safe both from Nets and Dogs, while the poor *Brocard* is chased unto death.

These being old, are also known by their teeth and horns, for they never change them; but it is questionable, whether they have any Hindes or females, although my Author informeth me, that he heareth there be also Hindes with horns like these, being not above one finger long; which if it be true, it is not improbable that these are the females of that kinde: whereunto I yeeld more easily, because the vulgar Hindes will not admit copulation with the *Brocard*, except they be constrained, and as it were ravished against their will, from whence it cometh that they are so rare and seldom bred: their flesh is much sweeter then the vulgar Harts.

I have therefore here expressed the figure of the head of this Beast with his horns, which is also called *Anamynta*, or a *Burgundian Brocard* whose horns are at the longest about eighteen inches long, and at the shortest about nine inches, whereof that part which cleaveth to the head is bunchy and indented: the longest as they grow in length, do more and more stand out one from another, turning up at the top like a bow, but the lesser do not stand out so far, and bend very little at the point; and whereas in the vulgar Harts the root of the horn is but in a round circle, as

The figure of the face and horns.

it were fastened upon the skull of the Beast, in this the bony roots lie within the skins much deeper, as may be easily discerned by comparing both together.

The reason why I call this *Burgundian* Hart, or *Subulon Anamynta*, is, because it not only wanteth the manifold branches of vulgar Harts, but that also which is called *Amynta*.

There are also another sort of Harts called *Achaini*, bred in *Creet* neer *Achæa*, whereas in all other parts of *Creet* there are no Harts, whereof it is affirmed by *Gaza*, that there was one of them which had a bough of green Ivie growing in his horns, it was conjectured that when it was young, some sprig of that Ivie was taken in a slifter of the horn, which by reason of some nourishment it found in the horn natural to that tree, being like a rocky substance, it there grew to more perfection. These are also called *Spathenæ*, although that term be also given unto vulgar Harts, to signifie their full age; yet some are of opinion, that this *Achaian* Hart was but an invention or figment made in bread; for there was in antient time a kinde of loaf called *Achaines* in the likeness of a Hart.

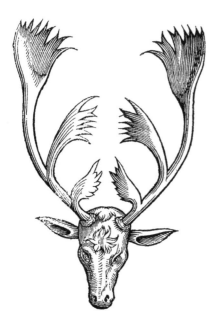

The picture of another face and horns.

I received also of that learned man *Iohn Cay*, another head out of *England*, which he conjectureth to be the head of the palmed Buck, as it was called by *Iulius Capitolinus*, which I do not take to differ from the fallow-Deer: and yet because this seemeth to be of the most excellent kinde, I have thought good to express it in this place, being far different from all other horns of this kinde of Beasts, and more beautiful.

Harts are bred in most Countries, but the Ancients do celebrate and prefer those of *Britain* before other, where they are of divers colours both white and black, as *Pausanias* affirmeth. In *Oedor*, a region of *Asia*, toward the Northern Ocean, they ride upon Harts; likewise there are Harts in *Scythia*: and the people cald *Meditæ*, which are subject to the Kings of *Tartaria*, make their Harts so tame, that they also ride upon them: there are none in *Creet*, except in the region of the *Cydonites*. There are also in the Woods of *Helvetia*, but not so many as in time past, because *Democraties* do not nourish game and pleasures like unto Monarchies, and therefore they are daily killed by the vulgar sort, there being no law against it.

The Harts of *Hellespont*, and about *Arginussa*, have one of their ears slit or cut asunder by nature in their dams belly; and therefore they never go over the Mountains into other regions: (as indeed it is the property of all Harts to love their native soils above all other places.) There is a City called *Dora*, in *Assyria*, near the banks of *Euphrates*, where are many flocks of Harts, of whom many times some are slain with Darts, and others as they swim away to their accustomed solitudes are oppressed in the water by the weight of Oares, and so taken. They are for the most part sand-coloured, and intermingled with some white spots, especially the Hindes and their Calves, and sometimes milk-white, which happeneth unto them by some defect in their nourishment before they be calved; and for natural imbecillity: so have I seen white Bears, Hares, Quails, Partridges, and Swallows.

When *Apollonius* and his Colleagues travelled by *Paraca*, a City of *India*, they suddenly heard a noise like the sound of a pipe, and while they looked about to see what it signified, they perceived that it was the pipe of a Keeper or Forrester, which governed a whole flock of white Harts: such an one was the Hart of *Sertorius* that noble Captain, whereby he led his Army, as they were perswaded by it, who affirmed that it was a *Spanish* Prophet or Wizard given to him by a certain *Lusitanian*, whom he took in an Island of *Portugal*; saying moreover, that she was inspired by *Diana*, and that she had authority from the Goddess to admonish him, and make the hearts of his Souldiers cleave fast unto him; and therefore if at any time he miscarryed in his proceedings, he could easily pacifie them from mutinies, in saying, that his Hart set him upon that enterprize, so putting off the fault cunningly from himself to the beast for fear of defection, wherefore also these were used in the *Bacchanals* of *Cracovia*, and their flesh being softer, is peculiarly tearmed by the French, Venaison. These do excell all other in the Beauty of horns, which are very high, yet grow they not to their bones or skelps, but to their skin, branching forth into many speers, being solid throughout, and as hard as stones, and fall off once every year, but if they remain abroad in the air, where some winde and rain fall upon them, so as now they are wet, and anon dry again, they grow as light as any vanishing or softer substance, as I have proved by experience, findeing some which have been lost by them in the Woods: wherefore I gather that they are of an earthly matter, concrete and hardned with a strong heat made like unto bones. It must be understood that the males only are horned, and yet have they small benefit by them, because (as I said) they grow but within their skin, and these also they lose every year in the Spring time. At one year old they have nothing but small bunches, as it were significations of their horns to come growing on their head; at two years old they appear more perfectly, but straight and simple; at three years they grow forked into two speers, at four into three, and so increase every year in their branches till they be six, and above that time you cannot certainly discern their age by their head, for their horns or speers grow not more in number, although their years make them greater in quantity: yet the old Harts do want these two branches, which the *Grœcians* call *Amynterai*, and the *Latines, Adminicula*; because they first come forth: and I have heard there were Harts horns in an Apothecaries shop of *Antwerp*, which had every one fifteen branches upon one stem, which if it be true, it goeth beyond all experience. Every year in the month of *April*, they loose their horns, and so having lost them, they hide themselves in the day time, inhabiting the shadowy places, to avoid the annoyance of flyes, and feed only during that time in the night. Their new horns come forth like bunches at the first, and afterward by the increase of the Suns heat, they grow more hard, covered with a rough skin, which the Hunters for honours sake call a Velvet head, and as that skin dryeth, they daily try the strength of their new head upon trees, which not only scrapeth off the roughness, but by the pain they feel in rubbing them, they are taught how long to forbear the company of their fellows; for at last, when in their chafing or fretting of their new horn against the tree, they can no more feel any smart or grief in them, they take it for high time to forsake their solitary dwellings, and return again to their former condition, like one that is supplyed with new arms, after the losing of his old. The tender and new horns the *Germans* call *Morchi*, and *Kolben*: these being taken from the Beast, are accounted among great Noble men a delicate dish of meat. *Cyprius* is said to have a Hart with four horns, which was called *Nicocreos*, and by him dedicated to *Apollo*, which I do therefore remember in this place, because it is seldom seen, that an Hart can bear naturally above two horns. Authors do generally affirm, that when a Hart hath lost his horns, he hideth them in some secret places, because he understandeth some secret vertues are contained in them, which mankinde seeketh for, and therefore he either envying the good of other, or fearing lest they bewray him hereafter to Hunters, taketh the best care and providence his discretion can afford, that they never come to the handling of men. When the people asked *Apollo*, what they should do with *Procles* their Tyrant, the Oracle answered, that he should go to that place where Harts cast their borns: whereby it was gathered, that he should be slain and buryed in the earth, and this caused the Proverb, *Ubi cervi abjiciunt cornua*, to signifie a desperate business: yet could it not be agreed, whether the Hart make more account of his right horn or his left, and therefore *Aristotle* affirmeth, that the left horn is never found; and *Pliny*, that the right horn is never found.

This difference may be reconciled with ease, for right and left are so tearmed for three causes, or three manner of ways. First, properly in all creatures, according to the beginning of motion. Secondly, for similitude or likeness, as the right and left side of Images, statues, &c. Thirdly, improperly when the right side of one thing standeth against the left side of another, being opposite, as when two men stand face to face, and by this reason may the left horn of *Aristotle*, and the right horn of *Pliny* signifie all one thing: but we know that the horns of Harts are found yearly both in Fields and Woods.

The wilde Harts of *Sarmatia* neer *Turkie*, have the greatest horns of all other, for it hath been proved, that one pair of them have weighed forty pounds *Troy* weight and above: and there they lose their horns in *March*, neither do they fall off together, but first one, and then the other, and after the first falling, it is manifest, that a certain worm getteth

225

on them, and maketh upon them many circles and little furrows, whereby the root or basis being weakened, the horn groweth very white in that place, and yet not without some appearance of blood remaining, which cleaveth to it, from the first falling off: for, when the head of this Beast is disarmed, there issueth blood from the skull, and in appearance the naked place is like a wound, and yet it is wonderful to mark, that within three days the same is heald and filled with the blood which congealeth in that place first to a sinew, and afterward to a hard bone, so as in *August* at the farthest, the horns are perfect; and therefore the *Egyptians* to describe a long-lived man, picture a Hart losing his horns every year, and new coming in their place. If any man be desirous to know the reasons, why only Beasts of this kinde lose their horns in this manner; I will not spare my pains to set down the best, which Authors have rendred for this wonder of nature.

First, because of the matter whereof they consist, for it is dry and earthy like the substance of green leaves, which fall off yearly, wanting glewing or holding moisture to continue them; and for this cause the horn of a Hart, cannot be bent. Secondly, from the place they grow upon, for they are not rooted upon the skull, but only within the skin. Thirdly, from their efficient cause, for they are hardned both with the heat of Summer, and cold of Winter, by means whereof the pores to receive their nourishment liquor, are utterly shut up and stopped, so as of necessity their native heat dyeth: which falleth not out in other Beasts, whose horns are for the most part hollow, and fitted for longer continuance, but these are of lesser, and the new bunches swelling up toward the Spring, do thrust off the old horns, being holp either by the boughes of trees, by the weight of the horns, or by the willing excussion of the beast that beareth them. *Democritus* and other (as *Gillius* and *Aelianus*) give other reasons, but because they seem to be far fetched, I will omit them. Yet by the way, it is to be noted, that if a Hart be libbed or gelded when he is young, he never beareth horns, or very small ones; and if his horns be upon him at the time of gelding, they never waxe less, or greater, or fall off. The Hindes never bear horns at all, as some have affirmed, but I rather believe *Cæsar, Maximilian*, and *Zenodotus*, who affirm upon their knowledge, that Hindes in some Countries have horns like the males: as likewise it is observed in the Elephants of *India*, and for this cause the Poets expressed the Hinde which nourished *Telephus* with horns, and that which *Hercules* took with golden horns, and it is for certain, that in *Ethiopia* and *Lybia*, both sexes have horns.

The face of this beast is fleshy, his nostrils flat, and his neck very long; his ears, some greater, and some smaller; but in the Mount *Elaphus* and *Hellespont*, they are slit. It is observed, that when a Hart pricketh up his ears, he windeth sharp, very far and sure, and discovereth all treachery against him, but if they hang down and wag, he perceiveth no danger. By their teeth is their age discerned, and they have four on both sides, wherewith they grinde their meat, and besides two other much greater in the male then in the female, and they bend downward to bite withall. All these beasts have worms in their heads bred underneath their tongue in a hollow place, where the neck-bone is joyned to the head, which are not bigger then such as flyes blow in rotten flesh. They are ingendered together one with another, and they are in number twenty, as some would have it; but I was given to understand by one that saw a head of this Beast dissected, wherein were many more Worms, and not contained in one place, but spread all over the head.

The breast is by the *French*-men called peculiarly *Hampan*, his blood is not like other Beasts, for it hath no *Fibres* or small veins in it, and therefore it is hardly congealed. His heart is very great, as it so falleth out in all fearful Beasts, having in it a bone like a Cross, as shall be afterward manifested. His belly is not of one fashion, as it falleth out in all other which chew the cud.

He hath no gall, which is one cause of the length of his life, and therefore also are his bowels so bitter, that the Dogs will not touch them, except they be very fat. The *Achaian* Harts are said to have their gall in their tails; and others say, that Harts have a gall in their ears. The Harts of *Briletum* and *Iharne*, have their reins quadrupled or four-fold. The genital part is all nervy, the tail small; and the Hinde hath udders betwixt her thighs with four speans like a Cow: Both male and female are wonderfully swift, and subtile, as shall be shewed in the discourse of their hunting. They are also apt and cunning to swim, although in their swimming they see no land, yet do they wind it by their noses. They chew the cud like other Beasts. It is reported, that when a Hart is stung by a Serpent, that by eating *Elaphoscum*; (that is, as some call it, Harts-eye; other Hart-thorn, or grace of God; others Wilde Ditany) it presently cureth the wound, and expelleth the poyson: the same vertue they attribute to *Polypodie*, against the wound of a Dart.

Having thus entred into mention of their food, it is to be farther observed, that the males of this kinde will eat Dwall or Night-shade, which is also called Deaths herb, and they also love above all other food wilde Elder, so as in the Summer time they keep for the most part in those places where these plants grow, eating the leaves only, and not the boughes or sprigs: but the Hinde will eat neither of both, except when she beareth a male in her belly, and then also by secret instinct of nature, she feedeth like a male. They will also eat Serpents, but whether for hatred to them, or for medicine they receive by them, it is questionable. A Hart by his nose draweth a Serpent out of her hole, and therefore the *Grammarians* derived *Elaphos*, a Hart, from *Elaunein tous opheis*, that is, of driving away Serpents.

I cannot assent to the opinion of *Aelianus*, that affirmeth the Serpents follow the breath of a Hart like some Philtre or amorous cup; for seeing that all Authors hold an hostility in natures betwixt them, it is not probable, that the Serpent loveth the breath of a Beast, unto whose whole body he is an enemy, with a perpetual antipathy. And if any reply, that the warm breath of a Hart, is acceptable to the cold Serpent, and that therefore she followeth it, as a Dog creepeth to the fire, or as other beasts to the beams of the Sun; I will not greatly gain-say it, seeing by that means it is most clear, that the breath doth not by any secret force, or vertue, extract, and draw her out of the den, but rather the concomitant quality of heat, which is not from the secret fire in the bones of the Harts throat, (as *Pliny* hath taught) but rather from her ordinary expiration, inspiration, and respiration. For it cannot be, that seeing all the parts of a Serpent are opposite to a Hart, that there should be any love to that which killeth her.

For my opinion, I think that the manner of the Harts drawing the Serpent out of her Den, is not as *Aelianus* and *Pliny* affirmeth, by sending into the Cave a warm breath, which burneth and scorcheth the Beast out of her Den; but rather when the Hart hath found the Serpents nest, she draweth the air by secret and violent attraction out from the Serpent, who to save her life followeth the air out of her den; as when a Vessel is broached or vented, the Wine followeth the flying air; and as a Cupping-glass draweth blood out of a scarified place of the body: so the Serpent is drawn unwillingly to follow her destroyer, and not willingly, as *Aelianus* affirmeth.

Unto this opinion both *Oribasius* in his Commentaries upon the Aphorisms of *Hippocrates*, and *Guniterius* his restorer do joyntly agree: but the Serpent being thus drawn forth, addeth greater force to her poyson, whereupon the proverbial admonition did arise. *Cave ne incideris in serpentem, cum extracta a latebris anhelitu cervi effugerit, tum enim propter iracundiam vehementius ei venenum est*, that is, Beware thou meet not with a Serpent drawn out of her hole by the breath of a Hart, for at that time by reason of her wrath, her poyson is more vehement. After this self same manner do the Sea-Rams, draw the Sea-Calfs hid in the *Subterranean* Rocks; for by smelling they prevent the Air that should come unto them for refrigeration.

There is many times strange conflicts betwixt the Hart and the Serpent, thus drawn forth; for the Serpent seeing her adversary, lifteth her neck above the ground, and gnasheth at the Hart with her teeth, breathing out very bitter hissings: on the contrary, the Hart deriding the vain endevour of his weak adversary, readier to fight then powerful to harm him, suffereth him to embrace both his neck and legs with his long and thin body, but at an instant teareth it into an hundred pieces. But the most strange combates are betwixt the Harts and Serpents of *Lybia*, where the hatred is deeper; and the Serpents watch the Hart when he lyeth a sleep on the ground, and being a multitude of them, set upon him together, fastening their poysonful teeth in every part of his skin; some on his neck and breast; some on his sides and back, some on his legs, and some hang upon his privy parts, biting him with mortal rage, to overthrow their foe.

The poor Hart being thus oppressed with a multitude, and pricked with venemous pains, assayeth to run away, but all in vain, their cold earthy bodies and winding tails, both over-charge his strength, and hinder his pace: he then in a rage with his teeth, feet, and horns assaileth his enemies, whose spears are already entred into his body, tearing some of them in pieces, and beating other asunder: they never the less (like men) knowing that now they must dye rather then give over, and yeeld to their pitiless enemy, cleave fast, and keep the hold of their teeth upon his body, although their other parts be mortally wounded, and nothing left but their heads, and therefore will dye together with their foe, seeing if they were asunder, no compassion can delay or mitigate their natural unappeaseable hatred.

The Hart thus having eased himself by the slaughter of some, (like an Elephant) at the sight of their blood, bestirreth himself more busily in the eager battail, and therefore treadeth some under foot in the blood of their fellows, other he persueth with tooth and horn, untill he see them all destroyed: and whereas the heads hang fast in his skin, for avoiding and pulling them forth, (by a divine natural instinct) he flyeth or runneth to the waters, where he findeth Sea-Crabs, and of them he maketh a medicine, whereby he shaketh off the Serpents heads, cureth their wounds, and avoideth all their poyson; this valiant courage is in Harts against Serpents, whereas they are naturally afraid of Hares and Conies, and will not fight with them.

It is no less strange that Harts will eat Serpents, but the reason is, for medicine and cure; for sometimes the pores of his body are dulled and shut up: sometimes the worms of his belly do ascend into the roof of his mouth, while he cheweth his cud, and there cleave fast: for remedy whereof the Hart thus affected, runneth about to seek for Serpents; for his devouring of a Serpent, is a cure of this malady.

Pliny saith, that when the Hart is old, and perceiveth that his strength decayeth, his hair change, and his horns dry above custom, that then for the renewing of his strength, he first devoureth a Serpent, and afterward runneth to some Fountain of water and there drinketh, which causeth an alteration in the whole body; both changing the hair and horn: and the Writer of the Gloss upon the 42. Psalm, which beginneth, *Like as the Hart desireth the water springs, so longeth my soul after God*; confirmeth this opinion.

230

Vincentius Belluacensis affirmeth, that Harts eat Serpents for to cure the dimness of their eye-sight. But for the ending of this question, we must corsider that there are two kindes of Harts; one which by the drawing forth of a Serpent out of her hole, doth presently kill her by stamping her under feet, this eateth that Serpent, and runneth to springing water, after that he feeleth the poyson to make his body swell, and then by drinking doth vomit forth the poyson, and in the mean time loseth both hair and horn; yet the Monks of *Mesaen* affirm, that the Harts thus poysoned doth only cover her body in the cold water, and not drink thereof, for that were exitial unto her; but she sendeth forth certain tears, which are turned into a stone, (called *Bezahar*) of which shall be more said hereafter. The other kinde of Harts, when he findeth a Serpent, killeth it, and doth not eat it, and immediately after the victory returneth to feed in the Mountains.

Harts are opposed by Wolves, for many Wolves together doth overcome a Hart; and therefore it is but a fable of *Strabo*, that the Wolves and Harts live tame together in the Woods of the *Veneti*. These kinde of Wolves are called *Thoes*, and they especially fear these Wolves when they have lost their horns, and feedeth only in the night season, which caused *Ovid* to write thus;

> *Visa fugit nymphe, veluti perterrita fulvum*
> *Carva lupum, &c.* ——— ———

They are afraid also of the first and second kinde of Eagles, for with their wings they raise much dust about the Harts, and then they being half blinde, the Eagles pull out their eyes, or else so beat their feathers about their faces, that they hinder their sight, and cause them to fall down headlong from the Mountains: they fear also the ganning of Foxes, and the Lynxes do likewise lye in wait to hurt them. These are above all other four-footed Beasts both ingenuous and fearful, who although they have large horns, yet their defence against other four-footed Beasts is to run away. For this cause, in ancient time a fugitive Boy or Servant was called a Hart; and if he ran away twice, *Cantharion*, which *Cantharion* was a *Spartan* fugitive, that first ran to the enemy, and afterward from them came back again to *Sparta*. And *Martial*

231

thus describeth *Alchæus*, who being overcome by *Philip* King of *Macedon* ran away like a Hart.

Trux spiritus ille Philippi,
Cervorum cursu præpete lapsus abit.

The Epithets expressing the qualities of this Beast are many: as nimble, or agile, winged, or swift-paced, full of years, quick-footed, horned, wandering, fearful, flying, fugitive, light, wood-hunter, wilde and lively. There are of them very audacious, for they will set upon men as they travel through the Woods: and it is observed, that the wrathful Hart hath few bunches on his horn, neither is it so long as others, but bunched at the root; yet all of them being pressed with Dogs or other wilde Beasts, will fly unto a man for succour.

It is reported by *Philip Melancthon*, that in *Locha* (a town of *Saxony*) there was a Hart, which before rutting time would every year leap over the walls, and run over Rocks and Mountains, and yet return home again, untill the time that Duke *Frederick* dyed, and then the Hart went forth, but never returned again. The male when he feeleth himself fat, liveth solitary and secret; because he knoweth the weight of his body will easily betray him to the Hunters, if he be hunted and pursued. The female commonly calveth neer the high ways, of purpose, to avoid noisome Beasts to her young one, who do more avoid the sight of man then her self. Also it is reported that *Mithredates* had a Bull, a Horse, and a Hart, for his guard, beside men, who would not be bribed to suffer Traytors to kill him, being a sleep. Moreover it is said of *Ptolomeus Philadelphe*, that having a Hinde-Calf given unto him, he brought it so familiarly tame, and accustomed it to words, that at length it seemed to understand the *Greek* language: And *Ælianus* affirmeth as much of the Harts of *India*, for that language.

When they are wounded with a Dart, and having gotten it out of their body by eating Dittany, they most carefully avoid the Sun-beams, lest they shine upon the green wound, for then it will hardly be cured: but above all other arguments of their understanding, none is more firm and evident, then their swiming; for the Harts of *Amanus, Libanus,* and *Carmell,* (Mountains of *Siria*) when they are to swim over the Sea, to the fruitful green trees of *Cyprus*, they come down to the Sea-shore, and there they tarry till they perceive a prosperous wind, and a calm water; which happening, the Captain or leader of them doth first of all enter into the water, and so the next followeth, laying his head upon the Captains buttocks, and so consequently all the residue resting their head upon the precedent. In the hindmost are the youngest and weakest, that so the violence of the floods being broken by the stronger which go before, the more infirm which follow may pass with less difficulty. Thus sail they along without star or compass to direct them, except their own sense of smelling, using their legs for Oares, and their broad horns for sails. And if the formost be weary, then slippeth he back to rest his head upon the hindmost, and so likewise the second and third, as they feel themselves enfeebled, untill they arrive at the happy port of good pasture; where growing stronger, like Beasts, fall to fighting for rule and government, but when the combate doth shew the victor and strongest, the residue do ever after yeeld obedience to him. In like sort do the Harts of *Epirus* swim to *Corcyra*, and of *Cilicia* to the Island of *Curiadactes*.

They are deceived with musick, for they so love that harmony, that they forbear their food to follow it. Also it is amazed at any strange sight, for if a Hunter come behinde a Horse or Bullock, laying over his back his Bow and Arrows, they stand staring upon the new formed Beast, untill the Dart do end their lives.

At the time of their lust or rutting, they are above measure fierce, fighting naturally for the female, and sometimes wounding one another to death; and this falleth out most commonly in the latter end of *August*, at which time *Arcturus* riseth with the Sun, and then it is most natural for the Hindes to conceive. In some places in *October* their lust ariseth, and also in *May*; and then whereas at other times the males live a part from the females, they go about like lascivious woers, seeking the company of their females, as it were at the Market of *Venus*.

The males in their raging desired lust, have a peculiar voyce, which the *French* call by a feigned word *Reere*; and the *Germans*, *Brulen*; and the *Latines* tearm *Rancere*; and the Beasts so affected *Ololygones*. When they finde the females, they are received with fear, then in short space one male will cover many females, continuing in this carnal appetite a

233

month or two: their females do seldom admit copulation, being herein like unto Cows, by reason of the rigour of the males genital: and therefore they sink down on their Buttocks when they feel the genital seed, as it hath been often observed in tame Harts, and if they can, the females run away, the males striving to hold them back within their fore-feet: but surely herein they differ from all other: it cannot well be said that they are covered standing, lying, or going, (but rather running) for so are they filled with greatest celerity.

When one Month or six Weeks of their rutting is past, they grow tame again, laying aside all fierceness, and return to their solitary places, digging every one of them by himself a several hole or Ditch, wherein they lie, to asswage the strong savour of their lust, for they stink like Goats, and their face beginneth to wax blacker then at other times; and in those places they live, untill some showers distill from the clouds; after which, they return to their pasture again, and live in flocks together as before.

The female being thus filled, never keepeth company with the male again untill her burthen be delivered, which is eight months; for so long doth she bear her young: before her Calving, she purgeth her self by eating *Seselis*, or *Siler* of the Mountain; and whereas she never purgeth untill that time, then she emptieth her self of pituitous and flegmatique humors.

Then go they to the places neer the high ways, and there they cast forth their Calf, (for the causes aforesaid) being more afraid of wilde Beasts then Men, whom she can avoid by flying: which when they have seen, they go and eat the *Seselis* aforesaid, and the skin which cometh forth of her own wombe covering the young one, finding in it some notable medicine, which the *Græcians* call *Chorion*, and not the herb *Arum*, and this she doth before she lye down to give her young one suck, (as *Pliny* affirmeth.)

They bring forth but one, or very seldom twain, which they lodge in a stable fit for them of their own making, either in some rock, or other bushy inaccessible place; covering them, and if they be stubborn and wilde, beating them with their feet untill they lie close and contented. Oftentimes she leadeth forth her young, teaching it to run and leap over bushes, stones, and small shrubs; against the time of danger; and so continueth all the Summer time, while their own strength is most abundant: but in the Winter time, they leave and forsake them, because all Harts are feeble in the Winter season.

They live very long, as by experience hath been often mentioned; not only because they have no gall (as the *Dolphin* hath none) but for other causes: also some affirm, that a Raven will live nine ages of a Man, and a Hart four ages of a Raven: whereunto *Virgil* agreeth in these verses;

> *Ter binis deci sque super exit in annos,*
> *Iusta senescentum quos implet vita virorum;*
> *Hos novies superat vivendo garrula cornix,*
> *Et quater egreditur cornicis sæcula cervus,*
> *Alipedem cervum ter vincit corvus: at illum*
> *Multiplicat novies Phœnix reparabilis ales:*

That is, as the life of a man is threescore and six, so a Raven doth live nine times so many years, (*viz.*) 528 years. The Hart liveth four times the age of the Raven, (*viz.*) 2112 years. The Crow exceedeth the Hart three times, (*viz.*) 6336. But the *Phenix* which is repaired by her own ashes, surmounteth the Crow nine times, and so liveth 57524 years. The which I have set down (not for truth) but for report, leaving every reader to the chiefest matter of credit, as in his own discretion he conceiveth most probable.

But it is confessed of all, that Harts live a very long life: for *Pliny* affirmeth, that an hundred years after the death of *Alexander Magnus*, there were certain taken alive which had about their necks golden Collars, with an inscription that they were put on by *Alexander*.

In *Calabria* (once called *Iapygia* and *Peucetia*) there was Collar taken off from the neck of a Hart by *Agathocles* King of *Sicily*, which was covered with the flesh and fat of the Hart; and there was written upon it *Diomedes Dianæ*: whereby it was conjectured, that it was put on by him before the siege of *Troy*: for which cause, the King brought the same and did offer it up in the Temple of *Iupiter*.

The like was in *Arcadia*, when *Arcesilaus* dwelt in *Lycosura*; for he confidently affirmed, that he saw an old sacred Hinde, which was dedicated to *Diana*, having this inscription in her Collar: *Nebros eoon ealoon ota es Ilion en Agapenor.* When *Agapenor* was in *Troy*, then was I a young Calf taken. By which it appeareth, that a Hart liveth longer then an Elephant, for indeed as they live long before they grow to any perfection, their youth and weakness cleaving fast unto them, so is it given to them to have a longer life, for continuance in ripeness and strength of years.

These Beasts are never annoyed with Feavers, because their flesh allayeth all adventitial and extraordinary heat. If he eat Spiders he instantly dyeth thereof, except he eat also Wilde Ivie, or Sea-crabs. Likewise Navew-gentil and Oleander, kill the Hart. When a Hart is in his chase, he is greatly pained in his bowels, by reason that the skin wherein they lie is very thin and weak, and apt to be broken with any small stroke; and for this cause he often stayeth to ease himself.

There is a kinde of thorn called *Cactus*, where withall if a young one be pricked in his legs, his bones will never make Pipes. Besides these Beasts are annoyed with Scabs and Itches in their head and skin, tearmed by the *French* by a peculiar name (*Froyer:*) I will not stand upon the idle conceit of *Albertus*, that Waspes and Emmets breed in the heads of Harts, for he mistaketh them for the worm, before mentioned.

The skins of this Beast are used for garments in some Countries, and in most places for the bottom of Cushions, and therefore they chuse such as are killed in the Summer time, when they are fat and most spotted; and the same having their hair pulled from them, are used for Breeches, Buskins, and Gloves. Likewise *Pliny* and *Sextus* affirmed, that if a man sleep on the ground having upon him a Harts skin, Serpents never anoy him: whereof *Serenus* made this Verse:

Aut tu cervina per noctem in pelle quicscis.

And the bons of young ones are applyed for making of Pipes. It is reported, that the bloud of Harts burned together with herb-dragon, orchanes, orgament, and mastick have the same power to draw Serpents out of their holes, which the Harts have being alive: and if there be put unto it wilde Pellitory, it will also distract and dissipate them again.

The marrow of a Hart hath the same power against Serpents, by ointment, or perfumed upon coles; and *Nicander* prescribeth a certain ointment to be made of the flesh of Serpents, of the marrow of a Hart, and Oils of Roses, against the bitings of Serpents. The fat of a Hart hath the like effects that the marrow hath. *Achilles* that Noble Souldier, was said never to have tasted of milk, but to be nourished with the marrow of Harts, by *Chiro*, as is affirmed by *Varinus* and *Etymologus*. The like operation hath the tooth (as *Serenus* saith)

Aut genere ex ipso dentem portabis amicum.

If the seed of a young Hinde Calf be drunk with Vinegar, it suffereth no poison of Serpents to enter into the body that day.

The perfume of the horn driveth away Serpents and noisome flies, especially from the young Calves, or from Horses if womens hair be added thereto, with the hoof of the Hart. And if men drink in pots wherein are wrought Harts horns, it will weaken all force of venom. The *Magicians* have also devised, that if the fat of a Dragons heart be bound up in the skin of a Roe, with the nerves of a Hart, it promiseth victory to him that beareth it on his Shoulder, and that if the teeth be so bound in a Roes skin, it maketh ones Master, Lord, or all superior powers, exorable and appeased toward their servants and suitors. *Orpheus* in his book of stones, commandeth a husband to carry about him a Harts horn, if he will live in amity and concord with his wife; to conclude, they also add another figment to make men invincible.

The head and tail of a Dragon, with the hairs of a Lion taken from between the browes, and his marrow, the froath or white-mouth of a victorious Horse, the nails of a Dog, and the nerves of a Hart and a Roe, bound up all together in a Harts skin: and this is as true as the wagging of a Dogs tail doth signifie a tempest. To leave these trifles scarce worthy to be rehearsed, but only to shew the vanity of men, given over to lying devises, let us come to the other natural and medicinal properties not as yet touched.

The flesh of these Beasts in their running time smelleth strongly like a Goats, the which thing is by *Blondus* attributed also to the flesh of the females with young, I know not how truly; but I am sure that I have

237

known certain Noble women, which every morning did eat this flesh, and during the time they did so, they never were troubled with Ague: and this virtue they hold the stronger, if the beast in dying, have received but one wound.

The flesh is tender, especially if the beast were libbed before his horns grew: yet is not the juice of that flesh very wholesome, and therefore *Galen* adviseth men to abstain as much from Harts flesh, as from Asses, for it engendereth melancholy, yet is it better in Summer then in Winter. *Simeon Sethi* speaking of the hot Countries, forbiddeth to eat them in Summer, because then they eat Serpents and so are venemous; which falleth not out in colder Nations, and therefore assigneth them rather to be eaten in Winter time, because the concoctive powers are more stronger through plenty of inward heat, but withal admonisheth, that no man use to eat much of them, for it will breed Palsies and trembling in mans body, begetting grosse humors, which stop the Milt and Liver: and *Avicen* proveth, that by eating thereof men in our the quartane Ague; wherefore it is good to powder them with salt before the dressing, and then seasoned with Peper and other things, known to every ordinary Cook and woman, they make of them Pasties in most Nations.

The heart and brain of a Hare or Cony have the power of Triacle for expelling of evill humors, but the Liver is intolerable in food: the horns being young are meat for Princes, especially because they avoid poison. It was a cruell thing of King *Ferdinand*, that caused the young ones to be cut out of the Dams belly and baked in Pasties, for his liquorous *Epicureal* appetite.

The whole nature and disposition of every part of this beast is against poison and venemous things (as before recited). His bloud stayeth the looseness of the belly and all fluxes, especially fryed with Oil, and the inferior parts anointed therewith, and being drunk in Wine, it is good against poisoned wounds and all intoxications.

The marrow of this beast is most approveable above other, and is used for sweet odour, against the Gowt, and heat of men in Consuptions, and all outward pains and weakness, as *Serenus* comprised in one sentence saying:

Likewise the fat and marrow, mollifieth or disperseth all bunches in the flesh and old swellings; all Ulcers except in the shins and legs, and with Venus-navil, the Fistula, mattery Ulcers in the ears; with Rozen, Pitch, Goose-greace, and Goat-sewet, the cleaving of the lips: and with Calves sewet the heat and pain in the mouth and jawes. It hath also vertue being drunk in warm water, to aswage the pain in the bowels and small guts, or Bloudy flux.

The gall of a Bull, Oil of bayes, Butter, and this marrow, by anointing, cureth pain in the knees and loins and other evils in the seat of man, in the hips, and in the belly when it is costive: It procureth flowers of Women, cureth the Gowt, Pimples in ones face, and Ringwormes. *Absyrtus* prescribeth it to be given in sweet wine with wax, unto a Horse for an old Cough proceeding of cold, after purging and heating, by holding the Horses tongue in ones hand while the medicine is thrust down his throat.

The same in Sheeps milk with Rubrick and soft Pitch, drunk every day or eaten to your meat, helpeth the Ptisick and Obstructions. *Anatolius* approved Bean meal sifted and sod with Harts marrow to be given to a Horse which stalleth bloud for three daies together. Also mingled with the powder of Oyster shels, it cureth Kibes and Chilblanes. A woman perfumed with the hairs of this beast, is preserved from abortements; and the same perfume helpeth the difficulty of urine, and little pieces cut off from the hide with a Pummise put in wine, and rubbing the body, helpeth the holy-fire. The powder of the bones burned, is an antidote against the falling evill, and the dispersing of the milt; and the bones beaten to powder, stayeth the Flux of the belly.

It were endless to describe all the virtues ascribed to the horn, and therefore I will content my self with the recital of few. *Pliny* and *Solinus* prefer the right horn, *Aristotle* the left, and the spires or tops are more medicinable then the hard and solide stem, but the horns found in the Woods lost by the beasts and grown light, are good for nothing. The other have their uses both raw and burned, which may be these which follow.

Take the horn and cut it into small pieces, then put it into an earthen pot anointed within with durt, and so set it in a furnace untill it become white, then wash it like a mineral and it will help the runnings and ulcers in the eyes; and the same also keepeth the teeth white, and the gums sound. The young horns while they be soft being eaten, are an antidote against Henbane and other poisonful herbs. The right horn hid by the Hart in the earth is good against the poison of Toades. The Harts horn hath power to dry up all humors, and therefore it is used in eye salves: and *Orpheus* promiseth to a bald man hair on his head again, if he anoint it with oil and powder of this horn: likewise the same with the seed of black mirtle, Butter and Oil, restraineth the falling away of the hair being anointed upon the head after it is newly shaven: with Vinegar it killeth Ringwormes. The same burned in the Sun, and afterward the face being rubbed and washed therewith thrice together, taketh away pimple-spots out of the face: the powder drunk in wine or anointed on the head killeth lice and nits; the same with Vinegar, Wine, or Oil of Roses, anointed upon the forehead, easeth the head-ach if it proceed of cold.

A perfume made of this horn with *Castoreum*, and Lime or Brimstone, causeth a dead childe strangled in his mothers womb to come forth; if the horn be taken raw and rubbed upon the gums, keepeth the cheeks from all annoyance of the tooth-ach, and fasteneth the loose teeth, as *Serenus* said:

> *Quod vero assumpsit nomen de dente fricando*
> *Cervino ex cornu cinis est.*

Galen prescribeth the powder of this horn for the Jaundise, and for him that spitteth bloudy matter, and to stay vomit being taken in a reere Egge. It comforteth also a rheumatick stomach, and it is tryed to cure the Kings evill, it pacifieth the milt, dryeth the Spleen, driveth all kind of Wormes out of the belly, being drunk with hony, and easeth the Colick, expelleth away mothers, helpeth the Strangury, and the pain in the bladder, stayeth Fluxes in women both white and red: being mingled with Barly meal, water, and twigs of Cedar, beside many other such properties.

The tears of this beast after she hath been hunted with a Serpent, are turned into a stone (called *Belzahard*, or *Bezahar*) of which we have spoken before: and being thus transubstantiated do cure all manner of venom (as *Avenzoar*, and *Cardinal Ponzetti* affirme) after many trials, and *Serenus* also expresseth in this Distichon:

> *Seminecis cervi lachrymam miscere liquori*
> *Convenit, atque artus illinc miscere calentes.*

The liver of this beast helpeth all sores in the feet, being worn in the shooes, the same dryed to powder with the throat or wind-pipe of the beast, and mingled with Hony, and so eaten helpeth the Cough, Ptisick, sighing and short breathing. *Pliny* and *Sextus* affirme, that when a Hinde perceiveth herself to be with young, she devoureth or eateth up a certain stone, which is afterward found either in her excrements or ventricle, and is profitable for all Women with childe and in travell, for by that only fact, the Hinde is most speedily delivered without great pain, and seldome or never suffering abortment; and there is also a little bone found in the heart of every one of these beasts, which performeth the same qualities, in stead whereof they have such a thing to sell at *Venice*, holding it at great price: but *Brasavola* affirmeth, that he opened the hearts of two Harts, and found in them a little gristle not much unlike to a crosse, whereof the one being of a Beast new killed, was very soft, but the other was much harder, because the beast was slain about six dayes before.

This bone is in the left side of the heart, upon which the Spleen moveth and sendeth forth her excrements by vapors, which by reason of their driness are there turned into a bone, and being first of all of the substance of the Harts bloud: and it is good against the trembling of the heart, and the Hemorrhoides, but this bone cannot be found in any, except he be killed betwixt the middle of *August* and the twelfth of *September*.

The skinny seed of the Hind-Calf, is above all other commended against poison, and the bitings of Serpents and of mad Dogs; likewise it stayeth all Fluxes of bloud, and spitting of bloud, and egestion of bloud: and it being eaten with Beets and Lentils, is profitable against the pain of the belly. The genital part and stones are wholesome (being taken in wine) against all bitings of Vipers, Adders, and Snakes, and the same virtue hath the natural seed supped up in a rere Egge.

The genital hath also a virtue to encrease lust in every creature, it being either dryed and drunk; or else bound fast to their privie parts. Likewise being warmed in water; and afterward dryed to powder and so drunk, helpeth the Colick, and the difficulty of making water, if you put it into a little Triacle.

The dung of Harts cureth the Dropsie, especially of a Subulon or young Hart: the urine easeth the pain in the Spleen, the wind in the ventricles and bowels, and infused into the ears, healeth their ulcers. In the tip of the tail lyeth poison, which being drunk, causeth extasie and death, if it be not helpt by a vomit made of Butter, Annise, and oil of *Sesamine,* or as *Cardinal Ponzetius* saith, that the Harts eye is an Antidote to this evill: It may be known by a yellowish-green colour, and therefore it is called the gall, for nature hath appointed that place to receive all the venom of the whole Body.

I should here end the discourse of this beast, after the method already observed in the precedents: but seeing the manner of the taking hereof (being a sport for Princes) hath yet been touched but very little, it shall not be tedious unto me, to abstain from the necessary relation of the subsequent stories, for the delightful narration of the hunting of the Hart: to the end that as the former treatise hath but taught how to know a Bird in a bush, that which insueth may declare the several wayes of catching and bringing the same to hand.

This is a beast standing amazed at every strange sight, even at the hunters bow and arrow, coming behind a stalking Horse (as is already declared:) and moreover, like as the Roes are deceived by the hissing of a leaf in the mouth of the hunter, so also is this beast, for while she hearkeneth to a strange noise, imitating the cry of a Hind-Calf, and proceeding from one man, she receiveth a deadly stroke by the other: so also if they hear any musical pipings, they stand still to their own destruction: for which cause the *Egyptians* decipher a man overthrown by flattery, by painting a Hart taken by musick: and *Varro* relateth upon his own knowledge, that when he supped in his Lordship bought of *M. Piso,* the Pastour or Forrester after supper, took but a Harp in his hand, and at the sound hereof, an innumerable flock of Harts, Boars, and other four-footed beasts came about their Cabanet, being drawn thither only by the musick; in so much as he though he had been in the *Roman Circus* or Theater, beholding the playing spectacles of all the *African* beasts, when the *Ædilian* Officers have their huntings: the like is also reported by *Ælianus*, saving that he addeth, that no toil or engine is so assured or unavoidable to draw these beasts within a labyrinth as is musick, whereby the Hunter getteth as it were the Hart by the ear, for if through attention he hold down his ears as he doth in musick, he distrusteth no harm, but if once he prick up his ears as he commonly doth, being chased by men and dogs, an infinite labour will not be sufficient to over-take and compass him. It is reported that they are much terrified with the sight of red feathers, which thing is affirmed by *Ausonius* in these Verses:

> *An cum fratre vagos dumeta per avia cervos*
> *Circundas maculis, & multa indagine pennæ.*

And *Ovid* also saying,

> *Nec formidatis cervos includite pennis.*

And *Lucan* also;

> —— *Sic dum pavidos formidine cervos*
> *Claudat odoratæ metuentes aera pennæ.*

Of which thing the Hunters make an advantage, for when they have found the beast, they set their nets where they imagine the beast will flie, and then one of them sheweth to the beast on the other side, the red feathers hanging on a rope, which scareth them in haste into the Hunters nets, as S. *Jerom* testifieth in one of his Dialogues, saying, *Et pavidorum more cervorum, dum vanos pennarum evitatis volatus, fortissimis retibus implicamini*. And you, saith he, (speaking to the *Luciferian* hereticks) run away from the vain shaking of feathers, like the fearfull Harts, while in the mean time you are inclapsed in unavoidable and inextricable nets. And this caused *Seneca* to write, that the babe feareth a shadow, and wilde beasts a red feather.

Many times the young Calf is the cause of the taking of his Dam: for the Hunter early in the morning before day light, watcheth the Hinde where she layeth her young one, untill she go and refresh her self with pasture; when he hath seen this, then doth he let loose his Dogs, and maketh to the place where the Hind-Calf was left by his mother.

The silly Calf lyeth immoveable as if he were fastened to the earth, and so never stirring, but bleating and braying suffereth himself to be taken, except there be rainy weather, for the impatience of cold and wet will cause him to shift for himself: which if it fall out, the Dogs are at hand to over-take him, and so being taken is committed to the keeper of the nets.

The Hinde both hearing and seeing the thraldom of her poor son, cometh to relieve him, without dread of Hound or Hunter, but all in vain, for with his dart he also possesseth himself of her; but if the Calf be greater, and so be able to run with the Dam among the herds, they are most hard to be taken, for in that age they run very fast, and the fear of Dogs increaseth their agility, in so much as to take them among the herds is impossible, every one fighting for them.

But the only way is to single one out of them from the flock, and so follow him until he be weary, for although he be very nimble, yet by reason of his tender age, his limbes are not able to continue long. The elder Harts are taken in snares and gins laid in ditches and covered with leaves, whereby the feet of this beast is snared in wood; this kind is described by *Xenophon* and *Pollux*, and is called in *Greek, Podestrabe*; in *Latin, Pedica*, of which also the Poets make mention, as *Virgil*:

> *Tunc gruibus pedicas & retia ponere cervis.*

And this kind is better described by *Gratius*, with whose words I will pass it over as a thing ont of use.

> *Nam fuit & laqueis aliquis curracibus usus.*
> *Cervino issere magis conterere nervo,*
> *Quidque dentatas iligno robere clausit:*
> *Sæpe habet imprudens alieni lucra laboris,*
> *Fraus tegit insidias habitu mentita ferino*
> *Venator pedicas, cum dissimulantibus armis.*

Their manner is when they are chased with Dogs to run away with speed, yet oftentimes stand still and look back, not only to hearken to the hunter, but also to rest themselves, for in their chase they are ever troubled in their belly (as is before declared) and sometime they grow so weary, that they stand still, and are pierced with arrows, sometime they run till they fall down dead, sometime they take themselves to the water and so are refreshed, or else to avoid the teeth of Dogs, they forsake the dry land, and perish in the floods, or else by that means escape scotfree: wherefore it must be regarded by every good hunter to keep him from the waters, either among the woods or other rough places.

But herein the subtilty of this beast appeareth, that when he is hunted, he runneth for the most part to the high wayes, that so the savour of his steps may be put out by the treadings of men, and he avoid the prosecution of the Hound. Their swiftnesse is so great, that in the *Champaine* and plain fields they regard not Dogs, for which cause in *France* they poison Arrows with an herb called *Zenicum* or *Toca*, and it is a kinde of *Aconite* or Wolfe-bane, which hath power to corrupt and destroy agility of body, and to stay celerity, and for their hunting in *France* by Dogs, it is most excellently described by *Budæus* and *Robertus Stephanus* in his *French* Dictionary.

This wilde, deceitful and subtil beast, (say they) by windings and turnings do often deceive their hunter, as the Harts of *Meandros* flying from the terrible cry of *Dianaes* hounds, wherefore the prudent hunter must frame his Dogs, as *Pythagoras* did his Scholars, (*Luuers qui ne parlent point*) with words of Art, to set them on, and take them off again at his pleasure; wherefore he must first of all compass in the beast, (*En son giste*) in her own lodging, and so raise her up in the sight of the Dogs, that so they may never lose her footing.

Neither must they set upon every one, either of the herd, or that wandereth solitary alone, nor yet a little one, but partly by aspect or sight, and partly by their footings in the soft earth, and also by their dung (*Les fumees*) they judge of their game, for a good Woodman must not stick to gather up the Deers excrement or soil, and keep them (*La trempe*) in his hunting horn: such things must the Kings huntsmen and forresters observe, as also the quantity of his bed or lodging when they finde it; being thus informed of their game, then (*Discoppler les chiens*) they take off their Dog couplings, and some on horseback, other on foot follow the cry with greatest art, observation, and speed, remembring and preventing (*Cer fruze*) the subtile turnings, and headings of the Hart, straining with all dexterity to leap hedge, pale, ditch, and rocks; neither fearing thornes, woods, down-hils, but providing a fresh horse in case the first tire, (*Chevaux de relatis*) and leaping on him with speed, untill he see (*un grand cerf l' escuyer du grand cerf*) the great Hart having ten speers on his horns, and his little squire-hart to attend him, which the Dogs once perceiving, only follow the great Hart, taking for a prohibition to follow any other.

The Dogs are animated by the winding of horns, and voices of the hunters, like Souldiers to a battel by the voice of a trumpet and other instruments: but sometimes the crafty great beast sendeth forth his little squire to be sacrificed to the Dogs and Hunters in stead of himself, lying close in the mean time, then must the retreat be sounded, and (*Rompre lechiens*) the Dogs be broken off and taken in (*Le limier*) that is, leame again untill they be brought to the fairer game, who ariseth in fear and rage, betaking himself to his surest legs, being pursued with all the cries of Hunters, ringing and ecchoing betwixt heaven and earth, dismaying him with the continual noise in his eares, no lesse dreadful and fearful then the voice of a passing bell to a sick man, or the sight of the executioner to a condemned caitife, yet still he striveth untill wearied and breathless, he be forced to offer up his bloud and flesh to the rage of all the observant pedissequants of the hunting Goddess *Diana*.

The vulgar sort call an old Hart a subtil and cunning beast, but the Nobles call him (*cerf sage*) a wise Hart, who to avoid all his enemies runneth into the greatest herds, and so bringeth a cloud of error upon the Dogs, to keep them from any further prosecution: sometime also beating of some of the herd into his own footsteps, that so he may more easily escape and procure a labyrinth to the Dogs, and then after a little while he betaketh himself to his heels again, running still with the wind, not only for refrigeration, but because he may the more easily hear the voice of his pursuers, whether they be far or neer.

At last, being (for all this) found out again by the observance of the hunters, and skill of the Dogs, he flyeth into the herds of Cattel, as Kie, Oxen, or Sheep, leaping upon an Ox, and laying his body or the fore-part thereof upon him, as a rider upon a Horse, that so touching the earth only with his hinder hoofs, to leave a very small or no sent at all behind for the Hounds to discern.

The chief huntsman or sergeant of the hounds unto *Lewis* the twelfth, called (*Le grand venieur*) affirmeth that on a time they having a Hart in chase, suddenly the Hounds fell at a fault, so as the beast was out of sight, and not a Dog would once stir his foot; whereat all the Hunters were amazed, like as in some jugling *Apollonian* trick, as though the hart had clean forsaken the earth, and with the wings of some fowl had been flown away; or as if the earth had opened her mouth to receive him into her protection, and had closed again over her head, or else some Witchcraft had cast a mist before the Dogs and Hunters eyes: At last by casting about (as it is usuall in such cases) they found the fraud of the horned beast, which is worth the memory.

There was a great white-thorne which grew in a shadowie steep place as high as a tree, and was invironed with other small shrubs about it, into the which the said Hart leapt, and there stood aloft the boughs spreading from one another, and there remained, whether because he could not get off again, or else for that he was stifled in that place, but surely he was there thrust through and so died, and so had they all rather perish any other way then by the teeth and tearing in pieces of angry and greedy Hounds.

Yet their maner is, that when they see themselves every where intercepted, to make force at him with their horns that cometh first unto him, except he be prevented by some sword or spear; which being done, the Hunter with his horn soundeth the fall of the beast, and then every one approacheth, luring with triumph for such a conquest, of whom the skilfullest openeth the beast, giving unto the Hounds such parts as belongeth to them, for their incouragement against another time; and for that purpose the Hunters dip bread in the skin and bloud of the beast, to give unto the Hounds their full satisfaction: and many such other things may the reader desirous of this knowledge find in the

Authors aforesaid, to whom I will commend him rather, then spend more time in this business, better manifested by experience, then by any written document, yet I would wish men to be sparing in this exercise, seeing it hath been seldom found that a man given to hunting, but he perished in his pleasure, as *Actæon* did by his own Dogs: and therefore *Alciatus* doth fitly compare together hunters and receivers of Theeves and Robbers, calling them new *Actæons*; who after they had received horns, must be destroyed by their own Dogs which they have nourished. The best use of these beasts is to keep them tame, as in *Helvetia*, where they hunt seldom, and to make good use of them for nourishment rather then for sport, as it is reported of a holy-man, who kept a Hinde so familiar with him, that in the Wilderness he lived upon her milk.

Concluding this discourse with the words of the Poet, for the instruction of Dogs to this pastime and practise of the beasts.

> *Veloces Spartæ catulos, acremque molossum,*
> *Pasce fero pingui, &c.*

And again;

> ——— ——— *Montesque per altos*
> *Ingentem clamore premes ad retia cervum.*
> ——— *Confertoque agmine cervi*
> *Torpent mole nova, & summis vix cornibus extant.*
> *Hos non immissis canibus, non cassibus ullis,*
> *Puniccæve agitent pavidos formidine pennæ:*
> *Sed frustra oppositum trudentes pectore montem*
> *Comminus obtruncant ferro, graviterque rudentes*
> *Cædunt, & magno læti clamore reportant.*

OF THE DYCTYES.

HERODOTUS in his fourth book affirmeth, that among the *African* Shepherds toward the East, there are bred in *Bassaria Hystriches* wilde Rams, *Thoes* and *Dyctyes*, of which last there is not any mention among all other writers, except in *Varinus* and *Hesychius*, who affirm that among the *Lacedemonians* a Glead or Kite was called *Dyctis*, but this spoken of *Herodotus* I conjecture to be some four-footed beast, being led with no other reason then that the other with whom he placeth it, are generally known to be creatures of that kind and nature: wherefore I thought good to express the name of it in this place, desiring the Reader to accept so much thereof as is already known, and to search farther for the description of it, at the hands of them who are eye-witnesses of the wonders of *Africa*.

OF THE DOG IN GENERAL.

A Dog is called in *Hebrew, Keleb,* and *Lamas* according to *Munster*; in *Chalde, Kalba*; in *Atabick, Kalbe*; in *Persia, Sag*; the *Saracens, Kep,* or *Kolph*; the *Grecians Kuon* because of his love to man, and vulgarly at this day *Skilos* and *Skule*; the *Medians, Spaco*; the *Germans, Hund*; the *Italians, Cane*; the *French, Chien*; the *Spaniards, Perro* or *Cavendo*, because his barking is as loud as an Artificial song, also *Catellus*; the *Illyrians, Pes* or *Pas*; and the *Latins, Canis*.

There is no region or Countrey in the world, where these are not bred in some store, as shall be declared afterward in the particular discourse of every kinde of Dogs. For as shall be manifested more at large, there are Dogs very great, some for hunting, some for War and defence, some for the Boar, Bull, or Bear, some for the Hare, Cony, or Hedge-hog: again some are smaller which are called Hounds, Braches, Beagles, Shepherds Dogs, House-curs, Spagnels both for the Water and Land; and some foisting Dogs for the pleasure of the rich.

In the first place there are to be handled the nature of Dogs in general, wherein they agree, and their common properties of nature, such as are not destroyed in the distinction of kinds, but remain like infallible and invariable truths in every kind and Countrey of the world. To begin with that which is outward, it is to be observed that Dogs are generally rough, and their hair indifferently long (which in Winter they lose every year) is a signe of a good constitution; but if it grow over long, the mangie scab will follow: the outward proportion of the head altereth as the kind altereth, being sometime like a Lion, sometime like a Hedge-hog, some long with a broad snowt, and sometime with a piked snowt, but the brain decreaseth and increaseth with the Moon, there is no commissure or seam in his scull (like as is in a Mans) but it is a continued bone without separation inward or outward.

The best Dogs have flat nostrils, yet round, solid and blunt, the mouth is long and slit, their teeth like saws, as it is in Fishes and Serpents: those which are called *Canine* before, are only changed, as it also falleth out in a Lion, and these they lose or change, both males and females, in the fourth moneth of their age: about which time they have new ones come forth to thrust off their old. By their teeth is their age discerned, for while they are white and sharpe, it assureth the youth of a Dog, but when they grow blackish, or duskie, they betoken the elder age.

The breast of a Dog is narrow and piked, his ventricle small and narrow, for which cause he never easeth his bodily excrements without pain, his bowels are like a Lions: he hath a long spleen like a Man, and a Hog: his yard and stones hang outward between his hinder-legs; a base natured cur striketh his tail betwixt his legs; his forelegs bend like the armes of a man, and he useth them in stead of Armes, having five distinct fingers, commonly called claws upon each foot before, and four upon each foot behind, which also have straight nails upon them, and that which hangeth higher upon the leg is crooked.

The females, because they bring forth many whelps at a time, have underneath their bellies great paps, with many speans to suck at, in a double rank or row on both sides, and the generous Bitches have 12. other but 10. They bear their young within their belly next to the midriffe, their fime is dry like a Wolves, and thereby his temperament is known to be hot and dry, considered in it self, but compared with others it varyeth, for to a Mans it is dry; to an Emmets, it is moist: again, in respect of a Man, it is hot; in respect of a Lion, it is cold.

The lowder and shriller voice of a Dog, is called barking, the lower and stiller, is called whining, or fawning. It was a monstrous thing, that a Dog should speak, and a Serpent bark, as it is believed in antiquity both came to passe, when *Tarquinius* was driven out of his kingdom. It is not causeless that the barking of Dogs, hath attributed unto it divers qualities, as for a man to dream of the same, presageth some treasonable harm by enemies, so likewise if they fawn and claw upon a man.

Among the precedent tokens of *Cæsars* death, they set down in certain Verses, the howling voices of Owls, the weeping drops of the Ivie tree, and the continual barkings of Dogs, as followeth.

> *Tristia mille locis Stygius dedit omina bubo,*
> *Mille locis lacrymavit ebur —— ——*
> *Inque foro circumque domos & templa deorum*
> *Nocturnos ululasse canes, &c.*

The *Egyptians* signifie these things by a Dog, a *Scribe*, a *Prophet*, a *Spleen*, *smelling, laughing*, and *neezing*. A *Scribe*, because as the Dog is silent more then he barketh, so must a perfect Scribe meditate more then he speaketh: for to bark at every one were to pleasure none, and to speak continually, were a signe of madness. Again, a *Prophet*, because a Dog doth most eagerly behold, and admire constantly at holy actions, and so ought the eyes and eares of a Prophet be attendant upon heavenly things. The *Spleen*, because a Dog hath little or no spleen, and thereof cometh his madness and death; whereof also it cometh that the servants which have the charge of Dogs, being with them in their sickness and latter end, for the most part prove Splenetick. *Smelling*, *Neesing*, and *Laughing*, because the Splenetick can do none of all these; but of this more afterward.

The voice of a Dog, is by the learned interpreted a railing and angry speech; whereof cometh *Canina facundia* among Authors, for railing eloquence. It is the nature of a Dog when he maketh water, to hold up his leg, if he be above six moneths old, or have been at procreation; the females do it for the most part sitting, yet some of the generous spirits do also hold up the legs. They ever smell to the hinder parts of one another, peradventure thereby they discern their kind and disposition of each other in their own natures. After they have run a course, they relieve themselves by tumbling and rowling to and fro: when they lie down, they turn round in a circle two or three times together, which they do for no other cause, but that they may the more commondiously lie round, and from the winde.

They sleep as doth a man, and therein dream very often, as may appear by their often barking in their sleep: but it must be diligently regarded of them that love to keep Dogs, that they permit them not to sleep much, especially after their meat when they are young, for as they are very hot, so in their sleep doth their heat draw much pain into their stomach and ventricle. The time of their copulation is for the most part at a year old, yet the females will lust after it at eight moneths old, howbeit they are not to be suffered, because it weakeneth their bodies, and dulleth in them all generosity; therefore after one year they may safely be suffered to come together, and not before. Neither is it material, whether in Summer or Winter, but it is best in the beginning of the Spring, but with this caution, that Whelpes of a litter or of one and the same Bitch, be never suffered to couple; for nature rejoyceth more in variety.

For then they grow salt and begin to be proud; yet in ancient time, for the more ennobling of their race of Dogs, they did not suffer them to engender till the Male were four year old, and the female three; for then would the Whelpes prove more strong and lively. By hunting, labour and travel, the males are made more fit for generation, and they prove best which have their sires of equal age. They are not suffered to engender all their life long, but untill ten and twelve year old, or rather

252

eight in the male, and six in the female. Yet there have been found which in one and other sex, have continued in procreation till they were twenty year old, but this exceeded all natural reason. When they begin to be proud, if you give them leaven mingled with milk and salt, they will not stray and range abroad. At the time of their copulation, they cleave together for a certain space, as if their hinder parts were glewed, and so they are filled at one time. They bear their young the fifth part of the year, that is, about two moneths and odd dayes; but this reckoning is not general, for some kinds bear their young three moneths, and some more. They bring forth many at a time, sometime five, seven, nine, or twelve, for so many cels hath the female in her womb.

Albertus relateth that he saw a Bitch of the Mastive kind, which brought forth at three litters fifty Whelpes, that is nineteen at the first, eighteen at the second, and thirteen at the third: but sometime she bringeth forth but one, which is a good argument to prove that she is filled at the first liming. They are purged of their menstruous fluxes seven or fourteen daies before they grow proud, and again, at their time of littering; at other times they suffer none.

The first they cast forth of their wombe is commonly a male, which resembleth the father, the other males and females as it happeneth, (but it is accounted a prodigious thing to litter all males or all females) wherein nature yeeldeth an excellent argument of divine providence, for the first born of all kinds hath more resemblance of the father then of the mother. They are also whelped blind, and so remain for nine or ten dayes, because through their multitude they cannot be perfected in the dams belly, which doth not happen to beasts which bear single, as Sheep and Goats. They use to carry them up and down in their mouths till they be seven dayes old, but not afterward, they have milk about five dayes before their littering. It is not good to preserve the first or second litter, but the third; and after they have littered it is good to give the Bitch Whay and Barly bread, for that will comfort her and encrease her milk; and in some places they take Goats milk and seethe in it broken bones of meat, whereby they conceive that the Dam and Whelpes are much bettered for that nutriment: there is not any great regard of the nourishment of Dogs, for they will eat much and that often and divers things, except Dogs flesh, for that cannot be so dressed and prepared by the art of man, but they finde it out by their nose and avoid it. It is good to let the Whelpes suck two moneths before they be weaned, and that of their own dam, for it is not so good for them to suck another, and in the mean time exercise them to meat, as Milk, Whay, Bread, and flesh; also from the Spring untill the Sun entreth *Cancer*, at which time it is good to let them grow lean according to the Verses of *Nemesian*.

> —— *Consuetam minuisse saginam*
> *Profuerit, tenuesque magis retinere cibatus,*
> *Ne gravis articulos depravet pondere molles.*
> *Nam tum membrorum nexas, nodosque relaxant.*

And afterward when they are six moneths old amend their diet again that they may grow strong.

> *Tunc rursus miscere sero Corealia dona.*
> *Conveniet, fortemque dari de frugibus escam.*

They will not eat Buck-mast wherewithal Hogs grow fat, for that breedeth in them the pain of the head. By eating the excrements of men they incur many diseases: they are mad drunk by the herb *Oenutta*, as Crowes bee; they cannot endure Wine, but bread sopped in wine they devoure, dryed flesh and bread in Milk is their safest food; if Cummin be now and then mixed in their bread, they are not much troubled with winde in their bellies. If you put a little Oil in their Water to drink or lap, they will prove more able and swift to run. If he refuse and loath his meat, take a little hot bread and give it him before meat, or dip brown bread in Vinegar, and so presse and squeese the liquor thereof into his nose and it will ease him.

There is much ado to chuse a Whelpe under the Dam that will prove the best in the litter. Some observe that which seeth last, and take that for the best; other remove the Whelpes from the kennel and lay them several and apart one from the other, then watch they which of them the Bitch first taketh and carryeth into her kennel again, and that they take for the best; or else that which vomiteth last of all. Some again give for a certain rule to know the best, that the same which weigheth least while it sucketh will prove best according to the Verses of *Nemesian*.

Pondere nam catuli poteris perpendere vires,
Corporibusque leves gravibus pernojcere cursu.

But this is certain that the lighter whelp will prove the swifter, and the heavier will be the stronger. Other make this experiment, first they compass in the Puppies in the absence of the Dam with a little circle of small sticks apt to burn, and stinking rags, then set they them on fire about the whelpes, and that Puppy which leapeth over first they take for the best, and that which cometh out last they condemn for the worst. As soon as the Bitch hath littered, it is good to chuse them you mean to preserve, and to cast away the refuse; keep them black, or brown, or of one colour; for the spotted are not to be accounted of. And thus much of the outward parts and the choise of Dogs. The manifold attributes of Dogs among all Writers, do decipher unto us their particular nature; as that they are called sharp, bitter, fierce, subtil, sounding, bold, eared for attention, affable, swift, speedy, clamorous, wilde, faithful, horrible, rough, fasting, cruell, ungentle, unclean, hurtful, biting, filthy, smelling, sent-follower, watchful, mad, hoarse, and quick-nosed; beside many such other both among the *Greeks* and *Latins*. And likewise you shall read of many particular Dogs, and their names appellative, both in *Greek* and *Latine*, which may be remembred also in this place, to shew what reckoning all ages have made of this beast; for it is necessary, that as soon as he beginneth to feed he presently receive a name, such are these, of two syllables or more, as *Scylax, Speude, Alke, Rome, Lacon, Acalanthis, Agre, Labros, Hylactor, Alleus, Argus* (one of *Ulysses* Dogs) *Asbolus, Augeas, Aura, Bria, Polis, Bremon, Kainon, Canache, Happarus, Charon, Chorax, Harpia, Lycitas, Chiron, Lycisca, Arcas, Dromas, Gnome, Eba, Hybris, Hyleus, Maira, Melampus, Orne, Lethargos, Nape*; besides infinite other among the antients; but among the latter writers, *Turcus, Niphus, Falco, Ragonia, Serpens, Ichtia, Pilaster, Leo, Lupus, Stella, Fulgur, Bellina, Rubinum, Satinus,* and *Furia*: so that every Nation, and almost every man hath a proper and peculiar name for his Dog, as well as for his Oxe.

There is not any creature without reason, more loving to his Master, nor more serviceable (as shall appear afterward) then is a Dog, induring many stripes patiently at the hands of his Master, and using no other means to pacifie his displeasure, then humiliation, prostration, assentation, and after beating, turneth a revenge into a more servent and hot love. In their rage they will set upon all strangers; yet herein appeareth their noble spirit, for if any fall or sit down on the ground and cast away his weapon, they bite him not; taking that declining for submissive pacification. They meet their Master with reverence and joy, crouching or bending a little, (like shamefast and modest persons) and although they know none but their Master and familiars, yet will they help any man against another Wilde beast. They remember voices, and obey their leaders hissing or whisling.

There was a Dog in *Venice* which had been three years from his Master, yet knew him again in the Market place; discerning him from thousands of people present. He remembreth any man which giveth him meat: when he fauneth upon a man he wringeth his skin in the forehead. The Dog which is broad faced like a Lion, is most full of stomach and courage; yet the tongue or skin of an *Hyæna* (by natural instinct) maketh him run away: sometimes they will agree with Wolves, for they have engendered together, and as the Lute strings made of a Wolfe and a Lambe cannot agree in musick, but one of them will break, so also will a Dogs and a Lambs.

Ælianus thinketh that Dogs have reason, and use Logick in their hunting, for they will cast about for the game, as a disputant doth for the truth, as if they should say either the Hare is gone on the left hand, or on the right hand, or straight forward, but not on the left or right hand, and therefore straight forward. Whereupon he runneth forth right after the true and infallible foot-steps of the Hare. There was a Dog in *Africa* in a ship, which in the absence of the Mariners came to a pitcher of oil to eat some of it, and the mouth of the pot being too narrow for his head to enter in (because the pot was not full) he devised to cast flint stones into the vessel, whereby the Oil rose to the top of the Pitcher, and so he eat thereof his fill, giving evident testimony thereby, that he discerned by nature, that heavy things will sink down, and light things will rise up and flie aloft.

There is a Nation of people in *Ethiopia* (called Nubæ) which have a Dog in such admirable estimation, that they give unto him the honor of their King; for they have no other King but he. If he faun, they take him for well pleased; if he bark or flie upon them, they take him for angry: and by his gestures and movings they conjecture his meaning, for the government of their state: giving as ready obedience to his significations, as they can to any lively speaking Prince of the world: for which cause the *Egyptians* also picture a Dog with a Kings robe, to signifie a Magistrate. Those people of *Egypt* also, observe in their religious processions, and gesticulations, dumb-idle-gods, to carry about with them two Dogs, one Hawk, and one *Ibis*, and these they call four letters: by the two Dogs, they signifie the two Hemispheres which continually watch and go over our heads: by the Hawk, the Sun; for the Hawk is a hot creature, and liveth upon destruction: by the *Ibis*, the face of the Moon; for they compare the black feathers in this bird to her dark part, and the white to her light. Other by the Dogs, do understand the two Tropicks, which are (as it were) the two porters of the Sun for the South and North: by the Hawk, they understand the Equinoctial or burning line, because she flyeth high: by the *Ibis*, the Zodiack: and indeed those Painters which could most artificially decipher a Dog (as *Nicias*) were greatly reverenced among the *Egyptians*.

The like folly (or impious beastliness) was that of *Galba*, who forsook the precedents of his predecessors in stamping their coin with their own image, and imprinted thereupon his sealing ring left him by his forefathers, wherein was engraven, a Dog bending upon his female. I know not for what cause, the Star in the midst of Heaven whereunto the Sun cometh about the Calends of *July*, was termed *Canis* (a Dog) and the whole time of the appearance of that Star, which is about thirty dayes, should be called *Dog-dayes*; but only because then the heat of the Sun doth torment the bodies of men twice so much as at other times: whereupon they attribute that to the Star (which they call *Sirius*) which rather is to be attributed to the Sun during that time every year.

Others fable, that there is another Star close to him (called *Orion*) who was an excellent hunter, and after his death was placed among the Stars, and the Star *Canis* beside him was his hunting Dog: but by this

Star called of the *Egyptians, Solachim*; and of the *Grecians, Astrocynon*, cometh that *Egyptian Cynick* year which is accomplished but once in 1460 years. Unto this Star were offered many sacrifices of Dogs in ancient time, whereof there can be no cause in the world, as *Ovid* well noteth in these Verses.

> *Pro Cane sidereo Canis hic imponitur aræ:*
> *Et quare fiat nil nisi nomen habet.*

As among the *Carians*, whereupon came the proverb of *Caricum Sacrificium*, for they sacrificed a Dog in stead of a Goat, and the young puppies or whelpes were also accounted amongst the most availeable sacrifices, for the pacifying of their Idoll gods.

The *Romans* and *Grecians* had also a custom to sacrifice a Dog in their *Lycæan* and *Lupercal* feasts, which were kept for the honour of *Pan*, who defended their flocks from the Wolf, and this was performed in *February* yearly, either because that the Dogs were enemies to Wolves, or else for that by their barking, they draw them away in the night time from their City: or else, because they reckoned that a Dog was a pleasing beast to *Pan*, who was the keeper of Goats: so also the *Grecians* did offer a Dog to *Hecate* who hath three heads, one of a Horse, another of a Dog, and the third head in the midst of a wilde man: and the *Romans* to *Genetha*, for the safe custody and welfare of all their houshold affairs.

Their houshold Gods (called *Lares*) were pictured and declared to the people sitting in Dogs-skins, and Dogs sitting besides them, either because they thereby signified their duty to defend the house and houshold: or else as Dogs are terrors to Theeves and evill beasts, so these by their assistance were the punishers of wicked and evill persons: or rather that these *Lares* were wicked spirits prying into the affaires of every private houshold, whom God used as executioners of his wrathful displeasure upon godless men.

There were Dogs sacred in the Temple of *Æsculapius*, because he was nourished by their milk; and *Jupiter* himself was called *Cynegetes*; that is, a *Dog-leader*, because he taught the *Arcadians* first of all to hunt away noisome beasts by the help of Dogs: so also they sacrificed a Dog to *Mars*, because of the boldness of that creature. To conclude, such was the unmemorable vanity of the Heathens in their gods and sacrifices, as it rather deserveth perpetuall oblivion then remembrance, for they joyned the shapes of men and beasts together (saith *Arnobius*) to make gods, *Omnigenumque deum monstra & latrator Anubis*, such were their *Cynocephali, Ophiocephali, Anubis, Hecate*; that is as much to say, as half Men, half Dogs, half Serpents, but generally all Monsters: and for the many imaginary virtues the ancients have dreamed to be in Dogs, they also in many places have given unto them solemn funerals in their hallowed Cemiteries, and after they were dead they ceased not to magnifie them, as *Alexander*, which built a City for the honour of a Dog.

All this notwithstanding, many learned and wise men in all ages have reckoned a Dog but a base and an impudent creature: for the *Flamen Dialis* of *Jupiter* in *Rome*, was commanded to abstain from touching of Dogs, for the same reason that they were prohibited and not permitted to enter into the Castle of *Athens*, and Isle of *Delos*, because of their publick and shameless copulation: and also that no man might be terrified by their presence from supplication in the Temples. The foolishness of a Dog appeareth in this, that when a stone or other thing is cast at him, he followeth the stone and neglecteth the hand that threw it, according to the saying of the Poet:

> *Arripit ut lapidem catulus, morsuque fatigat,*
> *Nec percussori mutua damna facit;*
> *Sic plerique sinunt vexos elabier hostes,*
> *Et quos nulla gravant noxia, dente petunt.*

Likewise men of impudent wits, shameless behaviors in taking and eating meat, were called *Cynicks*; for which cause *Athenæus* speaketh unto *Cynicks* in this sort, You do not O *Cynici* lead abstinent and frugal lives, but resemble Dogs: and whereas this four-footed beast differeth from other creatures in four things, you only follow him in his viler and baser qualities, that is, in barking and license of railing, in voracity and nudity, without all commendation of men.

The impudency of a Dog is eminent in all cases to be understood, for which cause that audacious *Aristogiton* son of *Cidimachus* was called a Dog, and the Furies of ancient time were pictured by black

Dogs, and a Dog called *Erinnys*: *Cerberus* himself with his three heads signified the multiplicity of Devils; that is, a Lions, a Wolfs, and a fawning Dogs; one for the Earth, another for the Water, and the third for the Air: for which cause *Hercules* in slaying *Cerberus*, is said to overcome all temptation, vice and wickedness, for so did his three heads signifie. Other by the three heads understand the three times; by the Lion the time present; by the Wolf, the time past; and by the fawning Dog, the time to come.

It is delivered by Authors, that the root of Oliander, or else a Dogs tooth bound about the arme, do restrain the fury and rage of a Dog: also there is a certain little bone in the left side of a Toade (called *Apocynon*) for the virtue it hath in it against the violence of a Dog. It is reported by *Pliny*, that if a live Rat be put into the pottage of Dogs, after they have eaten thereof, they will never bark any more; and *Ælianus* affirmeth so much of the Weasils tail cut off from him alive, and carryed about a man; also if one carry about him a Dogs heart or liver, or the skin wherein Puppies lie in their dams belly (called the Secundine) the like effect or operation is attributed to them against the violence of Dogs.

There is a little black stone in *Nilus* about the bigness of a Bean, at first sight whereof a Dog will run away. Such as these I saw at *Lyons* in *France*, which they called Sea-beans, and they prescribed them to be hanged about a Nurses neck to encrease her milk. But to conclude the discourse of the baseness of a Dog, those two proverbs of holy Scripture, one of our Saviour Mat. 7. *Give not that which is holy to Dogs*; and the other of St. *Peter*, 2 Epistle Chap. 2. The Dog is returned to the vomit; do sufficiently convince, that they are emblems of vile, cursed, rayling, and filthy men; which esteem not holy things, but eat up again their own vomits.

The skins of Dogs are dressed for Gloves, and close Boots, the which are used by such as have Ulcerous and swelling Legs or Limbs, for by them the afflicted place receiveth a double relief; first, it resisteth the influent humors; and secondly, it is not exasperated with Woollen. The *Turkes* colour their Dogs tails with red, and it is a custom of Hunters to take Dogs and tie them in the Woods unto trees by their stones, for by crying they provoke the Panther to come unto them.

260

It is not to be doubted but that the flesh of Dogs is used for meat in many places, although the opinion of *Rasis* be true and consonant to reason, that all devouring creatures, as Dogs, Foxes, and Wolves, have no good flesh for meat, because they engender melancholy; and yet *Galen* thinketh, that it is like to the flesh of a Hare, especially young Whelpes were held among the *Romans* a delicate meat, and were used by their Priests; and among Whelpes they attributed most virtue to their flesh which were eaten before they did see, for by them came no evill humor at all, as is often set down in *Plautus*.

Peter Martyr and *Scaliger* do affirm of *Cozumella* and *Lucatana*, and other Islands of the new World, that the people there do eat a kind of Dog which cannot bark: These Dogs are vile to look upon like young Kids. The inhabitants of *Corsica*, which are fierce, angry, wilde, cruell, audacious, dissemblers, active and strong, do also feed upon Dogs, both wilde and tame: and it is thought that their meat is a little furtherance to their inclination, for such is the natural disposition of Dogs. And *Sciltbergerus* in the Book of Peregrinations affirmeth also, that the *Tartarians* in *Ibissibur* do after the same manner feed upon the flesh of Dogs: from hence it cometh, that men resembling a Dog in a plain forehead and narrow, are said to be foolish; in a smooth and stretched out flatterers; those which have great voices like a Ban-dog, are strong; they which rail much (like often barking Dogs) are of a doggish, angry disposition. He that hath a great head like a Dog, is witty; he which hath a little head like an Asses, is blockish; they which have fiery eyes like Dogs, are impudent and shameless: thin lips with narrow folding corners, in Dogs is a token of generosity, and in men of magnanimity: they whose teeth hang over their canine teeth, are also adjudged railers, and virulent speakers: and as *Carnarius* observeth, vain glorious braggarts. A wide mouth, betokeneth a cruell, mad, and wicked disposition; a sharpe nose, an angry minde; as a round, blunt, and solid Nose, signifieth a Lions stomach and worthiness. A sharpe chin, vain babling and wantonness; they which are small in their girting stead about their loins, do much love hunting.

Stobæus in his wicked discourse or dispraise of Women affirmeth, that the curst, sharp, smart, curious, dainty, clamorous, implacable and wanton-rowling-eyed Women, were derived from Dogs: and *Hesiode* to amend the matter saith, when *Jupiter* had fashioned Man out of the earth, he commanded *Mercury* to infuse into him a *Canine* minde, and a clamorous inclination: but the Proverb of *Solomon* Chap. 30. concludeth the excellency of a Dog saying, *There be three things which go pleasantly, and the fourth ordereth his pace aright: The Lion which is the strongest among beast, and feareth not the sight of any body: a hunting Dog strong in his loins, a Goat, and a King against whom there is no rising up:* by all which is deciphered a good King; for the Lion riseth not against beasts, except he be provoked; the Dog riseth not against his friends, but wilde beasts; and the He-goat goeth before his flock like a guide and keeper.

OF THE GRAY-HOUND, WITH A NARRATION OF ALL STRONG AND GREAT HUNTING DOGS.

AMONG the divers kinds of hunting Dogs, the Gray-hound or *Grecian* Dog, called *Thereuticos* or *Elatica* (by reason of his swiftness, strength and sagacity to follow and devour wilde beast of great stature) deserveth the first place; for such are the conditions of this Dog, as *Plato* hath observed, that he is reasonably sented to finde out, speedy and quick of foot to follow, and fierce and strong to take and overcome: and yet silent, coming upon his prey at unawares, according to the observation of *Gratius*;

Sic Canis illa suos taciturna supervenit hostes.

Like the Dogs of *Acarnania*, which set upon their game by stealth. Of these are the greatest Dogs of the world, which in this place are briefly to be remembred.

These have large bodies, little heads, beaked noses, but flat, broad faces above their eyes, long necks, but great next to their bodies, fiery eyes, broad backs, and most generous stomachs, both against all wilde beasts and men also. Their rage is so great against their prey, that sometimes for wrath they lose their eye-sight. They will not only set upon Buls, Boars, and such like beasts, but also upon Lions, which *Mantuan* noteth in this verse;

Et truculentus Helor certare leonibus audens.

The greatest dogs of this kind are in *India*, *Scythia*, and *Hircania*, and among the *Scythians* they joyn them with Asses in yoak for ordinary labour. The Dogs of *India* are conceived by Tygres, for the *Indians* will take divers females or Bitches, and fasten them to trees in woods where Tygres abide: whereunto the greedy ravening Tyger cometh, and instantly devoureth some one or two of them, if his lust do not restrain him, and then being so filled with meat (which thing Tygers feldom meet withall) presently he burneth in lust, and so limeth the living Bitches, who are apt to conceive by him: which being performed, he retireth to some secret place, and in the mean time the *Indians* take away the Bitches, of whom come these valorous Dogs, which retain the stomach and courage of their father, but the shape and proportion of their mother, yet do they not keep any of the first or second litter, for fear of their Tygrian stomachs, but make them away and reserve the third litter.

Of this kinde were the Dogs given to *Alexander* by the King of *Albania*, when he was going into *India*, and presented by an *Indian*, whom *Alexander* admired, and being desirous to try what vertue was

263

contained in so great a body, caused a Bore and a Hart to be turned out to him, and when he would not so much as stir at them, he turned Bears unto him, which likewise he disdained, and rose not from his kennel; wherewithal the King being moved, commanded the heavy and dull Beast (for so he termed him) to be hanged up: his keeper the *Indian* informed the King, that the Dog respected not such Beasts, but if he would turn out unto him a Lyon, he should see what he would do.

Immediately a Lyon was put unto him, at the first sight whereof he rose with speed (as if never before he saw his match or adversary worthy his strength) and bristling at him, made force upon him, and the Lyon likewise at the Dog; but at the last, the Dog took the chaps or snowt of the Lyon into his mouth, where he held him by main strength, untill he strangled him, do the Lyon what he could to the contrary; the King desirous to save the Lyons life, willed the Dog should be pulled off, but the labour of men and all their strength was too little, to loosen those ireful and deep biting teeth which he had fastned. Then the *Indian* informed the King, that except some violence were done unto the Dog to put him to extream pain, he would sooner dye then let go his hold; whereupon it was commanded to cut off a piece of the Dogs tail; but the Dog would not remove his teeth for that hurt: then one of his legs were likewise severed from his body, whereat the Dog seemed not apalled; after that another leg, and so consequently all four, whereby the trunck of his body fell to the ground, still holding the Lyons snowt within his mouth; and like the spirit of some malicious man, chusing rather to dye then spare his enemy. At the last, it was commanded to cut his head from the body, all which the angry Beast endured, and so left his bodiless head hanging fast to the Lyons jaws: whereat the King was wonderfully moved, and sorrowfully repented his rashness in destroying a Beast of so noble a spirit, which could not be daunted with the presence of the King of Beasts: chusing rather to leave his life, then depart from the true strength and magnanimity of minde. Which thing the *Indian* perceiving in the King, to mitigate the Kings sorrow, presented unto him four other Dogs of the same quantity and nature, by the gift whereof he put away his passion, and received reward with such a recompence, as well beseemed the dignity of such a King, and also the quality of such a present.

Pliny reporteth also, that one of these did fight with singular courage and policy with an Elephant: and having got hold on his side, never left till he overthrew the Beast, and perished underneath him. These Dogs grow to an exceeding great stature; and the next unto them are the *Albanian* Dogs. The *Arcadian* Dogs are said to be generated of Lyons. In *Canaria*, one of the Fortunate Islands, their Dogs are of an exceeding stature.

The Dogs of *Creet* are called *Diaponi*, and fight with wilde Boars: the Dogs of *Epirus* called *Chaonides*, of a City *Chaon*, are wonderfully great and fierce; they are likewise called *Molossi*, of the people of *Epirus* so tearmed, these are sained to be derived of the Dog of *Cephalus*, the first Gray-hound whom stories mention: and the Poets say, that this Gray-hound of *Cephalus*, was first of all fashioned by *Vulcan* in *Monesian* brass, and when he liked his proportion, he also quickned him with a soul, and gave him to *Iupiter* for a gift, who gave him away again to *Europa*, she also to *Minos*, *Minos* to *Procris*, and *Procris* gave it to *Cephalus*: his nature was so resistable, that he overtook all that he hunted, like the *Teumesian* Fox. Therefore *Iupiter* to avoid confusion, turned both the incomprehensible Beasts into stones. This *Moloshus*, or *Molossus* Dog, is also framed to attend the folds of Sheep, and doth defend them from Wolves and Theeves, whereof *Virgil* writeth thus:

> *Veloces Spartæ catulos acremque Molossum*
> *Pasce sero pingui, nunquam custodibus illis*
> *Nocturnum stabulis furem incursusque luporum*
> *Aut imparatos a tergo horrebis Iberos.*

These having taken hold, will hardly be taken off again, like the *Indian* and *Persian* Dogs, for which cause they are called *incommodestici*, that is, *modi nescii*, such as know no mean, which caused *Horace* to give counsel to keep them tyed up, saying:

> *Teneant acres lora molossos.*

The people of *Epirus* do use to buy these Dogs, when they dye, and of this kinde were the Dogs of *Scylla*, *Nicomedes*, and *Eupolides*. The *Hircanian* Dogs are the same with the *Indian*. The *Pœonian*, *Persian*, and *Median*, are called *Syntheroi*, that is companions, both of hunting, and fighting, as *Gratius* writeth:

——— *Indociliis dat prœlia Medus.*

The Dogs of *Locus*, and *Lacene*, are also very great, and fight with Bores. There are also a kinde of people called *Cynamolgi*, neer *India*, so called, because for one half of the year they live upon the milk of great Dogs, which they keep to defend their Countrey from the great oppression of wilde Cattel, which descend from the Woods and Mountains of *India* unto them yearly, from the Summer solstice to the middle of Winter, in great numbers or swarms, like Bees returning home to their Hives and Hony-combes: These Cattel set upon the people, and destroy them with their horns, except their Dogs be present with them, which are of great stomach and strength, that they easily tear the wilde Cattel in pieces, and then the people take such as be good for meat to themselves, and leave the other to their Dogs to feed upon: the residue of the year they not only hunt with these Dogs, but also milk the females, drinking it up like the milk of Sheep or Goats. These great Dogs have also devouted men, for when the servant of *Diogenes* the *Cynick*, ran away from his master, being taken again and brought to *Delphos*, for his punishment he was torn in pieces by Dogs. *Euripides* also is said to be slain by Dogs; whereupon came the proverb *Cunos dike*, a Dogs revenge: for King *Archelaus* had a certain Dog which ran away from him into *Thracia*, and the *Thracians* (as their manner was) offered the same Dog in sacrifice, the King hearing thereof, laid a punishment upon them for that offence, that by a certain day they should pay a talent; the people breaking day, suborned *Euripides* the Poet (who was a great favourite of the Kings) to mediate for them, for the release of that fine: whereunto the King yeelded: afterward as the said King returned from hunting, his Dogs stragling abroad, met with *Euripides*, and tore him in pieces, as if they sought revenge on him, for being bribed against their fellow which was slain by the *Thracians*. But concerning the death of this man, it is more probable, that the Dogs which killed him, were set on by *Aridæus* and *Cratenas*, two *Thessalian* Poets, his emulators and corrivals in Poetry, which for the advancement of their own credit, cared not in most savage and barbarous manner, to make away a better man then themselves. There were also other famous men which perished by Dogs, as *Actæon, Thrasus,* and *Linus*; of *Thrasus, Ovid* writeth thus;

> *Prædaque sis illis quibus est Laconia Delos*
> *Ante diem rapto non adeunda Thraso.*

And of *Linus* and *Actæon* in this manner;

> *Quique verecundæ speculantem membra Dianæ,*
> *Quique Crotopiaden diripuere Linum.*

Lucian that scoffing Apostate, who was first a Christian, and afterward endevoured all his wit to rail at Christian Religion, even as he lacerated and rent his first profession, so was he rent in pieces by Dogs; and *Heraclitus* the Philosopher of *Athens*, having been long sick, and under the hands of Physitians, he oftentimes anointed his body with Bugils sewet, and on a day having so anointed himself, lying abroad sleeping in the Sun, the Dogs came, and for the desire of the fat tore his body in pieces. I cannot here forget that memorable story of two Christian Martyrs, *Gorgonius* and *Dorotheus*, which were put to death under *Diocletian* in the ninth persecution, and when they were dead, their carkases were cast unto hungry Dogs of this kinde, kept for such purposes, yet would not the Dogs once so much as stir at them, or come neer to touch them; and because we may judge that the ravening nature of these creatures was restrained by divine power: We also read that when *Benignus* the Martyr, by the commandment of *Aurelian*, was also thrown alive to be devoured of these Dogs, he escaped as free from their teeth, as once *Daniel* did from the Lyons den. I may also adde unto these the Dogs of *Alania* and *Illyria*, called *Mastini*, who have their upper lips hang over their neather, and look fierce like Lyons, whom they resemble in neck, eyes, face, colour, and nails; falling upon Bears, and Boars, like that which *Anthologius* speaketh of, that leaped into the Sea after a *Dolphin*, and so perished; or that called *Lydia*, slain by a Boar; whose Epitaph *Martial* made as followeth:

Amphitheatrales inter nutrita magistros
*   Venatrix silvis aspera, blanda domi,*
Lydia dicebar, domino fidissima dextro,
*   Qui non Erigones mallet habere Canem,*
Nec qui Dictæa Cephalum de gente secutus,
*   Luciferæ pariter venit ad astra deæ.*
Non me longa dies, nec inutilis abstulit ætas,
*   Qualia Dulychio fata fuere cani.*
Fulmineo spumantis apri sum dente perempta,
*   Quantus erat Calydon, aut Erymanthe tuus.*
Nec queror, infernas quamvis cito rapta per umbras:
*   Non potui fato nobiliore mori.*

There be in *France* certain great Dogs (called *Auges*) which are brought out of *Great Britain*, to kill their Bears, Wolves, and wilde Boars; these are singularly swift and strong, and their leaders, the better to arm them against the teeth of other Beasts, cover some of their parts with thick clouts, and their necks with broad collars, or else made of Badgers skins. In *Gallia Narbon*, they call them *Limier*, and the *Polonians* call all made Dogs for the Wolf, and such like Beasts, *Vislu*: and peculiarly for the Bear and Bore, *Charzii*, for Hares and Fowl, *Pobicdnizcii*, and Dogs of a middle scantling betwixt the first and the second, *Psii*.

Gray-hounds are the least of these kindes, and yet as swift and fierce as any of the residue, refusing no kinde of Beast, if he be turned up thereunto, except the Porcupine, who casteth her sharp pens into the mouth of all Dogs. The best Gray-hound hath a long body, strong and reasonable great, a neat sharp head, and splendent eyes, a long mouth, and sharp teeth, little ears and thin gristles in them; a straight neck, and a broad and strong breast, his fore-legs straight and short, his hinder-legs long and straight, broad shoulders, round ribs, fleshy buttocks, but not fat, a long tail, strong and full of sinews, which *Nemesian* describeth elegantly in these verses;

———— ———— Sit cruribus altis.
Costarum sub fine decenter prona carinam:
Renibus ampla satis validis diductaque coras
Sit rigidis, multamque gerat sub pectore lato,

268

Quæ sensim rursus sicca se colligat alvo:
Cuique nimis molles fluitent in cursibus aures.
Elige tuno cursu facilem, facilemque recursu,
Dum superant vires, dum læto flore juventus.

Of this kinde, that is a way the best to be chosen among the whelps, which weigheth lightest: for it will be soonest at the game, and so hang upon the greater beasts hindering their swiftness, untill the stronger and heavier Dogs come to help: and therefore besides the marks, or necessary good parts in a Gray-hound already spoken of, it is requisite that he have large sides, and a broad midriffe or film about his heart, that so he may take his breath in and out more easily; a small belly, for if it be great, it will hinder his speedy course; likewise that he have long legs; thin and soft hairs; and these must the Hunter lead on the left hand if he be a foot, and on the right hand if he be on Horseback.

The best time to try them, and train them to their game, is at twelve months old, howbeit some hunt them at ten months, if they be males, and at eight months, if they be female; yet is it surest not to strain them, or permit them to run any long course till they be twenty months old, according to the old verse;

Libera tunc primum consuescant colla ligari,
Iam cum bis denos Phœbe reparaverit ortus,
Sed parvos vallis spatio septove novelli
Nec cursus virtute parem, &c.

Keep them also in the leam or slip while they are abroad, untill they see their course, I mean, the Hare or Deer, and loosen not a young Dog, till the game have been on foot a good season, lest if he be greedy of the prey he strain his limbs till they break. When the Hare is taken, divide some part thereof among your Dogs, that so they may be provoked to speed by the sweetness of the flesh.

The *Lacedemon* Gray-hound was the best breed, they were first bred of a Fox and a Dog, and therefore they were called *Alopecides*, these admit copulation in the eight moneth of their age, and sometime in the sixt, and so continue bearing as long as they live, bearing their burthen the sixth part of a year, that is, about sixty days, one or two, more or less; and they better conceive, and are more apt to procreation while they are kept in labour, then when they lie idle without hunting. And these *Lacedemon* Dogs differ in one thing from all other Dogs whatsoever, for whereas the male out-liveth in vulgar Dogs of all Countries the female, in these the female out-liveth the male, yet the male performeth his labour with more alacrity, although the female have the sharper sense of smelling.

The noblest kinde of Dogs or the Hare keep home, unless they be led abroad, and seldom bark: they are the best which have the longest necks, for which cause they use this artificial invention to stretch their necks; they dig a deep hole in the earth, wherein they set the Gray-hounds meat, who being hungry, thrusteth down his head to take it, but finding it to be past his reach, stretcheth his neck above the measure of nature, by custom whereof, his neck is very much lengthened. Other place the Gray-hound in a ditch, and his meat above him, and so he reacheth upward, which is more probable. It is the property of these Dogs to be angry with the lesser barking Curs, and they will not run after every trifling Beast, by secret instinct of nature, discerning what kinde of Beast is worthy or unworthy of their labour, disdaining to meddle with a little or vile creature. They are nourished with the same that the smaller hunting Dogs are; and it is better to feed them with milk then whay. There are of this kinde called *Veltri*, and in *Italian*, *Veltro*; which have been procreated by a Dog and Leopard, and they are accounted the swiftest of all other. The Gray-hounds which are most in request among the *Germans*, are called *Windspill*, alluding to compare their swiftness with the winde, the same are also called *Turkischwind* and *Hetzhund*, and *Falco* a *Falcon*, is a common name whereby they call these Dogs. The *French* make most account of such as are bred in the Mountain of *Dalmatia*, or in any other Mountains, especially of *Turkey*; for such have hard feet, long ears, and bristle tails.

There are in *England* and *Scotland*, two kindes of hunting Dogs, and no where else in all the world; the first kinde they call in *Scotland*, *Ane Rache*, and this is a foot-smelling creature, both of wilde Beasts, Birds, and Fishes also, which lie hid among the Rocks; the female hereof in *England*, is called a *Brache*. The second kinde is called in *Scotland*, a *Sluth-hound*, being a little greater then the hunting Hound; and in colour for the most part brown, or sandy-spotted. The sense of smelling is so quick in these, that they can follow the foot-steps of theeves, and persue them with violence untill they overtake them; and if the theef take the water, they cast in themselves also, and swim to the other side, where they finde out again afresh their former labour, untill they finde the thing they seek for: for this is common in the Borders of *England* and *Scotland*, where the people were wont to live much upon theft; and if the Dog brought his leader unto any house, where they may not be suffered to come in, they take it for granted, that there is both the stollen goods, and the theef also hidden.

The Hunting Hound of Scotland called Rache, and in English a Hound.

The Sluth-Hound of Scotland, called in Germany a Schlatthund.

THE ENGLISH BLOOD-HOUND.

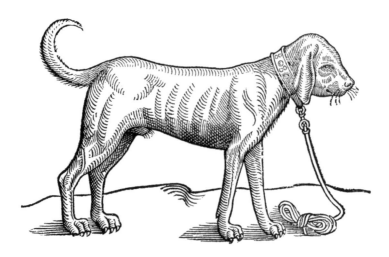

WE are to discourse of lesser hunting Dogs in particular, as we finde them remembred in any Histories & descriptions, Poets or other Authors, according to the several Countries of their breed and education; and first for the *British* Dogs, their nature and qualities hereafter you shall have in a several discourse by it self. The Blood-hound differeth nothing in quality from the *Scottish* Sluth-hound, saving they are greater in quantity, and not alway of one and the same colour; for among them they are sometime red, sanded, black, white, spotted, and of such colour as are other Hounds, but most commonly brown or red.

The vertue of smelling called in *Latine, Sagacitas,* is attributed to these as to the former hunting Hound, of whom we will first of all discourse, and for the qualities of this sense, which maketh the Beast admirable, *Plautus* seemeth to be of opinion, that it received this title from some Magicians or sage Wisards (called *Sagæ*) for this he saith, speaking of this Beast: *Ganem hanc esse quidein Magis par fuit: nasum ædepol sagax habet:* It is also attributed to Mice, not for smelling, but for the sense of their palace or taste; and also to Geese: In a Dog it is that sense which searcheth out and descryeth the rousts, fourms, and lodgings of wilde Beasts, as appeareth in this verrse of *Livius Andronicus.*

—— —— *Cum primis fida Canum vis*
Dirige oderisequos ad certa cubilia canes.

272

And for this cause it hath his proper Epithets, as *Odora canum vis, promissa canum vis, & naribus acres, & utilis: Pincianns* called this kinde *Plaudi*, for so did *Festus* before him, and the *Germans, Spurhund*; and *Leidthund, Iaghund*, because their ears are long, thin, and hanging down, and they differ not from vulgar Dogs in any other outward proportion, except only in their cry or barking voyce.

The nature of these is, being set on by the voyce and words of their leader, to cast about for the sitting of the Beast, and so having found it, with continual cry to follow after it till it be wearyed, without changing for any other; so that sometimes the Hunters themselves take up the Beast, at least wise the Hounds seldom fail to kill it. They seldom bark, except in their hunting chase; and then they follow their game through woods, thickets, thorns, and other difficult places, being alway obedient and attentive to their leaders voyce, so as they may not go forward when he forbiddeth, nor yet remain neer to the Hunters, whereunto they are framed by Art and discipline, rather then by any natural instinct.

The White Hounds are said to be the quickest sented and surest nosed, and therefore best for the Hare: the black ones for the Boar, and the red ones for the Hart and Roe: but hereunto I cannot agree, because their colour, (especially of the two later) are too like the game they hunt; although there can be nothing certain collected of their colour, yet is the black Hound harder and better able to endure cold, then the other which is white. In *Italy* they make account of the spotted one; especially white and yellowish, for they are quicker nosed: they must be kept tyed up till they hunt, yet so as they be let loose now and then a little to ease their bellies, for it is necessary that their kennel be kept sweet and dry.

It is questionable how to discern a Hound of excellent sense, (yet as *Blondus* saith) the square and flat nose is the best sign and index thereof: likewise a small head, having all his legs of equal length, his breast not deeper then his belly, and his back is plain to his tail, his eyes quick, his ears long hanging, but sometimes stand up: his tail nimble, and the beak of his nose alway to the earth, and especially such as are most silent or bark least.

There are some of that nature, who when they have found the Beast they will stand still untill their Hunter come, to whom in silence by their face, eye, and tail, they shew their game. Now you are to observe the

273

divers and variable disposition of Hounds in their finding out of the Beast: some, when they have found the footsteps go forward without any voyce or other shew of ear or tail. Again, another sort, when they have found the footings of the Beast, prick up their ear a little, but either bark, or wag their tails; other will wag their tail, but not move their ears, other again wring their faces, and draw their skins through over much intention, (like sorrowful persons) and so follow the sent, holding the tail immoveable.

There be some again, which do none of these, but wander up and down, barking about the surest marks, and confounding their own footsteps with the Beasts they hunt, or else forsake the way, and so run back again to the first head; but when they see the Hare, they tremble and are afraid, not daring to come near her, except she run away first: these with the other, which hinder the cunning labours of their colleagues, trusting to their feet, and running before their betters, deface the best mark, or else hunt counter (as they tearm it) take up any false sent for the truth, or which is more reprehensible, never forsake the high ways, and yet have not learned to hold their peace: unto these also you may adde those which cannot discern the footings or pricking of the Hare, yet will they run speedily when they see her, or else at the beginning set forth very hot, and afterward tyre, and give over lazily; all these are not to be admitted into the kennel of good Hunds.

But the good and approved Hounds on the contrary, when they have found the Hare, make shew thereof to the Hunter, by running more speedily, and with gesture of head, eyes, ears, and tail, winding to the Hares muse, never give over prosecution with a gallant noise, no not returning to their leaders, lest they lose advantage: they have good and hard feet, and are of stately stomacks, not giving over for any hate, and fear not the rocks or other mountain places, as the Poet expresseth:

> *Quæ laus prima canum? quibus est audacia præceps:*
> *Quæ nunc elatis rimantur naribus auras:*
> *Et perdunt clamore feram, dominumque vocando*
> *Insequitur tumulosque canis camposque per omnes.*
> *Venandi sagax virtus viresque sequendi,*
> *Et nunc demisso quærunt vestigia rostro.*

Increpitant quem si collatis effugit armis,
Noster in arte labor positus, spes omnis in illa, &c.

And therefore also it is good oftentimes to lead the Hounds to the Mountains for exercise of their feet, when you have no Hare or other Beast.

And whereas the nature of this Hare is, sometimes to leap and make headings, sometimes to tread softly, without any great impression in the earth, or sometimes to lye down and ever to leap or jump out & in to her own fourm or sitting, the poor Hound is so much the more busied and troubled to retain the small savour of her footings which she leaveth behinde her: for this cause also it is to be noted, that the Hound must be holp not only with the voyce, eye, and hand of the Hunter, but also with a seasonable time, for in frosty weather the savour congealeth and freezeth with the earth, so as you cannot hunt with any certainty untill the thaw thereof, or till the Sun arise.

Likewise if rain fall betwixt the going of the Hare and the hunting time, you cannot hunt till the water be dryed up, for the drops disperse the sent of the Hare, and the dry weather recollecteth it again. The Summer time also is not for hunting, by reason the heat of the earth consumeth the savour, and the night being then but short, the Hare travelleth but little, feeding only in the evening and morning. Likewise the fragrancy of every green herb yeeldeth such a savour, as doth not a little obliterate, and oversway the savour of the Beast: and therefore *Aristotle* in his Wonders, sheweth that in *Ætna* in the Summer time, there are such plenty of sweet smelling flowers, especially of Violets, which overcome the nostrils of the Hounds, so as in vain they follow the Hare. The best time therefore for hunting with these Hounds is the Autumn or fall of the leaf, because that then the odours of herbs are weakned, and the earth barer then at other times. The best manner to teach these Hounds, is to take a live Hare and trail her after you upon the earth, now one way, now another; and so having drawn it a convenient space, hide it in the earth; afterward set forth your Hound neer the trail, who taking winde, runneth to and fro neer the woods, fields, pastures, path-ways, and hedges, untill he finde which way the Hare is gone, but with a soft and gentle pace, untill at length coming neer the lodged Hare, he mendeth his pace, and bestirreth himself more speedily, leaping upon his prey like some Serpent, or as an arrow shot out of a Bow, and so tearing it in pieces or killing it with joy, loadeth himself with his conquest, and bringeth it to his Master with triumph, who must receive both Dog and it, with all tokens of love into his own bosome, which thing caused *Nemesian* to write thus;

> *Quæ freta si Morinum dubio refluentia ponto,*
> *O quanta est merces, & quantum impendia supra*
> *Si non ad speciem menturosque decores*
> *Protinus, hæc una est catulis jactura Britannis.*
> ——— *Diversa Britannia mittit*
> *Veloces, nostrique orbis venatibus aptos.*

There are divers Countrey Dogs like unto these, as the *Geloni* and *Gnosti*, which caused *Ovid* to reckon and call *Ichnobates* one of *Actæons* Dogs *Gnostus*: whom *Oppianus* compareth to the *Polypus* fish, which smelling in the waters the leaves of Olives, by the sent is drawn to the land to eat them. The *Spanish* Dogs whom the *French* call *Espagneulx*, have long ears, but not like a Braches, and by their noses hunt both Hares and Conies, they are not rough, but smooth haired. The *Tuscan* Dogs are commended by *Nemesian*; notwithstanding, they are not beautiful to look upon, having a deep shaggy hair, yet is their game not unpleasant.

> *Quin & Tuscorum uon est extrema voluptas*
> *Sæpe Canum: forma est illis licet obsita villo, &c.*
> *Haud tamen injucunda dabunt tibi munera prædæ, &c.*
> *Atque etiam leporum secreta cubilia monstrant.*

The *Umbrian* Dog is sharp nosed, but fearfull of his sport, as *Gratius* expresseth.

> ——— *Aut exigit Umber*
> *Nare sagax e calle feras,* ———
> *At fugit adversus idem quos efferent hostes,*
> *Tanta foret virtus; & tantum vellet in armis.*

The *Ætolian* Dogs have also excellent smelling noses, and are not slow or fearful, whom *Gratius* expresseth as followeth:

276

At clangore citat, quos nondum conspicit apros,
Ætola quæcunque Canis de stirpe (malignum
Officium) &c.
Seu frustra nimius properat furor, ——
Mirum quam celeres & quantum nare metentur:

The *French* Dogs are derived or propagated of the Dogs of Great *Britain*, and are swift and quick sented, but not all, for they have of divers kindes, as *Gratius* expresseth in these words;

Magnaque diversos extollit gloria Celtas.

They are very swift, and not sharp nosed, wherefore they are mingled in generation with the *Umbrian* Dogs, and therefore he celebrateth in many verses, the praise of the first Hunter (as he taketh him.) *Hagno Bæonius* and his Dog *Metagon*, and afterward the Dog *Petronius*: but it may be, that by *Metagon*, he meaneth the Dogs of *Lybia*, because there is a City of that name: and by *Petronius* the Dogs of *Italy*, for *Petronia* is a river that falleth into *Tiber*.

The *Grammarians* call a Dog engendered of a Hound, and an ordinary *French* Dog, *Vertagus*, a Tumbler: because he setteth himself to hunting, and bringeth his prey to his Master, whereupon *Martial* made this *Distichon*:

Non sibi, sed Domino venatur vertagus acer,
Illæsum leporem qui tibi dente seret.

The Water Spagnel.

277

Such be also other smelling Dogs, called in the *German* tongue (*Lochundle*) that is, Terriars or Beagles: these will set upon Foxes and Badgers in the earth, and by biting expel them out of their dens; whereof *Aristotle* reporteth a wonder, that one of them followed a Fox under the ground in *Bœotia*, and there made so great a noise by barking, that the Hunters went also into the Cave, where they saw many strange things which they related to the chief Magistrate.

Unto all these smelling Dogs, I may also adde the water Spagnel, called in *French, Barbeti*; and in *Germany* (*Wasserhund*:) who is taught by his Master to seek for things that are lost, (by words and tokens) and if he meet any person that hath taken them up, he ceaseth not to bay at him, and follow him till he appear in his Masters presence. These also will take water-fowl, and hunt Otters and Beavers, (although Hounds also will do the same) and watch the stroke of a Gun when the fowler shooteth, and instantly run into the water for the dead fowl, which they bring to their Master. They use to shear their hinder parts, that so they may be the less annoyed in swimming; whose figure is in the bottom of the former page described.

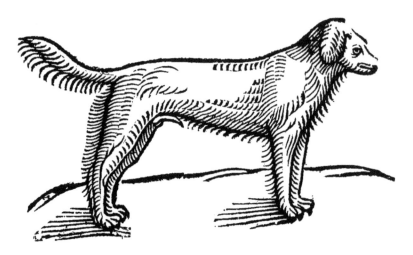

I may here also adde the Land-Spagnel, attending a Hawk, who hath no proper name in *English*, except from the fowl he hunteth; for which cause the *French* call them Dogs of the Quails; and the *Germans, Vogel-hund*, a fowl-Hound; although all Birds little fear Dogs, except the Bustard, who hath a heavy body, and is not able to fly far: yet are these taught by Falconers to retrive and raise Partridges, for they first take them into the fields, and shew them Partridges, whom after they have savoured twice or thrice, by custom they remember, and being uncoupled, will bestir themselves into all corners to finde them, being after a while very proud of employment, and very understanding in their game: they are for the most part white or spotted, with red or black: the *Polonians* call them (*Pobicnitzii*) and a Poet describeth them thus:

> *Nare sagax alius, campisque undisque volucres*
> *Quærit, & aduncus huc indefessus & illinc.*
> *Discurrit. ―――― ――――*

OF THE MIXT KINDE OF DOGS CALLED IN ENGLISH MANGRELS OR MONGRELS.

THOSE we call Mangrels, which though they be on both sides propagated by Dogs, yet are they not of one kinde: for as once Dogs coupled with Asses, Leopards, Lyons, Tygers, Apes, or any such Beasts, according to the old Verse;

> *Cani congeneres Lupus, Vulpes, Hyæna, Tygris.*

So now it is ordinary for the Gray-hound to couple with the Mastive, the Hound with the Gray-Hound, the Mastive with the Shepheards Dog, and the Shepheards Dog with any other Cur or Beagle: of these kindes we will now speak in order. And it is not to be omitted, that this commixtion of kindes have been invented by Hunters for the amendment of some natural fault, or defect they found in the *Monophyli*, that is, one single kinde, and so hereby they added some qualities to their kinde which they wanted before either in strength of body, or craft of wit: for they derive both of these from their Sires, wherefore *Oppianus* declareth, that in the commixtion of Dogs, the Ancients coupled together these kindes, the *Arcadians* with the *Eleians*, the *Cretensians* with the *Pæonians*, the *Carians* with the *Thracians*, the *Lacedemonians* with the *Tyrrhenian*, the *Sarmatian* with the *Iberian*,

279

and the *Gallican* Dogs with the *Umbrian*, because they want the quick sense of smelling: according to these verses:

> *Quondam inconsultis mater dabit Umbrica Gallis*
> *Sensum agilem, traxere animos de parte Gelonæ*
> *Hyrcano & vanæ tantum Calydonia linguæ*
> *Exibit vitium patre emendata Molosso.*

These Dogs so generated are peculiarly tearmed in *Greek, Hybris,* and *Hybrida,* as *Porphyrius,* writeth. The *French* Wolves were wont to have a Dog for their Captain or Leader, and it is ordinary for Wolves and Dogs to couple together, as by experience it hath been observed: And it is certain, that Mastive Dogs had their first beginning from this copulation, wherefore *Virgil* calleth one of these Dogs *Lycisca.*

> —— *Referensque lupum torvo ore Lycisca.*

The Dogs which are bred of *Thoes,* are commended for their rare qualities and understanding parts in the time of Wars, by *Hagnon Bœotius* in these verses;

> *Hic & semiferam thoum de sanguine prolem*
> *Seu norit voces, seu nudi ad pignora martis*
> *Et subiere astu, & parvis domuere lacertis*
> *Vulpina specie.* ——

The Dogs of *Hircania* do of themselves run into the Woods, (like adulterers) and seek out the Tygers to engender with them, which thing *Gratius* remembreth elegantly in many verses:

> —— *Ultroque gravis succedere Tigri*
> *Ausa canis, majore tulit de sanguine fœtum,*
> *Excutiet silva magnus pugnator adepta.*

In the rank of these Mangrels, I may adde in the next place those Dogs, called by the *Græcians, Symmaschi,* and *Somatophylakes,* because they attended upon men in their travels and labors to defend them, and are taught to fight for them, both against men and other beasts; wherein

280

they are as ready to take knowledge of violence offered to their Master, and also to revenge or hinder it, as a reasonable creature can be. These are called of the *Latines, Canes socii defensores*, sociable Dogs; of which there be two sorts, the first, is lesser, being of rough and long curled hair, his head covered with long hair, of a pleasant and tractable disposition, never going far from his Master, such was the Dog of *Tobit*, and the Dog of *Godrus* the Poet, called *Chiron*, whereof *Iuvenall* maketh mention; whose benevolence and ready minde toward their keepers and nourishers may appear by this story of *Colophonius*.

Upon a season, he with a Servant; and a Dog, went to a certain Mart to buy Merchandise, and as they travelled, his Servant which carryed the purse, diverted a little out of the way, to perform the work of nature, and the Dog followed him: which being done, he forgat to take up the Purse of mony that had fallen from him to the ground in that place, land so departed; the Dog seeing the purse, lay down beside it, and stirred not a foot; afterward the Master and man went forward, missing their Dog, and not their money, untill they came to their Mart or Fair, and then for want of mony were constrained to return back again without doing any farther thing: wherefore they resolved to go back again the same way they came, to see if they could hear of their mony, and at last when they came to the place where the servant had left the purse, there they found both Dog and mony together; the poor Cur scarse able to see or stand for hunger: when he saw his Master and the servant come unto him, he removed from the earth, but life not able to carry any longer in his body, at one and the same time in the presence of his friends and nourishers he also dyed, and took of them both his last farewel, through the faithful custody of their forgotten goods; for which it is apparent, that one part of their faithful disposition is, to keep their nourishers goods committed unto them, as shall be afterward more at large manifested.

Their watchful care over their Masters may appear also by these stories following, for the Dogs of *Xantippus* followed their Master to the Ship, at what time he was forewarned by the Oracle to depart out of *Athens*, by reason of the *Persians* war in *Greece*, and so they sailed with him to *Salamine*; and as they sailed by the way he commanded one of them to be cast into the Sea, who continued swimming after the Ship untill he dyed, for which cause his Master buryed him.

When *Gelon* the *Syracusan*, in his sleep had a fearful dream, that he was strucken with fire from Heaven, and with impression of fear, cryed out very lamentably: his Dog lying beside him, and thinking that some peril or theef was doing violence to his Master, he presently leaped up to the bed, and with scratching and barking awaked him, and so was he delivered from a horrible fear, by the barking of his Dog.

The *Tyrians* which have the best and the first purple in the world, are said in History to have it by the first occasion of *Hercules* Dog. *Hercules* falling in love with a Nymph called *Tyro*, and travelling toward her with his Dog, he saw the purple fish creeping upon a stone, the hungry Dog caught the fish to eat it and having devoured it, his lips were all dyed or coloured with the same: when the Virgin Nymph saw that colour upon the Dogs lips, she denyed the love of *Hercules*, except he could bring her a garment of that colour, whereupon the valiant man knowing by what occasion the Dogs lips received such a tincture, went and gathered all the purple fishes and worms he could finde, and pressing their blood out of them, therewithal coloured a garment, and gave it to the Nymph; for reward whereof, he possessed the Virgin, being by this means the first inventor of the *Phœnician* tincture.

Among these are to be remembred those loving Dogs, who either have fought for their Masters and so defended them, or else declared them that murdered their keepers, or that which is more admirable, leaped into the burning fires which consumed the dead bodies of their nourishers. Such an one was the Dog of *Calvus*, who being slain in a certain civil War at *Rome*, and his enemies coming about him to cut off his head, his poor Dog interposed his body betwixt the blows, and would not suffer any foe once to touch his Masters carcass, untill by more then six hundred souldiers the Dog was cut in pieces, so living and dying a most faithful companion and thankful friend to him that fed him.

The like was in a Dog of *Darius* the last King of the *Persians*, after he was slain by *Besus* and *Narbazanes* in the battel against *Alexander*, & so did the Dog of *Silanion* fight for his Master against theeves, and when he was slain, he departed not from the body, but kept it warily from

Dogs, Birds, or wilde Beasts, sitting upon his privy parts, and covering them untill the *Roman* Captains came and buryed it.

But most admirable was the love of a certain Dog to his Master punished with death, for the fact against *Germanicus*. Among other, this Dog would never go from the prison, and afterward when his Masters dead body was brought in the presence of many *Romans*, the Cur uttered most lamentable and sorrowful cryes; for which cause one of the company threw unto him some meat, to see if that would stop his mouth, and procure silence: but the poor Dog took up the meat, and carried to his masters mouth, not without the singular passion of the beholders: at last the body was taken up and cast into the river *Tiber*, the poor Dog leaped in after it, and endeavoured by all the means his weakness could afford, to keep it from sinking, in the presence of an innumerable multitude, which without tears could not look upon the loving care of this brute beast.

The Dogs of *Gelon, Hieron, Lysimachus, Pyrrhus* King of *Epirus, Polus* the *Tragœdian*, and *Theodorus*, leaped into the burning fires which consumed their masters dead bodies. *Nicias* a certain Hunter going abroad in the Woods, chanced to fall into a heap of burning coals, having no help about him but his Dogs, there he perished, yet they ran to the high ways, and ceased not with barking and apprehending the garments of passengers, to shew unto them some direful event: and at last one of the travellers followed the Dogs, and came to the place where they saw the man consumed, and by that conjectured the whole story. The like did the Dogs of *Marius Cæsarinus*, for by howling they procured company to draw him out of a deep Cave, whereinto he was fallen on Horse-back, and had there perished (being alone) except his Hounds had released him. But that Dogs will also bewray the murtherers of their friends and masters, these stories following, may evidently manifest.

As King *Pyrrhus* by chance travelled in his Countrey, he found a Dog keeping a dead corps, and he perceived that the Dog was almost pined, by tarrying about the body without all food, wherefore taking pity on the beast, he caused the body to be interred, and by giving the Dog his belly full of meat, he drew him to love him, and so led him away: afterward as *Pyrrhus* mustered his souldiers, and every one appeared in his presence, the Dog also being beside him, he saw the murtherers of his master, and so not containing himself, with voyce, tooth, and nail, he set upon them: the King suspecting that which followed, examined them if ever they had seen or known that Dog, they denied it, but the King not satisfied, charged them that surely they were the murtherers of the Dogs Master, (for the Dog all this while remained fierce against them) and never barked before their appearance, at the last their guilty consciences brake forth at their mouths and tongues end, and so confessed the whole matter.

The like was of two *French* Merchants which travelled together, and when they came into a certain Wood, one of them rose against the other for desire of his money, and so slew him and buryed him. His Dog would not depart from the place, but filled the Wood with howlings and cries; the murtherer went forward in his journey, the people and Inhabitants neer the said Wood, came and sound both the murdered corps, and also the Dog, which they took up and nourished till the Fair was done, and the Merchants returned, at which time they watched the high wayes, having the Dog with them, who seeing the murtherer, instantly made force at him without all provocation, as a man would do at his mortal enemy; which thing caused the people to apprehend him, who being examined, confessed the fact, and received condign punishment for so foul a deed.

To conclude this discourse with one memorable story more out of *Blondus*, who relateth that there was a certain woman neer *Paris*, who was beloved of two young men; one of them on a day took his staffe and his Dog, and went abroad (as it was thought, of purpose to go to his love) but it happened that by the way he was murthered and buryed, and the Dog would not depart from the grave of his Master: at the last, he being missed by his father and brethren, one of them went also to seek him, and see what was become of him, and so seeking, found the Dog lying upon his grave, who howled pitifully when he saw his Masters brother: the young man caused the ground to be opened, and so found the wounded corps of his brother, which he brought away, and caused to be buryed till the murtherer could be described: afterward in process of time, the Dog in the presence of the dead mans brethren espied the murtherer, and presently made force upon him very eagerly; which the brethren suspecting, apprehended him, and brought him before the Governours of the City, who examining him with all the policies they could invent, what should be the occasion, why the Dog should so eagerly fly upon him at all times, whensoever he was brought into his presence, could not get any confession of the fact from him: then the Magistrate adjudged, that the young Man and the Dog should combate together.

The Dog was covered with a dry sod skin in stead of armour, and the murtherer with a spear, and on his body a little thin linnen cloath, both came forth to fight, and so the man presently made force at the Dog, who leaping up to the face of the murtherer, took him fast by the throat, and overthrew him, whereat the wretch amazed, cryed out, saying, take pity on me you reverend Fathers, and pull off the Dog from my throat, and I will confess all; the which they performed, and he likewise declared the cause and manner of the whole murther, for which thing he was deservedly put to death. And thus far of the lesser sociable Dogs, now followeth the second kinde of the greater.

The greater sociable Dogs of defence are such as souldiers use in wars, or else are accustomed to keep houses or cattel. This kinde ought to be horrible, fierce, strange and unacquainted with all, except his Master, so that he be always at daggers drawing, and ready to fight with all which shall but lay their hands upon him, for which cause he ought to be instructed from his littering or infancy by art or continual discipline, to supply in him the defects of nature: let him be often provoked to wrath by boyes, and afterward as he groweth, let some stranger set upon him with weapon, as staffe or sword, with whom let him combate till he be wearied, and then let him tear some peece of the provokers garment, that so he may depart with a conceit of victory; after the fight tye him up fast, and suffer him not to straggle loose abroad, but feed him thus tyed up, so shall he in short time prove a strong defender, and eager combatant against all men and beasts which come to deal with him. Of this sort they nourish many in *Spain*, and in other places.

Such an one was the Dog of *Pheræus* the Tyrant of *Thessaly*, being a very great and fierce Beast, and hurtful to all, except them who fed him daily. He used to set this Dog at his chamber dore to watch and guard him when he slept, that who so ere was afraid of the Dog, might not approach near without exquisite torments. *Augeas* gave one of these to the Poet *Eupolis*, who taught him by many signes and gestures for the love of his meat, to observe his servant *Ephialtes*, if at any time he stole mony from him. And at the last, the wily Dog observed the servant so narrowly, that he found him robbing his Masters coffers: wherefore he instantly fell upon him and tore him in pieces. The which Dog afterward died for sorrow of his Masters death; whereupon *Ælianus* saith, that the place of his death in *Ægina* was called the place of mourning, to the day of his writing.

Nicomedes King of *Bythinia*, had one of these *Molossian* great Dogs, which he nourished very tenderly, and made it very familiar with himself: it fell out on a time, that this King being in dalliance with his wife *Ditizele*, in the presence of the Dog, and she again hanging about the Kings neck, kissing and provoking him to love with amorous gestures, the Dog thinking she had been offering some violence to his master the King, presently flew upon her, and with his teeth pulled her right shoulder from her body, and so left the amorous Queen to dye in the arms of her loving Husband: which thing caused the King to banish the Dog for ever out of his sight, for sorrow whereof he soon after dyed; but the Queen was most nobly buried at *Nicomedia* in a golden Sepulcher: the which was opened in the raign of the Emperour *Michael*, son of *Theophilus*, and there the womans body was found whole and not putrefied, being wrapped in a golden vesture, which taken off, and tryed in a furnace, yeelded above an hundred and thirteen pounds of pure gold.

When a Dragon was setting upon *Orpheus*, as he was occupied in hawking, by his Dogs his life was saved, and the Dragon devoured. And when *Cælius* one of the Senators of *Placentia* being sick, was set upon by certain lewd fellows, he received no wound till his Dog was slain.

There was never any thing more strange in the nature of Dogs, then that which happened at *Rhodes* besieged by the *Turk*, for the Dogs did there discern betwixt Christians and *Turks*; for towards the *Turks* they were most eager, furious, and unappeaseable but towards Christians, although unknown, most easie, peaceable and placidious, which thing caused a certain Poet to write thus:

His auxere fidem quos nostro fulva sub ære
Arva & Carpathii defendit littora ponti.
Pectora thoracum tunica sacrumque profano
Miratur, nutrit que Rhodes, custodibus illis
It noctes animosa Phalanx innexa trilici
Seligit, & blande exceptum deducit ad Urbem.

There were two hundred of these Dogs which brought the King of *Garamants* from banishment, rescuing him from all that resisted. The *Colophonian* and *Castabalensian*, or *Caspian* Dogs fought in all their battels: so likewise the *Cimbrian*, *Hircanian*, and *Magnesian* Dogs: these also the *Spaniards* used in *India*, to hunt out the naked people, falling upon them as fiercely as ever they would upon Bores, or other wilde Beasts, being pointed unto by their leaders finger. And for this cause was it, that *Vaschus* the *Spaniard* caused *Paera* an *Indian* Lord, and three other his wicked companions to be cast unto Dogs for their unnatural lust: but the Inhabitunts of *Caramair* and *Carib*, do drive astay the Dogs, for through their admirable activity in casting darts, they pierce the Dogs ere ever they come neer them with poysoned arrows. And thus much for the great warlike defensive Dogs.

In the next place followeth the Shepheards Dog, called by *Virgil*, *Pecuarius Canis*: and this cannot properly be tearmed a dumb keeper; for there is no creature that will more stir, bark, and move noise, then one of these against thief or wilde beast. They are also used by Heardsmen, Swine-heards, and Goat-Heards, to drive away all annoyances from their Cattel, and also to guide & govern them, in executing their masters pleasure upon signs given them, to which of the stragling Beasts they ought to make force. Neither is it requisite that this Dog be so large or nimble as is the Grey-hound, which is appointed for Deer and Hares.

But yet that he be strong, quick, ready, and understanding both for brauling and fighting, so as he may fear away and also follow (if need be) the ravening Wolf, and take away the prey out of his mouth; wherefore a square proportion of body is requisite in these Beasts, and a tolerable lightness of foot, such as is the Village Dog, used only to keep houses, and hereof also they are the best, who have the greatest or loudest barking voyces, and are not apt to leap upon every stranger or beast they see, but reserve their strength till the just time of imployment.

They approve also in this kinde above all other, the white colour; because in the night time they are the more easily discerned from the Wolf, or other noisome beast; for many times it falleth out, that the Shepheard in the twy-light, striketh his Dog in stead of the Wolf: these ought to be well faced, black or dusky eyes, and correspondent nostrils of the same colour with their eyes, black ruddy lips, a crooked camoyse nose, a flat chap with two great broches, or long straight sharp teeth growing out thereof, covered with their lips, a great head, great ears, a broad brest, a thick neck; broad and solid shoulders, straight legs, yet rather bending inward then standing outward; great and thick feet, hard crooked nails, a thick tail which groweth lesser to the end thereof, then at the first joint next the body, and the body all rugged with hair, for that maketh the Dog more terrible; and then also it is requisite that he be provided of the best breed, neither buy him of a Hunter (for such an one will be gone at the sight of a Deer or Hare) nor yet of a Butcher, for it will be sluggish; therefore take him young, and bring him up continually to attend Sheep, for so will he be most ready that is trained up among Shepherds.

They use also to cover their throat and neck with large broad collars, pricked through with nails, for else if the wilde beast bite them in those places, the Dog is easily killed: but being bitten at any other place he quickly avoideth the wound. The love of such to the Cattel they keep is very great, especially to Sheep; for when *Publius Aufidius Pontianus*, bought certain flocks of Sheep in the farthest part of *Umbria*, and brought Shepherds with him to drive them home; with whom the dogs went along unto *Heraclea*, and the *Metapontine* coasts, where the drovers left the Cattel; the Dogs for love of the Sheep yet continued and attended them, without regard of any man, and forraged in the fields for Rats and Mice to eat, untill at length they grew weary and lean, and so returned back again unto *Umbria* alone, without the conduct of men, to their first Masters, being many daies journey from them.

It is good to keep many of these together, at the least two for every flock, that so when one of them is hurt or sick, the herd be not destitute; and it is also good to have these male and female, yet some use to geld these, thinking that for this cause they will the more vigilantly attend the flock: howbeit I cannot assent hereunto, because they are too gentle and lesse eager when they want their stones. They are to be taken from their Dam at two moneths old, and not before: and it is not good to give them hot meat, for that wil encrease in them madness, neither must they taste any of the dead carkasses of the Cattel, lest that cause them to fall upon the living; for when once they have taken a smatch of their bloud or flesh, you shall seldom reclaime them from that devouring appetite. The understanding of these Shepherds Dogs is very great, (especially in *England*) for the Shepherds will there leave their Dogs alone with the flocks, and they are taught by custom, to keep the Sheep within the compass of their pasture, and discern betwixt grasse and Corn, for when they see the Sheep fall upon the Corn, they run and drive them away from that forbidden fruit of their own accord; and they likewise keep very safely their Masters garments and victuals from all annoyance untill their return. There is in *Xenophon* a complaint of the Sheep to the Shepherds concerning these Dogs: We marvel (said the Sheep) at thee, that seeing we yeeld thee milk, Lambs, and Cheese, whereupon thou feedest; nevertheless thou givest unto us nothing but that which groweth out of the earth, which we gather by our own industry; and whereas the Dog doth none of all these, him thou feedest with thine own hand, and bread from thine own trencher. The Dog hearing this complaint of the Sheep, replyed, That his reward at the Shepherds hand was just, and no more then he deserved, for (said he) I look unto you, and watch you from the ravening Wolf, and pilfering Theef, so as if once I forsake you, then it will not be safe for you to walke in your Pastures, for perill of death: whereunto the Sheep yeelded, and not replyed to the reasonable answer of so unreasonable a beast; and this complaint you must remember was uttered when Sheep could speak, as well as men, or else it noteth the foolish murmuring of some vulgar persons, against the chief Ministers of state, that are liberally rewarded by the Princes own hands, for their watchful custody of the Common-wealth. And thus much for the Shepherds Dog.

OF THE VILLAGE-DOG, OR HOUSE-KEEPER.

This Village Dog ought to be fatter and bigger then the Shepherds Dog, of an elegant, square and strong body, being black coloured, and great mouthed, or barking bigly, that so he may the more terrifie the Theef, both by day and night, for in the night the beast may seize upon the robber before he discern his black skin, and therefore a spotted, branded, party coloured Dog is not approved. His head ought to be the greatest part of his body, having great ears hanging down, and black eyes in his head, a broad breast, thick neck, large shoulders, strong legs, a rough hair, short tail, and great nails: his disposition must not be too fierce, nor yet too familiar, for so he will faun upon the Theef as well as his Masters friend. Yet is it good that sometime he rise against the household servants, and alway against strangers, and such they must be as can wind a stranger afar off, and descry him to his Master by barking as by a watch-word, and setting upon him, when he approcheth neer if he be provoked. *Blondus* commendeth in this kinde, such as sleep with one eye open and the other shaaut, so as any small noise or stir wake and raise him. It is not good to keep many of these curst Dogs together, and them few which be kept must be tyed up in the day time, that so they may be more vigilant in the night when they are let loose. There are of this kind which Mariners take with them to Sea, to preserve their goods on Ship-board, they chuse them of the greatest bodies and lowdest voice, like the *Croatian* Dog, resembling in hair and bigness, and such asare very watchful, according to the saying of the Poet:

> *Exagitant & lar, & turba Diania fures,*
> *Pervigilantque lares, pervigilantque Canes.*

And such also they nourish in Towers and Temples; in Towers, that so they may descry the approaching enemy when the Souldiers are asleep; for which cause, Dogs seen in sleep, signifie the careful and watchful wise, servants, or Souldiers, which foresee dangers and preserve publick and private good.

There was in *Italy* a Temple of *Pallas*, wherein were reserved the axes, instruments, and armour of *Diomedes* and his Colleagues, the which

Temple was kept by Dogs whose nature was (as the Author saith) that when *Grecians* came to that Temple, they would faun upon them as if they knew them; but if any other Countreymen came, they shewed themselves wilde, fierce, and angry against them. The like thing is reported of a Temple of *Vulcan* in *Ætna*, wherein was preserved a perpetuall and unquenchable fire, for the watching whereof, were Dogs designed; who would faun and gently flatter upon all those which came chastly and religiously to worship there, leading them into the Temple like the familiars of their God; but upon wicked and evill disposed leud persons, they barked and raged, if once they endevoured so much as to enter either the Wood or Temple; but the true cause hereof was, the imposture of some impure and deceitful, unclean, diabolical spirits. And by the like instinct, *Scipio Africanus* was wont to enter into the Capitol, and command the Chappel of *Jupiter* to be opened to him, at whom no one of the Keepers Dogs would ever stir, which caused the Men keepers of the Temple much to marvel, whereas they would rage fiercely against all other: whereupon *Stroza* made these Verses, falsly imputing this demonical illusion to divine revelation.

> *Quid tacitos linquam quos veri haud nescia Crete*
> *Nec semper mendax, ait aurea templa tuentes,*
> *Parcereque haud ulli solitos, (mirabile dictu)*
> *Docta Tyanæi Aratos senioris adora*
> *Non magico cantu, sed quod divinitus illis*
> *Insita vis animo, virtutis gnara latentis.*

The like strange thing is reported of a Temple or Church in *Cracovia*, dedicated to the *Virgin Mary*, wherein every night are an assembly of Dogs, which unto this day (saith the Author) meet voluntarily at an appointed hour, for the custody of the Temple, and those ornaments which are preserved therein against Theeves and Robbers: and if it fortune any of the Dogs be negligent and slack at the hour aforesaid, then will he bark about the Church untill he be let in, but his fellowes take punishment of him, and fall on him, biting and rending his skin, yea sometime killing him; and these Dogs have a set diet or allowance of dinner, from the Canons and Preachers of the Church, which they duely observe without breach of order; for to day two of them will goe to one Canons house, and two to anothers, and so likewise all the residue in turnes successively visit the several houses within the Cloister yard, never going twice together to one house, nor preventing the refection of their fellowes; and the story is reported by *Antonius Schnebergerus* for certain truth, upon his own knowledge.

OF THE MIMICK, OR GETULIAN-DOG, AND THE LITTLE MELITÆAN-DOGS OF GENTLEWOMEN.

THERE is also in *England* two other sorts of Dogs, the figure of the first is here expressed, being apt to imitate all things it seeth, for which cause some have thought that it was conceived by an Ape; for in wit and disposition it resembleth an Ape, but in face sharpe and black like a Hedge-hog, having a short recurved body, very long legs, shaggie hair, and a short tail: this is called of some (*Canis Lucernarius*) these being brought up with Apes in their youth, learn very admirable and strange feats, whereof there were great plenty in *Egypt* in the time of King *Ptolemy*, which were taught to leap and play, and dance, at the hearing of musick, and in many poor mens houses they served in stead of servants for divers uses.

These are also used by Players and Puppet-Mimicks to work strange tricks, for the sight whereof they get much money: such an one was the

Mimicks dog, of which *Plutarch* writeth that he saw in a publick spectacle at *Rome* before the Emperor *Vespasian*. The Dog was taught to act a play, wherein were contained many persons parts, I mean the affections of many other Dogs: at last there was given him a piece of bread, wherein, as was said, was poison, having virtue to procure a dead sleep, which he received and swallowed: and presently after the eating thereof he began to reel and stagger to and fro like a drunken man, and fell down to the ground, as if he had been dead, and so lay a good space not stirring foot nor limb, being drawn up and down by divers persons, according as the gesture of the Play he acted did require, but when he perceived by the time and other signes that it was requisite to arise, he first opened his eyes, and lift up his head a little, then stretched forth himself like as one doth when he riseth from sleep; at the last up he getteth and runneth to him to whom that part belonged, not without the joy and good content of *Cæsar* and all other the beholders.

To this may be added another story of a certain *Italian* about the year 1403 called *Andrew*, who had a red Dog with him of strange feats, and yet he was blind. For standing in the Market place, compassed about with a circle of many people, there were brought by the standers by many Rings, Jewels, Bracelets and pieces of gold and silver, and there within the circle were covered with earth, then the Dog was bid to seek them out, who with his nose and feet did presently find and discover them; then was he also commanded to give to every one his own Ring, Jewel, Bracelet, or money, which the blind Dog did perform directly without stay or doubt. Afterward the standers by, gave unto him divers pieces of coin, stamped with the images of sundry Princes, and then one called for a piece of *English* money, and the Dog delivered him a piece, another for the Emperors coin, and the Dog delivered him a piece thereof; and so consequently every Princes coin by name, till all was restored: and this story is recorded by *Abbus Urspergensis*, whereupon the common people said, the Dog was a Devill or else possessed with some Pythonical spirit: and so much for this Dog.

There is a Town in *Pachynus*, a Promontory of *Sicily* (called *Melita*) from whence are transported many fine little Dogs called, *Melitæi Canes*, they were accounted the Jewels of Women, but now the said

Town is possessed by Fisher-men, and there is no such reckoning made of those tender little Dogs, for these are not bigger then common Ferrets, or Weasils, yet are they not small in understanding, nor mutable in their love to men: for which cause they are also nourished tenderly for pleasure; whereupon came the proverb, *Militæa Catella*, for one nourished for pleasure, and *Canis digna throno*, because Princes hold them in their hands sitting upon their estate.

Theodorus the tumbler and dancer had one of these, which loved him so well, that at his death he leaped into the fire after his body. Now a dayes, they have sound another breed of little Dogs in all Nations, beside the Melitæan Dogs, either made so by art, as inclosing their bodies in the earth when they are Whelps, so as they cannot grow great, by reason of the place, or else, lessening and impayring their growth, by some kind of meat or nourishment. These are called in *Germany, Bracken Schosshundle* and *Gutschenhundle*; the *Italians, Bottolo*; other Nations have no common name for this kind that I know. *Martial* made this Distichon of a little *French* Dog; for about *Lions* in *France* there are store of this kinde, and are sold very dear; sometimes for ten Crowns, and sometimes for more.

> *Delicias parvæ si vis audire catellæ,*
> *Narranti brevis est pagina tota mihi.*

They are not above a foot, or half a foot long, and alway the lesser the more delicate and precious. Their head like the head of a Mouse but greater, their snowt sharp, their ears like the ears of a Cony, short legs, little feet, long tail, and white colour, and the hairs about the shoulders longer then ordinary, is most commended. They are of pleasant disposition, and will leap and bite without pinching, and bark prettily, and some of them are taught to stand upright holding up their fore legs like hands; other to fetch and carry in their mouths, that which is cast unto them.

There be some wanton women which admit them to their beds, and bring up their young ones in their own bosomes, for they are so tender, that they seldom bring above one at a time, but they lose their life. It was reported that when *Grego* in *Syracuse* was to go from home among other Gossips, she gave her maid charge of two things, one that she should look to her childe when it cryed, the other that she should keep the little Dog within doors.

Publius had a little Dog (called *Issa*) having about the neck two silver bels, upon a silken Collar, which for the neatness thereof, seemed rather to be a picture then a creature; whereof *Martial* made this elegant Epigram, comprehending the rare voice and other gestures in it.

Issa est puriot osculo columbæ,	*Sed blando pede suscit at toroque*
Issa est blandior omnibus puellis,	*Deponi monet, & rogat levari.*
Issa est carior Indicis lapillis,	*Caste tantus inest pudor catellæ.*
Issa est deliciæ catella Publii.	*Hanc ne lux rapiut suprema totam,*
Hanc ut, si queritur, loqui pulabis,	*Pictam Publius exprimit tabella,*
Sentit tristi tiamque gaudiumque.	*In qua tam similem vibebis Issam,*
Collo nexa cubat capitque somnos,	*Ut sit tam similis sibi nec ipsa,*
Ut suspiria nulla sentiantur,	*Issam denique pone cum tabella,*
Et desiderio coacta ventris	*Aut utramque putabis esse veram,*
Gutta pallia, non fefellit ulla.	*Aut utramque putabis esse pictam.*

Marcellus Empiricus reciteth a certain charm, made of the rinde of a wilde Figtree, held to the Spleen or Liver of a little Dog, and afterward hanged up in the smoak to dry, and pray that as the rind or bark dryeth, so the Liver or Spleen of the Dog may never grow; and thereupon the Dog (saith that foolish Emperick) shall never grow greater, then it was at the time that the bark was hanged up to drying. To let this trifle go, I will end the discourse of these little Dogs with one story of their love and understanding.

There was a certain noble Woman in *Sicily*, which understanding her husband was gone a long journey from home, sent to a lover (I should say an Adulterer) she had, who came, and by bribery and money given to her servants, she admitted him to her bed, but yet privately, more for fear of punishment, then care of modesty; and yet for all her craft, she mistrusted not her little Dog, who did see every day where she locked up this Adulterer: at last, her husband came home, before her lover was avoided, and in the night the little Dog seeing his true Master returned home, ran barking to the door and leaped up thereupon (within which the Whoremonger was hidden) and this he did oftentimes together, fauning and scraping his Lord and Master also; in so much as he mistrusted (and that justly) some strange event: at last, he brake open the door, and found the Adulterer ready armed with his sword, wherewithal he slew the good man of the house unawares; and so enjoyed the Adulterate woman for his wife: for Murther followeth if it go not before Adultery. This story is related by *Ælianus* to set forth a virtue of these little Dogs, how they observe the actions of them that nourish them, and also some descretion betwixt good and evill.

The Dogs of *Egypt* are most fearful of all other, and their custome is to run and drink, or drink of the River *Nilus* running, for fear of the Crocodiles: whereupon came the Proverb, of a man that did any thing slightly or hastily, *Ut Canise Nilo bibit. Alcibiades* had a Dog which he would not sell under 28 thousand Sesterces, that is, seven hundred *French* Crowns; it was a goodly and beautiful Dog, yet he cut off his tail, whereof he gave no other reason, being demanded why he so blemished his beast, but only that by that fact he might give occasion to the *Athenians* to talke of him.

The Dogs of *Caramania* can never be tamed, for their men also are wilde and live without all Law and Civility: and thus much of Dogs in special. In the next place I thought good to insert into this story the Treatise of *English* Dogs, first of all written in *Latin* by that famous Doctor in Physick *John Cay*, and since translated by *A. F.* and directed to that noble *Gesner*, which is this that followeth, that so the Reader may chuse whether of both to affect best.

THE PREAMBLE OR ENTRANCE INTO THE TREATISE FOLLOWING.

I wrote unto you (well beloved friend *Gesner*) not many years past, a manifold history, containing the divers forms and figures of Beasts, Birds, and fishes, the sundry shapes of Plants, and the fashions of Herbs, &c.

I wrote moreover unto you severally, a certain abridgement of Dogs, which in your discourse upon the formes of Beasts in the second order of milde and tamable beasts, where you make mention of Scottish Dogs, and in the winding up of your Letter written and directed to Doctor *Turner*, comprehending a Catalogue or rehearsal of your Books not yet extant, you promised to set forth in print; and openly to publish in the face of the world among such your works as are not yet come abroad to light and sight. But because certain circumstances were wanting in my breviary of *English* Dogs (as seemed unto me) I stayed the publication of the same, making promise to send another abroad, which might be committed to the hands, the eyes, the ears, the minds, and the judgements of the Readers.

Wherefore that I might perform that precisely, which I promised solemnly, accomplish my determination, and satisfie your expectation: which are a man desirous and capable of all kind of knowledge, and very earnest to be acquainted with all experiments: I will expresse and declare in due order, the grand and general kind of *English* Dogs, the difference of them, the use, the properties, and the divers natures of the same, making a tripartite division in this sort and manner. All *English* Dogs be either of a gentle kinde serving the game, a homely kinde apt for sundry necessary uses, or a currish kind, meet for many toies.

Of these three sorts or kinds so mean I to entreat, that the first in the first place, the last in the last room, and the middle sort in the middle seat be handled. I call them universally all by the name of *English* Dogs, as well because *England* only, as it hath in it *English* Dogs, so it is not with the *Scotish*, as also for that we are inclined and delighted with the noble game of hunting, for we *Englishmen* are addicted and given to that exercise and painful pastime of pleasure, as well for the plenty of flesh which our Parks and Forrests do foster, as also for the opportunity and convenient leisure which we obtain; both which the *Scots* want. Wherefore seeing that the whole estate of kindly hunting consisteth principally in these two points, in chasing the beast that is in hunting, or in taking the bird that is in fowling; It is necessary and requisite to understand that there are two sorts of Dogs by whose means the feats within specified are wrought, and these practises of activity cunningly and curiously compassed, by two kindes of Dogs, one which rouzeth the beast and continueth the chase, another which springeth the bird, and bewrayeth the flight by pursute. Both which kinds are termed of the *Latins* by one common name, that is, *Canes Venatici*, hunting Dogs. But because we *Englishmen* make a difference between hunting and fowling, for they are called by these several words, *Venatio*, *& Aucupium*, so they term the Dogs whom they use in these sundry games by dives names, as those which serve for the beast, are called *Venatici*, the other which are used for the fowl are called *Aucupaorii*.

The first kinde called *Venatici* I divide into five sorts, the first in perfect smelling, the second in quick spying, the third in swiftness and quickness, the fourth in smelling and nimbleness, the fifth in subtilty and deceitfulness, herein these five sorts excell.

OF THE DOG CALLED A HARIER; IN LATIN, LEVERARIUS.

THAT kinde of Dog whom nature hath endued with the virtue of smelling, whose property it is to use a lustiness, a readiness, and a couragiousness in hunting, and draweth into his nostrils the air or sent of the beast pursued and followed, we call by this word *Sagax*, the *Grecians* by this word *Ichneuten* of tracing or chasing by the foot, or *Rinelaten*, of the nostrils, which be the instruments of smelling. We may know these kinde of Dogs by their long, large and bagging lips, by their hanging ears, reaching down both sides of their chaps, and by the indifferent and measurable proportion of their making. This sort of Dogs we call *Leverarios, Hariers*, that I may comprise the whole number of them in certain specialities, and apply to them their proper and peculiar names, for so much as they cannot all be reduced and brought under one sort, considering both the sundry uses of them, and the difference of their service whereto they be appointed. Some for the Hare, the Fox, the Wolf, the Hart, the Buck, the Badger, the Otter, the Polcat, the Lobster, the Weasell, the Cony, *&c.* Some for one thing and some for another.

As for the Cony, whom we have lastly set down, we use not to hunt, but rather to take it, sometime with the net, sometime with a Ferret, and thus every several sort is notable and excellent in his natural quality and appointed practise. Among these sundry sorts, there be some which are apt to hunt two divers beasts, as the Fox other whiles, and other whiles the Hare, but they hunt not with such towardness and good luck after them, as they do that whereunto nature hath formed and framed them, not only in external composition and making, but also in inward faculties and conditions, for they swarve oftentimes, and do otherwise then they should.

OF THE DOG CALLED A TERRAR; IN LATIN, TERRARIUS.

ANOTHER sort there is which hunteth the Fox, and the Badger, or Gray only, whom we cal *Terrars*, because they (after the manner and custom of Ferrets in searching for Conies) creep into the ground, and by that means make afraid, nip, and bite the Fox and the Badger in such sort, that either they tear them in pieces with their teeth, being in the bosom of the earth, or else hale and pull them perforce out of their lurking Angles, darke dungeons, and close caves, or at the least through conceived fear, drive them out of their hollow harbors, in so much that they are compelled to prepare speedy flight, and being desirous of the next (albeit not the safest) refuge, are otherwise taken and intrapped with snares and nets laid over holes to the same purpose. But these be the least in that kinde called *Sagaces*.

OF THE DOG CALLED A BLOOD-HOUND; IN LATIN, SANGUINARIUS.

THE greater sort which serve to hunt, having lips of a large size, and eares of no small length, do not only chase the beast whiles it liveth (as the other do of whom mention above is made) but being dead also by any manner of casualty, make recourse to the place where it lyeth, having in this point an assured and infallible guide; namely, the sent and savour of the bloud sprinkled here and there upon the ground. For whether the beast being wounded, doth notwithstanding enjoy life, and escapeth the hands of the huntsman, or whether the said beast being slain is conveyed cleanly out of the Park (so that there be some signification of bloud shed) these Dogs with no lesse facility and easiness, then avidity and greediness can disclose and bewray the same by smelling, applying to their pursuite, agility and nimbleness, without tediousness; for which consideration, of a singular specialty they deserved to be called *Sanguinarii* Blood-hounds. And albeit peradventure it may chance, (as whether it chanceth seldom or sometime I am ignorant) that a piece of flesh be subtilly stolne, and cunningly conveyed away with such provisoes and precaveats, as thereby all appearance of bloud is either prevented, excluded, or concealed, yet these kinde of Dogs by certain direction of an inward assured notice and privie mark, pursue the deed-dooers, through long lanes, crooked reaches, and weary wayes, without wandering awry out of the limits of the land whereon these desperate purloiners prepared their speedy passage. Yea, the natures of these Dogs is such, and so effectual is their foresight, that they can bewray, separate, and pick them out from among an infinite multitude and an innumerable company, creep they never so far into the thickest throng, they will finde him out notwithstanding he lie hidden in wilde Woods, in close and overgrowen Groves, and lurk in hollow holes apt to harbour such ungracious guests.

Moreover, although they should passe over the water, thinking thereby to avoid the pursuite of the Hounds, yet will not these Dogs give over their attempt, but presuming to swim through the stream, persevere in their pursuite, and when they be arrived and gotten the further banck, they hunt up and down, to and fro run they, from place to place shift they, until they have attained to that plot of ground where they passed over. And this is their practise, if perdy they cannot at the first time smelling, finde out the way which the deed-doers took to escape. So at length get they that by art, cunning, and diligent endevour, which by fortune and luck they cannot otherwise overcome. In so much as it seemeth worthily and wisely written by *Ælianus* in his 6. Book and 39. Chapter, *To enthumaticon kai dialecticon*, to be as it were naturally instilled into these kind of Dogs. For they will not pause or breathe forth from their pursuite untill such time as they be apprehended and taken which committed the fact.

The owners of such Hounds use to keep them in close and dark kennels in the day, and let them loose at liberty in the night season, to the intent that they might with more courage and boldness practise to follow the fellon in the evening and solitary hours of darkness, when such ill disposed varlets are principally purposed to play their impudent pranks. These Hounds (upon whom this present portion of our treatise runneth) when they are to follow such fellowes as we have before rehearsed, use not that liberty to range at will, which they have otherwise when they are in game, (except upon necessary occasion whereon dependeth an urgent and effectual perswasion) when such purloyners make speedy way in flight, but being restrained and drawn back from running at random with the leame, the end whereof the owner holding in his hand is led, guided and directed with such swiftness and slowness (whether he go on foot, or whether he ride on horseback) as he himself in heart would wish for the more easie apprehension of these venturous varlets.

In the borders of *England* and *Scotland*, (the often and accustomed stealing of Cattel so procuring) these kind of Dogs are very much used, and they are taught and trained up first of all to hunt Cattel, as well of the smaller as of the greater grouth, and afterwards (that quality relinquished and left) they are learned to pursue such pestilent persons as plant their pleasure in such practises of purloining as we have already declared. Of this kind there is none that taketh the Water naturally, except it please you so to suppose of them which follow the Otter, which sometimes haunt the land, and sometime useth the water. And yet nevertheless all the kinde of them boyling and broyling with greedy desire of the prey which by swimming passeth through river and flood, plunge amids the water and passe the stream with their pawes.

But this property proceedeth from an earnest desire wherewith they be inflamed, rather then from any inclination, issuing from the ordinance and appointment of nature. And albeit some of this sort in *English* be called *Brache*, in *Scotish*, *Rache*, the cause thereof resteth in the she-sex, and not in the general kinde. For we *Englishmen* call Bitches belonging to the hunting kind of Dogs, by the tearm above mentioned. To be short, it is proper to the nature of Hounds, some to keep silence in hunting untill such time as there is game offered. Other some so soon as they smell out the place where the beast lurketh, to bewray it immediately by their importunate barking, notwithstanding it be far and many furlongs off, cowching close in his cabbin. And these Dogs the younger they be, the more wantonly bark they, and the more liberally; yet oftentimes without necessity, so that in them, by reason of their young years and want of practise, small certainty is to be reposed. For continuance of time, and experience in game, ministreth to these Hounds, not only cunning in running, but also (as in the rest) an assured foresight what is to be done principally, being acquainted with their Masters watchwords, either in revoking or imboldening them to serve the game.

OF THE DOG CALLED THE GASE-HOUND; IN LATIN, AGASÆUS.

THIS kinde of Dog which pursueth by the eye, prevaileth little, or never a whit, by any benefit of the nose, that is by smelling, but excelleth in perspicuity and sharpeness of sight altogether, by the virtue whereof, being singular and notable, it hunteth the Fox and the Hare. This Dog will chuse and separate any beast from among a great flock or herd, and such a one will it take by election as is not lanck, lean and hollow, but well spred, smooth, full, fat, and round, it followes by direction of the eyesight, which indeed is clear, constant, and not uncertain; if a beast be wounded and go astray, the Dog seeketh after it by the stedfastness of the eye, if it chance peradventure to return and be mingled with the residue of the flock, this Dog spyeth it out by virtue of his eye, leaving the rest of the Cattell untouched, and after he hath set sure sight upon it, he separateth it from among the company, and having so done, never ceaseth untill he have wearyed the Beast to death.

Our Countreymen call this Dog *Agasæum*, a Gase-hound, because the beams of his sight are so stedfastly setled and unmoveably fastned. These Dogs are much and usually occupied in the Northern parts of *England* more then in the Southern parts, and in fieldy lands rather then in bushie and woody places, horsemen use them more then footmen, to the intent that they might provoke their horses to a swift gallop (wherewith they are more delighted then with the prey it self) and that they might accustome their Horse to leap over hedges and ditches, without stop or stumble, without harme or hazard, without doubt or danger, and to escape with safegard of life. And to the end that the riders themselves, when necessity so constrained, and the fear of further mischief inforced, might save themselves undamnified, and prevent each perillous tempest by preparing speedy flight, or else by swift pursuite made upon their enemies, might both overtake them, encounter with them, and make a slaughter of them accordingly. But if it fortune so at any time that this Dog take a wrong way, the Master making some usual signe and familiar token, he returneth forthwith, and taketh the right and ready race, beginning his chase afresh, and with a clear voice, and a swift foot followeth the game with as much courage and nimbleness as he did at the first.

OF THE DOG CALLED THE GRAY-HOUND; IN LATIN, LEPORARIUS.

WE have another kinde of Dog, which for his incredible swiftness is called *Leporarius*, a Gray-hound, because the principal service of them dependeth and consisteth in starting and hunting the Hare, which Dogs likewise are indued with no lesse strength then lightness in maintenance of the game, in serving the chase, in taking the Buck, the Hart, the Doe, the Fox, and other beasts of semblable kinde ordained for the game of hunting. But more or lesse, each one according to the measure and proportion of their desire, and as might and hability of their bodies will permit and suffer.

For it is a spare and bare kind of Dog, (of flesh but not of bone) some are of a greater sort, and some of a lesser, some are smooth skinned, and some are curled, the bigger therefore are appointed to hunt the bigger beasts, and the smaller serve to hunt the smaller accordingly. The nature of the Dogs I finde to be wonderful by the testimony of all Histories. For, as *John Froisart* the Historiographer in his 4 *lib.* reporteth, A Grayhound of King *Richard* the second that wore the Crown, and bare the Scepter of the Realm of *England*, never knowing any man, besides the Kings person, when *Henry* Duke of *Lancaster* came to the Castle of *Flint* to take King *Richard*, the Dog forsaking his former Lord and Master came to Duke *Henry*, fauned upon him with such resemblances of good will and conceived affection, as he favoured King *Richard* before: he followed the Duke, and utterly left the King. So that by these manifold circumstances a man might judge his Dog to have been lightened with the lamp of foreknowledge and understanding, touching his old Masters miseries to come, and unhappiness nigh at hand, which King *Richard* himself evidently perceived, accounting this deed of his Dog a Prophecy of his overthrow.

Of the Dog called the Leviner, or Lyemmer; in Latin, Lorarius.

ANOTHER sort of Dogs be there, in smelling singular, and in swiftness incomparable. This is (as it were) a middle kinde betwixt the Harier and the Gray-hound, as well for his kind, as for the frame of his body. And it is called in *Latin, Levinarius, a Levitate,* of lightness, and therefore may well be called a Light-hound; it is also called by this word *Lorarius, a Loro,* wherewith it is led. This Dog for the excellency of his conditions, namely smelling and swift running, doth follow the game with more eagerness, and taketh the prey with a jolly quickness.

Of the Dog called a Tumbler; in Latin, Vertagus.

THIS sort of Dogs, which compasseth all by crafts, fraudes, and subtilties and deceits, we *Englishmen* call Tumblers, because in hunting they turn and tumble, winding their bodies about in circle wise, and then fiercely and violently venturing upon the beast, doth suddenly gripe it, at the very entrance and mouth of their receptacles, or closets before they can recover means, to save and succour themselves. This Dog useth another craft and subtilty, namely, when he runneth into a Warren, or fetcheth a course about a Conyburrough, he hunts not after them, he frayes them not by barking, he makes no countenance or shadow of hatred against them, but dissembling friendship, and pretending favour, passeth by with silence and quietness, marking and noting their holes diligently, wherein (I warrant you) he will not be overshot nor deceived. When he cometh to the place where Conies be of a certainty, he cowcheth down close with his belly to the ground, provided alwayes by his skill and policy, that the winde be never with him but against him in such an enterprise; and that the Conies spy him not where he lurketh. By which means he obtaineth the scent and savour of the Conies, carryed towards him with the winde and the air, either going to their holes or coming out, either passing this way, or running that way, and so provideth by his circumspection, that the silly simple Cony is debarred quite from his hole (which is the haven of their hope, and the harbour of their health) and fraudulently circumvented and taken, before they can get the advantage of their hole. Thus having caught his prey, he carryeth it speedily to his Master, waiting his Dogs return in some convenient lurking corner.

These Dogs are somewhat lesser then the Hounds, and they be lancker and leaner, beside that they be somewhat prick eared. A man that shall marke the form and fashion of their bodies, may well call them mungrel Gray-hounds if they were somewhat bigger. But notwithstanding they countervail not the Grey-hound in greatness, yet will he take in one dayes space as many Conies as shall arise to as big a burthen, and as heavie a load as a horse can carry, for deceit and guile is the instrument whereby he maketh this spoil, which pernicious properties supply the places of more commendable qualities.

OF THE DOG CALLED THE THEEVISH DOG, IN LATIN, CANIS FURAX.

THE like to that whom we have rehearsed, is the Theevish Dog, which at the mandate and bidding of his Master fleereth and leereth abroad in the night, hunting Conies by the air, which is sevened with the savour and conveied to the sense of smelling by the means of the winde blowing towards him. During all which space of his hunting, he will not bark, lest he should be prejudicial to his own advantage. And thus watcheth and snatcheth up in course as many Conies as his Master will suffer him, and beareth them to his Masters standing. The Farmers of the Countrey and uplandish dwellers, call this kind of Dog a Night Cur, because he hunteth in the dark. But let thus much seem sufficient for Dogs which serve the game and disport of hunting.

OF GENTLE DOGS SERVING THE HAWK, AND FIRST OF THE SPANIEL, CALLED IN LATIN, HISPANIOLUS.

SUCH Dogs as serve for fowling, I think convenient and requisite to place in the second Section of this treatise. These are also to be reckoned and accounted in the number of the Dogs which come of a gentle kind: and of those which serve for fowling, there be two sorts, the first findeth game on the land, the other findeth game on the water. Such as delight on the land, play their parts, either by swiftness of foot, or by often questing, to search out and to spring the bird for further hope of advantage, or else by some secret sign and privy token bewray the place where they fall. The first kind of such serve the Hawk, the second the net or train. The first kind have no peculiar names assigned unto them, save only that they be denominated after the bird which by natural appointment he is alotted to take; for the which consideration, some be called Dogs for the Falcon, the Phesant, the Partridge, and such like. The common sort of people call them by one general word, namely Spaniels; as though these kind of Dogs came originally and first of all out of *Spain*. The most part of their skins are white, and if they be marked with any spots they are commonly red, and somewhat great therewithall, the hairs not growing in such thickness but that the mixture of them may easily be perceived. Othersome of them be reddish and blackish, but of that sort there be but a very few. There is also at this day among us a new kind of Dog brought out of *France* (for we *Englishmen* are marvellous greedy gaping gluttons after novelties, and covetous cormorants of things that be seldom, rare, strange, and hard to get) and they be speckled all over with white and black, which mingled colours incline to a marble blew, which beautifieth their skins, and affordeth a seemly show of comeliness. These are called *French Dogs*, as is above declared already.

THE DOG CALLED THE SETTER; IN LATIN, INDEX.

ANOTHER sort of Dogs be there, serviceable for fowling, making no noise either with foot or with tongue, whiles they follow the game. These attend diligently upon their Master and frame their conditions to such becks, motions, and gestures, as it shall please him to exhibit and make, either going forward, drawing backward, it clining to the right hand, or yeelding toward the left, (in making mention of fowles, my meaning is of the Patridge and the Quail:) when he hath found the bird, he keepeth sure and fast silence, he stayeth his steps and will proceed no further, and with a close, covert, watching eye, layeth his belly to the ground and so creepeth forward like a worm. When he approacheth neer to the place where the bird is, he lies him down, and with a mark of his pawes betrayeth the place of the birds last abode, whereby it is supposed that this kind of Dog is called *Index*, Setter, being indeed a name most consonant and agreeable to his quality. The place being known by the means of the Dog, the fowler, immediately openeth and spreadeth his net, intending to take them; which being done, the Dog at the customed beck or usuall sign of his Master riseth up by and by, and draweth neerer to the fowle, that by his presence they might be the authors of their own insnaring, and be ready intangled in the prepared net, which cunning and artificial indevour in a Dog (being a creature domestical or houshold servant, brought up at home with offals of the trencher, and fragments of victuals) is not so much to be marvelled at, seeing that a Hare (being a wilde and skippish beast) was seen in *England* to the astonishment of the beholders, in the year of our Lord God 1564 not only dancing in measure, but playing with his former feet upon a tabberet, and observing just number of strokes (as a practitioner in that art) besides that nipping and pinching a Dog with his teeth and clawes, and cruelly thumping him with the force of his feet. This is no trumpery tale, nor trifle toy (as I imagine) and therefore not unworthy to be reported, for I reckon it a requital of my travell, not to drown in the seas of silence any special thing, wherein the providence and effectual working of nature is to be pondered.

OF THE DOG CALLED THE WATER SPANIEL, OR FINDER; IN LATIN, AQUATICUS SEU INQUISITOR.

THAT kinde of Dog whose service is required in fowling upon the water, partly through a natural towardness, and partly by diligent teaching, is indued with that property. This sort is somewhat big, and of a measurable greatness, having long, rough, and curled hair, not obtained by extraordinary trades, but given by natures appointment; yet nevertheless (friend *Gesner*) I have described and set him out in this manner, namely powled and notted from the shoulders to the hindermost legs, and to the end of his tail, which I did for use and customs cause, that being as it were made somewhat bare and naked,

307

by shearing off such superfluity of hair, they might atchieve the more lightness, and swiftness, and be lesse hindered in swimming, so troublesome and needless a burden being shaken off. This kinde of Dog is properly called *Aquaticus*, a Water Spaniel, because be frequenteth and hath usual recourse to the water where all his game lyeth, namely water fowls, which are taken by the help and service of them, in their kind. And principally Ducks and Drakes, whereupon he is likewise named a Dog for the Duck, because in that quality he is excellent. With these Dogs also we fetch out of the water such fowl as be stung to death by any venemous Worm; we use them also to bring us our bolts and arrows out of the water (missing our mark) whereat we directed our levell, which otherwise we should hardly recover, and oftentimes they restore to us our shafts which we thought never to see, touch, or handle again, after they were lost: for which circumstances they are called *Inquisitores*, searchers and finders. Although the Duck otherwhiles notably deceiveth both the Dog and the Master, by diving under the water, and also by natural subtilty, for if any man shall approach to the place where they build, breed and sit, the Hens go out of their nests, offering themselves voluntarily to the hands, as it were, of such as draw neer their nests. And a certain weakness of their wings pretended, and infirmity of their feet dissembled, they go slowly and so leasurely, that to a mans thinking it were no masterie to take them. By which deceitful trick they do as it were entise and allure men to follow them, till they be drawn a long distance from their nests, which being compassed by their provident cunning, or cunning providence, they cut off all inconveniences which might grow of their return, by using many careful and curious caveats, lest their often hunting bewray the place where the young ducklings be hatched. Great therefore is their desire, and earnest is their study to take heed, not only to their brood, but also to themselves. For when they have an inkling that they are espied, they hide themselves under turses or sedges, wherewith they cover and shroud themselves so closely and so craftily, that (notwithstanding the place where they lurk be found and perfectly perceived) there they will harbour without harm, except the Water Spaniel by quick smelling discover their deceits.

308

OF THE DOG CALLED THE FISHER; IN LATIN CANIS PISCATOR.

THE Dog called the Fisher, whereof *Hector Boetius* writeth, which seeketh for Fish by smelling among rocks and stones, assuredly I know none of that kind in *England*, neither have I received by report that there is any such, albeit I have been diligent and busie in demanding the question as well of Fishermen as also huntsmen in that behalf, being careful and earnest to learn and understand of them if any such were, except you hold opinion that the Beaver or Otter is a Fish (as many have believed) and according to their belief affirmed, as the bird *Pupine*, is thought to be a fish, and so accounted. But that kind of Dog which followeth the fish to apprehend and take it (if there be any of that disposition and property) whether they do this thing for the game of hunting, or for the heat of hunger, as other Dogs do which rather then they will be famished for want of food, covet the carcases of carrion and putrified flesh. When I am fully resolved and disburthened of this doubt, I will send you certificate in writing. In the mean season I am not ignorant of that both *Ælianus* and *Aetius*, call the Beaver *Kunapotamion* a water Dog, or a Dog-fish, I know likewise thus much more, that the Beaver doth participate this property with the Dog, namely, that when fishes be scarce they leave the water and range up and down the land, making an insatiable slaughter of young Lambs untill their paunches be replenished, and when they have fed themselves full of Flesh, then return they to the water from whence they came. But albeit so much be granted that this Bever is a Dog, yet it is to be noted that we reckon it not in the beadrow of *English* Dogs as we have done the rest. The sea Calfe, in like manner, which our Countrey men for brevity sake call a Seel, other more largely name a *Sea Veale*, maketh a spoil of fishes between rocks and banks, but it is not accounted in the Catalogue or number of our *English* Dogs, notwithstanding we call it by the name of a Sea-Dog, or a Sea-Calf And thus much for our Dogs of the second sort, called in *Latin*, *Aucupatorii*, serving to take fowl either by land or water.

Of the delicate, neat, and pretty kind of Dogs called the Spaniel Gentle, or the Comforter; in Latin, Melitæus, or Fotor.

THERE is besides those which we have already delivered, another sort of Gentle Dogs in this our *English* soil, but exempted from the order of the residue, the Dogs of this kind doth *Callimachus* call *Melitæos* of the Island *Melita*, in the sea of *Sicily* (which at this day is named *Malta*) an Island indeed, famous and renowned with couragious and puissant Souldiers, valiantly fighting under the banner of Christ their unconquerable Captain) where this kind of Dogs had their principal beginning.

These Dogs are little, pretty, proper, and fine, and sought for to satisfie the delicateness of dainty dames and wanton womens wils, instruments of folly for them to play and dally withal, to trifle away the treasure of time, to withdraw their mindes from more commendable exercises, and to content their corrupted concupiscences with vain disport (a silly shift to shun irksome idleness.) These puppies the smaller they be, the more pleasure they provoke, as more meet playfellowes for minsing mistresses to bear in their bosomes, to keep company withal in their Chambers, to succour with sleep in bed, and nourish with meat at bord, to lay in their laps, and lick their lips as they ride in their Waggons: and good reason it should be so, for courseness with fineness hath no fellowship, but featness with neatness hath neighbourhood enough. That plausible proverb verified upon a Tyrant, namely, that he loved his Sow better then his Son, may well be applyed to these kind of people, who delight more in Dogs that are deprived of all possibility of reason, then they do in children that be capeable of wisdom and judgement. But this abuse peradventure reigneth where there hath been long lack of issue, or else where barrenness is the best blossom of beauty.

The virtue which remaineth in the Spaniel Gentle, otherwise called the Comforter.

NOTWITHSTANDING many make much of those pretty puppies called Spaniels Gentle, yet if the question were demanded what property in them they spie, which should make them so acceptable and precious in their sight, I doubt their answer would be long a coining. But seeing it was our intent to travail in this treatise, so, that the Reader might reap some benefit by his reading, we will communicate unto such conjectures as are grounded upon reason. And though some suppose that such Dogs are fit for no service, I dare say, by their leaves, they be in a wrong box. Among all other qualities therefore of nature, which be known (for some conditions are covered with continual and thick clouds, that the eye of our capacities cannot pierce through them) we finde that these little Dogs are good to asswage the sickness of the stomach, being oftentimes thereunto applyed as a plaister preservative, or born in the bosom of the diseased and weak person; which effect is performed by their moderate heat. Moreover the disease and sickness changeth his place and entreth (though it be not precisely marked) into the Dog, which to be truth, experience can testifie, for these kinde of Dogs sometimes fall sick, and sometimes die, without any harme outwardly inforced, which is an argument that the disease of the Gentleman, or Gentlewoman or owner whatsoever, entreth into the Dog by the operation of heat intermingled and infected. And thus have I hitherto handled Dogs of a gentle kind whom I have comprehended in a triple division. Now it remaineth that I annex in due order, such Dogs as be of a more homely kinde.

DOGS OF A COURSE KINDE SERVING MANY NECESSARY USES, CALLED IN LATIN CANES RUSTICI, AND FIRST OF THE SPEPHERDS DOG, CALLED IN LATIN, CANIS PASTORALIS.

THE first kinde, namely the Shepherds hound, is very necessary and profitable for the avoiding of harmes, and inconveniences which may come to men by the means of beasts. The second sort serve for succour against the snares and attempts of mischievous men. Our Shepherds Dog is not huge, vast and big, but of an indifferent stature and growth, because it hath not to deal with the bloudthirsty Wolfe, sithence there be none in *England*, which happy and fortunate benefit is to be ascribed to the puissant Prince *Edgar*, who to the intent that the whole Countrey might be evacuated and quite cleared from Wolves, charged and commanded the

Welshmen (who were pestered with these butcherly beasts above measure) to pay him yearly tribute (note the wisdom of the King) three hundred Wolves. Some there be which write that *Ludwal* Prince of Wales paid yearly to King *Edgar* three hundred Wolves in the name of an exaction (as we have said before.) And that by the means hereof, within the compass and term of four years, none of those noisom and pestilent beasts were left in the coasts of *England* and *Wales*. This *Edgar* wore the Crown royal, and bare the Scepter imperial of this Kingdom, about the year of our Lord Nine hundred fifty nine. Since which time we read that no Wolf hath been seen in *England*, bred within the bounds and borders of this Countrey, marry there have been divers brought over from beyond the Seas, for greediness of gain and to make money, for gazing and gaping, staring and standing to see them, being a strange beast, rare, and seldom seen in *England*. But to return to our Shepherds Dog: This Dog either at the hearing of his Masters voice, or at the wagging and whistling in his fist, or at his shrill and hoarse hissing bringeth the wandering weathers and straying Sheep into the self same place where his Masters will and wish is to have them, whereby the Shepherd reapeth this benefit, namely that with little labour and no toil or moving of his feet he may rule and guide his flock, according to his own desire, either to have them go forward, or to stand still, or to draw backward, or to turn this way, or take that way. For it is not in *England*, as it is in *France*, as it is in *Flanders*, as it is in *Syria*, as it is in *Tartaria*, where the Sheep follow the Shepherd, for here in our Countrey the Shepherd followeth the Sheep. And sometimes the straying Sheep when no Dog runneth before them, nor goeth about and beside them, gather themselves together in a flock, when they hear the Shepherd whistle in his fist, for fear of the Dog (as I imagine) remembring this (if unreasonable creatures may be reported to have memory) that the Dog commonly runneth out at his Masters warrant, which is his whistle. This have we oftentimes diligently marked in taking our journey from Town to Town, when we have heard a Shepherd whistle we have rained in our horse and stood still a space, to see the proof and tryall of this matter. Furthermore, with this Dog doth the Shepherd take Sheep for the slaughter, and to be healed if they be sick, no hurt or harm in the world done to the simple creature.

Of the Mastive, or Bandog; called in Latin, Villaticus, or Catenarius.

THIS kind of Dog called a Mastive or Bandog is vast, huge, stubborn, ugly, and eager, of a heavie and bourthenous body, and therefore but of little swiftness, terrible, and frightful to behold, and more fierce and fell then any *Arcadian* cur (notwithstanding they are said to have their generation of the violent Lion.) They are called *Villatici*, because they are appointed to watch and keep farm-places and Countrey Cotages sequestred from common recourse, and not abutting upon other houses by reason of distance, when there is any fear conceived of Theeves, Robbers, Spoilers, and Night-wanderers. They are serviceable against the Fox and Badger, to drive wilde and tame Swine out of Medowes, Pastures, Glebelands, and places planted with fruit, to bait and take the Bull by the ear, when occasion so requireth. One Dog or two at the utmost is sufficient for that purpose, be the Bull never so monstrous, never so fierce, never so furious, never so stern, never so untamable. For it is a kind of Dog capeable of courage, violent and valiant, striking cold fear into the hearts of men, but standing in fear of no man, in so much that no weapons will make him shrink, nor abridge his boldness. Our *Englishmen* (to the intent that their Dogs might be more fell and fierce) assist nature with art, use and custom, for they teach their Dogs to bait the Bear, to bait the Bull and other such like cruell and bloudy Beasts (appointing an overseer of the game) without any Collar to defend their throats, and oftentimes they train them up in fighting and wrestling with any man having for the safegard of his life, either a Pikestaffe, a Club, or a sword, and by using them to such exercises as these, their Dogs become more sturdy and strong. The force which is in them surmounteth all belief, the fast hold which they take with their teeth exceedeth all credit, three of them against a Bear, four against a Lion are sufficient, both to trie masteries with them, and utterly to overmatch them. Which thing *Henry* the seventh of that name, King of *England* (a Prince both politick and warlike) perceiving on a certain time (as the report runneth) commanded all such Dogs (how many so ever were in number) should be hanged, being deeply displeased, and conceiving great disdain, that an ill favoured rascal Cur should with such violent villany, assault the valiant Lion King of all beasts. An example for all subjects worthy remembrance, to admonish them, that it is no advantage to them to rebell against the regiment of their Ruler, but to keep them within the limits of loyalty. I read an History answerable to this of the self same *Henry*, who having a notable and an excellent fair Falcon, it fortuned that the Kings Falconers, in the presence and hearing of his grace, highly commended his Majesties Faulcon, saying, that it feared not to intermeddle with an Eagle, it was so venturous a Bird and so mighty; which when the King heard, he charged that the Falcon should be killed without delay, for the self same reason (as it may seem) which was rehearsed in the conclusion of the former history concerning the same king. This Dog is called in like manner, *Catenarius*, a *Catena*, of the chain wherewith he is tyed at the gates in the day time, lest being loose he should do much mischief, and yet might give occasion of fear and terror by his big barking. And albeit *Cicero* in his Oration had *pro S. Ross.* be of this opinion, that sueh Dogs as bark in the broad day light should have their legs broken, yet our Countrymen on this side the Seas, for their carelesness of life setting all at cinque and sice are of a contrary judgement. For Theeves rogue up and down in every corner, no place is free from them, no not the Princes palace, nor the Countrymans cotage. In the day time they practise pilfering, picking, open robbing, and privie stealing, and what legerdemain lack they? not fearing the shameful and horrible death of hanging.

The cause of which inconvenience doth not only issue from nipping need and wringing want, for all that steal are not pinched with poverty, some steal to maintain their excessive and prodigal expences in apparel, their lewdness of life, their haughtiness of heart, their wantonness of manners, their wilful idleness, their ambitious bravery, and the pride of the sawcy *Salacones me galorrounton*, vain glorious and arrogant in behaviour, whose delight dependeth wholly to mount nimbly on horse-back, to make them leap lustily, spring and prance, gallop and amble, to run a race, to winde in compass, and so forth, living altogether upon the fatness of the spoil. Other some there be which steal, being thereto provoked by penury and need, like masterless men applying themselves to no honest trade, but ranging up and down, impudently begging and complaining of bodily weakness where is no want of ability. But valiant *Valentine* the Emperor, by wholesome lawes provided that such as having no corporal sickness, sold themselves to begging, pleaded poverty with pretended infirmity, and cloaked their idle and slothful life with colourable shifts and cloudy cozening, should be a perpetual slave and drudge to him, by whom their impudent idleness was bewrayed, and laid against them in publick place, lest the insufferable slothfulness of such vagabonds should be burthenous to the people, or being so hateful and odious, should grow into an example.

Alfredus likewise in the Government of his Common-wealth, procured such encrease of credit to justice and upright dealing by his prudent Acts & Statutes, that if a man travelling by the high way of the Countrey under his dominion, chanced to lose a budget full of Gold, or his capcase farsed with things of great value, late in the evening, he should finde it where he lost it, safe, sound, and untouched the next morning, yet (which is a wonder) at any time for a whole moneths space if he sought for it, as *Ingulphus Croyladensis* in his history recordeth. But in this our unhappy age, in these (I say) our devilish days, nothing can escape the clawes of the spoiler, though it be kept never so sure within the house, albeit the doors be lockt and boulted round about. This Dog in like manner of the *Grecians* is called *Oikouros.*

Of the *Latinists, Canis Coltos;* in *English,* the *Dog-keeper.*
Borrowing his name of his service, for he doth not only keep Farmers houses, but also Merchants mansions, wherein great wealth, riches, substance and costly stuffe is reposed. And therefore were certain Dogs found and maintained at the common costs and charges of the Citizens of *Rome* in the place called *Capitolium,* to give warning of Theeves coming. This kind of Dog is called,

In *Latin, Canis Laniarius,* in *English,* the *Butchers Dog.*
So called for the necessity of his use, for his service affordeth great benefit to the Butcher as well in following as in taking his Cattel, when need constraineth, urgeth, and requireth. This kinde of Dog is likewise called,

In *Latin, Molossicus,* or *Molossus,*

after the name of a Countrey in *Epirus* called *Molossia,* which harboureth many stout, strong, and sturdy Dogs of this sort, for the Dogs of that Countrey are good indeed, or else there is no trust to be had in the testimony of writers. This Dog is also called,

In *Latin, Canis Mandatarius,* a *Dog messenger,* or *Carrier,*

upon substancial consideration, because at his Masters voice and commandement, he carryeth letters from place to place, wrapped up cunningly in his leather collar, fastned thereto, or sowed close therein, who lest he should be hindred in his passage, useth these helpes very skilfully, namely resistance in fighting if he be not overmatched, or else swiftness and readinesse in running away, if he be unable to buckle with the Dog that would fain have a snatch at his skin. This kinde of Dog is likewise called,

In *Latin, Canis Lunarius;* in *English,* the *Mooner.*

Because he doth nothing else but watch and ward at an inch, wasting the wearisome night season without slumbring or sleeping, bawing and wawing at the Moon (that I may use the word of *Nonius*) a quality in mine own opinion strange to consider. This kind of Dog is also called,

In *Latin, Aquarius;* in *English,* a *Water-drawer.*

And these be of the greater and the weightier sort, drawing water out of wels and deep pits, by a wheel which they turn round about by the moving of their burthenous bodies. This Dog is called in like manner,

Canis Carcinarius in *Latin,* and may aptly be *Englished,* a *Tinkers Cur.*

Because with marvellous patience they bear big budgets fraught with Tinkers tools, and metal meet to mend kettels, porrage-pots, skillets, and chafers, and other such like trumpery requisite for their occupation and loytering trade, easing him of a great burthen, which otherwise he himself should carry upon his shoulders; which condition hath challenged unto them the foresaid name. Besides the qualities which we have already recounted, this kind of Dogs hath this principal property ingraffed in them, that they love their Masters liberally, and hate strangers despightfully; where-upon it followeth that they are to their Masters in travelling a singular safegard, defending them forcibly from the invasion of villains and Theeves, preserving their lives from losse, and their health from hazzard, their flesh from hacking and hewing, with such like desperate dangers. For which consideration they are meritoriously termed,

In *Latin, Canes defensores; Defending Dogs* in our mother tongue.

If it chance that the Master be oppressed, either by a multitude, or by the greater violence, and so be beaten down that he lie groveling on the ground, (it is proved true by experience) that this Dog forsaketh not his Master, no not when he is stark dead: But induring the force of famishment and the outragious tempests of the weather, most vigilantly watcheth and carefully keepeth the dead carkasse many dayes, indevouring furthermore, to kill the murtherer of his Master, if he may get any advantage. Or else by barking, by howling, by furious jarring, snarring, and such like means betrayeth the malefactor as desirous to have the death of his aforesaid Master rigorously revenged. An example hereof fortuned within the compasse of my memory. The Dog of a certain wayfaring man travelling from the City of *London* directly to the Town of *Kingstone* (most famous and renowned by reason of the triumphant coronation of eight several Kings) passing over a good portion of his journey, was assaulted and set upon by certain confederate Theeves lying in wait for the spoil in *Come-packe*, a perillous bottom, compassed about with Woods too well known for the manifold murders and mischievous robberies there committed. Into whose hands this passenger chanced to fall, so that his ill luck cost him the price of his life.

And that Dog whose sire was *English*, (which *Blondus* registreth to have been within the banks of his remembrance) manifestly perceiving that his Master was murthered (this chanced not far from *Paris*) by the hands of one which was a suiter to the same woman, whom he was a wooer unto, did both bewray the bloudy Butcher, and attempted to tear out the villains throat, if he had not sought means to avoid the revenging rage of the Dog. In fires also which fortune in the silence and dead time of the night, or in stormy weather of the said season, the older Dogs bark, baul, howl, and yell, (yea notwithstanding they be roughly rated) neither will they stay their tongues till the houshold servants awake, rise, search, and see the burning of the fire, which being perceived they use voluntary silence, and cease from yolping. This hath been, and is found true by triall, in sundry parts of *England*.

There was no fainting faith in that Dog, which when his Master by a mischance in hunting stumbled and fell, toppling down a deep ditch being unable to recover of himself, the Dog signifying his Masters mishap, rescue came, and he was haled up by a rope, whom the Dog seeing almost drawn up to the edge of the ditch, cheerfully saluted, leaping and skipping upon his Master as though he would have imbraced him, being glad of his presence, whose longer absence he was loath to lack. Some Dogs there be, which will not suffer fiery coles to lie scattered about the hearth, but with their pawes will rake up the burning coles, musing and studying first with themselves how it might conveniently be done. And if so be that the coles cast too great a heat, then will they bury them in ashes and so remove them forward to a fit place with their noses. Other Dogs be there which execute the office of a Farmer in the night time. For when his Master goeth to bed to take his natural sleep; And when,

> *A hundred bars of brasse and iron bolts,*
> *Make all things safe from starts and from revolts,*
> *When Janus keeps the gate with Argus eye,*
> *That dangers none approach, no mischief nie,*

As *Virgil* vaunteth in his Verses: Then if his Master biddeth him goe abroad, he lingereth not, but rangeth over all his lands thereabout, more diligently, I wys, then any Farmer himself. And if he finde any thing there that is strange and pertaining to other persons besides his Master, whether it be man, woman, or beast, he driveth them out of the ground, not medling with any thing that do belong to the possession and use of

318

his Master. But how much faithfulness, so much diversity there is in their natures.

For there be some, which bark only with free and open throat, but will not bite, some which do both bark and bite, and some which bite bitterly before they bark.

The first are not greatly to be feared, because they themselves are fearful, and fearful Dogs (as the Proverb importeth) bark most vehemently.

The second are dangerous, it is wisdom to take heed of them, because they sound as it were, an *Alarum* of an afterclap, and these Dogs must not be over much moved or provoked, for then they take on outragiously, as if they were mad, watching to set the print of their teeth in the flesh. And these kinde of Dogs are fierce and eager by nature.

The third are deadly, for they fly upon a man without utterance of voyce, snatch at him, and catch him by the throat, and most cruelly bite out collops of flesh. Fear these kinde of Curs, (if thou be wise and circumspect about thine one safety) for they be stout and stubborn Dogs, and set upon a man at a suddain unawares. By these signes and tokens, by these notes and arguments our men discern the towardly Cur from the couragious Dog, the bold from the fearful, the butcherly from the gentle and tractable. Moreover they conjecture, that a Whelp of an ill kinde is not worth keeping and that no Dog can serve the sundry uses of men so aptly and conveniently as this sort, of whom we have so largely written already. For if any be disposed to draw the above named services into a Table, what man more clearly, and with more vehemency of voyce giveth warning either of a wastful Beast, or of a spoyling theef then this? who by his barking (as good as a burning Beacon) foresheweth hazards at hand. What manner of Beast stronger? What servant to his Master more loving? What companion more trusty? What Watchman more vigilent? What revenger more constant? What Messenger more speedy? What Water-bearer more painful? Finally, what Pack-horse more patient? And thus much concerning *English* Dogs, first of the gentle kinde, secondly of the courser kinde. Now it remaineth that we deliver unto you the Dogs of a Mungrel or Currish kinde, and then will we perform our task.

CONTAINING CURS OF THE MUNGREL AND RASCAL SORT, AND FIRST OF ALL THE DOG CALLED IN LATINE, ADMONITOR, AND OF US IN ENGLISH, WAPPE, OR WARNER.

OF such Dogs as keep not their kinde, of such as are mingled out of sundry sorts, not imitating the conditions of some one certain spice, because they resemble no notable shape, nor exercise any worthy property of the true, perfect and gentable kinde, it is not necessary, that I write any more of them, but to banish them as unprofitable implements, out of the bounds of my Book; unprofitable I say, for any use that is commendable, except to entertain strangers with barking in the day time, giving warning to them of the House, that such and such be newly come, where-upon we call them admonishing Dogs, because in that point they perform their Office.

OF THE DOG CALLED TURNESPIT, IN LATINE, VERUVERSATOR.

THERE is comprehended, under the Curs of the coursest kinde, a certain Dog in Kitchin-service excellent. For when any meat is to be roasted, they go into a wheel, which they turning round about with the weight of their bodies, so diligently look to their business, that no drudge nor scullion can do the feat more cunningly. Whom the popular sort hereupon call Turn-spits, being the last of all those which we have first mentioned.

OF THE DOG CALLED THE DANCER, IN LATINE, SALTATOR OR TYMPANISTA.

THERE be also Dogs among us of a Mungrel kinde, which are taught and exercised to dance in measure at the Musical sound of an instrument, as at the just stroke of the Drum; at the sweet accent of the Cittern, and tuned strings of the harmonious Harp, shewing many pretty tricks by the gesture of their bodies; as to stand bolt upright, to lye flat upon the ground, to turn round as a ring, holding their tails in their teeth, to beg for their meat, and sundry such properties, which they learn of their Vagabundical Masters, whose instrument they are to gather gain withall in the City, Countrey, Town, and Village. As some which cary old Apes on their shoulders in coloured Jackets to move men to laughter for a little lucre.

OF OTHER DOGS, A SHORT CONCLUSION, WONDERFULLY INGENDRED WITHIN THE COAST OF THIS COUNTREY.

OF these there be three sorts; the first bred of a Bitch and a Wolf, called in *Latine, Lyciscus*; the second of a Bitch and a Fox, in *Latine, Lacæna*; the third of a Bear and a Bandog, *Vicanus*. Of the first we have none naturally bred within the borders of *England*. The reason is for the want of Wolves, without whom no such Dog can be ingendred. Again, it is delivered unto thee in this discourse: how and by what means, by whose benefit, and within what circuit of time, this Countrey was clearly discharged of ravening Wolves, and none at all left, no, not the least number, or to the beginning of a number, which is an *Unarie*.

Of the second sort we are not utterly void of some, because this our *English* soil is not free from Foxes, (for indeed we are not without a multitude of them, insomuch as divers keep, foster and feed them in their houses among their Hounds and Dogs, either for some malady of minde, or for some sickness of body) which peradventure the savour of that subtill Beast would either mitigate or expell.

The third which is bred of a Bear and a Bandog, we want not here in *England*, (A strange and wonderful effect, that cruel enemies should enter into the work of copulation, and bring forth so savage a Cur.) Undoubtedly it is even so as we have reported, for the fiery heat of their flesh, or rather the pricking thorn; or most of all, the tickling lust of lechery, beareth such swing and sway in them, that there is no contrariety for the time, but of constraint they must joyn to engender. And why should not this be consonant to truth? why should not these Beasts breed in this land, as well as in other forein Nations? For we read that Tygers and Dogs in *Hircania*, that Lyons and Dogs in *Arcadia*, and that Wolves and Dogs in *Francia* couple and procreate. In men and women also lightned with the Lantern of reason (but utterly void of vertue) that foolish, frantick, and fleshly action (yet naturally seated in us) worketh so effectually, that many times it doth reconcile enemies, set foes at friendship, unanimity, and atonement, as *Moria* mentioneth. The *Urcane* which is bred of a Bear and a Dog,

> *Is fierce, is fell, is stout and strong,*
> *And biteth sore to flesh and bone.*
> *His furious force indureth long,*
> *In rage he will be rul'd of none.*

That I may use the words of the Poet *Gratius*. This Dog exceedeth all other in cruel conditions, his leering and fleering looks, his stern and savage visage, maketh him in sight fearful and terrible, He is violent in fighting, and wheresoever he set his tenterhook teeth, he taketh such sure and fast hold, that a man may sooner tear and rend him asunder, then loose him and separate his chaps. He passeth not for the Wolf, the Bear, the Lyon, nor the Bull, and may worthily (as I think) be companion with *Alexanders* Dog which came out of *India*. But of these, thus much, and thus far may seem sufficient.

A START TO OUT-LANDISH DOGS IN THIS CONCLUSION, NOT IMPERTINENT TO THE AUTHORS PURPOSE.

USE and custome hath entertained others Dogs of an Out-landish kinde, but a few and the same being of a pretty bigness, I mean Island Dogs, curled and rough all over, which by reason of the length of their hair make shew neither of face nor of body: And yet these Curs, forsooth, because they are so strange, are greatly set by, esteemed, taken up, and many times in the room of the Spaniel gentle or comforter. The nature of men is so moved, nay, rather maryed to novelties without all reason, wit, judgement or perseverance, *Eromen allotrias, paroromen suggeneis.*

> *Out-landish toys we take with delight,*
> *Things of our own Nation we have in despight.*

Which fault remaineth not in us concerning Dogs only, but for Artificers also. And why? it is manifest that we disdain and contemn our own Work-men, be they never so skilful, be they never so cunning, be they never so excellent. A beggerly Beast brought out of barbarous borders, from the uttermost Countreys Northward, &c. we stare at, we gaze at, we muse, we marvail at, like an Ass of *Cumanum*, like *Thales* with the brazen shanks, like the man in the Moon.

The which default *Hippocrates* marked when he was alive, as evidently appeareth in the beginning of his Book *Peri Agmon*, so entituled and named:

And we in our work entituled *De Ephemera Britannica*, to the people of *England* have more plentifully expressed. In this kinde look which is most blockish, and yet most waspish, the same is most esteemed, and not among Citizens only and jolly Gentlemen, but among lusty Lords also, and Noblemen. Further I am not to wade in the soord of this discourse, because it was my purpose to satisfie your expectation with a short treatise (most learned *Conrade*) not wearisome for me to write, nor tedious for you to peruse. Among other things which you have received at my hands heretofore, I remember that I wrote a several description of the *Getulian* Dog, because there are but a few of them, and therefore very seldom seen. As touching Dogs of other kindes you your self have taken earnest pain in writing of them both lively, learnedly, and largely. But because we have drawn this libel more at length then the former which I sent you (and yet briefer then the nature of the thing might well bear) regarding your most earnest and necessary studies; I will conclude, making a rehearsal notwithstanding (for memory sake) of certain specialities contained in the whole body of this my breviary. And because you participate principal pleasure in the knowledge of the common and usual names of Dogs (as I gather by the course of your letters) I suppose it not amiss to deliver unto you a short table containing as well the *Latine* as the *English* names, and to render a reason of every particular appellation, to the intent that no scruple may remain in this point, but that every thing may be sifted to the bare bottom.

A Supplement Or Addition, Containing A Demonstration Of Dogs Names How They Had Their Original.

THE names contained in the general Table, forsomuch as they signifie nothing to you being a stranger, and ignorant of the *English* tongue, except they be interpreted: as we have given a reason before of the *Latine* words, so mean we to do no less of the *English*, that every thing may be manifest unto your understanding. Wherein I intend to observe the same order which I have followed before.

Sagax, in *English*, *Hund*, is derived of our *English* word hunt. One letter changed in another, namely T into D, as Hunt, Hund, whom if you conjecture to be so named of your Countrey word Hund, which signifieth the general name (*Dog*) because of the similitude and likeness of the words, I will not stand in contradiction (friend *Gesner*) for somuch as we retain among us at this day many *Dutch* words, which the *Saxons* left at such time as they enjoyed this Countrey of *Britain*. Thus much also understand, that as in your language *Hand* is the common word, so in our natural tongue (*Dog*) is the universal, but Hund is particular and a special, for it signifieth such a Dog only as serveth to hunt, and therefore it is called a Hund.

Of the Gase-Hound.

The Gase-hound called in *Latine, Agasæus*, hath his name of the sharpness and stedfastness of his eye-sight. By which vertue he compasseth that which otherwise he cannot by smelling attain. As we have made former relation, for to gase is earnestly to view and behold, from whence floweth the derivation of this Dogs name.

Of the Gray-Hound.

The Gray-hound called *Leporarius*, hath his name of this word Gre, which word soundeth, *Gradus* in *Latine*, in *English*, Degree. Because among all Dogs these are the most principal, having the chiefest place, and being simply and absolutely the best of the gentle kinde of Hounds.

Of the Levyner or the Lyemmer.

This Dog is called a *Levyner*, for his lightness, which in *Latine* soundeth *Levitas*. Or a Lyemmer, which word is borrowed of Lyemme, which the *Latinists* name *Lorum*: and wherefore we call him a Levyner of this word *Levitas*: (as we do many things besides) why we derive and draw a thousand of our terms out of the *Greek*, the *Latine*, the *Italian*, the *Dutch*, the *French*, and the *Spanish* tongue; (Out of which Fountains indeed, they had their Original issue.) How many words are buried in the grave of forgetfulness; grown out of use; wrested awry; and perversly corrupted by divers defaults; we will declare at large in our Book entituled, *Symphonia vocum Britannicarum*.

Of the Tumbler.

Among Hounds the Tumbler called in *Latine, Vertagus*; which cometh of this word Tumbler, flowing first from the *French* Fountain. For as we say Tumble, so they *Tumbier*, reserving our sense and signification, which the *Latinists* comprehend under this word *Vertere*. So that we see thus much, that Tumbler cometh of *Tumbier*, the Vowel I, changed into the Liquid L, after the manner of our speech. Contrary to the *French* and the *Italian* tongue: In which two Languages, a Liquid before a Vowel for the most part is turned into another Vowel; as may be perceived in the example of these two words, *Implere & plano*, for *Impiere & piano*, L, before E, changed into I, and L, before A, turned into I also. This I thought convenient for a tast.

After such as serve for hunting, orderly do follow such as serve for hawking and fowling, among which the principal and chiefest is the Spaniel, called in *Latine, Hispaniolus*, borrowing his name of *Hispania*, wherein we *English* men not pronouncing the Aspiration H, nor the Vowel I, for quickness and readiness of speech, say roundly a Spagnel.

Of the Setter.

The second sort is called a Setter, in *Latine, Index*. Of the word (*Set*) which siginifieth in *English* that which the *Latinists* mean by this word *Locum designare*, the reason is rehearsed before more largely, it shall not therefore need to make a new repetition.

Of the Water Spaniel or Finder.

The Water Spaniel consequently followeth, called in *Latine,* *Aquaticus*; in *English* a Water Spaniel, which name is compound of two simple words, namely Water, which in *Latine* soundeth *Aqua*, wherein he swimmeth, and *Spain, Hispania*, the Countrey from whence they came; not that *England* wanteth such kinde of Dogs, (for they are naturally bred and ingendered in this Countrey) but because they bear the general and common name of these Dogs since the time they were first brought over out of *Spain*. And we make a certain difference in this sort of Dogs, either for something which in their qualities is to be considered, as for an example in this kinde called the Spaniel, by the apposition and putting to of this word Water, which two coupled together sound Water Spaniel. He is called a Finder, in *Latine, Inquisitor*; because that by serious and secure seeking, he findeth such things as be lost, which word Finde in *English* is that which the *Latines* mean by this Verb *Invenire*. This Dog hath this name of his property, because the principal point of his service consisteth in the premises.

Now leaving the surview of hunting and hawking Dogs, it remaineth that we run over the residue, whereof some be called fine Dogs, some course, othersome Mungrels or Rascals. The first is Spaniel gentle called *Canis Melitæus*, because it is a kinde of Dog accepted among Gentils, Nobles, Lords, Ladies, &c. who make much of them, vouchsafing to admit them so far into their company, that they will not only full them in their laps, but kiss them with their lips, and make them their pretty play-fellows. Such a one was *Gorgons* little puppy mentioned by *Theocritus* in *Syracusis*, who taking his journey, straightly charged and commanded his Maid to see to his Dog as charily and warily as to his childe: To call him in always that he wandred not abroad, as well as to rock the babe a sleep, crying in the Cradle.

This Puppetly and pleasant Cur, (which some frumpingly tearm Fysting Hound) serves in a manner to no good use, except (as we have made former relation) to succour and strengthen qualing and qualming stomachs, to bewray bawdery, and filthy abhominable lewdness (which a little Dog of this kinde did in *Sicilia*) as *Ælianus* in his 7. Book of Beasts, and 27. chapter recordeth.

Of Dogs under the courser kinde, we will deal first with the Shepheards Dog, whom we call the Bandog, the Tydog, or the Mastive, the first name is imputed to him for service, *Quoniam pastori famulatur*, because he is at the Shepheards his Masters commandment. The second a *Ligamento* of the band or chain wherewith he is tyed. The third a *Sagina*, of the fatness of his body.

For this kinde of Dog which is usually tyed, is mighty, gross, and fat fed. I know this that *Augustinus Niphus* calleth this *Mastinus*, (which we call *Mastivus*) and that *Albertus* writeth how the *Lyciscus* is ingendred by a Bear and a Wolf. Notwithstanding the self same Author taketh it for the most part *pro Molosso*, a Dog of such a Countrey.

Of Mungrels and Rascals somewhat is to be spoken: and among these, of the Wappe of Turnspit, which name is made of two simple words, that is, of Turn, which in *Latine* soundeth *Vertere*, and of Spit which is *Veru*, or spede, for the *English* word inclineth closer to the *Italian* imitation, *Veruvorsator*, Turnspit. He is called also Waupe, of the natural noise of his voyce Wau, which he maketh in barking. But for the better and readier sound, the vowel U, is changed into the consonant P, so that for Waupe we say Wappe. And yet I wot well that *Nonius* borroweth his *Baubari* of the natural voyce Bau, as the *Græcians* do their *Bautein* of Wau.

Now when you understand this, that *Saltare* in *Latine* signifieth *Dansare* in *English*. And that our Dog is thereupon called a Dancer, and in the *Latine*, *Saltator*; you are so far taught as you were desirous to learn: and now I suppose, there remaineth nothing, but that your request is fully accomplished.

Thus (Friend *Gesner*) you have, not only the kindes of our Countrey Dogs, but their names also, as well in *Latine* as in *English*, their Offices, Services, Diversities, Natures, and Properties, that you can demand no more of me in this matter. And albeit I have not satisfied your minde peradventure (who suspectest all speed in the performance of your request imployed, to be meer delays) because I staid the setting forth of that unperfect pamphlet, which five years ago I sent to you as a private friend for your own reading, and not to be printed and so made common, yet I hope (having like the Bear lickt over my young) I have waded over in this work to your contentation, which delay hath made somewhat better, and *Deuterai phrontides*, after wit more meet to be perused.

Now it is convenient to shut up this treatise of Dogs, with a recital of their several diseases and cures thereof; for as all other creatures, so this beast is annoyed with many infirmities. First, therefore if you give unto a Dog every seventh day, or twice in seven days broath or pottage, wherein Ivy is sod, it will preserve him sound without any other medicine, for this herb hath the same operation in Dogs to make wholesome their meat, that it hath in Sheep to clense their pasture. The small fruits of Ellebor which are like to Onions, have power in them to purge the belly of Dogs: Other give them Goats-milk, or Salt beaten small, or Sea-crabs beaten small and put into water, or Staves-acre, and immediately after his purgation, sweet Milk. If your Dog be obstructed and stopped in the belly, which may be discerned by his trembling, sighing, and removing from place to place, give unto him Oaten meal and water to eat, mingled together and made as thick as a Pultess, or leavened Oaten bread, and sometime a little Whay to drink.

The Ancients have observed that Dogs are most annoyed with three diseases, the swelling of the throat, the Gowt, and madness; but the later Writers have observed many noysome infirmities in them. First, they are oftentimes wounded by the teeth of each other, and also of wilde Beasts: for cure whereof, *Blondus* out of *Maximus* writeth these remedies following: First, let the sinews, *fibres*, or gristles of the wound be laid together, then sow up the lips or upper skin of the wound with a needle and thred, and take of the hairs of the Dog which made the wound, and lay thereupon, untill the bleeding be stanched, and so leave it to the Dog to be licked; for nature hath so framed the Dogs tongue, that thereby in short space he cureth deep wounds.

And if he cannot touch the sore with his tongue, then doth he wet his foot in his mouth, and so oftentimes put it upon the maim: or if neither of these can be performed by the Beast himself, then cure it by casting upon it the ashes of a Dogs head, or burned salt, mingled with liquid pitch poured thereupon. When a Dog returning from hunting is hurt about the snowt, by the venemous teeth of some wilde Beast, I have seen it cured by making incision about the wound, whereby the poysoned bloud is evacuated, and afterward the sore was anoynted with Oyl of Saint Johns-wort. Wood-worms cure a Dog bitten by Serpents. When he is troubled with Ulcers or rindes in his skin, pieces of Pot-sheards beaten to powder and mingled with Vinegar and Turpentine, with the fat of a Goose; or else Water-wort with new Lard, applyed to the sore, easeth the same: and if it swell, anoynt it with Butter.

For the drawing forth of a thorn or splinter out of a Dogs foot, take Colts-foot and Lard, or the powder thereof burned in a new earthen pot; and either of these applyed to the foot, draweth forth the Thorn, and cureth the sore: for by *Dioscorides* it is said, to have force to extract any point of a Spear out of the body of a man. For the Worms which breed in the Ulcers of their heels, take *Unguentum Egyptiacum*, and the juyce of peach-leaves: There are some very skilful Hunters which affirm, that if you hang about the Dogs neck sticks of Citrine, as the wood dryeth, so will the Worms come forth and dy. Again, for this evill they wash the wounds with water, then rub it with Pitch, Thyme, and the dung of an Oxe in Vinegar; afterward they apply unto it the powder of Ellebor. When a Dog is troubled with the Mangie, Itch, or Ring-worms, first let him blood in his fore-legs in the greatest vein: afterward make an Ointment of Quick-silver, Brimstone, Nettle-seed, and twice so much old Sewet or Butter, and therewithall anoint him, putting thereunto if you please decoction of Hops and Salt water.

Some do wash Mangy Dogs in the Sea-water; and there is a Cave in *Sicily* (saith *Gratius*) that hath this force against the scabs of Dogs, if they be brought thither, and set in the running water which seemeth to be as thick as Oyl. Flegm or melancholy doth often engender these evils, and so after one Dog is infected, all the residue that accompany or lodge with him, are likewise poysoned: for the avoiding thereof, you must give them Fumitory, Sorrel, and Whay sod together; it is good also to wash them in the Sea, or in Smiths-water, or in the decoction aforesaid.

For the taking away of Warts from the feet of Dogs, or other members, first rub and friccase the Wart violently, and afterward anoint it with Salt, Oyl, Vinegar, and the powder of the rinde of a Gourd; or else lay unto it Aloes beaten with Mustard-seed, to eat it off, and afterward lay unto it the little scories or iron chips, which fly off from the Smiths hot iron while he beateth it, mingled with Vinegar, and it shall perfectly remove them.

Against Tikes, Lyce, and Fleas anoint the Dogs with bitter Almonds, Staves-acre, or roots of Maple, or Cipers, or froth of Oyl, if it be old; and anoint also their ears with Salt-water, and bitter Almonds, then shall not the flies in the Summer time enter into them. If Bees or Wasps, or such Beasts sting a Dog, lay to the sore burned Rue, with Water; and if a greater Fly, as the Horner, let the Water be warmed. A Dog shall be never infected with the Plague, if you put into his mouth in the time of any common Pestilence, the powder of a Storks craw, or Ventricle, or any part thereof with Water: which thing ought to be regarded, (for no creature is so soon infected with the Plague as is a Dog and a Mule) and therefore they must either at the beginning receive medicine, or else be removed out of the air, according to the advice of *Gratius*:

> *Sed varii ritus, nec in omnibus una potestas;*
> *Disce vices, & quæ tutela est proxima, tenta.*

Wolf-wort, and *Apocynon*, whose leaves are like the leaves of Ivie, and smell strongly, will kill all Beasts which are littered blinde; as Wolves, Foxes, Bears, and Dogs, if they eat thereof: So likewise will the root of *Chamæleon* and *Mezereon*, in Water and Oyl, it killeth Mice, Swine, and Dogs. *Ellebor*, and *Squilla*, and *Faba Lupina*, have the same operation. There is a Gourd (called *Zinziber* of the Water) because the taste thereof is like to Ginger, the Flower, Fruit, and Leaf thereof killeth Asses, Mules, Dogs, and many other four-footed Beasts. The Nuts *Vomicæ*, are poyson to Dogs, except their ear be cut presently and made to bleed. It will cause them to leap strangely up and down, and kill him within two hours after the tasting, if it be not prevented by the former remedy. *Theophrastus Chrysippus* affirmeth, that the water wherein Sperage hath been sod given to Dogs, killeth them: the fume of Silver or Lead hath the same operation.

If a Dog grow lean, and not through want of meat, it is good to fill him twice or thrice with Butter, and if that do not recover him, then it is a sign that the worm under his tongue annoyeth him, (which must be

330

presently pulled out by some Naul or Needle) and if that satisfie not, he cannot live, but will in short time perish. And it is to be noted, that Oaten bread leavened, will make a sluggish Dog to become lusty, agile, and full of spirit. Dogs are also many times bewitched, by the only sight of Inchanters, even as Infants, Lambs, and other creatures, according to *Virgils* verse;

Nescio quis teneros oculus mihi fascinat agnos.

For the bewitching spirit entereth by the eye into the heart of the party bewitched: for remedy whereof, they hang about the neck a chain of Corral, as for holy Herbs I hold them unprofitable.

To cure the watry eyes of Dogs; take warm water, and first wash them therewith, and then make a plaister of meal and the white of an Egge, and so lay it thereunto. By reason of that saying, Eccles. 20. cap. *Bribes and gifts blinde the eyes of Iudges, even as a dumb Dog turneth away Correction.* Some have delivered, that green Crow-foot forced into the mouth of a Dog, maketh him dumb, and not able to bark: When a Dog becometh deaf, the Oyl of Roses with new pressed Wine infused into his ears, cureth him: and for the Worms in the ears, make a plaister of a beaten Spunge and the white of an Egge, and that shall cure it.

The third kinde of Quinancy (called *Synanche*) killeth Dogs, because it bloweth up their chaps, and includeth their breath. The Cough is very noysome to Dogs, wherefore their keepers must infuse into their Nostrils two cups of Wine, with bruised sweet Almonds: but *Tardinus* for this disease prescribed great Parsley sod with Oyl, Honey, and Wine, and so given to the Dog. For the shortness of the breath, bore him through the ear, and if there be any help, that will prevail.

If a bone stick in the mouth of a Dog, hold up his head backward, and pour Ale into his mouth untill he cough, and so shall he be eased. When a Dog hath surfeited, and falleth to loath his meat, he eateth the herb *Canaria*, and is relieved (both against his furfeit, and also the bitings of Serpents.) For the Worms in the belly, he eateth Wheat in the stalk. The Gowt maketh the Dogs legs grow crooked, and it is never so cured, but that after a course or two they grow lame again. When his skin flyeth from his nails, take meal and water, and binde them thereunto for a remedy; and these are for the most part, those diseases wherewithall Dogs are infected, and the other are either cured by heat, or by eating of grass: and so for this part, I conclude both the sickness and cure of Dogs, with the saying of *Gratius*:

Mille tenent pestes, curaque potentia major.

Concerning the madness of Dogs, and their venemous bitings, we are now to speak: and first of all, no reasonable man ought to doubt, why the teeth of a mad Dog should do more harm then of a sound and healthy one: because in rage and anger, the teeth of every Beast and creature, receive venome and poyson from the head (as it is well observed by *Ægineta*) and so at that time fastning their teeth, they do more harm then at other times. Against the simple biting of a Dog, it is sufficient but to use the urine of a Dog, for there is not much venome in those wounds; and the urine also will draw out the prickles of a Hedge-hog, because such wounds have in them but little poyson. Also (as *Aetius* prescribeth) it is very soveraign in such wounds, first of all to cover and rub the sore with the palm of ones hand, and then pour into it Vinegar and *Nitre*, so as it may descend to the bottom of the wound, and afterward lay unto it a new spunge wetted in the same Vinegar and *Nitre*, and let it be so continued for the space of three days, and by the working thereof it shall be whole.

Also it is generally to be observed in all the bitings of men by Dogs, that first of all it is requisite, that the wound be well rubbed over by the palm of the hand with Vinegar, then pour into the wounds Vinegar mixed with water or with *Nitre*, laying also a spunge thereupon, and so binde it upon the place, having first wetted the cloaths wherewithall you binde it with the said Vinegar mixed, so let it remain bound up three days together, and afterward follow the common course of curing, as in every vulgar wounds, or else, lay thereunto Pellitory of the Wall, mingled and beaten with Salt, changing it every day, untill the crust or upper skin fall away.

It is also good sometimes, the holes being small, to wet Lint in Vinegar, and to purge the wound with powder of Anise-seed, or Cumin; laying the Lint upon the Anise for two or three days. The same being thus purged, take a medicine of the equall parts of Hony, Turpentine,

Butter, Goose-grease, Marrow of a Hart, or Calf, melted betwixt the teeth of a man, and lay it thereunto, for it also cureth the bitings of men: but if the sore be inflamed, then lay unto it Lentils sod with the parings of Apples, and dryed, or the crums of bread with the juyce of Beets, and a little Oyl of Roses, made like a plaister.

Divers Authors have also prescribed these outward medicines against the bitings of Dogs in general, namely Vinegar spunged, the Lees of Vinegar, with *Nigella Romana*, *Venus* Hair, Alabaster, Brine with Lint, Garlick mixed with Honey, and taken into the body, Lees of Wine, Almonds both sweet and bitter mingled with Honey, dryed Anise-seeds burned, the leaves of black Hore-hound, or Archangel beaten with Salt, Scallions with Honey and Pepper of the case, the juyce of Onyons with Rue and Honey, or raw Onyons with Hony and Vinegar, but sod ones with Honey and Wine, (if they be green) let them ly to the wound three days: the ashes of Vine-trees with Oyl, ashes of a Fig-tree with a Sear-cloth, beside infinite other elaborate medicines, drawn from Trees, Fruits, Fields, Gardens, and all other creatures; as if Nature had only stroven to provide sundry ready cures for this evill above all other.

Leaving therefore the simple bitings of Dogs, let us proceed to the madness of Dogs and their bitings, wherein the greater danger must be considered, with greater circumspection of remedies. First therefore, the Ancients have derived *Rabiem*, of *Raviem*, madness, of the hoarsness of voyce, (because a Dog at that time hath no perfect voyce.) But it is more probable, that *Rabies* cometh of *Rapiendo*, because when a Dog beginneth to be oppressed herewith, he biteth, snatcheth, runneth to and fro, and is carryed from home and Master, to his own perdition: this by the *Græcians* is called *Lytta*, and *Cynolossos*.

By this evill, not only Dogs perish, but all other creatures (except a Goose) bitten by them: and a man doth not escape without great perill. For *Albertus* relateth a story, of a man whose arm was bitten by a mad Dog, and after twelve years the sore brake forth again, and he dyed within two days; and the reason hereof was (as in all likelihood that of *Cælius*) that when one and the same nature infecteth each other, as Dogs do Dogs, and men do men, then by reason of their similitude and natural sympathy, they receive the consuming poyson with all speed: but if another nature infect that, betwixt whom in inclination and passion, there is a dissimilitude and antipathy, (as is betwixt a Dog and a Man) then will the poyson receive greater opposition, and be so much the longer before it receive predominant operation, because the first overcometh Nature by treason, against which there is no resistance; and the second by open force and proclamation of War, against which all the strength and force of nature is combined and opposed.

Hereof also it came to pass, that the Noble Lawyer *Baldus*, playing with his Dog at *Trent*, was bitten by him in his lip, and neglecting the matter (because he never suspected the Dogs madness) after four moneths the poyson wrought upon him, and he perished miserably. Those Beasts which have teeth like saws, (as Dogs, Wolves, and Foxes) go mad by nature, without the bitings of others, but those which have no such teeth (as Asses and Mules,) fall not mad at any time untill they be bitten by other.

Also it hath been observed, that sometimes a mad Dog hath bitten, and there hath followed no harm at all, whereof this was the reason, because poyson is not equally in all his teeth; and therefore biting with the purer and wholesomer, the wound became not perillous.

A man bitten with a mad Dog, falleth mad presently when he cometh under the shadow of a Corn-tree; as it is affirmed by most Physitians, for that shadow setteth the poyson on fire: but a man falling mad, of all creatures avoideth a Dog, and a Dog most of all falleth upon men. There are many things which ingender madness in Dogs, as hot wheaten bread dipped in Bean-water, melancholy bred within them, and not purged by *Canaria*, or other herbs, the menstruous pollutions of Women, and the pain of his teeth. Their madness is most dangerous in the Dog-days, for then they both kill and perish mortally; for at that time their spittle or fome, falling upon mans body, breedeth great danger; and that if a man tread upon the Urine of a mad Dog, he shall feel pain by it if he have a sore about him: from whence it came to pass, that a stone bitten by such a Dog, was a common proverb of discord. Also it is observed, that if a wound be dressed in the presence of man or woman, which hath been bitten by a mad Dog, that the pain thereof wil be encreased: and which is more, that abortment will follow upon Beasts with young, or Egges covered by the Hen, by their presence: But for remedy, they wash their hands and sprinckle themselves, or the Beasts with that water, whereby the evill is to be cured.

If the gall of a mad Dog, about the bigness of a Lentill seed be eaten, it killeth within seven days, or else doth no harm at all, if it pass seven days without operation. When a mad Dog had suddenly tore in pieces a garment about ones body; the Taylor or Botcher took the same to mend, and forgetting himself, put one side of the breach into his mouth to stretch it out to the other, and fell mad immediately. Men thus affected, fear all waters, their virile member continually standeth, they suffer many Convulsions, and oftentimes bark like Dogs.

There was a certain Mason at *Zurick*, who had his finger grievously bitten with a mad Dog about *Iuly*, whereunto he laid Garlick, Rue, and Oyl of Scorpions, and so it seemed to be healed, wherefore he took no counsel of any Physitian. About *August* following, he was taken with a Feaver, being first very cold, then very hot, and so continued sweating for a day or two, and could not endure the cold air. He thirsted much, yet when water or drink was brought him, he was so afraid thereof that he could not drink: his sweat was cold, and when he felt any cold air, he cryed out for fear it had been water: thus he remained trembling, and offering to vomit at the sight of water, many times howling, and so perished after two days ended.

When a Dog is mad it may be known by these signes, for he will neither eat nor drink, he looketh awry and more sadly then ordinary; his body is lean, he casteth sorth thick fleam out of his nostrils or mouth: He breatheth gaping, and his tongue hangeth out of his mouth. His ears is limber and weak, his tail hangeth downward: his pace is heavy and sluggish untill he run, and then it is more rash, intemperate and uncertain. Sometimes running, and presently after standing still again: he is very thirsty, but yet abstaineth from drink, he barketh not, and knoweth no man, biteing both strangers and friends. His head hangeth downward; he is fearful, and runneth into secret places from his whelps or fellows, who often bark at him, and will not eat of bread upon which his bloud hath fallen. His eyes grow very red; he many times dyeth for fear of water: some discern it by laying Nuts or grains of Corn to the bitten place, and afterward take them away and cast them to Hens or Pullen, who for hunger will eat them, and if after the eating the fowl live, the Dog will not be mad; but if it dye, then for certainty the Dog will fall mad. The which passions do also agree with them that are bitten by him; and it is not to be forgotten, that the bitings of the female bring more danger then the males.

The bodies of them that are thus wounded grow very dry, and are pressed with inward burning Feavers, if by Musick and delightful sports they be not kept waking; many times they dye suddenly, or else recover for a small time, and then fall into a relapsed malady.

Some give this to be the cause of their fear of water, because their body growing dry, seemeth to forget all participation with humidity: but *Rufus* affirmeth, this cometh from melancholy, wherewithall these persons are most commonly affected: which agreeth with an imagination they have, that they see Dogs in the water, and indeed it cannot be but their own countenance, which in these passions is very red, doth wonderfully afflict them, both in the water, and in all looking glasses.

When a certain Philosopher (being bitten by a mad Dog) entred into a Bath, and a strong apparition of a Dog presented it self unto him therein, he strove against this imagination with a singular confident courage to the contrary, saying within himself; *Quid Cani commune est cum Balneo?* what hath a Dog to do in a Bath? and so went in and overcame his disease: which thing had seldom chanced, that a man hath recovered this malady after he fell into fear and trembling, except *Eudemus* and *Themiso*, who obeying the request of a friend of his, entred likewise into the water, and after many torments was recovered.

To conclude, some men in this extremity suffer most fearful dreams, profusion of seed, hoarsness of voyce, shortness of breath, retention of urine, which also changeth colour, being sometimes black, sometimes like milk, sometime thick, sometime thin as water, rumbling in the belly, by reason of crudity, redness of the whole body, distention of nerves, heaviness of minde, love of darkness, and such like. Yet doth not this operation appear presently upon the hurt, but sometimes at nine days, sometimes at forty days, sometimes at half a year, or a year, or seven, or twelve year, as hath been already said.

For the cure of these Dogs, and first of all for the preventing of madness, there are sundry invented observations. First, it is good to shut them up, and make them to fast for one day, then purge them with *Hellebor*, and being purged, nourish them with bread of Barley-meal. Other take them when they be young whelps, and take out of their tongue a certain little worm, which the *Græcians* call *Lytta*; after which time they never grow mad, or fall to vomiting, as *Gracius* noted in these verses;

> *Namque subit nodis qua lingua tenacibus hæret*
> *Vermiculum dixere, mala atque incondita pestis, &c.*
> *Iam teneris elementa mali, causasque recidunt.*

But immediately it being taken forth, they rub the tongue with Salt and Oyl. *Columella* teacheth that Shepheards of his time, took their Dogs tails, and pulled out a certain nerve or sinew, which cometh from the Articles of the Back-bone into their tails, whereby they not only kept the tail from growing deformed and over-long, but also constantly believed, that their Dogs could never afterward fall mad: whereunto *Pliny* agreeth, calling it a castration or gelding of the tail, adding, that it must be done before the Dog be forty days old. Some again say, that if a Dog taste of a Womans milk which she giveth by the birth of a Boy, he will never fall mad. *Nemesian* ascribeth the cure hereof to *Castoreum* dryed and put into milk, but this is to be understood of them that are already mad, whose elegant verses of the cause, beginning, and cure of a mad Dog, I have thought good here to express:

> *Exhalat seu terra sinus, seu noxius aer*
> *Causa mali; seu cum gelidus non sufficit humor,*
> *Torrida per venas concrescunt semina flammæ.*

Whatsoever it be, he thus warranteth the cure.

> *Tunc virosa tibi sumes, multumque domabis*
> *Castorea, adtritu silicis lentescere coges.*
> *Ex ebore huc trito pulvis lectove feratur*
> *Admiscensq diu facies concrescere utrumque.*
> *Mox lactis liquidos sensim superadde fluores,*

337

Ut non cunctantes hanstus infundere cornu.
Inserto possis, furiasque repellere tristes.

Armetia a King of *Valentia*, prescribeth this form for the cure of this evill: let the Dog be put into the water, so as the hinder-legs do only touch the ground, and his fore-legs be tyed up like hands over his head, and then being taken again out of the water, let his hair be shaved off, that he may be pieled untill he bleed: then anoint him with Oyl of Beets, and if this do not cure him within seven days, then let him be knocked on the head, or hanged out of the way.

When a young male Dog suffereth madness, shut him up with a Bitch; or if a young Bitch be also oppressed, shut her up with a Dog, and the one of them will cure the madness of the other.

But the better part of this labor, is more needful to be employed about the curing of men, or other creatures which are bitten by Dogs, then in curing or preventing that natural infirmity. Wherefore it is to be remembred, that all other poysoned wounds are cured by incision and circumcising of the flesh, and by drawing plaisters, which extract the venom out of the flesh, and comfort nature; and by Cupping-glasses, or burning Irons, (as *Cœlius* affirmeth) upon occasion of the miraculous fiction of the Temple door Key of S. *Bellious*, neer *Rhodigium*; for it was believed, that if a mad man could hold that Key in his hand red hot, he should be delivered from his fits for ever.

There was such another charm or incantation among the *Apuletans*, made in form of a prayer against all bitings of mad Dogs, and other poysons, unto an obscure Saint (called *Vithus*) which was to be said three Saterdays in the evening, nine times together, which I have here set down for no other cause but to shew their extream folly.

Aime Vithe pellicane   *Irasque canum mitigas,*
Oram qui tenes Appulam, *Tu sancte rabiem asperam*
Littusque Polygnanicum, *Rictusque canis luridos,*
Qui morsus rabidos levas, *Tu sævam prohibe luem.*
I procul hinc rabies, procul hinc furor omnis abesto.

But to come to the cure of such as have been bitten by mad Dogs: First I will set down some compound medicines to be outwardly applyed to the body: Secondly, some simple or uncompounded medicines: In the third place such compounded and uncompounded potions, as are to be taken inwardly against this poyson.

For the outward compound remedies, a plaister made of *Opponax* and Pitch, is much commended, which *Menippus* used, taking a pound of Pitch of *Bruttas*, and four ounces of *Opponax* (as *Ætius* and *Actuarius* do prescribe) adding withall, that the *Opponax* must be dissolved in Vinegar, and afterward the Pitch and that Vinegar must be boyled together, and when the Vinegar is consumed, then put in the *Opponax*, and of both together make like taynters or splints, and thrust them into the wound, so let them remain many days together, and in the mean time drink an Antidote of Sea-crabs and Vinegar, (for Vinegar is alway pretious in this confection.) Other use *Basilica*, Onyons, Rue, Salt, rust of Iron, White bread, seeds of Horehound, and Triacle: but the other plaister is most forcible to be applyed outwardly, above all medicines in the world.

For the simple and uncompounded medicines to be taken against this sore, are many: As Goose-grease, Garlike, the root of wilde Roses drunk; bitter Almonds, leaves of Chickweed, or Pimpernel, the old skin of a Snake pounded with a male-Sea-crab, Betony, Cabbage leaves, or stalks, with Parsneps and Vinegar, Lime and Sewet, powder of Sea-crabs with Hony; powder of the shels of Sea-crabs, the hairs of a Dog laid upon the wound, the head of the Dog which did bite, mixed with a little *Euphorbium*; the hair of a Man with Vinegar, dung of Goats with Wine, Walnuts with Hony and Salt, powder of Fig-tree in a Sear-cloth, Fitches in Wine, *Euphorbium*; warm Horse-dung, raw Beans chewed in the mouth, Fig-tree-leaves, green Figs with Vinegar, fennel stalks, *Gentiana*, dung of Pullen, the liver of a Buck-Goat, young Swallows burned to powder, also their dung; the urine of a Man, an *Hyæna* skin, Flower-deluce with Honey, a Sea-hearb called *Kakille, Silphum* with Salt, the flesh and shels of Snayls, Leek-seeds with Salt, Mints, the tail of a Field-mouse cut off from her alive, and she suffered to live, roots of Burs, with Salt of the Sea-Plantain, the tongue of a Ram with Salt, the flesh of all Sea-fishes, the fat of a Sea-calf and Vervine; beside many other superstitious Amulets which are used to be bound to the arms necks, and

339

breasts, as the Canine-tooth bound up in a leaf and tyed to the arm; a Worm bred in the dung of Dogs hanged about the neck; the root of *Gentian* in an *Hyænaes* skin, or young Wolfs skin, and such like; whereof I know no reason beside the opinion of men.

The inward compound potions or remedies against the bitings of Dogs may be such as these. Take Sea-crabs, and burn them with twigs of white Vines, and save their ashes, then put to them the powder of *Gentian* root well cleansed, and small beaten, and as oft as need requireth take two spoonfuls of the first, and one of the second, and put them into a cup of pure and unmixed Wine, and so drink it for four days together, being well beaten and stirred, so as the Wine be as thick as a Cawdle; and there is nothing more forcible then Sea-crabs, *Hiera, Diascincum,* powder of Walnuts in warm rain Water, Triacle, *Castoreum,* Pills, Spurge-seed, and a decoction of *Indian* thorn with Vervine given in water. These may serve for several compound inward remedies against these poysons, and now follow the simple.

First eating of Garlike in our meat, drinking of Wormwood, Rams flesh burned and put into Wine so drunk. There is an Herb called *Alysson,* by reason of the power it hath against this evil, which being bruised and drunk, cureth it. The liver of a Boar dryed and drunk in Wine, hath the same operation Jews lime drunk in water, Leeks and Onyons in meat, Dogs bloud, the head, the vein under the tongue (commonly supposed to be a worm) and the liver of the Dog which hath done the hurt, are also prescribed for a remedy of this evill: but especially the liver or rennet of a young Puppey, the rinde of a wilde Fig-tree, a dram of *Castoreum,* with Oyl of Roses, Centaury, or *Chamæleon*; the root of a wilde Rose; (called *Cynorrhodon* and *Cynosbaton*) *Ellebor*; the brain of a Hen drunk in some liquor, Sorrel, Honey, Mints, and Plantaine: but *Pimpinella Germanica* is given to all Cattel which are bitten by a mad Dog. Besides many other such like, which for brevity sake I omit, concluding against all superstitious curing by Inchantments or supposed Miracles, such as is in a certain Church of S. *Lambert,* in a City of *Picardy,* where the Mass Priests, when a man is brought unto them having this evill, they cut a cross in his forehead, and lay upon the wound a piece of S. *Lamberts* stole burning, (which they say (though falsly) is reserved to this day without diminution) then do they sow up the wound again, and say another plaister upon it, prescribing him a dyet; which is to drink water, and to eat hard Egs, but if the party amend not within forty days, they binde him hand and foot in his bed, and saying another bed upon him, there strangle him, as they think without all sin) and for preventing of much harm that may come by his life, if he should bite another. This story is related by *Alysius*, and it is worth the noting, how murther accompanieth superstitious humane inventions, and the vain presumptuous confidence of Cross-worshippers: and thus much of the madness of Dogs, and the cure thereof in men and beasts.

In the next place, the conclusion of this tedious discourse followeth, which is the natural medicines arising out of the bodies of Dogs, and so we will tye them up for this time.

Whereas the inward parts of men are troubled with many evils, it is delivered for truth, that if little *Melitæan* Dogs, or young sucking Puppies, be laid to the breast of a childe or man that hath infectious passions or pains in his entrails, the pain will depart from the man into the beast; for which cause they burned them when they were dead. *Serenus* doth express this very elegantly, saying;

> *Quin etiam catulum lactentem apponere membris*
> *Convenit, omne malum transcurrere fertur in illum.*
> *Cui tamen extincto munus debetur humandi,*
> *Humanos quia contactus mala tanta sequuntur,*
> *Et junctum vitium ducit de conjuge conjux.*

If a Whelp be cut asunder alive, and laid upon the head of a mad melancholike woman, it shall cure her, and it hath the same power against the Spleen. If a woman grow barren after she hath born children, let her eat young Whelp-flesh, and *Polypus* fish sod in Wine and drink the broth, and she shall have ease of all infirmities in her stomach and womb. Water distilled out of Whelps, causeth that pieled or shaven places shall never have more hair grow upon them.

With the fat of whelps, bowelled and sod till the flesh come from the bones, and then taken and put into another Vessel, and the weak, resolute, or paralytike members being therewith anointed, they are much eased if not recovered. *Alysius* saith, he made experience of Puppies sod alive in Oyl, whereby he cured his Gowty legd Horses, and therefore it cannot chuse but be much more profitable for a man.

The skin of a Dog held with the five fingers, stayeth Distillations; it hath the same operation in gloves and stockins, and it will also ease both Ach in the belly, head, and feet, and therefore it is used to be worn in the shoes against the Gowt.

The flesh of mad Dogs is salted, and given in meat to them which are bitten by mad Dogs for a singular remedy. The bloud is commended against all intoxicating poysons and pains in the small guts, and it cureth scabs. The fat is used against deafness of the ears, the Gowt, Nits in the head, and incontinency of urine, given with Alum. A plaister made of the Marrow of a Dog and old Wine, is good against the falling of the fundament. The hair of a black Dog easeth the Falling sickness, the Brains of a Dog in Lint and Wool laid to a mans broken bones for fourteen days together, doth consolidate and joyn them together again, which thing caused *Serenus* to make these excellent verses:

> *Infandum dictu cunctis procul absit amicis,*
> *Sed fortuna potens omen convertat in hostes,*
> *Vis indigna novo si parserit ossa fragore,*
> *Conveniet cerebrum blandi Canis addere fractis,*
> *Lintea deinde super que inductu nectere lanas*
> *Sæpius & succos conspergere pinguis olivi,*
> *Bis septem credunt revale scere cuncta diebus.*

The brain-pan or skull of a Dog clove asunder, is applyed to heal the pain in the eyes; that is, if the right eye be grieved, thereunto apply the right side of the skull, if the left eye, the left side.

The vertues of a Dogs head made into powder are both many and unspeakable, by it is the biting of mad Dogs cured; it cureth spots and bunches in the head; and a plaister thereof made with Oyl of Roses, healeth the running in the head: it cureth also all tumors in privy parts, and in the fear, the chippings in the fingers, and many other diseases.

The powder of the teeth of Dogs, maketh Childrens teeth to come forth with speed and ease, and if their gums be rubd with a Dogs tooth, it maketh them to have the sharper teeth: and the powder of these Dogs teeth rubbed upon the gums of young or old, easeth Tooth-ach, and abateth swelling in the gums. The tongue of a Dog is most wholesome both for the curing of his own wounds by licking, as also of any other creatures. The Rennet of a Puppey drunk with Wine, dissolveth the Colick in the same hour wherein it is drunk: and the Vomit of a Dog laid upon the belly of a Hydropick man, causeth water to come forth at his stool. The gall healeth all wheals and blisters after they be pricked with a Needle, and mingled with Honey it cureth pain in the eyes, and taketh away white spots from them: likewise infused into the ears, openeth all stoppings, and cureth all inward pains in them.

The Spleen drunk in Urine, cureth the Spleenetick; the milt being taken from the Dog alive, hath the same vertue to help the milt of man. The skin of Bitches wherein they conceive their Puppies (which never touched the earth) is pretious against difficulty in Childe-birth, and it draweth the Infant out of the womb. The milk of a Bitches first whelping, is an antidote against poyson, and the same causeth hair never to come again, if it be rubbed upon the place where hairs are newly pulled off: Also infused into the eyes, driveth away the whiteness of them. Likewise there is no better thing to anoint the gums of young children withall, before they have teeth, for it maketh them to come forth with ease: it easeth likewise the pain of the ears, and with all speed healeth burnt mouths by any hot meat: *Ora ambusta cibo sanabis lacte Canino.*

The urine of a Dog taketh away spots and warts, and being mingled with Salt of *Nitre*, wonderfully easeth the Kings Evill. The dung of Dogs (called by the Apothecaries *Album Græcum*) because the white is best, being ingendred by eating of bones, and therefore hath no ill favour; *Galen* affirmeth, that his Masters in Physick, used it against old sores, Bloody flixes, and the Quinsie; and it is very profitable to stanch the bloud of Dogs; and also against the inflamations in the breast of Women mingled with Turpentine. It was well prescribed by *Avicen*, to expell congealed bloud out of the stomach and bladder, being taken thereof so much in powder as will lye upon a Golden Noble.

OF THE ETHIOPIAN EAL.

THERE is bred in *Ethiopia* a certain strange Beast about the bigness of a Sea-horse, being of colour black or brownish: it hath the cheeks of a Boar, the tail of an Elephant, and horns above a cubit long, which are moveable upon his head at his own pleasure like ears; now standing one way, and anon moving another way, as he needeth in fighting with other Beasts, for they stand not stiffe, but bend flexibly; and when he fighteth, he alway stretcheth out the one, and holdeth in the other, of purpose as it may seem, that if one of them be blunted and broken, then he may defend himself with the other. It may well be compared to a Sea-horse, for above all other places it loveth best the waters.

OF THE ELEPHANT.

THERE is no creature among all the Beasts of the world, which hath so great and ample demonstration of the power and wisdom of Almighty God as the Elephant: both for proportion of body and disposition of spirit; and it is admirable to behold the industry of our ancient fore-fathers, and noble desire to benefit us their posterity, by searching into the qualities of every Beast, to discover what benefits or harms may come by them to mankinde: having never been afraid either of the wildest, but they tamed them; the fiercest, but they ruled them; and the greatest, but they also set upon them. Witness for this part the Elephant, being like a living Mountain in quantity and outward appearance, yet by them so handled, as no little Dog became more serviceable and tractable.

Among all the *Europæans* the first possessor of Elephants, was *Alexander Magnus*, and after him *Antigonus*, and before the *Macedonians* came into *Asia*, no people of the world, except the *Africans* and the *Indians*, had ever seen Elephants. When *Fabritius* was sent by the *Romans* to King *Pyrrhus* in Ambassage, *Pyrrhus* offered to him a great sum of money, to prevent the War, but he refused private gain; and preferred the service of his Countrey: the next day he brought him into his presence, and thinking to terrifie him, placed behinde him a great Elephant, shadowed with cloth of Arras; the cloth was drawn, and the huge Beast instantly laid his trunk upon the head of *Fabritius*, sending forth a terrible and direful voyce: whereat *Fabritius* laughing, perceiving the policy of the King, gently made this speech;

Neque heri aurum, neque hodie bestia me permovit.

I was neither tempted with thy Gold yesterday, nor terrified with the sight of this Beast to day: and so afterward *Pyrrhus* was overcome in War by the *Romans*, and *Manlius Curius Dentatus* did first of all bring Elephants in Triumph to *Rome*, calling them *Lucanæ Boves*, Oxen of the Wood, about the 472 year of the City; and afterward in the year of *Romes* building 502 when *Metellus* was high Priest, and overthrew the *Carthaginians* in *Sicily*, there were 142 Elephants brought in Ships to *Rome* and led in triumph, which *Lucius Piso* afterward, to take away from the people opinions of the fear of them, caused them to be brought to the stage to open view and handling, and so slain; which thing *Pompey* did also by the slaughter of five hundred Lions and Elephants together; so that in the time of *Gordianus*, it was no wonder to see thirty and two of them at one time.

An Elephant is by the *Hebrews* called *Behemah*, by way of excellency, as the *Latins* for the same cause call him *Bellua*, the *Chaldeans* for the same word, Deut. 14. translate *Beira*; the *Arabians, Behitz*; the *Persians, Behad*; and the *Septuagint, Ktene*; but the *Grecians* vulgarly *Elephas*, not *Quasi Elebas*, because they joyn copulation in the water, but rather from the *Hebrew* word *Dephil*; signifying the Ivory tooth of an Elephant (as *Munster* well observeth.) The *Hebrews* also use the word *Schon* for an Elephants tooth. Moreover *Hesychius* called an Elephant in the *Greek* tongue *Perissas*; the *Latins* do indifferently use *Elephas* and *Elephantus*; and it is said that *Elephantus* in the *Punick* tongue, signifieth *Cæsar*: whereupon when the Grandfather of *Julius Cæsar* had slain an Elephant, he had the name of *Cæsar* put upon him.

The *Italians* call this beast *Leofante*, or *Lionfante*; the *French, Elephante*; the *Germans, Helfant*; the *Illyrians, Slon*. We read but of three appellative names of Elephants; that is of one, called by *Alexander* the great *Ajax*, because he had read that the buckler of great *Ajax* was covered with an Elephants skin, about whose neck he put a Golden collar, and so sent him away with liberty. *Antiochus* one of *Alexanders* successors had two Elephants, one of them he likewise called *Ajax*, in imitation of *Alexander*, and the other *Patroclus*, of which two this story is reported by *Antipater*. That when *Antiochus* came to a certain ford or deep water, *Ajax* which was alway the Captain of the residue, having sounded the depth thereof, refused to passe over, and turned back again, then the King spake to the Elephants and pronounced, that he which would passe over should have principality over the residue: whereupon *Patroclus* gave the adventure, and passed over safely, and received from the King the silver trappings and all other prerogatives of principality; the other seeing it (which had alway been chief till that time) preferred death before ignominy and disgrace, and so would never after eat meat but famished for sorrow.

They are bred in the hot Eastern Countries, for by reason they can endure no cold, they keep only in the East and South. Among all, the *Indian* Elephants are greatest, strongest, and tallest, and there are among them of two sorts, one greater (which are called *Prasii*) the other smaller (called *Taxilæ*) They be also bred in *Africa*, in Lybia, much greater then a *Nysæan* Horse, and yet every way inferiour to the *Indian*; for which cause, if an *African* Elephant do but see an *Indian*, he trembleth, and laboureth by all means to get out of his sight, as being guilty of their own weakness.

There are Elephants also in the Isle *Taprobane*, and in *Sumatra* in *Africa*. They are bred in *Lybia*, in *Æthiopia*, among the *Troglodytæ*, and in the Mountain *Atlas, Syrtes, Zames*, and *Sala*, the seven Mountains of *Tingitania*, and in the Countrey of *Basman*, subject to the great *Cham*. Some Authors affirm, that the *African* Elephants are much greater then the *Indian*, but with no greater reason then *Columella* writeth, that there be as great beasts found in *Italy* as Elephants are: whereunto no sound Author ever yeelded.

Of all earthly creatures an Elephant is the greatest: for in *India* they are nine cubits high, and five cubits broad; in *Africa* fourteen or fifteen full spans, which is about eleven foot high and proportionable in breadth, which caused *Ælianus* to write, that one Elephant is as big as three Bugils; and among these the Males are ever greater then the Females. In the Kingdom of *Melinda* in *Africk*, there were two young ones not above six monthes old, whereof the least was as great as the greatest Ox, but his flesh was as much as you shall finde in two Oxen; the other was much grater.

Their colour is for the most part mouse-colour, or black; and there was one all white in *Ethiopia*: The skin looketh pieled and scabby; it is most hard on the back, but softer underneath the belly, having no covering of hair or gristles, nor yet help by his tail to drive away the flies, for that evill doth this beast feel in his great body, but alway hath crevises in his skin, which by their savour do invite the little flies to a continual feast, but when by stretching forth they have received the swarmes, by shrinking together again, they inclose the flies, and so kill them: so that these crevises in his skin, are unto him in stead of a main, tail, and hair: yet there are some few hairs which grow scattering upon his hide, whereof some have been brought out of *America* into *Germany*, which were two palms long, but not so stiffe as Swines.

Their skin is so hard and stiffe, that a sharpe sword or iron cannot pierce it. Their head is very great, and the head of a man may easily enter into their mouth, as a finger into the mouth of a Dog; but yet their ears and eyes are not equivalent to the residue of their proportion: for they are small like the wings of a Bat or a Dragon, those of the *Ethiopian*

347

Sambri want ears altogether. Their eyes are like the eyes of Swine, but very red; they have teeth of either side four, wherewith they grind their meat like meal, and they have also two other which hang forth beyond the residue, in the males downward, and these are the greater and crooked; but in the females upward and they are the smaller and straight: the one of them they keep alwayes sharp, to revenge injuries, and with the other they root up plants and trees, for their meat; so that nature hath armed both sexes with these for their chiefest defence; and with these the females are calved at the first, and indued from the mothers belly, and appear so soon as they come forth; the males not so quickly, but rather after the manner of Bores and Sea-horses, they hang out of their mouthes, and grow to be ten foot long, whereof they make posts of houses in some Countreys, and call them *Ebora*, that is, young Ivory; which caused *Martial* to write thus;

> *Grandia taurorum portant qui corpora, quæris*
> *An Lybicas possint sustinuisse trabes.*

There is a certain Book extant, without the name of the Author, written of *Judea* or the *Holy land*, wherein the Author affirmeth that he saw an Elephants tooth sold to a *Venetian* Merchant for six and thirty Ducats, it being fourteen spans long, and four spans broad, and it weighed so heavy, that he could not move it from the ground.

Vartomanus also saith, that he saw in the Isle of *Sumatra*, two Elephants teeth, which weighed three hundred six and thirty pounds. This is certain, that the teeth of those Elephants which live in the Marishes and watry places, are so smooth and hard, as they seem intractable, and in some places they have holes in them, and again certain bunches as big as hail-stones, which are so hard, as no art or instrument can work upon them.

The Elephants of the Mountains have lesser and whiter teeth, fit to be applyed to any work, but the best of all, are the teeth of the *Campestrial* and field Elephants, which are whitest and softest, and may well be handled without all pain. The teeth of the female are more pretious then of the male, and these they lose every tenth year; which falling off, they bury and cover in the earth, pressing them down by sitting upon them, and then heal them over with earth by their feet, and so in short time the grasse groweth upon them: for, as when they are hunted they know it is for no other cause then their teeth; so also when they lose their teeth, they desire to keep them from men, lest the virtues of them being discovered, they which bear them should enjoy the lesse peace and security.

It is admirable what devises the people of *India* and *Africa* have invented by natural observation, to finde out these buried teeth, which unto us living in the remote parts of the world, we would judge impossible by any ordinary or lawful course, except we should turn up the earth of a whole Countrey, or go to work by diabolical conjuration; yet have they found out this facile and ready course. In the woods or fields where they suspect these teeth to be buried, they bring forth pots or bottles of water, and disperse them, here one, there another, and so let them stand, and tarry to watch them, so one sleepeth, another singeth, or bestoweth his time as he pleaseth; after a little time, they go and look in their pots, and if the teeth lie near their bottles, by an unspeakable and secret attractive power in nature, they draw all the water out of them that are neer them, which the watchman taketh for a sure sign, and so diggeth about his bottle, till he finde the tooth: but if their bottles be not emptied, they remove to seek in another place.

These Ivory teeth have been alway of great estimation among all the Nations that ever knew them, the *Ethiopians* payed for a tribute unto the King of *Persia* every third year twenty of these teeth hung about with gold and Jet-wood. These are sold by weight, and there be many which deceive the world with the bones of Fishes in stead hereof, but the true Ivory is paler and heavier, and falling upon the ground will easily break, whereas the bones of Fishes are more tenacious, light and strong. It is like to the *Chernites* wherein *Darius* was entombed, and the Marble called *Lapis Coraliticus*, Coral stone: like unto this is the *Alagi* stone, and the *Pæderos* Jewel. With this Ivory they made images and statues for their Idol gods, as one for *Pallas* in *Athens*, for *Esculapius* in *Epidaurus*, for *Venus* under the name of *Urania* by *Phidias*, whereupon she was called *Elephantina*, for *Apollo* at *Rome*: and therefore *Pausanias* wondereth at the *Grecians* that spared no cost for the vain worship of their gods, for they brought of the *Indians* and *Ethiopians* Ivory to make their Images with more pomp and ostentation: besides of Ivory they make the hafts of knives, and also the best combs, and *Solomon* as appeareth 3 Reg. 10. had a throne of Ivory covered all over with gold, for the costs and charge whereof he could not expend lesse then thirty thousand talents.

The greatness of these appeareth by their use, for *Pelybius* reporteth by the relation of *Galussa* a Noble man and a great traveller in *Africa*, that with them they made posts for houses, and racks to lay their Cattels meat upon, and likewise folds to enclose them. *Apelles* made an Ink of Ivory, which was called Elephants inke, and he painted therewith. It hath been affirmed by *Ælianus* and some writers following *Pliny*, that these teeth are horns, and that Elephants are horned beasts, which errour rose upon the occasion of these words of *Pliny; Elephantos & arietes candore tantum cornibus assimilatis, in Santonum littore reciprocatos destituit Oceanus*: where *Ælianus* finding a resemblance betwixt Rams and Elephants in their white horns, was contented to apply that name to them both, which appertaineth only to one; for *Pliny* himself *lib.* 18. sheweth his meaning by another like speech, of their whetting their horns upon trees, and *Rhinocerotes* upon stones: for except he had named horns in the first place it might have been questioned whether *Rhinocerotes* had any horns, but rather teeth in the second place.

But whatsoever were the words or opinion of *Pliny*, it is most certain, that after *Herodotus* and other ancient writers, it is safer to call these teeth then horns, and I will briefly set down the reasons of *Philostratus*, that will have them to be teeth; and afterward of *Grapaldus, Ælianus*, and *Pausanias*, that would make them horns, and so leave the Reader to consider whether opinion he thinketh most agreeable to truth. First, that they are not horns, it is alleadged that horns fall off and grow every year again, especially of Harts, and grow forth of their heads; but teeth which are called *Fannæ* or *Gang-teeth*, standing out of the mouth, fall off together, and are given for weapon and defence to beasts, and such are an Elephants. Again, a horn hath a certain line or circle neer the root, which is covered every year, but this cometh up like a stony substance, without all circle or cover, and therefore it cannot be a horn. Moreover, those creatures are said to have horns that have cloven hoofs, this hath no cloven hoof, but only five distinct fingers upon a foot. Lastly, all horned beasts have an empty hollowness in their horns (except Harts) but this is found and full thoroughout, except a little passage in the middle like a hole into a tooth: and thus say they which will have them called teeth.

Now on the contrary, those which will have them horns, make these arguments. First, as the Elks have their horns grow out of their eye-lids, the *Rhinocerotes* or *Ethiopian* Buls out of their nose, so as it is not unnatural for the Elephant to have his horns grow out of his mouth. Again, horns fall off and come again in old beasts, but teeth do not so, and therefore these are horns and not teeth; the power of fire cannot alter teeth, but these teeth break if you go about to change their porportion or figure, but horns of Oxen and Elephants may be stretched, bended, altered, straightned, and applyed to what fashion soever you will. Again, teeth grow out of the gums and cheek-bone, as it is apparent, but horns grow out of the scull and temples, and so do the Elephants, as by observation every man may discern. Lastly, as nature hath given another shape and greater proportion of body to Elephants then to any other beasts, so also it is not unreasonable that it vary in the placing of his horns, for they grow downward, and the very mole and quantity of his body is sufficient to arme him against the fear of death. Thus they argument for the horns of Elephants.

The Poets have a pretty resemblance of dreams, comparing true dreams to horns, and false dreams to Ivory, because falshood is ever more burnished, then naked and ragged truth. And besides the eye of man is translucent, and containeth in it a horny substance, and by the eye we alway receive the best assurance, but by the mouth (signified by teeth) are many falshoods vented: and for that horns turn upward to heaven, the fountain of truth, but the teeth of an Elephant grow downward towards the earth the mother of error. And for this cause *Aeneas* by *Virgil* and *Homer*, is said to come in at the horny gate of *Somnus*, and to go forth at the Ivory: *Virgils* Verses are these:

> *Sunt geminæ Somni portæ, quarum altera fertur*
> *Cornea, qua veris facilis datur exitus umbris.*
> *Altera candenti perfecta nitens Elephanto,*
> *Sed falsa ad cœlum mittunt insomnia manes.*

351

His ubi dum natum Anchises, unaque Sibyllam
Prosequitur dictis, portaque emittit eburna.

And here we will leave, and prosecute no further this discourse of their horns and teeth, but proceed to the other outward parts of this beast.

The tongue is very small though broad, his trunck called *Proboscis* and *Promuscis*, is a large hollow thing hanging from his nose like skin to the groundward; and when he feedeth it lyeth open, like the skin upon the bill of a Turkey-cock, to draw in both his meat and drink, using it for a hand, and therefore improperly it is called a hand. For by it he receiveth of his keeper whatsoever he giveth him, with it he overthroweth trees, and wheresoever he swimmeth, through it he draweth breath. It is crooked, gristly, and inflexible at the root next to the nose: within it hath two passages, one into the head and body by which he breatheth, and the other into his mouth, whereby he receiveth his meat: and herein is the work of God most wonderful, not only in giving unto it such a divers proportion and anatomy, but also giving him reason to know this benefit of it, that so long as he is in the water and holdeth up that trunck, he cannot perish.

With this he fighteth in war, and is able to take up a small piece of money from the earth: with it he hath been seen to pull down the top of a tree, which twenty four men with a rope could not make to bend. With it he driveth away his Hunters when he is chased, for he can draw up therein a great quantity of water, and shoot it forth again, to the amazement and overthrow of them that persecute him. The *Moers* say that he hath two hearts, one wherewithal he is incensed, and another whereby he is pacified.

But the truth is, as *Aristotle* in the dissection of the heart observed, there is a double ventricle and bone in the heart of an Elephant. He hath a Liver without any apparent gall, but that side of the Liver being cut, whereon the gall should lie, a certain humour cometh forth like a gall. Wherefore *Ælianus* saith, he hath his gall in his maw-gut, which is so full of sinews, that one would think he had four bellies; in this receiveth he his meat, having no other receptacle for it. His intrails are like unto a Swines, but much greater.

His Liver four times so great as an Oxes, and so all the residue except the Milt. He hath two pappes a little beside his brest under his shoulders, and not between his hinder legs or loins, they are very small and cannot be seen on the side. The reasons hereof are given, first that he hath but two pappes, because he bringeth forth but one at a time, and they stand under his shoulders like an Apes, because he hath no hoofs but distinct feet like a mans, and also because from the breast floweth more aboundance of milke.

The genital part is like a Horses, but lesser then the proportion of his body affordeth: the stones are not outwardly seen, because they cleave to his reins. But the female hath her genital betwixt her thighes: the forelegs are much longer then the hinder legs, and the feet be greater. His legs are of equall quantity, both above and beneath the knees, and it hath ancle bones very low. The articles do not ascend so high as in other creatures, but kept low neer the earth. He bendeth his hinder legs like a mans when he sitteth, but by reason of his great weight he is not able to bend on both sides together, but either leaneth to the right hand or to the left, and so sleepeth: It is false that they have no joints or articles in their legs, for when they please they can use, bend, and move them, but after they grow old, they use not to lie down or strain them, by reason of their great weight, but take their rest leaning to a tree: and if they did not bend their legs, they could never go any ordinary and stayed pace. Their feet are round like a Horses, but so as they reach from the middle every way two spans length, and are as broad as a bushel, having five distinct toes upon each foot, the which toes are very little cloven, to the intent that the foot may be stronger, and yet parted, that when he treadeth upon soft ground, the weight of his body presse not down the leg too deep. He hath no nails upon his toes, his tail is like an Oxes tail, having a little hair at the end, and the residue thereof peeled and without hair: He hath not any bristly hairs to cover his back. And thus much for their several parts and their uses.

There is not any creature so capable of understanding as an Elephant, and therefore it is requisite to tarry somewhat the longer in expressing the several properties, and natural qualities thereof, which sundry and variable inclinations, cannot choose but bring great delight to the Reader. They have a wonderful love to their own Countrey, so as although they be never so well delighted with divers meats and joyes in other places, yet in memory thereof they send forth tears, and they love also the waters, rivers, and marishes, so as they are not unfitly called *Riparii*, such as live by the rivers sides: although they cannot swim by reason of their great and heavie bodies, untill they be taught. Also they never live solitary, but in great flocks, except they be sick or watch their young ones, and for either of these they remain adventurous unto death, the eldest leadeth the herd, and the second driveth them forward, if they meet any man they give him way, and go out of his sight.

Their voice is called by the word *Barrire*, that is, to bray, and thereupon the Elephants themselves are called *Barri*; for his voice cometh out of his mouth and nostrils together, like as when a man speaketh breathing, wherefore *Aristotle* calleth it Raucity, or hoarsness, like the low sound of a Trumpet, this sound is very terrible in battails as shall be afterward declared.

They live upon the fruits of Plants and roots, and with their truncks and heads, overthrow the tops of trees, and eat the boughs and bodies of them, and many times upon the leaves of trees he devoureth Chamæleons, whereby he is poisoned and dyeth, if he eat not immediately a wilde Olive. They eat earth often without harm, but if they eat it seldom, it is hurtful and procureth pain in their bellies, so also they eat stones. They are so loving to their fellows, that they will not eat their meat alone, but having found a prey, they go and invite the residue to their feasts and chear, more like to reasonable civil men, then unreasonable brute beast. There are certain noble Melons in *Ethiopia*, which the Elephants being sharp smelling beasts, do winde a great way off, and by the conduct of their noses come to those Gardens of Melons, and there eat and devour them. When they are tamed they will eat Barlie either whole or ground: of whole at one time is given them nine *Macedonian* Bushels, but of Meal six, and of drink either wine or water, thirty *Macedonian* pints at a time, that is, fourteen gallons; but this is observed, that they drink not wine except in war, when they are to fight, but water at all times, whereof they will not tast, except it be muddy and not clear, for they avoid clear water, loathing to see their own shadow therein; and therefore when the *Indians* are to passe the water with their Elephants, they chuse dark and cloudy nights wherein the Moon affordeth no light. If they perceive but a Mouse run over their meat, they will not eat thereof, for there is in them a great hatred of this creature. Also they will eat dryed Figs, Grapes, Onions, Bulrushes, Palmes, and Ivy leaves: There is a Region in *India*, called *Phalacrus*, which signifieth Balde, because of an herb growing therein, which causeth every living thing that eateth thereof, to lose both horn and hair, and therefore no man can be more industrious or wary to avoid those places, then is an Elephant, and to forbear every green thing growing in that place when he passeth thorough it.

It will forbear drink eight dayes together, and drink wine to drunkenness like an Ape. It is delighted above measure with sweet savours, ointments, and smelling flowers, for which cause their keepers will in the Summer time lead them into the medowes of flowers, where they of themselves will by the quickness of their smelling, chuse out and gather the sweetest flowers, and put them into a basket if their keeper have any; which being filled, like dainty and neat men, they also desire to wash, and so will go and seek out water to wash themselves, and of their own accord return back again to the basket of flowers, which if they find not, they will bray and call for them. Afterward being led into their stable, they will not eat meat untill they take of their flowers and dresse the brims of their mangers therewith, and likewise strew their room or standing place, pleasing themselves with their meat, because of the savour of the flowers stuck about their cratch, like dainty fed persons which set their dishes with green herbs, and put them into their cups of wine.

Their pace is very slow, for a childe may overtake them by reason of their high and large bodies (except in their feare) and for that cause cannot swim: as also by reason that the toes of their feet are very short and smally divided. When they are brought into a Ship, they have a bridge made of wood, and covered with earth, and green boughs are set on either side, so that they imagine they go upon the land untill they enter into the Ship, because the boughs keep them from sight of the Sea. They are most chast, and keep true unto their males without all inconstant love or separation, admitting no adulteries amongst them, and like men which tast of *Venus* not for any corporal lust, but for desire of heirs and successors in their families; so do Elephants without all unchast and unlawful lust, take their venereal complements, for the continuation of their kinde, and never above thrice in all their dayes, either male or female suffer carnall copulation (but the female only twice.) Yet is their rage great when the female provoketh them, and although they fight not among themselves for their females, (except very seldom) yet do they so burn in this fury, that many times they overthrow trees and houses in *India* by their tuskes, and running their head like a Ram against them, wherefore then they keep them low and down by subtraction of their meat, and also bring some stranger to beat them. There was a certain cunning Hunter sent into *Mauritania*, by the *Roman* Emperor, to hunt and take Elephants; on a day he saw a goodly young Elephant in copulation with another, and instantly a third approached with a direful braying, as if he would have eaten up all the company, and as it afterward appeared, he was an arrival to the female, which we saw in copulation with the other male: when he approached neer, both of them set themselves to combat, which they performed like some unresistable waves of the Sea, or as the hils which are shaken together by an earthquake, wherein each one charged the other most furiously for their love, to the terror and admiration of all the beholders, and so at last became both disarmed of their teeth and horns by their often blowes, before one had overcome the other, and so at last by the hunters were parted asunder, being ever afterward quiet from such contentions about their females for copulation.

The *Indians* separate the stables of the females far asunder from the males, because at that time they overthrow their houses. They are modest and shamefast in this action, for they seek the Deserts, Woods, and secret places for procreation, and sometimes the waters, because the waters do support the male in that action, whereby he ascendeth and descendeth from the back of the female with more ease: and once it was seen, that in *Virgea* (a Countrey of the *Corascens*) two Elephants did engender out of *India*, otherwise they couple not out of their own Countries. When they go to copulation, they turn their heads towards the East, but whether in remembrance of Paradise, or for the *Mandragoras*, or for any other cause I cannot tell: the female sitteth while she is covered. They begin to engender, the male at six, ten, twelve, fifteen or twenty year old, the female not before ten years old. They couple but five dayes in two years, and never after the female is filled till she have been clear one whole year; and after the second copulation, he never more toucheth his female. At that time the male breatheth forth at his nose a certain fat humour like a menstruous thing, but the female hath them not till her place of conception be opened: and alway the day after her filling, she washeth herself before she return to the flock.

The time of their going with young is according to some, two years, and according to other, three; the occasion of this diversity is, because their time of copulation cannot certainly be known, because of their secrecy, for the greater bodies that beasts have, they are the lesse fruitful. She is delivered in great pain, leaning upon her hinder legs. They never bring forth but one at a time, and that is not much greater then a great Cow-calfe (of three monthes old) which she nourisheth six or eight year. As soon as it is Calved, it seeth and goeth, and sucketh with the mouth, not with the trunck, and so groweth to a great stature.

The females when they have calved are most fierce, for fear of their young ones, but if a man come and touch them, they are not angry, for it seemeth they understand that he toucheth them not for any desire to take or harm them, but rather to stroke and admire them. Sometimes they go into the water to the belly, and there calve for fear of the Dragon: the male never forsaketh her, but keepeth with her for the like fear of the Dragon, and feed and defend their young ones with singular love and constancy unto death; as appeareth by the example of one, that heard the braying of her calf fallen into a ditch, and not able to arise, the female ran unto it, and for hast fell down upon it, so crushing it to death, and breaking her own neck with one and the same violent love.

As they live in herds, so when they are to passe over a river or water, they send over the least or youngest first, because their great bodies together should not cause the deep water to swell or rise above their height: the other stand on the bank and observe how deep he wadeth, and so make account that the greater may with more assurance follow after the younger and smaller, then they the elder and taller; and the females carry over their Calves upon their snowts, and long eminent teeth binding them fast with their truncks, (like as with ropes or male girts, that they may not fall) being sometime holpen by the male; wherein appeareth an admirable point of natural wisdom, both in the cariage of their young, and in sending of the lesser foremost, not only for the reason aforesaid, but also because they being hunted and prosecuted, it is requisite that the greatest and strongest come in the rear and hindmost part, for the safegard of the weaker, against the fury of their persecutors, being better able to fight then the foremost, whom in natural love and policy, they set farthest from the danger.

Mutius which had been thrice Consul affirmeth, that he saw Elephants brought on shore at *Puteoli* in *Italy*: they were caused to go out of the Ship backward, all along the bridge that was made for them, that so the sight of the Sea might terrifie them, and cause them more willingly to come on land, and that they might not be terrified with the length of the bridge from the continent. *Pliny* and *Solinus* affirm, that they will not go on shipboard, untill their keeper by some intelligible signe of oath, make promise unto them of their return back again.

They sometimes, as hath been said, fight one against another, and when the weaker is overcome, he is so much abased and cast down in minde, that ever after he feareth the voice of the conquerour.

They are never so fierce, violent, or wilde, but the sight of a Ram tameth and dismayeth them, for they fear his horns; for which cause the *Egyptians* picture an Elephant and a Ram, to signifie a foolish King that runneth away for a fearfull sight in the field. And not only a Ram, but also the gruntling clamour or cry of Hogs: by which means the *Romans* overthrew the *Carthaginians* and *Pyrrhus* which trusted overmuch to their Elephants. When *Antipater* besieged the *Megarians* very straitly with many Elephants, the Citizens took certain Swine and anointed them with pitch, then set them on fire and turned them out among the Elephants, who crying horribly by reason of the fire on their bodies, so distempered the Elephants, that all the wit of the *Macedonians* could not restrain them from madness, fury, and flying upon their own company, only because of the cry of the Swine. And to take away that fear from Elephants, they bring up with them when they are tamed, young Pigges and Swine ever since that time. When Elephants are chased in hunting, if the Lions see them, they run from them like Hinde-calves from the Dogs of Hunters, and yet *Iphicrates* sayeth, that among the *Hesperian* or western *Ethiopians*, Lions set upon the young Calves of Elephants and wound them: but at the sight of the mothers, which come with speed to them, when they hear them cry, the Lions run away, and when the mothers finde their young ones imbrued in their own bloud, they themselves are so inraged that they kill them, and so retire from them, after which time the Lions return and eat their flesh. They will not indure the savour of a Mouse, but refuse the meat which they have run over: in the river *Ganges* of *India*, there are blew Wormes of sixty cubits long having two armes; these when the Elephants come to drink in that river, take their trunks in their hands and pull them off. There are Dragons among the *Ethiopians*, which are thirty yards or paces long, these have no name among the inhabitants but Elephant-killers. And among the *Indians* also there is as an inbred and native hateful hostility between Dragons and Elephants: for which cause the Dragons being not ignorant that the Elephants feed upon the fruits and leaves of green trees, do secretly convey themselves into them or to the tops of rocks: covering their hinder part with leaves, and letting his head and fore part hang down like a rope, on a suddain when the Elephant cometh to crop the top of the tree, she leapeth into his face, and diggeth out his eyes, and because that revenge of malice is too little to satisfie a Serpent, she twineth her gable like body about the throat of the amazed Elephant, and so strangleth him to death.

Again they marke the footsteps of the Elephant when he goeth to feed, and so with their tails, net in and entangle his legs and feet: when the Elephant perceiveth and feeleth them, he putteth down his trunck to remove and untie their knots and gins; then one of them thrusteth his poisoned stinging head into his Nostrils, and so stops up his breath, the other prick and gore his tender belly-parts. Some again meet him and flie upon his eyes and pull them forth, so that at the last he must yeeld to their rage, and fall down upon them, killing them in his death by his fall, whom he could not resist or overcome being alive: and this must be understood, that forsomuch as Elephants go together by flocks and herds, the subtil Dragons let the foremost passe, and set upon the hindmost, that so they may not be oppressed with multitude.

Also it is reported that the bloud of an Elephant is the coldest blood in the world, and that Dragons in the scorching heat of Summer, cannot get any thing to cool them, except this bloud; for which cause they hide themselves in rivers and brooks whither the Elephants come to drink, and when he putteth down his trunck they take hold thereof, and instantly in great numbers leap up unto his ear, which is naked, bare and without defence: whereout they suck the blood of the Elephant untill he fall down dead, and so they perish both together.

Of this blood cometh that ancient *Cinnabaris*, made by commixture of the bloud of Elephants and Dragons both together, which alone is able, and nothing but it, to make the best representation of blood in painting. Some have corrupted it with Goats-blood, and call it *Milton*, and *Mimum*, and *Monocroma*: it hath a most rare and singular vertue against all poisons, beside the unmatchable property aforesaid.

These Serpents or Dragons are bred in *Taprobana*, in whose heads are many pretious stones, with such naturall seals or figurative impressions, as if they were framed by the hand of man, for *Podisippus* and *Tzetzes* affirm, that they have seen one of them taken out of a Dragons head, having upon it the lively and artificial stampe of a Chariot.

Elephants are enemies to wilde Buls, and the *Rhinocerots*, for in the games of *Pompey*, when an Elephant and a *Rhinoceros* were brought together, the *Rhinoceros* ran instantly and whet his horn upon a stone, and so prepared himself to fight, striking most of all at the belly of the Elephant, because he knew that it was the tenderest and most penetrable part of the body.

The *Rhinoceros* was as long as the Elephant, but the legs thereof were much shorter, and as the *Rhinocerotes* sharpen their horns upon the stones, so do the Elephants their teeth upon trees: the sharpness of either yeeldeth not to any steel. Especially the *Rhinocerot* teareth and pricketh the legs of the Elephant. They fight in the woods for no other cause, but for the meat they live upon, but if the *Rhinocerot* get not the advantage of the Elephants belly, but set upon him in some other part of his body, he is soon put to the worst, by the sharpness of the Ivory tooth which pierceth through his more then buffe-hard skin (not to be pierced with any dart) with great facility, being set on with the strength of so able an adversary. The Tygre also feareth not an Elephant, but is fiercer and stronger, for he leapeth upon his head and teareth out his throat, but the Gryphins which overcome almost all beasts, are not able to stand with the Lions or Elephants.

The females are far more strong, chearful, and couragious then the males, and also they are apt to bear the greater burthens; but in War the male is more graceful and acceptable, because he is taller, giving more assured ensignes of victory and fortitude: for their strength is admirable, as may be conjectured by that which is formerly recited of their trunck, as *Vartoman* affirmeth, that he saw three Elephants with their only heads, drive a great Ship out of the Sea-water where it was fastened unto the shore. When he is most loaded he goeth surest, for he can carry a wooden Tower on his back with thirty men therein, and their sufficient food and warlike instruments.

The King of *India* was wont to go to war with 30000 Elephants of war, and beside these he had also followed him 3000 of the chiefest and strongest in *India*, which at his command would overthrow Trees, Houses, Wals, or any such thing standing against him: and indeed upon these were the *Indians* wont to fight, for the defence of their Coast and Countrey. The farthest region of that continent is called *Partalis*, inhabited by the *Gangarides* and *Calingæ*, the King whereof was wont to have seven hundred Elephants to watch his Army, and there was no mean Prince in all *India* which was not Lord of many Elephants. The King of *Palibotræ* kept in stipend, eight thousand every day, and beyond his Territory was the King of *Modubæ* and *Molindæ*, which had four hundred Elephants. These fight with men, and overthrow all that come within their reach, both with their truncks and teeth.

There were certain officers and guiders of these Elephants, which were called *Elephantarchæ*, who were the governors of sixteen Elephants, and they which did institute and teach them Martial discipline, were called *Elephantagogi*. The Military Elephant did carry four persons on his bare back, one fighting on the right hand, another fighting on the left hand, a third which stood fighting backward from the Elephants head, and a fourth in the middle of these holding the rains and guiding the beast to the descretion of the Souldiers, even as the Pilot in a Ship guideth the stern, wherein was required an equall knowledge and dexterity, for they understand any language quickly; for when the *Indian* which ruled them said, Strike here on the right hand, or else on the left, or refrain and stand still, no reasonable man could yeeld readier obedience. They did fasten by iron chains, first of all upon the Elephant that was to bear ten, fifteen, twenty, or thirty men, on either side two panniers of iron bound underneath their belly, and upon them the like panniers of wood hollow, wherein they place their men at armes, and covered them over with small boards, for the trunck of the Elephant was covered with a mail for defence, and upon that a broad sword, and two cubits long: this (as also the wooden Castle or panniers aforesaid) were fastened first to the neck, and then to the rump of the Elephant. Being thus armed, they entred the battel, and they shewed unto the beast to make them more fierce, wine, red liquor made of Rice, and white cloth, for at the sight of any of these, his courage and rage increaseth above all measure; then at the sound of the Trumpet he beginneth with teeth to strike, tear, beat, spoil, take up into the air, cast down again, stamp upon men under feet, ovethrow with his trunck, and make way for his riders to pierce with Spear, Shield, and Sword; so that his horrible voice, his wonderful body, his terrible force, his admirable skill, his ready and inclinable obedience, and his strange and seldom seen shape, produced in a main battel no mean accidents and overturns. For this cause we read how that *Pyrrhus* first of all produced Elephants against the *Romans* in *Lucania*: afterward *Asdrubal* in *Africa, Antiochus* in the East, and *Jugurtha* in *Numidia*.

Against this new kinds of Castle-fighting, and Souldier-bearing beasts, on the contrary they invented new kinds of stratagems, as is before set down, and also new instruments of war, for a *Centurion* in *Lucania* with a new devised sharp Sword cut off the trunck of this beast, again other invented, that two armed Horses should draw a Chariot, and in the same armed men with Javelins and sharp Spears, the speedy Horses should with all force run upon the Elephants, and the spear-men directing their course and weapons, some upon the beast, other upon the riders, did not only wound the beast, but also by celerity of the Horses, escape all danger.

Other again sent against him armed Souldiers, having their Armour made full of sharp pricks or piercing piked Nailes, so that when the beast did strike at them with his trunck, he received grievous wounds by his own blowes. Again there were certain young men Souldiers, armed with light armour, which being mounted upon swift Horses, could cast Darts with singular facility, and without the reach of the beast, many times wounding him with long Spears, and so by example of the Horse-men, the Foot-men, grew more bold, and with piles in the earth annoyed the belly of the beast, and utterly vanquishing it and the rider. Again, they devised slings to cast stones, whereby they beat off the riders, and many times overthrew the Castle-bearer, as it were by some violent stroke of a Cannon shot; neither was there ever any more easie way to disaster these monster-seeming Souldiers, then by casting of stones; and lastly they would suffer their Elephants and their riders by poor hopes and appearances of fear, to enter into the midst among them, and so begirt and inclose them, that they took the Elephants alive; and also more shooters of Darts carryed in Chariots with the strong course of horses, did so annoy them, that whereas their bodies were great and unweildy, not nimble to stir out of place, it became more easie to kill an Elephant then a Horse, because many shooters at one time could pierce so fair a mark with unresistible weapons. And these things are related by *Vegetius*.

At the last the fight with Elephants turned into a publick game or pastime, both to see them fought withall by men, and also among themselves. When certain prisoners of the *Romans* were taken by *Annibal*, he first constrained them to skirmish among themselves, and so slew one another except only one; and he was by the like commandement forced to fight with an Elephant, but upon condition of liberty if he escaped alive: and thereupon joyned combate, and slew the Elephant, to the great grief and amazement of all the *Carthaginians*; but going home, according to agreement, *Annibal* fearing that by this fact those great beasts would grow into contempt, sent certain Horse-men to kill him by the way.

Their trunck or hand is most easie to be cut off; for so it *happened* in the ædility or temple-office of *Claudius*, *Antonius* and Posthumus being Consuls, and afterward in the *Circus*, when the *Luculli* were the commons officers. And when *Pompey* was Consul the second time, there were 17 or 20 which at one time fought within the *Circus*, at the dedication of the Temple of *Venus* the *Victoria*, where the *Getulians* fought with them with Spears and Darts; for there happened an admirable accident, one of the Souldiers who having a hurt in his feet did creep upon his knees betwixt the legs of the Elephants, and cast up the Darts over his head into the beasts belly, which fell down round about him, to the great pleasure of the beholders, so that many of the Elephants perished rather by Art then the strength of the Souldier. No lesse was the Miracle of another slain with one stroke, for a pile ran into his temples through his eye, and there stuck so fast, that it could not be pulled forth again; which thing was afterward assayed by *Julius Cæsar*, and in the third time of his Consulship, there were twenty Elephants, which in the Games fought with five hundred men, and so many with Towers on their backs, bearing threescore men in every Tower.

To conclude, Elephants are afraid of fire, and *Martial* made this *Epigram* of a Bull slain by an Elephant, which was wont to domineer in all their triuphant games, wherewithal I will conclude this discourse.

> *Qui modo per totam flammis stimulatus arenam*
> *Sustulerat raptas Taurus in astra pilas,*
> *Occubuit tandem cornuto ardore petitus,*
> *Dum facilem tolli sic Elephanta putat.*

In the next place it is good to relate the story of the taking and taming of Elephants, for in *Lybia* about the *Troglodytæ*, the hunting and taking of Elephants have given many names to severall Towns, as *Elephantina*, and *Elephantis*, *Epitheræ*, *Philothera*, and the hunting of Elephants by *Ptolemais*, by the Port *Saba*, the City *Daraba*, and *Lycha*. In *Africk* they take them in great ditches, whereinto when they are fallen, the people presently with boughs, mattocks, leaves, and digging down of high raised places, take them out again, and so turn them into a valley wrought by the labour of man, most firmely walled on both sides, where with famine they tame him; for when he would gently take a bough at the hand of a man, they adjudged him tamed, and grew familiar with him, leading him away without all scruple.

But the *Indians* use a more ingenious and speedy means to tame them, which is this; first, they dig also a great ditch, and place such meat therein as the beast loveth, who winding it, and coming thereunto, for desire thereof falleth into the fosse or ditch: being so fallen in, and not able to come forth again, one cometh to him with Whips, beating him very grievously for a good space, to the great grief of the beast, who through his inclosing can neither run away nor help himself; then cometh another during this time of punishment, and blameth the first man for beating the beast, who departeth presently as one afraid of his rebuke, the other pitieth the beast, and stroaketh him, and so goeth away; then cometh the whipper again, and scourgeth the Elephant as before and that more grievously to his greater torment for a good space together: whereupon the time fulfilled, the other cometh again and fighteth with the whipper, and forcibly seemeth to drive him away, and relieve the poor beast; and this they do successively three or four times; so at the last, the Elephant groweth to know and love his deliverer, who by that means draweth him out and leadeth him away quietly: While this thing is doing, the smiter and whipper useth a strange and unwonted kind of habit, so as he may never be known by the Elephant after he is tamed, for fear of revenge: of which you shall hear more afterward, in the farther discourse and opening the nature of this beast.

Arrianus and *Strabo* relate another way whereby the *Indians* take their Elephants, which because they write upon their own eye sight, of the things they knew assuredly, I have thought good to expresse the devise; Four or five Hunters first of all chuse out some plain place, without Trees or Hils, but declining, by the space of some four or five furlongs; this they dig like a wide ditch as aforesaid, and with the earth they take up, they raise wals about it like a trench, and in the sides of the trench they make certain dens with holes, to convey in light to the Watch-men, whom they place therein, to give notice and observe when the Elephants are inclosed; then make they a narrow bridge covered with earth at the farther end of the trench, that the beasts may dread no fallacy; and for the more speedy effecting and compassing their desire, they also include in the trench three or four tame female Elephants, to entise and draw into them the wilde ones.

Now these beasts in the day time feed not so boldly as in the night, and therefore they cannot easily be deceived or taken in the light; but in the night great flocks of them follow the Captain (as we have already shewed) and so coming neer this trench, partly by the voice, and partly by the savour and smell of the females, they are drawn into the trench; then the Watch-men with all speed, pull down the bridge, and other of them go into the next Townes to call for help, who upon the first notice thereof, come to the place mounted upon the best and strongest tame Elephants, and so compasse them about, giving meat in their presence to the tame, but besieging the inclosed, they keep them from all meat and food, until they be so weakned that they dare enter in among them, but in this manner, they turn in their tame Elephants, and go under their bellies, and so when they come near the wilde Elephants, they speedily convey themselves under his belly, and lay unavoidable fetters upon their feet: then provoke they the tame ones to beat and fight with the wilde, who by reason of the manacles upon their feet are easily overthrown and fall to the ground; being on the ground, they put halters upon their necks made of raw Oxe hides, and so bind them to the tame and domestical Elephants: And while they lie on the ground, they get upon them, and to the intent that their Riders may be without danger of harm by them, they cut the skin of their necks round about in a circle, with a sharp sword, and upon the wound they tie and fasten a rope, that so the pain may constrain the beast to be quiet, so that by this they begin to feel their own weakness, and leave off their wildeness, betaking themselves to the mercy of their new Masters.

But thus raised from the earth again, and yoaked by the necks and legs to the tamed Elephants, they are safely led home into stables, where they are fastened to great pillars by their necks, and if they refuse to eat their meat, with Tymbrels, Cymbals, Harpes, and other musical instruments, they are so entised from sullen wildeness, that they forget their first natures, and yeeld all loving obedience to men, as to their victorious conquerors and unresistible Masters.

These beasts by their sagacity and natural instinct, do sometime foresee their own peril, and discover the trains and secret intentions of the Hunters, so as they cannot be drawn into the ditches and fosses by any allurements, but presaging their own misfortunes, turn back again upon their Hunters, even through the midst of them, and so seek to save themselves by flight overthrowing their enemies that dare approach unto them. At which time there is a fierce fight, to the great slaughter many times both of men and beasts; for the men to stay his flight, bend their spears, and charge their darts and arrowes, to strike the Elephant directly on the face, and if the beast perceive that he hath overthrown any man instantly he maketh to him, taketh him in his teeth, lifting him up into the air, and casting him down again, stampeth upon him, wounding him many times with his teeth or horns, whereby he putteth him to cruel torments, and leaveth him not till he be dead.

And when they invade or set upon a man, they spread forth their broad ears, (which are fashioned like the winges of Ostriches) as the sails of a ship, and drawing up their trunck under their teeth their noses stand forth like the beak of some ship, and so rush they with unresistible violence upon the weak bodies of men, overturning them in no other sort, then a mighty great Hulk or man of war, the little Oares or Whirries in the Sea.

And as the Trumpets in war give the signes of fighting, so do these send forth such terrible yelling and roaring clamors, as bringeth no mean astonishment to his persecutors: beside the lamentable and mournful voices of men, by them wounded and fallen to the earth; some having their knees and bones broken, other their eyes trod out of their head, other their noses pressed flat to their faces, and their whole visages so disfigured and disfavoured in a moment, that their neerest friends, kindred and acquaintance cannot know them. These also fil the spacious air with direful cries, that are heard a great way off, into the Towns and Cities adjoyning, having no other means to escape out of the way, and from the teeth of the beast, except he strike his tooth into some root and there it stick fast untill the poor overthrown man can creep aside and save himself by flight.

In this conflict, sometime the Elephants, and sometimes men are the conquerors, by bringing upon the beasts divers terrors and manacles, out of which they are not very easily delivered: for men also have their trumpets, and so make the woods and fields ring with them, the ratling of their Armour and Shields, and their own howling and whooping, kindling fires on the earth, casting both fire-brands and burning Torches into the face of the Elephant, by all which the huge beast is not a little disgraced and terrified. So that being bereft of their wits, they turn back and run into the ditch which they so carefully avoided before.

But if their rage proceed undeterred, and men be forced to yeeld unto them, forth they go into the woods, making the trees to bend unto them as a Dog or an Ox doth the standing corn at harvest: breaking off their tops and branches, which hinder their course and flight, as another beast would crop off the ears of corn; but where they are taller then the woods, there they strain every joynt and member in them to get ground land overgo their Hunters; which they may perform and attain more easily, because of their customary aboad in those places: and when they are escaped out of the sight of their followers, and make account that they are freed from further persecution, then cast they off all fear, and compound their distracted senses into a remembrance of meat, and so gather their food from Palms, Trees or bushes; afterward betaking themselves to rest and quietness.

But if their Hunters come again into their sight, they also again take them to their heels, untill they have gotten more ground from them, and then they rest again; and if the Sun decline, and light of day fail the Hunters, and darkness make an end of the chase; then do they compasse in the beasts way, and set the wood a fire, (for Elephants fear fire as much as Lions:) So that by all this it appeareth; that the fabulous tales of *Gabinius* the *Roman* writer of Elephants, are not to be believed, when he affirmeth, that Elephants will fight against and resist the violence of fire.

The *Troglodytæ* hunt and take Elephants after another manner, for they climbe up into the trees, and there sit till the flocks of Elephants passe by, and upon the last, the Watch-man suddenly leapeth (with great courage) taking hold upon his tail and so sliding down to his legs, and with a sharp Axe which he hath hanging at his back cutteth the nerves and sinews of his legs with so great celerity, that the beast cannot turn about to relieve it self, before she be wounded and made unable to revenge her harm, or prevent her taking: and sometimes she falleth down on the wounded side, and crusheth the Hunter watch-man to death, or else with her force in running, dasheth out his brains against a tree.

The Elephant-eaters (called *Elephantophagi*) do observe the like policy, for by stealth and secretly they set upon the hindmost, or else the wandring solitary Elephant, and cut his sinews, which causeth the beast so cast down and taken.

Other among the aforesaid *Troglodytæ*, use a more easie, cunning and lesse perillous kinde of taking Elephants; for they set on the ground very strong charged bent-bowes, which are kept by many of their strongest youngmen, and so when the flocks of Elephants passe by, they shoot their sharp arrowes dipped in the gall of Serpents, and wound some one of them, and follow him by the bloud, untill he be unable to make resistance. There are three at every bow, two which hold it, and one that draweth the string. Other again, watch the trees whereunto the beast leaneth when he sleepeth, neer some waters, and the same they cut half asunder, whereunto when he declineth his body, the tree is overturned and the beast also, and being unable to rise again because of the short nerves and no flexions in his legs, there he lyeth till the Watch man come and cut off his head.

Aristotle describeth another manner of taking Elephants in this sort; The Hunter (saith he) getteth up upon a tamed Elephant, and followeth the wilde one till he have overtaken it, then commandeth he the tame beast to strike the other, and so continueth chasing and beating him, till he have wearyed him and broken his untameable nature. Then doth the rider leap upon the wearyed and tyred Elephant, and with a sharp pointed Sickle doth govern him after the tame one, and so in short space he groweth gentle. And some of them when the rider alighteth from their backs, grow wilde and fierce again; for which cause they binde their forelegs with strong bands, and by this means they take both great and small old and young ones; but as the old ones are more wilde and obstinate, and so difficult to be taken, so the younger keep so much with the elder, that a like impossibility or difficulty interposeth itself from apprehending them.

In the *Caspian* lake, there are certain fishes (called *Oxyrinchi*) out of whom is made such a firme glew, that it will not be dissolved in ten dayes after it hath taken hold, for which cause they use it in the taking of Elephants.

There are in the Island *Zeira* many Elephants, whom they take on this manner: In the Mountains they make certain cloysters in the earth, having two great trees standing at the mouth of the cloysters, and in those trees they hangup a great par-cullis gate, within that cloyster they place a tame female Elephant at the time of their usual copulation: the wilde Elephants do speedily wind her, and make to her, and so at the last having found the way betwixt the two trees, enter into her; sometime twenty, and sometime thirty at a time: then are there two men in the said trees, which cut the rope whereby the gate hangeth, so it falleth down and includeth the Elephants, where they suffer them alone for six or seven dayes without meat, whereby they are so infeebled and famished, that they are not able to stand upon their legs.

Then two or three strong men enter in among them, and with great slaves and clubs, belabour and, cudgel them, till by that means they grow tame, and gentle; and although an Elephant be a monstrous great beast and very subtil, yet by these and such like means do the inhabitants of *India* and *Ethiopia*, take many of them with a very small labour to their great advantage.

Against these sleights of men, may be oposed the subtil and cautelous evasions of the beast, avoiding all the footsteps of men, if they smell them upon any herb or leaf, and for their fight with the Hunters, they observe this order. First of all, they set them foremost which have the least teeth, that so they may not be afraid of combate, and when they are weary, by breaking down of trees they escape and flie away. But for their hunting, they know that they are not hunted in *India* for no other cause, then for their teeth, and therefore to discourage the Hunters, they set them which have the worst teeth before, and reserve the strongest for the second encounter: for their wisdom or natural discretion is herein to be admired, that they will so dispose themselves in all their battails when they are in chase, that ever they fight by course, and inclose the youngest from perill, so that lying under the belly of their Dams they can scarce be seen: and when one of them flyeth they all flie away, to their usual resting places, striving which of them shall go foremost: And if at any time they come to a wide and deep Ditch, which they cannot passe over without a bridge, then one of them descendeth, and goeth down into the Ditch, and standeth transverse or crosse the same, by his great body filling up the empty parts, and the residue passe over upon his back as upon a bridge.

Afterward when they are all over, they tarry and help their fellow out of the Ditch or Trench again, by this sleight or devise, one of them putteth down to him his leg, and the other in the Ditch windeth his trunck about the same, the residue standers by cast in bundles of sprigs with their mouthes, which the Elephant warily and speedily putteth under his feet, and so raiseth himself out of the Trench again, and departeth with his fellowes.

But if they fall in and cannot finde any help or means to come forth, they lay aside their natural wilde disposition, and are contented to take meat and drink at the hands of men, whose presence before they abhorred; and being delivered they think no more upon their former condition, but in forgetfulness thereof, remain obedient to their deliverers.

Being thus taken, as it hath been said, it is also expedient to express by what art and means they are cicurattd and tamed. First of all therefore when they are taken, they are fastened to some Tree or Pillar in the earth, so as they can neither kick backward nor leap forward, and there hunger, thirst, and famine, like two most strong and forcible Riders abate their natural wildeness, strength, fear and hatred of men: Afterward when their keepers perceive by their dejection of minde, that they begin to be mollified and altered, then they give unto them meat out of their hands, upon whom the beast doth cast a far more favorable and cheerful eye, considering their own bondage, and so at the last necessity frameth them unto a contented and tractable course and inclination.

But the *Indians* by great labour and industry take their young Calves at their watering places, and so lead them away, inticing them by many allurements of meat to love and obey, them, so as they grow to understand the *Indian* language, but the elder *Indian* Elephants do very hardly and seldom grow tame, because of their remembrance of their former liberty, by any bands and oppression; nevertheless by instrumental musick, joyned with some of their Countrey songs and ditties, they abate their fierceness, and bring down their high untractable stomachs, so as without all bands they remain quiet, peaceable and obedient, taking their meat which is layed before them.

Pliny and *Solinus* prescribe the juyce of Barly to be given to them for their mitification, whereunto also agreeth *Dioscorides* (calling that kind of drink *Zythus*) and the reason hereof is, because of the tart sharpness in Barly water if it stand a little while; and therefore also they prescribe Vinegar and ashes to rub the beasts mouth, for it hath power in it to pierce stones, all sharp things penetrate deep into his flesh, and alter his nature; the invention whereof is attributed to *Democritus*.

Being thus tamed, they grow into civill and familiar uses, for *Cæsar* ascended into the *Capitol* betwixt four hundred Elephants, carrying at either side burning Torches, and *Heliogabalus* brought four Waggons drawn with Elephants in *Vaticanum*, and men commonly ride upon them, for *Apollonius* saw neer the River *Indus*, a Boy of thirteen year old riding alone upon an Elephant, spurring and pricking him as freely as any man will do a lean horse.

They are taught to bend one of their hinder legs to take up the Rider, who also must receive help from some other present standers by, or else it is impossible to mount on the back of so high a Palfrey. They which are not accustomed to ride upon these beasts, are affected with vomiting and casting, like men when they first of all take the Sea. They are ruled without bridle or rains, only by a long crooked piece of wood bending like a Sickle, and nailed with sharp nails, no man can sit more safely and more softly upon a Horse or Mule then they do which ride upon the Elephants. The *Indians* with their lesser Elephants (which they call bastard Elephants) plow their ground and corn.

The common price of Elephants is at the least five hundred Nobles, and sometimes two thousand. The *Indian* women are most chast and continent, yet for an Elephant they take a great pride to be hired for whores, for they imagine that the fame and received opinion of their beauty doth countervail and cover the shameful losse of their honesty (as *Arrianus* writeth in his book of *Indians*.)

Since the time that Elephants have been tamed, their natures and dispositions have been the better observed and discovered; for they willingly obey their keepers, learning all feats of Armes, to take up stones and cast them, and to swim; so that *Strabo* affirmeth, there was no possession or wealth comparable to a Chariot or Waggon of Elephants.

Mutianus which was thrice Consul, affirmed to *Pliny*, that he saw an Elephant which learned the *Greek* letters, and was able with his tongue to write these words, *Antos egos Tadegrapsa laphura te kelt' anetheca*; that is, I wrote these things and dedicated the *Celtican* spoils: but in these actions of writing, the hand of the teacher must be also present to teach him how to frame the letters, and then, as *Ælianus* saith, they will write upon Tables, and follow the true proportion of the Characters expressed before their face, whereupon they look as attentively as any *Grammarian*. In *India* they are taught many sports, as to Dance and leap, which caused *Martial* to write thus;

> *Turpes esseda quod trabunt bisontes,*
> *Et molles dare jussa quod choreas*
> *Nigro bellua nil legat magistro,*
> *Quis spectacula non putet deorum?*

When the Prizes of *Germanicus Cæsar* were played, there were many Elephants which acted strange feats or parts, four of them went upon Ropes and over the Tables of meat, whereon they set their feet so warily that they never touched any of the ghests, the boardes or standing cups being fully furnished. And also they learned to dance after Pipes by measure, sometime dancing softly, and sometime apace, and then again leaping upright, according to the number sung or played upon the instrument; and they are apt to learn, remember, meditate, and conceive such things as a man can hardly perform.

Their industrious care to perform the things they are taught, appeareth herein, because when they are secret and alone by themselves, they will practise leaping, dancing, and other strange feats, which they could not learn suddenly in the presence of their Masters: as Pliny affirmeth for certain truth of an Elephant which was dull and hard of understanding, his keeper found him in the night practising those things which he had taught him with many stripes the day before, and could not prevail by reason of the beasts slow conceit.

There was an Elephant playing upon a Cymbal, and others of his fellowes dancing about him, for there was fastened to either of both of his forelegs one Cymbal, and another hanged to his trunck, the beast would observe just time, and strike upon one, and then the other, to the admiration of all the beholders. There was a certain banquet prepared for Elephants upon a low bed in a parlour set with divers dishes and pots of Wine, whereinto were admitted twelve, six males, apparelled like men, and six females apparelled like women: when they saw it, they sat down with great modesty, taking here and there like discreet temperate ghests, neither ravening upon one dish or other, and when they should drink, they took the cup receiving in the liquor very mannerly, and for sport and festivity would through their truncks squirt or cast a little of their drink upon their attendants; so that this beast is not only of an admirable greatness, but of a more wonderful meekness and docibility.

They are said to discern betwixt Kings and common persons, for they adore and bend unto them, pointing to their Crowns, which caused *Martial* to write this *Tetrastichon*;

> *Quod pius & supplex Elephas te Cæsar odorat,*
> *Hic modo qui tauro tam metuendus erat,*
> *Non sacit hoc jussus, nulloque docente magistro:*
> *Crede mihi, numen sentit & ille tuum.*

The King of *Indians* was watched with four and twenty Elephants, who were taught to forbear sleep, and to come in their turns at certain hours, and so were they most faithful, careful and invincible. And as there be of them three kinds, the *Palustrians* or Marishie Elephants are hair brained and inconstant, the Elephants of the Mountains are subtil and evill natured, lying in wait to destroy and devoure, but the *Campestrial* Elephants are meek, gentle, docible, and apt to imitate men. In these is the understanding of their Countrey language, of obedience to Princes, government, and offices; the love and pleasure of glory and praise: and also that which is not alway in men; namely, equity, wisdom, and probity.

They have also a kind of Religion, for they worship, reverence, and observe the course of the Sun, Moon, and Stars; for when the Moon shineth, they go to the Waters wherein she is apparent; and when the Sun ariseth they salute and reverence his face: and it is observed in *Ethiopia*, that when the Moon is changed untill her prime and appearance, these beasts by a secret motion of nature, take boughs from off the trees they feed upon, and first of all lift them up to heaven, and then look upon the Moon, which they do many times together, as it were in supplication to her. In like manner they reverence the Sun rising, holding up their trunck or hand to heaven, in congratulation of her rising.

Iuba was wont to say, that this beast was acceptable to those Gods which ruled Sea and Land, because of their reverence to Sun and Moon, and therefore *Ptolomeus Philopator*, offered four Elephants in a sacrifice (to recover the quietness of his minde) thinking that the Gods would have been well pleased therewith, but finding that his fearful dreams and visions departed not from him, but rather his disquietness increased, fearing that the gods were angry with him for that action, he made four Elephants of Brass, and dedicated them to the Sun, that so by this deed he might purchase pardon for the former offence.

This Religion of theirs, also appeareth before their death, for when they feel any mortal wounds, or other natural signes of their later end, either they take up the dust, or else some green herb, and lift it up to Heaven in token of their innocency and imploration of their own weakness: and in like manner do they when they eat any herb by natural instinct to cure their diseases: first they lift it up to the Heavens (as it were to pray for a divine blessing upon it) and then devoure it.

I cannot omit their care, to bury and cover the dead carkases of their companions, or any other of their kinde; for finding them dead, they pass not by them till they have lamented their common misery, by casting dust and earth on them, and also green boughs, in token of sacrifice, holding it execrable to do otherwise: and they know by a natural instinct some assured fore-tokens of their own death. Besides when they wax old and unfit to gather their own meat, or fight for themselves, the younger of them feed, nourish, and defend them, yea they raise them out of Ditches and Trenches into which they are fallen, exempting them from all labour and perill, and interposing their own bodies for their protection: neither do they forsake them in sickness, or in their wounds, but stand to them, pulling out Darts of their bodies, and helping both like skilful Chirurgions to cure wounds, and also like faithful friends to supply their wants.

Again, how much they love their young, which is a natural part, of religion we have shewed before. *Antipater* supposeth that they have a kinde of divination or divine understanding of law and equity, for when King *Bocohus* had condemned thirty men to be torn and trod in pieces by Elephants, and tying them hand and foot to blocks or pieces of wood, cast them among thirty Elephants, his servants and Officers could not by all their wit, skill, or provocation, make the Beasts touch one of them: so that it was apparent, they scorned and disdained to serve any mans cruel disposition, or to be the ministers of tyranny and murther. They moreover have not only an observation of chastity among themselves, but also are revengers of whoredom and adulterers in other, as may appear by these examples in History.

A certain Elephant seeing his Master absent, and another man in bed with his Mistress, he went unto the bed and slew them both. The like was done at *Rome*, where the Elephant having slain both the adulterer and adulteress, he covered them with the bed-clothes untill his Keeper returned home, and then by signes drew him into his lodging place, where he uncovered the Adulterers, and shewed him his bloudy tooth that took revenge upon them both for such a villany: whereat the Master wondering, was the more pacified, because of the manifest-committed iniquity. And not only thus deal they against the woman, but they also spare not to revenge the adultery of men; yea of their own Keeper: for there was a rich man which had marryed a wife not very amiable or lovely, but like himself for wealth, riches, and possessions, which he having gained, first of all set his heart to love another, more fitting his lustful fancy, and being desirous to marry her, strangled his rich ill-favoured Wife, and buryed her not far from the Elephants stable, and so marryed with the other, and brought her home to his house: the Elephant abhorring such detestable murther, brought the new marryed Wife to the place where the other was buryed; and with his teeth digged up the ground and shewed her the naked body of her predecessor, intimating thereby unto her secretly, how unworthily she had marryed with a man, murtherer of his former wise.

Their love and concord with all mankinde is most notorious, especially to their Keepers and Women: for if through wrath they be incensed against their Keepers, they kill them, and afterward by way of repentance, they consume themselves with mourning: And for the manifesting of this point *Arrianus* telleth a notable story of an *Indian*, who had brought up from a foal a white Elephant, both loving it, and being beloved of it again, he was thereupon carryed with great admiration. The King hearing of this white Elephant, sent unto the man for it, requiring it to be given to him for a present, whereat the man was much grieved, that another man should possess that which he had so tenderly educated and loved, fitting him to his bow and purposes, and therefore like a rival in his Elephants love, resolved to deny the King, and to shift for himself in some other place: whereupon he fled into a Desert region with his Elephant, and the King understanding thereof, grew offended with him, sent messengers after him to take away the Elephant, and withal to bring the man back again, to receive punishment for his contempt.

When they came to the place where he remained, and began to take order for their apprehension, the man ascended into a steep place, and there kept the Kings messengers off from him by casting of stones, and so also did the Beast, like as one that had received some injury by them, at last, they got neer the *Indian*, and cast him down, but the Elephant made upon them, killing some of them, and defending his Master and nourisher, put the residue to flight, and then taking up his Master with his trunk, carryed him safe into his lodging, which thing is worthy to be remembred, as a noble understanding part both of a loving friend and faithful servant.

The like may be said of the Elephant of *Porus*, carrying his wounded Master the King in the battel he fought with *Alexander*, for the Beast drew the Darts gently out of his Masters body without all pain, and did not cast him untill he perceived him to be dead, and without bloud and breath, and then did first of all bend his own body as near the earth as he could, that if his Master had any life left in him, he might not receive any harm in his alighting or falling down. Generally, as is already said, they love all men after they be tamed, for if they meet a man erring out of his way, they gently bring him into the right again, yet being wilde are they afraid of the foot-steps of men if they winde their treadings before they see their persons, and when they finde an herb that yeeldeth a suspicion of a mans presence, they smell thereunto one by one; and if all agree in one savour, the last Beast lifteth up his voyce and cryeth out for a token and watch-word to make them all fly away.

Cicero affirmeth that they come so near to a mans disposition, that their small Company or Nation seemeth to over-go or equall most men in sense and understanding.

At the sight of a beautiful woman they leave off all rage and grow meek and gentle; and therefore *Ælianus* saith, that there was an Elephant in *Egypt*, which was in love with a woman that sold Corrals, the self same woman was wooed by *Aristophanes*; and therefore it was not likely, that she was chosen of the Elephant without singular admiration of her beauty, wherein *Aristophanes* might say as never man could; that he had an Elephant for his rivall; and this also did the Elephant manifest unto the man: for on a day in the market, he brought her certain Apples, and put them into her bosom, holding his trunk a great while therein, handling and playing with her breasts. Another likewise loved a *Syrian* woman, with whose aspect he was suddenly taken, and in admiration of her face stroked the same with his trunk, with testification of farther love: the Woman likewise failed not to frame for the Elephant amorous devices with Beads and Corrals, Silver, and such things as are grateful to these brute Beasts, so she enjoyed his labour and dilgence to her great profit, and he her love and kindeness without all offence to his contentment, which caused *Horat* to write this verse:

Quid tibi vis mulier nigris dignissima barris?

At last, the woman dyed, whom the Elephant missing, like a lover distracted betwixt love and sorrow fell beside himself and so perished. Neither ought any man to marvel at such a passion in this Beast, who hath such a memory as is attributed unto him, and understanding of his charge and business, as may appear by manifold examples: for *Antipater* affirmeth that he saw an Elephant that knew again, and took acquaintaince of his Master which had nourished him in his youth, after many years absence.

When they are hurt by any man, they seldom forget a revenge, and so also they remember on the contrary to recompense all benefits, as it hath been manifested already. They observe things done both in weight and measure, especially in their own meat. *Agnon* writeth that an Elephant was kept in a great mans house in *Syria*, having a man appointed to be his Overseer, who did dayly defraud the Beast of his allowance: but on a day as his Master looked on, he brought the whole measure and gave it to him: the Beast seeing the same, and remembring how he had served him in times past, in the presence of his Master exactly divided the Corn into two parts, and so laid one of them aside: by this fact shewing the fraud of the servant to his Master. The like story is related by *Plutarch* and *Ælianus*, of another Elephant, discovering to his Master the falshood and privy theft of an unjust servant.

About *Lycha* in *Africk* there are certain springs of water, which if at any time they dry up, by the teeth of Elephants they are opened and recovered again. They are most gentle and meek, never fighting or striking Man or Beast, except they be provoked, and then being angred, they will take up a man in their trunk and cast him into the air like an arrow, so as many times he is dead before he come to the ground. *Plutarch* affirmeth, that in *Rome*, a boy pricking the trunck of an Elephant with a goad, the Beast caught him, and lift him up into the air to shoot him away and kill him: but the people and standers by seeing it, made so great a noise and cry thereat, that the Beast set him down again fair and softly without any harm to him at all; as if he thought it sufficient to have put him in fear of such a death.

In the night time they seem to lament with sighs and tears their captivity and bondage, but if any come to that speed, like unto modest persons they refrain suddenly, and are ashmed to be found either murmuring or sorrowing. They live to a long age, even to 200 or 300 years; if sickness or wounds prevent not their life: and some but to a 120 years; they are in their best strength of body at threescore, for then beginneth their youth.

Iuba King of *Lybia* writeth, that he hath seen tame Elephants which have descended from the Father to the son, (by way of inheritance) many generations: and that *Ptolemæus Philadelphus* had an Elephant, which continued alive many Ages, and another of *Seleucus Nicanor*, which remained alive to the last overthrow of all the *Antiochi*.

The Inhabitants of *Taxila* in *India* affirm, that they had an Elephant at the least three hundred and fifty years old, for they said it was the same that fought so faithfully with *Alexander* for King *Porus*, for which cause *Alexander* cald him *Aiax*, and did afterward dedicate him to the Sun, and put certain golden chains about his teeth with this inscription upon them: *Alexander filius Iovis Aiacem Soli: Alexander* the son of *Iupiter* consecrateth this *Aiax* to the *Sun*. The like story is related by *Iuba*, concerning the age of an Elephant, which had the impression of a Tower on his teeth and was taken in *Atlas* 400 years after the same was engraven.

There are certain people in the world which eat Elephants, and are therefore called of the *Nomades* (*Elephantophagi*) Elephant-eaters, as is already declared: there are of these which dwell in *Daraba*, neer the Wood *Eumenes*, beyond the City *Saba*, where there is a place (called the hunting of Elephants. The *Troglodytæ* live also hereupon, the people of *Africk* cald *Asachæ*, which live in Mountains, do likewise eat the flesh of Elephants, and the *Adiabaræ* or *Megabari*. The *Nomades* have Cities running upon Charriots, and the people next under their Territory, cut Elephants in pieces, and both sell and eat them.

Some use the hard flesh of the back, and other commend above all the delicates of the world the reins of the Elephants; so that it is a wonder that *Ælianus* would write, that there was nothing in an Elephant good for meat, except the trunck, the lips, and the marrow of his horns, or teeth. The skin of this Beast is exceeding hard, not to be pierced by any dart; whereupon came the Proverb, *Culicem haud curat Elephas Indicus*, the *Indian* Elephant careth not for the biting of a Gnat, to signifie a sufficient ability to resist all evill, and Noble mindes must not revenge small injuries.

It cannot be but in such huge and vast bodies there should also be nourished some diseases, and that many (as *Strabo* saith) wherefore first of all there is no creature in the world less able to endure cold or Winter, for their impatiency of cold bringeth inflamation. Also in Summer, when the same is hottest, they cool one another by casting dirty and filthy water upon each other, or else run into the roughest Woods of greatest shadow. It hath been shewed already, that they devour Chamæleons, and thereof perish, except they eat a wilde Olive.

When they suffer inflamation and are bound in the belly, either black Wine, or nothing will cure them. When they drink a Leach they are grievously pained: for their wounds by darts or otherwise, they are cured by Swines-flesh, or Dittany, or by Oyl, or by the flower of the Olive. They fall mad sometime, for which I know no other cure, but to tye them up fast in Iron chains. When they are tyred for want of sleep, they are recovered by rubbing their shoulders with Salt, Oyl and Water. Cows milk warmed and infused into their eyes, cureth all evils in them, and they presently like reasonable men acknowledge the benefit of the medicine.

The medicinal vertues in this Beast are by Authors observed to be these: The bloud of an Elephant and the ashes of a Weasil, cure the great Leprosie: and the same bloud is profitable against all Rhumatick fluxes, and the *Sciatica*. The flesh dryed and cold, or heavy fat and cold is abominable: for if it be sod and steeped in Vinegar with Fennel-seed, and given to a Woman with childe, it maketh her presently suffer abortment. But if a man taste thereof salted and steeped with the seed aforesaid it cureth an old cough. The fat is a good Antidote either by Ointment or Perfume: it cureth also the pain in the head.

The Ivory or tooth is cold and dry in the first degree, and the whole substance thereof corroborateth the heart and helpeth conception; it is often adulterated by Fishes and Dogs bones burnt, and by white Marble. There is a *Spodium* made of Ivory in this manner; Take a pound of Ivory cut into pieces; and put into a raw new earthen pot, covering and glewing the cover with lome round about, and so let it burn till the pot be throughly hardned: afterward take off the pot, and beat your Ivory into small powder, and being so beaten, sift it, then put it into a glass, and pour upon it two pound of distilled Rose-water, and let it dry. Thirdly, beat it unto powder again, and sift it the second time, and put into it again so much Rose-water as at the first, then let it dry, and put thereunto as much Camphire as will ly upon three or four single Groats, and work it all together upon a Marble stone into little Cakes, and so lay them up where the air may not corrupt and alter them. The vertue hereof is very pretious against spitting of bloud, the Bloudy-flix; and also it is given for refrigeration without danger of binding or astriction.

After a man is delivered from the Lethargy, Pestilence, or sudden forgetfulness, let him be purged and take the powder of Ivory and *Hiera Ruffi*, drunk out of sweet water: This powder with Hony-Attick, taketh away the spots in the face: the same with wilde Mints drunk with water, resisteth and avoideth the Leprosie at the beginning. The powder of Ivory burnt and drunk with Goats-bloud, doth wonderfully cure all the pains, and expell the little stones in the reins and bladder: Combes made of Ivory are most wholesome, the touching of the trunk cureth the Headach: The Liver is profitable against the Falling-evill, the same vertue hath the gall (if he have any) against the Falling-evill.

The fime by anointing, cureth a lowsie skin, and taketh away that power which breedeth these vermine: the same perfumed easeth Agues, helpeth a woman in travail, and driveth Gnats or marshflies out of a house.

OF THE ELK.

As the Elphant last handled, could not live in any Countrey of the world, but in the hot Eastern, and Southern Regions; so the Elk on the contrary is most impatient of all heat, and keepeth not but in the Northern and cold Countries: for *Polonia*, and the Countreys under that Climate will not preserve an Elk alive, as it hath been often tryed by experience: for which cause, they are not found but in the colder Northern Regions; as *Russia*, *Prussia*, *Hungaria*, and *Illyria*, in the Wood *Hercynia*, and among the *Borussian-Scythians*, but most plentiful in *Scandinavia*, (which *Pausanias* calleth the *Celtes*) for all the Ancients called the Kingdoms of *Germany*, and the North, *Celtarum Regiones*, Countreys inhabited by the *Celts*.

The Figure of the *ELK* with *Horns*.

The *ELK* without *Horns*.

This Beast is called in *Greek*, *Alke*; and in *Latine*, *Alces*, or *Alce*; which was a name of one of *Actæons* Dogs in *Ovid*: the *Turks*, *Valachians*, the

Hungarians, Iajus; the *Illyrians* and *Polonians, Los;* in the singular, and plurally, *Lossie,* for many Elks. *Albertus Magnus* calleth it *Alches* and *Aloy,* and afterward *Equicervus,* a Horse-Hart. The *Germans, Elch, Ellend,* and *Elent,* by a *Metathesis* of *Alke,* or *Alce:* and for my part I take it to be the same Beast which *Pliny* calleth *Machlis,* for there is nothing attributed to an Elk which also doth not belong to *Machlis.*

I finde not any unreconcileable difference among Authors concerning this Beast, except in *Cæsar, lib.* 6. of his Commentaries, who by the relation of other, (not by his own sight) writeth that there are Elks in the *Hercynian* Wood, like unto Goats in their spotted skins, who have no horns, nor joints in their legs to bend withall, but sleep by leaning unto trees like Elephants, because when they are down on the ground, they can never rise again. But the truth is, that they are like to Roes or Harts, because Goats have no spotted skins, but Deer have, and there may easily be a slip from *Caprea,* a Roe, to *Capra,* a Goat: and *Cæsar* himself confesseth, that the similitude is in their spotted skins, which are not competible in Goats, but in Roes.

And whereas he writeth that they have no Horns, the error of this relator may be this, that either he had only seen a young one before the horns came forth, or else an old one, that had lately lost his horns; and by this I suppose that the authority of *Cæsar* is sufficiently answered, so as we may proceed to the description of this Beast collected out of the ancient Writers, *Pausanias, Vapiscus, Cæsar,* and *Solinus, Pliny,* and the later Writers consenting with them in all things, (excepting *Cæsar* in the two things aforesaid) *Albertus Magnus, Mathæus, Michuanus, Seb. Munster, Erasmus, Stella, Iohannes, Bonarus,* Baron of *Balizce* a *Polonian, Johannes Kentmannus, Jo. Pontanus, Antonius Schnebergerus, Christophorus Wirsungus,* and that most worthy learned man *Georgius Joachimus* of *Rhætia,* and *Baoron Sigismund.*

Pausanias supposeth it to be a Beast betwixt a Hart and a Camel, and *Albertus,* betwixt a Hart and a Horse; who therefore, as it hath been said, calleth it *Equi-cervus,* a Horse-Hart; but I rather by the horns afterward described, and by the foot which *Bonarus* had, do take and hold it to be as big every way as two Harts, and greater then a Horse, because of the labour and qualities attributed thereunto: whereunto also agreeth *Albertus.*

384

In *Swedia* and *Riga* they are tamed, and put into Coaches or Charriots to draw men through great snows, and upon the ice in the Winter time they also are most swift, and will run more miles in one day, then a Horse can at three. They were wont to be presents for Princes, because of their singular strength and swiftness; for which cause *Alciatus* relateth in an emblem, the answer of *Alexander* to one that asked him a question about celerity whether haste doth not alway make waste: which *Alexander* denied by the example of the Elk in these Verses:

Alciatæ gentis insignia sustinet Alce,
    Unguibus & [meeden] fert [anaballomenos]
Constat Alexandrum sic respondisse roganti,
    Qui tot obivisset tempore gesta brevi,
Nunquam inquit differre volens, quod & indicat Alce,
    Fortior hæc dubites, ocyor anne siet?

Pliny affirmeth (in my opinion) very truly that this Beast is like an Oxe, except in his hair, which is more like to a Hart, his upper lip is so great, and hangeth over the neather so far, that he cannot eat going forward, because it doubleth under his mouth, but as he eateth he goeth backward like a Sea-crab, and so gathereth up the grass that lay under his feet. His mane is divers both upon the top of his neck, and also underneath his throat it buncheth like a beard or curled lock of hair, howbeit, they are alway maned on the top of the neck. Their neck is very short, and doth not answer to the proportion of the residue of his body, and therefore I have expressed both figures of the Elks.

Their fore-head is very broad, two spans at the least: it hath two very large Horns, which we have here also expressed, both for the right side and the left: so as they bend toward the back in the plain edge, and the spires or pikes stand forward to the face: both males and females have horns, they are solid at the root, and round, but afterward branched, and grow out of their eye-lids, they are broader then a Harts, and are also very heavy, for they weigh at the least twelve pounds, and are not above two foot long, and the breadth measured from the longest spire to the other opposite side, about ten inches: the root next to the skin, is more then a man can well griple in his hand, and therefore here is expressed the figure

385

of both horns, both in male and female; for there is not any difference in their natures that I can learn, and these horns they lose every year. His ears and back are very long, and hanging down, the colour for the most part like a Hart, and sometime white; and *Munster* affirmeth, that in the Summer they are of russet colour, and in the Winter brown or blackish coloured. His fore-legs without all joynts to bend, herein resembling an Elephant, and therefore it sleepeth leaning to Posts or Trees, and not lying on the ground. His hoofs are cloven like a Harts, and with the fore-feet he pierceth the Dogs that hunt him, for the fighteth not with his horns, but with his fore-legs. It is a melancholick Beast, and fearful to be seen, having an ambling pace, and keeping in the wet, watry, and marshy places, delighting in nothing but in moisture. The flesh is fat and sweet, but ingrateful to the palate, and engendereth melancholy. The *Germans* call this Beast *Ellend*, which in their language signifieth miserable or wretched, and in truth if the report thereof be not false, it is in a most miserable and wretched case, for every day throughout the year it hath the Falling-sickness, and continueth in the pangs thereof, untill the hoof of his right fore-foot touch his left ear, which comes not to pass but by the extream torments of the body, for whilest the members are reached and stretched with many strains and Convulsions (as it falleth out in that sickness) by chance the aforesaid foot rubbeth the said ear, and immediately thereupon the Beast is delivered from his pangs: whereby we are to admire the works of our Creator, which having laid so heavy an infirmity upon this poor Beast, wherewith he is dayly tormented, yet hath he also provided a remedy for that evil in the hoof of his own foot, making the torments of the disease to be the Apothecary for applying the remedy to the place of cure.

They live in heards and flocks together in *Scandivania*, and when the waters are frozen up, the wilde Mountain Wolves set upon them in great multitudes together, whom they receive in battel upon the Ice, fighting most fiercely and cruelly till one part be vanquished: In the mean time the Husbandmen of the Country observe this combate, & when they see one side go to the wall, they persecute them, & take the victors part, for it is indifferent to take either the one side or the other; but most commonly the Elks are conquerers by reason of their fore-feet, for with them they pierce the Wolves or Dogs skins, as with any sharp pointed Spear or Javelin.

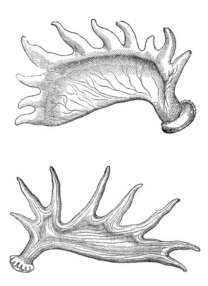

Some have been of opinion that these are wilde Asses, but they are led hereinto with no reason, except because they are used for travel and burthen as is before said, for there is no proportion or resemblance of body betwixt them: besides, they have cloven hoofs, for the most part, although *Sigismundus Baro* affirm, that there are some of this kinde which have their hoofs whole and undivided. Being wilde it is a most fearful creature, and rather desireth to ly hid in secret, then to fly, except persued by Hunters; and there is no danger in hunting of this Beast, except a man come right before him, for on his sides he may safely strike and wound him; but if the Beast fasten his fore-feet on him, he cannot escape without death. Notwithstanding it is a Beast (as hath been said) as great as two Harts, yet is it above measure fearful, and if it receive any small wound, or shot, instantly it falleth down and yeeldeth to death, as *Bonarus* hunting with *Sigismund* the second King of *Polonia* in the Woods of *Lituania* tryed with his own hand, for with his hunting Spear he pierced one a very little way in the skin in the presence of the King, who presently fell down dead.

In some Countries of ancient time (saith *Pausanias*) they took them on this manner. They having found out the field or hill where the Beasts are lodged, they compass it in by the space of a thousand paces round in circle with welts and toils invented for that purpose, then do they draw in their nets round like a purse, and so inclose the Beasts by multitude, who commonly smelling his Hunters, hideth himself in some deep ditch or cave of the earth; for the nature of this Beast hath framed to it self a most sharp sagacity, or quick sent of smelling, being not herein inferiour to any of the best Dogs in the world, because it can a great way off discover the Hunters, and many times while men are abroad in hunting of other Beasts, this is suddenly started out of her lodging place, and so discovered, chased, and taken.

Other again take it by the same means that they take Elephants, for when they have found the trees whereunto they lean, they so cut and saw them, that when the Beast cometh, he overthroweth them, and falleth down with them, and so is taken alive.

We read that there were Elks in the triumph of *Aurelian* at *Rome*, and in the games dedicated by *Apollo* and *Diana*, and celebrated by *Valerius Publicola*, were many Elephants, Elks, and Tygers. Likewise there were ten Elks at *Rome* under *Gordianus*. When they are chased eagerly, and can finde no place to rest themselves in and lie secret, they run to the waters, and therein stand, taking up water into their mouths, and within short space do so heat it, that being squirted or shot out of them upon the Dogs, the heat thereof so oppresseth and scaldeth them, that they dare not once approach or come nigh her any more.

The greatest vertue of medicine that I can learn or finde to be in this Beast, is in the hoof, for that worn in a Ring, it resisteth and freeth a man from the Falling evill, the Cramp, and cureth the fits or pangs, if it be put on when he is in his foming extremity: also scraped into powder and put into Wine and drunk, it is used in *Polonia* against the same evill. In like sort they mingle with Triacle, and apply it to the heart, or else hang it about their neck for an Amulet to touch their skin against that disease: and because that both in ancient time, and also now adays, this Beast is seldom seen, and more seldom taken, the hoof thereof being so often approved for the uses before said, the rarity (I say thereof) maketh it to be sold very dear, which would be (if they could be found or taken) in more plentiful manner.

Some Mounte-banks sell in stead thereof a Bugles hoof, but it may easily be described by scraping, for (it is said) it smelleth very sweet, whereas a Bugles savoureth very ill and strong. It is observed also, that it hath not this vertue except it be cut off from the Beast while he is yet alive, and that in the months of *August* and *September*, at what time these Elks are most of all annoyed with the Falling-sickness, and then it hath strongest vertue to cure it in others.

Others affirm, it wanteth his operation if it be cut off from a young one, which never tasted of carnal copulation, and so hath not been dulled thereby: but howsoever, this is certain, that some-times it cureth, and sometime it faileth, and as there can be given no good reason of the cure, so I rather ascribe it to a superstitious conceit or belief of the party that weareth it, rather then to any hidden or assured work of nature. The skins of this Beast are dressed by Tawyers, with the fat of fishes and Alum, to make breast-plates; and to shelter one from rain, and they sell them for three or four Nobles a piece; but in *Cracovia* for fifteen Florens. It may be discerned from a Harts skin by blowing upon it, for the breath will come through like as in a Buffe, and the hairs also of this Beast have also hollow passages in them when they grow upon the back of the Beast, or else soon after the skin is taken off.

Some also use the Nerves against the Crampe, binding the offended member therewith, and herewith do we conclude this story of an Elk, referring the reader to the fable of *Acida* related before in *Cacus*, if he have desire to know it for the affinity betwixt the name thereof, and *Alces* an Elk.

OF THE FERRET.

I take it to be most true without all exception, that the *Græcians* call a Ferret *Gala Agria*, a wilde Weasil, *Ictys* and *Phereoikos*, although *Erymologus* and *Hesychius* ascribe the reason of this latter name to her lodging under Oaks and Olive-trees. *Ictys* also was a common name of all Weasils, to those *Græcians* which never knew or saw any other then one kinde of them, or as *Scaliger* against *Cardan* will have it to signifie a wilde *Campestrial* Weasil, and not a tame kinde, being domestical and living in houses, and that these differ only from one another in place and manner of living, and not in colour, stature or qualities. And where *Aristophanes* citeth it among other Beasts which are devourers of fish; in my opinion there is no Beast that more desireth Fish, then Ferrets and Cats; and for this cause it hath his name *Ictys quasi Ichthus*, of eating of Fish; and yet I cannot consent unto them which will have it descend and hunt Fish in the waters, like Otters or Beavers: for it abhorreth both swimming or diving, but neer to the waters it hunteth Fish, where for the most part being wilde it remaineth.

The *Latines* call this Beast *Viverra*, and *Furo*, and *Furetus*, and *Furectus*, because (as shall be afterward manifested) it preyeth upon Conies in their holes, and liveth upon stealth, and in the earth will kill a Cony six times as big as herself, but being abroad on the land, in the open air is nothing so wilde, strong or full of courage. From *Ictys* is derived *Iltissus*, and the *German, Iltis*, for a Ferret: this is called by the *French, Furon, Furet*, and *Fuson*, and *Fuset*: by the *Spaniards, Furon*, and *Furam*, and from the *English, Ferret*, is the *German Fret*, derived by a common *Syncope*, and in the time of *Georgius Agricola*, it was called in *Germany, Furette*, and *Frettel*; and the *English* word seemeth also to be derived from *Fretta* in *Latine*, which by a like *Syncope* is contracted of *Viverra*, as to any indifferent learned man it may appear at the first sight of derivation.

But herein seemeth an unreconcileable diffrence, that it is reported of the *Ictys* by *Gaza*, the intepreter of *Aristotle*, that it was most greedy of Honey, and for that cause it will seek out the Hives of Bees, and enter them without all fear of stings. But when *Pliny* speaketh of *Ictys*, he doth not call it *Viverra*, or once attribute unto it the love of Honey, but rather the hatred and loathing thereof, in so high a degree, that if he tast of it, he falleth into Consumptions, and hardly escapeth death. And these things

Scaliger alleadgeth against *Cardan*, only to prove that *Ictys* and *Viverra*, are two distinct Beasts, and that *Cardan* was mistaken in affirming, that they were but several names, expressing one and the same Beast.

The answer whereunto may be very easie, for although *Pliny* leaveth without rehearsal their love of Hony, it doth not necessarily follow, that they love it not (as *Aristotle* before him constantly affirmeth) and *Scaliger* nameth no Author, nor bringeth any reason to demonstrate their hate of Honey, or any harm which insueth them by eating thereof: and therefore against his authority may *Strabo* be opposed, who in his third Book, speaking of the Conies of *Spain*, and of their Hunters and starters, out of their holes, he taketh and nameth indifferently without all distinction and exception, *Viverra*, and *Ictys*, for the one and other. *Niphus* translateth *Ictys*, a Marrel, but without reason; for the same man finding in *Aristotle*, that there is war betwixt Locusts and Serpents, which is fitly called *Ophiomachia*; whereas *Aristotle* nameth *Akris*, a Locust, he falleth in doubt whether it were not better to be *Ictys*, a Martel, or as other copies have it *Aspis*, an Aspe, which can by no means agree unto them, for there is a kinde of Locusts (called *Ophiomachum*) because of their continual combates with Serpents. And therefore not to stand any longer upon this difference, omitting also the conjecture of *Tzetzes*, which confoundeth *Ictys* with *Milvus*, a Glead or Kyte, which cannot stand reasonable, because *Homer* saith, there was a kinde of Caps made of the hairs of *Ictys*, nor yet of *Albertus* his new found name of *Anbatinos*, nor *Avicenna* his *Katyz*, or the *French*, *Fissau*, which is a Poul-Cat.

I will descend to the description of the parts and qualities, wherein the Authors themselves at variance, make their own reconcilement, by attributing the same things to the *Icta*, and Ferret, except that of an obscure Author, which saith that *Ictys* is *Ankacinor*, as big as a Grayhound, and that it is wiser and more industrious in his youth and tender age, then in his perfection of strength and years.

These Ferrets are lesser then the *Melitean* or Gentlewomens Dogs, and they were first of all brought out of *Africk* into *Spain*, and therefore are called by *Strabo*, *African* Weasils, because of their similitude with Weasils: for *Spain*, *Italy*, *France*, and *Germany*, have not this Beast bred among them, but brought to them out of other Countries. But in

England they breed naturally of the quantity aforesaid, and they are tamed to hunt Conies out of the earth. It is a bold and audacious Beast, enemy to all other, except his own kinde, drinking and sucking in the bloud of the Beast it biteth, but eateth not the flesh. When the Warrener setteth it down to hunt, he first of all maketh a great noise to fray all the Conies that are abroad into their holes, and so having frighted them, pitcheth his Nets, and then putteth his tame Ferret into the earth, having a long string or cord with Bels about her neck, whose mouth he muzzleth, that so it may not bite the Cony, but only terrifie her out of her borough and earth with her presence or claws; which being performed, she is by Dogs chased into the nets, and there overwhelmed, as is aforesaid in the history of the Conies.

Their body is longer for the proportion then their quantity may afford, for I have seen them two spans long, but very thin and small. Their colour is variable, sometime black, and white on the belly, but most commonly of a yellowish sandy colour, like Hermeline or Wool, dyed in urine. The head little like a Mouses, and therefore into whatsoever hole or chink she putteth it in, all her body will easily follow after. The eyes small, but fiery, like red hot iron, and therefore she seeth most clearly in the dark: Her voyce is a whyning cry, neither doth she change it as a Cat: She hath only two teeth in the neather chap, standing out, and not joyned or growing together. The genital of the male is of a bony substance, (wherein *Pliny* and *Scaliger* agree with *Cardan* and *Strabo* for the *Ictys* also) and therefore it alway standeth stiffe, and is not lesser at one time then at other. The pleasure of the sense in copulation is not in the yard or genital part, but in the nerves, muscles, and tunicles wherein the said genital runneth. When they are in copulation, the female lyeth down or bendeth her knees, and continually cryeth like a Cat, either because the Male pincheth and claweth her skin with his sharp nails, or else because of the rigidity of his genital. And when the female desireth copulation, except she be with convenient speed brought to a male, or he suffered to come to her, she swelleth and dyeth. They are very fruitful in procreation, for they bring forth seven or eight at a time, bearing them in their little belly not above forty days. The young ones newly littered are blinde 30 days together, and within forty days after they can see, they may be set to hunting. The Noble men of *France* keep them for this pleasure, who are greatly given to hunt Conies, and they are sold there for a *French* crown. Young boys and scholars also use them to put them into the holes of rocks and walls to hunt out birds, and likewise into hollow trees, where-out they bring the Birds in the claws of their feet.

They are nourished being tamed with Milk, or with Barley bread, and they can fast a very long time. When they go, they contract their long back and make it stand upright in the middle, round like a bowl. When they are touched, they smell like a Martel, and they sleep very much: being wilde, they live upon the bloud of Conies, Hens, Chickens, Hares, or other such things, which they can finde and over-master. In their sleep also they dream, which appeareth by whyning and crying in their sleep. Whereas a long fly (called a Fryer) flying to the flaming candles in the night, is accounted among poysons, the Antidote and resister thereof is by *Pliny* affirmed to be a Goats gall or liver, mixed with a Ferret, or wilde Weasil, and the gall of Ferrets is held pretious against the poyson of Aspes, although the flesh and teeth of a Ferret be accounted poyson. Likewise the gall of a Ferret is commended against the Falling disease, and not only the gall (saith *Marcellus*) but the whole body, if it be rosted, dressed, and eaten fasting, like a young pig. It is said by *Rasis* and *Albertus*, that if the head of a Wolf be hanged up in a Dove-cote, neither Cat, Ferret, Weasil, Stoat, or other noysome Beast dare to enter therein. These Ferrets are kept in little hutches, in houses, and there fed, where they sleep much: they are of a very hot temperature and constitution, and therefore, quickly digest their meat, and being wilde by reason of their fear, they rather seek their meat in the night then in the day time.

OF THE FITCH OR POUL-CAT.

THE difference of a Poul-Cat, from the Wilde-Cat, is because of her strong stinking savour, and therefore is called *Putorius*, of *Putore*, because of his ill smell: for all Weasils being incensed and provok't to wrath, smell strongly, and especially the Poul-Cat; likewise when in the Spring time they endeavour procreation, for which cause among the *Germans*, when they would express an infamous Whore or Whoremaster, they say they stink like an *Iltis*, that is a Fitch or Poul-Cat. The *French* call this Beast *Putois*, and *Poytois*, as it is to be found in *Carolus Figulus*; the *Savoyans*, *Pouttett*; the *Illyrians* and *Bohemians*, *Tchorz*; and the *Polonians*, *Viidra*; and *Scaliger* calleth it in *Latine* (*Catum fuinam*) by another name then *Putorius*. It is greater then an ordinary Weasil, but lesser then the wilde Martel, and yet commonly fatter: the hairs of it are neither smooth and of one length, or of one colour; for the short hairs are somewhat yellowish, and the long ones black, so as one would think that in many places of the body, there were spots of divers colours, but yet about the mouth it is most ordinarily white.

The skin is stiff, harsh, and rugged in handling, and therefore long lasting in Garments, yet because the Beast is alway fat, the savour of it is so rank, that it is not in any great request, and moreover it is said, that it offendeth the head, and procureth ach therein; and therefore it is sold cheaper then a Fox skin, and the fattest is alway the worst of all. The Skinners approve the skins of Fitches and Martels best, which are killed in Winter, because their flesh and lust is much lower, and therefore rendereth a less hurtfull smell then at other times. The tail is not above two hands or palms long, and therefore shorter then is a Martels. In all other parts of the body it equalleth a Martell, or exceedeth very little, having thinner necks, but larger and greater bellies, the tail, legs, and breast, are also of a blacker colour, but the belly and sides more yellow. Some have delivered that the left legs thereof are shorter then the right legs, but this is found untrue by daily experience: They keep in the tops of houses and secret corners, delighting to kill and eat Hens and Chickens, whose craft in devouring his prey is singular; for to the intent that the silly creatures to be devoured may not bewray them to the House-keepers, the first part that they lay hold upon with their mouths is the head of the Hen and Chicken, and by that means stayeth his crying by cropping off the head. Some of these Fitches wander and keep in the Woods, and thereby live upon Birds and Mise, and such things: some again live by the Sea sides in Rocks, and they take Fishes like Beavers and Otters: and some creep into the Caves of hollow trees, where they eat Frogs, and most of all they delight to be near stals of Cattel, Hay-houses, and houses, where they meet oftentimes with Egges, wherein they delight above all other kindes of meat. And thus much for this Beast.

OF THE FOX.

A Fox is called in *Hebrew, Schual*; and in *Chaldee, Thaal*; and therefore in Psal. 61. where the *Hebrew* readeth *Schualim*, there the *Chaldee* translateth it *Thealaia*; the *Arabians* call him *Thaleb*; and *Avicen* calleth a Fox sometime *Chabel*, and also *Chalchail*; the *Greek* Septuagints, *Alopekon*, and vulgarly *Alopex*, and *Alopon*; the *Latine, Vulpes*, and *Vulpecula* of *Volipes*, his tumbling-pace; the *Italians, Volpe*; the *French, Regnard*, and a little Fox *Regnardeau*; the *Spaniards, Rapoja*, of ravening; the *Germans, Fuchs*; the *Flemings, Vos*; and the *Illyrians, Lisska*.

The Epithets expressing the nature hereof among Writers, both Poets and others, are these: crafty, wary, deceitful, stinking, strong-smelling, quick-smelling, tayled, warlike or contentious, wicked and rough; the *Græcians* fiery colored, and subtil for slaughter; and therefore Christ called *Herod* a Fox, because he understood how by crafty means he sought to entrap and kill him: and all the Ancients called such kinde of men *Vulpiones*, which every Nation under Heaven doth imitate.

There are store of Foxes in the *Alpine* regions of *Helvetia*, and amongst the *Caspians* they abound, so that their multitude maketh them tame, comming into the Cities, and attending upon men like tame Dogs. The Foxes of *Sardinia* are very ravenous, for they kill the strongest Rams and Goats, and also young Calves; and in *Egypt* they are lesser then in *Græcia*, and most commonly all Foxes are of stature like to a shepherds Dog. Their colour is reddish and more white toward the head: In *Muscovia* are both black and white, *viz* about the river *Woga*, black and ash-coloured, and in the Province of *Usting* all black, and these are of the smaller sort, which are nourished to make caps of their skins, and are therefore sold at twenty or thirty Florens a skin. In *Spain* they are all white, and their skins are often brought by the Merchants to be sold at *Francford* Mart.

In the Septentrional or Northern Woods, there are black, white, and red Foxes, and such as are cald *Crucigeræ*, that is Cross-bearing Foxes, for on their backs and orethwart their shoulders there is a black cross, like an Asses: and there are Foxes aspersed over with black spots, and all these are of one and the same malignant and crafty nature: and these (saith *George Fabritius*) are distinguished by their regions or habitations: for it is most commonly seen, that Foxes which keep and breed toward the South and West, are of an ash colour, and like to Wolves, having loose hanging hairs, as is to be seen both in *Spain* and *Italy*; and these are noted by two names among the *Germans*, from the colour of their throat. One kinde of them is called *Koler*, whose throat seemeth to be sprinkled and darkned with cole-dust, upon white, so as the tops of the hair appear black, the foot and stalk being white.

The other *Birkfuchse*, because their throat is all white, and of this kinde the most splendent white, is most pretious. A second there is (called *Kreutzfuchse*) because of the cross it beareth upon his back and shoulders down to his fore-feet, being in other parts like the former, except the throat which is blacker then any of the other before spoken of, and these are not bred in *Germany*, but brought thither from other Nations.

A third kinde is of a bright skie-colour (called *Blauwfuchse*) and this colour hath given a different name to Horses, which they call *Blauwschimmel*, but in the Foxes it is much more mingled, and these Foxes which have rougher and deeper hair are called *Braudfuchse*.

The *Moscovians* and *Tartarians* make most account of the black skins, because their Princes and great Nobles wear them in their garments: yet are they more easily adulterated, and counterfeited by the fume or smoke of Torches made of pitch. The white and blew skins are less esteemed, because the hair falleth off, and are also lesser then the other: the red ones are most plentiful; and *Scaliger* affirmeth that he saw skins brought into *France* by certain Merchants, which had divers white hairs disposed in rows very elegantly upon them, and in divers places they grew also single. In *Norvegia* and *Suetia*, as there are white Hares and Bears, so there are also white Foxes; In *Wolocha* they are black, as it is affirmed by *Sigismundus Liber*, the picture of the Cross-bearing-Fox which is less then the former is here following expressed and set down.

THE CRUCIGERAN FOX.

SERPENTS, Apes, and Foxes, and all other dangerous harmful Beasts, have small eyes, but Sheep and Oxen which are simple, very great eyes. The *Germans* when they describe a good Horse, they decipher in him the outward parts of many Beasts, from whom (it seemeth) he partaketh his generosity, and from a Fox they ascribe unto him short ears, a long and bushy tail, an easie and soft treading step, (for these belong to a Fox.) The male Fox hath a hard bony genital, his tail is long and hairy at the end, his temperament and constitution is hot, as appeareth both because of his resemblance or similitude with Dogs and Weasils, and also his rank and strong smelling savour; for being dead, his skin hath power in it of heating, and his fat or oyl after a decoction is of the same force and condition.

The greatest occasion of his hunting is the benefit of his skin, for his flesh is in all things like a Dogs, and although *Galen, Mnesimachus*, and

Silvius affirm, that in the Autumn or latter part of the year, some men use to eat the flesh of Foxes, (especially being Cubs) that is young, tender, and not smelling: but *Ætius* and *Rasis* affirm, (and that with great reason) that their flesh, and the flesh of Hedg-hogs and Hares, is not agreeable to the nature of man.

But their skin retaineth the qualities of the hot Beast being pulled off, by reason of the long and soft hair growing thereupon; and the skins of Cubs which are preferred before the elder, are of least value, because their hair is apt to fall off, which being thin doth not admit any deep rootings of the hair. The *Thracians* in the time of *Xenophon*, wore Caps of Foxes skins upon their heads and ears, in the coldest and hardest Winters, and from hence it cometh, that in some Authors the covers of mens heads, (commonly called in *Greek, Pericephalæa*) are tearmed *Alopecia,* or *Alopecis*: and for this purpose in *Germany* at this day, they slit asunder the skin of Foxes tails, and sow it together again, adding to it a sufficient number till it be framed into a Cap: but the skin of the belly and sides is of more pretious estimation, because it is more soft and smooth, and therefore is sold for twice so much as the other parts.

In the Summer time the skins are little worth, because that then the beasts are troubled with the *Alopecia*; that is, the falling off or looseness of the hair; and therefore then also they are dangerous to be used, because of that disease: men which have the Gowt, shrinking up of the sinews, or other old fluxions of the Rhewme in their legs, can use no better or more wholesome thing then to wear buskins of the skins of Foxes; the *Scythians* make them shooes, and soal them with the backs of Fox and Mise skins, upon which they go. The *Latins* have a proper word for the voice of a Fox, which is, *Gannio Gannire,* to Ganne, and it is also metaphorically applyed to men, when by scrieching clamors they trouble others; as *Terence* in *Adelph. Quid ille gannit? Quid vult?* And *Plautus* also, *Gannit odiosus omni toti familiæ*; and for this voice did *Mantuan* write his Verse;

> ——— *Putes ululare lupos, gannire sagaces*
> *Vulpeculas* ——— ———

But yet as *Albertus* and *Constantinus* have truly observed, that in the time of his hunting he will bark like a little Dog, and the Harts are greatly afraid of this ganning of Foxes.

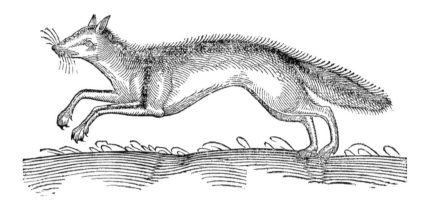

It hath been already shewed in the story of the Badger, how the Fox by laying his excrements in the Badgers den, getteth the same to his own use; for the abode of Foxes in the day time is in the caves and holes in the earth, and come not abroad till the night. These dens have many caves in them, and passages in and out, that when the Terriars shall set upon him in the earth, he may go forth some other way: and forasmuch as the Wolf is an enemy to the Fox, he layeth in the mouth of his den, an Herb (called Sea-onion) which is so contrary to the nature of the Wolf, and he so greatly terrified therewith, that he will never come neer the place where it either groweth or lyeth; the same is affirmed of the Turtle to save her young ones, but I have not read that Wolves will prey upon Turtles, and therefore we reject that as a fable.

When *Aristomanes* was taken by the *Lacædemonians*, and included into a rock or quarrey of stones, he escaped out of their hands, by digging another passage out of it then where he was put in; saying, that it was a shame for a Man to have lesse wit then a Fox. When they are in their dens, they lie upon their bellies with their hinder legs stretched forth at length, like as a man when he sleepeth on his belly, and therefore it seemeth that their legs are so framed to creep and pierce under the earth and dig out their way after their own pleasure.

This is such a devouring beast, that it forsaketh nothing fit to be eaten, for it killeth Hares and Conies, and with his breath draweth field

Mice out of their holes, like as a Hart draweth out Serpents with his breath, and devoureth them. He devoureth also all kinde of Pullen, they also eat Grapes, Apples, and Pears; whereupon came the proverb in *Plautus, Tam facile vinces quam vulpes pyrum comest*; Thou shalt as easily overcome him, as a Fox eateth a Pear: which is applyed to any easie or dispatchable business. In *Arabia*, and *Syria Palestina*, they are so ravenous, harmful, and audacious, that in the night by ganning and barking, they invite one another (as it were) by a Watchword, to assemble in great multitudes together, for to prey upon all things, and they fear not to carry into their dens, old shooes and vessels, or instruments of husbandry: for which cause, when the Husbandmen hear thereof, they gather all things into their houses and watch them.

But as it falleth out in all gluttonous ravening persons, that while they strive to fill their bellies, they poison their lives, so also it fareth with Foxes, for nature hath so ordained, that if a Fox, eat any meat wherein are bitter Almonds, they die thereof if they drink not presently: and the same thing do Aloes in their meat work upon them, as *Scaliger* affirmeth upon his own sight or knowledge. *Apocynon* or Bear-foot given to Dogs, Wolves, Foxes, and all other beasts which are littered blind, in fat or any other meat killeth them, if vomit help them not, which falleth out very seldom, and the seeds of this herb have the same operation. It is reported by *Democritus*, that if wilde Rue be secretly hunge under a Hens wing, no Fox will meddle with her; and the same writer also declareth for approved, that if you mingle the gall of a Fox, or a Cat, with their ordinary food, they shall remain free from the dangers of these beasts.

When they engender and admit copulation, they are joyned like Dogs, the male upon the female: and the female when she perceiveth her womb filled, she departeth and liveth very secret, for it falleth out very seldom that a female or Bitch-fox is taken great with young. She bringeth forth ordinarily four at a time, and those blind and imperfect, without Articles in their legs, which are perfected and framed by licking, for Bears, Wolves, Lions, Foxes, Dogs, and *Thoes* which are *Multipara* and *Multifida*, that is, fruitful, bearing many at one time, and also Cloven or slit-footed into many clawes, have not the benefit of nature to perfect their young ones in their wombes.

Kites, Vultures, and Eagles lie in wait to destroy the Foxes Cubs or Whelps. Foxes do not only engender with their own kinde, but also with Wolves, Dogs, or any other beasts of equall proportion, both of quantity and time of going with young: so the *Laconian* Dogs are engendred by a Dog and a Fox; and the *Hyæna*, of a Wolf and a Fox (as *Albertus* affirmeth) and the *Simivulpa* of an Ape and a Fox, as is already in the story of Apes declared.

There be also many evils wherewithal Foxes are annoyed, and first of all he falleth sometime into madness as a Dog, and the same evils follow a mad Fox, which already are manifested to accompany a mad Dog, and that more often in Summer then in Winter.

When a Fox feeleth himself sick, nature hath taught him to eat the gum of Pinetrees, wherewithal he is not only cured, but also receiveth length of dayes. They are also vexed with the falling away of their hair, called therefore *Alopecia*, because Foxes are most commonly vexed therewith, and as we see in Plants, that some of them dry and consume through want of moisture to feed them, other are suffocated and choaked by abundance, and as it were drowned in humidity: so it happeneth in hair, which groweth out of the body of beasts, and the heads of men, no otherwise then Plants out of the earth, and are therefore to be nourished by humours; which if they fail and wax dry, the hair also shorteneth with them, and as it were rotteth away in length: but if they abound and overflow, then do they loosen the roots of the hair, and cause them to fall off totally.

This disease is called *Alopecia*, and the other *Ophiasis*, because it is not general, but only particular in one member or part of the body or head, and there it windeth or indenteth like a Serpents figure.

Michael Ferus affirmeth, that sometime the liver of the Fox inflameth, and then it is not cured but by the Ulcerous blood flowing to the skin, and that evill blood causeth the *Alopecia*, or falling away of the hair, for which cause (as is already said) a Foxes skin is little worth that is taken in the Summer time.

The length of the life of a Fox is not certainly known, yet as *Stumpsius* and others affirm, it is longer then the life of a Dog. If the urine of a Fox fall upon the grasse or other herbs, it dryeth and killeth them, and the earth remaineth barren ever afterward. The savour of a Fox is more strong then of any other vulgar beast, he stinketh at nose and tail, for which cause *Martial* calleth it *Olidam Vulpem*, an *Olent* or smelling beast.

Hic olidam clamosus ages in retia vulpem.

Touching the hunting or taking of Foxes, I approve the opinion of *Xenophon*, who avoucheth, *Leporum capturam venatico studio quam vulpium digniorem*; that is, the hunting of the Hare is a more noble game or pastime then the hunting of the Fox.

This beast is more fearful of a Dog then a Hare, for the only barking of Dogs causeth him to rise many times from his den or lodgings out of the earth, or from the middle of bushes, briars, and brambles, wherein he hid himself: and for his hunting this is to be observed, that as in hunting of a Hart it hath been already related, the Hunter must drive the beast with the winde, because it hindereth his refrigeration; so in hunting of a Fox he drive him against the winde, and then he preventeth all his crafty and subtill agitations and devises; for it stayeth his speed in running, and also keepeth his savour fresh alway in the nose of the Dogs that follow him: for the Dogs that kill a Fox must be swift, strong and quick sented, and it is not good to put on a few at once, but a good company together, for be assured the Fox will not lose his own bloud till he hazzard some of his enemies, and with his tail which he windeth every way, doth he delude the Hunters: when the Dogs are pressed neer unto him, and are ready to bite him, he striketh his tail betwixt his legs, and with his own urine wetteth the same, and so instantly striketh it into the Dogs mouths, whereof when they have tasted, so many of them as it toucheth will commonly leave off and follow no farther.

Their teeth are exceeding sharp, and therefore they fear not to assault or contend with beasts, exceeding their stature, strength, and quantity. Sometime he leapeth up into a tree, and there standeth to be seen and bayed at by the Dogs and Hunters, like as a Champion in some Fort or Castle, and although fire be cast at him, yet will he not descend down among the Dogs; yea he endureth to be beaten and pierced with Hunters spears, but at length being compelled to forsake his hold and give over to his enemies, down he leapeth, falling upon the crew of barking Dogs, like a flash of lightning, and where he layeth hold there he never looseth teeth, or asswageth wrath, till other Dogs have torn his limbs, and driven breath out of his body.

If at any time he take the earth, then with Terriar Dogs they ferret him out of his den again. In some places they take upon them to take him with nets, which seldom proveth, because with his teeth he teareth them in pieces; yet by *Calentius* this devise is allowed in this Verse;

Et laqueo Vulpes & decipe casse fuinas.

But this must be wrought under the earth in the caves, dens, or surrowes, made of purpose, which is to be performed two manner of wayes, one by placing the Gin in some perch of wood, so as that as soon as the beast is taken by the Neck, it may presently flie up and hang him, for otherwise with his teeth he will shear it asunder and escape away alive: or else that neer the place where the rope is fastened, to slip upon the head of the Fox, there be placed some thick collar or brace, so as he can never bite it asunder.

The *French* have a kinde of Gin to take by the legs (which they call *Hausepied*) and I have heard of some which have found the Foxes leg in the same Gin, bitten off with his own teeth from his body, rather putting himself to that torment with his own teeth, then to expect the mercy of the Hunter, and so went away upon three feet: and other have counterfeited themselves dead, restraining their breath and winking, not stirring any member when they saw the Hunter come to take them out of the Gin, who coming and taking his leg forth, not suspecting any life in them, so soon as the Fox perceiveth himself free, away he went and never gave thanks for his deliverance: for this cause *Blondus* saith truly, that only wise and old Hunters are fit to take Foxes, for they have so many devises to beguile men, and deliver themselves, that it is hard to know when he is safely taken, untill he be throughly dead.

They also use to set up Gins for them baited with Chickens in bushes and hedges: but if the setter be not at hand so soon as the Fox is insnared, it is dangerous but that the beast will deliver it self. In some places again they set up an iron toile, having in it a ring for the Fox to thrust in his head, and through that sharp pikes, at the farther end whereof is placed a piece of flesh, so that when the hungry Fox cometh to bite at the meat and thrusteth in his head, the pikes stick fast in his neck, and he inevitably insnared. Moreover, as the harmefulness of this beast hath troubled many, so also they have devised more engins to deceive and take him; for this cause there is another policy to kill him by a bow, full bent, with a sharp arrow, and so tenderly placed as is a trap for a Mouse, and as soon as ever the Fox treadeth thereon, presently the arrow is discharged into his own bowels, by the weight of his foot.

Again, for the killing of this beast they use this sleight, they take of Bacon-grease or Bacon as much as ones hand, and rost the same a little, and therewith anoint their shooe-soles, and then take the liver of a Hog cut in pieces, and as they come out of the wood where the beast lodgeth, they must scatter the said pieces in their foot-steps and draw the carcasse of a dead Cat after them, the savour whereof will provoke the beast to follow the foot-steps, then have they a cunning Archer or handler of a Gun, who observeth and watcheth in secret till the beast come within his reach, and so giveth him his great and deadly wound.

But if the Fox be in the earth, and they have found his den, then they take this course to work him out. They take a long thing like a Bee-hive, and open at one end, and iron wiers at the other like a grate, and at the open end is set a little door to fall down upon the mouth, and to inclose the Fox when he entreth in by touching of a small rod that supporteth that door. This frame is set to the Foxes dens mouth, and all the other passages watched and stopped. The Fox having a desire to go forth, and seeing light by the wiers, misdeemeth no harm, and entreth into the hive which is wrought close into the mouth of his den, and being entred into it, the rod turneth the door fast at the lower end or entrance, and so the Fox is intrapped, to be disposed of at the will of the taker.

Foxes are annoyed with many enemies; and to begin with the least, the small flies, called Gnats, do much trouble and infect them, against whom the Fox useth this policy; He taketh a mouthful of straw or soft hay, or hair, and so goeth into the water, dipping his hinder parts by little and little, then the flies betake themselves to his head, which he keepeth out of the water, which the Fox feeling, dippeth or diveth also the same under water to his mouth, wherein he holdeth the hay as aforesaid, whereunto the flies runne for sanctuary or dry refuge, which the Fox perceiving, suddenly casteth it out of his mouth, and runneth out of the water, by this means easing himself of all those enemies.

In like manner, as all beasts are his enemies, and he friend and loving to none, so with strength, courage, and policy, he dealeth with every one, not only against the beasts of the Land, but also against the monsters of the Sea. When he findeth a nest of Waspes in the earth, or in other places, as in trees, he layeth his tail to the hole, and so gathereth into it a great many of them, which he presently dasheth against the wall, or tree, or stones adjoyning, and so destroyeth them, and thus he continueth untill he have killed them all, and so maketh himself executor to their heaps of hony.

His manner is when he perceiveth or seeth a flock of fowl to flie in the air, to rowl himself in red earth, making his skin to look bloody, and lie upon his back, winking with his eye, and holding in his breath as if he were dead, which thing the birds, namely Crows, Ravens and such like observing, because of the hatred of his person, they for joy alight and triumph at his overthrow, and this the Fox endureth for a good season, till opportunity serving his turn, and some of the fowl come neer his snowt, then suddenly he catcheth some one of them in his mouth, feeding upon him like a living and not a dead Fox, and so doth devour and eat him, as the Leopard doth devour and eat Apes, and the Sea frog other little fishes.

In like sort he deceiveth the Hedge-hog, for when the Hedge-hog perceiveth the Fox coming to him, he rowleth himself together, like a foot-ball, and so nothing appeareth outward except his prickles, which the Fox cannot indure to take into his mouth, and then the cunning Fox to compasse his desire, licketh gently the face and snowt of the Hedge-hog, by that means bringing him to unfold himself again, and to stand upon his legs, which being done, he instantly devoureth, or else poisoneth the beast with the urine that he rendereth upon the Hedge-hogs face: and at other times he goeth to the waters, and with his tail draweth fishes to the brim of the River, and when that he observeth a good booty, he casteth the Fishes clean out of the water upon the dry land, and then devoureth them.

405

All kindes of Hawkes are enemies to Foxes, and Foxes to them, because they live upon Carrion, and so in the Province of *Ula*. *Avicen* saw a Fox and a Crow fight together a long season, and the Crow with his talons so be-gripling the Foxes mouth that he could not bark, and in the mean time she beat and picked his head with her bill untill he bled again. The Eagles fight with Foxes and kill them; and *Olaus Magnus* affirmeth, that in the Northern Regions they lay Egges and hatch their young in those skins which they themselves have stripped off from Foxes and other beasts.

The Kites, Vultures, and Wolves, are Enemies to Foxes, because they are all flesh-devouring creatures, but the Fox which hath so many enemies, by strength or subtilties overcometh all. Whereupon *Persius* calleth a subtil man a Fox, saying,

Astutam vapido servas sub pectore vulpem.

The medicinal uses of this beast are these, First, (as *Pliny* and *Marcellus* affirm) a Fox sod in water till nothing of the Fox be left whole except the bones, and the legs or other parts of a gowty body washed and daily bathed therein, it shall drive away all pain and grief, strengthning the defective and weak members; so also it cureth all the shrinking up and pains in the sinews: and *Galen* attributeth the same virtue to an Hyæna sod in Oil, and the lame person bathed therein, for it hath such power to evacuate and draw forth whatsoever evill humour aboundeth in the body of man, that it leaveth nothing hurtful behind.

Neverthelesse, such bodies are soon again replenished through evill diet, and relapsed into the same disease again. The Fox may be boyled in fresh or salt water with Annise and Thyme, and with his skin on whole and not slit, or else his head cut off, there being added to the decoction two pintes of Oil.

The flesh of a Fox sod and layed to a sore bitten by a Sea-hare, it cureth and healeth the same. The Foxes skin (as is already said) is profitable against all moist Fluxes in the skin of the body, and also the Gowt, and cold in the sinews. The ashes of Foxes flesh burnt and drunk in wine, is profitable against the shortness of breath and stoppings of the Liver.

The bloud of a Fox dissected and taken forth of his urine alive, and so drunk, breaketh the stone in the bladder; or else (as *Myrepsus* saith) kill the Fox, and take the bloud and drink a cupful thereof, and afterward with the same wash the genital parts, and within an hour the stone shall be voided: the same virtue is in it being dryed and drunk in Wine with Sugar.

Oxycraton and Foxes blood infused into the Nostrils of a lethargick Horse, cureth him. The fat is next to a Buls and a Swines, so as the fat or lard of Swine may be used for the fat of Foxes, and the fat of Foxes for the Swines grease in medicine. Some do herewith anoint the places which have the Cramp, and all trembling and shaking members. The fat of a Fox and a Drake inclosed in the belly of a Goose, and so rosted, with the dripping that cometh from it, they anoint paralytick members.

The same with powder of Vine twigs mollified and sod in lie, attenuateth and bringeth down all swelling tumours in the flesh. The fat alone healeth the *Alopecias* and looseness of the hair; it is commended in the cure of all Sores and Ulcers of the head; but the gall and fime with Mustard-seed is more approved. The fat is also respected for the cure of pain in the ears, if it be warmed and melt at the fire, and so instilled; and this is used against tingling in the ears. If the hairs rot away on a Horse tail, they recover them again by washing the place with Urine and Bran, with Wine and Oil and afterward anoint it with Foxes grease. When Sores or Ulcers have procured the hair to fall off from the head, take the head of a young Fox burned with the leaves of black *Orchanes* and *Alcyonium*, and the powder cast upon the head recovereth again the hair.

If the brain be often given to Infants and sucking children, it maketh them that they shall remain free from the falling evill. *Pliny* prescribeth a man which twinkleth with his eyes, and cannot look stedfastly, to wear in a chain the tongue of a Fox; and *Marcellus* biddeth to cut out the tongue of a live Fox, and so turn him away, and hang up that tongue to dry in purple thred, and afterward put it about his neck that is troubled with the whiteness of the eyes, and it shall cure him.

But it is more certainly affirmed, that the tongue either dryed or green, layed to the flesh wherein is any Dart or other sharp head, it draweth them forth violently, and renteth not the flesh, but only where it is entred. The Liver dryed and drunk cureth often sighing. The same or the Lights drunk in black wine, openeth the passages of breathing. The same washed in wine and dryed in an earthen pot in an Oven, and afterward seasoned with Sugar, is the best medicine in the world for an old Cough, for it hath been approved to cure it, although it hath continued twenty years, drinking every day two spoonfuls in wine.

The Lights of Foxes drunk in water after they have been dryed into powder, helpeth the Milt; and *Myreplus* affirmeth, that when he gave the same powder to one almost suffocated in a Plurisie, it prevailed for a remedy. *Archigene* prescribeth the dryed Liver of a Fox for the Splenetick with Oxymel: and *Marcellinus* for the Milt drunk after the same manner; and *Sextus* adviseth to drink it simply without composition of Oxymel.

The Gall of a Fox instilled into the ears with Oil, cureth the pain in them; and mixed with Hony Attick and anointed upon the eyes, taketh away all dimness from them, after an admirable manner. The Milt bound upon the tumors and bunches of the brest, cureth the Milt in mans body. The reins dryed and mingled with Hony, being anointed upon kernels, take them away. For the swelling of the chaps, rub the reins of a Fox within, the mouth. The genitals because of their gristly and bony substance, are approved for the dispersing of the stone in the bladder.

The stones take away pimples and spots in the face. The dung pounded with Vinegar, by anointment cureth the Leprosie speedily.

These and such other virtues Medicinal both the elder and later Physitians have observed in a Fox, wherewithal we will conclude this discourse; saving that many writers have devised divers witty inventions and fables of Foxes, under them to express vices of the world, as when they set a Fox in a Fryers weed, preaching to a sort of Hens and Geese, following the fiction of *Archilochus* Fox, to signifie how irreligious Pastors in holy habits beguile the simple with subtility. Also of a Fox teaching a Hare to say his *Credo* or Creed betwixt his legs, and for this cause almighty God in his word compareth false Prophets to Foxes, Ezek. 13. destroying the young Grapes and Plants. The Weasil brought a Fox into a Garner of Corn through a small hole, and when he had filled his belly, he assayed to come out again at the same place, but in vain, because his body swelled with over eating, and therefore he was constrained to come out as empty and hungry as he came in: whereupon this conference was betwixt them;

Forte per angustam tenuis Vulpecula rimam,
Repserat in cameram frumenti, postea rursus
Ire foras pleno tentabat corpore frustra.
Cui mustela procul, Si vis, ait, effugere isthinc,
Macra cavum repetes arctum, quem macra subisti.

OF THE GENNET-CAT, CALLED GENETHA.

THIS beast is called *Genitocatus*, either for the similitude it holdeth with a Cat, or else because it hath been believed that it was engendred by a Cat, but I rather do assent that the right name thereof is *Ginetta* or *Ginetha*, because they are bred in *Spain* with the *Gennet* horses, and so taketh his name from the place. *Albertus* (though a learned man, yet many times he was deceived in the names of beasts) called this creature *Genocha*, and the *Germans* call it *Ein Gennithkatz*. The quantity or stature hereof is greater then a Cat, but lesser than a Fox, and therefore I think it about the mold or bigness of a young Fox of six moneths old. It is a meek and gentle creature, except it be provoked; for in *Constantinople* they are kept came, and are suffered to go up and down from house to house like Cats. Being wilde, they love the vallies and low places, especially the Marishes or land neer the waters, for the steep rocky mountains they cannot endure. And these *Cardan* taketh to be of the Weasil kinde, because the forme and disposition thereof, especially to the tame and Domestical Weasil, and in *Spain* they are cald *Foinai*, being black and ash-coloured, distinguished and variably interlined with many spots.

But *Scaliger* who was delighted to contradict *Jerom Cardan*, cannot endure to hear of this comparison betwixt Weasils and Ginnet-cats, because he saith, the skin of a *Gennitta* is bigger then three Weasils, and that it resembleth a Weasil in nothing except in the ears; but *Cardans* comparison toucheth not the quantity, but only the outward form and qualities, and he himself disagreeth not that it is equall in quantity to an Otter. But certainly the skin thereof is admirable and beautiful to behold, and if they were not common, but rare and seldom found beasts, it is no question but the price thereof and due estimation would excell many others: For the abundance of spots, their natural and uniform order, their shining splendor and brightness, give place to no other party-coloured beast, as you may observe in the true figure thereof here declared.

In the next place I have thought good to express the figure of the skin taken off, which skin, from the head to the top of the tail, was about four spans and one palm long, and the tail was as long as the body being severed from the skin: the latitude or breadth thereof in the middle, was about one span in breadth, the middle of the belly, and the upper part of the neck, were ash coloured, and in the tail were eight black circles and so many white, one successively following the other; the whole body aspersed with black spots, and the residue yellowish white.

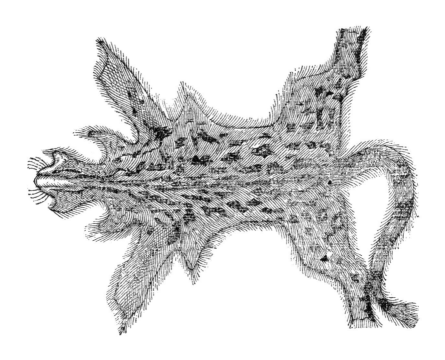

The skin smelt sweetly and somewhat like to a Musk-cat, and from *Lyons* in *France* they are brought into *Germany*, three or four of them being sold for a Noble. It is very probable that it is a little kinde of Panther or Leopard, for there is a little Panther which hath such spots, and besides of such a stature and harmless disposition, whose skin in old time was pretiously used for garments, and the favour thereof was very pleasant, and therefore I supersede any further discourse hereof, till we come to the declaration of the greater beast.

OF THE GOAT, MALE AND FEMALE.

THE male or great Goat-Buck, is called in *Hebrew, Atud*, and the lesser *Seir*, and *Zeir*. The *Chalde* translateth it, Gen. 13. *Teias-jait*, and Numb. 15, *Ize*; the *Arabians, Teus* and *Macz*; the *Persians, Asteban*, and *Busan*; the *Grecians, Tragos*, or devouring or ravening in meat, according to the Verse;

Tragus ab Edendo quod grana fracta pane.

Also *Chimaron* and *Enarchan*; the *Latins, Hircus*, and sometime *Caper*, which word properly signifieth a Gelded Goat, as *Martial* useth in this Verse:

Dum jugulas hircum, factus es ipse Caper.

The *Italians, Beccho*; the *Germans, Bock*, and for distinction sake, *Geissbook*, and *Reechbock*, and *Bœck*; the *Spaniards, Cabron*; the *French, Bouc*, the *Illyrians, Kozel*.

The reason of the *Latin* word *Hircus*, is derived of *Hirtus* (signifying rough) by reason of the roughness of their bodies. And it is further to be understood, that the general kind of Goats (which the *Latins* distinguish by *Hircus, Capra*, and *Hœdus*, that is, by their sex, or by their age; the *Hebrews* call them singularly *Ez*, and plurally *Izim*, Numb. 15. for a Goat of a year old, you shall read *Izbethschneth*. The *Chalde* useth also the general word *Oza*; the *Arabian, Schaah*; the *Persian, Buz*, and whereas Levit. 16. *Seir* is put for *Caper* a gelded Goat, there the *Chalde* rendereth it *Zephirah*; the *Arabians, Atud*, and the *Persian Buzgalaie*. And in the same Chapter you shall read *Azazel*, which *David Kimhi* rendereth for the name of a mountain neer *Sinai* where Goats use to feed and lodge: and the *Septuagints* translate it *Apopompaion*, signifying emission or sending away, and for this cause I suppose, that when the Scape-goat was by the Priest sent out of the Temple, he went to that mountain, and therefore the word *Azazel* seemeth to be compounded of *Ez*, a Goat, and *Azal Iuit*, that is, he went; for the Scape Goat went and carryed away the evill.

The *Grecians* call the female Goat *Aix*, which seemeth to be derived of *Ez* the *Hebrew* word. The *Arabians, Dakh*, and *Metaham*, as I find in *Avicen*; the *Saracens, Anse*; the *Italians, Peccho*, changing *B* from the male into *P*; and the *Spaniards, Capron*; the *French, Cheuer* or *Chieuere*; the *Germans, Geiss*; the *Illyrians, Koza*; and the *Tuscanes* at this day call a female Goat *Zebei*. And this may suffice for the names of both male and female.

Their nature is to be declared severally, except in those things wherein they agree without difference: and first of all, the male is rightly termed *Dux & maritus Caprarum*, the guide and husband of the females, and therefore *Virgil* saith of him not improperly, *Vir gregis ipse Caper*, The He-goat is the husband of the flock and except in his genitals and horns, he differeth not in any proportion or substance from the female. His horns are longer and stronger then are the females, and therefore upon provocation he striketh through an ordinary piece of Armor or Shield at one blow: his force and the sharpness of his horns are so pregnable. He hath many attributes among the learned, as left-sided, aged, greedy, bearded, swift, long-legged, horn-bearer, captain of the flock, heavy, rough, hoarse-voiced, rugged, unarmed, unclean, strong-smelling, lecherous, bristler, wanderer, vile, wanton, sharp, stinking, two-horned, and such like: whereof his nature and qualities are so deciphered, as it needeth no long treatise of explication.

There is no beast that is more prone and given to lust then is a Goat, for he joyneth in copulation before all other beasts. Seven dayes after it is yeaned and kiddened, it beginneth and yeeldeth seed, although without proof. At seven moneths old it engendereth to procreation, and for this cause that it beginneth so soon, it endeth at five years, and after that time is reckoned unable to accomplish that work of nature. When the *Egyptians* will describe fecundity or ability of generation, they do it by picturing of a male Goat.

That which is most strange and horrible among other beasts is ordinary and common among these, for in them scarce the Brother joyneth with the Sister, and a Camel can never be brought to cover his Dam: but among these the young ones being males, cover their Mother, even while they suck their milk. If they be fat, they are lesse venereous then being macilent or lean. *Herodotus* declareth that in his time a Goat of *Mendesia* in *Egypt*, had carnal copulation with a woman in the open sight of men, and afterward was led about to be seen. When they desire copulation they have a proper voice wherewithal (as it seemeth) they provoke the female to love. This is called it in *Italy*, *Biccari* and *Biccarie*, which the *Venetians* apply to all lecherous companions as commonly as a proverb, and this they never use but at that time. By reason of his lust, his eyes sink deep into the corners of their holes (called *Hirqui*) and *Apuleius* with other *Grammarians* do derive the word *Hircus*, whereby this beast is called, from that disposition.

By drinking salt water they are made desirous and apt to procreation. At that time they fight mutually one with another for their females, and it is a term among the late writers, to call those men *Hirci*, Goats, which are contented to permit other men to lie with their wives in publick, before their own faces for gain, because they imagine that such is the property of Goats. But I know not with what reason they are moved hereunto, for there is a memorable story to the contrary.

In *Sibaris* there was a young man called *Crathis*, which being not able to retain lust, but forsaken of God, and given over to a reprobate sense, committed buggery with a female Goat, the which thing the master Goat beheld and looked upon, and dissembled, concealing his mind and jealousie for the pollution of his female. Afterward finding the said young man asleep, (for he was a Shepherd) he made all his force upon him, and with his horns dashed out the buggerers brains. The man being found dead on this manner, and the Goat which he had ravished delivered of a monster, having a Mans face, and a Goats legs, they call it *Silvanus*, and place it in the rank of idoll Gods, but the wretched man himself was buried with more honour then beseemed, for they gave him a noble funeral, and finding a River in *Achaia* which mingled water with another, they called it *Crathis*, after the name of that unnatural and beastly monster; whereupon also came the *Italian Crathis* which *Strabo* remembreth. By which story it is evident, that jealous rivality resteth as well in Goats as in Men of more reasonable capacity and understanding.

The females desire of copulation is no lesse then the males, for while they suck they admit the male, and at the seventh month they conceive. The best time of their admission to procreation is about the end of Autumn (according to *Columella* his opinion) They are not filled the first day of copulation, but the second or third, and those which are joyned in *November* do bring forth their young in the Spring when all things grow fresh and green: wherefore if they chance to be slack, and not willing to engender or couple, their keepers use this sleight or policy, to procure and stir up their lust. They rub their udders with Nettles untill they constrain bloud, and afterward with a handful of Salt and Nitre, or else with Pepper or Myrrhe; after which rubbing, their desire of copulation much increaseth, and it maketh the female to provoke the male and undergo him more willingly; and this thing also procureth in them aboundance of milk (as *Aristotle* affirmeth) he had seen tryed by making experiment thereof upon the brests of Women, Virgins, and Widows: And generally all the keepers of Cattel do herewith rub their genitals, for the furthering and provoking in them carnal copulation, with the things aforesaid.

They being filled and with young, they carry them in their belly five moneths before deliverance. After three years old the female ceaseth to retain in her self or confer to her Kids the strength of nature, and the male after four, so that it is not a part of good husbandry to keep their young which they bring forth after those years, but rather to kill them and make them away: So also it is not good to keep their firstings, or those which are first of al engendred, but rather the second or third seed of procreation. Some of them bring forth twins, and some more, as it is reported of the Goats of *Egypt*, which bring forth five at a time, because they drink of the fruitful river of *Nilus*: for the Goat-herds of the Countrey do give thereof to their Cattel, and fetch it into all parts of that region, and in *Illyria* they breed twice a year, bringing sometime three, four, or five at once, but three at a time are never to be kept, but killed and eaten, for they are accounted not worth their bringing up; only cold maketh them to suffer abortments, and sometimes they bring forth monsters like to other Cattel (for all little beasts are more apt to engender monsters then the greater.)

Concerning the time that they bear young, it is in *Italy* eight years, and being fat they are not apt to conceive, wherefore they make them lean before they admit them to their bucks. One male is sufficient for ten females, and some (saith *Varro*) provide but one for 15 (as *Menas*) and other but one for 20 (as *Murus*.) There is no creature that smelleth so strongly as doth a male Goat, by reason of his immoderate lust, and in imitation of them the *Latins* call men which have strong breaths (*Hircosi*) Goatish: wherefore *Plautus* saith to an old lecherous fellow which could not keep his lips from slavering of women,

> *Cum sis jam ætatis plenus, anima fœtida,*
> *Senex hircose tu osculere mulierem.*

And therefore *Tiberius Cæsar* who was such a filthy and greasie-smelling old man, was called (*Hircus vetulus*) an old Goat, in the *Atellanican Comœdie*. They conjecture of men that have hairy legs to be unchast and full of lust, by reason of their similitude with a Goat, and those which have a shril and clamorous voice, the *Grecians* call *Margoi*, (that is, blockheads.) Those which have eyes like to Goats they call *Aegopoi*, Goat-eyes, that is very red eyes. The *Egyptians* affirm that their female Goats when *Sirius* the Star in the beginning of Dog-dayes riseth with the Sun, do continually look upon the East, and that their attentive observation is a most certain argument of the revolution, that is the appearance and departure of the said Dog dayes. The like things do the *Lybians* report of their Goats concerning that Star, and moreover that they foresee and foreshew change of weather, for they depart from their stables, and run want only abroad before showers, and afterward having well fed of their own accord return to their folds again.

Concerning the description of their several parts, it is good to follow the direction of *Cossinius*, first to look to their age (as is before said) if men desire to provide Goats for herd-breed and profit, so as their Kids may be like them, and they bear young or continue procreation eight years at the least. And for their outward parts, let them be firm, great, well compacted, full of muscles, and the superficies of their whole body be soft and equall, without bunches or indentures: therefore a thick hair, two dugs hanging under their snowt or chin, are good signes of the best Goats.

There are two kindes of Goats, one horned, and of this sort the long sharp-horned beasts, with broad foreheads, are the most approved, and by the circles of their horns their age is discerned: But the unhorned are best for breed, procreation and milk, and such are the *Caspian* Goats, which are for the most part white, flat nosed, and little of growth. Their eyes are very deep in their heads, and therefore their sight sharp, strong and continual seeing bright and clear in the night, but the colour of their eyes variable, like to the colour of their bodies; The males have more teeth then the females, for the females want their upper teeth: But males and females have large beards under their chins, and this is called *Aruncus* (saith *Eryngus*) but the reason hereof is, because that when a Goat is taken by the beard and drawn out of the fold, all the residue stand amazed, and so also when any of them hath eaten Sea-holly (cald *Eryngium:*) so that *Aristotle* confoundeth *Eryngium* for *Aruncum*, and so taketh one for another. Once in *Lemnos* there was a male Goat which had so much milk wrung out of his paps growing betwixt his legs, that therewith a Calf, by licking it received the beestings, but afterward the male Kid begotten by the same Goat had the like udders, whereat the owner being much amazed, because it was a prodigious thing, for his satisfaction asked counsel at the Oracle, from whom he received this answer, that it betokened nothing but plentiful encrease of his Cattel. The females have two udders under their loins next to the small of their belly, except the *Lybian* Goats, and their udders lie under their breast or forepart of their belly, like an Apes. In *Naxus* the Goats have greater Gals then in any other part of the world, and the forepart is held prodigious: On the contrary, in *Chalcis* the Goats have no gall at all. They have many bellies and a round Milt, which thing no other horned-beast hath, except a Sheep. The males have harsher hairs then their females, and the *Lybian* Goats have hair as long as womens, and very rough curled, which the inhabitants shear off every year, and therewith the Ship-wrights make cable ropes: but in *Cilicia* and *Phrygia*, they shear them and make the stuffe called *Zambelot*: and another kinde of Cloth called *Mathaliaze*. In *Arabia* they make Tents of Cloth compiled of Asses and Goats hair, and it seemeth that *Cilicia* received his name of this kinde of Cloth, which is called in *Latin, Cilicium*, or else that this Cloth was first invented among them, whereupon it received that denomination; but among the *Grammarians* and Poets, *Lana Caprina* (Goats wool) grew to a proverb, to signifie a thing of no weight or moment, as it is in *Horace*;

> *Alter rixatur de lana sæpe caprina,*
> *Propugnat nugis armatus* ———

There are another sort of Goats which are called *Syrian* Goats, and of some *Mambrin* Goats, and most commonly *Indian* Goats, because they are most noble in that Countrey, and that in *Coytha*; and likewise in the Region of *Damiata*, for *Mambre* is a Mountain neer *Hebron*, from whence it is probable, that the word *Mambrin* cometh; wherefore I have thought good to expresse the figure both of the greatest of that kinde, as it was taken by *Antonius Musa Brasovalus*, Physitian to the Noble Duke *Hercules de Este*, at *Ferraria*, by one of these Goats brought thither to be seen.

These lesser were found pictured in an old manuscript in *Germany*, which book did intreat of the Holy Land. The greater Goat I conjecture to be the same which *Leo Afer* calleth *Adimain*, and is found in *Mauritania*, being as tall as an Asse, and hath very long broad ears pendant, and under them next to their necks two things like dugs or paps, which hang down from their throat, and these are most fruitful in milk, and with these the *Lybians* plow, and keep them in stead of Kie and other Cattel, for they milk them, and of their milk make Butter and Cheese. Their hair is very short, and they very gentle and familiar; so that the said *Leo* affirmeth, that when he was a young man, and loved those rash and wanton sports wherewithal youth are delighted, he got up upon one of these, and rode quietly upon the back of it above a quarter of a mile. They keep, being wilde, in the Deserts of *Lybia*, and if at any time they stray or wander into *Numidia*; and

419

the fields thereof, it is accounted by the people and inhabitants a prodigious and monstrous thing.

The lesser kinde I conjecture to be the right *Mambrine* or *Syrian* Goat, although some of the late writers call it an *Indian* Goat; the reason is, because (as hath been said) they call all strange beasts by the names of *Indians*, if they finde them not in their own Countrey. The ears of it are large and broad, as the picture describeth, and such ears have the Goats of *Gallia-Narbon*, being at the least as broad as a mans span; they are of colour like wilde Goats, their horns very sharp, and standing not far distant one from the other, and have stones like a stone Horse, being in all other parts not unlike to the vulgar and common Goat.

Some curious herdsmen (as *Alcmæon* and *Archelaus*) have delivered to the world, that Goats take breath through their ears; and *Phyles* approveth their conceit, because he had seen an experiment of a Goat, that his mouth and nostrils being stopped fast, nevertheless he seemed not to be troubled for want of breath: and for this also is alleadged the authority of *Oppianus*, who writeth of certain Goats (called *Aegari*) that they have a certain hole or passage in the middle of their head, betwixt the horns, which goeth directly unto the liver, and the same stopped with liquid Wax, suffocateth or stifleth the beast.

If this be true (as I would not any way extenuate the authority of the writer) then it is very likely that some have (without difference) attributed to all kindes of Goats that which was proper to this kinde alone, for the former opinion is not reasonable: Nevertheless I leave every man to his own liberty of believing or refusing.

There is no beast that heareth so perfectly and so sure as a Goat, for he is not only holp in this sense with his ears, but also hath the Organ of hearing in part of his throat, wherefore when the *Egyptians* describe a man which hath an excellent ear, they express him by a Goat. There are some kinde of Goats in *Illyria* which have whole hoofs like a Horse, and these are only found in that Region. In all other Nations of the World they are cloven footed.

The use of their several parts is singular, and first of all to begin with their skin, the people of *Sardinia* (as saith *Nymphidorus*) nourish Goats for their skins, whereof they make them garments, being dressed with the hair upon them; and they affirm strange virtue in them, namely, that they heat their bodies in the Winter, and cool them in the Summer; and the hairs growing upon those skins are a cubit long, therefore the man that weareth them in Winter time, turneth the hairy side next to his body, and so is warmed by it; and in Summer the raw side, and so the hair keepeth the Sun from piercing his skin and violence of heat: And this also is usual in *Suevia*, where the women wear garments of Goats hair in the Winter, and also make their childrens coats thereof, according to *Virgils* saying in *Moreto*,

> ——— *Et cinctus villosæ tegmine Capræ.*

For this cause the Merchants buy them rough in those parts of *Savoy* neer *Geneva*, and their choice is, of the young ones which die naturally; or are kild, or else such as were not above two years old. The *Tyrians* in the *Persian* war, wore upon their backs Goat-skins. In ancient time they made hereof *Dipthera*, that was a kinde of Parchment, whereon they wrote on both sides, and had the name in *Greek* from that use: which

Hermolaus by a metaphorical allusion, called *Opistographi*. From the use of these in garments, came the appellation of harlots to be cald *Pellices*, and a whores bag was called *Penula Scortea*, such a one is used by Pilgrims which go to visit the Church of Saint *James* of *Calec*, and such Carriers or Foot-posts had wont to use in their journies, which caused *Martial* to write thus;

> *Ingrediare viam cœlo licet usq sereno,*
> *An subitas nusquam scortea cepit aquas.*

The Sandals which men were wont to wear on their feet in the East Countries, were also made of Goats skins, and there was a custome in *Athens*, that men for honour of *Bacchus*, did dance upon certain Bottles made of Goats skins, and full of wind, the which were placed in the middest of the Theatre, and the dancer was to use but one leg, to the intent that he might often fall from the slippery bottles, and make the people sport; whereunto *Virgil* alluded this saying;

> *Mollibus in pratis unctos saliere pro utres.*

There is also a *Ladanum* tree in *Carmania*, by the cutting of the bark whereof there issueth forth a certain gum, which they take and preserve in a Goats skin; their use in War wherein the Souldiers were wont to lie all Winter, and therefore we read that *Claudius* the Emperour had given him thirty tents of Goats skins for his Souldiers attend upon the Judges, and the Mariners also by these defended themselves from the violence of storms upon the Sea: and so I leave this part of the beast, with remembrance of that which is written in holy Scripture, Heb. 11. that the people of God in ancient times did flee away from the rage of superstition, being anparelled, or rather meanly disguised in Goat skins, being charitably holped by the beasts, that were cruelly put to death by wretched men.

In the next place the milke of Goats cometh to be considered, for that also hath been, is, and will be of great account for Butter and Cheese, which the Writers call *Tyropœia*, and *Virgil* celebrateth the singular commendation both of the Wool and of the Milke, in these Verses;

Hæc quoque non cura nobis leviore tuenda,
Nec minor usus erit, quamvis Milesia magno
Vellera mutent ur Tyrios incocta rubores.
Densior hinc soboles, hinc largi copia lactis;
Quo magis exhausto spumaverit ubere mulctra,
Læta magis pressis manabunt flumina mammis.
Nec minus interea barbas, incanaque menta
Cyniphii tondent hirci setasque comantes
Usum in Castrorum: & miseris velamina nautis.

Therefore their Milk is profitable for Butter, although inferior to a Cows, yet equal to a Sheeps, and the herdsmen give their Goats salt before they be delivered of their young, for this maketh them to abound in milk. Others with Goats milk preserve their Wine from corruption by sowreness; first they put into their Wine the twentyeth part so much as is of the Wine, and so let it stand in the same vessell covered three or four dayes, afterward they turn it into a sweet and fresh vessel, and so it remaineth preserved from all annoyance of sowreness.

Cheeses made of Goats milk were wont to be called *Velabrenses Casei*, because amongst the *Romans* they were made at *Velabrum*, and that with smoak, whereupon *Martial* made this *Distichon*;

Non quemcunque focum, nec fumum caseus omnem,
Sed Velabrensem qui bibit, ipse sapit.

Aristotle and *Julius Pollux* do commend the *Sicilian* Cheese, which was made of Sheep and Goats milke together, and by *Athenæus* it is called, *Caseus Tromilicus*, and by *Simonides Stromilius*. In *Rhætia* of *Helvetia* there are excelent Cheeses made of Goats milk and Cow milk mixed together. The milk also of a Goat mixed to a Womans milk is best for the nourishment of man, because it is not too fat; yet *Galen* saith, if it be eaten without Hony, Water, and Salt, it curdleth in the belly of a man like a Cheese and strangleth him; and being so used it purgeth the belly: from thence came the fiction of the Poets, that *Jupiter* was noursed by a Goat, and that afterward in his War against the *Titanes* or Giants, he slew that Goat by the counsel of *Themis*, and wore her skin for an armor, and so having obtained victory, placed the Goat among

423

the Stars, whereupon she was called *Aix ourania*, a heavenly Goat, and so *Germanicus Cæsar* made this Verse upon him, and *Jupiter* himself was called *Aigiochus*.

> ――― ――― *Illa putatur*
> *Nutrix esse Jovis, si verè Jupiter infans*
> *Ubera Cretææ suxit fidissima Capræ,*
> *Sydere quæ claro gratum testatur alumnum.*

The flesh of male Goats is not wholesome for mans body, but the flesh of a female in the Spring and Fall of the leaf, by reason of the good nourishment may be eaten without danger. They are worse then Bull-beef, because they are sharper in concoction and hotter, wherefore if they digest not well, they increase melancholy. The liver of a Goat being eaten, doth bring the Falling sickness; yet being salted a good space, and then sod with Vine-branches, or other such broad leaves, to keep them asunder, and some Wine poured into the Water when they almost sod, they become are very which and delicate meat; and theresore the *Athenians* praised the *Lacædemonians*, that in their feast sweet they called *Copidæ*, they slew a Goat; and held it for a divine meat.

Also *Cletomachus* an *Academick* of *Carthage*, relateth of a certain *Thebane* Champion, which excelled in strength all the Champions of his time, and that he did eat continually Goats flesh, for it is very strong and remaineth a long season in the body, and doth much good being digested, notwithstand|ing the strong and rank smell thereof, otherwise it is dangerous, as is already said, therefore *Fiera* having commended the Kyd, when he cometh to speak of the Goat he writeth thus:

> *Cum male olet siccat, fit jam caper improbus, absit,*
> *Et cadat ante foces victima Bacche tuos.*

But *Pliny* affirmeth, that if a male Goat eat Barley bread, or Parsneps washed, the same day that he is killed, then there is no poyson in his flesh: the stones of a Buck goat, resist concoction, and beget evill humors in the body: wherefore such a banquet is called in *Greek (Tragos Hulibertas)* for Goats after their copulation, have an evill flesh, not fat, but dry, and the remedy to make their flesh sweeter, is to geld the male when he is young and tender, for so his temperature is amended by a cold and moist constitution.

The Inhabitants of *Portugal* eat Goats flesh, and account it delicate meat; especially such as dwell in the Mountains. In *Germany* they make of it a kinde of meat which is called *Klobuusst*, and is prepared on this manner: they take a Goats heart newly taken out of the body, and slit it into small pieces, and break six Egges upon it, and the crums of white bread, seasoned with spices and Saffron, and so put into a bag, and sod or roasted: afterward they are served upon the table, and strewed over with Kitchin Sugar.

The guts being salted, are called (*Hilla*) which the *French* stuffe like puddings, and call them (*Saulcisses*) from whence cometh our *English* Sawsadge, of this sewet and fat of Goats are the best candles made, because it is hard and not over liquid. The bloud of a Goat hath an unspeakable property, for it scoureth rusty iron better then a file, it also softneth an Adamant stone, and that which no fire is able to melt, nor iron to break, being of such an invincible nature, that it contemneth all violent things, yet is it dissolved by the warm bloud of a Goat. The Load-stone draweth iron, and the same being rubbed with garlick, dyeth and loseth that property, but being dipped again in Goats-bloud, reviveth and recovereth the former nature.

Osthanes prescribeth for a remedy of love, the urine of a Goat to be mingled with Spikenard, and so drunk by him which is overcome with that passion, assuring him thereby that they shall fall in as great loathing as ever before they were in loving. With the hoofs of a Goat they drive away Serpents, and also with the hairs by burning and perfuming them in the place where the Serpents lodge. With the horns of Goats they make bows; for in *Delos* there was dedicated the horn of a Goat, which was two cubits long and a span; and hereat ought no man to wonder, for that noble Bow of *Pandarus*, which *Homer* commendeth, was made of a horn of a female Goat.

Affricanus declareth, that in ancient time they made fruitful their Vine-yards by this means: they took three horns of a female Goat, and buried them in the earth with their points or tops downward, to the root of the Vine-stocks, leaving the hollow tops, standing a little out of the ground, and so when the rain descended, it filled the horns, and soked to the root of the Vine, perswading themselves thereby that they received no small advantage in their Grapes. The gall of a female Goat put into a vessel, and set in the earth, is said by *Albertus* to have a natural power to draw Goats unto it, as though they received great commodity thereby. Likewise, if you would have white hairs to grow in any part of a Horse; shave off the hair and anoint the place with a gall of a Goat, so shall you have your desire. The *Sabæans*, by reason of continual use of Myrrhe and Frankincense, grow to a loathing of that savour: for remedy of which annoyance, they perfume their houses by burning storax in Goats-skins. And thus much for the several parts of a Goat.

There were in ancient time three kindes of Heards-men which received dignity one above another; the first were called (*Bucolici*) Neat-heard, because they keep the greater Cattel: the second were (*Opiliones*) Shepheards, of their attendance upon Sheep: the third, last, and lowest kinde, were termed *Aepoli*, and *Caprarii*, that is, Goat-heards, or Keepers of Goats, and such were the *Locrensians*, who were called *Ozolæ*, because of their filthy smell, for they had the most part of their conversation among other Beasts.

A Goat-heard or Keeper of these Cattel must be sharp, stern, hard, laborious, patient, bold and chearful, and such a one as can easily run over the Rocks through the Wilderness, and among the bushes without fear or grief, so that he must not follow his flock like other heards, but go before them: they must also be light and nimble, to follow the wandering Goats, that run away from their fellows, and so bring them back again, for Goats are nimble, moveable, and inconstant, and therefore apt to depart away, except they be restrained by the herd and his Dog. Neither have Goats a Captain or Bell-bearer like unto Sheep, whom they follow, but every one is directed after his own will, and herein appeareth the pride of this Beast, that he scorneth to come behinde either Cattel, or Sheep, but always goeth before; and also in their own herds among themselves, the Buck goeth before the female for the reverence of his beard, (as *Ælianus* saith) the labour of the Goat-herd must be to see his Cattel well fed abroad in the day time, and well foulded at night; the first rule therefore in this husbandry is to divide the flocks, and not to put any great number of them together, for herein they differ from Sheep, who love to live together in multitudes, as it were affecting society by which they thrive better, and mourn not so much as when they are alone: but Goats love singularity, and may well be called Schismaticks among Cattel, and therefore they thrive best lying together in small numbers, otherwise in great flocks they are soon infected with the pestilence, and therefore in *France*, they care not to have *Magnos Greges, sed plures*: not great flocks, but many.

The number of their flock ought not to exceed fifty, whereupon *Varro* writeth this story of *Gabinus* a *Roman* Knight, who had a field under the Suburbs containing a thousand Akers of pasture ground, who seeing a poor Goat-herd bring his Goats every day to the City, and received for their milk a peny a peece, he being led with covetousness, proponed to himself this gain, that if he stored his said field with a thousand Milch-female-goats, he also should receive for their milk a thousand pence a day; whereupon he added action to his intent, and filled his field with a thousand Goats, but the event fell out otherways then he expected: for in short time the multitude infected one another, and so he lost both milk and flesh: whereby it is apparent, that it is not safe to feed great flocks of these Cattel together.

In *India* in the Region *Coitha*, the Inhabitants give their Milch-goats dryed fishes to eat, but their ordinary food is leaves, tender branches, and boughs of trees, and also bushes or brambles; whereupon *Virgil* wrote in this manner:

> *Pascuntur verò silvas & summa Lycæi,*
> *Horrenfesque rubos & amantes ardua dumos.*

They love to feed on the Mountains better then in the Vallies and green Fields; always striving to lick up the Ivie or green plants, or to climbe upon trees, cropping off with their teeth all manner wilde herbs, and if they be restrained and enclosed in fields, then they do the like to the plants that they finde there; wherefore there was an ancient law among the *Romans*, when a man let out his ground to farm, he should always condition and except with the Farmer that he should not breed any Goat in his ground, for their teeth are enemies to all tender plants: their teeth are also exitiable to a tree, and *Pliny* and *Varro* affirm, that the Goat by licking the Olive-tree maketh it barren; for which cause in ancient time, a Goat was not sacrificed to *Minerva* to whom the Olive was sacred.

There is no creature that feedeth upon such diversity of meat as Goats, for which cause they are elegantly brought in by *Eupolis* the old Poet, bragging of their belly chear, wherein they number up above five and twenty several things, different in name, nature, and taste: and for this cause *Eustathius* defended by strong argument against *Disarius*, that men and cattel which feed upon divers things, have less health then those Beasts which eat one kinde of fruit alone. They love Tamerisk, Aldern, Elm-tree, Assaraback, and a tree called *Alaternus*, which never beareth fruit but only leaves: also three-leaved-grass, Ivie, the herb *Lada*, which groweth no where but in *Arabia*, whereby it cometh to pass, that many times the hair of Goats is found in the gumb called *Ladanum*, for the peoples greedy desire of the gumb, causeth them to wipe the juyce from the Goats beard.

For the increase of milk in them, give them Cinquefoyl five days together before they drink, or else binde Dittany to their bellies, or (as *Lacuna* translateth the words out of *Alricanus*) you may lay milk to their bellies, belike by rubbing it thereupon. The wilde Goats of *Creet*, eat *Dittany* aforesaid against the strokes of Darts: and *Serapion* avoucheth by the experience of *Galen*), that Goats by licking the leaves of Tamarisk, lose their gall; and likewise that he saw them licking Serpents which had newly lost their skins, and the event thereof was, that their age never turned or changed into whiteness or other external signes thereof.

Also it is delivered by good observation, that if they eat or drink out of vessels of Tamarisk, they shall never have any Spleen; if any one of them eat Sea-holly, the residue of the flock stand still and will not go forward, till the meat be out of his mouth. The *Grammarians* say that *Chimæra* was killed by *Bellerophon* the son of *Glaucus*, in the Mountain *Lycius*, and the reason hereof is, that the Poets faigned *Chimæra* to be composed of a Lyon, a Dragon, and a Goat, and in that Mountain all those three were kept and fell: for in the top were Lyons, in the middle were Goats, and also at the foot thereof Serpents. If they suffer heat or cold they are much endangered, for such is their nature that they avoid all extremity, and the females with young are most of all molested with cold; if they have conceived in the Winter, then many Abortments or casting their young followeth.

In like sort it hapneth if they eat Walnuts (and not to their full) unripe, therefore either they must be suffered to eat of them to society, or else they are not to be permitted to them.

If at any time they eat Scammony, Hellebore, Lesseron, or Mercury, they are much troubled in their stomach, and lose their milk, especially the white Hellebore. The Publicans in the Province of *Cyrene*, have all the government of the pastures, and therefore they permit not Benzwine to grow in their Countrey, finding thereby great gain; and if at any time their Sheep or Goats meet with any branch thereof, they eat it greedily, but the Sheep immediately fall to sleep, and the Goats to Neezing. *Ægolethros* and *Sabine* are poyson to Goats. The Herb called in *Greek, Rhododendron*, and may be *Englished* Rose-tree, is poyson to Goats, and yet the same helpeth a man against the venome of Serpents.

The prickle or spindle tree (called also *Euonymus*) which groweth in the Mount *Occynius* called *Ordyne*) about the bigness of a Pine-apple-tree, having soft leaves like the same, and it buddeth in *September*, and the flower is like to a white Violet flower, this killeth Goats, except they be purged with black Hellebore immediately after they have eaten thereof. The *Egyptians* when they will describe a man devouring Sheep or Goats, they picture the herb *Curilago* or *Conyza*, because it also killeth them. Also as *Clodrysippus* affirmeth they avoid Cumin, for it maketh them mad, or bringeth upon them Lethargies, and such like infirmities.

He avoideth also the spettle of man, for it is hurtful to him, and to the Sea-fish *Scolopendra*, and yet he eateth many venemous herbs and groweth fat thereby; and this also may be added, that Goats grow fat when they are with young, but by drinking of Honey they are weakned, and indangered of death. Concerning their drink, it is necessary for a skilful Goat-herd to observe the nature of the beast, and the best time and place of their watering, according to the saying of *Virgil*:

> —— *Jubeo frondentia Capris*
> *Arbuta sufficere, & fluvios præbere recentes.*

In the Summer they are to be watered twice a day, and at other times once only in the afternoon: but it is reported of the Goats of *Cephalenia*, that they drink not every day like other Goats, but only once or twice in six months, and therefore they turn themselves to the winde or cold air of the Sea, and by yawning, suck into their mouths or bellies that which serveth them in stead of water. When the Sun declineth, they ly and look not upon one another but on the contrary, and they which lodge in the fields take up their rest amongst their acquaintance. But if they be used to fold or house, they remember it, and repair thither of their own accord, which thing caused the Poet to write in this manner:

> *Atque ipsæ memores redeunt in tecta, suosque*
> *Ducunt: & gravido superant vix ubere limen.*

Concerning their stables or houses to lodge in, for their defence against the cold, the diligent herd-man must observe, that nothing must be laid under the Goat to ly upon, and it is best to make his stable upon stones, or some such hard floor, and the same must be kept and turned dry every day from the annoyance of their dung, for that hurteth their heads. It is good to set the window of their stable to the Sun, and from the winde, according to the counsel of *Virgil*;

> *Et stabula a ventis hyberno opponere soli,*
> *Ad medium conversa diem, cum frigidus olim*
> *Jam cadit extremoque irrorat Aquarius anno.*

Although Goats be stronger then Sheep, yet they are never so sound, for in buying and selling or them, he was never accounted a wise man, that either hoped to buy, or promised to sell without fault. It was sufficient in open Market places, when and where Goats were to be sold, to promise, *Hodie capras recte esse & bibere posse & eas licite habere*, that is, that the day of their sale they were well, and could drink, and they were his own, and it was lawful for him to have them.

But farther no man was urged, for (*Archelaus* saith) they are ever *Febricitantes*, because their breath is hotter, and their copulation more fiery, and therefore their herdmen must not be unprovided of good and sufficient medicine to help them, and not only against their natural diseases, but also their continual horn-wounds which they give one another by their often fightings, and also when they aspire to climbe upon steep and craggy pointed rocks or trees, they often fall and are wounded, in such cases they have no such Physitian as their Keeper, whose bag and box must be as an Apothecaries shop to yeeld continual remedies to all their grievances.

The best means to preserve them in health, next to a good diet and warm lodging, is, to plant *Alysson* neer to their stabling houses. And their continual Ague spoken of before is profitable to their body, for when it departeth and leaveth them, presently they perish and dy. Sheep and Goats have a natural foresight of the Pestilence or Murrain, of Earthquakes, and of wholesome temperate weather, and of abundance and store of fruits; but neither of both shall be ever infested by the Pestilence, if you give them the powder of a Storks Ventricle or maw one spoonful thereof in water every day.

And whereas all other kinde of Cattel when they are sick, consume and pule away by little and little, only Goats perish suddenly, insomuch as all that are sick are unrecoverable, and the other of the flock must be instantly let bloud and separated before the infection overspread all; and the reason of their sudden death, is because of their aboundance of food, which ministreth speedy flax for the fire of their disease to burn. At such times they must not feed all the day long, but only thrice or four times a day be led forth to grass, and brought in again to their stables.

If any other sickness annoy them, they are to be cured with Reed, and the roots of white Thorn beat together with Iron Pestles, and mingled with rain Water; and so given to the Cattel to be drunk: but if this medicine help not, then either sell them away, or else kill them, and salt them till you minde to eat them. Goats are not troubled with Lice or Nits, but only with Tickes.

There is a certain Wine called *Melampodion*, the report is, that one *Melampos* a Shepherd had it revealed unto him, to cure the madness of Goats: it is made of black Hellebore, and Goats milk. Goats are also molested and subject to the Falling sickness, and this is known by their voyce and cold moist brains; and therefore the *Roman* Priests were commanded to abstain from touching such Beasts.

431

They are also troubled with the Gowt; the Female-goat easeth the pain of her eyes by pricking them upon a Bull-rush, and the Male-goat by pricking them upon a Thorn, and so pituitous matter followeth the prick, whereby the sight is recovered without any harm done to the Apple; and from hence it is supposed, that the Physitians learned their *Parakentesis* pricking of sore eyes with a Needle.

The Females never wink in their sleep, being herein like the Roe-bucks. There are certain Birds (called *Capri-mulgi*) because of their sucking of Goats, and when these or any of them have sucked a Goat, she presently falleth blinde. If at any time she be troubled with the Dropsie, an issue must be made under her shoulder, and when the humour is avoided, stop up the hole with liquid pitch. They drink the seed of *Seselis* to make them have an easie deliverance of their young, and for that cause *Columella* prescribeth a pinte of sod Corn and Wine to be infused into their throats in that extremity; their other maladies being like unto Sheep, we will reserve their description and cure to that History.

These Goats have in ancient times been used for Sacrifices, not only by the Soveraign command of Almighty God, but also by the practise of Heathen people; for their perfect sacrifice which consisted of a Ram, a Goat, a Hog, and a Bull, was called *Hecatombe* and *Tryttis*.

The reason why Swine and Goats were sacrificed among the Heathen, was, because the Swine dig up the earth with their noses, and root out the Corn, they were sacrificed to *Ceres*; and the Goats spoil the Vines by biting, for which cause they sacrificed him to *Bacchus*; that so the drunken God might be pacified with the bloud of that Beast, whose hallowed grapes he had devoured; whereupon the Poet writeth thus:

> *Sus dederat pœnas: exemplo territus horum*
> *Palmite debueras abstinuisse, Caper.*
> *Quem spectans aliquis dentes in vite prementem,*
> *Talia non tacito dicta dolore dedit:*
> *Rode caper vitem, tamen hinc cum stabis ad aras,*
> *In tua quod spargi cornua possit, erit.*

When they sacrificed a Goat in *Græcia*, they tryed him by giving him Pease or cold water to drink, which if he refused, they also refused him for sacrifice, but if he tasted it, they took and offered him.

Martiall having seen, or rather heard of a Countrey Priest, sacrificing a Goat, and being assisted by a Countreyman, when the Beast was slain, the Priest commanded the poor Countrey man to cut off the stones, *Teter ut immundæ carnis abiret odor*, to let the unwholesome vapour of the unclean flesh out of the body. Afterward the Priest being busie about the Sacrifice, and stooping down to the carkass of the Beast, his cods appeared behinde him betwixt his legs, the which when the Countrey-man saw, he suddenly cut them off with his sharp knife, thinking that the ancient ceremony of fasting required this to be done: whereupon *Martial* wrote this Epigram,

> *Sic modo qui Tuscus fueras, nunc Gallus aruspex,*
> *Dum jugulus hireum, factus es ipse caper.*

The *Mendesians* worshipped Goats both males and females, because as they imagine they were like to their God *Pan*. The *Egyptians* also deified the male Goat for his genital members, as other Nations did *Priapus*. The *Gentiles* had also a brazen Goat, whereupon *Venus* rode in brass, which picture they called (*Pandemon*) and *Venus* (*Epitragia*:) I think that lust could not be better described then by this emblem, for venereous persons will suffer their whores to do any disgrace unto them, for their carnal pleasure. And thus much for these male and female Goats, now follow the stories of the wilde Goats and the Kids in order.

OF THE GOAT CALLED BY PLINY A DEER.

THERE is no man that shall see this Beast, but will easily yeeld unto my opinion, that it is a Goat, and not a Deer, the hair, beard, and whole proportion of body most evidently demonstrating so much, neither is there any difficulty herein, except for the horns which turn forward at the point, and not backward, which thing yet swarveth not so much from a Goat as from a Deer, and therefore can be no good reason to alter my opinion. There are of this kinde, as Doctor *Cay* affirmeth, in the Northern part of *England*, and that figure which is engraven at *Rome* in a Marble pillar, being a remembrance of some Triumph which *Pliny* setteth forth, differeth in no part from this Beasts description and proportion: Yet I take it that it may be brought into *England* from some other Nation, and so be seen in some Noble mans house, but that it should be bred there, I cannot finde any monument of authority, but I rather conjecture the same to be bred in *Spain*. Of these kindes there are three Epigrams in *Martial*, whereby is declared their mutual fights killing one another; their fear of Dogs, and their flesh desired both of men and beasts.

The first Epigram describing their wilful fight, one killing another, and so saving a labour to the Hunter, for they kill themselves to his hand, is thus;

> *Frontibus adversis molles concurrere damas*
> *Vidimus, & fati sorte jacere pari.*
> *Spectavere Canes prædam, stupuitq; superbus*
> *Venator, cultro nil superesse suo.*
> *Unde leves animæ tanto caluere furore?*
> *Sic pugnant Tauri, sic cecidere viri.*

The second Epigram is a Dialogue speaking to the Emperour, who took care to encrease his game, seeing not only men were enemies to them, but they also to one another, whereupon he writeth this distichon;

Aspicis imbelles tentent quàm fortia damæ
Prælia; tam timidis quanta sit ira feris.
In mortem parvis concurrere frontibus audent,
Vis Cæsar damis parcere? mitte Canes.

The third Epigram is a complaint of their weak and unarmed state, having neither teeth like Bores, nor horns like Harts to defend themselves, but lie open to the violence of all their enemies:

Dente timetur Aper, defendunt cornua ceroum,
Imbelles damæ quid nisi præda sumus?

These are of a whitish yellow colour on the back, and are nourished sometime for the pleasure, and sometime for the profit of their possessors, for they will suffer hunting like a Deer, and also be tamed for milk like a Goat. And hereof I finde no other especial mention among Authors, beside that which is already rehearsed.

OF THE WILDE GOAT, AND THE FIGURE OF THE HELVETIAN, ALPIAN, WILDE OR ROCK-GOAT.

Wilde-goats are transfigured into many similitudes, and also dispersed into many Countries beyond the Seas and in the *Alpes*, the picture of the *Alpine* wilde Goat is here set down. They are also to be found in *Italy*, in the Mountains of *Fiscela* and *Tetrica*, in so much as the tame Goats which are nourished there, are said to be derived of these wilde Goats, these are called *Cynthian* Goats, because they are bred in the Mountains of *Delos* called *Cynthus*. There are of these which are found in the tops of the *Lybian* Mountains as great as Oxen, whose shoulders and legs abound with loose shaggy hair, their shins small, their faces are round, their eyes are hollow and hard to be seen.

Their horns crooking backward to their shoulders, not like other Goats, for they stand far distant one from another: and among all other

435

Goats they are indued with a most singular dexterity of leaping, for they leap from one top to another, standing a great way asunder, and although many times they fall down upon the hard rocks, which are interposed betwixt the Mountains, yet receive they no harm: for such is the hardness of their members, to resist that violence, and of their horns to break their falls, that they neither are offended thereby in head nor legs.

Such are the Goats of *Soractum* as *Cato* writeth, which leapeth from Rock to Rock, above threescore foot: of this kinde are those Goats before spoken of in the History of the tame Goat, which are thought to breath out of their ears, and not out of their nostrils; they are very swift and strong horned; the love betwixt the Dams and the Kids in this kinde, is most admirable; for the Dam doth most carefully educate and nourish her young; the young ones again, do most thankfully recompense their mothers carefulness, much like unto reasonable men, which keep and nourish their own Parents in their old decrepit age, (which the love of God and nature doth enjoyn them) for satisfaction of their own education; so do these young wilde Goats, toward their own mothers; for in their age they gather their meat and bring it to them, and likewise they run to the rivers or watering places, and with their mouths suck up water, which they bring to quench the thirst of their Parents: and when as their bodies are rough and ugly to look upon, the young ones lick them over with their tongues, so making them smooth and neat.

And if at any time the Dam be taken by the Hunters, the young one doth not forsake her till he be also insnared: and you would think by the behaviour of the imprisoned Dam towards her young Kids, and likewise of the Kid towards his Dam, that they mutually contend one to give it self for the other: for the Dam foreseeing her young one to hover about her in the hands of her enmies, and continually to follow; with sighs and tears seemeth to wish and perswade them to depart, and to save themselves by flight, as if they could say in the language of men, *Fugite filii infostos venatores, ne me miseram capti materno nomine private*; that is to say, Run away my sons, save your selves from these harmful and greedy Hunters, lest if you be taken with me, I be for ever deprived of the name of a mother. The young ones again on the other side wandring about their Mother, bleat forth many a mournful song, leaping to the Hunters, and looking in their faces, with pitiful aspects, as if they said unto him; We adjure you (oh Hunters) by the Maker of us all, that you deliver our Mother from your thraldom, and in stead of her take us her unhappy children, bend your hard hearts, fear the laws of God which forbiddeth innocents to be punished, and consider what reverence you owe to the old age of a mother; therefore again (we pray you) let our lives satisfie you for our Dams liberty. But poor creatures, when they see that nothing can move they unexorable minde of the Hunters, they resolve to dye with her whom the cannot deliver, and thereupon of their own accord, give themselves into the hands of the Hunters, and so are led away with their mother.

Concerning the *Lybian* Goats before spoken of, which live in the tops of Mountains, they are taken by nets, or snares, or else killed by Darts and Arrows, or some other art of hunting. But if at any time they descend down into the plain fields, they are no less troubled, then if they were in the waves of some great water. And therefore any man of a slow pace may there take them, without any great difficulty.

The greatest benefit that ariseth from them is their skin and their horns; with their skins they are clothed in Winter time against Tempests, Frosts, and Snow, and it is a common weed for Shepherds and

Carpenters. The horns serve them in steed of Buckets, to draw water out of the running streams, wherewithall they quench their thirst, for they may drink out of them, as out of cups; they are so great, that no man is able to drink them off at one draught, and when cunning artificers have the handling of them, they make them to receive three times as much more.

The self same things are written of the Wilde Goats of *Egypt*, who are said never to be hurt by Scorpions. There is a great City in *Egypt* (called *Coptus*) who were wont to be much addicted to the worship of *Isis*, and in that place there are great abundance of Scorpions, which with their stings and poyson, do oftentimes give mortal and deadly wounds to the people, whilest they mourn about the Chappel (for they worship that Goddess) with funeral lamentation: against the stinging of these Scorpions, the *Egyptians* have invented a thousand devises, whereof this was the principal; At the time of their assembly, they turn in wilde female Goats naked among the Scorpions lying on the ground, by whose presence they are delivered and escape free from the wounds of the Serpents, whereupon the *Coptites* do religiously consecrate these female Goats to divinity, thinking that their Idoll *Isis* did wholly love them, and therefore they sacrificed the males, but never the females.

It is reported by *Plutarch*, that wilde Goats do above other meat love meal and figs, wherefore in *Armenia* there are certain black fishes which are poyson; with the powder or meal of these fishes they cover these figs, and cast them abroad where the Goats do haunt, and as soon as the Beasts have tasted them, they presently dy. Now to the Wilde Goat before pictured, called in *Latine*, *Rupicapra*, and *Capricornus*; and in *Greek*, a *Gargos*, and *Aigastros*, and of *Homer Ixalon*; of the *Germans*, *Gemmes*, or *Gemmus*; the *Rhetians* which speak Italian, call it *Camuza*; the *Spaniards*, *Capramontes*; the *Polonians*, *Dzykakoza*; the *Bohemians*, *Korytanski Kozlik*; that is to say, a *Carinthian* Goat, because that part of the *Alpes* called *Carinthia* is neer bordering upon *Bohemia*.

Bellonius writeth, that the *French* call him *Chambris*, and in their ancient tongue *Ysard*, this is not very great of body, but hath crooked horns which bend backward to his back, whereupon he stayeth himself when he falleth from the slippery Rocks or Mountains.

These horns they are not fit to fight they are so small and weak, and therefore nature hath bestowed them upon them for the cause aforesaid. Of all other Goats this is the least, it hath red eyes, but a quick eye-sight, his horns are black, being nine or ten fingers long, and compassed about with divers circles, but at the top none at all, which is sharp and crooked like a hook. They arise at the root *Parallelwise*, that is by equal distance one from another, being hollow the breadth of ones thumb, the residue solid like the Harts.

The Males in this kinde differ not from the Females, neither in horn, colour, or proportion of body: they are in bigness like the common Goat, but somewhat higher. Their colour is betwixt brown and red. In the Summer time they are red, and in the Winter time they are brown. There hath been seen of them which were white and black, in distinct colour one from another: and the reason hereof is; because they change colour many times in the year. There are some of them altogether white, but these are seldom found; they inhabit for the most part the Rocks or Mountains, but not the tops like the Ibecks, neither do they leap so far as the foresaid Goats. They come down sometime to the roots of the *Alpes*, and there they lick sand from the Rocks, like as the Village-tame-goats to procure them an appetite.

The *Helvetians* call these places in their natural tongue *Fultzen*, that is *Salares*: about these places do the Hunters hide themselves, and secretly with guns, bows, or other such instruments, they suddenly shoot and kill them. When they are hunted they step up to the steepest Rocks, and most inaccessible for Dogs, by that means providing their own safety: but if the Hunters press after them and climbe upon the Rocks with hands and feet, they leap from thence, from stone to stone, making their way to the tops of the Mountains, so long as they are able to go or climbe, and then they hang by the horns of their head, as if they were ready to fall, which caused *Martial* to write thus:

Pendentem summa Capream de rupe videbis,
Casuram speres, decipit illa Canes.

Where the Poet attributeth that to the Roe which belongeth to the Wilde Goat, and there they hang many times till they perish, because they cannot loose themselves again, or else they are shot with Guns, or fall down headlong, or else are driven off by the Hunters. From the day of Saint *James* they use themselves to the coldest parts of the Mountains, that by degrees they may be accustomed to the cold. I have known some of these made tame, so that they have descended down to the flocks of tame Goats, whom they do not avoid like the *Ibex*.

From these wilde Goats hath that same herb (called *Doronicum*) and of the *Græcians*, *Doronicu*, given a name among the *Germans*, *Gemesseh Wort*; that is, Wilde-goats-herb, being excellent to cure the Colick, and therefore highly esteemed among the *Arabians, Græcians*, and *Mauritanians*. It is hot and dry in the second degree; and the Countrey people in *Helvetia*, do give it against diziness in the head, because these wilde Goats oftentimes feed upon the same, and yet are never troubled with that infirmity, although they run round about the Mountains.

There are Hunters which drink the bloud of this Goat coming hot out of his body, immediately after the wound given, against that sickness. The fat and milk of a wilde Goat mingled together, have cured one long sick of the Ptisick. The wilde Goats of *Creet*, being wounded with poysoned darts, run presently and eat of the herb *Dittani*, by the vertue and juyce whereof, they not only avoid the arrow which sticketh in their skin, but also death, and cure the poyson.

OF THE KID.

HAVING formerly discoursed of several kindes of Goats, now it followeth that we should also intreat of the Kid, which is the issue of a Goat; and first of the several names thereof. It is called in *Hebrew, Egedi*; which because it signifieth also a Lamb, they put unto it *Haissim*, and the plural Masculine is *Gedaiim*, and the feminie *Gedioth*, Gen. 35. where the *Chaldean* translation hath *Gadeia*; the *Persian, Buskabale*, or else *Cahali buson*; for the *Persians* render *Cahale* for *Sheter*; in *Hebrew, Busan*, for *Issim*. The *Septuagints* render *Erifon*; and vulgarly at this day, the *Græcians* call him *Eriphon*; but the truth is, that *Eriphoi* are Kids of three or four months old, and after that time untill their procreation, they are called *Chimaroi*; the *Latines* call him *Hoedi ab edendo*, from eating (as *Isidorus* saith) for then their flesh is tender and fat, and the tast thereof pleasant. The *Italians* call it *Cauretto*, or *Capretto*, and *Ciaverello*; the *Rhetians* which speak *Italian*, *Ulzol*: the *Spaniards*, *Cabrito*; the *French*, *Chereru*; the *Germans*, *Gitse*, or *Kitslæin*; the *Polonians*, *Coziel*.

It was a question whether nature would finish her parts upon a young one out of the dams belly, wherefore a triall was made upon a Kid which never saw his dam, for upon a season a dissection was made upon a Female-goat great with young, and out of her belly was a young one taken alive, so as it could never see the mother; the same Kid was put into a house where were many bowls full of Wine, Oyl, Milk, and Hony, and other liquid things: there also lay beside him divers kindes of fruits, both of the Vine, of Corn, and of Plants; at last this Kid was seen to arise and stand upon his feet, and as if some body had told him that his legs were made to walk upon, he shook off all that moistness which he brought with him out of his mothers belly, afterward he scratched his side with his foot, and then went and smelled at all the former vessels, and at last coming to the milk bowl, he supped and licked thereof, which when the beholders saw, they all cryed out that *Hippocrates* rule was most true, *Animalium naturas esse indoctas*, that is to say, the natures of creatures are not formed by art, but of their own inclination.

There is nothing more wanton then a Kid, whereupon *Ovid* made this verse:

Splendidior vitro, tenero lascivior hœdo.

They often jump and leap among themselves, and then they promise fair weather, but if they keep continually with the flocks, and depart not from their mothers, or continually suck or lick up their meat, they fore-shew a storm, and therefore they must be gathered to their folds, according to the Poets saying;

———— Si sine fine modoque
Pabula delibent cum tutas vesper adire
Compellat caulas, monstrabunt adfore nimbos.

If Geese swallow the hairs of Kids or Goats, they dy thereof Kids are not to be separated from their Dams, or weaned till they be three months old, at which time they may be joyned to the flocks: they are nourished when they are young after the same manner as they be at a year old, except that they must be more narrowly looked unto, lest their lasciviousness overthrow their age: and besides their Milk, you must give unto them Three-leaved-grass, Ivie, and the tops of Lentils, tender leaves, or small twigs of trees: and whereas commonly they are brought forth in twins, it is best, to choose out the strongest headed Kid for the flock, and to sell the other away to the Butchers. Out of the rennet of the Calves or Kids is the Coagulation.

There was a certain law (as appeareth by *Baisyus*) in the Books of the civill Lawyers, that shooes should be made of the skins of Kids, as appeared by ancient Marble monuments at *Rome*, which thing *Martiall* approveth in his verses to *Phebus*; shewing how time altereth all things, and that the skins of Kids which were wont to cover bald heads, are now put upon bare legs; the verses are these that follow,

> *Hœdina tibi pelle contegenti*
> *Nudæ tempora verticemque calvæ,*
> *Festive tibi, Phœbe, dixit ille*
> *Qui dixit caput esse calceatum.*

Out of the hide of a Kid is made good glew; and in the time of *Cicero* they stuffed beds with Kids hair: their flesh hath been much esteemed for delicate meat; and for that cause dressed and trimmed sundry ways; the best Kids for meat have been said to come from *Melos*, or *Umbralia*, or *Viburtinum*, which never tasted grass, but have more milk in them then bloud, according to the saying of *Juvenal*.

> *De Viburtino veniet pinguissimus agro*
> *Hœdulus & toto grege mollior, inscius herbæ,*
> *Nec dum ausus virgas humilis mordere salicti.*

For this cause they may safely be eaten all the year long while they suck, both of men of temperate and hot constitution, for they are less hurtful then the Rams, and do easily digest, and nourish temperately, for they engender thin and moist bloud, and also help all hot and temperate bodies, and they are at the best when as they are neither two old, that is above six moneths, nor too young, that is under two moneths.

The red or sandy coloured are the best, yet is their flesh hurtful to the Colick. *Simeon Sethi* affirmeth, that if a man eat a Kids liver before he drink in the morning, he shall not be over drunk that day. *Celtus* also prescribeth it in the sickness of the Holy-fire. They are wholesome, sod, roasted, or baked, but the ribs are best sod. *Platina* teacheth one way whereby it was dressed in his time for a delicate dish; they took some field Herbs and fat broth, two whites of an Egge well beaten together, with two heads of Garlick, a little Saffron, and a little Pepper, with the Kids flesh, put all together into a dish, rosted before at the fire upon a spit (with Parsely, Rosemary, and Lawrel leaves) and so serv'd out with that sauce, and set on the table: but if they did not eat it before it was cold, it weakened the eye-sight, and raised up venereal lust.

The bloud also of a Kid was made into a bludding, and given to be eaten of them which have the Bloudy-flix. They have also devised to dress a Kid hot, and to fill his belly with Spices and other good things: likewise it is sod in Milk with Lawrel, with divers other fashions, which every Cook is able to practise without the knowledge of learning.

And thus I might conclude the discourse of Kids with a remembrance of their constellation in the Waggoner, upon the Bulls horn, which the Poets observe for signes and tokens fore-shewing rain and clowdy weather, according to *Virgils* verse:

Quantus ab occasu veniens pluvialibus Hœdis.

These Stars rise in the Evening about the Nones of *October*, and in *December*, they wont to sacrifice a Kid with Wine to *Faunus*. There is a Bird called *Captilus*, which is a great devourer of Kids and Lambs, and the same also is hunted by a Dragon, for when she hath filled her self with these Beasts, being wearyed and idle, the Dragon doth easily set upon her and overtake her. Also when they fish for the Worm seven cubits long in the River *Indus*, they bait their hook with a Lamb or Kid, as is reported by *Ælianus*; and the Ancients were wont by inspection into the intrails of Kids, to declare or search into things to come, as *Gyraldus* amongst other their superstitious vanities rehearseth.

The manifold medicinal properties of Goats come now in the end of this story to be declared, and first of all it is to be noted, that these properties are several, both in the male, female, and Kid; and therefore they are not to be confounded, but as the diligence of learned Authors hath invented, and left them severally recorded, so they require at our hands which are the heirs of such beneficial helps, the same care and needful curtesie.

There are some which do continually nourish Goats in stables neer their dwelling houses, with an opinion that they help to continue them in health, for the Ancients ordained that a man which had been bitten or stroke by Serpents, and could not easily be cured thereof, should be lodged in a Goats stable. The hairs of a Goat-buck burned and perfumed in the presence, or under a man whose genital is decayed, it cureth him.

The powder of a Wine bottle made of a Goats skin with a little Rozen, doth not only stanch the bloud of a green wound, but also cure the same. The powder of the Horn with Nitre and Tamarisk seed, Butter, and Oyl, after the head is shaven, by anointing it therewith, strengthneth the hair from falling off, when it groweth again; and cureth the *Alopecia*, and a horn burnt to powder and mingled with meal, cureth the chippings in the head, and the scabs: for taking away the smell of the arm-pits, they take the horn of an old Goat, and either scrape or burn the same, then adde they to it a like quaintity of Myrrhe, the Goats gall, and first scrape or shave off the hair, and afterward rub them therewith every day, and they are cured by that perfrication.

The bloud fryed in a pan, and afterwards drunk with Wine, is a preservative against intoxications, and cureth the Bloudy-flix, and the bloud in a Sear-cloth is applyed against the Gout, and cleanseth away all Leprosies, and if the bloud come forth of the nose without stay, then rub the nose with this bloud of a Goat. It being fitted to meat cureth all the pains of the inward parts: being sod upon coals stayeth the looseness of the belly, and the same applyed to the belly mixed with fine flowre, and Rozen, easeth the pain in the small guts; the same mixed with the marrow of a Goat, which hath been fed with Lentils, cureth the Dropsie;

and being drunk alone, breaketh the stones in the reins; and with Parsley drunk in Wine, also dissolveth the stone in the bladder, and preventeth all such calculating gravel in time to come.

There is a Medicine called by the Apothecaries *Divina manus*, Gods hand, against the Stone, and they make it in this manner. When Grapes begin to wax ripe, they take a new earthen pot, and pour into it water, and seethe the same till all the scum or earthy substance thereof be ejected: and the same pot cleansed, then take out of the flock a Male-goat of four year old, or thereabouts, and receive his bloud as it runneth forth of his slaughtered body into that pot, so as you let go the first and last stream thereof to the ground, and save the residue: then let it thicken in the pot, and so being therein congealed, break it into many pieces with a reed, and then covering it with some linnen cloth, set it abroad in the day time where it may gather dew, and then the next day set it abroad in the Sun again to exhale the same dew, (if in the mean time there fall no rain) then let it dry, and afterward make thereof a powder, and preserve it in a box, and when the evill pincheth, use a spoonful of it with Wine of *Creet*: and *Philagrius* commendeth the manifold benefit hereof, for he had often tryed it, and with a medicine made of an *African* Sparrow mixed with this, he procured one to make water, and to void a great stone which had not vented his urine in many days, and lived in the mean time in horrible pains; and the same vertue is attributed hereunto, if it be anointed neer the bladder; and one be bathed in the warm air, and so oftentimes both the Bath and the Oyntment be reiterated. *Marcellus* teacheth how one may make tryal of the vertue of this bloud, for if he take a Male-goat, and put him up close seven days, feeding him in the mean time continually with Bays, and afterward cause a young Boy to kill him, and receive his bloud in a bladder, and put in the said bladder sandy stones, like unto those that are ingendered in the bladder of a man, within a short time he shall see those stones dissolved, and scarse to be found in the bladder of bloud, by which he confidently affirmeth, that nothing in the World is of like power to remove the Stone; but withal he willeth some superstitious observations, as namely, that he be killed by a chaste person; and on a Thursday, or Sunday, or such like: but the conclusion is, that the said Bloud must be dryed to powder in an Oven, and afterward prescribeth that three ounces hereof, one ounce of Thyme, one ounce of Pennyroyal, three ounces of burned *Polypus*, one ounce of white Pepper, one ounce of *Apian*, and one ounce of Lovage seed to be given to the party in sweet Wine fasting, and having no meat in his stomach undigested, and having digested the medicine, he must eat presently.

And therefore if it be true, as all antiquity and experience approveth, that the Goats bloud breaketh and dissolveth the Adamant stone; then much more (saith *Jacobus Silvius*) may it work upon the stone in a mans bladder. The flesh of Goats decocted in water, take away all bunches and kernels in the body. The fat of this beast is more moist then a Females or a Kids, and therefore it is most strong in operation, to scatter, dissolve, and resolve more then a Sheep.

It cureth all Fissures in the lips mixed with Goose-grease, Rozen, Pitch, and the marrow of a Hart. Also if one be troubled with swellings in his Temples or in his Legs, let him use of this sewet half a pound, and a pound of Capons-grease mixed therewith, and spreading it upon a cloth like a Sear-cloth, let him apply it to the sore, and it shall help mightily.

Also when the neck of an Ox swelleth, it hath been proved for a golden remedy, to take and anoint it with Goats-grease, liquid Pitch, the Marrow of a Bugle or Ox, and old Oyl, and may as well be called *Tetrapharmacum*, as that of *Galen* made of Wax, Rozen, Pitch, and Goats-sewet. Also if the bloud be fallen into an Oxens legs, it must be let forth, or else it will breed the mangy; and therefore first of all the place must be cut with a knife, and then rubbed with clouts wet in Salt and Oyl, and last of all anoynted with old Sewet and Goats-grease.

Two ounces of this Goats-grease, and a pinte of green Oyl mixed together, and melted in a pot, and infused into one that hath the Bloudy-flix, cureth him speedily: when the hot dung or fime of a Goat is mixed with Saffron, and applyed to the gowty members Hydropick, it worketh upon them a strange cure: and some adhere unto the stalks of Ivy beaten, Mustard-seed, and the flower of a wilde Cucumber.

The Liver of this Beast laid upon a man that hath been bitten by a mad Dog, causeth him never to be afraid of water: the same being sod, yeeldeth a certain liquor, and sore eyes being anointed with that liquor, within twelve times recover; and drunk in sharp Wine, and laid to the Navel, stayeth the Flux; also sod in Wine, no scum or froth being taken off from it, but permitted to joyn with it, helpeth the Bloudy-flix.

The entrails of a Goat eaten are profitable against the Falling-sickness. The gall killeth the Leprosie, all swelling and botches in such bodies, and being mingled with Cheese, Quick silver, and powder of Sponge, and made as thick as Honey, taketh away the spots and burls in the face. It also rooteth out and consumeth dead flesh in a wound, and also mingled with Bran and the Urine of a Bull, cureth the scurffe in the head. *Aetius* also teacheth women how to conceive with childe, if she dip a purple cloth in Goats blood, and apply it to her Navell seven dayes, and afterward lie with a man in the prime and encrease of the Moon. The Gall of a wilde Goat is commended privately for the help of them that are purblind, and for all whiteness and Ulcers in the eyes: and when the hairs which trouble the eyes be pulled up, if the place be anointed with the Gall of Goats, the hair will never grow any more.

The Milt being sod, helpeth the Flux, and the Spleen taken out of the beasts belly, and applyed to the Spleen of a Man, doth within short time ease it of all pain, if afterward it be hanged up in any fume or smoak to be dryed. *Albertus* and *Rasis* say, that if a Man eat two Goats stones, and presently lie with his wife, she shall bring forth a male childe, but if he eat but one, then shall the childe have but one stone. The fime decocted with Hony, and laid to Ulcers and swellings, dissolveth or draweth them, and mingled with Vinegar, is most profitably used to take away black spots in the face.

And if he which is sick of the falling evill do eat thereof fifteen pils, or little bals, it shall procure unto him much ease. If it be mingled with Mouse-dung, toasted at the fire and sprinkled with Hony, and so anointed upon bald places, where you would have the hair to grow again, and mingled with Vinegar wherein a Sea-onion hath been steeped, and bound to the forehead or temples, asswageth the pain of the bran-pan.

The Pastoral *Carthaginians*, to the intent that the humour flowing out at their Childrens noses, may never hurt them, burn a vein in the crown of the head with Wool, when they are four year old, and thereby they conceive that they are kept and conserved in perpetuall good health: and if when they burnt their children, they fell into a Cramp, they eased them presently by casting upon them the urine of Goats. When a Man is thick of hearing, mingle together the Gall of an Ox, and the Urine of a Goat, and infused into the ears, although there be in them a very mattery substance.

Galen prescribeth this portion to evacuate that Water which lyeth betwixt the skin by Urine, if one drink Hysope water and the Urine of a Goat; Likewise it helpeth the Dropsie, and the dust of an Elephants tooth drunk in this Goats Urine, it dissolveth the stone in the reins and bladder, without all fearful peril and danger.

The medicines arising out of the female Goat are these, We finde that the female Goat, and the land toad being sodden together, are cures of singular worth for the diseases of all living four-footed beasts. The (*Magi*, or) wisemen say, that the right eye of a green living Lizard, being taken out, and his head forthwith struck off, and put in a Goats skin is of a great force against quartan Agues. The ashes of a Goats hide besmeared over with Oil, taketh away the spots in the face. The same ashes made of a Goats hide, recovereth the blisters and gals of the feet. The shaving of the Goats skin being rubbed with Pumice stone, and mixed with Vinegar, is an excellent approved good remedy for the Smalpox.

If a Woman bleed overmuch at the nose, let her breasts be bound with a thong made of a Goats skin. The same being sodden with the hair on it, the juyce being soked up, stayeth the belly. It is not good for those that have the falling sickness to sleep or lie in a Goats skin, if at any time the passion moveth them to it; yet it is hurtful for their head, by reason of the rank smell, and not for any other particular private cause.

Goats hairs being burnt, do appease all issues of bloud, which being mixed with Vinegar they are good to stanch the bleeding at nose, and you may blow in their nostrils Goats hairs burnt and whole, and also Myrrhe mixed with Goats hairs so burnt. The same also burned and mingled with Pitch and Vinegar, helpeth the bleeding at nose, and being put in the nose they stir up lethargies.

The favour of the Goats horn, or of the hair doth the like, Goats dung in sweet water, doth expell the stone in the body, so doth the ashes of Goats hair in like manner, which being burned and bruised, and given in a medicine, they do mightily help and recover the Strangury. It is also reported that Goats horn and the hair being burnt, will drive away Serpents: and their ashes soked or anointed, is very good against strokes or stinging of Serpents.

To stay the Flux in the belly, take the hairs that grow behind on the Goats sitting place, and burn them, which being tempered with beaten Barley and Oil, must be perfumed under a mans seat.

Goats flesh being rosted by the fire where dead men are burnt, is good for those that have the Falling-sickness. The same is a good remedy against the falling sickness. It is good for such to abstain from Hogs flesh, Beef, or Goats flesh. They that drink Goats bloud, wax pale presently on it, which is excellent to get out spots of any thing: it is also good against those that are intoxicate with poison, and therefore must be drunk with wine, and being sod with marrow, it is good against the same disease, so is the male Goats bloud. The root of Cinkefoyle drunk in wine, helpeth ill humors Goats bloud also, either of the male or female, asswageth the inwards and the flowings or laskes of the belly: it is good for those that have the Dropsie, being tempered with Hony, and also sodden with marrow.

Some use it against the Bloudy flux and pain of the belly, being also sodden with marrow, it is good against the same disease. If you mix Goats bloud with Chisel steept in broath, and a little Rosin put into it, whereof make a plaister, and lay it to the belly or other parts, and it recovereth any pain thereabouts.

The fat of a male Goat is more faster, and therefore good for those that have the Bloudy flux. The substance of a Goat is fat, yet is not the fat of a Goat so moist as a Swines, but for bitings, and those that are grieved in their belly Goats fat is better then Swines, not because it hath more operation in it to expell the grief, but by reason it is thick, whereas the Swines grease will run about like oil: neither is the fat of Kids so warm and dry as female Goats, neither the male Goats so fat as the gelded Goats, in *Latin* called *Hircus*; also female Goats fat is more binding then the Tallow of Oxen, but the males fat is good against Scorpions made in a perfume. It is also good for those that are poisoned with *French* green flies, called *Cantharides*. Being tempered with Wax, it taketh away the stinging of Serpents; it helpeth any biting or wound. If a Womans breast grieve her after her delivery of childe, let her seethe husked Barley and Scallions, and the fat of a male Goat, whereof let her drink a little. Against the ache of the eyes, take Goats fat and Sheeps together, with a little warm water.

Almost every grief of the body if it be no wound, will be more easily recovered by plaisters, but if the grief be as it were grounded, (or an old grief) let it be burned, and upon the place so scorched, put Butter or the fat of a male Goat; it will also recover and heal kibes and Chilblanes. It helpeth the Kings evill; so doth the fat of the female Goats help the same disease. The males fat mixed with *Arsenicke*, taketh away the roughness of the nails: it also healeth the nails of the Leprosie without any pain, it expelleth the *Cantharidans* being applyed with the juyce of the Grape that groweth on a wilde Vine. This Goats fat is profitable to help any about the straightness of their mouths or lips, being tempered with wax it allayeth Sores and Blisters, and with Pitch and Brimstone it healeth them, and being applyed with Hony and the juice of a Brambel, it cureth the swellings arising in the hands or fingers, especially in curing of Fellons.

The fat of a Bull well salted, or if it be in an ach or grief, dipt in oil without Salt, and so after the same manner is the male Goats fat used, which being tempered with Roses, taketh away the wheales or blisters that rise in the night: being also dropped into the ears of one that is deaf, it recovereth him.

It helpeth the Falling sickness, putting thereto as much of the gall of Buls, just of the same weight, and seethe it together, and then lay it in the skin of the gall that it touch not the ground, and drink it out of the water. It is also good against the stinging of Scorpions, being applied with Butter and the meal of *Zea*, warmed and washed with red Wine.

The broath that is confected of Goats fat sodden, is excellent for those that are troubled with the Ptisick, to sup now and then a few; also it helpeth the Cough being tempered with new sweet wine, that an ounce may be put in a goblet, and so mixed with a branch of Rue. It being also sodden with husked Barley, easeth those that have fretting in the guts.

The same also sodden with Barley flowre and Wine made of Pomgranates and Cheese, let it be given to those that are troubled with the Bloudy flux, and let them take it with the juice of husked Barly.

Rasis also saith, that the fat of a fierce Lion is of such singular account, that if a Glyster be made of it, with the water of Barly sod, either with the water of tosted meal, and boyled *Sunach*, and so dissolved with Wax, it is a most pretious remedy for the swelling of the inwards. But Goats fat doth much help the griefs of the inward parts that nothing cometh forth but cold water. The fat of the Buck Goat many use (being sod with bread and ashes) against the Bloudy flux; and also the She Goats fat being taken out of her back alone being a little cold, and then supped up: Other allow the fat to be sodden with Barly flower, Cinnamon, Annise, and Vinegar mixed together. The same fat taken so out of the back mixed with Barly, Bran, and Cinnamon, Annise, and Vinegar, of each of them alike, and seethe thereof, and being strained give it the patient that is diseased with the Bloudy flux, and it shall most speedily help him.

The same also mixed with Pellitory and Cyprian Wax, may be laid to the Gowt. Also sodden with Goats dung and Saffron, and layed on the Gowt it asswageth the grief.

The marrow of the female Goat, in the fourth place next after the marrow of the Hart, the Calf and the Bull is commended of *Dioscorides*, but the last of all is the Sheeps fat. The Harts is most renowned of all, next the Calves, then the Buck Goats, and last of all the female Goats. To help the grief of the eye, take the marrow of Goats and anoint your eyes, and it will cure them. Goats bloud sod with marrow may be taken against all toxical poison.

Pliny saith, that their dung being anointed with Hony, is good for the watering or dropping of the eys, and their marrow against aches. The bloud of Goats, their marrow, and their Liver, is very good to ease the belly. Goats bloud sodden with the marrow, helpeth the Bloudy flux, and those that have the Dropsie; and I think that the Bucks is more effectual and of greater operation, so it be eaten with Mastick. Also the Goats marrow is good for the eyes of Horses.

The right horn of a Goat is of some held to be of more effect then the other, which I rather hold to be superstitious; whatsoever other reason or secret quality the Horn may afford for the bitings of Serpents, take Goats horn and burn the hairs of them, and the ashes of them soked in water, and Goats milk with the horn, and wilde Marjoram, and three cups of Wine put together, and being drunk against the stinging of an adder expelleth the poison.

The ashes of Goats horn being all anointed with Oil, tempered with Mirtle, stayeth the sweating of the body. Harts horn and Goats being burned, and (if it be requisite) is good to wash the teeth withal, and it will make them look white, and the gums soft. It is also good against the Bloudy flux and watering of the eyes in regard they are most usual; yet they neither asswage the griefes nor consume them, which are of a cold and dry nature.

Harts horn being burnt as also a Goats horn, taketh away bitings. Goats dung or the horn being burnt to ashes, and dipped in Vinegar, stoppeth the bloud. The corrupt bloud that cometh out of a Buck Goat, is more effectual and of a better operation; and the ashes of a Goats horn or dung soked in Wine or Vinegar, and anoint the Nostrils, stayeth bleeding at the Nose.

Goats horn being burned at the end, and the pieces or scorchings that arise thereof, must be shaken into a new vessel untill the horn be quite consumed, then beat and bruise them with Vinegar made of Sea onions, and anoint the evill called Saint Anthonies fire; and it is of a miraculous operation.

It will make one sleep that is troubled with the weakness of his head and watching, if it be laid under their pillow. It being mixed with Bran and Oil of Mirtle, it keepeth the hairs fast that are falling off the head. The savour of the horn burned descrieth the Falling sickness; so doth the smell of the intrails of a Goat or the Liver eaten; likewise it raiseth up a Lethargick man. They use also the horns of Harts and Goats to make white the teeth, and to fasten the gums. The same shorn or shaven into mixt hony, represseth the flux of the belly. In the pain of the belly perfume the shavings of the same, mingled with Oil and burned Barly; the same perfume is good to be laid upon the Ulcers of Horses.

The hoofs of Goats are prescribed by *Palladius* to be burned for the driving away of Serpents, and the dust of them put into Vinegar cureth the *Alopecias*. The dust of their hoofs is good to rub the teeth withall, also to drive away the swellings in the disease called St. Anthonies fire, burn the foot of the Goat with the horn, and reserve the dust thereof in a box, and when you will use it, wet the place first with Wine, and afterwards cast on the powder.

The juice of a Goats head sod with hair, is commended for burstness in the belly, and the ancient Magicians gave the brain of the Goats to little infants against the Falling sickness, but pressed through a gold Ring, the same cureth Carbunkles in the belly being taken with Hony.

If the body or head be rubbed with that water or meat which falleth out of the mouth of a Goat; mingled with Hony and Salt, they kill all kinde of Lice, and the same thing giveth remedy to the pain of the belly, but if it be taken overmuch it purgeth. The broth of the entrails to be gargarized in the mouth, cureth the exulceration of the tongue and arteries.

The Liver of the female Goat sod and eaten, is given against the Falling evill, and taketh from them Convulsion, and with the liquor thereof, after it is sod, it is good to anoint the purblind eyes, also it is good to hold the eyes open over it while it seetheth, and to receive into them the fume, and the reason hereof is, because Goats see as perfectly in the night as in the day time, and therefore *Celsus* saith, that this medicine is most agreeable to them that cannot see at all in the night, as it hapneth to Women whose monethly courses are stopped, and then it is good for them to anoint their eyes with the bloud of a Goat, and eat the Liver sod or rosted. The powder of the Liver burnt purged and drunk in Wine cureth the Colick.

If a woman in travel or with childe be swollen up, let her take a Goats liver rowled in warm ashes, and let her eat it in four dayes, and drink old wine thereunto, so shall she be delivered. The Gall is contrary to all poisoned Witch-craft made upon the rustick Weasil; and if the Kings evill be daily touched therewith at the beginning, it will keep it from overspreading, and with beaten Alum it disperseth Scabs. The old Magicians were wont to say, that when a Man rubbed his eyes when he lay down, and put it underneath his pillow, he should sleep soundly; it driveth away scabbes in the head if it be mingled with Fullers chaulke, so as the hairs may be dry a little; and the same with Hony helpeth the eyes, according to the saying of *Serenus*;

> *Hyblæi mellis succi cum felle caprino*
> *Subveniunt oculis dira caligine pressis.*

The Physitians in application hereof to the cure of eyes take many wayes, and mix it with other drugs, as when they give it against whiteness in the eyes with Hellebore, against wounds and Pin and Webs with Wine; and against the broken tunicles with a womans milk, and therefore *Rasis* and *Albertus* do justly call the Gall of a Goat an Eye-salve, and also being instilled into the ears when they are full of pain, it cureth them, first mingling it with a scruple of Hony in an earthen sheard, and so infusing into the ear, and shutting it in with a little wool.

Also all the pains in the ears are cured by the stalkes or juyce of Leeks, Gall of Goats, and sweet water; and if there be any Rupture in the ear, then use therewith a womans milk, or warm Oil of Roses: likewise against the Cankers in the gums, and the Squinancy, it is profitable to use it with Hony. For all tumors or swellings in the neck, take equal quantities of this Gall, of Goose-grease, and the yolk of an Egge, and these being all mingled together, let the offended place be rubbed therewith.

The same with the juyce of *Cyclamine* and a little Alum looseneth the belly, and Wool being well dipped therein and bound to the Navel of the belly, expelleth the Worms, it cureth the faults in the seat by anointment; it also hath another virtue in it expressed by the Poet in this Verse;

> *Languidus antiquo purgatur penis Iaccho,*
> *Ac super illinitur fœcundæ felle capellæ.*

The melt sod cureth the Bloudy-flix, and the bladder burnt and given in posset-drink is good for them that cannot contain urine in their sleep, and the secunds of a female Goat being drunk in Wine of women after their delivery, ejecteth and casteth forth their seconds also. The milk is many ways available, for *Democrates* the Physitian, in the recovery of

454

Confidia the daughter of *Servilius*, which had been Consul, used the milk of Goats a long season which he fed with Lentils: Sea-crabs mixed with this milk, expelleth poyson; and the first milk of a Goat which is milked from her after the weaning of the Kid, drunk by him that hath a quartane Ague, easeth the fits thereof. And some of the ancient Physitians gave as much dung of Swallows as will ly upon three groats, mixed with this milk against a quartane Ague, and when young Lambs were sick, the shepheards cured them by infusing into their chaps the milk of Goats; the powder of Betony drunk out of Goats milk stayeth bleeding.

The holy fire is a disease of Sheep almost incurable, because if any remedy do but touch them, they fall mad: but they only in this malady admit for the recreation or remedy Goats milk. The root of the greater Siler decocted in Goats milk, cureth those cold ustions in the flesh or belly, when the place looketh black or loseth sense: and *Aesculapius* taught his followers and patients to drink it against the Itch, or any biting, and if at any time there be any strain in any member of the body, so that the Article seemeth to decline and lose his former strength and humor, it is recovered again by binding unto it Lyne-seed sod in Goats milk. *Funerius* adviseth to wash the face therewith, that the beauty of it may be more splendant. Take seven Sea-crabs, and being beaten to powder, mingle them with one pinte of Goats milk, and a cup of Oyl, and so strain them diligently, and infuse them into a Horses mouth which is sick of the Head-ach, and it shall cure him.

The milk also by the counsel of *Philistion*, with the juyce of Cabages, Salt, and Hony, is given against the shortness of breath; and if the right eye of a *Chamæleon* be pulled out of her alive, and put into Goats milk, and applyed to the eyes, it cureth the whiteness of the eyes.

The fat of a Bull mixed with this milk, and infused into the ears, cureth their mattery evils, and causeth them to hear more assuredly and firmly. The gums of children anointed therewith, causeth their teeth to come forth with less pain, and fasteneth the loose teeth by often rubbing: the corners in the throat, and the Arteries are delivered from exulcerations by gargarizing this milk, either warmed at the fire, or else as it cometh forth of the udder.

The seed of Cresses decocted in this milk, and drunk, easeth the pains in the stomach, and also purgeth being mixed with Salt and Hony. *Marcellus* prescribeth this excellent purgation, which shall never make the party sick, that is a pinte of Goats milk, two ounces of salt ammoniack, and one ounce of the best *Mecis*, beat them all together, and give them to the patient fasting, and so let him walk a good while, till the medicine be wrought in his body; and if a woman be with childe, and oppressed with Head-ach, or have an Ague, she may safely take this milk sod with Hony.

The Physitians make a special drink of this milk, which they call *Schiston*; it is sod in a new earthen pot, and hath put into it the branches of a fig-tree, and so many cups of sweet water, as there were pintes of milk, and when it boyleth, keep it from seething over, by putting into it a silver vessel with cold water, & being taken from the fire, divide it into many vessels till it be cold, so the whay will part from the milk: and some take the whay and seethe it again till the third part be only left, and afterward set it abroad in the Sun to cool, and this may be safely drunk five days together (every day a pinte) at five several times, against the Falling evill, Melancholy, Palsies in Leprosies, Gowts or pains in the Articles, and the sickness of the Liver, which is like to a Pleuresie. Or let him drink the Goats milk, the third part thereof mingled with Hony (as *Hippocrates* prescribeth) or with the seed of *Mathrum*, (as *Serenus* counselleth) in this verse:

────── ────── *Stomacho medentur*
Semina Mathri sactæ cum lacte capella.

A draught of Goats milk sodden with Mallows, and a little Salt put to it, represseth the gripings of the belly, and if you put a little Rennet unto it, it will be more profitable. Goats milk tempered with Rennet, before it be altogether strained, while it is warm, it must be given to those that have the Bloudy-flix to drink, and it will help them presently: put also to a good potion of sweet Wine mingled with Goats milk, and a little Rennet of a Kid (as much as a Nut-kernel is) which being tempered with the hand, let it be given to the patient, labouring with the Bloudy-flix, before it be strained, for the space of three days. Let this drink be given one that is fasting about the time he riseth, and being boyled, put sufficient-Barley flowre to it, and being in like manner like pap or pottage; you must give it to the patient to drink for the same disease.

Goats milk being sodden half away, may be given to those that have the Bloudy-flix. If they that be troubled with fretting of the guts, and the Flix, are weakened by reason of their often going to the stool.

The broath of a fat Hen sod with Butter or Goats milk, or Sheeps, warmed by it self; or else sod with Butter, is very good to be given unto them. Take three ounces of *Amylum*, being a kinde of meat, three moneths old, into as much goats milk sod as you shall think fit, and so give it the patient by suppository means for the Bloudy-flix. Oxen, Sheeps, or Goats milk, stayeth the exulcerations and flowings of the belly, so it be sod on the coals, after the use of glysters, if a mans secret inwards do abound with filth, but if not, after the foments be laid to the roots and stock of the yard, fresh Goats milk must be applyed about the measure *Hemian*, and no less, but it must not be done all together, but apart. The next day let the milk seethe till the one half be diminished, still taking away that which is uppermost (I mean the skin or froth that gathereth in setling) and so use it.

For the risings and flowings of the belly and the Flix, it is very good to get Cows milk or Goats, as is before mentioned of the Cow. Panick being sod in Goats milk, helpeth the belly, being taken twice a day, and so it is good for the fretting of the guts. Old bread tempered with Goats milk, being given those that have the Flux in their belly twice a day, in manner of supping, it is a present help.

The juyce of planted pease, soaked with Goats milk, helpeth the lask of the belly. The milt is good with Goats milk, after one hath fasted two days, let him drink Goats milk, that are fed with Ivy, without any other kinde of meat, for three days together.

They that are troubled with the pain in the milt, the best remedy is this: let milch Goats be kept fasting three days, and in the third day let him eat Ivy only, and let them be milked before they drink; and let the fasting patient grieved about his milt, take three Sextaries warm of that milk, so soon as she is milked, and so let him drink it the space of three days, during which time he shall not eat nor drink any other meat, and it shall help him marvellously. He that hath the Consumption of the Spleen, let him drink the whay of Goats that are fed with Ivy. Goats milk also half sodden, so it be of them that feed on Ivy only, it may be given to children that are troubled with the pain in the milt. A drink made of Goats milk and rennet put to it (as Cheese is accustomed to be made) and given to those that have the Dropsie, they shall be holpen. Also Goats milk killeth the Worms.

Those that are troubled with the grief of the reins, let them take three cups of Cretian sod in Wine, and so much of Goats milk, and three and thirty grains of Cowcumber-seed, all well bruised together, which he may drink at one draught. *Anatolius* saith, that a porrenger full of Goats milk, with as much *Amylum*, which is as much as three porrengers of Sheeps milk, and three ounces of Oyl, all which well tempered together, must be given through a horn to a Horse that pisseth bloud, and it will remedy the same: and *Polygonius* saith, that Goats milk and *Amylum*, with three Egges and the juyce of Pellitory, is good for the same disease in Horses. The meal of Betony soaked out of Goats milk, stayeth the bloud dropping out of the paps. Physitians do drink certain medicines made of Goats milk that increase *Venus*.

The men of *Thessalia* drink another root of a certain herb (called *Orchim*) being softer and nothing inferior with Goats milk to stir up men to carnal copulation, and they drink the harder kinde of root so tempered to stay it. The root *Raguort* (as some call it) being given to women with childe, it maketh them that they cannot conceive, being of watery condition: against which Goats milk soaked with Honey, is an excellent remedy.

If the hinder parts that are somewhat fleshy stand further out then the rest, and open, anoint them with Goats milk warmed. If any mans Sheep be sick, let him take Goats milk mingled with Wine, and so let him give it them to drink. If Lambs be troubled with Agues or sickness, let Goats milk be given them through a horn.

Cheese made of Goats milk is an excellent help for those that have drunk Miselden. For other bitings of Beasts, (besides that of a mad Dog) Goats Cheese well dryed with wilde Marjoram must be drink. The same also is excellent against the stinging of Serpents; for all other bitings and stingings of lesser Beasts, it is also a very good remedy. Being dryed out of Vinegar and Honey, taketh away Ulcers and Blisters.

This same Cheese when it is new, so it be well pressed, and no whay left in it, and mixed with Honey, is most excellent against the quartain Ague. Goats cheese also represseth all dolors and punctions; and being soft and new, and made with Honey, and covered with a woollen or linnen cloth, taketh away the puffing up of the flesh. It being dryed with scallions, you may anoint Saint *Antonies* fire with it. Being dryed out of Honey and Vinegar, (when men do bath) without Oyl it may be anointed on black wheals. That which is fresh and well riwated, being laid on the eyes, it quickly asswageth the pain. It is also exceeding good for the pricking of the eyes, the grief of the head and feet, it is also good for the dropping of the eyes, with a little warm water applyed unto it, and if it be a swelling of the eyes, then out of Honey, either of which griefs is to be kept warm with whay.

For the grief of a mans Yard, seethe Goats Cheese and Honey, of a like quantity in a Poultess made in a new earthen pot, and so laid thereunto twice a day, but first wash the place with old Wine that is to be cured. It is good for Carbuncles; and if a woman be sick of her womb, and troubled with a Fever, let her take half a *Chænix* of Pettispurge, and so much Nettle-seed, and half a *Chænix* of Goats Cheese scraped, being tempered with old Wine, and afterward being sodden, let her sup it up, and if she have the Flix, let her drink the black wilde Grape, and the rinde of a Pomgranate, and a Nut-kernel, and the rennet of a Bull, these being washed in black Wine, Goats Cheese, and Wheat-flower, put them together.

The fime or dung of such Females as live in the Mountains drunk in Wine, cureth the Falling evill; and in *Galens* time they gave the trindles of Goats in Wine against the Jaundise, and with the fime they anoint them that have the Flux, and made into a Poultess, is very helpful against the Colick; but *Marcellus* prepareth it on this manner: first it must be steeped in water and strained, with sixty grains of Pepper, and three porringers of Sweet water, and so divide it into three equal potions to be drunk, in three several days: but the body of the patient must be first washed or anointed with *Acopus*, so as all perfrictions by sweat may be avoided.

Aetius against the hardness of the Spleen, prescribeth a plaister made of Goats dung, Barley meal, and the dung alone against all tumors or swellings of the milt. Against water lying betwixt the skin, and the skin and the flesh this is prepared many ways, and first against the Dropsie, they seethe it the in urine of a Boy which hath tasted of poyson, or in the Goats urine, till it be as thick that it will stick and cleave, and it will purge all by the belly, and also the shavings of hides which Coriers make, sod in Vinegar with Goats dung is accounted in *England* a singular medicine to repress all hydropick swelling in the legs and belly.

The fime of Female-goats drunk in sweet water expelleth the Stone out of the Bladder. Against the pain in the hips, the *Arabians* prescribe it in this manner, which they call adustion (betwixt the thumb and the hand) there is a hollow place wherein they put Wool dipped in Oyl; afterward they set on fire little piles of Goats dung in the same Wooll, and there let it burn till the fume and vapour thereof be sensibly felt in the hip-bone: some use to apply this to the fat, but in our time it is all out of use, and seeing yet the pains of the hip do rather fall into the thighs, shins and legs, then ascend up into the Arms and shoulders, *Aetius* and *Cornarius* say, that this adustion for the hips was used in the ancient time divers ways, and some on this manner, holding the burning dung in a pair of tongs unto the leg of that side where the pain lyeth, untill the adustion be felt in the hip, and this course used *Dioscorides*.

Quintillius used another way, which was this: he first of all heat the Goats dung, and therewithall burned the soft and fleshy part of the great toe, neer unto the nail, untill it pierced to the sick place; after such ustions, they lay beaten leaves of Leeks with Salt to the place, but in the hard bodies of Country men inured to labour, they apply the Dung of Goats with Barley meal and Vinegar.

The same with Saffron and Goats sewet, applyed to the Gowt, healeth it; or else Mustard-seed, stalks of Ivy, Bettony, or the flower of Wilde-cowcumber, the same drunk with Spikenard, or other Spice, stirreth up a Womans flowres, and causeth easie deliverance, but being beaten into Meal and Vinegar, and laid to a Womans belly, with Wooll and Frankincense, stayeth all Fluxes and Issues: also little bals of the same with hairs, and the fat of a Sea-calf, wrought al together and perfumed under a woman, hath the same effect, or else the liver of a Sea-calf, and the shavings of Cedar-wood.

Pliny affirmeth, that the Mid-wives of his time stayd the greatest Flux of the belly by drinking the urine of a Goat, and afterwards anointing it with the dung of a Horse that hath bruised his hoof; Goats bloud with Vinegar cureth the same, and if an Aple-tree have worms in it, the dung of a Goat and the urine of a man laid to the root drive them away.

The urine of Goats bloud drunk with Vinegar, resisteth the stinging of Serpents, and also being laid to bunches and swellings in the flesh, in what part soever they be, it disperseth and expelleth them. Against the stifness of the neck, which they call *Opisthotones*, take urine of a Goat, and the heads of Scallions bruised to juyce, and infuse them into the ears; and the same mingled with the Oyl of Roses and a little Nitre, cureth the pain in the ears by infusion, or by the smoke perfumed in a Goats horn twenty days together.

Against natural deafness take the horn of a Goat newly slain, and fill it with urine, and hang it up nine days in the smoke, and afterwards use it. The urine of a Goat made warm, and instilled into the ears, and the fime anointed with fat, is good for the veins of the throat. For the Dropsie drink one spoonful mingled with *Carduus*, and warm it at the fire: also mingled with Wine or Water, it expelleth the Stone in the Bladder, according to the saying of *Serenus*:

Nec non obscœnus capræ potabitur humor,
Obruit hic morbum tabefactaque saxa remittis.

The same Physitian prescribeth Goats trindles to be drunk in Wine against the Jaundise, and to stay the fluxes of women, the same dung tyed in a cloth about unquiet children, especially women-kinde, maketh them more still; being mingled with Wine, cureth the bitings of Vipers, and the dung taken out of the Goats belly and anointed upon the sore, cureth it with all speed; the same vertue it hath to heal men wounded by Scorpions, being decocted in Vinegar, it cureth also the biting of a mad Dog, mixed with Honey and Wine.

Being laid upon a Wound it keepeth it from swelling, it hath the same vertue mingled with Barley-meal, but healeth the Kings evill. It is used also

461

to ripen sores and ruptures, being applyed to the suppurations, it keepeth down the swellings of womens brests, being first dryed, and then steeped in new Wine, and so laid to the sore, for it digesteth inflamation.

When the eye-lids be thick, hard red and bald, take Goats dung and Mouse dung, of either a like quantity burned, and twice so much of the powder of the *Græcian* canes, with Honey Attick; and anoint them therewith; being heat with Vinegar, and put upon the sore, it cureth Tetters and Ring-worms, and disperseth Carbuncles in the belly: also being heated in Vinegar with Cow milk, Oyl of Cipress and Laurel, it purgeth and cureth all wounds of the legs and shins, it pulleth out thorns or sharp pricks out of the body, as that learned Physitian *Mytiæ* hath proved, as Sheeps dung also doth: laying it round about the wound, it cureth burnings and draweth out heat, with Oyl of Roses and Vinegar (as *Galen* writeth.)

It is also commended for broken joynts, because it suffereth them not to swell or start out, being once set, therefore it must be used with Honey and Wine, and it hath the same operation for broken ribs, for it openeth, draweth and healeth: also it being decocted with Vinegar, it healeth the pains in the nerves, although they be ready to rot, and easeth the pain in the joynts: the fime of a fat Goat cureth the Gout, and the contraction or shrinking of the nerves, being dressed with Vinegar, and made as thick as Honey, it helpeth the trembling members. It is very dry, and therefore (*Arnoldus* saith) it cureth the Fistula, making a plaister thereof with the meal of Beans, Wine and Leigh, which hath been seen wonderfully to dry up the Fistula. With Oxymel and Vinegar it cureth the *Aleptius*, but it must be burned.

Take seaven bals of Goats dung, work them in Vinegar, then anoint your fore-head therewith, and it easeth the pain in the head, or else mingle it with Oyl of Roses, and spread it upon a cloth laying it to your temples, change it morning and evening, and you shall finde great ease thereby.

If the eyes be swoln at any time, binde this dung unto them: being mingled with liquid pitch and Honey, healeth them which are sick of the Quinsie; being gargarized in the mouth, he which is sick of an old Cough, let him take the dryed trindles and put them into the best Wine, and drink it off, so shall he presently avoid his fleam and filthy humor, and be healed.

The same vertue which are in the Goats before spoken of, do also belong to the wilde Goats, the bloud taketh away bunches in the flesh; and being mingled with Sea-palm, causeth the hair to fall off. An Ointment made of the fat of Goats, is profitable to them which have webs in their eyes; and the fat of Mountain Goats, helpeth infected Lights: His liver broiled upon coals and taken alone, helpeth the Flix, but most certainly when it is dryed and drunk in Wine: the gawl is good for many things; especially it is a Treacle against poyson, suffusions, whiteness and blindness of the eyes, by anointing, it cureth the purblinde and the webs in the eye; and generally it hath the same properties in every part as the tame Goats before spoken of.

The like may be said of the Kids or young Goats, and first of all a Kid being slit asunder alive, and his warm flesh said to a poysoned wound, doth most assuredly heal the same. Others take the warm flesh of Kids and perfume them with hair, by the savour whereof they drive away Serpents: the skin newly pulled off, and put upon the body beaten with stripes, taketh away their pain: others again use it against the Cramp; and not without reason, for the tender skins of Lambs & Goats, being sprinkled or dipped in warm Oyl, giveth very much strength and patience to endure the Convulsion.

Praxagoras prescribeth the flesh against the Falling evill; and by gargarizing the broath when it was sod, cureth the Quinsie and soreness of the throat. *Demetrius* saith, that the brain being drawn through a gold ring, and given to a Hawk which hath the Falling sickness, it will work admirably upon her. The bloud being dryed and decocted with marrow, is good against all intoxicate passions, and being mingled with sharp Vinegar before it be congealed, it helpeth the spitting of bloud: the same being eaten, cureth all kinde of Flixes, being taken three days together. *Galen* rehearseth in the Antidote of Urbane, among other things, the bloud of Kids to draw the dead young ones out of the Dams belly.

With the fat there is an Ointment made with Rose water, to heal the fissures of the lips and nose, which is much desired of Women, not only for the before rehearsed vertue, but also because by anointing they keep by it their face from Sun-burning. The *French* and *Italians* call it

(*Pomato*) because it smelleth like Apples, they put also into it Musk and Rose water, a pound of Kids sewet, and warm it in a Bath untill all be white, and so wash it with the said Rose water, and afterward repose it in a glass: The Ointment which is called (*Unguentum album*) is like unto it: the ashes of the thighs of a Kid, healeth burstness, and stancheth bloud: the rennet is also commendable against Hemlock, or Toad-stool, and against all the poysonful strokes of Sea-beasts; being drunk in Wine, it stayeth bleeding, and refresheth excreations of bloud; being taken with Vinegar it helpeth also the flix; being drunk fasting, it hath some operation to stay womens flowers. The lights of a Kid sod and eaten fasting, preserveth from drunkenness that day; and the powder of it burned, easeth the itching of the eyes; and peel'd eye-lids, if it be applyed like *Stibium*: likewise the bladder of a female Kid drunk in powder, helpeth the inconstancy of urine: the milt laid upon the spleen of an infant, asswageth the pain and tumors thereof; the liver is not fit for temperate men, but for weak cholerick men.

The Inhabitanes of the Mount *Atlas* do gather *Euforbium*, and corrupt it with Kids milk, but it is discerned by fire; for the good *Euforbium* being burned, yeeldeth an unacceptable savour, and so we conclude this story, with the two Emblems of *Alciatus*. One against them that take much pain, and make good beginnings, but evill ends, like a Goat which giveth a good mess of milk, and over-turneth it with her foot:

> *Quod fine egregios turpi maculaveris orsus*
> *Innoxamque tuum verteris officium,*
> *Fecisti quod Capra sui mulctraria lactis*
> *Cum ferit, & proprias calce profundit opes.*

The other Emblem is upon a Goat, the which by her Keeper was constrained to give a young Wolf suck, who afterward notwithstanding that good turn, devoureth his Nurse: and it may be applyed unto them which nourish their own harms, and save a theef from the gallows.

> *Capra lupum nen sponte meo nunc ubere lacto,*
> *Quod male pastoris provida cura jubet:*
> *Creverit ille simul, mea me post ubere pascit:*
> *Improbitas nullo flectitur obsequio.*

There is a pretty comparison of a Harlots love to a fisherman, which putteth upon him a Goats skin with the horns, to deceive the *Sargus*-fish, for that fish loveth a Goat above all other creatures, and therefore the fisher-man beguileth her with a false appearance, as the flattering love of Harlots doe simple mindes by fained protestations.

OF THE GULON.

THIS Beast was not known by the Ancients, but hath been since discovered in the Northern parts of the World, and because of the great voracity thereof, it is called (*Gulo*) that is, a devourer in imitation of the *Germans*, who call such devouring creatures *Vilsiuss*, and the *Swedians*, *Gerff*; in *Lituania* and *Muscovia*, it is called *Rossomokal*. It is thought to be engendered by a *Hiæna* and a *Lioness*, for in quality it resembleth a *Hiæna*, and it is the same which is called (*Crocuta*:) it is a devouring and an unprofitable creature, having sharper teeth then other creatures. Some think it is derived of a Wolf and a Dog, for it is about the bigness of a Dog: it hath the face of a Cat, the body and tail of a Fox; being black of colour: his feet and nails be most sharp, his skin rusty, the hair very sharp, and it feedeth upon dead carkases.

When it hath found a dead carkass he eateth thereof so violently, that his belly standeth out like a bell; then he seeketh for some narrow passage betwixt two trees, and there draweth through his body, by pressing whereof, he driveth out the meat which he had eaten: and being so emptied returneth and devoureth as much as he did before, and goeth again and emptieth himself as in former manner; and so continueth eating and emptying till all be eaten. It may be that God hath ordained such a creature in those Countries, to express the abominable gluttony of the men of that Countrey, that they may know their true deformed nature, and lively ugly figure, represented in this Monster-eating-beast: for it is the fashion of the Noble men in those parts, to sit from noon till midnight, eating and drinking, and never rise from the table, but to disgorge their stomachs, or ease their bellies: and then return with refreshed appetites to ingurgitate and consume more of Gods creatures: wherein they grow to such a heighth of beastliness, that they lose both sense and reason, and know no difference between head and tail. Such they are in *Muscovia*, in *Lituania*, and most shameful of all in *Tartaria*.

These things are reported by *Olaus Magnus*, and *Mathias Michou*; But I would to God that this same (more then beastly intemperate gluttony) had been circumscribed and confined within the limits of those unchristian or heretical-apostatical countries, and had not spread it self and infected our more civil and Christian parts of the World; so should not Nobility, Society, Amity, good fellowship, neighbourhood, and honesty, be ever placed upon drunken or gluttonous companions: or any man be commended for bibbing and sucking in Wine and Beer like a Swine: When in the mean season no spark of grace, or Christianity, appeareth in them: which notwithstanding they take upon them, being herein worse then Beasts, who still reserve the notes of their nature, and preserve their lives; but these lose the markes of humanity, reason, memory and sense, with the conditions of their families, applying themselves to consume both patrimony and pence in this voracity, and forget the Badges of Christians, offering sacrifice to nothing but their bellies. The Church forsaketh them, the spirit accurseth them, the civil world abhorreth them, the Lord condemneth them, the Devil expecteth them, and the fire of Hell it self is prepared for them; and all such devourers of Gods good creature.

To help their digestion, for although the *Hiena* and *Gulon*, and some other monsters are subject to this gluttony, yet are there many creatures more in the world, who although they be Beasts and lack reason, yet can they not by any famine, stripes, or provocations be drawn to exceed their natural appetites, or measure in eating or drinking. There are of these Beasts two kindes, distinguished by colour, one black, and the other like a Wolf, they seldom kill a Man, or any live Beasts, but feed upon carrion and dead carkasses, as is before said; yet sometimes when they are hungry, they prey upon Beasts, as Horses, and such like, and then they subtilly ascend up into a tree, and when they see a Beast under the same, they leap down upon him and destroy him. A Bear is afraid to meet them, and unable to match them by reason of their sharp teeth.

This Beast is tamed, and nourished in the Courts of Princes, for no other cause then for an example of incredible voracity. When he hath filled his belly, if he can finde no trees growing so near together, as by sliding betwixt them, he may expel his excrements; then taketh he an Aldor-tree, and with his fore-feet rendeth the same asunder, and passeth through the midst of it, for the cause aforesaid. When they are wilde, men kill them with bows and gins, for no other cause than for their skins which are precious and profitable; for they are white spotted, changeably interlined like divers flowers; for which cause the greatest Princes, and richest Nobles use them in garments in the Winter time, such are the Kings of *Polonia, Sweveland, Goatland*, and the Princes of *Germany*; neither is their any skin which will sooner take a colour, or more constantly retain it. The outward appearance of the said skin is like to a damaskt garment, and besides this outward part, there is no other memorable thing worthy observation in this ravenous Beast, and therefore in *Germany*, it is called a four-footed Vulture.

OF THE GORGON OR STRANGE LYBIAN BEAST.

AMONG the manifold and divers sorts of Beasts which are bred in *Africk*, it is thought that the *Gorgon* is brought forth in that Countrey. It is a fearful and terrible beast to behold, it hath high and thick eye-lids, eyes not very great, but much like an Oxes or Bugils, but all fiery-bloudy, which neither look directly forward; nor yet upwards, but continually down to the earth, and therefore are called in *Greek, Catobleponta*. From the crown of their head down to their nose they have a long hanging mane, which make them to look fearfully. It eateth deadly and poysonful herbs, and if at any time he see a Bull or other creature whereof he is afraid, he presently causeth his mane to stand upright, and being so lifted up, opening his lips, and gaping wide, sendeth forth of his throat a certain sharp and horrible breath, which infecteth and poysoneth the air above his head, so that all living creatures which draw in the breath of that air are grievously afflicted thereby, losing both voyce and sight, they fall into lethal and deadly Convulsions. It is bred in *Hesperia* and *Lybia*.

The Poets have a fiction, that the *Gorgones* were the daughters of *Midusa* and *Phorcynis*, and are called *Steingo*, and by *Hesiodus Stheno*, and *Euryale*, inhabiting the *Gorgadian* Islands in the *Æthiopick* Ocean, over against the gardens of *Hesperia*. *Medusa* is said to have the hairs of her head to be living Serpents, against whom *Perseus* fought, and cut off her head; for which cause he was placed in Heaven, on the North side of the Zodiack above the Waggon, and on the left hand, holding the *Gorgons* head. The truth is, that that there were certain *Amazonian* women in *Africk*, divers from the *Scythians*, against whom *Perseus* made war; and the Captain of those Women was call *Medusa*, whom *Perseus* overthrew, and cut off her head, and from thence came the Poets fiction, describing it with Snakes growing out of it as is aforesaid. These *Gorgons* are bred in that Countrey, and have such hair about their heads, as not only exceedeth all other Beasts, but also poysoneth when she standeth upright. *Pliny* called this *Catablepon*, because it continually looketh downward, and saith that all the parts of it are but small, excepting the head, which is very heavy, and exceedeth the proportion of his body, which is never lifted up, but all living creatures dy that see his eyes.

By which there ariseth a question, whether the poyson which he sendeth forth, proceed from his breath, or from his eyes. Whereupon it is more probable, that like the Cockatrice he killeth by seeing, then by the breath of his mouth, which is not competible to any other Beasts in the world. Besides when the Souldiers of *Marius* followed *Jugurtha*, they saw one of these Gorgons, and supposing it was some Sheep, bending the head continually to the earth, and moving slowly, they set upon him with their swords, whereat the Beast disdaining, suddenly discovered his eyes, setting his hair upright, at the sight whereof the Souldiers fell down dead.

Marius hearing thereof sent other Souldiers to kill the Beast, but they likewise dyed as the former. At last the Inhabitants of the Countrey, told the Captain the poyson of this Beasts nature, and that if he were not killed upon a sudden, with the only sight of his eyes, he sent death into his hunters: then did the Captain lay an ambush of Soldiers for him, who slew him suddenly with their spears, and brought him to the Emperour; whereupon *Marius* sent his skin to *Rome*, which was hung up in the Temple of *Hercules*, wherein the people were feasted after the triumphs; by which it is apparent that they kill with their eyes, and not with their breath.

So that the fable of *Servius*, which reporteth that in the furthest place of *Atlas*, these *Gorgons* are bred, and that they have but one eye a piece, is not to be believed, except he mean, as else-where he confesseth, that there were certain maids which were sisters, call *Gorgons*; and were so beautiful, that all young men were amazed to behold them. Whereupon it was said, that they were turned into stones: meaning that their love bereft them of their wit and sense. They were called the daughters of *Cetus*; and three of them were made Nymphs, which were called *Pephredo*, *Enyo*, and the third *Dinon*: so called as *Geraldus* saith, because they were old women so soon as they were born, whereunto was assigned one eye and one tooth. But to omit these fables, it is certain that sharp poysoned sights are called *Gorgon Blepen*, and therefore we will follow the authority of *Pliny* and *Atheneus*. It is a Beast all set over with scales like a Dragon, having no hair except on his head, great teeth like Swine, having wings to fly, and hands to handle, in stature betwixt a Bull and a Calf.

There be Islands called *Gorgonies*, wherein these Monster-*Gorgons* were bred, and unto the days of *Pliny*, the people of that Countrey retained some part of their prodigious nature. It is reported by *Xenophon*, that *Hanno* King of *Carthage* ranged with his Army in that Region, and found there certain women of incredible swiftness and pernicity of foot. Whereof he took two only of all that appeared in sight, which had such rough and sharp bodies, as never before were seen. Wherefore when they were dead, he hung up their skins in the Temple of *Juno*, for a monument of their strange natures, which remained there untill the destruction of *Carthage*. By the consideration of this Beast there appeareth one manifest argument of the Creators divine wisdom and Providence, who hath turned the eyes of this Beast downward to the earth, as it were thereby burying his poyson from the hurt of man: and shadowing them with rough, long, and strong hair, that their poysoned beams should not reflect upwards, untill the Beast were provoked by fear or danger, the heaviness of his head being like a clog to restrain the liberty of his poysonful nature; but what other parts, vertues, or vices are contained in the compass of this Monster, God only knoweth, who peradventure hath permitted it to live upon the face of the earth, for no other cause but to be a punishment and scourge unto mankinde; and an evident example of his own wrathful power to everlasting destruction. And thus much may serve for a description of this Beast, untill by Gods Providence, more can be known thereof.

OF THE HARE.

A Hare is a four-footed Beast of the earth, which the *Hebrews* call *Arnebet*, in the feminine gender, which word gave an occasion to an opinion that all Hares were females, or at the least that the males bring forth young as well as females: whereof we shall see more in the sequell of this story. And the *Jews* say, that it signifieth nothing else in *Hebrew*

470

but a Hare; for which word Deut. 14. the *Chaldee* translateth *Arneba*; the *Arabians, Ernab*; the *Persians, Kargos. Avicenna* calleth it *Arneberri; Silvaticus, Arnaberri, Arnebus,* and *Arnaben*; the *Saracens, Arneph*; the *Græcians, Lagoos, Lagos, Lageoos,* because of his immoderate lust. It is called *Ptoox* for his fear, and in *Latine, Lepus,* of *Levipes,* signifying swiftness of feet, and that it is not heard when it goeth; howsoever some men derive it from *Leporis* the *Greek* word, others derive *Lagos* from *La,* betokening elevation, and *Oos,* signifying an ear, because she pricketh up one of her ears when she runneth. The *Italians,* call it *Livora*; the *French, Lieure,* and *Leurault, Leureteau*; the *Spaniards, Liebre*; the *Germans, Hass,* or *Haas*; the *Ilyrians, Zagicz.*

There be four sorts of Hares, some live in the Mountains, some in the Fields, some in the Marishes, and some every where without any certain place of abode. They of the Mountains are most swift, they of the fields less nimble, they of the marshes most slow, and the wandring Hares are most dangerous to follow: for they are so cunning in the ways, and muses of the field, running up the hils and rocks, because by custom they know the nearest way, and forbearing down hils, sometime making heads upon the plain ground, to the confusion of the Dogs, and the dismaying of the Hunter.

Pollux saith, that there be certain Hares called *Elymæi* (almost as big as Foxes) being blackish, of long bodies, and large white spots upon the top of their tails; these are so called of their countrey (like the *Elymæan* Dogs.) There be also Hares called *Moschiæ*, so called because of their sweet smell, or else that they leave in their foot-steps such a strong savour, whereunto when the Dogs smell, they are said, to be almost mad. At *Pisa* the Hares be very great, because there they have more gratefull meat then in other places.

In the neither *Pannonia* they are much fatter and better tasted than they be in *Italy,* the *Italian* Hare hath its fore-legs low, a part of his back-pale or yellowish, the belly white, the ears long: In *Gallia* beyond the *Alpes*; they are also white, and therefore some have thought that in the Winter time they eat snow: and this is certain, that when the snow melteth, their colour is much altered. There hath been white haired Conies, whose skin was black, and *hair* of their ears black. They are bred in *Lybia*, in *Scythia*, and in *Italy*, in the top of the Mountains, and so brought into other Countries. Some again have been white in the Winter, and return to their former colour in Summer. There are great store of white Conies in *Vilna*; and *Lethuania*, but they are lesser esteemed and sold cheaper. (*Schineborgerus* saith) the back of a Hare is commonly russet, or like Olive colour interlined with some black spots: the common Hare of the *Alpes* never changeth colour, and it is greater than the ordinary Hare. There are white Hares also in *England*, and in *Muscovia*, there are a multitude of Hares of all colours, but no where so many as in the Desert Islands, because there are no Foxes there to kill the young ones, or Eagles, which frequent the highest Mountains in the Continent, and the people that inhabit there regard not hunting.

In *Athens* (*Maucrates* saith) there were no Hares, but *Alceus* affirmeth the contrary. Hares brought into *Ithaca*, dy presently, and if they range a little about the Countrey, yet return they back to the haven where they came to land, and depart not from the shore till they be dead. *Hegesander Delphus* writeth, that in the reign of *Antigonus*, there was such a number of Hares in *Astipalea*, (and afterward in *Leros*) that the Inhabitants were constrained to go to the Oracle, and demand counsel how to resist the Hares, from whom they received answer, that they must nourish Dogs and kill them; and whereas they so abounded in *Leros*, which at the peoples own request and care, multiplyed to their great harm; afterward a sign of the Hare was placed in Heaven, to remember them, that nothing so much hurteth man-kinde, as their own desires: yet in ancient time there was not a Hare in those Countries.

In the next place we are to describe all the parts and members of Hares, for it is admirable to behold how every limb and part of this Beast is composed for celerity: and first of all the head is round, nimble, short, and of convenient longitude, prone to turn every way; the ears long and lofty like an Asses, for Nature hath so provided, that every fearful and unarmed creature should have long and large ears, that by hearing it might prevent its enemies, and save it self by flight. The lips continually move sleeping and waking, and from the slit which they have in the middle of their nose, cometh the term of Hare-lips, which are so divided in men; for if a Woman with childe see one of them suddenly, it is dangerous, if the childe prove not Hare-lipt. They have also teeth on both sides.

Whatsoever Beast be born in your flock, having that mark upon them, which is commonly called Hares-tooth, never suffer them to suck their dam, but cast them away as unprofitable and bastard cattel; the neck of a Hare is long, small, round, soft, and flexible, the shoulder-bone straight and broad, for her more easie turning; her legs before soft and sound, standing a little asunder, very flexible, broader behind then before, and the hinder legs longer then the former; a breast not narrow, but fitted to take breath in course; a nimble back, and fleshie belly, tender loins, hollow sides, fat buttocks filled up, comely, strong, and nervy loins, the fore-feet very flexible; only it wanteth a commodious tail for course. The eyes are brown, it is a subtile Beast, but not bold; it seldom looketh forward, because it goeth by jumps. The eye-lids coming from the brows, are too short to cover their eyes, and therefore this sense is very weak in them; and besides their over-much sleep, their fear of Dogs and swiftness, causeth them to see the less; when they watch, they shut their eyes; and when they sleep they open them.

Wherefore the *Egyptians* when they will signifie and open a manifest matter, they picture a Hare sleeping. They watch for the most part all the night: when the eye-lid of a man is pulled back, so as it will not cover the ball of the eye; the *Græcians* call it *Lagophthalmous*, that is, Hares-eyes, for so doth *Cœlius* define it, it cometh sometimes, when in the cure it is cut away too much, or else when the hinder lid falleth down, and standeth not up to meet the other, but concerning the colour of their eyes, it is not very possible to discover it, as well for the causes aforesaid, as also because it is seldom taken but dead; yet this is certain, that with what colour it beginneth, in that it continueth to the last, according to *Virgils* verses:

> *Quem fuga non rapit ore Canum, non occulit umbra,*
> *Concolor immonum sub Jove terra tegit.*

The liver is so parted asunder, that a man would think there were two livers in one body, and *Pliny* is bold to affirm, that in *Briletum, Thirne, Propontis, Sycynum, Bolba,* and other places they are all such. *Archelaus* upon this occasion affirmeth, that a Hare beareth young both male and female, so that the *Grammarians* know not of what sex to make it. *Albertus* and *Democritus* are absolute in this point.

Blondus confesseth he cannot tell; the common sort of people suppose, they are one year male, and another female. *Ælianus* also affirmeth so much, and by relation of his friend, he ventureth the matter, and saith moreover, that a male Hare was once found almost dead, whose belly being opened, there were three young ones alive taken out of her belly, and that one of them looked up alive, after it had lien a while in the Sun, and it put out the tongue as though it desired meat, whereupon milk was brought to it, and so it was nourished.

But all this is easily answered, if a man follow the counsel of *Archadius*, and look upon the secrets of nature, he shall finde a most plain distinction: but the Hunters object that there be some which are only females, and no more: but no male that is not also a female, and so they make him an *Hermaphrodite*. *Niphus* also affirmeth so much, for he saw a Hare which had stones and a yard, and yet was great with young, and also another which wanted stones; and the males genital, and also had young in her belly. *Rondelius* saith, that they are not stones, but certain little bladders filled with matter, which men finde in female Hares with young, such as are upon the belly of a Beaver, wherein also the vulgar sort are deceived, taking those bunches for stones, as they do these bladders. And the use of these parts both in Beavers and Hares is this; that against rain both one and other sex suck thereout a certain humor, and anoint their bodies all over therewith, and so are defended in time of rain. The belly of a Sow, a Bitch, and a Hare, have many cels in them, because they bring forth many at a time, when a Hare lyeth down, she bendeth her hinder legs under her loins, as all rough-footed Beasts do.

They are deceived, which deliver by authority of holy Scriptures, that Hares love to lodge them upon Rocks, but we have manifested elsewhere, that those places are to be understood of Conies. They have fore-knowledge both of winde and weather, Summer and Winter by their noses, for in the Winter they make their forms in the Sun-shine, because they cannot abide frost and cold, and in the Summer they rest toward the North, remaining in some higher ground, where they receive colder air.

We have shewed already that their sight is dim, but yet herein it is true that *Plutarch* saith, they have *Visum indefessum*, an indefatigable sense of seeing, so that the continuance in a mean degree, countervaileth in them the want of excellency. Their hearing is most pregnant; for the *Egyptians* when they signifie hearing, picture a Hare; and for this cause we have shewed you already that their ears are long like horns, their voyce is a whining voyce, and therefore Authors call it *Vagitum*, as they do a young childes, according to the verse of *Ovid*:

Intus ut infanti vagiat ore Puer.

They rest in the day time, and walk abroad to feed in the night, never feeding near home, either because they are delighted with forein food, or else because they would exercise their legs in going, or else by secret instinct of nature, to conceal their forms and lodging places unknown; their heart and bloud is cold, which *Albertus* assigneth for a cause of their night-feeding: they eat also Grapes, and when they are overcome with heat, they eat of an herb called *Lactuca Leporina*, and of the *Romans*, and *Hetrurians*, *Ciserbita*, of the *Venetians*, *Lactucinos*; of the *French*, *Lacterones*; that is, Hares-lettice, Hares-house, Hares palace; and there is no disease in this Beast the cure whereof she doth not seek for in this herb. Hares are said to chew the cud in holy Scripture, they never drink, but content themselves with the dew, and for that cause they often fall rotten. It is reported by *Philippus Belot*, that when a Hare drunk Wine, she instantly dyed; they render their urine backward, and their milk is as thick as a Swines, and of all creatures they have milk in udders before they deliver their young.

They are very exceedingly given to sleep, because they never wink perfectly: some Author's derive their name *Lagon* in *Greek*, from *Laein* to see, and thereupon the *Græcians* have a common proverb *Lagos Catheudon*, a sleeping Hare for a dissembling and counterfeiting person, because the Hare seeth when she sleepeth; for this is an admirable and rare work of Nature, that all the residue of her bodily parts take their rest, but the eye standeth continually sentinel. Hares admit copulation backward, and herein they are like to Conies, because they breed every moneth for the most part, and that many; at that time the female provoking the male to carnal copulation, and while they have young ones in their belly they admit copulation, whereby it cometh to pass, that they do not litter all at a time, but many dayes asunder, bringing forth one perfect, and another bald without hair, but all blinde like other cloven-footed-beasts. It is reported that two Hares brought into the Isle *Carpathus*, filled that Island with such abundance, that in short time they destroyed all the fruits, whereupon came the proverb *Carpathius Leporem*, to signifie them which plow and sow their own miseries.

It falleth out by divine Providence, that Hares and other fearfull Beasts which are good for meat, shall multiply to greater numbers in short space, because they are naked and unarmed, lying open to the violence of men and beasts, but the cruel and malignant creatures, which live only upon the devouring of their inferiours, as the Lyons, Wolves, Foxes, and Bears, conceive but very seldom, because there is less use for them in the world, and God in his creatures keepeth down the cruel and ravenous, but advanceth the simple, weak, and despised: when the female hath littered her young ones, she first sicketh them with her tongue, and afterward seeketh out the male for copulation.

Hares do seldom wax tame, and yet they are amongst them, which are neither *Placidæ* nor *Feræ*, tame nor wilde, but middle betwixt both, and *Cardane* giveth this reason of their untameable nature, because they are perswaded that all men are their enemies. *Scaliger* writeth; that he saw a tame Hare in the Castle of Mount-*Pesal*, who with her hinder legs would come and strike the Dogs of her own accord, as it were defying their force, and provoking them to follow her. Therefore for their meat they may be tamed and accustomed to the hand of man, but they remain uncapable of all discipline, and ignorant of their teachers voyce, so as they can never be brought to be obedient to the call and command of their teacher, neither will goe nor come at his pleasure.

It is a simple creature, having no defence but to run away, yet it is subtile, as may appear by changing of her form, and by scraping out her footsteps when she leapeth into her form, that so she may deceive her Hunters, also she keepeth not her young ones together in one litter, but layeth them a furlong one from another, that so she may not lose them all together, if peradventure men or beasts light upon them. Neither is she careful to feed her self alone, but also to be defended against her enemies, the Eagle, the Hawk, the Fox, and the Woolf, for she feareth all these naturally, neither can there be any peace made betwixt her and them, but she rather trusteth the scratching brambles, the solitary woods, the ditches and corners of rocks or hedges, the bodies of hollow trees, and such like places, then a dissembling peace with her adversaries.

The wilde Hawk when she taketh a Hare, she setteth one of her talons in the earth, and with the other holding her prey, striving and wrestling with the Beast untill she have pulled out his eyes, and then killeth him. The Foxes also compass the poor Hare by cunning, for in the night time when he falleth into her foot-steps, he restraineth his breath, and holdeth in his savour, going forward by little and little, untill, he finde the form of the Hare, and then thinking to surprize her, on a sudden leapeth at her to catch her; but the watchful Hare doth not take sleep after a careless manner, delighting rather in suspition than security, when she perceiveth the approaching of such a guest, (for she windeth him with her nostrils) and thinketh it better to go from home, than make a feast to her foe.

Wherefore she leapeth out of her form and runneth away with all speed she can. The Fox also followeth, but a far off, and she hearing her adversary no more, betaketh her self to rest again, under some bramble, or other bush, supposing that the ground she hath gotten shall never be recovered of her again: but the Proverb is old and true, Fair and softly goeth far; so the Fox which seldom getteth meat, but winneth it with his wit and his heels, followeth as fast as he can; for a slow pace over-taketh the Hare at rest, which when she perceiveth, forth she goeth again, forsaking her quiet sleep, for the safe-gard of her life, and having gone so much ground as she did before, she betaketh her to rest the second time, hoping that now she hath quit her self from her foe; but the Foxes belly hath no ears, and therefore hunger is to him like a thousand whips, or a whole kennel of Hounds, forcing him forward after his game.

The Hare for her better safegard getteth up into some small tree, being sleepy and weary through the Foxes pursute; the Fox cometh to the tree and shaketh it by the roots, and will not suffer the Hare to take any rest, for he hopeth that time and travel will bring her to his dish; she leaps away again, and letteth no grass grow under his feet, hoping that her heels shall deliver her from the Foxes teeth: After follows the Fox, and at length (as the greater purse over-weigheth the smaller, and the great Horse of War over-wearieth the little hunting Nag,) so doth the lusty limbs of the Fox, out-last the weak legs of the Hare, and when she can go no more, needs must her weakness betray her to her foe, and so was her flight and want of rest like a sickness before her death, and the Foxes presence like the voyce of a passing bell.

And on the contrary, all the labour of the Fox, like a gentle and kinde exercise for the preparing of his stomach to such a feast. The fift and least kinde of Wolves are also enemies to Hares, and the Weasil do craftily sport and play with the Hare untill he have wearied him, and then hangeth fast upon her throat, and will not lose her hold, run the Hare never so fast, till at last through want of breath, and loss of bloud, she falleth into the hands of her cruel play-fellow, who turneth sport into good earnest, and taketh nothing from her but her bloud, leaving her carcase to be devoured by the hands of others, and in this manner is the silly Hare hunted by beasts: Now let us hear how she is hunted of men.

It is before expressed, that every limb of a Hare is composed for celerity, and therefore she never travelleth but jumpeth, her ears lead her the way in her chase, for with one of them she harkeneth to the voyce of the Dogs, and the other she stretcheth forth like a sail to hasten her course, always stretching her hinder-feet beyond her former, and yet not hindering them at all; but sometimes when her ardent desire maketh her strain to fly from the Dogs, she falleth into the nets, for such is the state of the miserable, that while they run from one perill, they fall into another; according to the saying of holy Scripture, Isa. 24. *He that scapeth out of the snare, shall fall into the ditch.* And this is to be noted, that if the Hare had the wit to run forthright, and never to turn, she could not be so easily over-taken; but because of her love to the place of her breed, there she is taken and loseth her life where she had her beginning: for she preferreth that place above all other for safety. Again some of the elder Hares; as soon as they hear the Dogs, fly to the tops of the high Mountains, for they more easily run up the hill, then down.

Wherefore the Hunter must studiously avoid that disadvantage, and keep her down in the vallies. In paths and high ways she runneth more speedily, wherefore they must be kept from that also. The Hares of the Mountains do oftentimes exercise themselves in the plain, and through practise grow acquainted with the neerest ways to their own lodging; so that if at any time the husbandmen set upon them in the fields, they dally with them till they seem to be almost taken, and then on a sudden take the neerest way to the Mountains, not suspected by the Hunters, and so take sanctuary in the unaccessible places, whither Dogs nor Horse dare ascend. For the Hares which we keep in the bushes are not able to endure labour, and not very swift (by reason of the pain in their feet) growing fat through idleness and discontinuance of running, they must be hunted on this sort: first of all they go through young woods and hedges, such as grow not very thick, for the thicker hedges they leap over, but when they come to many thick places that they must leap over, they quickly fall down and are tired.

The Dogs first of all go from them carelessly, because they cannot see them through the trees, but suffer them to run in the Woods following a far off by the scent, untill at last they get the sight of her, and through their better exercise and skill, easily overtake her: but the campestrial or Field-hare being leaner of body, and oftner chased, is taken with more difficulty, by reason of her singular agility, she therefore when she begins her course, leapeth up from the ground as if she flew; afterward passeth through brambles and thick bushes with all expedition; and if at any time she come into deep grass or corn she easily delivereth her self and slideth through it. And as it is said of the Lyons, that with their tails they stir up their strength and courage; so are the ears of this Beast like Angels wings, Ships sails, and rowing Oars, to help her in her flight; for when she runneth she bendeth them backward, and useth them in stead of sharp spurs to prick forward her dulness, and in her course she taketh not one way, but maketh heads like labyrinths to circumvent and trouble the Dogs, that so she may go whither she will, always holding up one ear, and bending it at her pleasure to be the moderator of her chase. Neither is she so unprovident or prodigal of her strength, as to spend it all in one course, but observeth the force of her prosecutor, who if he be slow and sluggish, she is not profuse of her celerity, but only walketh gently before the Dogs, and yet safely from their clutches, reserving her greatest strength to her greatest necessity; for she knoweth that she can out-run the Dogs when she pleaseth, and therefore it is a vain conceit to trouble her self more then she is urged. But if there be a Dog following her more swiftly then the residue, then she setteth forward with all the force she can, and when she hath left both Hunters and Dogs a great way behinde her, she getteth to some little hill or rising of the earth, there she raiseth her self upon her hinder legs, like a Watch-man in his Tower, observing how far or near the enemy approacheth, and perceiving that she is delivered from persuit of all danger, seemeth to deride the imbecillity of their forces.

The younger Hares by reason of their weak members, tread heavier upon the earth then the elder, and therefore leave the greater savour behinde them: and in ancient time, if the Hunters had taken a young Leverit, they let her go again in the honour of *Diana*. At a year old they run very swift, and their savour is stronger in the Woods then in the plain fields.

The Hare is followed by the foot and so descryed, especially in soft grounds or high-ways, but if they go to the Rocks, to the Mountains, or to the hollow places, they are more uncertain, if they ly down upon the earth (as they love to do) in red fallow grounds they are easily descryed.

When they are started in the plain fields they run far, but in the Woods they make short courses: If they hear the Dogs, they raise themselves on their legs and run from them; but if fearful imagination oppress them, as they oftentimes are very sad and melancholy, supposing to hear the noise of Dogs where there are none such stirring, then do they run to and fro, fearing and trembling, as if they were fallen mad.

Their footsteps in the Winter time are more apparent then in the Summer, because as the nights be longer, so they travel farther: neither do they smell in the Winter mornings so soon as it is day, untill the frost and ice be thawed, but especially their footsteps are uncertain in the full Moon, for then they leap and play together, scattering and putting out the savour; nor in the Spring time also when they do ingender, they confound one anothers footsteps by multitude.

They which will go forth to hunt or take pleasure in that pastime, must rise early, lest they be deprived of the smell of her footsteps, so shall not the Dogs be able any way to finde the Hare, nor the Hunters their game and pastime: for the nature of the footstep remaineth not long, but suddenly in a manner vanisheth away every hour. Again, they must set the Hils and Rocks, the Rivers, and also the Brooks with nets and gins, thereby as it were stopping up the starting holes, paths, and ways, wherein the Hare for the most part trusteth, whether they be broad or narrow: The best time for the effecting and bringing hereof is after the Sun-rising, and not in twylight or break of the day, lest the nets be set neer the Hares form, and she be scared away, but if they be set a far off, there is no danger of her departure after the Sun is up, because then she giveth her self to sleep: the nets must be set on this manner, let the rodes be pitched upright, fastning their snares to the tops, raising the net in the middle, and hang a long stone at one side, that when the Hare is in the net she may not go out again. When the Hare is raised, he which followeth her to the nets, must drive her in with a great cry, and being in the net, he must gently restrain the Dogs, and make signification to the hunter that she is taken, or else if it fail, let him shew the contrary.

The keeper of the nets must keep silence, lest by hearing of his voice she be averted, and the hunter must take the Dogs and go to the forme, there to start the Hare; and the fashion was in ancient time among the *Pagans*, first of all to call upon *Apollo* and *Diana*, (their imagined Gods of hunting) to speed their sport, and to whom they promised part of their game. But when the Dog is sent forth, and after much winding and casting about, falleth into the footstep of the Hare, then let him loose another, and seeing them run in one course, uncouple all the Hounds, let him follow after, speaking to his Dogs by name, saying now *A*, then *B. Hoïka C.* and such like words of Art, not pressing them too eagerly at the beginning, but gently encouraging them to the pursuit.

The Dogs take this for a sign of joy, and being glad to gratifie their Masters run along with a gallant cry, turning over the doubtful footsteps; now one way, then another, like the cuts of Indentures, through rough and plain, crooked and straight, direct and compass, wagging of their tails, and glistering with their eyes, untill they finde the Hares form: then they make signification thereof to the hunter with their tails, voices, and paces; now running together, now standing still divided asunder, they set upon the beast, who suddainly riseth and turns the cry of the Hounds after her flight, then must the Hunters cry out, *Jo Dogs, there boyes, there, Jo, A, Jo, B, Jo, C,* and the shortest word is fittest to applaud the Dogs.

Let the Hunter also run after, so as he never meet the Hare and trouble the hounds, the poor Hare gets her out of sight, and runs to the place where she was first started, but if she fall into the nets by the way, the keeper of the nets must give token to the Hunters by his hollowing voice, after the usual manner of woodmen: *O oha, O ohe,* that the game is at an end, and then call the Dogs by name. If the Hare run far, and stand long on foot, and if the Dogs passe over the Hares footsteps and discry them not, then must the Hunter recall them with a peculiar hunting term, and lead them to the place, or casting himself about it as near as he can, rebuking the Dogs that range at uncertainties, and exhorting them that be diligent; who when they have found the footings again, run on as before, with all alacrity. In the mean season let the Hunter stand still till the Dogs do infallibly demonstrate unto him that they have found the game again, then let the Hunter proceed as before, exhorting his Dogs to the sport, and if it last all day, the Hunter must regard that he restrain and keep the Dogs to the wearied Hare, lest if they start a fresh one, their labour be lost. If it be in Summer about noon, let him rest his Dogs for strengthning of their feet till the heat be over; if it be snowie weather, and the winde set Northerly, the footsteps remain long and are not easily melted, but if the South winde blow, the footsteps are very quickly shortned: and neither when the snow falleth fast, or the winde bloweth strong, must the Dogs be led forth to hunting, for the snow burneth the Dogs nose, and the frost killeth the heat of the Hares foot; then let the Hunter take his nets and some other companion with him, and go to the Woods or Mountains, tracing out the footsteps of the beast in the snow unto the form, which is in some steep or shadowed place, where the windes blow over the snow, for in such places doth the

Hare seek her lodging; having found it, let him not come too neer, lest he raise her from her seat, but cast round about, and if he find no footings from that place, he may take it for granted that the Hare is found.

Having so done, let him leave her, and seek another before the snow be melt, and the footings dashed, having respect to the time of the day, that so he may inclose and take them before the evening: then let him draw his nets round about them, compasing the whole plat wherein she resteth, and then raise her from her stool: if she avoide the net, he must follow her by the foot unto her next lodging place, which will not be far off, if he follow her close, for the snow doth weary her and clot upon her hinder feet, so as the Hunter may take her with his hand, or kill her with his staffe.

Blondus showeth another way of taking Hares: The Hunters spread and divide themselves by the untilled and rough wayes, leading a Gray-hound in a slip, beating the dushes, hedges, and thorns, and many times sending before them a quick smelling Hound, which raiseth the Hare out of her muse, and then let go the Gray-hound with hunting terms, and cryes, exhorting him to follow the game; and many times the Dogs tear the Hare into many pieces, but the Hunters must pull them bleeding from the mouth of their Dogs.

Others again lie in wait behinde bushes and trees to take the Hare on a sudden, and some in the Vineyards, for when they are fat and resty, they are easily overtaken, especially in the cold of Winter. *Cyrus* (as appeareth in *Xenophon*) was taught to make ditches for the trapping of Hares in their course, and the Eagles and Hawkes watch the Hare when she is raised and hunted by the Hounds; and set upon her on the right side, whereby they kill and take her, so that it is true which was said at the beginning, that Hares are hunted by Men and Beasts.

Having thus discoursed of Hunting and taking of Hares, now it followeth also in a word or two to discourse of Parks or inclosed Warrens, wherein Hares, Conies, Deer, Bores, and other such beasts may alwayes be ready, as it were out of a store house or Seminary, to serve the pleasure and use of their Masters. *Grapaldus* saith, that the first *Roman* that ever inclosed wilde beasts, was *Fulvius Herpinus*, and *Gellius* saith, that *Varro* had the first Warren of Hares: the manner was (saith *Columella*) that Richmen possessed of whole Towns and Lordships, neer some Village, inclosed a piece of land by pail, mudwall, or bush, storing the same with divers wilde beasts, and such a one there was in the Lordship that *Varro* bought of *Marcus Piso* in *Tusculanum*; and *Quintus Hortensius* saw at *Lauretum* a wood inclosed, containing fifty Acres, wherein were nourished all sorts of wilde beasts, within the compass of a wall.

Quintus Althea commanded his Forrester to call the beasts together before him, and his guests sitting at Supper, and instantly he sounded his pipe, at the voice whereof there assembled together a great company of all sorts, to the admiration of the beholders. *Quintus Fulvius* had a Park in *Tarquinium*, wherein were included not only all the beasts before spoken off, but also wilde Sheep, and this contained forty Acres of ground besides he had two other, *Pompeius* erected a Parke in *France*, containing the compass of three thousand paces, wherein he preserved not only Dear, Hares, and Conies, but also Dor-mise, Bees, and other Beasts: the manner whereof ought to be thus; first that the wals or pales be high, or close joynted, so as neither Badgers, nor Cats may creep through, or Wolves, or Foxes, may leap over: Wherein ought also to be bushes, and broad trees for to cover the beasts against heat and cold, and other secret places to content their natures, and to defend them from Eagles and other ravening Fowls: In which, three or four couple of Hares do quickly multiply into a great Warren. It is also good to sow Gourds, Miseline, Corn, Barly, Peas, and such like, wherein Hares delight and will thereby quickly wax fat. For their fatting the Hunters use another devise, they put Wax into their ears, and so make them deaf, then turn them into the place where they should feed, where being freed from the fear of sounds (because they want hearing) they grow fat before other of their kinde.

Concerning the use of their skins, in some Countries they make sleeves and breeches of the them, especially lynings for all outward cold diseases, *Heliogabalus* lay upon a bed filled with flew or wool of Hares, for than that, there is nothing more soft, for which cause the *Grecians* made spunges thereof, to clense the eyes of men. The Goldsmiths use the feet or legs of Hares in stead of brushes or brooms, to take of the dust from their plate. The flesh of Hares hath ever been accounted a delicate meat (among all other four-footed beasts) as the Thrush among the fowls of the air, according to the saying of *Martial*:

> *Inter aves Turdus, si quis me judice certet,*
> *Inter quadrupedes, gloria prima lepus.*

In ancient time (as *Cælius* saith) the *Britans* were forbidden to eat Hares, like as the *Jews* by the law of *Moses*, Lev. 11. Deut. 14. Plutarch enquireth the reason why the Jews worship Swine, and Hares, because they did not eat their flesh: whereunto answer was made, that they abstained from Hares, because their colour, ears and eyes, were like Asses; wherein the ignorance of Gods law appeared, for they abstained from Hares at Gods commandment, because they were not cloven-footed, for the *Egyptians* accounted all swift creatures to be partakers of Divinity.

Their flesh ingendereth thick bloud, therefore it is to be prescribed for a dry diet, for it bindeth the belly, procureth urine, and helpeth the pain in the bowels: but yet it is not good for an ordinary diet, it is hot and dry in the second degree, and therefore it nourisheth but little being so hard, as *Gallen* witnesseth.

The bloud is far more hot then the flesh, it is thin, and therefore watery like the bloud of all fearfull beasts; the hinder parts from the loins are most delicate meat, called in *Latin, Pulpamentum*, it was wont to be dressed with salt, and Coriander seed, yet the forepart is the sweeter, for the manner of the dressing whereof I leave to every mans humour. It was once believed that the eating of the hinder loins of a Hare would make one fair, or procure beauty, whereupon *Martial* received a Hare from *Gellia* a friend of his with this message;

> *Formosus septem Marce diebus eris.*

And he retorted the jest in this manner upon *Gellia*;

> *Si me non fallis, si verum (lux mea) diois,*
> *Edesti nunquam, Gellia, tu leporem.*

Lampridius writeth that a certain Poet played upon *Alexander Severus* the Emperour for eating Hares flesh, which made him fair, whereas in truth he was very black; In this manner:

> *Pulchrum quod vides esse nostrum regem,*
> *Quem Syrum suum detulit propago,*
> *Venatus facit, & lepus comesus,*
> *Ex quo continuum capit leporem.*

The Emperour seeing those Verses, for Emperours have long ears and hands, made answer unto them as followeth;

> *Pulchrum quod putas esse vestrum regem*
> *Vulgari (miserande) de fabella,*
> *Si verum putas esse, non irascor;*
> *Tantum tu comedas velim lepusculos,*
> *Ut fias animi malis repulsis*
> *Pulcher, ne invideas livore mentis.*

If any man finde fault with the Emperours Verses, *Erasmus* hath already answered the objection, that Kings and Emperours are not subject to laws of versifying; besides his answer was in *Greek*, and this but translated.

The eating of Hares procureth sleep, and thus much for the flesh and parts. The Epithets of a Hare expressing their natures are, Eared, trusting their feet, fearful, careful, fruitful, flying, raging, unhorned, little, crafty, tender, sharp-smelling, swift, whining, and wandring, besides many other *Greek* names. When *Xerxes* gathered his Army to go against *Grecia*, a Mare brought forth a Hare, which foreshewed that great Army should work no strange effect. And another Mare of three years old brought forth an Hare which spake as soon as it was littered, biting her mother with her teeth, and killing her, and while they looked upon her, sucking her dams bloud, feathers grew out of her back in fashion of wings, which being done, the monster lifting up the voice, spake in this manner; *Fundite jam lachrymas & suspiria miseri mortales, ego hinc abeo*: that is to say, O ye wretched mortal men weep and sigh, I go away: at which words she flew away and was never seen more.

486

There were present at the sight hereof seven publick notaries, which called witnesses and made instruments thereupon, (as *Antonius Bautius* writeth in his Epistle to *Petrus Toletus* of *Lyons* in the year 1537 in *December*:) whereunto the said *Toletus* made this answer, The dayes shall come (saith he) except the mercy of God prevent them, that children shall think they do obedience to their Parents if they put them to death.

They shall grieve because they were born, and say they are adulterate, as the Hare that was born of the Mare. Likewise it is reported by *Lisander*, that when the *Corinthians* refused the conduct of the *Lacdemonians*, and the *Lacedemonians* besieging the City, fell to be very much afraid, and unwilling to scale the wals; whiles they stood in this amaze, suddenly a Hare leaped out of the town ditch; which thing when *Lisander* saw, he exhorted his Souldiers, saying, Be not afraid (O ye *Spartans*) of this sluggish and unexercised people, for you see they stir not out of the City, but suffer Hares to lodge under their wals; whereupon came the proverb (*Dormire lepores sub mœnibus*) Hares sleep under their wals, to signifie a slothfull, secure, sluggish, idle, and unthrifty people.

The Eagles of *Norway* lay their young ones in Hares skins, which themselves pull off. There is also a bird in *Scythia*; about the bigness of a Bustard, which bringeth forth two at a time, and keepeth them in a Hares skin which he hangeth upon a bough. Hares were dedicated to love, because (*Xenophon* saith) there is no man that seeth a Hare but he remembreth what he hath loved.

They say the City *Bocas* of *Laconia* was built by a sign of good fortune taken from a Hare, for when the Inhabitants were driven out of their Countrey they went to the Oracle to desire a place to dwell in, from whom they received answer, that *Diana* should shew them a dwelling place: they going out of their Countrey a Hare met with them, which they consented to follow, and there to build where the Hare should lodge, and they followed her to a Myrtle tree, where the Hare hid her self, in which place they built their City, and ever afterwards retained with veneration a Myrtle tree. And thus I will conclude this moral discourse of Hares, with that *Epigram* of *Martial* made upon occasion of a Hare that in sport passed through the mouth and teeth of a tame Lion, saying that she was ambitious in offering her life to the Lions teeth in this wise:

Non facit ad sævos cervix nisi prima leonet,
Quid fugis hos dentes, ambitiose lepus?
Scilicet a magnis ad te descendere tauris,
Et quæ non cernunt frangere colla velint.
Desperanda tibi est ingentis gloria fati:
Non potes hoc tenuis præda sub hoste mori.

The powder of a Hare with oil of myrtle, driveth away pain in the head, and the same burned cureth the Cough: the powder thereof is good for the stone in the bladder: also the bloud and fime of a Hare burnt in a raw pot to powder, afterwards drunk fasting with Wine and warm water, it cureth the stone: and *Sextus* saith, he made triall of it by putting a spoonful of the powder into water wherein was a sand stone, and the same stone did instantly melt and dissolve: so likewise a young Hare cut out of the dams belly and burnt to powder, hath the same operation. A wastcoat made of Hares skins straighten the bodies of young and old: also the same dipped in Oil laid to the sore places of a Horses legs where the skin is off by over reaching, it often cureth the sore: the bloud taken warm out of the body amendeth Sun burning, freckles, pimples, and many other faults in skin and face; which *Celsus* prescribeth to be done, first by washing the place many hours together, in the morning with the bloud, and afterwards anointing it with oil: the same virtue is in the fat of Swans mingled with oil, according to the saying of *Serenus*:

Cygnæos adipes hilari misceto Lyæo,
Omne malum propere maculoso ex ore fugabis,
Sanguine vel leporis morbus delabitur omnis.

It also cureth and taketh away the thick skin of the eye, it adorneth the skin, produceth hair in bald places, and easeth the Gowt.

Orno cutim, produco piles, & sedo podagram,
Sanguine si fuerint membra peruncia meo.

It being fryed, helpeth the Bloudy flux, Ulcers in the bowels, and old laske, and taketh away the poison of an arrow; it being anointed upon a hot outward Ulcer, it ripeneth it. After a bath, it cureth a great Leprosie by washing. The Rennet of a Hare stayeth looseness, the flesh is profitable for Ulcers in the bowels, it breaketh the stone being beaten, and being decocted like a Fox easeth the Gowt and the shrinking up of the sinews. The fat with the flowers of beans beaten together, draweth thorns out of the flesh: If a nail stick in the sole of the foot, beat together the fat of a Hare and a raw Sea-crab, then lay it to the place, and right against it upon the same foot lay also two or three Bean flowers, and let it lie a day and a night, and so it shall be cured: and the same draweth a poisoned Arrow out of a Horse; *Andreas* reporteth to *Gesner*, that he hath often heard that the sewet of a Hare layed to the crown of a Womans head, expelleth her secunds, and a dead childe out of the womb. The powder made of this wool or Hair stancheth bleeding, if the hairs be pulled off from a live Hare, and stopped into the nose.

The powder of the wool of a Hare burned mingled with the Oil of Myrtles, the gall of a Bull, and Allum warmed at the fire, and anoint it upon the head, fasteneth the hair from falling off: also the same powder decocted with hony, helpeth the pain in the bowels, although they be broken: being taken in a round ball the quantity of a Bean together; but these medicines must be used every day.

Arnoldus preseribeth the hair to be cut short, and so to be taken into the body against burstness: A perfume made of the dung and hairs of a Hare, and the fat of a Sea calfe, draweth forth Womens flowers. The seed of a wilde Cowcumber, and an Oyster shell burned, and put into Wine, mingled with the hair of a Hare, and wool of a Sheep, with the flower of Roses, cureth inflamations of Womens secrets after their child-birth. Also *Hippocrates* prescribeth the shell of a Cuttlefish to be beaten into Wine and layed in Sheeps wool and Hares hair, helpeth the falling down of the womb of a Woman with childe. If a mans feet be scorched with cold, the powder of a Hares wool is a remedy for it. The head of a Hare burned and mingled with fat of Bears and Vinegar, causeth hair to come where it is fallen off, and *Galen* saith that some have used the whole body of a Hare so burned and mingled for the foresaid cure, being layed in manner of a plaister.

By eating of a Hares head, the trembling of the Nerves and the losse of motion and sense in the members receiveth: singular remedy. There things also preserve teeth from aking: the powder of a Hares head burned with salt mingled together, rubbed upon the teeth, or if you will put thereunto the whitest Fennel, and the dryed beans of a Cutle fish.

The *Indians* burn together the Hares head and Mice for this purpose. When ones mouth smelleth strong, this powder with Spicknard asswageth the smell. The brain is good against poison. The heart of a Hair hath in it a theriacal virtue also. The brain is proved to have power in it for comforting and repairing the memory. The same sod and eaten helpeth trembling which happen in the accessions; of sickness, such an one as is in the cold shaking fit of an Ague: It is to be noted, that all trembling hath its original cause from the infirmity or weakness of the Nerves, as is apparent in old age, although the immediate causes may be some cold constitution, as abundance of cold humors, drinking of cold drink, and such like; all which tremblings are cured by eating the brain of a Hare roasted, (saith *Dioscorides* and *Egineta*.) It also helpeth children to breed teeth easily, if the gums be rubbed therewith, for it hath the same power against inflamation, that hony and better hath: being drunk in Wine and the stones thereof rosted and eaten, it is good for him that hath any pain in his bladder, and if the Urine exceed ordinary, for staying thereof, take the brain hereof to be drunk in wine.

The tooth of a Hare layed to that part where the teeth ake, easeth them. Take the Maw with the dung, in it, and wash it in old wine so as the dung may mingle there with, and then give it to one sick of the Bloudy-flux, and it shall eare him. The Rennet hath the same virtue that is in a Calves or Kids, and whereas *Nicander* praiseth it in the first place, for the virtue it hath in it against poison, *Nicoon* an ancient Physitian giveth it the second place, for it is full of sharp digesting power, and therefore hath a drying quality. It dissolveth the congealed and coagulated milk in the belly, and also clotted bloud within in the stomach more effectually then the Rennet of any other beast, being alway the better for the age.

Being mingled with Vinegar, it is drunk against poison; and also if a Man or Beast be anointed with it, no Serpent, Scorpion, Spider or wilde

Mouse, whose teeth are venomous will venture to sting the body so anointed; or else inwardly take thereof three spoonfuls with Wine against the said bitings, or of any Sea-fish or Hemlock after the wound received; and with Vinegar it is soveraign against all poison of *Chamæleons*, or the bloud of Buls.

The same being drunk in Vinegar, or applyed outwardly to womens breasts, disperseth the coagulated milk in them: also being mingled with Snails, or any other shelfish, which feed upon green herbs or leaves, it draweth forth Thornes, Darts, Arrowes, or Reeds out of the belly: or mingled with gum of Frankincense, Oil, bird lime, and Bees-glew, of each an equall quantity with Vinegar, it stancheth bloud, and all issues of bloud flowing out of the belly: and it also ripeneth an old sore, according to the saying of *Serenus*;

Si inducas leporis aspersa coagula vino.

Being layed to the Kings evill in Lint with Vinegar, it disperseth and cureth it: also it healeth Cankers, it cureth a Quartan Ague; also mixed with Wine and drunk with Vinegar, against the Falling evill and the stone in the bladder: If it be mixed with *Sagapanum* and Wine *Amyny*, and infused into the ears, giveth help, as also the pain of the teeth. It dissolveth bloud in the lights, and easeth the pain of bloud congealed in your stomach: when one spitteth bloud, if he drink *Samia* and Myrtle with the Rennet of a Hare, it shall give him very present ease.

The latter learned Physitians take a drink made of Vinegar and Water, and give it warm to eject and expell bloud out of the Lights; and if any drop thereof cleave in the bowels, then do they three or four times together iterate this potion, and after apply and minister all binding astringent medicines and emplasters, and for the Bloudy flux it is good to be used: It is held also profitable by *Dioscorides* and other the ancients, that if the pap or brest of a Woman be anointed therewith, it stayeth the sucking Infants looseness in the belly, or else given to the childe with Wine, or (if it have an Ague) with Water.

There is, saith *Aristotle*, in the Rennet a fiery quality, but not in the highest degree, for as fire dissolveth and discerneth, so doth this in milk distinguish the airy part from the watery, and the watery from the earthy:

Wherefore when one tasteth an old Rennet, he shall think he tasteth an old putrified Cheese, but as leaven is to bread, which hardneth, joyneth, and seasoneth the same, so is Rennet to Cheese; and therefore both of them have the same qualities of dissolving and binding; *Galen* affirmeth that he cured one of Gowty tumours and swellings, by applying thereunto old and strong putrified Cheese beaten in a morter, and mixed with the salted fat or leg of a Swine. If a Man sick of the Bloudy flux drink thereof in a reer Egge two scruples for two dayes together fasting, it will procure him remedy.

For pacifying the Colick, drink the Rennet of a Hare: the same mingled with Goose grease, stayeth the incontinencie of Urine, it also retaineth womens flowers. If it be drunk with Vinegar it helpeth the seconds, and being applyed with Saffron and the juyce of Leeks, driveth a dead childe out of the womb. If it be drunk three or four dayes together after childe-birth, it causeth barrenness. There are (saith *Pliny*) a kind of Wormes which being bound to Women before the Sun rising in a Harts skin, cause them that they cannot conceive: this power is called *Asocion*.

Masarius saith, that if a Woman drink this Rennet to her meat before she conceive with childe, she should be delivered of a Male child: and such is the foolish opinion of them which affirm at this day, that if men eat parsly or white buds of black ivie, it maketh them unable to carnall copulation.

The Rennet of a Hare easeth and disperseth all tumors and swellings in Womens brests: the Lights of a Hare powdred with salt, with Frankincense, and white wine, helpeth him that is vexed with the Falling sickness, if he receive it thirty dayes together. *Sextus* ascribeth the same remedy to the Hart, and *Pliny* commendeth the Lights to heal the pain in the eyes. Being drunk in powder, it cureth the secrets. If the heels be troubled with Kibes they are healed with the fat of Bears; but if they be wrung with a cold, they are healed with the dust of a Hares hair, or the powder of the Lights; Likewise when the foot is hurt with strait shooes, it hath the same operation. The ancient *Magi* took the skin of an Oxe in powder, with the Urine of Boyes, and sprinkled it on the toes of their feet, binding the heart of a Hare to the hands of him that hath a Quartan Ague: and some cure it by hanging the heart of a young Hare or Leveret to the neck or arme, in the beginning of the fit of him that is so visited. The heart of a Hare dried mixed with Frankincense or Manna in white wine drunk thirty dayes together, cureth the Falling sickness.

For the pain in the belly take the same medicine, and drunk with warm water mingled with Samia, cureth the fluxes of women; also if a man that hath the flux eat the Liver of a Hare dipped in sharp Vinegar it helpeth him if he be Liver sick: or if one have the Falling sickness, eat the quantity of an ounce thereof, and it helpeth him. The Gall of a Hare, the Heart, Lungs, Lights and Liver of a Weasel, mixed together, three drams, one dram of *Castoreum*, four drams of Myrrha; a dram of Vinegar and Hony beat together, cureth him that hath a swimming or dizziness in his brain. The gall newly taken forth mingled with a like portion of hony, and warm in the skin of an onion, and so put into the ear, giveth remedy to him that can hear nothing.

If he that is sick in the milt, that is, if it be over hard, swallow down the milt of a Hare not touching it with his teeth, or seeing it with his eyes, it cureth him. The belly of a Hare with the intrails tosted and burned in a frying-pan mixed with Oil, and anointed upon the head, restoreth decayed hairs. The reins of a Hare inveterated and drunk in Wine, expelleth the stone, and being sod, cut and dryed in the Sun, helpeth the pain in the reins, if it be swallowed down and not touched with the teeth. The reins of a Hare, and of a Moor-hen, cureth them that are poisoned by Spiders, the stones of a Hare roasted and drunk in Wine, stayeth the incontinency of Urine. In the pain of the loins, and of the hip bones, they have the same operation. The secrets and stones of Hares are given to Men and Women to make them apter to copulation and conception, but this opinion hath no other ground beside the fœcundity of the beast that beareth them. They which carry about with them the ankle bone of a Hare, shall never be pained in the belly (as *Pliny* saith) So likewise *Sextus* and *Marcellus*.

Take the ankle bone out of a live Hare, and hairs from her belly, therewithal make a threed and bind the said bone to him that hath the Colick, and it shall ease him. The said bone also beaten to powder is reckoned among the chief remedies against the stone. When Women have hard travel, put it into Cretick-wine with the liquor of Penyroyal, and it procureth speedy delivery, being bound to the benummed joynts of a mans leg bringeth great ease: so also do the feet being bruised and drunk in warm Wine, relieve the arteries and shortness of breath: and some belive that by the foot of a Hare cut off alive, the Gout is eased.

The fime of a Hare cureth scorched members, and whereas it was no small honour to Virgins in ancient time, to have their brests continually stand out, every one was prescribed to drink in Wine or such other things, nine grains of Hares dung: the same drunk in Wine in the evening stayeth Coughing in the night; in a potion of warm wine it is given to them that have the Bloudy flux, likewise if a man be sick of the Colick, and drink three pieles thereof in sweet Wine, it procureth him much ease: being decocted with hony and eaten every day, the quantity of a Bean in desperate cases, mendeth Ruptures in the bowels.

Asclepiades in his medicine whereby he procured fruitfulness to Noble Women, he gave them four drams of Myrrha, two drams of Flower-deluce, two of Hares dung, confected with Collyrial water, & so put up into their bellies after ceasing of the flowers, before they lay with their Husbands. *Albertus* and *Raphael* prescribe this medicine to help a woman that wanteth milk in her brests, *Crystal*, white Mustard-seed, and Hares dung put into broath made with Fennel.

OF THE HEDGE-HOG.

FORASMUCH as there be two sorts of Hedge-hogs, one of the Sea, and another of the Land, our purpose in this place is only to discourse of the Land Hedge-hog, the *Hebrews* call him *Kipod*, which in the 14. of Isa. and Zepha. 2. is so translated by the *Septuagints*; although that some of the *Hebrews* would have it to signifie, a ravening bird, but seeing that I find the word *Kapaz* in most *Hebrew* dictionaries to signifie *Claudere* and *Contrahere*, and that is most proper to shut up and draw together, I do rather believe that the proper meaning thereof is a Hedge-hog, because this beast so draweth it self together, when it is in danger, as we shall hear more at large afterwards, according to the old Verse;

Implicitumque sinu spinosi corporis erem.

494

The *Arabians* call him *Ceufud*, or *Coufed*; the *Caldeans, Caupeda*; the *Septuagints, Mugale. Silvaticus* calleth it *Agilium*; *Avicen, Aduldus*, and *Aliherha* signifieth a great Mountain Hedge-hog: the *Grecians, Cher*, and *Acanthonocos*, or *Echinos*, by reason of the prickes upon his back. The *Latines, Echinus, Ericius, Ricius, Herix*, and *Erinaceus*; the *Italians, Riccio*, and *Rizo*; the *Spaniards, Erizo*; the *Portingals, Ouriso*, or *Orizo, Cache*, because of hiding themselves; the *French, Herison*; the *Germans, Igal*, as in lower *Germany*; in *Holland, Een Yseren Verchen*; in *English* a *Hedge-hog*, or an *Urchine*; by which name we call a Man that holdeth his neck in his bosome: the *Italians, Gess, Malax*: and the *Illyrians, Azvuiier, Zatho*, and *Otzischax*. So then for the entrance of our discourse, we take it for granted, that *Herinaceus* and *Echinus* signifie one thing, except one of them signifie that kinde which is like to a Hog, and the other that kinde which is like to a Dog, for they differ in place, or in habitation: some of them keep in the Mountains, and in the Woods or hollow trees, and other about Barnes and Houses: in the Summer time they keep neer Vineyards and Bushie places, and gather fruit, laying it up against Winter.

It is about the bigness of a Cony, but more like to a Hog, being beset and compassed all over with sharp thorny hairs, as well on the face as on the feet: and those sharp prickles are covered with a kind of soft mosse, but when she is angred or gathereth her food she striketh them up by an admirable instinct of nature, as sharp as pins or needles: these are hair at the beginning, but afterwards grow to be prickles, which is the lesse to be marvelled at, because there be Mise in *Egypt* (as *Pliny* saith) which have hair like Hedge-hogs. It hath none of these prickles on the belly, and therefore, when the skin is off, it is in all parts like a Hog.

His stones are inward and cleave to his loins like as a birds, he hath two holes under his tail, to eject his excrements, which no creature living hath besides him. His meat is Apples, Wormes, or Grapes; When he findeth apples or grapes on the earth, he rowleth himself upon them, untill he have filled all his prickles, and then carryeth them home to his den, never bearing above one in his mouth. And if it fortune that one of them fall off by the way, he likewise shaketh off all the residue, and walloweth upon them afresh, untill they be all setled upon his back again, so forth he goeth, making a noise like a cart wheele. And if he have

495

any young ones in his nest, they pull off his load wherewithal he is loaded, eating thereof what they please, and laying up the residue for the time to come.

When they are nourished at home in houses and brought up tame, they drink both milk and Wine: But there is an Herb (called *Potomagiton*) whereof if they tast, they die presently.

When they are in carnall copulation they stand upright, and are not joyned like other beasts, for they imbrace one another, standing belly to belly: but the prickly thornes upon their backs will not suffer them to have copulation like Dogs or Swine, and for this cause they are a very little while in copulation, because they cannot stand long together upon their hinder legs. When the female is to bring forth her young ones, and feeleth the natural pain of her delivery, she pricketh her own belly, to delay and put off her misery, to her further pain, whereupon came the proverb (as *Erasmus* saith) *Echinus partum differt*, the Hedge-hog putteth off the littering of her young; which is also applyed against them which put off and defer those necessary works, which God and nature hath provided them to undergo; as when a poor man deferreth the payment of his debt, untill the value and sum grow to be far more great then the principal.

The inward disposition of this beast, appeareth to be very crafty and full of subtlety, by this, because (*Lycophron* saith) that *Nauplius* had a cunning crooked wit, and was called by him a Hedge-hog. When they hide themselves in their den, they have a natural understanding of the turning of the winde, South and North, and they that are nourished came in houses, immediately before that change remove from one wall to another; the wilde ones have two holes in their cave, the one North, the other South, observing to stop the mouth against the winde, as the skilful manner, to steer and turn the rudder or sails, for which occasion *Aristotle* saith, that some have held opinion, that they do naturally foreknow the change of weather.

There is mortal hatred betwixt the Serpent and the Hedge-hog, the Serpent seeketh out the Hedge-hogs den, and falleth upon her to kill her, the Hedge-hog draweth it self up together round like a foot-ball, so that nothing appeareth on her but her thorny prickles; whereat the Serpent biteth in vain, for the more she laboureth to annoy the Hedge-hog, the more she is wounded and harmeth herself, yet notwithstanding the height of her minde, and hate of her heart, doth not suffer her to let go her hold, till one or both parties be destoyed.

The Hedge-hog rowleth upon the Serpent piercing his skin and flesh, (yea many times tearing the flesh from the bones) whereby he scapeth alive and killeth his adversary, carrying the flesh upon his spears, like an honorable banner won from his adversary in the field. The Wolf also is afraid of, and flyeth from the Hedge-hog; and there is also a story of hatred between the Hare and the Hedge-hog, for it is said, that a Hare was seen to pluck off the prickles from the Hedge-hog, and leave her bald, pieled and naked, without any defence. The Fox is also an enemy to the poor, Hedge-hog, and lyeth in wait to kill it, for the proverb is true, *Multa novit Vulpes, Echinus vero unum, magnum*; that is to say, the Fox knoweth many devises to help himself; but the Hedge-hog knows but one great one, for by rowling up her self (as before said) she opposeth the thorns of her back, against the Foxes teeth: which alone were sufficient to secure her from a greater adversary; but the wily Fox perceiveth that he can no where fasten his teeth without danger of himself, pisseth upon the Hedge-hogs face and poisoneth her: whereupon the poor beast is forced to lay open himself, and to take breath against the Foxes stinking excrement: which thing the Fox espying, loseth no opportunity, but presently teareth the Hedge-hog in pieces; thus the poor beast ayoiding the poison, falleth into the mouth of her enemy.

The manner of Hedge-hogs is, that whensoever they are hunted by Men, they draw up their legs and put down their head to the mossie part of their belly, so as nothing of them can be taken but their prickles: and perceiving that shift will not serve the turn, but their case growing desperate, they render out of their own bodies a certain urine hurtful to their skin and back, envying that any good thereby should ever come to mankinde; and therefore seeing they naturally know the manifold uses of their own hides, here is the cunning of her hunting, to cause her first of all to render her urine, and afterward to take her, for the urine maketh the thornes of her back to fall off every day, and therefore they take this course for their last, refuge. But in these cases the Hunters must poure upon the Hedge-hog warm water, for feeling warmth she presently unfolds her self, and lyeth open; which the Hunter must observe, and instantly take her by one of her hinder legs, so hanging her up till she be killed with famine; otherwise there cometh no benefit by her taking.

With the same skin flead off, brushes are made for garments, so that they complain ill which affirm, that there is no good or profitable condition coming to mankind by this beast. Again this is to be reserved and used for dressing of flax (as *Massarius* saith) and also it is set upon a Javeline at the dore to drive away Dogs. In ancient time they did not eat the flesh of Hedge-hogs, but now a dayes men eat thereof, (of them which are of the swinish kind) When the skin is off their bodies, they scald it a little in Wine or Vinegar, afterward lard it and put it upon a spit, and there let it be roasted, and afterwards eaten, but if the head be not cut off at one blow, the flesh is not good.

The Epithets belonging to this beast are not many; it is called red, sharp, marine, volible, and rough, whereupon *Erasmus* said,

Ex hirco in lævem nunquam mutabis Echinum.

And thus much for the natural and moral parts of this beast. Now followeth the medicinall. Ten sprigs of Lawrel, seven grains of Pepper, and of *Opepanax*, as big as a Pease, the skin of the ribs of a Hedge-hog, dryed and beaten cast into three cups of Water and warmed, so being drunk of one that hath the Colick, and let rest, he shall be in perfect health; but with this exception, that for a man it must be the membrane of a male Hedge-hog, and for a woman a female.

The same membrane or the body of all Hedge-hogs burnt to ashes, hath power in it of cleansing, digesting, and detracting, and therefore it is used by Physitians for taking down of proud swelling wounds, and also for the cleansing of Ulcers and Boyles, but specially the powder of the skin hath that virtue; also it being roasted with the head, and afterwards beat unto powder and anointed on the head with hony, cureth the *Alopecias*.

The same powder restoreth hair upon a wound if it be mingled with Pitch, and if you add thereunto Bears grease, it will restore unto a bald man his head of hair again, if the place be rubbed untill it be ready to bleed. The same powder cureth the Pistula, and some mingle red Snails with this dust, applying it in a plaister to Ruptures and Swellings in the cods, and being mingled with oil by anointment, it taketh away the burles in the face, and being drunk in wine is a remedy against the pains of the reins or the water betwixt the skin and the flesh.

A suffumigation made of a Hedge-hogs skin, under them that have their Urine stopped, by Gods help (saith my Author) the stopping shall be removed, if it proceed not from the stone, nor from an impostume. The flesh salted, dryed, and beat to powder, and so drunk with sweet Vinegar, helpeth the pain in the reins, the beginning of Dropsies, Convulsions, and Leprosies, and all those affections which the *Grecians* call *Cachectæ*. The Mountain Hedge-hog is better then the domestical, having prickles like Needles points, but legs like to the other: the meat is of better taste, and doth more help to the stomach, softning the belly, and provoking the Urine more effectually, and all this which is attributed to Hedge-hogs is much more powerful in the Porcupine.

The Hedge-hog salted and eaten is good against the Leprosie, the Cramp, and all sickness in the Nerves and Ptisick and pain in the belly, rising of windiness and difficulty of digestion: the powder anointed on Women with childe, always keepeth them from abortment. The flesh being stale given to a mad Man, cureth him; and being eaten keepeth one from the Strangury; also being drunk in wine, expelleth the stone in the bladder, and is good against the Quotidian Feaver, and the bitings of

Serpents. The fat of a Hedge-hog stayeth the flux of the bowels: If the fat with warm water and hony be gargarized, it amendeth a broken and hoarse voice; the left eye being fryed with Oil, yeeldeth a liquor which causeth sleep, if it be infused into the ears with a quill. The gall with the brain of a Bat and the milk of a Dog, cureth the reins; likewise, the said gall doth not suffer uncomely hairs to grow again upon the eye-browes, where once they have been pulled up. It maketh also a good eye salve.

Warts of all sorts are likewise taken away by the same; the milt sod and eaten with meat, it healeth all pains in the milt, and the reins dryed are good against a Leprosie or Ptisick coming by Ulcer, or the difficulty of Urine, the Bloudy flux and the Cough. The dung of a Hedge-hog fresh, and *Sandaracha* with Vinegar and liquid pitch, being layed to the head, stayeth the falling away of the hair.

When a man is bitten with a mad Dog, or pricked with prickles of a Hedge-hog, his own Urine laid thereunto with a spunge or wool, is the best cure: or if the thornes stick in the wound of his foot, let him hold it in the warm Urine of a Man, and it shall easily shake them forth: and *Albertus* and *Rasis* affirm, that if the right eye of a Hedge-hog be fryed with the oil of *Alderne* or Linseed, and put in a vessel of red brasse, and afterward anoint his eyes therewith, as with an eye-salve, he shall see as well in the dark as in the light. And thus I will conclude this discourse with one story, that a Hedge-hog of the earth was dedicated to the good God among the foolish *Pagans*, and the water Hedge-hog to the evill, and that once in the City of *Phrygia* called *Azanium*, when a great famine troubled the inhabitants, and no sacrifice could remove it; one *Euphorbus* sacrificed a Hedge-hog, whereupon the famine removed, and he was made Priest, and the City was called *Traganos* upon the occasion of that sacrifice.

OF THE HORSE.

When I consider the wonderful work of God in the creation of this Beast, enduing it with a singular body and a noble spirit, the principal whereof is a loving and dutiful inclination to the service of Man; wherein he never faileth in Peace nor War, being every way more neer unto him for labour and travel: and therefore more dear (the food of man only excepted) we must needs account it the most noble and necessary creature of all four-footed Beasts, before whom no one for multitude and generality of good qualities is to be preferred, compared or equalled, whose commendations shall appear in the whole discourse following.

It is called in *Hebrew, Sui*, and a Mare *Susah*, the which word some derive from *Sis*, signifying Joy; the *Syrians* call it *Rekesh* and *Soustas*; the *Arabians, Ranica*; and the *Caldeans, Ramakim, Susuatha*; the *Arabians, Bagel*; the *Persians, Asbaca*; the *Grecians, Hippos*, and at this day *Alogo*; the *Latins, Equus*, and *Caballus*; the *Italians* and *Spaniards, Cavallo*; the *French, Chevall*; the *Germans, Kossz*; the *Bohemians, Kun*; the *Illyrians, Kobyla*; the *Polonians, Konii*.

It is also profitable to consider the reason of some of these names, both in the *Latin* and *Greek* tongue; and first of all *Equus* seemeth to be derived, *Ab æqualitate*, from equality; because they were first used in Charets and draughts, and were joyned together being of equal strength, legs and stature; *Caballus* seemeth to be derived from the *Greek* word *Caballes*, which was a common name for ordinary Hackney-horses, and

Horses of carriage, whereupon *Seneca* commendeth *Marcus Cato*, that in his triumph of Censorship, *Uno Caballo contentum et ne toto quidem, partem enim sarcinæ ab utroque latere dependentes occupabant*; that is to say, that he was contented with one Horse for his own saddle, and yet not totally one neither, for the packes that hang on either side of him, possessed the greatest part, and the true derivation of this word, seemeth to accord with *Caxe*, which signifyeth a manger, and *Alis* aboundance, because riding Horses are more plentifully fed, and these Horses were also used for plowing, according to the saying of *Horace*;

Optat ephippia bos piger, optat arare Caballus.

The *Grecians* call it *Hippos*, which seemes to be derived from standing upon his feet, and this beast only seemeth to be one of the number of them, which are called *Armenta*.

And besides all Histories are filled with appellative names of Horses, such as these are, *Alastor, Aethon, Nicteus,* and *Orneus,* the Horses of *Pluto. Aetha* a Mare of *Agamemnon* remembred by *Homer. Aethion, Statio, Eous, Phlego, Pyrois;* the Horses of the Sun: *Lampus, Podargus, Xampus, Arnon,* the Horses of *Erymus:* by whose aid *Hercules* is said to overcome *Cygnus,* the Son of *Mars: Balius, Xanthus,* and *Padasus,* the Horses of *Achilles. Boristenes,* for whom *Adrianus* made a grave (as *Dion* writeth) *Bromius, Cærus, Calydon, Camphasus, Cnasius, Corithe,* and *Herpinus,* two names of *Britain* Horses cited by *Martial* and *Gillius. Cylarus,* the swift Horse of *Castor, Dimos,* and *Phobos,* the Horses of *Mars. Euriole, Glaucus,* and *Sthenon,* the Horses of *Neptune, Parthenia,* and *Euripha,* Mares belonging to the *Centaurs* of *Hippodamia,* slain by *Ornomaus. Harpe,* another Mare. *Phœnix,* and *Corax,* the Horses of *Eleosthenes. Epidaminus,* who wan the prizes in the sixty sixth *Olympiade,* and caused a statue to be made in *Olympus,* and his said Horses and Chariot called *Pantarces,* and beside these, other *Cnacias* and *Samus.*

Also *Podarces, Rhœbus, Strymon, Tagus, Theron, Thoes, Volneris,* which was a Horse of *Prasinum,* and it is repoted, that *Verus* the Emperor so much affected this Horse, that he not only caused him to be brought into his own Palace, and to have his meat alway given in his presence, but made of him a picture with a manger, wherein were Grapes and Corn, from whence came the first Golden Horses or prizes of Chivalry;

Primus equum volucrem Massyli munera regis
Haud spernenda tulit: —— ——

Unto these may be added the affected names of Poets in love of their favorites, as *Rholandus, Vegiantinus, Baiardus,* the Horse of *Rainaldus, Rubicanus* of *Argalifas, Hippogrysus* of *Rugerius, Frontinus* and *Fratalatus* of *Sacrapan,* and *Rondellius* of *Oliverius.*

The Epithets that belong to Horses, are either general or particular, the general may be rehearsed in this place, such as these are following; brasse-footed, continual, horn-footed, sounding-footed, foming, bridle-bearer, neighing, maned, dusty, four-footed, fretting, saddle-bearing, watery, or sweating, whole-footed; and many such others both among the *Greeks* and *Latins,* which howsoever they may contain divers Allegories in them, and therefore may seem to be figuratively sed down, yet I thought good being of other opinion to reckon them in the beginning, that so the Reader may consider, that I would be unwilling to omit any thing in this story, which might any way tend to the dignity of the subject we intreat of, or the expressing of his nature. Wherefore we will first of all begin with the description of the natural parts of a good Horse.

The hair of a Horse falleth off every year, the neather eye lid or brow hath no long hairs growing upon it, and therefore *Nicon* that famous painter of *Greece,* when he had most curiously limbed forth a Horses perfection, and faild in no part of nature of art, but only in placing hairs under his eye, for that only fault he received a disgraceful blame.

The hair of the manes ought to be long, that part which groweth betwixt the ears, upon the Temples, hanging down betwixt the eyes, the *Grecians* term *Procomion,* the *Latins, Caprona,* and in *English* it may be called a fore-top, which is granted to Horses not only for ornament sake, but also for necessity to defend their eyes. The Horses are naturally proud of these locks and manes, as may appear by those Mares which are kept for procreation of Mules, by copulation with Asses, which at the first despise to ingender with those shaveling and short haired Stalions. Wherefore their keepers shave off their manes, and their fore-tops, afterwards leading them to the waters, wherein while the Mares behold their own deformity, they grow so shamed, dejected, and discouraged, that ever after they admit with quietness the Asses to cover them. Therefore it is never good to cut the mane or the fetter-locks, except necessity require, for the mane and fore-top is an ornament to the neck and head, and the fetter-locks to the legs and feet: and he that keepeth Horses must as well regard to have them comely for outward grace, as strong and able for necessary labour. Many use to cut the necks of their riding Horses, even as they do of their drawing Horses, which thing although it may seem to be done for greater encrease, and farther growth of hair, yet is it unseemly for an honest rider: some again cut it to stand compass like a bow, and many use the *Armenian* fashion, cutting the Mane by rowes, leaving some longer then other, as it were the batlements of a Church; but the best fashion of all is the *Persian* cut, whereby the one half of the thickness is cut away on the left side, and the other on the right side smoothly turned over and combed, according to the saying of *Virgil*:

Densa juba & dextro jactata recumbit in armo.

But if the Horse be double maned, and so the hair fall half on the one side, and half on the other, then cut all the middle hairs away, and leave both the sides whole; for such was the intention of the *Parthians*. In a Colt or young fole, the hinder part is higher then the forepart, but as he grows in years, so likewise the forepart groweth higher then the hinder.

This beast hath two bones in his head, and other two descending from his forehead to the Nostrils, two inferiour Gumbes, or cheek-bones, forty teeth, that is to say, four and twenty grinders, four canine, and twelve biting teeth; there are seven crosse ribs in his neck, and seven from his reins to his hole, his tail hath twelve commissures, and two *Ragulæ* in his fore-shoulders, from his shoulders to his legs other two, from his legs to his knees two more, in his knees there are two supporters, and from the shin to the Articles two more, there are sixteen small bones in the bottom of his hoof, and but one in his brest, in the inward parts there are six and twenty ribs, from the hinder parts to the top of his reins, the two grinding bones; and from them to the hinder part of the head there are two more, and two little ribs from the upper part of the thigh to the *Gamba*, and from thence to the hairs of the pasterns, there are two, and the little ones to the hooves sixteen; so all the bones in number are accounted a hundred and seventy.

Now it followeth to declare the measure and number of the members; there are twelve steps or degrees in the roof of his mouth, his tongue is half a foot long, the upper lip hath twelve inches, the under lip five, every one of the cheeks ten: from the fore-lock to the Nostrils he hath one foot in length, his two ears contain six inches, and his eyes four inches a piece. From his fore-lock to the *Mercurius*, there are contained eight inches, the back-bone containeth three and thirty crosse ribs. From the convulsion of the reins to the top of the tail, are twelve commissures, the length of his *Sagula* containeth also twelve inches, from his shoulders to his legs six, from his legs to his knees a foot in length, from the Articles to the hoofs four inches, in his whole length six feet. And this is the stature of a couragious and middle Horse, for I know there are both bigger and lesser.

The quality and the measure of the nerves or sinews is this, from the middle nostrils through the head, neck and back-bone, is a dubble file or threed to the top of the tail, which containeth twelve foot in length. The two broad sinews in the neck do contain four-foot, from the shoulders to the knees, there are two sinews, from the knee to the bottom of the foot there are four sinews, in the fore-legs there are ten sinews, in the hinder-legs there are other ten sinews, from the reins to the stones there are four sinews, so the whole number amounteth to thirty four. Consequently the number of the veins is to be declared. In the palat or roof of the mouth, their are two veins, under the eyes other two, in the brest other two, and in the legs other two, four under the pasternes, two in the ancles, four in the crown of the pasternes, four out of the thighes, two out of the loins, two out of the Gambaes, one out of the rail, and two in the womb or Matrix, so the whole number is nine and twenty.

There are certain veins above the eyes which are divided in Horses, wherein they are let bloud, by making to them small incisions, the bloud also is taken out of the veins, in the palat or roof of the mouth. There was an ancient custome of letting Horses bloud upon Saint *Stevens* day, by reason of many holy dayes one succeeding another, but that custom is now grown out of use. Also some take bloud out of the Matrix veins, but that is not to be admitted in Geldings, because with their stones they lose a great part of their heat, excepting extream necessity, but out of the palat bloud may be let every moneth, and stallions when they are kept from Mares if the vein of their mouths be opened, fall into blindness, although it is no good part of husbandry to let them bleed that year, wherein they admit copulation, for the vacuation of bloud and seed, is a double charge to nature.

But the Organical vein of the neck, is the best letting of bloud, both in stoned and gelded Horses. The later Leaches make incision in the great vein called *Fontanella*, and in *Inen Thymus* or *Jugulis*. The eyes of a Horses are great or glassie, and it is reported by *Augustus*, that his eyes were much more brighter then other mens, resembling Horses: these eyes see perfectly in the night, yet their colour varieth as it doth in Men, according to the caprine and glazie humour. And sometimes it falleth out, that one, and the same Horse hath two eyes of distinct colours. When the eyes of a Horse hang outward, he is called *Exophthalmos*. Such fair eyes are best, for *Bucephalus* the Horse of *Alexander* had such eyes, but when the eyes hang inward, they are called *Cœloph-Thalmoi*, and the *Parthians* count them the best Horses, whose eyes are of divers colours, and are therefore called *Heteroph Thalmoi*, because the breed of that Horse was said to take the beginning from the *Parthians*, and the reason why the people loved not these Horses, was, because they were fearful, and apt to run away in wars.

The ears of a Horse, are tokens and notes of his stomach, as a tail is to a Lion, his teeth are changed, yet they grow close together like a mans. It is a hard thing for a Horse to have a good mouth, except his stallion teeth be pulled out, for when he is chafed or heated, he cannot be held back by his rider, but disdaineth the bridle: wherefore after they be three year and a half old, those teeth ought to be pulled forth. In old age, a Horses teeth grow whiter, but in other creatures blacker.

506

A Mare hath two udders betwixt her thighes, yet bringeth forth but one at a time: many of the Mares have no paps at all, but only they which are like their Dams. In the heart of a Horse there is a little bone, like as in an Oxe, and a Mule; he hath no gall like Mules and Asses, and other whole-footed-beasts, howsoever (some say) it lyeth in his belly; and others, that it cleaveth to his liver, or to the gut-colon. The small guts of a Horse lie near that gut, that so one side of his belly may be free and full of passage; and from hence it cometh, that the best Horses, when they run or travel hard, have a noise or rumbling in their belly. The Hip-bone of a Horse is called by some the haunch, as the *Arabians* say; the tail (because therewith he driveth away flies) is called *Muscartum*, it ought to be long, and full of hairs. The legs are called *Gambæ* of *Campo*, signifying treading: the hoofs of a Horse ought neither to be high nor very low, neither ought the Horse to rest upon his anckles, and those Horses which have straight bones in the Articles of their hinder knees, set hard on the ground, and weary the Rider: but where the bones are short in the same places, as they are in Dogs, there the Horse also breaketh, and woundeth one leg with another; and therefore such Horses are called *Cynopodæ*. They have also quick flesh in their hoofs, and their hoofs are sometimes called horns, upon which for their better travel, men have devised to fallen iron plates or shooes. This hoof ought to be hard and hollow, that the Beast may not be offended, when he goeth upon stones; they ought not to be white, nor broad, but almost kept moist, that so they may travel the better, having strong feet, hard and sound hoofs, for which cause the *Græcians* call them *Eupodes*.

Forasmuch as it is requisite for every man to provide him Horses of the best race, and their kindes are divers in most places of the world, so the coursers of Horses do many times beguile the simpler sort of buyers, by lying and deceitful affirmation of the wrong Countreys of the best Horses, which thing bringeth a confusion: for there are as many kindes of Horses as Nations. I will therefore declare severally the Countreys breeding the Horses, for the Region and air maketh in them much alteration, that so the Reader may in a short view see a muster of Horses made of all Nations. The Wilderness of *Acarnania*, and *Etolia* is as fit for feeding Horses as *Thessaly*. The Horses of the *Greeks, Armenians*, and *Trojans* are fit for war, of the *Greckish* I will speak more afterward.

507

Alexandria was wont to take great delight in Horses, and combates of Horses: *Apollonius* writeth *Lib. 5. Æthiopia* (as it is reported) breedeth Horses having wings and horns. *Varro* commendeth the *Apulian* Horses, and *Volatteranus* writeth, that they and the Horses of *Rosea* are most fit for war: he meaneth above all the Horses of *Italy*. There have been very fruitful pastures in *Arcadia* for cattel, especially for breeding Horses and Asses that are Stallions, for the procreation of Mules, and the breed of the *Arcadian* Horses excelleth. The same man preferreth the Horses of *Thessalia* and the *Greekish* Horses, for they are sound of their feet and head, but not of comely Buttocks, they have their back bone whole, great and short.

The latter two I might have referred to the whole body of the Horse. The Horses of *Armenia* are very necessary and convenient for war, for they and the *Capadocians* do breed of the *Parthian* Horses, saving their heads are somewhat bigger. Of the *Hackney* or common Horses, I will say more afterward, where I touch the difference of Horses, and of their pace. The *Barbarian* Horses are the same as the *Lybian* Horses. *Vegetius* commendeth the Horses of *Toringa* and *Burgundia*, after them of *Vonusci*. *Britain* breedeth little Horses and Amblers. Of Horses that are celebrate of the *Calpian* Mountain: See in the *Spanish*. The Horses of *Cappadocia* and *Armenia* have the breed of the *Parthians*; but their heads are bigger, and are of a most famous Nobility, for that Countrey before any other land, is most commodious for the nourishing of Horses, according to the verses of *Nemesian*:

> *Cappadocumque notas referat generosa propago*
> *Armata, & palmas nuper grex omnis avorum.*

The *Cappadocians* do pay to the *Persians* every year, beside silver, a thousand and five hundred Horses, &c. The *Medes* have the double of these, and they sur-name the *Cappadocians* Horses famous and swift; for he saith, that whiles these are young, they are accounted weak by reason of their young teeth, and their body feeding on milk; but the older they grow, so much the swifter they are, being very couragious, and apt for war and hunting, for they are not afraid of weapons, neither to encounter with wilde Beasts. *Mazaca* is a City of *Cappadocia*, situate under the Mountain *Argæus*, now called *Cæsarea*, as *Eusebius* remembreth in his Chronicles, and from that City cometh the *Mazacenian* Horse, for the *Cappadocian* Horse. And not only the Countrey, but the City it self sometime was called *Cappadocia* from this City or walled Town, I suppose the Horses of *Mazaca* were so called, which *Oppianus* calleth *Mazaci*, of these also and more, I will set down these verses of *Nemesian*:

> *Sit tibi præterea sonipes, Maurusia tellus*
> *Quem mittit, modo sit gentili sanguine firmus,*
> *Quemque coloratus Mizax deserta per arva*
> *Pavit, & assiduos docuit tolerare labores.*
> *Ne pigeat quod turpe caput, deformis & alvus*
> *Est illis, quodque infrenes, quod liber uterque,*
> *Quodque jubis pronos carvix diverberet armos.*
> *Nam flecti facilis, lasci vaque colla secutus*
> *Paret in obsequium lentæ moderamine virgæ.*
> *Verbera sunt præcepta sugæ, sunt verbera fieni.*
> *Quin & promissi spatiosa per æquora campi,*
> *Cursibus acquirunt commoto sanguine vires,*
> *Paulatimque avidos comites post terga relinquunt.*
> *Hand secus effusis Nerei per cærula ventis,*
> *Cum se Threicius Boreas super extulit antro, &c.*
> *Horum tarda venit longi fiducia cursus:*
> *His etiam emerito vigor est juvenilis in ævo.*
> *Nam quæcunque suis virtus bene florius annis,*
> *Non priut est animo quam corpore passa ruina.*

And peradventure *Nem sianus* understood certain Horses of *Lybia*, by the name of the *Mizacian* Horses, when as he joyns them with the *Maurasian* Horses, and calls them painted *Mauzacian* Horses, which agreeth not with *Cappadocian*; writing also, that they are ruled with a stroke of air in stead of a bridle, which thing we have read in Authors writing of the *Massylian* Horses, in the Countrey of *Lybia*, and whereof we will speak when we discourse of the *Lybian* Horses. But the *Cappadocian* Horses are swift and lusty in their old age, as it is related by *Oppianus*. Again, if *Mazacian* Horses be the same that the *Cappadocian* are; what is the reason why *Oppianus* doth name them apt, unless peradventure every *Mazacian* Horse is a *Cappadocian*, and not otherwise? The Horses of *Chalambria*, are so named of a place in *Lybia*; the *Chaonian* Horses are the same with the *Aprirolan* Horses. The *Colophonians* and *Magnetians* do bestow great labour in breeding of Horses; for the *Colophonians* dwell in a plain, as I have read in a certain *Greek* Author. *Strabo lib.* 14. writeth, that the *Colophonians* in times past did abound with Sea-forces, and have much excelled in Horse-men; that wheresoever in any Nation there was waged war, they hired and required the aid of the *Colophonian* Horse-men, and so it was made a common Proverb: *Colophonem addidit. Erasmus.* The Horses of *Crete* are commended by *Oppianus*, and elsewhere. From their loins upward they are as big as the *Cyrenian* Horses, with well set thighes, excellent for the soundness of their feet, and holding their breath a long time in riding, and therefore fit for single races or in Chariots.

The *Epean* Horses are remembred of *Oppianus*, and the *Epeans* are a people of *Achaia*, and the *Achaian* Horses are commended of the same. The *Lipidanean* kinde of Horses is more excellent, and he preferreth the *Thessalian* Horses before those of *Epidauria*, but the *Epicotian* Horses are biting and stubborn: *Absyrtus* saith, that the *Epicotian* Horses, and the *Samerican* and *Dalmatian*, although they are stubborn and will not abide the bridle, and besides are base and contemptible, yet they are bold in war and combates, and therefore the *Epicotian* Horses and the *Sicilian* despise not, if their qualities and comely parts be apparent in them, although sometime he hath run away from the enemy, as the Poet saith:

> *Quamvis sæpe fuga versos ille egerit hostes,*
> *Et patria Epirum referat.* ———

Epiria and *Chaonia*, is also a part of *Epirus Alpestrian*, although sometimes it be taken for the whole Countrey of *Epirus*. The Horses of *Chaonia* are commended, as *Gratius* remembreth, writing of the *Sicilian* Horses, in these verses to this effect, that no man hath presumed to strive with the *Chaonians*, and the *Achaian* hand doth not express their deserts:

───── *Queis Chaonias contendere contra*
Ausit, vix merita quas signat Achaia palma.

There are people of *Arabia* called *Erembi*, which some call *Ichthyophagans*, and *Troglodytans*. *Vegetius* in the third place commendeth the *Frysian* Horses for swiftness, and long continuance of course, after the *Hunnian, Burgundians*. The *French* Horse is the fame that the *Menapians*, and S. *Hierom* writeth, that worldly men are delighted with the *French* Geldings; but *Zachartes* Ass loosed from his bands, rejoyceth good men. *Lucius Apuleius* hath commended the *French* Beasts, for if the young fole be derived of a generous kinde, it is an argument it will prove a Noble Beast.

The *Gelanoian* Horses are a kinde of base Horses, not fit for war; whether this name proceed of a strange Countrey, I have no certain knowledge thereof. There is a certain River in *Sicilia* called *Gelas*, of which Countrey, the Horses are of great value and much set by. And also the *Gelons* are a people of *Scythia*, who in their flight fight upon Horses, of which *Lucanus* writeth to this effect;

> *Massagetes quo fugit equo, fortesque Geloni:* And *Virgil*,
> *Bisaltæ quo more solent, acerque Gelonus,*
> *Cum fugit in Rhodopen, aut in deserta Getarum,*
> *Et lao concretum cum sanguine potat equino.*

Signifying thus much, that the *Massagetes* & valiant *Gelons* fly away upon Horses like the *Bisaltans*, when they fly into *Rhodope*, or into the Wilderness of the *Gelans*, and drink milk mixed with Horse-bloud for hunger and famine: But these fearful Horses are not meet for war. *Germania* hath greater Horses and hard trotters, whose pace is very hard and troublesome. The *Getican* Horses run most swiftly. The Horses of the *Greeks* have good sound broad feet, and of a great body, a comely fine head, their fore-part somewhat high of stature, straight and well compacted, and of a well fashioned body, but the joyning of their buttocks not so agreeable and answerable to the rest: they are most swift and couragious, yet notwithstanding in all *Greece* the *Thessalian* Horses are most esteemed; *Nemesianus* writeth also of the

Greekish Horses: *Greece* therefore yeeldeth choice Horses, and well hoofed. In *Helvetia* the Horses are fitted, and very expert in war, and especially the *Algecian* Horses, which will last and continue a long time.

In *Spain* also the Horses are of a great stature of body, well proportioned and straight, having a fine head; the joynts of their bodies very well divided, set apart, and ready or flexible, simple and short buttocks, but not very strong and comely. They are strong and able to sustain the undergoing or compassing of journeys; neither are they slender bodied or subject to leanness; but they are nothing nimble for course, as shall appear by the words of the Authors following, neither are they spurred when they are ridden: from their growing even to their middle age, they are pliant, and easie to be handled, afterward they wax wilde and biting. The *Cappadocian* Horse is renowned, the like, or the next triumph or victory have the *Spanish* Horses in running the ring. Neither doth *Sivilia* yeeld Horses inferior for the ring then those: and *Africa* is accustomed to bring forth the most swift Horses by copulation with the *Spanish* bloud to the use of the saddle.

Oppianus saith that their *Iberian* Horses are more excellent, and do so much surpass other Horses in swiftness, how much the Eagle or the winding Hawk in the air, and the Dolphin in the Sea, excelleth other birds and fishes; but they are small, and of little strength, and no courage: although *Absyrtus* affirmeth (if you read him well) that they are of a great stature of body, they being rid but a little way do lose their swiftness of pace: they are of a comely body; but their hoofs are not hollow or hard.

The *Spanish* Horses are desired of great Princes and Peers, and the *Magnates*, because their opinion is, that they are swift and nimble; and out of *Spain* they are respected for lightness and elegancy. The judgement of the Ancients for the general breed of Horses, was this; that the greatest Horses are bred from the third Climate, to the end of the sixt; and most of all in *Spain*: yet we have seen stronger and bigger Horses bred in the seventh Climate, and those more able to endure labour then those that are under the third or fourth climate.

The Horses of the *Celtiberans* somewhat a dusty colour: and they change if they be transported into the farther *Spain*; and the *Parthian*

Horses are like them in regard they excel in nimbleness and dexterity of running, whereof *Martial* writeth thus, *Videbis altam Liciane Bilbilim, equis & armis nobilem*: which *Bilbilis* is a City of *Celtiberia*. Of the *Callacians* and *Gennets*, we will speak also in the *Spanish* Horses that are bred in the *Calpian* Mountain, afterward, when we entreat of the differences of Horses according to their degree.

The *Huns* bring up their Horses hardly, able to endure cold and hunger, and they have great and crooked heads, staring eyes, strait nostrils, broad chaps, and strong and rough necks, and long manes down to their legs; great ribs, straight backs, bushy tails, strong shanks or legs, small feet, full and wide hoofs, their flanks hollow, and their whole body full of holes. There is no fatness in their hanch or buttocks, they have no strings in their sinews or arteries, and they exceed in length more then in height, having great bellies hanging down, big-boned, and leanness (which is a deformity in other Horses) in these it sheweth their stateliness: their courage is moderate and wary, and these are able to endure wounds. These *Hunnian* Horses elsewhere he calleth them *Hunnican* Horses, and the same in times past *Huns*: but they are called now a days *Ungarian* Horses.

The Companies or Armies of *Huns*, wandering up and down with most swift Horses, filled all things with slaughter and terrour. They are biting and kicking Horses, as most *Pannonicks* are, (for they call *Pannonia* at this day *Hungaria*) of which there is a Proverb of Malignity sprung up; *Non nisi irritati opinione aut offensæ metu ferociunt*: that is to say; They wax not stern, or rage not, but either by opinion, or fear of offence, affirming that the *Pannonians* are very fit for War. There is not any that can hold and constrain or draw the bridles in, or loose them forth, that rideth an *Indian* Horse when he pranseth and runneth violently, but such a one that hath been trained up from his childehood in the skill of Horses: these men have accustomed to hold them with the bridle, and also to break their wilfulness by snaffles or hits, and those that are well skilled in handling Horses, do compell them from their unruliness, as restrain them within a small circuit. Yet notwithstanding to make this circle and finish it, it requireth the help of hands, and it is a great skil belonging to Horsemen.

They which are most skilful of this Art, and cunning doers of it, know very well how to bring their course into a circle, whose compass is not to be regarded chiefly when it can bear but two Souldiers fighting together at one time. There are among the *Indian Psyllans* (for there are also other *Africks* of that name) Horses bred no bigger then Rams, and they say that in *India* there are Horses with one horn, of which horn drinking cups may be made, having this vertue in them; that if you put poyson into them, and a man drink thereof, it shall not hurt him, because the horn doth drive away or expell the evill or poyson. Whereof you shall see more at large in the History of *Monocerotes*: and *Ælianus* himself elsewhere, and *Philes* following him, write the same thing of a cup made of the horn of an *Indian* Ass, having one horn.

The *Istrian* Horses are of good able feet, very straight, whole backt, and hollow; but swift of course. The *Moores* Horses (saith *Oppianus*) are most excellent, as well to hold out long courses, as also to endure hard labours: the *Lybians* next unto these are of a most durable celerity: they are shaped alike, except that the *Lybian* Horses are big, and of a longer body, having thicker ribs and sides, and their brest is larger before on their crest; they can easily abide the heat of the Sun and daily thirst.

Africa hath been accustomed to put the most swiftest Horses of the *Spanish* brood to the use of the saddle: (and *Livius* saith) in *lib* 23. that it was a custom to the *Numidians*, being in battel, to lead two Horses together, and in manner of vauters oftentimes, in the most sharp conflict could leap from the weary Horse to a fresh, (so great was the dexterity of the rider, and the docibility of the beast.) From *Tunis* of *Africa*, *Massalia*, and *Numidia*, there are also brought very singular Horses, passing for running, which the common people call *Barbary* Horses. The *Massylians* (a people of *Lybia*) have very good Horses, which they govern with a rod without a bridle, from whence *Virgil* in his fourth of his *Æneidos*, calleth them untamed and wilde *Numides*: and *Silius* saith also, the *Numides* a Nation having no skill of the bridle, do leap up and down, here, and there, and every where:

> *Hic passim exultant Numidæ gens inscia freni,*
> *Quis inter geminas per ludum nobilis aures*
> *Quadrupedem flect it non cedens virga lupatis.*

Also the rod rules the *Massylian* Horse: the same *Nemesianus* writeth of those which he calleth *Mazacians*, (as I have before spoken of the *Cappadocian* Horses). The *Dorcadian* Horses although they are of a marvellous swiftness, yet they are inferiour to the *Lybian* Horses in running. The *Lybian* Mares are taken with a pipe, and by these allurements they are made tame and leave off all wilde qualities, and whithersoever the pipe shall allure them, thither they follow, and the Shepheard when he stands, they leave off marching forward; and if he sing more pleasantly, they are so delighted with it, that they cannot hold tears. The Shepheards of these flocks, make their Shepheards pipe of the tree (called *Rhododaphus*) the sound whereof delighteth those that go before the herd. *Gratius* also writeth to this effect;

Fingit equos Pisis Numidæ, &c. ⸺
Audax & patiens operum genus ille: vigebit
Centum actus spatiis, atque eluctabitur iram,
Nec magni culius sterilis quodcunque remisit
Terra sui, tenuesque sitis producere rivi.

Although the place be not perfect, yet that that is spoken concerning the *Numidian* and *Lybian* Horses, is manifested as well by the words of *Oppianus* before recited, as also by that which *Ælianus* setteth down for (saith he) I have heard these things touching the *Lybian* Horses of the men of that Nation, that of all other Horses they are the swiftest, and that they have no sense of their labours, being lank by reason of their slenderness and thinness of their shape, and are wholly of themselves fit to endure their masters negligence, for their masters give them no meat or fodder, neither doth any man rub or dress them with the curry combe after they have laboured or travelled: neither do they lay any litter or straw for them to ly on, nor pare their hoofs, but so soon as they have ended their journey, leaping off their backs, they turn them to seek their food, and in like manner the men of *Lybia* worn with leanness, and all besmeared with filth, do ride on Horses of this sort.

The Horses and Oxen of *Africa*, which dwell between *Getulia* and us, are as ours, that is, having longer lips, (the Interpreters translate it hoofs.) Their Kings take delight in troops of Horses, so that there are numbred to him every year four hundred thousand Colts.

The *Chalambrian Lybians* are before spoken of and the *Nasavions* we will speak of hereafter. *Barbary* breedeth very few Horses; but the *Arabians* which inhabit in the Desert, and the people of *Lybia* do breed very many, and they do not so much accustom them to journeys and warfare, as to hunting, and feeding them with Camels milk only twice a day and night, whereby they keep them fine, but very lean, and in the time of grass they turn them out to feed in the field, but they ride not on them.

The Horses of *Massylia* are equal with the *Lybians*. The people of *Magnetia* have been renowned in feeding and bringing up Horses, and they are very skilful in combate on Horse-back (as *Lucanus* saith.) The *Magnetians* are famous for Horses, and the Nation of *Nycata* for Oars: *Magnetia* is a countrey of *Macedonia*, bordering upon *Thessaly*, so the City and Countrey of *Asia* lyeth toward *Mæandrus*. *Oppianus* commendeth the *Magnetian* Horses. The *Moores* fight often on Horse back with Spears, but their Horses are naked, and their bridles made of rushes.

The *Massylians* following the *Lybians* (for the most part) are furnished after that manner, and they resemble others, having little Horses, both swift, obedient, and easily to be ruled with a rod.

The collars of their Horses are made of wood or hair, whereby the bridles hang. The principal Horses of *Barbary* are not swift, but in respect they live on fodder, they are more handsome and better in flesh, which they use in eminent danger, when it standeth them upon to escape the rage of their enemies. Thus far I have related the words of *Oppianus*, touching the nourishing of Horses, among the *Lybians*, where he sheweth that they are all alike, both in shape and other proportion. Touching the *Nemesian* Horses, they are all one with the *Maurans* and *Marusans*, (as *Strabo* witnesseth) calling them nimble and swift kindes amongst the *Moores*.

The *Sicilians* are swifter then the *Moores*, and the *Moores* are of a more valiant courage then the *Sicilians*, or some such like other thing, who are furnished with yellow colours, and shew to the eye most shining and splendant, and which is more, they only desire the roaring of a Lyon, for which when they come to other wilde Beasts by way of hunting, he commendeth them to be excellent: then he saith that the yellow is the best colour.

In the Countrey of *Mauritania* are great store of Lyons, and of the *Nazacanos* we have spoke of before sufficiently. The *Median* Horses are of exceeding greatness, and the men of that Countrey are so bewitched with the rich attire and shape of their bodies, and also their Horses being so loose with superfluity or rankness, that the Horses take delight in their Masters, both in greatness and in fairness of body, and such costly furniture upon their backs, that they seem to perceive their own stature and comeliness. The *Medes* every year by way of custome pay three thousand Horses. *Herodotus* also calleth the *Nisean* Horses the *Medes*, whereof more shall be spoke afterwards. The *Menapians* amongst our Country-men, the only men which I suppose were once call'd *French* of *Cæsar*, and the *Rugians*, (as Warriours) for the most part are in estimation. I also finde that the *Rugians* inhabited that Countrey which is now called *Rugerland*, and that *Paulus Diaconus* remembreth them, *lib.* 1.

Touching the affairs of *Longobardus*, there are that say they departed into *Mechelburgia*. These are the right off spring of the *Germans* (saith *Althametus*), they are counted as *Germans*, both in language and vertue. *Gratius* writeth of the *Marcibians*, saying the *Marcibians* scarse yeeld their tough neck to the sword. *Virgill* also declareth *Mycenia* to be a Countrey of most notable Horses: and *Gratius* commendeth a Horse fit for hunting highly in these verses:

> *Consule Penei qualis perfunditur amne*
> *Thessalus, aut patriæ quem conspexere Mycenæ*
> *Glaucum, nempe ingens, nempe ardua fundet in auras*
> *Crura, quis Eleas potior lustravit arenas?*
> *Ne tamen hoc attingat opus, jactantior illi*
> *Virtus, quam silvas durumque lacessere Martem.*

The *Mysian* Horses were once great in estimation (as *Camerarius* writeth.) Also the *Nasamonians* are people of *Lybia*, living as spoylers of the ships in the *Syrtes*. Of all these Horses before said, the *Nisæan* Horse is the goodliest, and fittest to carry the body of a King, they are of a passing good shape, an easie pace, and very submissive to the bridle; having a little head, and a long and thick mane, with yellow or brown hairs hanging down on both sides: *Armenia* is very fit for feeding Horses, wherein is a certain medow called *Hippoboans*, by which they make their journey which pass from *Persia* and *Babylon* into the *Caspian* Border, in which place they feed five hundred Mares which belong unto their King.

The *Nisæan* Horses (written with *Jota* and simple *Sigma*, as *Eustathius* writeth) are the most excellent and best; some say that they have their generation from *Germany*, others out of *Armenia*, but they have a certain kinde of shape like the *Parthians*.

In *India* most of their living creatures are far greater then in other places (except Horses) for the *Nisæan* Horses, do exceed the *Indian* Horses, (as *Herodotus* writeth) in his seaventh Book, describeing the *Persian* Horse. Behinde the spears (saith be) came ten Horses in most sumptuous furniture, which were *Nisæans*, so called, because there is a great field named *Nisæus* in the Countrey of *Media*, which yeeldeth Horses of a great stature. After these followed *Jupiters* Chariot drawn with eight Horses, after which *Xerxes* was caryed in a Chariot drawn by *Nisæan* Horses, and by how much the greater the *Lybian* Elephant is then the *Nisæan* Horse, so much the greater are the *Nisæan* Horses then the *Indian* (as the same man saith) in his first Book: but the King was about to offer a white Horse, that is of the *Nisæan* Horses, having a better mark as some expounded.

There are that say that *Nisæus* is a plain of *Persis*, where the most famous and notable Horses are bred. Some interpret it to the yellow *Nisæan* Horse, because all the Horses of *Nisæan* are of this colour. Between *Susinax* and *Bactria*, there is a place which the *Greeks* call [*Nisos*] in which the most singular fine Horses are bred. There are also that suppose they are had from the red Sea, and all those to be of a yellow colour. *Herodotus* writing of *Nisæus*, maketh it a part of *Media*. *Orpheus* also writeth, that there is a place in the red Sea called *Nisa*. *Stephanus* also maketh mention of [*Nisæan Pedion*] with the *Medes*, of which people the Horses are so called. *Cœlius Rhodiginus* reproved a certain man which translated the *Islandish* Horses for the *Nisæan* Horses. *Plutarch* saith that *Pyrrhus* had an apparition of a *Nisæan* Horse armed and furnished with a Rider, that *Alexander* the Great was Captain thereof.

The *Medes* have Colts of a most noble kinde of Horses, which (as antient Writers do teach us, and as we our selves have seen) men when they begin the battel with a fierce encounter are wont to prance valiantly, which are called *Nisæan* Horses.

Touching the *Paphlagonians*, about the education of their Horses, see more among the *Venetians*: The *Parthian* Horses are of a large body, couragious, of a gentle kinde, and most sound of their feet. Concerning those Horses which have but one eye, commended among the *Parthians*, and of those which are distinguished by diversity of colours, from those that come forth first, I have spoke already out of *Absyrtus*, The *Armenian* and *Parthian* Horses are of a swifter pace then the *Sicilians*, and the *Iberi* swifter then the *Parthians*, whereof *Gratius* writeth to this effect:

> *Scilicet & Parthis inter sua mollia rura*
> *Mansit honor: veniat Caudini saxa Taburni,*
> *Garganumque trucem, aut Ligurinas desuper Alpes,*
> *Ante opus excussis cadet unguibus; & tamen illi*
> *Est animus fingetque meas se nisus in artes;*
> *Sed juxta vitium posuit Deus. ———*

That is to say, among the *Parthians* there hath remained honour for their soft Countries; but let him come to the Rocks of *Caudmus*, *Tabernus*, and too rough *Garganus*, or upon the *Ligurian Alpes*, then he will quickly shake off his hoofs, and make a shew of great valiantness. The Horses of the *Celtiberians* are somewhat white; and if they may be brought into *Spain* they change their colour. But the *Parthians* are alike, for they excel all others in nimbleness and dexterity of running: How the *Parthians* do make their pace easie in the trotters and hard footing Horses, after the manner of Geldings, shall be declared afterwards, for *Persia* preferreth these Horses above the censure of their patrimonies as well to carry, (having an easie pace) and being of most excellent dignity: As for their pace it is thick and short, and he doth delight and lift up the Rider, being not instructed by art, but effecteth it by nature.

Amongst these ambling Nags, (called of the *Latines* among the common sort of *Totenarii*) their pace is indifferent, and whereas they are not alike, they are supposed to have something common from both; as it hath been proved: whereof *Vegetius* writeth in this manner.

In a short journey they have the more comeliness and grace in going, but when they travel far, they are impatient, stubborn, and unless they be tamed, will be stubborn against the Rider; and that which is a more greater marvel, when they are chafed, they are of a delightful comeliness, their neck turneth in manner of a Bow, that it seemeth to ly on their breast. The *Pharsalian* Mares evermore bring Foals very like their Syre, and therefore very well so named, *Equæ probæ*. We read of the *Phasian* Horses which receive their name (from the mark or brand of a bird so named) or else because of their excellent beauty and comeliness.

The *Rosean* Horses, *Varro* so nameth of *Rosea*, which *Volatteranus* writeth to be most fit for War: and this *Rosea*, otherwise *Roscea*, *Festus* saith, that it is a Countrey in the coasts of the *Reatians*, so called, because the fields are said to be moist with that dew. The Horses of *Sacæ*, if they happen to throw down their Rider, they forthwith stand still, that they may get up again. *Vegetius* having commended the *Persian* Horses saith, that the *Armenians* and *Sapharens* do follow next. This *Saphirine* verily is an Island in the *Arabian* coast, and the people of *Saphiria* lye beside *Pontus*. The Horses of *Epirota*, *Salmarica*, and *Dalmatia*, although they will not abide to be bridled, yet they shew that they are warlike by their legs.

The *Sardinian* Horses are nimble and fair, but lesser then others. The *Sarmatican* kind of Horses is feat and well fashioned in this kind, very fit for running, unmixt, having a well set body, a strong head, and a comely neck. Some Horses they call *Aetogenes*, from a certain mark which they have in their shoulders and colour, which the *Sarmatians* do take unto themselves as very good, with which they do contend about their cruelty, wherefore they imploy them in warlike out-rodes, but those that bear the Eagles mark in their buttocks and tail, they are disallowed of them; and they report that they mark them so, because they will not use them, by reason lest they should quickly be destroyed or run into some trouble.

The *Sarmatians* when they entend any long journeys, the day before they keep them fasting, giving them a little drink, and so they will ride them a hundred and fifty miles continually going. These Horses are very fit for War, and many of them are sound gelded in their tender age, and they say they never lose their teeth. It is a custome of *Scythia* and *Sarmatia* to geld their Horses to make them more gentle: they are swift, little, and fierce, but very stubborn and untamed; neither doth *Circo*, (situate near *Sicilia*) breed Horses inferiour to the *Spanish*, as *Vegetius* writeth. The *Epirotan* and *Siculian* Horses are not to be despised, if they were well bred and educated, they want not comeliness and good qualities.

The *Siculian* Horses are most swift. *Lilybæum* is a promontory of *Sicilia* lying towards *Lybia*, which a certain verse maketh more plain: but as I understand it is the Three-clift-topt-mountain *Ætna*, which casteth forth fire, and covereth the carkcase of *Enceladus* the Giant, lying there under (whereof *Oppianus* writeth) and some others also. But (saith he) the *Armenians* and *Parthians*, have swifter coursers by far, then the *Siculians*. Now, let us hear *Gratius* himself, discoursing of the *Siculian* Horses, as well as of the *Lybican*.

> *Sic & Strymonio facilis tutela Bisaltæ,*
> *Possent Ætneas utinam se ferre per artes.*
> *Qui ludus Siculis: quid tum si turpia colla,*
> *Aut tenuis dorso curvatur spina? per illos*
> *Cantalus Graiis Agragas, victæque fragosum*
> *Nebroden liquere feræ. O quantus in armis*
> *Ille meis, cujus dociles pecuaria fœtus*
> *Sufficient, queis Chaonias contendere contra*
> *Ausit, vix merita quas signat Achaia palma.*

But as for *Gratius*, I suspect the place to be unperfect; for *Agragas* is a Mountain of *Sicilia*, having a Town situate in the top of it, bearing the same name, where their Ancestors were wont to nourish and bring up the best Horses. There is also in *Sicilia* a Mountain called *Nebrodes*, which some think to be so called by reason of the plenty of Dear, but they have no Author for it, and as for the printed Book of *Gratius*, I finde it expresseth it not so well as *Virgill* setteth it down, *saying*, that *Agragas* was a breeder of most couragious and notable Horses: but yet *Servius* saith, (according to *indarus*) that the *Agrigentines* in times past sent their Horses to the justing or combates of *Græcia*, returning with victory from thence, and we have also read, that in *Cappadocia* whole troops of Horses have been destroyed. The men of *Delphos* by the answer of *Apollo* got herds and great store of Horses from *Agrigentine*, and those were excellent. *Aristophanes* calleth those great *Ætnean* Horses (*Canthari*) either of the greatness of the Mountain, or else great *Canthars* are bred in it, or of the Horses of *Ætna*, being notable for swiftness and running. The Horses that are bred in *Creet* and *Cappadocia* are also most excellent.

In *Greece* there are most notable Horses of *Thessaly*, which *Absyrtus* saith be the best in all *Greece*. The words of *Gratius* the Poet speaking of the *Thessalian* Horses are before recited. The Mares of *Aametus* were the most excellent, but as *Homer* reporteth the *Thessalian* were before them. The Solitude or Wilderness of *Arcananus* is as commodious to feed Horses, as *Thessalia*. It is certain that *Thessalia* excels with Horses, from whence *Xerxes* is said to have made a combate, that he might try his Horses there where he understood the best breed of *Greekish* Horses to be, and from whence this proverb arose, *Decernatur equa Thessalia* (*viz.*) let the *Thessalian* Mare be tryed by battail, a proverb of excellent worth, because in old time the chiefest praise was of the *Thessalian* Mares: which is very apparent by the Oracle that was delivered to the *Æginensians*. *Suidas* relateth (but I know not out of what Author) that *Thessalia* hath excellent Horsemen; *Thracia* expert shooters; and *India* light armour: so hath likewise *Creet* and *Caria*.

Erasmus writeth, that *Thessalia* is most fit to feed Horses, who do far excel the *Arcadians* and *Epidaures*, as *Strabo* witnesseth, *lib.* 8. *Caesar* was said (when he was Dictator) to have made the first shew among the *Romans* of the Horses, fighting against Buls, and killing them, whereof *Lucanus* writeth thus:

Thessalius sonipes bellis feralibus omen.

That is to say; the *Thessalian* Horse is profitable for fence and deadly conflicts. There is also in *Thessalia* a City (named *Pella*) from whence I deem the *Pellæan* Horses are so called of *Gratius*, yet there be other places called *Pella* (as *Macedonia* and *Achaia*) whereof *Gratius* writeth thus:

> *Spadices vis Pellæi valuere Cerauni,*
> *Et tibi devotæ magnum pecuaria Cyrrhæ*
> *Phœbe decus nostras agere in sacraria tonsas.*

Which (*Cerauni*) are Mounts of *Epirus*, and *Cyrrha* is a Town of *Phocis*, situate at the foot of the hill *Parnassus*, where *Apollo Cyrrhæus* was worshipped. The *Tyrrheans* being excellent warriors, are commended of *Oppianus*. Out of the Islands of the *Tyrrhenian* Sea (especially *Corsica* and *Sardinia*) there be very short Horses, but they are of good courage, and gentle withall.

The *Thracian* Horses are foul and ill shapen, being rough all over their bodies, and having very great shoulders, which in the *Greek* is named (*Calomysten*) such a one as will cast down the rider on the ground from off his back, they are crook-backt, or bunched out; or else of divers kindes; and therefore they have an unsure and reeling pace, and their course is very unconstant. *Absyrtus* saith, the *Thracian* Horses are the best. The *Thuringian* Horses are neighbours to *Hessis*, which *Pliny* and *Volatteranus* supposed, are called (*Mediterranean Cimbri.*)

There be some that suppose the *Venetians* to descend from a people of *Paphlagonia* (called *Venetans*) which after the destruction of *Troy* came to these places, and by these they make an argument, conjecturing it to be good, in regard they are wholly imployed about breeding Horses, which at this time faileth altogether, but in former days they were very careful to follow their business about the training up of young Mules, whereof *Homer* writeth. And *Dionysius* the Tyrant of *Sicilia* ordained, that the breed of Horses should be fetcht from hence, to make warlike combates with them, that among the *Græcians* the excellency of the *Venetian* breed should remain, and that a great while after that breed of Horses got the praise. *Vuallachus* this day is called of the *Saxons* a gelded Horse, and brought out of that Countrey, which sometimes was called *Dacia*. The *Lycospades* and *Lycophotians* shall be spoken of hereafter.

OF THE CHOICE OF GOOD HORSES.

PALLADIUS adviseth to observe four things in choice of a Stallion Horse, the form or outward proportion, the colour, the merit, and the beauty, all which are necessary to be observed in the choice of Colts or elder Horses, that they may be of a generous race, having soft legs, lofty paces, gently treading, such as will lead the way, and be not afraid of any water, bridge, or sudden noises; having a gentle neck, a sharp head, a short belly, a fat back, a dapple colour, nimble ears, thick mane lying on the right side, a double bone descending by his loins, a sounding hoof, and legs that cannot stand still, which *Virgil* expresseth in these words.

> *Nec non & pecori est idem delectus equino.*
> *Tu modo, quos in spem statuis summittere gentis,*
> *Præcipuum jam inde a teneria impende laborem.*
> *Continuo pecoris generosi pullus in arvis*
> *Altius ingreditur, & mollia crura reponit.*
> *Primus & ire viam, & fluvios tentare minaces*
> *Audet, & ignoto sese committere ponti:*
> *Nec vanos horret crepittus, illa ardua cervix,*
> *Argutumque caput, brevis alvus, obesaque terga:*
> *Luxuriatque toris animosum pectus, honesti*
> *Spadices glaucique: color deterrimus albis*
> *Et gilvo: tum, si qua sonum procul arma dedere,*
> *Stare loco nescit, micat auribus & tremit artus:*
> *Collectumque premens volvit sub naribus ignem.*
> *Densa juba, & dextro jacta recumbit in armo.*
> *At duplex agitur per lumbos spina, cavatque*
> *Tellurem, & solido gravites sonat ungula cornu.*

Varro sheweth that at the first foaling of a Colt, a man may observe by certain signes how he will prove when he is in perfection: for if he be chearful, bold, and not terrified at any strange sight, if he run before the company, be wanton, and contend with his equals in course, and over-

524

run them: if he leap over a ditch, go over a bridge, or through water, and being provoked appeareth meek; these are the most true signes of an elegible Colt.

Also it is to be considered, whether they rise quickly, being stirred from their rest, and run away speedily, if their bodies be great, long, full of muscles, and sharp, having a little head, black eyes, open and wide nostrils, sharp pricked ears, a soft and broad neck, not long, a thick mane curled, and falling on the right side, a broad and full breast, large shoulders, and shoulder-bones, round ribs, a little belly, a double back-bone, or at the least not thin, bunchy, and extended; his loins pressed downwards, broad, and well set, little and small stones, a long tail, with curled hair, high, straight and equal legs, round knees, not great, not bending inward; round buttocks, brawny and fleshy thighs, high, hard, hollow, and round hoofs, well set to the crown of their pastern, having veins conspicuous and apparent over all his body. That Colt which at the time of his foaling hath the most highest legs, is likeliest by common reason to prove most able and noble in his age, for of all the joynts in the body the knees and legs grow least, and they which have flexible joynts in their infancy, will be more nimble and flexible in their age. And thus much for the parts of a Colt. Now, in the next place we must likewise take consideration of a Horse untamed, and ready for the saddle. For the outward parts of his body, saith *Xenophon*, yeeld evident signification of his minde, before he be backed.

Plato willeth that the state of his body be straight, and articulate, his head bony, his cheeks little, his eyes standing out, and not sunk into his head, flaming like bloud, looking cruelly if the body be black; but black eyes if the body be white, do argue a gentler and better disposition; short and little ear, the crown of his head greater then the residue, broad nostrils, whereby he not only looketh more terribly, but breatheth more easily; for when one Horse is angry with another, in their rage they are wont to stretch out their nostrils vehemently.

The beak or snowt of a Horse, ought not to stand out like a Swines, but to bend down a little crooked, the head to be so joyned to the neck, as it may bend more commodiously, that is, if the neck be small next to the head, so will the neck stand before the rider, and his eyes appear before his feet: and although he be full of stomach, yet will he never be violent or stiffe necked. It ought also to be considered, whether his cheek bones be sharp, tender, or unequal, standing one above another, for their imparity maketh the Horses neck to be hard and stubborn.

The back-bone above his shoulders higher, commodious to set the saddle upon, and his whole body the better compacted, if the back-bone be double, and smooth; for then shall the Rider sit more easily, and the form of the Horse appear more delectable. A large breast sheweth his comeliness and strength, making him fit to take longer reaches without doubling of his legs, because in a broad breast the legs stand further asunder: large side or ribs swelling out above the belly, for they shew the ability of the Horse both to his food and work, a round even belly, and his loins being broad and short, causeth the fore-legs to be lifted up more easily, and the hinder-legs to follow; for the small loins do not only deform, but enfeeble and oppress the Horse, therefore the loins ought to be double, the ribs broad and fleshy, agreeable to the breast and sides, buttocks solid and broad, with a long tail reaching down to the heels of his hinder-legs, Thighs full of sinews, the bones of his legs thick like posts of the whole body, but that thickness ought neither to be of veins nor flesh, for then they are quickly inflamed and wounded, when they travel in rough and sharp ways: for if the flesh be cut a little, the commissures part asunder, and causeth the Horse to halt, and above all other things have a regard to his feet, and therein especially to his hoof, for being thick, it is better then being thin, likewise if they be hard, causeth the pastern to stand higher from the ground, for so in their pace the soft and hard parts of the foot do equally sustain one another, and the hard hoof yeeldeth a sound like a Cymbal, for the goodness of a Horse appeareth by the sound of his feet.

Now on the contrary side it is good also to set down the faults and signes of reprobation in Horses, and first of all therefore, a great and fleshy head, great tears, narrow nostrils, hollow eyes, a long neck, a mane not hairy, a narrow breast, hollow shoulders, narrow sides, and little fleshy sharp loins, bare ribs, hard and heavy legs, knees not apt to bend, weak thighs, not strong, crooked legs, thin, full fleshy, plain and low hoofs; all these things are to be avoided in the choise of your Horse.

NOW in the next place, let us consider the choise of Horses and Mares appointed for breed and procreation, and we have shewed already, that in a Stallion, we are principally to consider the colour, form, merit, and beauty. This Stallion is called in *Italy, Rozzone*; in *France, Estalon*; in *Germany, Ein Springhengst*; and in *Latine, Admissarius, quia ad generandam sobolem admittitur*, because he is sent to beget and engender. The *Græcians, Anabates*, or *Ocheutes*. First of all therefore, to begin with the colour: that Horse is best which is of one continued colour, although oftentimes (as *Rufus* saith) Horses of a despicable colour prove as noble as any other.

The chief colours are these; bay, white, carnation, golden, russet, mouse-colour, flea-bitten, spotted, pale and black: of all those the black or bay is to be preferred. *Oppianus* maketh distinction of Horses by their colour in this manner, the gray or blewish spotted is fittest for the hunting of the Hart, the bright bay for the Bear and Leopards, the black with flaming eyes against the Lyons. The natural colour of the wilde Horses are an ash colour, with a black strake from the head along the back to the tail; but among tame Horses there are many good ones of black white, brown, red, and flea-bitten colour. But yet it is to be remembred, that seldom or never Colts be foaled white, but rather of other colour, degenerating afterward by the increase of their age, for such Horses are more lively, durable, and healthy, then other of their kinde, and therefore *Plutarch* commendeth a white Horse of *Sylla* for his swiftness of foot and stomach: among all colours, first the black, then the bay, next the white, and last the gray are most commended.

Camerarius commendeth a certain colour called in *Latine, Varius*, and may be englished daple gray, because of the divers in-textures of colours, which although many Nations do disallow, yet undoubtedly that colour (saith he) is a signe and argument of a good nature, constituted and builded upon a temperate commixture of humors. Where black, white, and yellow hairs appear, so that the sight of one of these is nothing inferiour to the equestrial party coloured caparisons: Among Horses which are divers coloured, they which have stars in their fore-head, and one white foot, were most commended; such were the *Thracian* Horses not admitted in copulation, of which *Virgil* speaketh in this manner;

—— *Thracius albis*
Portat equus bicolor maculis, vestigia primi
Alba pedis frontemque ostentans arduus albam.

Black Horses also which have one russet or swart spot in their faces, or else a black tongue are highly commended for generation, but the pale coloured Horses are no wayes to be admitted to cover Mares, because their colour is of no account: and likewise it is seldom seen that the Foal proveth better then the Sire. The bay colour hath been received without exception for the best travellers, for it is supposed, that *Baudius* (amongst the *Latines*) is derived of *Vadium, quia inter cætera animalia fortius vadat*: because among other creatures he goeth most surely.

It is also behoveful that in a Stallion Horse, the mane be of the same colour with the body. Horse-keepers have devised to make their Mares conceive strange colours, for when the Mares would go to the Horse, they paint a Stallion with divers colours, and so bring him into the sight and presence of the Mare; where they suffer him to stand a good while, untill she perfectly conceive in her imagination the true *Idea* and full impression of those pictures, and then they suffer him to cover her; which being performed, she conceiveth a Foal of those colours: In like manner; Pigeons conceive young ones of divers colours.

The *Germans* to mingle the colour of Horses hairs (especially to bring black among white) take the roots of Fearn, and of Sage, and seethe them together in lee, and then wash their Horses all over therewith. For the making of their Horses white, they take that fat which ariseth from the decoction of a moul in an earthen pot, and therewithall anoint the places they would have white, Also they shave off the hairs, and put upon the bald place crude Hony, and Badgers grease, which maketh the hairs to arise white: and many other means are used by Horse-leaches, as afterward shall be shewed. In the old age of a Horse his hair doth naturally change white, above all other beasts that we know, and the reason is, because the brain-pan, is a more thin and slender bone, then

528

the greatness of his body would require, which appeareth by this, that receiving a blow in that place, his life is more endangered then by hurting any other member, according to the observation of *Homer*:

Et qua setæ hærent capiti, lethaleque vulnus
Præcipue sit equis. ———

And thus much shall suffice for the colour of a Stallion: now followeth the form or outward proportion of the body, which ought to be great and solid, his stature answerable to his strength, his sides large, his buttocks round, his breast broad, his whole body full and rough, with knots of muscles, his foot dry and solid, having a high hoof at the heel. The parts of his beauty are these, a little and dry head, the skin almost cleaving to the bones, short and pricked ears, great eyes, broad nostrils, a long and large mane and tail, with a solid and fixed rotundity of his hoofs, and such an one, as thrusteth his head deep into the water when he drinketh; his ribs and loins like an Oxes, a smooth and straight back, his hanches or hips long, broad, and fleshy, his legs large, fleshy and dry, the sinews and joynctures thereof great, and not fleshy near the hoofs: that the hinder part of his body be higher then his forepart, like as in a Hart, and this beauty better appeareth in a lean body then in a fat, for fatness covereth many faults; the former parts are thus expressed by *Horace*:

Regibus hic mos est ubi equos mercantur, opertos
Inspiciunt, ne si facies ut sæpe decora
Molli sulia pede est, emptorem inducat hiantem,
Quod pulchri clunes, breve quod caput, ardua cervix.

If you will make trial of your Stallion, whether he be fit for procreation, *Hipparchus* teacheth you this experiment: press the genital member with your two fingers, and with locks of Wooll draw out his seed, which being so drawn out, if it cleave and hang together, so as it will not be cut nor easily parted, it is a demonstration of a good Stallion; but if it hang not together like birdlime, but easily go asunder like Milk or Whay, such a Horse is not to be admitted to cover your Mares. When Horses be old among other faults, they engender Foals lame in their feet, and therefore they are to be kept, and not to be admitted to copulation nor War; for his rage is like a weak fire among wet stuble, according to these verses:

> ——— *Morbo gravis aut segnior annis*
> *Deficit, abde domo, nec turpi ignosce senectæ.*
> *Frigidus in venerem senior, frustraque laborem*
> *Ingratum trahit: & si quando ad prælia ventum est,*
> *Ut quondam in stipulis magnus sine viribus ignis,*
> *Incassum furit.* ———

Therefore it behoveth that a Stallion Horse be not under three years old when he covereth a Mare, and it is best for him to begin at five, for so he will endure in generation, not only till he be twenty year old, but also to thirty or forty years, as in some Countreys hath been often proved. They are not to be admitted to cover above fifteen in one year at the most, and a young Horse not above ten or twelve in one year; the residue may be suffered with observation of their strength and nature.

The King of *Babylon* beside his Horses for war had eight hundred Stallions, which were admitted to cover six thousand Mares, so that every one had twenty a peece; there is also a place in *Syria* near *Apamia*, where in one plot of ground were nourished thirty thousand Mares, and three thousand Stallions (as *Cælius* saith) so that every Stallion had an hundred Mares to cover (in that place) which number exceedeth the proportion of nature. It is also to be remembred, that Stallions are to be separated from Mares all the year long, except at the time of procreation, and then also he must be largely fed according to these verses:

> *His animadversis, instant sub tempus, & omnes*
> *Impendunt curas denso distendere pingui,*
> *Quem legere ducem, & pecori duxere maritum:*
> *Florentesque secant herbas, fluviosque ministrant,*
> *Farraque: ne blando nequeant superesse labori:*
> *Invalidique patrum referant jejunia nati:*
> *Ipsa autem macie tenuant armenta volentes.*
> *Atque ubi concubitus primos jam nota voluptas*

Sollicitat, frondesque negant, & fontibus arcent.
Sæpe etiam cursu quatiunt, & Sole fatigant:
Cum graviter tunsis gemit area frugibus: & cum
Surgentem ad Zephyrum paleæ jactantur inanes.
Hoc faciunt, nimio ne luxu obtustor usus
Sit genitali arvo, & sulcos oblimet inertes,
Sed rapiat sitiens Venerem, interiusque recondat.

It is also to be observed, that the males which are designed for procreation be not over much labored, for then he will be the more weak for generation, nor yet suffered to be too idle, for then a certain fleamy humor is increased in them, which likewise disableth them in copulation; and thus much for the males.

Almost all the same things which have been said of the male, belong to the female, except the belly of the female ought to be greater; but if there be any white speckles or spots in the eyes of the female, such as are not contracted by accident, but breed in them by nature, such a one is refused for breed; for an Horse born of such a Mare, when he cometh to be old, will likewise be affected with the same blindness; but if it be a female, by reason of her yearly purgation, she may peradventure avoid that mischief.

It behooveth therefore that the Mares appointed for race, be well compacted, of a decent quality, being fair and beautiful to look upon, the belly and loins being great, in age not under three nor above ten years old.

Concerning their admission to generation, it is to be remembred, that the *Latins* have a proper term to signifie the appetite of the female to the male, which they call, *Equire*, that is, Horsing, and they continue in that lust sixty dayes together; the signes whereof are these, They forsake their company, running not toward the East and West, but the contrary, to the North and South: neither permit they any body to come near them, untill they either be wearied or meet with the male, and if they meet with a female like themselves, they joyn neer to her, and seem to rejoyce at her society, lifting up the tail, changing of the voice, and sending forth of her secrets, a certain thin humour, somewhat like the seed of a Horse, which is called *Hippomanes*.

They also make water more often then at other times, so that among all the females in the world, there is none, beside a Woman, that is more greedy of procreation then a Mare, because they want a menstruous purgation, and yet eat aboundance of meat, which *Virgil* expresseth, setting down their unlimitable rage, which carryeth them over Mountains and Rivers, in the time of this fury.

> *Scilicet ante omnes furor est insignis equarum,*
> *Et mentem Venus ipsa dedit, quo tempore Glauci*
> *Potniades malis membra absumpsere quadrigæ.*
> *Illas ducit amor trans Gargara, transque sonantem*
> *Ascanium, superant montes & flumina tranant.*

Also at that time, their genital hangeth forth more then at other times, but if their manes be shorn off, their lust is extinguished. It is reported also by *Columella* that in *Spain*, in the Mountain *Tegro* which reacheth into *Portugal* upon the Ocean, there be Mares which rage so far in lust, that by their ardent desire of copulation they conceive by the Southwest winde, without the company of a Horse, (even as Hens do lay egges being not troad by a Cock) which are called *Hypenemia*, but those Foales live not till they be above three year old. And it is the property of these Mares (saith *Avicen*) by kicking against the winde with their hinder legs, to open their own womb, and to receive in that delectable air, wherewithal they are satisfied.

Also he saith, that he heard of an old man, which was born in the Isle of *Pealtupha*, that the Mares thereof never cease running, from the one end of the Island to the other, when the rage of their lust is upon them; which thing is elegantly described by a Poet, how they turn themselves to the West, standing upon the rocks, and there draw in the cold aire, which oftentimes maketh them conceive, wondering that they conceive not rather by the East sunrising or South, then by the Westerly winde bordering upon the North; the Poets words are these:

> *Continuoque avidis ubi subdita flamma medullis,*
> *Vere magis (quia vere calor redit ossibus) illa*
> *Ore omnes versæ in Zephyrum, stant rupibus altis*
> *Exceptantque leves auras: & sæpe sine ullis*
> *Conjugiis vento gravidæ (mirabile dictu)*
> *Saxa per, & scopulos, & depressas convalles*

Diffugiunt, non Eure tuos neque Solis ad ortus:
In Boream Caurumq; aut unde nigerrimus auster
Nascitur, & pluvis contristat frigore cœlum.

Sometimes Horses and Mares admit copulation at two year old, but those Foales never prove excellent, but at three year old or thirty moneths, they suffer conjunction safely and with profit, because they cease to lose their teeth. They continue in their generation, bearing every second year, the male untill he be thirty year old, and the female as long as she liveth; but the male engendereth yearly: And it is reported of a Horse in *Opus*, that covered a Mare after he was forty year old, being only holp up and down from the Mare.

Pliny, Oppianus, Ælianus, and *Aristotle* do confidently affirm, that when the King of *Scythia* had all his generous breed of Horses destroyed by a pestilence (except one of his best Mares and a Stallion which was a Foale of that Mares) being desirous to continue the breed, caused his Horse-keeper to put the Son and the Mother together, but the Horse refused copulation with his own Parent. Afterward the Horse-keeper covered the Mare with artificial skins, and likewise dressed the Horse in such manner, as one could not know the other, whereupon being brought together the second time, the Stallion covered his own Mother: Afterward the Horse-keeper discovered them, the one to the other, whereby they knew the fraud, and grew guilty in themselves of incestuous commixtion: Whereupon they took no other revenge upon themselves, but ran to the top of an high rock, and there successively threw down themselves, one after another, so ending their miserable days, and preventing their Masters hopes; to teach all mankinde that they ought not to seek to thrive by sins against nature: the like is before rehearsed of a male Camel.

The very like story is reported of a Horse in the coasts of *Rea*, yet this is not held to be general: for beasts (as *Aristotle* saith) do promiscuously cover one another; the Father the Daughter, the Son the Mother, the Brother the Sister, and this maketh them to be perfect beasts; and the stories before recited may be true, yet are they extraordinary: otherwise the common rule of *Ovid* remaineth true, That it is not a filthy thing for beasts to observe no degrees of nature.

—— Coeunt animalia nullo
Cætera delectu, nec habetur turpe juvencæ
Ferre patrem tergo, fit equo jua filia conjux.

The best time of the year for the joyning of Horses and Mares for copulation, is from the vernall æquinoctial to the Summer solstice, because then the Colts which are soaled in due time, have the green herbs and all the warm weather for the succour of their infancy: and if the Mare (after she have been once covered) refuse the male, let her rest ten days, and then bring her to the male again; if she refuse the second time, you may take it for granted, that she is filled already. Wherfore seeing it is known certainly that a Mare goeth twelve moneths with young, it is an easie matter so to order the time of her copulation, that her foale may alwayes be delivered in a warm and seasonable time of the year; for which cause there is an invention for stirring up of the lust both in the male and female: the *Hymenæan* shepherds, by the sweetness of songs upon their pipes, stirred up their Horses and Mares to copulation, but the more assured way is, to follow the direction of *Columella* and *Absyrtus*, to provoke them by natural means, like as Buls and Kine.

And first of all for the male, give him the tail of a Hart burned, mingled with wine, and anoint therewithal his stones and genital member, and so shall the dull Stallion be more prone to venery; also there is a kind of *Satyrium*, which they give to them in drink, or the powder of a Horses stones: likewise if the female refuse, take shrimpes beaten soft with water (as thick as hone) therewithal touch the nature of the Mare in her purgation, and afterwards hold it to her nose; or else take Hens dung mixed with Rozen and Turpentine, and anoint the secrets of the Mare, which shall so far increase her lust, as it cureth the lothsomeness better then the shrimps, and increaseth lust. But you must regard, that no lean and ill favoured Mare be anointed, because the Horse is quickly wearyed from his lust, and so delighteth only to be tickled therewith without doing any thing.

Other again do first of all bring some vulgar Horse to the Mare, who provoketh and stirreth her to lust, and when he is neer the very fact of filling her, they lead her away to a more generous Stallion, to be covered by him: And so if none of these means do prevail with her, they do rub

534

her secrets with a Nettle, and that causeth her to suffer the Horse to enter.

Democritus also saith that it is in our power to cause our Horses to bring forth males or females; for if we suffer them to couple when the North winde bloweth, or the third day before the full Moon, or bind his left stone, he shall get a male; but if when the South winde bloweth, or three days after the full Moon, or bind the right stone of the Horse, it will prove a female.

Also if at the time of copulation, the Horse leap off from the Mare on the right side, it is a token it will be a male, but if on the left side, it will be a female. Carnal copulation is most acceptable to Horses, and lesse grievous unto them then to Neat, for there is no kind (man only excepted) that is so venereous and nimble in generation as is a Horse or Mare.

The males know their females with whom they live, although they have been but a few days together; and if strange females fall into their company, they expell them away by biting, feeding single and alone with their female by themselves; but if any male or other stone Horse come within their walke, then presently they make force at him; if their female stir from them, they restrain her by biting: and in this time of their rage, they neither regard the rider, nor their adversary, nor the bridle, nor cruell stripes, nor steep hils, nor rocks, nor caves of the earth, if they winde the amorous savour of their fellowes; according to the saying of *Virgil* in these Verses;

Nonne vides, ut tota tremor pertentet equorum
Corpora, si tantum notas odor attulit auras?
Ac neque eos jam frena virum, nec verbera sæva,
Non socpuli, rupesq cavæ, atque objecta retardant
Flumina, correptos unda torquentia montes.

It hath been also received, that a barren Mare shall conceive if you take a bunch of leeks bruised smal and put into a cup of Wine and twelve *French* flies called *Cantharides* in water, put them two dayes together into the genital of a Mare, like a Glyster, and afterwards put her to a Horse anointing her secrets with the said ointment two several times, when the Horse leaps down from her; or else they take Niter, Sparrows dung, Rozen, and Turpentine, thrusting the same into the Mares genital, whereby it hath been proved, that fecundity oftentimes followed.

Also some use Siler of the Mountains to procure conception in Mares and Cowes, and the true sign of conception is, when their nature (that is) the fluent humour out of their secrets ceaseth for a moneth, or two, or three: and *Pliny* saith, that when a Mare is filled, she changeth her colour, and looketh more red, which is to be understood not of her hair, but of her skin, lips and eyes, her hair standing more full then before. Then let them be separated from the males, exempting them from moist places, cold and labour, for all these are enemies to her foaling, and cause abortment.

Likewise they must not have too much meat nor too little, but only a temperate diet, and soft lodging, their better ordering is elegantly described in *Virgil*, by these Verses.

> *Non illas gravibus quisquam juga ducere plaustris,*
> *Non saltu superare viam sit passus, & acri*
> *Carpere prata fuga: fluviosque innare rapaces.*
> *Salribus in vacuis pascant: & plena secundum*
> *Flumina, muscus ubi & viridissima gramine ripa,*
> *Speluncæque tegant: & saxea procubet umbra.*

This is most certain, that if a Woman in her flowers, touch a Mare with foal (or sometime do but see her) it causeth to cast her foal, if that purgation be the first after her Virginity: In like manner if they smell of the snuffe of a Candle, or eat Buck-mast or *Gentian*. The *Egyptians* when they will describe a Woman suffering abortment, they picture a Mare treading upon a Wolf, for if a Mare kick at a Wolf, or tread where a Wolf hath troad, she casteth her foale: If an Asse cover a Mare which a Horse hath formerly filled, there followeth abortment; but if a Horse cover a Mare which an Asse hath formerly filled, there followeth no abortment, because the Horses seed is hotter then the Asses. If a Mare be sick of abortment or foaling, *Polypody* mingled with warm water given her in a horn, is a present remedy.

536

The *Scythians* when they perceive their Mares to be quick with foale, they ride upon them, holding opinion that thereby they cast forth their foales with lesse pain and difficulty. They carry their young one in their wombs, as hath been already said, twelve moneths, but sometimes they come at eleven moneths and ten dayes, and those are commonly males, for the males are sooner perfected in the womb then the females, and commonly the females are foaled at twelve moneths and ten days, and those which tarry longer are unprofitable and not worth education. A Mare is most easily delivered of her young among other beasts, and beareth most commonly but one at a time, yet it hath been seen that twins hath proceeded from her. At the time of her delivery, she hath lesse purgation of bloud, then so great a molde of body can afford, and when she hath foaled, she devoureth her seconds, and also a thing that cleaveth to her foales forehead, being a piece of black flesh called *Hippomanes*, neither doth she suffer her young one to suck until she have eaten that, for by smelling thereunto, the young and old Horses, or other of that kind would fall mad: and this thing have the imposters of the world, used for a *Philtre* or amorous cup, to draw women to love them, *Virgil* speaketh thus of it;

> *Quæritur & nascentis Equi de fronte revulsus*
> *Et matris præreptus amor* ———

And again;

> *Hinc demum Hippomanes vero quod nomine dicunt*
> *Pastores, lentum distillat ab inguine virus*
> *Hippomanes, quod sæpe malæ legere novercæ,*
> *Miscueruntque herbas & non innoxia verba.*

This poison made into a Candle (*Anaxilaus* saith) in the burning thereof, there shall be a presentation of many monstrous Horses-heads. There is very great poison contained in this *Hippomanes*, for the *Arcadian Phormis* made a Horse of brasse at *Olympia*, & put *Hippomanes* into the same, and if the Horses at any time seen this Brazen Horse, they were so far inraged with lust, that no halters or bands could hold them, but breaking all, run and leaped upon the said Brazen horse, and although it wanted a tail, yet would they forsake any beautiful Mare, and run to cover it; neither when they came unto it, and found it by their heels to be sounding and hard brasse, would not they despair of copulation, but more and more, with noise of mouth, rage, and endevor of body, labour to leap upon the same, although the slippery brasse gave them no admission or stay of abode upon the back of that substance, neither could they be drawn from the said Brazen Image, untill by the great strength and cruell stripes of the riders they were forcibly driven away.

Some think this little piece of flesh to cleave to the forehead, others to the loins, and many to the genitals; but howsoever it is an unspeakable part of Gods providence, to make the Mares belly a sepulchre for that poison; for if it should remain in the males as in the females the whole race of Horses would utterly perish and be destroyed through rage of lust, for which cause the keepers and breeders of Horses do diligently observe the time of their Mares foaling, and instantly cut off the same from the Colt, reserving it in the hoof of a Mare, to procure the Stallions to carnal copulation, and the Colt, from which they cut this piece of flesh, they sacrificed it, for it is manifest saith *Ælianus*, that the Mare will never love that foal, from whence she hath not eaten and consumed this piece of flesh.

And this poison is not only powerful in brute beasts, but also in reasonable men, for if at any time by chance or ignorantly they tast hereof, they likewise fall to be so mad and præcipitate in lust, raging both with gestures and voice, that they cast their lustful eyes upon every kind of Women attempting wheresoever they meet them to ravish or ingender with him: and besides because of this oppression of their minde, their body consumeth and fadeth away: for three dayes after the Colt is soaled he can hardly touch the ground with his head. It is not good to touch them, for they are harmed by often handling, only it is profitable, that it be suffered with the dam in some warm and large stable, so as neither it be vexed with cold nor in danger to be oppressed by the Mare through want of room. Also their hoofs must be looked unto, lest their dung sticking unto them burn them, afterward when it waxeth stronger, turn him out into the field with his dam, lest the Mare over-mourn her self for want of her foal, for such beasts love their young ones exceedingly.

538

After three dayes let the Mare be exercised and rid up and down, but with such a pace as the foal may follow her, for that shall amend and encrease her milk. If the Colt have soft hoofs, it will make him run more speedily upon the hard ground, or else lay little stones under their feet, for by such means their hoofs are hardned, and if that prevail not, take Swines grease, and Brimstone never burned, and the stalks of Garlick bruised and mingled all together, and therewithal anoint the hoofs.

The Mountains also are good for the breeding of Colts, for two causes, first for that in those places their hoofs are hardened; and secondly by their continual ascending and descending, their bodies are better prepared for induring of labour. And thus much may suffice for the educating and nursing of foals.

For their weaning observe this rule, first separate them from their dams twenty four hours together, in the next morning let them be admitted to suck their belly full, and then removed to be never more suckled: at five moneths old begin to teach them to eat bread or hay, and at a year old give them Barly and Bran, and at two years old, wean them utterly.

Of handling, taming, or breaking of Horses.

THEY which are appointed to break Horses are called by the *Grecians, Eporedicæ, Hippodami,* and *Hippocomi*; the *Latins, Equisones, Arulatores,* and *Cociones*; in *Italian, lo Rozone. Absyrtus* is of opinion that foals are to be used to hand, and to be begun to be tamed at 18 moneths old, not to be backed but only tyed by the head in a halter to a rack or manger, so that it may not be terrified for any extraordinary noise, for which cause they use them to brakes, but the best time is at three years old, as *Crescetiensis* teacheth in many Chapters, wherefore when they begin to be handled, let him touch the rough parts of his body, as the mane and other places, wherein the Horse taketh delight to be handled: neither let him be over severe and Tyrannous, and seek to overcome the beast by stripes, but as *Cicero* saith, by fair means, or by hunger and famine.

Some have used to handle them sucking, and to hang up in their presence bits and bridles, that so by the sight and hearing the gingling thereof in their ears, they might grow more familiar. And when they came to hand to lay upon their backs a little boy flat on his belly; and afterward to make him sit upon him formally, holding him by the head, and this they do at three year old, but commit him to no labour untill he be four year old, yet domestical and small Horses for ordinary use are tamed at two year old, and the best time for the effecting hereof, is in the moneth of *March*.

It is also good in riding of a young Horse to light often, and to get up again, then let him bring him home and use him to the stable, the bottom whereof, is good to be paved with round stones, or else planks of Oak, strewing litter upon it when he lyeth down, that so he may lie soft and stand hard. It is also good to be regarded, that the planckes be so laid, as the Urine may continually run off from them, having a little close ditch to receive it, that so the Horses feet may not be hurt thereby, and a good Master of Horses must oftentimes go into his stable, that so he may observe the usage of this beast. The manger also ought to be kept continually clean for the receiving of his provender, that so no filth or noisome thing be mingled therewith: there ought also to be partitions in it, that so every beast may eat his own allowance, for greedy Horses do not only speedily raven up their own meat, but also rob their fellows. Others again have such weak stomachs that they are offended with the breath of their fellows, and will not eat except they eat alone.

The rack also is to be placed according to their stature, that so their throat may not be too much extended, by reaching high, nor their eyes or head troubled, because it is placed too low. There ought also to be much light in the stable, lest the beast accustomed to darkness, be offended at the Sun light, and wink over much, being not able to indure the beams when he is led abroad; but yet the stable must be warm and not hot; for although heat do preserve fatness, yet it bringeth indigestion and hurteth a Horses nature, therefore in the Winter time the stable must be so ordered, as the beast may not be offended or fall into diseases by overmuch heat or suddain cold. In the Summer time let them lodge both night and day in the open air.

This also in stabling of your Horses must be avoided, namely, the sties of Swine; for the stink, the breath, the gruntling of Hogs, is abominable for Horses, and nature hath framed no sympathy or concord betwixt the noble and couragious spirit of a Horse, and the beastly sluggish condition of a Swine. Remove also far away from your Horses stables all kinde of fowl, which were wont to haunt those places to gather up the remnant grains of their provender, leaving behind them their little feathers, which if the Horse lick up in his meat, stick in his throat, or else their excrements which procureth the looseness of his belly.

It must also be regarded, that the stable must be kept neat, sweet, and clean, so as in absence of the Horse, it may not lie like a place for Swine. The instruments also, and implements thereof, such as are the Horse cloathes, the Curry-combs, the Mane-combs, Saddles and Bridles, be disposed and hung up in order behind the Horse, so as it may neither trouble him eating or lying, nor yet give him occasion to gnaw, eat, and devour them to their own damage or hurt, for such is the nature of some wanton Horses, to pull asunder and destroy whatsoever they can reach.

They are therefore oftentimes to be exercised and backed, and principally to be kept in a good diet, for want of food dejecteth the spirit of the noblest Horse, and also maketh the mean Horse to be of no use; but on the contrary a good diet doth not only make a mean Horse to be serviceable, but also continue the worth and value of the beast: which thing Poets considered, when they fained that *Arion* the Horse of *Neptune* and some others were made by *Ceres* the Goddess of Corn, which any mean witted man may interpret to signifie, that by abundance of provender the nature of Horses was so far advanced above ordinary, that like the Sons of the Gods they perform incredible things: whether therefore they eat chaffe, or hay, or grasse, or grain, according to the diversities of Countries, let it be wholesome, clean, fresh, and sweet, without dust, gravel, mustiness, or evill smell.

In the morning give them Barly or provender, a little at a time in distinct or several portions, twice or thrice one after another, so as he may chew and eke digest it throughly, otherwise if he raven it in, as he will do having much at a time, he rendreth it in his dung whole and not digested. About three hours after, he hath eaten his provender, give him

541

a little of hay, and three hours after that, his dinners allowance of grain, as in the morning, and afterwards about two or three a clock hay again, and then some drink; last of all give him his allowance of provender for supper, with a bottle or two of hay, which ought to be more plentiful then the former servings: and yet these rules are not to be understood as though they might not be altered, for the times prefixed may be prevented if occasion require. Their best provender is Oats and Barley, yet Barly ingendreth the thinner and better bloud, and therefore it is to be preferred, only the measure of the provender is left to the discretion of the Horse-keeper, and there is no meat more wholesome for a Horse, then Barly and Chaffe; because it will make him full of life, and also able to indure labour, yet not over fat.

In *England* in many places they give their Horses bread made of Fitches, Beans, and Pease. When one is to make a journey on horse-back, let him not give his Horse too much provender the noon before, but so much the more hay, and bread steeped in wine, and also let him serve him sooner at night then ordinary, that so the beast may take the more rest. There be which refuse to give Horses wet provender or steeped bread, because they conceive that it will breed in them loathsomeness of meat; but the truth is, a reasonable Horse-keeper preventeth that mischief; and besides, the meat of a Horse is altogether so dry, that the beast himself is indangered to be sick of that disease; and therefore it is as safe to give him moistened food sometimes, as well as to give him bread mingled with salt.

When a Horse is weary or sweateth, let him not drink nor eat provender, but after he is walked a little while, give him hay, first of all covering him with a large cloth, and remember, that hay is not to be cast before a Horse, as it is out of the reek, but first of all it must be pulled, and shaken betwixt the hands, for the avoiding of dust and other filth. Restrain the Horse as much as you may from eating the litter under his feet, for even the best meat so defiled is unwholesome. It is also good sometimes to suffer him to pick up his meat on the ground betwixt his forelegs, that will make his neck to grow thinner, leaner and more comely. Let his neck be fast bound in the stable with a Leathern collar, and binde with a manicle his fore-leg to the hinder-leg on the contrary side, and so shall his be preserved in more health, because they cannot move out of their place but with difficulty.

Concerning the drink of Horses, something more is to be added in this place, and namely brackish and troubled water, such as runneth softly, as in great ponds, is fittest for Horses, because that water, being hot and thick nourisheth better, but the swift Water is colder, and therefore more unwholesome, but in hot times (as in Summer) the sweet and clearer water is more convenient if custome be not against it. And because a Horse (except he drink freely) can never be fat, let his mouth oftentimes be washed within with Salt and Wine, and that will make him eat and drink more liberally: and yet the running water is more wholesome for Horses, because whatsoever is moveably fluent, is lesse subject to poison then that which standeth still; but if a Horse sweat or be weary, it is not safe to let him drink any thing, except he first stale, for in such cases followeth distention. And it is better to turn or lead forth your Horse to water, then to bring it unto them. And if at any time necessity cause this to be done, then let the Water be very clear and fresh.

His stable or lodging ought to be ordered, as neither it offend him by cold in Winter, nor yet through heat in Summer, for both these extremities are pernicious: and therefore when the weather is extream cold, then must the Horses back and belly be covered with a cloth; and when on the contrary it exceedeth in heat, then must his litter be taken away. Also in heat he must be covered with linnen to avoid flies, and in cold with woollen to help nature: likewise it is good toward night to pick, cleanse, and open his hoofs, with some artificial instrument, and to thrust into the hollow Cow-dung, or in defect thereof Horse-dung with a little straw, that so he may not shake it out again: but this is not good to be done every day, but rather every second day, and it is good to mingle therewith sewet or grease, or else a new laid Egge with warm ashes. In ancient time they used not to shooe their Horses with iron, untill the dayes of *Catulius*, who remembreth this custome, saying.

Ferream ut soleam tenaci in voragine mula:

So that it seemeth that this devise was first of all invented for Mules. The Horse-shooes ought to be round like his feet, and not heavie, lest the

543

Horses nimbleness be thereby hindered; and great care must be had in nailing or setting them on, lest the tender and fleshie part of the foot be thereby pierced.

Another charge of a Horse-keeper is to keep his Horses lips soft, tender, and gentle, so as he may more sensibly feel his bit: and for this cause let him often rub them with his hands and warm water, and if need require with oil also: and in handling of a Horse this must be observed for a general rule, That neither he come to the Horse right before his face, nor behind his tail, because both these are dangerous to the rider; lest by his heels or mouth he harme him, but on his side he may safely set upon him or handle his Horse, and when he leadeth him, he must likewise go on his side.

Likewise good and painful dressing of Horses is no small means to retain him in sound and perfect health; and therefore he must often be touched with the Curry-comb, and afterward with a handful of straw, so as the hand may follow the stroke to lay the hair smooth: and their fashion was in old time to brush over their Horses with a little linnen instrument made like a sword, whereby they excusse all dust from the beast: and herein it is wisdom to begin at the head and mane, and so to descend to other parts, and to touch the Horses back gently: he may wash the head and mane because it being so bony, it is dangerous lest the comb offend and grieve the beast, except it be layed on very tenderly, but it is not good to wash the legs, because dayly washing loftneth the hoof by sliding down of the water, and therefore it is sufficient only to stroke them down with his hands.

The neather part also of the belly is not to be kept over clean, for the more it is cleansed with water, the more is the Horse pained therein: when a Horse is dressed, it is good to bring him out of the stable, that so in the open air he may be tyed in a longer halter, and seem to be at liberty, whereby he shall be brought to more cleanness and tractable gentleness, standing upon some smooth stones, till all the dust and loose hairs both by the Comb and Brush be driven away, and in the mean time the stable be emptied, and this is to be performed before the Horses watering. You must also regard the skin wherein the Horses yard runneth be kept clean, for if it be stopped it hindereth urine, and maketh the Horse sick, and when your Horse is in dressing, let him have before him no manner of meat either of hay or provender.

Let them be led to the Water twice a day, and wash therein both legs and belly, except in the Winter time, wherein it is not safe to wet the Beast so often: and if there be in them any appearance of sickness and infirmity, or if you have any purpose to give unto them any kind of medicine, then must you altogether forbear to water them. Some use to wash their Horses legs with warm wine-lees to refresh their joints and sinews after hard journies, which custome seemeth very allowable: other use in stead thereof warme dish-water out of the kitchin, and the backes they wash with cold water and salt.

Underneath their tails, and near their yards, you shall find them in the Summer time to be much annoyed with flies, and therefore it is a needful part of the Horse-keepers watchfulness to look in those places and drive them away, for so his charge will take the better rest.

And evermore there must be nourished a mutual benevolence betwixt the Horse and Horse-keeper, so as the Beast may delight in the presence and person of his attendant; and for this cause he may be kept from hunger, wet litter, cold in the Winter, and flies in the Summer: and furthermore a diligent caution must be had, that the Beast be not provoked through overmuch severity, for if the Horse by his keepers violence be often driven to his rack and manger to avoid stripes, either he hurteth his shoulders or legs by his own weight or force, or else groweth into a trembling at the presence of a man, and so never yeeldeth any loving obedience; or else falleth into some furious and unreclaimable evill qualities. The Master therefore ought often to enter into his stable, and take a view of his Horses usage, whereby the Beast will quickly take notice of him, especially if he have but one, for it is a great folly and piece of ill husbandry to trust Servants and not to oversee them. *Cato* was wont to say, *Frons occipitio prior*: that is, as the forehead is before the nape of the neck; meaning thereby that nature hath set him highest and formost, which should not hide himself, but take his place upon him and discharge it, for it is not safe or any part of wisdome, to see by another mans eyes, or work altogether by Deputies.

Men must also be affraid of lending their Horses, for the *Germans* have a pretty proverb, that they will not trust their wives at great feasts out of their sight, for commonly they learn some evill fashion or other more then they had before; and so much more Horses (after lending) return home again to their Masters with alteration of strength and quality.

OF ADORNING AND FURNISHING HORSES.

I cannot approve them that cut off their Horses tail or foretop; one received beginning from an ignorant perswasion of increasing the strength of the Horses back, and the other from an imagined comliness, by trimming it with ribben or some devised knot, or that it hindred the Horses sight. In the first the Beast is wronged and deprived of his help against the flies, and decency of his hinder parts; and in the second nature accused, for not adorning the Horses forehead with more gaudy and variable coloured hairs, and providing a bunch of hair to weaken his eyes; but neither of these are tolerable, for a wise man once to imagine, and therefore I will not spend any more time to confute this vain adorning of Horses.

Let the horse-keeper take heed that he harm not the Beast when he putteth on his Bridle, for a little negligence quickly bringeth a great offence, by touching, wringing, and oppressing any tender part in the Horses head or mouth. He must alway put on his Bridle on the left side, and if the Horse of his own accord do not open his mouth to the bit, then must he gently open his mouth with one finger, and so put it upon him; and if by that means he open not his mouth, then presse or wring his lip upon his great canine tooth, which thing causeth any Horse to open his mouth.

Also it must be regarded that the Horse in leading be not drawn after you, for so will he be made hard headed, unwilling to follow. Again his Cheeks must not be pinched by the Bridle, left the skin grow senseless; and also it must not hang long or loose in his mouth, for so he will be alway biting his bit, and give lesse obedience to his Rider.

Camerarius writeth that he hath seen some put Salt upon their bits, whereof the Horse licking or tasting, became more willing to take it into

546

his mouth; and for the better performance hereof, it is necessary to observe by often triall, what kind or fashioned bit best beseemeth and fitteth the Horses mouth, and finding it, keep him thereunto continually: and when it is put on, neither wring his Cheeks, or let him rowl it betwixt his teeth.

The Saddle also must be so fastened to his back, as that it may not turn or rowl upon the same; wherefore he which layeth it thereupon, must come on the left side, and gently without violence or noise, set it upon the Beast; so that neither girths, peytril, sturrops, trappings, or crupyard, fall betwixt the Back and Saddle, neither covering therewith the Horses wither, nor yet touching his hips or loins.

First of all let the peytrill on the breast be buckled, then the girths in order neer the forelegs, not upon the belly, for upon the belly they will be sliding off, and that is against the rules of riding; for *Bene equitant qui bene cingunt*; that is to say, they ride well which bind fast: and this ought to be done in an open place, where both the Rider and the Horse may have more liberty: wherewithal a generous and great stomached Beast is much delighted: neither must he be tyed or drawn too hard till the Rider be seated. Look also often to the girths, that they wring not the sides, or pull off the skin.

OF RIDING AND SITTING ON HORSEBACK.

WHEN you are to get up and mount on Horseback, take hold on the lower part of the Bridle neer the Bit, with the left hand, with such a distance as may both keep him from rising, nor give him offence, if you take advantage to get into the Saddle, and with the right hand take the rains on the top of the shoulders and the mane, and so hold them, as you give no check to the Horses mouth in mounting: there are other rules for this among Riders, wherewithal I will not meddle, only it is good to use your Horse to backing both sadled and bare, as well from the plain ground, as from blocks, and risings invented for the ease of man.

Therefore before you go to Horseback, first stroke your Horse, and make much of him with gentle words, or other convenient sound which the Horse understandeth, and so will he stand more willingly till you be on his back: for this thing there is in *Plutarch* an excellent story of

547

Alexander the great, when *Bucephalus* was first of all presented to his Father King *Philip*, by a *Thessalian*, called *Philonix*: For when the King was perswaded to go forth into the field to try the qualities of this beast, which was so highly commended for rare parts, and valued at such a price, as none but a King might yeeld for him, then the Horse began to snort, and kick, and to admit no man to come unto him within the length of the rains, but kept aloft like a wilde and untamed Horse; yeelding no obedience to voice or other signes of the Riders: whereat the King fell exceeding angry, and bid them lead away the unruly and untamed Horse: *Alexander* being present, complained of the ignorance and fearfulness of the Riders, and that they were the cause why such a generous and gallant beast was no better manned. At the hearing whereof, King *Philip* smiled, and yet so carryed himself as though he had not heard the words of his Son, untill *Alexander* repeated his saying the second time; whereunto his Father replyed, What (sir Boy) will you make your self more skilfull then these old cunning Riders? will you lay on them an imputation of fear and ignorance? Yes, said *Alexander*, I will adventure to handle this Horse better then any other: Yea but (said *Philip*) what punishment then wilt thou undergo if thou fail and perform not what thou hast said? What punishment? (said *Alexander*) why I will give them the price of the Horse: Whereat the King laughed and struck up the wager, and so had *Alexander* the rains of the Horse delivered to him, who presently turned him about against the Sun-rising, that so he might not be terrified with the shadow of the beholders, and so led him up and down softly two or three turns, and at last wan the Horse to hand, which he gently stroked and applauded: and when he had gotten perfect intelligence and understanding of the Horses stomach, he cast off his cloak, and addressed himself to mount on his back, so holding the rains and bearing his hand and whole body as he did not check or pinch the Horses mouth: so he inclined him first of all to lay away his stirred and angry minde, and afterward paced him to and fro gently, which the Horse endured: At last he put Spurs unto him, and made him run, leap, carreer, and curvet, to the terrour, at the first, of all the beholders, and afterward to the singular admiration and praise of himself: which caused the company or train to applaude this fact, and forced the old man his Father, to send forth tears for joy; and when *Alexander* descended from his Horse, he could not contain himself, but he must needs go kisse and embrace such a Son; whereby it is manifest, that when a Man is to ride on a generous spirited Horse, he shall bend him to endure the burthen by gentleness and familiarity, so as the Beast may still know and love his Rider.

Likewise when the Master mounteth, it is requisite that the servant be on the other side of the Horse to hold the stirrop, for so shall he get up more surely, and set himself more softly. Some Horses are taught to bend their knees to take up their aged and sick Masters, that so they may be the lesse offended in ascending to their backs, and this custom (saith *Pollux*) did first of all begin among the *Persians*.

The ancient *Germans* were so singularly exercised in Horsemanship, that standing upon the ground and holding a Spear or Lance in their hands, they mounted without other stirrop or vantage upon their Horses backs; and not only when they were ordinary attired in common garments, but then also when they were armed, (though *Julius Cæsar* take from them all glory of Chivalry) yet now adayes the invention of Saddles with stirrops, is most easie both for Horse and Horsemen, being then better the *Pelethronian* invention time.

When the Rider is in his Saddle, and is well seated, he must not sit as in a Chair or Chariot, bended together, but rather keep his body upright, only bowing outward his knees, for so shall he be better able to defend himself, or offend his adversary; for he must rather seem to stand then to sit on horseback.

The Rider or Master of Horses must spare his Horse in the heat of Summer, (about Dog-dayes) and in the cold of Winter, and never at any time to Ride past the twylight of the evening. The Horse being empty, is more prone to make water then being full, and therefore must not be hindered in that desire: and alway after his staling, ride him not too fast, untill his nerves which were extended to let forth the Urine be contracted, setled and drawn together again.

If in the Winter time a Horse be to passe over a foord of water (which will ascend up above his belly) let him stale first, lest he fall into the Strangury, and also be a little eased of his load.

There is no beast that rejoyceth more in celerity and swiftness then a Horse, because so soon as he is turned out of hand, he instantly runneth away speedily, and doth walke softly as at other times: and this is a pleasure to them, except when they are provoked above their desires: and the counsell of *Xenophon* when you are to Ride fast or for a wager, is this, bend the upper part of the body forward, stretching out the hand which carryeth the rains; now drawing it in, and then letting it at length again; and therefore it is good in such cases to use short rains, and if the Horse in his course stretch forth the rains of his own accord, then is it a sign of an unskilful Rider, or of a weak and tireable Horse. Add not Spurs but in great necessity, but guide and provoke him with voice and riding rod, for quick and good metled Horses are by the Spur made fierce; and gentle natured Beasts made sluggards like Asses, which by often beating seem to neglect and despise stripes.

You must also shorten and lengthen your journies and times of Ridings, so as they may neither be certain to the Beast, nor yet over long; and specially after a long journey, take a shorter if you Ride upon the same Horse.

First of all let him be used to plain and equal wayes, and if he be to leap or go up a hill, it was a precept of the old *Grecians*, that then the Rider must lay the rains in his neck.

If the Horse at any time be either more fierce or sluggish then ordinary, he may be holp by these means. Wildeness and fierceness of Horses, is like to anger and rage in men; and therefore occasions of offence in word and deed must be avoided: therefore as soon as the Rider is upon his back, let him rest a little before he set forward, and then also let the Horse move but his own pace: for as men are offended with suddain violence and imperious gestures, so also are Horses: but if the Horse being stirred to his race, be more forward and hot then ordinary, he must be gently restrained by the bridle; and it is better to qualifie their rage in long and spacious direct journies, then in often windings and turnings.

But if any man be so simple as to think that by length of journey or race, his Horse will be more meek, because he may be tyred, he deceiveth himself; for as rage in man inventeth hurtfull revenge, and turneth into malice by continuance, so also in Horses it procureth a headlong ruine (if it be not prevented) both to Horse and Rider: and therefore if your Horse be of a generous spirit, never provoke him to ferocity, for as they are wilde and fierce, so are they wicked and harmful.

It is also better to use light and gentle bridles then heavy and sharp, except the Rider can by his art so frame the sharp as the gentle bit: and also the Rider must so frame himself in his art of riding, that in the commotion of his Horse, he may not touch any member or part of him, but only his back whereupon he sitteth.

He must also learn his different terms, to incite and stir up his Horse to run forward, which the *Grecians* call *Clogmos*, or else to restrain him and keep him in, which they call *Poppysmus*, the one closeth the lips, and the other toucheth the palat.

If the Horse be fearful of any thing, you must shew the thing to him plainly, that so by custom he may learn not to be skittish, and let him smell thereunto, till he learn not to be afraid; but if men beat them, they do but fear them more; for while they are so ill handled, they suspect that the things whereof they are afraid are the cause of their stripes. In like sort when they go on the one side, or turn back again, it is good to use the Spurs, because they encrease their terrour and perverseness; and therefore as peaceable encouragement and friendly perswasion is the best means to perswade a man in his fear, the like course must be taken with a Horse, that so he may go straight on without doubt or trembling; and learn not to account any thing horrible to his nature.

When a Horse is so tyred and wearied in his journey that a man would judge him unfit for any labour, take off his saddle and burthen, and put him into some stable or green field, where he may tumble and rowle over and over, and he shall easily recover. In ancient time, if Horses were to be travelled through snow, they made them boots of sackcloth to wear in their journey.

OF THE DISPOSITION OF HORSES IN GENERAL.

AMONG the flocks or heards of Horses, there is not a Captain or leader going before or governing the residue, as among Oxen, Sheep, and Elephants; because the nature of these is more instable and moveable it being a swift and high spirited Beast, and therefore hath received a body furnished with such members as are apt to be swayed by such spirit: for *Lactantius* truly observeth in them a desire of glory, because after victory, the conquerours exsult and rejoyce, but the conquered or overcome, mourn and hang down their heads; which thing *Virgil* expresseth in this Verse;

> *Insultare solo, & gressus glomerare superbos.*

But more plainly *Ovid*, the triumph of the conquering Horse; saying,

> *Hic generosus honos & gloria major equorum;*
> *Nam capiunt animis palmam, gaudentque triumpho,*
> *Seu septem spatiis circo meruere coronam.*
> *Nonue vides victor quanto sublimius altum*
> *Attollat caput, & vulgi se venditet aura,*
> *Celsave cum cæso decoratur terga leone,*
> *Quam tumidus, quantoque venit spectabilis actu:*
> *Compescatque solum, generoso concita pulsu,*
> *Ungula sub spoliis graviter redeuntis opimis.*

And *Pliny* affirmeth that when they are joyned together in Chariots, they understand their encoragements of glory and commendation: and therefore there is not any beast of so high a stomach as a Horse.

OF THE NATURAL DISPOSITION OF HORSES.

THEY love wet places and bathes, for which cause they are called *Philolutra*, they also love musick, as hath been already declared, and the whole hoast of Army or the *Sybarites*, taught their Horses to dance at the sound of a Pipe: and *Cælius* writeth hereof in this manner, So great (saith he) was the riot and wantonness of the *Sybarites*, that at their common feasts they brought in Horses to dance before men; which thing being known by the *Crotoniatæ*, they offered them War, and agreed upon the fight: whereupon in the day of battle, the *Crotoniats* brought with them divers Pipers and Minstrils, who upon a sign given to them, sounded their instruments, whereupon the *Sybaritan* Horses came running and dancing among their adversaries, and so betrayed themselves and their Riders to the enemy.

The like story is reported by *Athenæus*, of the people called *Cardiani*, for they also taught their Horses to dance upon their hinder legs, and to work many strange feats with their fore-feet, at the hearing of certain measures played upon Pipes.

The *Bisaltans* waged War against the *Cardians*, and they had to their Captain a certain man called *Onaris*, who when he was a Boy was sold to *Cardia*, and there he served with a Barber: In the time of his service he oftentimes heard, that the Oracle had foretold, how the *Cardians* should be overcome by the *Bisaltans*, and therefore he to prevent the worst, run away from his Master, and came home safe to *Bisalta* his own Countrey, and was by his Countrey-men created Captain of all their warlike forces: he understanding what tricks the *Cardians* taught their Horses in dancing, brought out of *Cardia* certain Pipes, and taught divers *Bisaltans* to sound and play the measures upon them, which the *Cardians* taught their Horses: whereupon when as they joyned battle with the *Cardian* Horses (for all the force of the *Cardians* lay in their Horses) he commanded his Piping *Bisaltans* to sound their musick, which the Horses understood, who presently stood up upon their hinder-legs, and would not fight any more, or go any further, so as they were overthrown by their adversaries.

They have also a singular pleasure in publick spectacles, and therefore have been observed to be provoked not only by pipes or such instrumentall musick, but also by Songs or vocall harmony, by variety of colours, and by burning Torches. *Dion* also writeth that he saw a Horse taught to know and to do reverence to a King.

And *Textor* affirmeth that he saw a Horse at *Paris* at the trumphs, Tilt, and Turnaments made for the mariage of *Lewis* the twelfth to *Mary*, a Lady of *Britain*, which being commanded by his Rider to salute the Queen, presently did bend both his knees unto her, and then rose again running away as fast as a bird could flie.

Homer seemeth also to affirm that there are in Horses divine qualities, understanding things to come, for being tyed to their mangers they mourned for the death of *Patroclus*, and also fore shewed *Achilles* what should happen unto him: for which cause *Pliny* saith of them, that they lament their lost Masters with tears, and foreknow battles; *Virgil* writeth thus of the Horse of *Pallas*;

> *Post bellator equus, positis insignibus, Æthon*
> *It lachrymans, guttisque humectat grandibus ora.*

Accursius affirmeth, that *Cæsar* three dayes before he died, found his ambling Nag weeping in the stable, which was a token of his ensuing death, which thing I should not believe, except *Tranquillus* in the life of *Cæsar*, had related the same thing, and he addeth moreover, that the Horses which were consecrated to *Mars* for passing over *Rubicon*, being let to run wilde abroad without their Masters, because no man might meddle with the Horses of the Gods, were found to weep aboundantly, and to abstain from all meat. Whereof there could be no cause given, but the love of their former Masters. It is also reported of *Rodatus*, a Captain to *Charles* the great, who after the death of the Emperour was made a Monk, his Horse would never suffer any to come on his back except his Master, who likewise had abstained from riding many years: But it happened that certain *Pagans* brake in upon the said Monastery, whereupon poor *Rodatus* went unto his Horse, who after many years discontinuance, willingly took up his aged Master upon his back, and so carryed him untill he triumphed over his adversaries; and no marvel, for Dogs and Horses are most loving to men, if they be brought up carefully, and liberally, they recompense the good turns of their benefactors. It is observed in the nature of Horses, that they seldom hurt a man or childe, except in their madness, yet are there malicious Horses as well as men. It is reported by *Pliny* and *Tzetzes*, that when a foal hath lost his dam, the residue of the Mares which give suck, bring it up, and that they are seldom found at variance, except the barren Mares pull away the foals from the natural dams. For there is no creature so loving to their young ones, as are Mares, neither any so desirous of young; for which cause, when they are barren themselves, they labour to steal them away from others.

They which were wont to races, would perform it upon Mares newly delivered of foals they tyed up the foals at home, and led the Mares to the beginning of the race, making the end thereof at the foals stable; and so putting the Beast forward, she runneth homewards more speedily for the remembrance of her foal.

OF THE FEAR OF HORSES, AND THEIR ENEMIES IN NATURE.

HORSES are afraid of Elephants in battle, and likewise of a Camel; for which cause when *Cyrus* sought against *Cræsus*, he overthrew his Horse by the sight of Camels, for a Horse cannot abide to look upon a Camel. If a Horse tread in the foot-path of a Wolfe, he presently falleth to be astonished: Likewise if two or more drawing a Chariot, come into the place where a Wolf hath trod, they stand so still as if the Chariot and they were frozen to the earth, saith *Ælianus* and *Pliny*. *Æsculapius* also affirmeth the same thing of a Horse treading in a Bears footsteps, and assigneth the reason to be in some secret, betwixt the feet of both Beasts.

We have shewed already, that if a Mare strike a Wolf, or tread in the foot-steps thereof, she presently casteth her Foal; and therefore the *Egyptians*, when they signifie a Woman suffering abortment, picture a Mare kicking a Wolf. The *Dextanian* Horses being not Gelded, dare fight with Lions, but being gelded, like all other Horses, they are so afraid of Lions, that no stripes, or spurs, is able to bring them in their presence, the *Caropian* Horses excepted.

All kinde of Swine are enemies to Horses; the Estridge also is so feared of a Horse, that the Horse dares not appear in his presence. The like difference also is betwixt a Horse and a Bear. There is a Bird which is called *Anclorus*, which neyeth like a Horse, flying about, the Horse doth many times drive it away, but because it is somewhat blind, and cannot see perfectly, therefore the Horse doth oftentimes catch it, and devour it, hating his own voice in a creature so unlike himself.

It is reported by *Aristotle*, that the Bustard loveth a Horse exceedingly, for seeing other Beasts feeding in the Pastures, despiseth and abhorreth them, but as soon as ever it seeth a Horse, it flyeth unto him for joy, although the Horse run away from it; and therefore the *Egyptians*, when they see a weak man driving away a stronger, they picture a Bustard flying to a Horse. Horses are also taught to leap, if a Man take him by the rains, and go over the ditch before him, holding him fast, and pulling him to him. But if he be unwilling, then let another come behind him and strike him with a whip, or with a rod, so will he leap over without delay; and thus when you have used him to leap empty, likewise accustome him loaded. First over smaller, and then over greater hedges. But at the beginning let him leap in soft ground, and being well practised in harder; and when he beginneth to leap, let the Rider put spurs unto him, for so will he performe his leap with more safety to himself and the Rider; and by custome he may leap and run as well down the hill as up hill; and therefore the *Persians*, and *Nodrisians* use and accustome their Horses to run both down hill, and up hill.

These Epithets following, do serve and express the nature of Horses; full of stomach, generous, magnanimous, strong, ardent, sharp, covetous, fierce, bolde, threatning, terrible, foaming; such were the Horses of *Acarnania, Argos, Mycena, Aria, Elis, Epid, Spain, Thessali, Farsalis*, of which Countrey was *Bucephalus*, the Horse of *Alexander. Ballasia*, a Province addicted to *Mahomet*, hath many of these excellent, great and swift Horses, whose hoofs are so hard, that they need no iron shooes, although they travel over rocks and mountains.

The *Arabians* also have such Horses, and in the Kingdom of *Senega*, they have no breed of Horses at all, by reason of the heat of their Countrey, which doth not only burn up all pasture, but also cause Horses to fall into the Strangury; for which cause they do buy Horses very dear, using in stead of Hay, the stalkes of Pease dryed and cut asunder, and Millet seed in stead of Oats, wherewithal they grow exceeding fat; and the love of that people is so great to Horses, that they give for a Horse furnished nine bond-slaves, or if it please them well, fourteen; but when they have bought their Horses, they send for Witches, and observe therein this ceremony.

They make a burning fire with stickes, putting therein certain fuming herbs, afterwards they take the Horse by the bridle, and set him over the smoaking fire, anointing him with a very thin ointment, muttering secretly certain charmes, and afterwards hanging other charmes about their Neck in a red skin, shut them up close for fifteen dayes together: then did they bring them forth, affirming that by this means they are made more valiant and couragious in war.

THE LOVE AND KNOWLEDGE OF HORSES TO MEN.

AND to this discourse of Horses belongeth their nature, either of loving or killing men. Of the nature of *Alexanders* Horse before spoken of, called *Bucephalus*, is sufficently said, except this may be added, that so long as he was naked and without furniture, he would suffer any man to come on his back; but afterwards being sadled and furnished, he could endure none but *Alexander* his Master: For if any other had offered to come near him, for to ride him, he first of all terrified him with his neighing voice, and afterwards trod him under foot if he ran not away. When *Alexander* was in the *Indian* Wars, and riding upon this Horse in a certain battle, performed many valiant acts, and through his own improvidence, fell into an ambush of his foes, from which he had never been delivered alive, but for the puissancy of his Horse, who seeing his Master beset with so many enemies, received the Darts into his own body, and so with violence pressed through the middest of his enemies, having lost much bloud, and received many wounds, ready to die for pain, not once stayed his course till he had brought his Master the King safe out of the battle, and set him on the ground; which being performed, in the same place he gave up the ghost and dyed, (as it were comforting himself with this service) that by his own death he had saved the life of such a King: for which cause, after *Alexander* had gotten victory, in that very place where his Horse died, he built a City and called it *Bucephalon*.

It is also reported that when *Licinius* the Emperour would have had his Horses to tear in pieces his Daughter, because she was a Christian, he himself was by one of them bitten to death. *Neocles* the Son of *Themistocles* perished by the biting of a Horse: neither herein only is the nature of Horses terrible, because also they have been taught to tear men in pieces: for it is said that *Busiris* and *Diomedes* did feed their Horses with mans flesh, and therefore *Hercules* took the like revenge of *Diomedes*, for he gave him to his Horses to be eaten: of *Diomedes* were these Verses made;

Ut qui terribiles pro gramen habentibus herbis,
Impius humano viscere pavit equos.

557

The like also is reported of *Glaucus* (the Son of *Sysiphus*) who fed Horses with mans flesh at *Polnia* a City of *Bœotia*, and afterward when he could make no more provision for them, they devoured their Master: whereof *Virgil* writeth thus;

> *Et mentem Venus ipsa dedit, quo tempore Glauci:*
> *Potniades malis membra absumpsere quadrigæ.*

But this is thought a fiction, to expresse them which by feeding and keeping of Horses, consume their wealth and substance. And thus much for the natural inclination of Horses.

OF SEVERAL KINDES OF HORSES.

THERE be several kinds of Horses which require a particular tractate by themselves, and first of all the Martial or great warlike Horse, which for profit the Poet coupleth with Sheep:

> *Laniferæ pecudes & equorum bellica proles.*

The parts of this Horse are already described in the Stallion, the residue may be supplyed out of *Xenophon* and *Oppianus*. He must be of a singular courage and docibility, without maime, fear, or other such infirmity.

He must be able to run up and down the steepest hils, to leap, and bite, and fight in battle, but with the direction of his Rider: for by these is both the strength of his body and minde discovered; and above all, such a one as will never refuse to labour, though the day be spent: wherefore the Rider must first look to the institution and first instruction of his Horse, for knowledge in martial affaires is not natural in Men or Horses, and therefore except information and practice adorne nature, it cannot be, but either by fear or heady stubborness, they will overthrow themselves and their Riders. First of all they must not be Geldings, because they are fearful, but they must be such as will rejoyce and gather stomach at the voice of musick, or Trumpets, and at the ringing of Armour: they must not be afraid of other Horses, and refuse to combate, but he able to leap high and far, and rush into the battle, fighting (as is said) with heels and mouth.

The principal things which he must learn are these: first to have a lofty and flexible neck, and also to be free, not needing the spur; for if he be sluggish and need often agitation to and fro by the hand of the Rider, or else if he be full of stomach and sullen, so as he will do nothing but by flattery and fair speeches, he much troubleth the minde of the Rider: but if he run into the battle with the same outward aspect of body, as he doth unto a flock or company of Mares, with loud voice, high neck, willing mind, and great force, so shall he be both terrible to look upon, and valiantly puissant in his combate. Wherefore the Rider must so carry his hand, as the rains may draw in the Horses neck, and not so easily, as in a common travelling Gelding, but rather sharply to his grievance a little, by which he will be taught as it were by signes and tokens to fight, stand still, or run away.

The manner of his institution may be this; after the dressing and furnishing of your Horse as aforesaid, and likewise the backing, first of all move, stir or walk your Horse gently, untill he be well acquainted with the cariage of your hand and whole body, and afterward accustome him to greater and speedier pace or exercise, use him also to run longer races, and also by drawing in your hand to stay or stop suddenly; for there are Horses so instructed, that they can stay themselves in their speediest course upon an instant, without any circumambulation, shaking off the violence of their course, like an ordinary trotting Nag, by mounting up a little with their forefeet.

And alway it is to be remembred that after the mounting on horse-back, you must first of al begin on the left hand, bending your hand that way, and also to the right hand when you would have your Horse to turn on that side. And above all other things Horses are delighted with crooked, bending and round courses, such as are in circles and Rings, and he must be accustomed to run from other Horses leaving them behind him, and likewise turning toward them and making at them with his face to them: but headlong and precipitate courses, such as hunters make without guiding body, hand or Horse, are evermore to be avoided, for many men have perished from theis Horses, as the Poets witness of

Nipheus, Leucagus, Liger, Clonius, Remulus, Amycus. And also among the *Historiographers, Agenor, Fulco* of *Jerusalem, Philip* son of *Ludovicus Crassus* King of *France*, and *Bela* King of *Pannonia*.

Of Horse-men, and the orders of Chivalry and Knighthood.

THE principal Horse-men of the world celebrated in stories, for training, ruling, and guiding their Horses according to the art of War, may for the dignity of Knighthood (wherewithal they are honoured) and from whom that Equestrial order is derived, be recited in this place. It is manifest by *Sipontinus*, that the *Roman* Equestrial order, was in the middle betwixt the Senatours and the common people, for at the first there was no difference betwixt *Equites* and *Judices*, for both of them had for a badge, cognisance, or note of their honour, power to wear a ring of gold, and in the Consulship of *Marcus Cicero* the title was turned to Equestrial, or name of a Knight, or man at Armes, by that means reconciling himself to the Senate, and affirming that he was derived from that order, and from that time came the *Equester ordo*, being, as is said before, the people, and recorded after the people, because of the latter creation thereof: yet had they not their beginning at this time, but only now they first came into the orders of the Common-wealth; for they were called *Celeres* under *Romulus*, of one *Celer* who at the command of *Romulus* slew *Remus*; and he was made the chief Judge of three hundred. They were afterward called *Flexanimes*, either because they swayed the minds of them whom they judged, or else which is more probable, because of martialling and instructing their Horses for war: afterward because they took a great company of horse-men, without all and of footmen, at the City *Trossulum* in *Thuscia*, they were called *Trossulani*, and *Trossuli*, and yet some ignorant persons honoured with the title of *Trossuli* in remembrance of that victory, were ashamed thereof as unworthy their dignities.

They were forbidden to wear purple like as were the Senatours, and their golden Ring was a badge both of Peace and War. The Master of the Horse among the *Romans*, called by the *Grecians, Hipparchus*, and by the *Latins, Magister Equitum*, was a degree of honour next to the *Dictator*, and *Marcius* the *Dictator* made the first Master of horse-men, who was called *Spurius*, and set him in place next to himself. These Equestrial men or Knights of State were wont to be publicans at the least, and it was ordained that no man should be called into that order, except both he, his Father, and Grandfather were free men, and were worth in value twenty thousand pound: *Turon* and *Tiberius* made this law, but afterward it grew remisse and not observed; whereby both Bondmen and Scribes were rewarded with this dignity from the Emperour, for Orations and pleasing speeches: yet were the Decurial Judges chosen out of this rank; for indeed by primary institution, they were the flower and seminary of the *Roman* Gentry. *Pliny* complaineth that this dignity which was wont to be a reward for Military men, who had adventured their lives for the honour of their Countrey, was now bestowed corruptly, and for money upon mean bribing persons. It should seem they had every one a Horse of honour given to him for his note, for if one of them had grown fat and unweeldy, not able to manage and govern this Horse, it was taken from him. And *Cato* took away the Horse from *Scipio Astaticus*, because he had intercepted money; and from hence came the terms of their allowance, as *Equestre æs*, for that money which was paid for a Horse to one Knight, and *Pararium æs*, for a double fee to an Equestrial man.

Among the *Athenians*, the highest order was of them which were called *Pentacosiomedymni*, which had plowed so much sand as had sowed an 100 bushels of Corn; and the next degree were their *Equites*, Knights, or Horse-men, because for the defence of their City, they were able every one to nourish a Horse of war. There were of these in ancient time but 600, and afterward they were increased unto 1200, and the sacrifices which were made for their pomps and triumphs, were called *Hippades*: and they had liberty to nourish their long hair which was forbidden to other men, and their tax to the sacrifice was at the least half a talent, (which is at the least 300 Crowns) and this sacrifice was made for the health of their Horses. There were two Masters created over these, to wage and order war; and ten inferiour Governours or Wardens to look to the provision and nourishing of Horses.

Among the *Lacedemonians* they had four Governments; the *Monarchy* for the Kings, the *Aristocraty* for the Old-men, the *Oligarchie* for their *Ephori* or Commissioners, the *Democratie* for their Young-men, which governed, managed, and instructed Horses. *Nestor* that ancient Knight was commended for his skill, and had therefore given him the title of *Hippotes*.

Among the *Calcidensians* there was not a rich man but they took him into this Order, and the *Cretians* likewise did ever highly account hereof, and made it their highest degree of honour, for even the *Romans* did sometime govern whole Provinces with no other then these; and *Egypt* had this in peculiar, that no other Order, no not a Senator might be President or Govern among them. The *Achæans* had this degree in high estimate, like as the *Germans* their *Batavi* or States. The Citizens of *Capua* were and are disguised with a perpetuity of this honour, because in the *Latins* war, they did not revolt from the *Romans*; and among all other, the *Gaditan* were most honoured herewith, for at one time and for one battle: they created 400. This title hath spred and adorned it self with many more degrees, as that among the *French*, *Caballarii* and *Equites aurati*, and such as are Knights of *Jerusalem* and divers others, some for Religion, and some for feats of Armes: whereas the *Persians* used a certain kind of garment in War, called *Manduas*, from hence cometh the Knights upper garment to be called a mantle, for all the *Persians* were Horsemen. The noblest Horses and such as could run most speedily and swiftly were joyned together in chariots for races, courses, spectacles, games and combates, for great values and prizes.

> ――― ――― *Nempe volucrem*
> *Sic laudamus equum: facili cui plurima palma*
> *Fervet, & exultat rauco victoria circo.*

And again *Ovid* saith;

> *Non ego nobilium venio spectator equorum.*

And *Horace*;

> *Nec te nobilium sugiat certamen equorum.*

562

There was one *Anniceris* a *Cyrenian* most skilful in this practise, and according to the vain humors of men, was not a little proud hereof, and for his love to *Plato* would needs in the *Academy* shew him and his Scholars his skill, and therefore joyning his Horses and Chariot together, made many courses with such an even and delineate proportion, that his Horses and wheels never wandered a hair breadth from the circle or place limited, but alway kept the same road and footsteps, whereat every one marvelled: but *Plato* reproved the double diligence and vain practice of the man, saying to him in this manner, It cannot be, that a man which hath travelled and laboured so much in an art or skill of no worth or use in the Common-wealth, that ever he can addict his mind to grave, serious and profitable business, for while he applyeth all his parts and powers of body and soul to this, he is the lesse able and more unapt to those things which are alone more worthy of admiration.

The ancient custom was, to use other mens Horses in this combate, and therefore in the funeral of *Patroclus*, *Homer* bringeth in *Menelaus*, using the Horse of *Agamemnon*. There were four several places wherein these games of Horses and Chariots were wont to be observed and kept, and they were called after these places, *Olympia*, *Pythia*, *Nemea*, and *Isthmia*, and of all these the *Olympiads* were the chief, whereof all stories are full, for they were celebrated in *Olympus* every fifth year inclusively, that is, after the end of every fourth year.

The writers of Chronicles do agree that the games of *Olympus* were first instituted by *Hercules* in the 2752 year of the world, beginning the world from *Noahs* flood, and they begin to record and number the first *Olympiad* to be about the 3185 year of the world, about seventeen year before the building of *Rome*.

There were of these *Olympiads* 328 and the last of these by computation or account fell about the year of our Lord 534 after the birth of Jesus Christ the blessed Saviour of the world.

The perfection of these games began the twenty five *Olympiad*, at what time *Pagondas* the *Theban* was pronounced victor: for then were swift Horses brought into the games, and were called *Teleioi*, that is, perfect in agility and growth; and these are called by *Pindarus*,

563

Monampycia; afterward came in *Synaris* with two Horses, and in succession both Colts, Mares, and Mules: their courses are thus expressed by *Virgil*;

———— *Ergo animos ævumque notabis,*
Et quis cuique dolor victo, quæ gloria palmæ,
Nonne vides? cum præcipiti certamine campum
Corripuere, ruuntque effusi carcere currus,
Cum spes arrectæ invenum, exultantiaque haurit
Corda pavor pulsans, illi instant verbere torto,
Et proni dant lora: volat vi fervidus axis.
Jamque humiles, jamque elati sublime videntur
Aera per vacuum ferri atque assurgere in auras,
Nec mora, nec requies: at fulvæ nimbus arenæ
Tollitur: humescunt spumis, flatuque sequentum:
Tantus amor laudum, tantæ est victoria curæ.
Sin ada bella magis studium turmasque feroces,
Aut Alphæarotis prælabi flumina Pisæ,
Et Jovis in luco currus agitare volantes:
Primus equi labor est, animos atque arma videre
Bellantum, lituosque pati, tractuq; gementem
Ferre rotam, & stabulo frenos audire sonantes.

And *Horace* expresseth it in this manner:

Sunt quos curriculo pulverem Olympicum
Collegisse juvat, metaque fervidis
Evitata rotis, palmaque nobilis
Terrarum dominos evehit ad deos.

Women were wont to be excluded from these games, untill *Cynisca* the daughter of *Archidamus* King of the *Spartans*, first of all other women nourished and trained Horses for these currule and Chariot games, and when she brought her Horses to *Olympus*, she obtained the prize; therefore her Horses were consecrated to *Jupiter Olympius*, and their figures remained in Brass in his Temple.

It is also said that *Echarates* a *Thessalian* overcame in the *Olympian* games with a Mare great with foal: And it is also reported that *Miltiades* the son of *Cimon Stesagora* (one of the ten Captains of *Athens*) ran away from *Pisistratus* the Tyrant, and in the time of his absence, he was twice Victor at *Olympus* by four Mares, the first time he bestowed the glory upon his cousen German *Miltiades*, his mothers brothers son, and the second time he took it to himself; for which cause he was slain by the sons of *Pisistratus*; his Mares were also buryed over against him, with an inscription, that they had won four games in *Olympus*, so that it appeared, he ran divers times and never missed victory. At *Athens* they observed these courses with Horses in honour of *Theseus*, and called the place of the running, *Hippodromus*.

The *Latines* call it *Stadium*, and *Curriculum*, and it was appointed in some plain valley, according to the proverb, *Equus in planiciem*; in the midst whereof was a building called *Circus*, whereon the beholders stood to look upon the pastime, and there were also places to contain the Horses and Chariots, till they were turned out to run, (called *Carceres*) according to the verses of *Silius*:

> *Sic ubi prosiluit piceo de carcere præceps*
> *Ante suos it victor Equus.* ———

And *Horace* also,

> *Ut cum carceribus missos rapit ungula currus,*
> *Instat equis auriga suos vincentibus, illum*
> *Præteritum temnens extremos inter euntem.*

And hereof came the proverb (*A carceribus ad calcem*) signifying from beginning of the race to the latter end. *Erichthonius* invented a Chariot called *Harma*, and was the first that ever ran in *Olympus* with four Horses in the same, of whom *Virgill* writeth thus:

> *Primus Erichthonius currus & quatuor ausus*
> *Jungere Equos rapidisque insistere victor.*

And from hence came the tearm *Quadriga*, for a Chariot with four Horses. There was a Chariot in *Athens* drawn by one Horse, and the games thereof were called *Polemysteria*. Likewise at *Rome* in the Consul-

feasts celebrated for the honour of *Neptune*, they ran with Horses both joyned and single.

There were likewise games at *Rome*, called *Equitia*, and *Equitia*, celebrated every year, the twelfth of the Calends of *May*, wherein after the Horses they coursed Foxes tyed to pieces of wood set on fire; this is called in *Latine* also *Turneamentum*; and in *Italian* by *Scoppa, Hagiostra*; and in *French Formierim*. There is also a play with Horses for children cal'd *Troia*, first invented by *Ascantus*, when he besieged *Alba*, and by him brought and taught to the *Romans*, of which *Virgill* speaketh, saying;

> *Incedunt pueri, pariterque ante ora parentum*
> *Frenatis lucent in equis, ———*
> *Cornea bina ferunt præfixa hastilia ferro:*
> *Pars læves humero pharetras. ———*
> *Tres equitum numero turmæ, ternique vogantur*
> *Ductores: pueri bisseni quemque secuti.*
> *——— Signum clamore paratis*
> *Æpytides longe dedit, insonuitque flagello.*
> *Olli discurrere pares, atque agmina terni*
> *Diductis solvere choris, rursusque vocati*
> *Convertere vias, infestaque tela tulere.*
> *Inde alios ineunt cursus, aliosque recursus*
> *Adversis spatiis, alternosq orbibus orbes*
> *Impediunt, pugnæque cient simulachra sub armis.*
> *Et nunc terga: fugæ nudant, nunc spicula veriunt*
> *Infensi: facta pariter nunc pace feruntur.*
> *Hunc morem cursus, atque hæc certamina primus*
> *Ascanius, long am muris cum cingeret Albam.*
> *Rectulit, & priscos, docuit celebrare Latinos.*
> *——— Hinc maxima porro*
> *Accepit Roma, & patrium servavit honorem:*
> *Trojaque nunc pueri, Trojanum dicitur agmen.*

OF THE GREATEST HORSE-MASTERS AND NOURISHERS OF HORSES.

IT is reported of King *Solomon*, that he had forty thousand stables of Horses for Chariots, and twelve thousand for war. The *Lybians* when they went to war, did fight out of their Chariots, and therefore they were said to fight upon two Horses. The *Centaures* were the first that ever taught men to fight on Horse-back, and the *Roman Turnia* consisted of two and thirty Horse-men, the Captain whereof was called *Breoutio*. The people of *Nomades* called *Surgatii*, brought eight thousand Horse-men at one time into the field, which neither used armour nor brass, nor iron, except only their daggers, and a rope of leather thongs, wherewithall they entred the battail, and joyning with their enemy, they made certain gins, or loops thereupon, which they cast upon the necks of Horses and men, and so with multitudes drew them unto them, in which draught they strangled them.

The *Indians* use the very self same Armour on Horse-back that they do on foot, but yet they lead empty Horses and Chariots to leap up and down upon, and to refresh their fighting Horses; and the number of their Horse-men were at one time fourscore thousand.

When *Pharnuches* the *Arabian*, was riding on Horse-back, there was a Dog ran betwixt his Horses legs, wherewithall the Horse being amazed, suddenly leaped upright, and cast off his Rider, who being bruised with the fall, fell into a Consumption: whereupon the Servants at the commandment of their Master, brought the said Horse into the place where he cast his Rider, and there cut off his legs about the knees. There was also a fashion for Horses to fight in battails without bridles: For *Fulvius Flaccus*, when the *Romans* overthrew the *Celtiberians* in *Spain*, caused them to pull off their bridles from their Horses, that so they might run with all violence, without restraint of Riders upon their enemies; whereupon followed victory: for many times it falleth out that the Horse hath more courage then his Rider, wherefore a good Horse-man must have skill to annoy his enemy, and defend himself; and likewise, to make his Horse to come off and on without fear or dread, according to necessity.

There is a proverb in *Greek, (Choris hippeis)* that is, (*Seorsim equites*) the Horsemen are asunder, whereof *Suidas* giveth this reason: when *Darius* invaded the territory of the *Athenians* ranging and destroying at his pleasure, no man daring to abide his forces, at his departure, the *Ionians* climed up into trees, and signified unto the *Athenians*, that the

Horse-men had broken rank and were asunder. Whereupon *Miltiades* set upon the scatered company, and obtained a noble victory.

OF FIGHTING IN WAR UPON HORSES.

THE most cruel and fearful kinde of fight, is the arming of Horses, which were called in antient time *Catafracti*, and *Clibanarii*, and *Acatafracti*, and *Færentarii*, fighting first of all with spear, and afterwards with sword and shield, casting sometimes also darts at one another, and bearing bows to shoot arrows, their Horses making room for them, which way soever they went: for with sharp pikes and other crooked-keen-cutting-instruments, fastened to their Armour or Chariot-wheels, in the violence of their course, they wounded, killed, over-turned, or cut asunder whatsoever flesh came in their reach.

The ancient Horsemen of the *Romans* had no breast-plates, (as *Polybius* affirmeth) and therefore they were naked in their fore-parts, providing for the danger that was behinde them, and defending their breast, by their own celerity: their shields were made of Oxe skins plighted and pasted together, being a little round in compass like the fashion of a mans belly.

There was also great use of swift Horses in War, for the *Roman* Souldiers carried with them two Horses a peece, being taught and exercised like *Indians*, when they had need to flie, to leap upon their empyty Horse, for their sparing of the other: and they were therefore called *Amphippi* being apt to carry their Masters out of danger, and from hence (*Ælianus* saith) the *Romans* took the pattern of their *Phalanx*, (called *Antistomus*) with which they used to terrifie the Barbarians, setting their Horses in a double front, so as they appeared headed both waves; and this was also the custom of all the *Germans*, when the number of their Horse-men was not equall, they mingled the Foot-men, with their Light-horses, who being experienced to run suddenly with the Horse men, leaped into the battail, and surprized the enemies flying away: and the same fashion did the *Spaniards* aso use (*Strabo* saith) for the terrifying of their enemies, making the Foot-men to fall into the battell among the Horse-men.

568

Those which did shoot Darts on Horse-back, were called *Hippotoxotæ*, and therefore *Aristophanes* in his discourse of Birds, calleth Hawks by that name, for the resemblance betwixt them and Horses, bearing these Riders. The Hawks are so called in swiftness of their course; and because the talons of the Hawk are crooked like bows. *Arrianus* writeth that the Horse-men of *Alexander* carryed spears in their hands fourteen cubits long, whereunto I cannot consent; for eight cubits is a common size, as much as any Souldier on Horse-back is able to use.

In battail there are wings of Horse-men, which are so called, because like wings they cover and protect the Army. And there were also Legionary Horse-men, because they were joyned to the Legions of Souldiers, and the company of Elephants, Foot-men, and Horse-men which were wont to go before the King, were called *Agema*. A company of Horses set like a Tower in a Quadrangular form in a field, was called *Pergus*. The Armour of Horses on his front or fore-part, is called *Prometopidia*, upon the ears *Parotia*, upon the cheeks *Paria*, upon the breast *Prosternidia*, upon the sides *Parapleuridia*, upon the loins *Parameridia*, upon the legs *Paracnemidia*. And the time of arming a Horse is known of every Souldier.

OF RIDING.

THE *Medes, Persians*, and *Armenians*, were the first that invented the art of riding and shooting, (as *Strabo* saith) *Pausanias* cald *Neptune Hippeus* for no other cause, but that it was supposed he was the first invented the art of riding. *Polydorus* ascribeth it to *Bellerophon. Lysias* the Orator saith, that the *Amazonian* women were the first of all mortal creatures that first adventured to back Horses. Others ascribe it to the *Centaures*: But to leave the Invention, and come to the Art. *Damis* in the life of *Apollonius*, setteth down the sum of the Art of riding, which briefly is this; To sit straight upon his Horse, to rule him valiantly, to turn him with the bridle which way soever he pleaseth, to beat him when he is stubborn, to avoid Ditches, Gulfs, and Whirlpools when he rideth through waters; going up a hill, to lengthen the rains, and to restrain and draw them in going down the hill; now and then to stroke his hair, and not always to use stripes.

Martial hath an excellent Epigram upon one *Priscus* a rash-headed-hunter, who neither feared Hedges, Hils, Dales, Ditches, Rocks, Rivers, nor other perils; using a bridle to his Horse, but none to his affections; and therefore he telleth him, that he may sooner break a Hunters neck, then take away a Hares life: for there are deceits in the Rocks, Hils, and plain Fields, to shake the Rider from Horse-back to the earth. Thus followeth the Epigram;

> *Parcius utaris moneo rapiente veredo,*
> *Prisce, nec in lepores tam violentus eas.*
> *Sæpe satis fecit prædæ venator, & acri*
> *Decidit excussus nec rediturus equo.*
> *Insidias & campus habet: nec fossa, nec agger,*
> *Nec sint saxa licet, fallere plana solent.*
> *Non deerunt qui tanta tibi spectacula præstent:*
> *Invidia fati sed leviore cadunt.*
> *Si te delectant animosa pericula, Thuscis*
> *(Tutior est virtus) insidiemur apris.*
> *Quid te frena juvant temeraria? Sæpius illis*
> *Prisce datum est equitem rumpere, quam leporem.*

The best place for riding, is a barren and plain Countrey. It is reported of *Claudius*, that when he had road a great way in the Countrey upon his enemies, and met no body, he returned back again into his own Camp, and blamed the sluggishness of his enemies, because no one of them was seen abroad.

It is reported by *Aristotle*, that the further a man rideth, the more apt he shall be to weep; and the reason is, because of all the motions of the body, riding is the wholesomest, both for the stomach and for the hips; for a man must not sit on Horse-back, as if he were carryed in a Coach; but rather keep his back-bone upright, not only to be moved by his Horse that beareth him, but also by himself; and there he must sit close to the Horses hips, extending his legs to the uttermost, using not only his eyes to look before him, but also lifting up his neck to help his sight: for so the soft pace of the Horse doth corroborate the spirit above all other exercises; likewise, the body and stomach; also it purgeth the senses, and maketh them sharp: yet sometimes by the violent course of a Horse, the breast of a Man, or some other part about the reins receive damage, (as some have observed:) yet is it not so much to be ascribed to the motion of riding, as to the uneasie pace, or rather to the uneasie seat of the Rider.

The *Scythians* above all other Nations have the loosest and broadest bodies; and the reason is, because they wrap not their children in swadling cloaths as other people, and likewise because they have no regard unto their sitting upon Horse-back; and lastly, for their continual sloath and ease: for the men use much to ride in Chariots, and Litters, before they get on Horse-back; but after they are accustomed thereunto, they ride so much, that their hips and bones fall full of ach, and they are also thereby made unfit for generation, because in a journey of an hundred miles, they never light to ease themselves and their Beasts.

These men hereafter named, were excellent Riders and tamers of Horses. *Automedon*, servant of *Achilles; Idæus*, servant to *Paraimus; Metiscus*, servant to *Turnus; Myrtilus*, servant to *Oenomaus; Ceberes*, servant to *Darius; Anniceris*, servant to *Cyreneus; Picus* to *Mesapus;* and *Lausus Silius* remembreth *Cyrnas, Durius, Atlas*, and *Iberus*.

The instruments of Riding appertaining to a Horse.

A good Rider must consider the hardness or softness of his Horses mouth, that so he may temper his bit; for a stiffe-necked Horse, is not so much to be guided by rod and Spur, as by bit, and bridle: wherefore it must sometime be hard, and sometimes gentle. The hard bits are called *Lupati*, because they are unequal, and indented to a Wolves teeth, whereunto the Horse being accustomed, groweth more tractable and obedient to a gentle bit. According to the saying of *Ovid*:

Tempore paret equus lentis animosus habenis,
Et placido dutos accipit ore lupos.

And *Virgill* again speaketh to like effect:

571

―――― *prensisque negabunt*
Verbera lenta pati, & duris parere lupatis
Asper equus, duris contunditur or a lupatis.

And *Silius* saith:

Quadrupedem flectit non cedens virga lupatis.

There is also another instrument made of Iron or Wood (called *Pastomis*) and *Englished, Barnacles*; which is to be put upon the Horses nose, to restrain his tenacious fury from biting, and kicking, especially at such time, as he is to be shod or dressed. The *Indians* were wont to use no bridles, like the *Græcians* and *Celts*, but only put upon their Horses mouth a piece of a raw Oxe skin, fastened round about, containing in it certain iron pricks standing to the Horses lips, putting a long round trench through his mouth, to the edge whereof they fasten the rains, wherewithall they guide the beast. The *Turkish* Horses, and *Spanish* Jennets have bits, with open circles in the middle, consisting of Leather, or Iron, to restrain the Horses fury. The rains are called *Habenæ*, because they make the Horses, Habiles, that is, tractable, and rulable, to be turned, restrained, or put forward, at our pleasure, according to the saying of *Silius*;

Ferrato calce, atque effusa largus habena,
Cunctantem impellebat equum. ――――

And *Virgill*:

Ipse ter adducta circum caput egit habena.

Neither is there any Horse swift, or slow, noble, or unnoble, that can be guided without these; which must be held continually in the hand of the Rider, they must not be unequal, one longer then another, neither thick, neither weak, nor brickle.

There was a certain golden chain (called *Ampix*) wherewithal the fore-tops of Horses were wont to be bound or tyed up, and thereupon *Homer* calleth the Horse of *Mars, Chrysampix*; and from hence that custom of womens frontlets, to be adorned with gold and pretious stones. There are

572

also other ornaments of Horses called trappings; and in *Latine, Phaleræ*, derived from *Phalon* in *Greek*, signifying bright, because they were wont to put a great deal of gold and silver upon them, (as *Livius* saith) which Horses so trapped, were presents for great Princes: And there is a kind of *Achates* stone, wherewithal the *Indians* do adorn their Horse-trappings: and it was apparent in *Homers* time, that they used little Bels, or sounding pieces of Brass to be fastened to their Horses bridles and trappings; they hanged likewise Jewels and Pearls to the beast of their Horses, which *Virgill* expresseth in this manner:

> *Instratos ostro alipedes, pictisque tapetis*
> *Aurea pectoribus, demissa monilia pendent.*
> *Tecti auro, falvum mandunt sub dentibus aurum.*

A good Horse-man must also have a paring knife, wherewithal to purge and open his Horses feet: this is called by *Rusius, Rossneta*; and by others *Scalprum*. There is a kinde of Manicle for the pasterns of Horses, (called *Numella*.) Moreover a good Rider must provide him stirrops, (called *Subsellares* and *Staphæ*) which although it be but a new devise, yet are they so necessary for every Rider, as without them they cannot long continue. They must not be made too straight for the foot, because that then they do not only hinder motion in that part, and so make it benummed and cold, but also give occasion of great hurt to the Rider in case the Horse fall, except he can so temper himself to put but a very little part of his foot therein.

There are also Spurs requisite to a Rider (called *Calcaria*) because they are fastened to the heel of a man, wherewithal he pricketh his dull Horse when he would have him hasten the journey, and the *Greeks* derive it from *Muops*, signifying a pricking fly, from imitation of which creature it may seem they took this invention: but this must be remembred, that they are prepared for the dull and sluggish Horse, and not for the free and full of life; for such a Horse being pricked therewith, runneth forth rather with rage and disdain, then for love of the journey, and many times the torment thereof maketh him by kicking out his heels to cast off his Rider.

Lastly, he must have regard to his Saddle, whereon he must sit: for the Barbarians did use to ride upon bare Horses backs; but since that time, the wiser sort of Horse-men have invented a seat for their own security. *Martiall* writeth hereof thus:

> *Stragula succincti venator sume veredi,*
> *Nam solet a nudo surgere ficus equo.*

OF HUNTING HORSES.

HUNTING Horses because of their swiftness, were wont to be called *Veredi*; according to the saying: *Sunt & veredi, cursu pernices*: Although they use this kinde also for posts, and performance of speedy journeys. The males are much better then the females, and therefore they seldom use Mares in hunting, because they are not so well able to leap, or endure the Woods, for which cause *Gratius* writeth in this manner of them;

> *Restat equos finire notis, quos arma Dianæ*
> *Admittant: non omne meas genus audet in artes.*
> *Est vitium ex animo: sunt quos imbellia fallant*
> *Corpora: præveniens quendam est incommoda virtus.*

Oppianus in his discourse of hunting Horses, (as we have said already) adviseth to make choise of them by the colour, unto whom *Gratius* consenteth, saying:

> *Venanti melius pugnant color, optima nigri.*

They that are of blewish colour, having variable spotted legs (he saith) are fittest to hunt Harts: they that are of a bright gray, to hunt Bears, and Leopards; they that are bay, or of a reddish colour, to hunt the Boars: they that are black, having glazen eyes, are good against Lyons: and thus much for the hunting Horses.

OF COURSERS, OR SWIFT LIGHT RUNNING HORSES.

AFTER the use of Wagons, and Chariots, which men had invented for their ease in travel, and growing to be weary thereof, by reason of many discommodities, they came also to the use of single Horses, which therefore they called Coursers, and now a days a Horse for Saddle, whereupon men perform their journeys; and the Poets say, the inventer hereof was *Bellerophon* the son of *Neptune*, to whom his father gave *Pegasus* the flying Horse; which therefore they describe with wings, and place for a star in Heaven like an Angel, because of his incredible celerity: others attribute it to the invention of *Sesostris*, otherwise called *Sesonchosis*, a King of *Egypt*; some to *Orus*, when he waged war against his brother *Typhon*; For these Horses, are no less profitable in war, then in peace, although none use them in these days, but common Souldiers; yet in antient time the greatest Nobles rode upon them. The Emperor *Probus* had one of these Horses, which was nothing comely, nor very high, yet would he endure ordinary journeys, to run a hundred mile a day, whereupon his Master was wont to say merrily; that he was better for a flying, then a fighting Souldier. The Horses of *Spain* are of this kinde, which they call Jennets, of *Genibus* their knees; because when the Rider is on their backs, he must hold his knees close to the Saddle and sides, for his better ease. Like unto these are the *Barbary* Horses, whom they geld, to keep them from the hardness of the Nerves, which happenth unto them in their heat and travel. There are a kinde of Horses called *Lycospacles*, and the reason of this name is, as some say; because when they were Foals, they escaped the teeth of Wolves, being set on by them: and therefore they run the more speedily to their dying day, for the wounds of Wolves make a Horse light footed; but this is not likely, for fear cannot put that into them which is not bred of nature; even as we say, that *Ulysses* by avoiding *Circes* cup, or *Cyclops*, was therefore made wise; but rather on the contrary; because he was wise, therefore he did avoid *Circes* cup; so likewise we say, that these Horses are not lighter of foot, nor fuller of courage, because they were set upon by Wolves, and delivered by fear; but because nature hath framed them, nimble, valiant, and couragious; therefore they did avoid the Wolf.

Ælianus also saith, that these Horses had a wonderful knowledge, and sagacity, to discern betwixt *Græcians* and other Nations; for when a *Græcian* came unto them, they loved them, stood still, and took meat at their hands; but if a *Barbarian*, or stranger came unto them, they discerned them by their nose, as a Dog doth the foot-steps of a Beast, lifting up their voyce, they ran as fast away from them as they would from any ravening Beast. These loved not only their familiars; but above all other things to be neat, fine, and cleanly in Chariots: For if at any time they came through water, drawing of a Chariot, they took a pride in cleansing themselves from all durt and filthiness, cleaving to their legs or face. And that which is more strange, they were unwilling in race, to be stayed or taken out thereof, as appeared by this story, related by *Festus*. There is saith he in *Rome* a great gate called *Ratumena*, which took his name from the death of a young man, an *Hetrurian*, who perished there in a race of Chariots, being Conqueror, because his Horses would not stay untill they came into the Capitol, and saw the framed earthen Chariots, which were placed in the porch of *Jupiters* Temple by the *Romans*, and were appointed to be fashioned in earth by the hand of a cunning Potter, the which being wrought in earth, and put into the furnace, they grew so great that they could not be taken out whole; at the sight of these, the Horses of *Ratumena* stood still, but first of all, their master was slain in the course by falling off.

The Horses of *Tartaria* are so incredibly swift, that they will go twenty *German* miles in one day. There was a race of Horses at *Venice* (called *Lupiferæ*) which were exceeding swift, and the common same is, that they came upon this occasion. There was a certain merry fellow, which would become surety for every man, for which he was commonly jested at in the whole City. It fortuned on a day, as he travelled abroad in the Woods; that he met with certain Hunters that had taken a Wolf, they seeing him, asked him merrily, if he would be surety for the Wolf, and make good all his damages that he had done to their flocks, and foals, who instantly confessed he would undertake for the Wolf, if they would set him at liberty; the Hunters took his word, and gave the Wolf his life, whereupon he departed without thanks to the Hunters.

Afterward in remembrance of this good turn, he brought to the house of his surety a great company of Mares without mark or brand, which he received, and branded them with the Images of a Wolf, and they were therefore called *Lupiferæ*, from whom descended that gallant race of swift Horses among the *Veneti*: upon these ride the posts, carrying the letters of Kings and Emperors to the appointed places, and these are said to refuse copulation with any other Horses that are not of their own kinde and linage.

The *Persian* Horses are also exceeding swift, which indeed have given name unto all others. The messengers of the great *Cam* King of *Tartaria*, have their posts so appointed at every five and twenty miles end, of these running light Horses, that they ride upon them, two or three hundred miles a day: And the *Pegasarian* coursers of *France*, by the like change of Horses, run from *Lyons* to *Rome* in five or six days.

The Epithets of a swift running courser are these, winged or wing-bearing, Lark-footed, breathing, speedy, light, stirred, covetous of race, flying, sweating, not slow, victorious, rash, violent, and *Pegasæan*. *Virgil* also describeth a swift and sluggish Horse most excellently in these verses; sending one of them to the Ring, and victory of running, without respect of Countrey or food, they are to be praised for enriching his master, and the other for his dulness to the mill, the verses are these following.

> —— *Nempe volucrem*
> *Sic laudamus equum, facili cui plurima palma*
> *Fervet, & exultat rauco victoria Circo.*
> *Nobilis hic, quocunque venit de gramine, cujus*
> *Clara fuga ante alios, & primus in æquore pulvis,*
> *Sed venale pecus Corithæ, posteritas &*
> *Hirpini, si rara jugo victoria sedit,*
> *Nil tibi majorum respectus, gratia nulla*
> *Umbrarum, dominos pretiis mutare jubentur*
> *Exiguis, tritoque trahunt Epithedia collo*
> *Segnipedes, dignique molam versare Nepotis.*

One of these swift light Horses is not to be admitted to race or course untill he be past three year old, and then may he be safely brought to the ring, and put to the stretching of his legs in a composed or violent pace, as *Virgil* saith:

> *Carpere mox gyrum incipiat gredibusque sonare*
> *Compositis, sinuetque alterna volumina crurum.*

Pliny affirmeth, that if the teeth of Wolves be tyed to these Horses, it will make them never to give over in race, and when the *Sarmatians* were to take long journeys, the day before they gave their Horses very little drink, and no meat at all, and so would they ride them an hundred and fifty miles out right.

The *Arabians* also in many regions use to ride upon Mares, upon whom they perform great journeys, and King *Darius* did also fight his battails upon Mares which had foals; for if at any time their affairs went to rack, and they in danger, the Mares in remembrance of their foals at home would carry them away more speedily then any other Horse: and thus much for the light or swift Horses.

OF THE GELDING.

THEY have used to lib their Horses, and take away their stones, and such an one is called in *Latine, Canterius,* or *Cantherius,* which is drived of *Cauterium,* because they were seared with hot irons, or else from the stronger boughs or branches of Vines, so called, because they were pruned. In *French, Cheval Ogre, Cantier, Cheuron,* and *Soppa* doth interpret the *Spanish, Janetto,* to be a Gelding. It is said of *Cato Censortus,* that he was carryed and rode upon a Gelding; and of these the *Turkish* Horses receive the greatest commendations.

Forasmuch as many Horses by their seed and stones are made very fierce, truculent, and unruly, by taking away of them, they are made serviceable and quiet, which before yeelded unto man very little profit: and this invention may seem first of all to be taken from them which fed divers together in one herd, being taught the intolerable rage of their stoned Horses towards their Colleagues and guides; for abating whereof they took from them their male parts.

Of the manner hereof you may read plentifully in *Rusius,* and he affirmeth that the *Scythians* and *Sarmatians,* who keep all their Horses in herds, were the first devisers thereof: For these people using to rob and forrage, were many times by the neighing of their unruly Horses discovered; for their property is to neigh not only at Mares, but also at every stranger that they see or winde, and for males they were so headstrong, that they would divers times carry away the Rider perforce, and against his will, to his own destruction, in the rage of their natural lust.

If they be gelded under their dams when they suck, it is reported by some; that from such their teeth never fall away; and beside, in the heat of their course their nerves are not hardned, for which cause they are the best of all to run withall.

They use to geld them in *March*, in the beginning of the Spring, afterward being well nourished, they are no less strong, able and couragious then other unlibbed; also there is a pretty proverb, *Cantherius in Fossa*, a Gelding in a Ditch, which is then to be used, when a man undertaketh a business which he is not able to manage; for a Horse can do much in a plain, but nothing at all in a Ditch. It is reported that *Jubellius Taurea*, and *C. Assellius*, fought a combate on Horse-back near the City *Capua*, and when one had provoked another a good while in the plain fields, *Taurea* descended into a hollow way, telling his fellow combatant, that except he came down unto him, it would be a fight of Horses, and not of Horse-men; whereunto *Assellius* yeelded, and came down unto the Ditch: at whom his adversary jested, asking him, if he did not know, that a Gelding could do nothing in a ditch, from whence came the common proverb aforesaid.

There is also another proverb (*Cantherius in Porta*) A Gelding in the gate, to signifie a man who after he had undertaken the performance of a great exploit, his heart faileth in the very entrance, for it is reported of one *Sulpicius Galba*, who riding out of the City, his Horse tyred in the gate.

There is likewise another adage in *Plautus*, which is this; *Crete hac mulier Cantherino ritu astans somniat*. That is to say, this Woman sleeps standing like a new dressed Horse, and is applyed against them which in a kinde of foolish jesture shut their eyes when they talk or work: and thus much for the Gelding.

OF CAREERING HORSES FOR POMP OR TRIUMPH.

THE nature of these Horses is to lift up themselves and rise before, standing upon their hinder legs, which is not possible for any to do without a generous and gallant spirit, and also nimble and strong loins to bear up the hinder legs, for it is not as many suppose, that this power of rising before from the softness of his legs, but rather from his loins and hips betwixt his hinder legs, for when his mouth is a little checked with the bridle he presently bendeth his hinder pasterns and anckles, and so lifteth up his fore-parts, that his belly and yard do appear, and in doing hereof the Rider must not bear his hand hard, but give him the bridle, that so he may do it willingly and with greater grace of the beholders.

There are some which teach Horses to lift up themselves by knocking their pasterns with a rod, which the Horse understandeth as well as he doth his race, when he is stroke on the back by the Rider. And in teaching of a Horse this feat, it must be observed, that he never have rest untill he have learned it, and that at certain signs and tokens, he be taught of his own accord to perform divers and sundry gestures: but if after long riding and copious labour, he begin to understand his Masters pleasure, and rise twice or thrice together, then you may give him the rains, nothing doubting but that he understandeth and will be obedient to the pleasure of the Rider. And in this kinde he is accounted the best careering Horse, which will rise high and oftnest together; neither is there any quality so commendable in a Horse as this, or that so draweth and (as it were) so imprisoneth the eyes of old and young, and other beholders, for which cause Martial Horses for service of War, are to be instructed herein; and thus much for this Horse.

OF LOAD OR PACK-HORSES.

WHERE they keep Horses in herds and flocks, they have some which are not fit for the saddle, nor for the wars, and therefore are to be employed for the carrying of burthens, or to the Cart; although (as *Festus* saith) Mules were first used for carrying and draught; but forasmuch as all Nations have not Mules, they are therefore inforced to use Horses, and for this purpose the Geldings are much better then the stoned Horses; wherefore the Countrey-men of most Nations take Horses, for this purpose, after they be old, past breeding, or have some other blemish in winde or limb, whereby they are disabled to travel under a man: for so great is the greediness of our age, that Horses are not spared so long as they be able to live; according to the common proverb, (*Asinis, equis, Mulis feriæ nullæ*) Horses, Mules, and Asses, keep no Holy-days: where the Law of God concerning the Sabbath is not observed; for the nourishing of Horses doth countervail the charges. Among these may be remembred those little Nags called *Hinni*, and *Ginni*, spoken of already in the discourse of Asses, whereof some are generated betwixt a Horse and an Ass, and others fall to be very little, through some sickness which happeneth unto them in their dams belly: these are used with shorn manes according to the saying of *Propertius: huc mea detonsis aucta est Cynthia mannis.* They are used for pleasure, to carry the young sons of Noble-men and Gentle-men. There are also Horses called *Equi funales*, because in their triumphs they were led with a halter next after the triumph.

OF WILDE-HORSES, THE SEA-HORSE, AND THE HART-HORSE, CALLED HIPPELAPHUS.

IN the days of *Gordianus* there were brought to *Rome* forty wilde Horses, and in the map of *Gordianus* Wood, there were pictured three hundred. They are called in *Latine, Equiferi*; and in *Greek, Hippagroi*, they abound in *Spain*, and in the *Alpes*, and in the Deserts of *Æthiopia* there are many of them, which have two long venomous teeth standing out of their mouth: they differ also in their hoofs from other Horses, for they are cloven-footed like Harts, and they have a long mane growing all along their back to their tail: And if at any time the Inhabitants take them by gins and other slights, they fall so sullen, that they abstain from meat and drink, disdaining to be kept in any servitude or bondage; the Wilde Horses of *India* have but one horn: In the *Alpes* they are of an ash-colour, with a black list down their backs. The wilde Horses of *Scythia*, near the River *Hypanis*, are clean white. The wilde Horses of *Syria* live in flocks and herds together, and in every herd they have one Captain or Master over the residue, and if it fortune that any of the younger Horses leap upon a Mare, this Captain-horse runneth after him, never giving over till he hath bit off his stones.

There are wilde Horses in *Brushia* which are like to other Horses in all parts, excepting their backs, which are so soft and weak, that they cannot endure to be sat upon, neither are they easily tamed, and the people of the Countrey eat their flesh: In *Polonia* there is a kinde of wilde Horse which hath horns like a Hart, and therefore I take it to be the same which is called *Hippelaphus*, whose picture is here described as it was taken here in *England*, by that learned Physitian Doctor *Cay*.

THE FIGURE OF HIPPELAPHUS.

THIS beast was brought out of *Norway*, having a mixt form, betwixt a Hart and a Horse, having a well compacted body, a long and lean leg, a cloven hoof, a short tail, and in all parts you would judge him to be a Hart, but in his head and ears you would judge him to be a Mule, and in his horns a Roe, the upper lip hanging over the neather almost as much as an Elks; his mane like a Horses, but thinner and standing more upright, without other alteration from their shoulders to their tail, they have a like bristling mane growing on the back-bone, as long as their other hair; a bunch under their chaps, and upon that a bunch or shaggy hair, the hair about their shoulders is more longer then ordinary, but their necks so short, that they can neither drink their drink, nor eat their meat upon the ground, except they bend down upon their knees. The males in this kinde do only bear horns, and such as do not grow out of the Crowns of their head, but as it were out of the middle on either side, a little above the eyes, and so bend to the sides: They are sharp, and full of bunches like Harts, no where smooth but in the tops of the speers, and where the veins run to carry nutriment to their whole length, which is covered with a hairy skin: they are not so rough at the beginning, or at the first prosses, specially in the fore-part, as they are in the second, for that only is full of wrinckles: from the bottom to the middle they grow straight, but from thence they are a little recurved; they have only three speers or prosses, the two lower turn away, but the uppermost groweth upright to heaven; yet sometimes it falleth out (as the Keepers of the said Beast affirmed) that either by sickness, or else through want of food, the left horn hath but two branches: In length they are one *Roman* foot and a half, and one finger and a half in breadth, at the root two *Roman* palms. The top of one of the horns is distant from the top of the other three *Roman* feet and three fingers, and the lower speer of one horn is distant from the lower of the other, two *Roman* feet measured from the roots: in substance and colour they are like to Harts horns, they weighed together with the dry broken spongy bone of the fore-head, five pound and a half, and half an ounce, (I mean sixteen ounces to the pound:) they fall off every year in the month of *April*, like to Harts, and they are not hollow. The breadth of their fore-heads betwixt the horns is two *Roman* palms and a half, the top of the crown betwixt the horns is hollow on the hinder part, and in that siecel lyeth the brain which descendeth down to the middle region of the eyes.

Their teeth are like Harts, and inwardly in their cheeks they grow like furrows, bigger then in a Horse; the tooth rising out sharp above the throat, as it should seem that none of his meat should fall thereinto unbruised. This Beast in young age is of a Mouse or Ass colour; but in his elder age it is more yellowish, especially in the extream parts of his body: the hair smooth, but most of all on his legs, but under his belly, in the inner part of his knee, the top of his neck, breast, shoulders, and back-bone, not so smooth: In height it was about twenty two handfuls and three fingers, being much swifter then any Horse; the female beareth every year, as the Keeper said in *Norway*, two at a time; but in *England* it brought forth but one.

The flesh of it is black, and the fibres broad like an Oxes; but being dressed like Harts flesh and baked in an Oven, it tasted much sweeter. It eateth commonly grass; but in *England* seldom after the fashion of Horses, which forbear hay when they may have bread; but leaves, rindes of trees, bread and oats, are most acceptable unto it. It reacheth naturally thirty hand breadths high, but if any thing be higher which it doth affect; it standeth up upon the hinder-legs, and with the fore-legs there imbraceth or leaneth to the tree, and with his mouth biteth off his desire.

It drinketh water, and also *English* Ale in great plenty, yet without drunkenness; and there were that gave it Wine, but if it drink plentifully it became drunk. It is a most pleasant creature being tamed; but being wilde, is very fierce, and an enemy to mankinde, persecuting men, not only when he seeth them by the eye, but also by the sagacity of his nose following by foot more certainly then any Horse, for which cause they which kept them near the high ways, did every year cut off their horns with a saw: It setteth both upon Horse and Foot-men; trampling and treading them under-foot whom he did over-match, when he smelleth a man before he seeth him, he uttereth a voice like the gruntling of a Swine being without his female: it doth most naturally affect a woman, thrusting out his genital (which is like a Harts) as if it discerned sexes. In *Norway* they call it an *Elk*, or *Elend*, but it is plain they are deceived in so calling it, because it hath not the legs of an Elk, which never bend, nor yet the horns, as by conference may appear. Much less can I believe it to be the *Hippardius*, because the female wanteth horns, and the head is like a Mules; but yet it may be that it is a kinde of Elk, for the horns are not always alike, or rather the Elk is a kinde of Horse-hart, which *Aristotle* calleth *Arrochostus* of *Arracolos* a region of *Assya*, and herein I leave every man to his judgement; referring the Reader unto the former discourses of an Elk, and the *Tragelaphus*.

OF THE SEA-HORSE.

THE Sea-horse, called in *Greek, Hippotomos*, and in *Latine, Equus Fluviatilis*; It is a most ugly and filthy Beast, so called because in his voyce and mane he resembleth a Horse, but in his head an Oxe or a Calf; in the residue of his body a Swine, for which cause some *Græcians* call him sometimes a Sea-horse, and sometimes a Sea-oxe, which thing hath moved many learned men in our time to affirm, that a Sea-horse was never seen; whereunto I would easily subscribe (such *Bellonius*) were it not that the antient figures of a Sea-horse, altogether resembled that which is here expressed; and was lately to be seen at *Constantinople*, from whom this picture was taken. It liveth for the most part in *Nilus*; yet is it of a doubtful life, for it brings forth and breedeth on the land, and by the proportion of the legs, it seemeth rather to be made for going, then for swimming: for in the night time it eateth both hay and fruits, sorraging into corn fields, and devouring whatsoever cometh in the way; and therefore I thought it fit to be inserted into this story. As for the Sea-calf, which cometh sometimes to land only to take sleep; I did not judge it to belong to this discourse, because it feedeth only in the waters.

This picture was taken out of the *Colossus* in the *Vatican* at *Rome*, representing the River *Nilus*, and eating of a Crocodile: and thus I reserve the farther discourse of this beast unto the History of Fishes, adding only thus much, that it ought to be no wonder, to consider such monsters to come out of the Sea, which resemble Horses in their heads, seeing therein are also creatures like unto Grapes and Swords.

The *Orsean Indians* do hunt a Beast with one horn, having the body of a Horse, and the head of a Hart. The *Æthiopians* likewise have a Beast, in the neck like unto a Horse, and the feet and legs like unto an Ox. The *Rhinocephalus* hath a neck like a Horse, and also the other parts of his body, but it is said to breath out air which killeth men. *Pausanias* writeth, that in the Temple of *Gabales*, there is the picture of a Horse, which from his breast backwards is like a Whale. *Lampsacenus* writeth, that in the *Scythian* Ocean, there are Islands wherein the people are called *Hippopodes*, having the bodies of men, but the feet of Horses; and *Lamia* hereafter to be declared, hath the feet of a Horse, but in other things the members of a Goat: and thus much for the several kindes of Horses, both for them that are properly so called, and also for any other, which like bastards retain any resemblance of nature with this Noble and profitable kinde of Beast.

OF THE DIET OF HORSES, AND THEIR LENGTH OF LIFE.

HAVING thus discoursed of the kindes of Horses, and their several accidents, and uses both for War, and Peace, pleasure, and necessity; now likewise it followeth, that we should proceed to their diet, and manner of feeding: wherein we are first of all to consider, that the natural constitution of a Horse is hot and temperate. Hot, because of his Levity, and Velocity, and length of life; temperate, because he is docible, pleasant, and gentle towards his Master and Keeper. He therefore that will keep Horses, must provide for them abundance of meat; for all other Cattel may be pinched without any great danger, only Horses can endure no penury. *Varro* saith, that in feeding of Horses, we must consider three things; First of all, what food the Countrey wherein we live doth yeeld: Secondly, when it must be given: Thirdly, by whom, but specially the place of feeding Horses is to be considered; for although Goats can live in the Mountains, better then in the green fields, yet Horses live better in the green fields, then they can in the Mountains. For which cause when we chuse pasture for Horses, we must see that it be fat, such as groweth in Meddows, that in the Winter time it may be Sunny, and in the Summer it may be open and cold, neither so soft under-foot, but that the Horses hoofs may feel some hardness, for Horses, Mules and Asses, do love well green grass, and fruits, yet principally they grow fat with drinking; when they are in the stables, let them have dry Hay. A Mare when she hath foaled give her Barly, and generally at all times in the Winter season *Bullimung*, or a mixture of all kindes of grain is fit for them in the house, according to these verses of *Nemetian*:

> *Inde ubi pubentes calamos duravert æstas,*
> *Lactenesque urens herbas siccaverit omnem*
> *Mensibus humorem, culmisque armarit aristas,*
> *Ordea tum, paleasque leves, præbere memento.*
> *Pulvere quinetiam, puras secernere fruges*
> *Cura sit, atque toros manibus percurrere equorum,*
> *Gaudeat ut plausu sonipes letumque relaxit*
> *Corpus, & altores rapiat per viscera succos,*
> *Id curent famuli, comitumque animosa juventus.*

We have shewed already, that they must have straw, or litter to ly upon, and *Pollux* doth set down the kindes of meats for Horses, as barley, hay, or *French* wheat, rice, and hay; for hard and dry meat is fittest for Horses, because it doth not fill them with winde; but all green meat is the less approved, by reason of inflamation. Three-leaved grass is also good for Horses, especially if they be young, for chaffe, hay, grass, and oats, are their natural and pleasing food: and although grass be moist, yet in the young age of a Horse, he delights in moist meats, for they stretch out his belly, and encrease his growth, but when he is elder, then ought he to be nourished with dryer food; as chaff, Barley, Oats, and such things. For although chaff, by reason of their dryness, make not a Horse fat, yet do they preserve him in perfect strength, for all hard things which are dissolved with difficulty, do retain their force of nutriment longer, but softer meats do not so; therefore the best dyet or habitude for Horses, is, to retain the mean betwixt fatness and leanness. For fatness ministreth many humors to the nourishment of sickness, and leanness diminisheth natural strength, maketh the body deformed. In some Countreys they give their Horses Vine branches in the Autumn, to move their bellies, and increase their strength.

The herb *Medica*, which aboundeth in *Media*, is very nourishable to Horses, but the first stalks are refused, saith *Aristotle*, the residue being watered with stinking water, is most commodious. In *Italy* they fat their Horses with *Trifoly*; in *Calabria* with *Sulla*, or *Arthritica*; and the *Thracians*, near the River *Strymon*, with a green Thistle.

In the Spring time give your younger Horses *Bullimung* for many dayes together, for that will not only make them fat, but also purge their bellies: for this purgation is most necessary for Horses, which is called soyling, and ought to continue ten days together, without any other meat, giving them the eleventh day a little Barley, and so forward to the fourteenth; after which day, continue them in that dyet ten days longer, and then bring them forth to exercise a little, and when as they sweat, anoint them with Oyl; and if the weather be cold, keep a fire in the stable: And you must remember when the Horse beginneth to purge, that he be kept from Barley and drink, and give him green meat, or *Bullimung*, whereof that is best that groweth near the Sea side.

But if the Horse go to soil in *April*, after five days, bring him forth, and wash him all over with water, then wiping his hair from all wet and filth, and loose hairs, pour upon him Wine and Oyl, pressing it smooth upon his back, down to his skin; so let him be wiped all over again, and carryed into the stable, to be dieted with *Masline*, or *Bullimung*, as before, except he be troubled with the Glanders, and then he must not feed on it in the day time, lest through the heat of the Sun, he fall into the mangie, or into madness.

It is also requisite, that while we feed our Horses with green Corn, they be let bloud in the veins of the breast, and also cut in the roof of their mouths, that so those places being emptyed which were stuffed with corruption, the vacuity may be replenished with better bloud; a Horse thus dyeted, shall not only live in more health, and free from sickness, but also be more strong to undergo his labour.

With the bloud that cometh out of him, mingled with Nitre, Vinegar, and Oyl, you shall anoint him all over, if so be he be subject to the Glaunders, or to the Mangie; and then keep him in the stable five days together, suffering no Curri combe to come upon him, untill the sixt day, feeding him in the mean time with green Corn or *Bullimung*; and then bring him forth again, washing him all over with water, and rubbing him with a hard whisp, untill the humor or moistures be wholly wiped off, and he fed as before fourteen days together.

If you please not to keep him in the stable, then in the Spring time, turn him out in some meddow, or green pasture, and there let him feed at his own pleasure; for it hath been often proved, that such a dyet hath recovered may sick Horses.

It is reported of the *Horotæ*, and *Gedrusti*, and men of *Freeseland*, the *Macedonians*, and *Lydians*, do seed their Horses with fishes: Likewise the *Pæonians* which inhabit about *Prasius* near the Mountain *Orbelus*, do feed their Horses, and all Cattel which they yoak with fishes.

Concerning the drink of Horses we have spoken elsewhere, and therefore we shall not need to say any thing of it here, except that the drinking much, and the Horse thrusting his head in deep into the troubled water, is an unfallible sign of his goodness; and the custom of some is, for to give their Horses mashes made of water and corn sod together, or else Bear, Ale or Wine, by drinking whereof, they encrease their spirits and stomach.

Albertus saith, that some to make their Horses fat, take Snails, and beat them in pieces, so putting them into their meats, whereby they grow to a false fatnesse, which is easily dissolved. By eating of black Hellebor, Oxen, Horses and Swine are killed: and thus much for the food of Horses.

Concerning the voice of Horses, the *Latins* call it *Hinnitum*, and the *Grecians, Phruma*, and *Phrumatesta*; but this is certain, that from their very foaling, the females have a shrill and sharper voice then the males, which is fuller and broader, untill they be two year old, and after copulation their voice encreaseth, so continuing untill they be twenty year old, after which time, it falleth and decreaseth again.

The length of a Horses life (according to *Aristotle*) is eighteen or twenty years, and if they be well tended and regarded in their youth, it hath been found, that some have lived unto five and twenty, or thirty year old. The females live longer then the males, because of their generation, for the immoderate lust of Horses, shortneth their dayes. And it hath been found that a Mare hath lived to forty or fifty years, and a Horse to three and thirty: wherefore I do leave the relation of *Pliny* and *Athenæus*, to be censured by the Reader, who affirm, that Horses in their time, lived threescore or seventy years.

Albertus also affirmeth, that a Souldier told him for a certain truth, that he knew a Horse which lived till he was threescore years old, and at that age did service in the field. And *August. Niphus* also affirmeth, that the Riders of *Ferdinand* the first, told him there was a Horse in their Masters stable of seventy year old. The age of a Horse may be known by his teeth, and the *Persian, Bohemian, Epirian*, and *Sicilian* Horses, live longer then the *Spanish* or *Numidian*. In their years, the female never groweth after five, nor the male after six in height or length, so as the males are sooner perfited in the womb then the females, on the contrary the females do sooner grow to their perfection after their foaling then the Males.

The males have more teeth then the females, and in each sex they which have fewest teeth, live not so long, and in their old age their teeth grow white. Now their age is discerned by their teeth on this manner, the first four, that is two above and two beneath, be changed after they be thirty year old, and a year after the four next are changed in like manner, again after another year four more are changed, so that after four year and six moneths, he looseth no teeth, except canine, which cometh again in the fist and sixt year; so that afterwards their age cannot be discerned, because in the seaventh year, they are all filled. Another unfaigned note of their age, is the hollowness of their temples, and their eye-lids beginning to wax gray, and their teeth hanging out of their mouths. They have also little blacks in the middle of their teeth. Some try the age of their Horses, as a wife and learned man writeth, by considering twelve teeth, six above, and six beneath, for the old Horses have longer and thinner teeth, which are black at the top, and there are certain broaches or wrinckles in their teeth, which being filled, the mark is said to be out of their mouth.

Some try the age of their Horses by their cheeks, for they pull up the skin from the bones, and if it will quickly fall back again into his former place, they take it for an assured token of the Horses youth: but if it stand out and fall slowly down, then on the contrary, they judge the Horse to be old, and thus much for the age and diet of Horses.

THERE are certain people in *Scythia*, which were called *Hippophagi*, because they lived upon Horse-flesh; such also were the *Sarmatians* and the *Vandals*: likewise in *Scythia* the lesse, neer *Taurica Chersonnesus*, the people do not only eat the flesh of Horses, but also their milk, and make Cheese thereof.

Athenæus also affirmeth, that the manner of the ancient *Persians* was, upon the feasts of their nativities to roast an Ox, an Asse, a Horse, and a Camel whole, and so set them before their guests.

In like sort, they eat Horse-flesh and Camels-flesh at *Damascus*; and in *Polonia* wilde Horses, especially that part which groweth under the mane. The *Sarmatians* made meat of Millet-seed, and mingle it with Mares milk, or with bloud taken out of the veins of their legs, wherewithal they make puddings, and this is their chief food. So wikewise do the *Tartarians*, who having a Horse sick, cut off his Ulcer or wound, and so kill him and eat his flesh. The *Gothes* also in the dayes of *Virgil* did drink the bloud of Horses, as appeareth in these Verses;

> *Profuit incensos æstus avertere, & inter*
> *Ima ferire pedis, salientem sanguine venam:*
> *Bisaltæ, quo more solent, acerque Gelonus,*
> *Cum fugit in Rhodopen, atque in deserta Getarum,*
> *Et lac concretum cum sanguine potat equino.*

The Poets do also fain, that *Pelias* the Son of *Tirus* and *Neptune*, was educated by a Mare, and *Metabus* brought up his Daughter *Camilla* with Mares milk, because she was born wilde, he also bred her among the bushes, according to these Verses;

> *Hic natam in dumis, interque horrentia lustra*
> *Armentalis equæ mammis, & lacte ferino*
> *Nutribat, teneris immulgens ubera labris.*

The *Tartarians* drinke Mares milke, which they dresse like white wine, and call it *Chumis*, whereof *Paulus Venetus* rehearseth this story: The King of *Tartar*, saith, he, nourisheth above ten thousand milk-white Horses and Mares, and every year, upon the eight and twenty day of *August*, they observe a solemn feast, wherein the milk of these white Mares is dressed and set forth in comely vessels.

Afterward the King taketh a bowl full thereof, and powreth it on the ground round about him, being so taught by his *Magitians*, to offer Sacrifice to the gods of his Countrey: For they perswade him that the Gods lick up that milk spilt on the ground, and afterwards the King drinketh up the residue, and besides him no body that day, except it be of the Kings linage, or of the Countrey of *Horiach* (for the people of that Countrey have liberty to tast thereof that day) because of a battle which once they obtained for the great *Cam*.

The property of this milk is to loosen the belly; and because it is thin and hath no fat in it, therefore it easily descendeth, and doth not curdle in the stomach, and it is said, that the *Scythians* can keep it twelve dayes together, therewithal satisfying their hunger, and quenching their thirst. And thus much shall satisfie for the natural discourses of Horses: hereafter followeth the moral.

The moral discourse of Horses, concerning Fictions, Pictures, and other devises.

And first of all for the moral dignity of Horses, there is a celestial constellation called *Hippos*, according to these Verses of *Aratus* thus translated;

> *Huic Equus ille jubam quatiens fulgore micanti*
> *Summum contingit caput alvo stellaque jungens*
> *Una.* ———

The *Latins* call this star *Pegasus*, and they say that he is the Son of *Neptune* and *Medusa*; who with striking his foot upon a Rock in *Helicon* a mountain of *Bœotia*, opened a Fountain, which after his name was called *Hippocrene*. Others tell the tale in this sort, at what time *Bellerophon* came to *Prætus* the Son of *Abas* the King of the *Argives*, *Antia* the Kings wife fell in love with her guest, and making it known unto him, promised him half her husbands Kingdom if he would lie with her, but he like an honest man abhorring so foul a fact, utterly refused to accomplish the desire and dishonesty of the lustful Queen; whereupon she being afraid lest he should disclose it unto the King, prevented him by her own complaint, informing the King that he would have ravished her: when the King heard this accusation (because he loved *Bellerophon* well) would not give punishment himself, but sent him to *Schenobeus* the Father of Queen *Antia*, that he in defence of his Daughters chastity might take revenge upon him, who presently cast him to *Chimæra*, which at that time depopulated all the coast of *Lycia*: but *Bellerophon* by the help of the Horse *Pegasus* did both overcome and avoid the monster, and being weary of his life, perceiving that there was no good nor truth upon the earth, determined to forsake the world and flie to heaven: who coming neer to heaven, casting down his eyes to the earth, trembled to see how far he was distant from it, and so his heart fainting for fear, fell down backward and perished, but his Horse kept on his flight to heaven, and was there placed among the Stars by *Jupiter*. *Euripedes* telleth the tale otherwise, for he saith that *Chiron* the *Centaure* had a Daughter nourished in the mountain *Pelius* which was called *Theas* and afterward *Hippe*, because of her exceeding hunting on horse-back, she was perswaded by *Æolus* (the Son of *Hellen*, a Nephew of *Jupiters*) to let him lie with her, whereupon she conceived with childe, and when the time of her deliverance came, she fled from her Father into the woods, for fear the loss of her Virginity should be known unto him; but he followed her to see what was the cause of his Daughters departure, whereupon she desired of the Gods that her father might not see her in travel, her prayer was granted, and she after her delivery, was turned into a Mare, and placed among the Stars.

Others say that she was a Prophetesse, and because she revealed the counsels of the Gods, was therefore metamorphozed in that shape in the place aforesaid. Others say, that because she gave over to worship *Diana*, she lost her first presence. But to return to the first tale of *Bellerophon*, who after the death of *Chimæra*, growing proud for his valor attempted to flie to heaven, but *Jupiter* troubled his Horse with a Fury, and so he shooke off his Rider, who perished in the field, *Alecus apo tese alese*, because of his errour: and *Pegasus* was placed in heaven.

But to come nearer to the description of the Poeticall Horse, *Albertus Magnus* and some others say, that it is a Beast bred in *Ethiopia*, having the head and feet of a Horse, but horned, and wings much greater then the wings of an Eagle, which he doth not lift up into the air like a bird, but only stretcheth them out when he runneth, whereby his only presence is terrible to all creatures, unto whom he is enemy, but especially to Men. But for the truth hereof (although *Pliny* and some others seem to affirm as much) yet will I set down nothing for truth and certainty, because as the Poets call every swift Horse *Volucres*, and *Alipedes*; so the errour of that figure, hath rather given occasion to the framing of this new Monster *Pegasus*, then any other reasonable Allegory.

Likewise I know no cause why the Poets should fain, that *Ceres* was turned into a Mare, and hid her self in the herds of *Oncius*; *Neptune* falling in love with her, followed her to those fields, and perceiving that he was deceived, turned himself also into a Horse, and so had to do with her, whereat *Ceres* was grievously offended, and fell into a great fury, for which cause she was called *Erinnys*: yet afterwards she washed her self in the River *Ladon*, laying aside all her rage and fury, at the fulness of time she brought forth *Arion*.

And the *Arcodians* also had a certain Den, wherein they had a great remembrance of this ravishment of *Ceres*, sitting in a Den, wherein they say she hid her self from all creatures, and whereunto they offer divine worship. They picture her in a Colts skin, sitting like a woman in all parts, with a long garment down to her ancles, but the head of a Horse with the pictures of many Dragons, and other such wilde beasts, holding in one of her hands a Dolphin, and in the other a Dove.

By all which it is not uneasie for every man to know & conceive their meaning, that plenty of food signified by *Ceres*, doth not only maintain Men, Fowls, Beasts and Fishes, but also the immoderate use thereof draweth men to inordinate lust and concupiscence, and that the Gods of the Heathen were more rather to be accounted Beasts then Men.

Diana also among the *Arcadians* was called *Eurippa*, for the finding out of those Mares which *Ulysses* had lost: which *Ulysses* erected a statue for *Neptune* the great Rider, and they say that *Hippolytus* being torn in pieces by Horses, through the love of *Diana*, and skill of *Æsculapius*, by the vertue of certain herbs he was restored unto life again: Whereupon *Jupiter* being sore vexed and angry with *Æsculapius* for such an invention, deluding as it were the fury of the Gods, killed him with lightning, and thrust him down into hell, because no wretched man would fear death if such devises might take place: which fact *Virgil* describeth in these Verses:

At Trivia Hippolytum secretis alma recondit
Sedibus, & nymphæ Ægeriæ nemorique relegat,
Solus ubi in silvis Itolis ignobilis ævum
Exigeret, verscque ubi nomine Virbius esset.
Unde etiam Triviæ templo lucisque sacratis
Cornipedes arcentur equi, quod littore currum
Et juvenem monstr is pavidi effudere marinis.

The Poets also do attribute unto the night, black Horses, and unto the day white. *Homer* saith, that the names of the day Horses are *Lampus* and *Phaethon*; to the Moon they ascribe two Horses, one black and another white; the reason of these inventions for the day and the night is, to signifie their speedy course or revolution by the swiftness of Horses, and of the darkeness of the night by the black Horses, and the light of the day by the white; and the Moon which for the most part is hid and covered with earth, both increasing and decreasing, they had the same reason to signifie her shadowed part like a black Horse, and her bright part by a white one.

The like Fiction they had of *Hecate*, whom *Ausonius* calleth *Tergemina*, because she is described with the head of a Horse, a Dog, and a wilde Man, the Horse on the right hand, the Dog on the left hand, and the wilde Man in the middle: whereby they declared how vulgar, illiterate, and uncivilized men, do participate in their conditions, the labours and envie of brute beasts.

We may also read in the *Annales* of *Tacitus*, that in his time there was a Temple raised to Equestrial fortune, that is, for the honour of them which managed Horses to their own profit, and the good of their Countrey, and that *Fulvius* the *Prætor* in *Spain*, because he obtained the victory against the *Celtiberians*, by the valour and diligence of his Horse-men, was the first that builded that Temple. Likewise, there was another Temple in *Bœotia* for the same cause dedicated unto *Hercules*.

The ancient *Pagans* call the God of Horses *Hippona*, as the God of Oxen *Bubona*. It is also apparent, that many Nations use to sacrifice Horses, for at *Salentinum* a Horse was cast alive into the fire and offered to *Jupiter*. Likewise the *Lacedemonians* sacrificed a Horse to the winds. At *Rome* also they sacrificed a Horse to *Mars*, and thereof came the term of *Equus October*, which was sacrificed every year in *October*, in *Campus Martius*. This Horse was often take out of a Chariot, which was a Conqueror in race, and stood on the right hand; as soon as he was killed, some one carried his tail to a place called *Regia*, and for his head there was a continual combate betwixt the inhabitants of the streets, *Suburra*, and *Sacravia*, which of them should possesse it; for the *Suburrans* would have fastened it to the wal of *Regia*, and the *Sacravians* to the Tower *Mamillia*.

The reason why they Sacrificed a Horse, some have conjectured because the *Romans* were the off-spring of the *Trojans*, and they being deceived by a Horse, their posterity made that Sacrifice for punishment of Horses: but it, is more reasonable, that because they Sacrificed a conquering Horse, they did it only for the honour of *Mars* (the God of victory) or else because they would signifie, that flying away in battle was to be punished by the example of Sacrificing of a swift Horse.

The *Carmani* did also worship *Mars*, and because they had no Horses to use in War, they were forced to use Asses, for which cause they Sacrificed an Asse unto him. There is another fable amongst the Poets, that the *Methimnæans* were commanded by the Oracle to cast a Virgin into the Sea to *Neptune*, which they performed: now there was a young man whose name was *Ennallus*, which was in love with the said Virgin, and seeing her in the Waters, swum after her to save her, but both of them were covered with the waters of the Sea; yet after a certain space *Ennallus* returned back again, and brought news that the Virgin lived among the Pharies of the Sea, and that he after that he had kept *Neptunes* Horses, by the help of a great wave escaped away by swimming; for the Poets fain that *Neptunes* Chariot was drawn by Horses of the Sea, according to these Verses of *Gillius*;

Non aliter quotiens perlabitur æquora curru
Extremamque petit Phœbæa cubilia Tethyn
Frænatis Neptunus equis ———

They also faign that the Sun is drawn with two swift white Horses, from whence came that abomination, that the Kings of *Judea* had erected Horses and Chariots in honour of the Sun, which were set at the entrance of the Temple of the Lord; which Horses were destoyed by *Josias*, as we read in holy Scripture. And the manner of their abomination was, that when they did worship to the Sun, they road upon those Horses from the entrance of the Temple to the chamber of *Nethan-melech*. The *Persians* also Sacrificed a Horse to *Apollo* according to these Verses of *Ovid*:

Placat equo Persis, radiis Hyperiona cinctum,
Ne detur sceleri victima tarda deo.

And for this cause the *Massagetes* sacrificed a Horse (the swiftest of all Beasts) unto the Sun, the swiftest of all the Gods. *Philostratus* also recordeth, that *Palamedes* gave charge to the *Grecians* to Sacrifice to the Sun rising a white Horse. The *Rhodians* in honor of the Sun did cast yearly away into the Sea, the Chariots dedicated to the Sun, in imagination that the Sun was carryed about the World in a Chariot, drawn by six Horses.

As the Army of the *Persians* did proceed forward on their journey, the fire (which they did call Holy and Eternal) was lifted up on silver Altars; presently after this, there followed the Wise-men, and after those Wise-men came 165 young men, being cloathed with as many red little garments as there are dayes in the year: Instantly upon the same, came the holy Chariots of *Jupiter*, which was drawn by white Horses; after which, with a resplendent magnitude the Horse of the Sun was seen to appear (for so it was called) and this was the manner of their Sacrifices.

The King of *Indians* also (as is said) when the dayes began to wax long, he descended down to the River *Indus*, and thereunto sacrificed black Horses and Buls; for the Buls in ancient time were consecrated to the Rivers, and Horses also were thrown thereinto alive, as the *Trojans* did into *Xanthus*.

The *Veneti* (which worshiped *Diomedes* with singular honour) did Sacrifice to him a white Horse: when the *Thebanes* made war on the *Lacedemonians*, it is said that *Cædasus* apeared in a vision to *Pelopidas*, one of the *Thebane* Captains, and told him that now the *Lacedemonians* were at *Leuctra*, and would take vengeance upon the *Thebanes*, and their Daughters; Whereupon *Pelopidas* to avert that mischief, caused a young foal to be gallantly attired, and the day before they joyned battle, to be led to a Sepulcher of their Virgins, and there to be killed and sacrificed.

The *Thessalians* observed this custome at their marriages and nuptial Sacrifices, the man took a Horse of War armed and furnished, which he led into the Temple; after the Sacrifice ended he delivered the rains of the Bridle into the hands of his Wife, who led the same Horse home again: but for what signification or cause this rite was observed, *Ælianus* which relateth the story sheweth not, but saith he referreth himself to the *Thessalians* to declare their own reasons of this observation. And thus much shall suffice concerning the Sacrificing of Horses.

Another moral-honour done unto them was their burial; For we have shewed already that *Volucer* the Horse of *Verus* the Emperour was honourably buried, the Mares of *Cinon* which had won three games at *Olympus*, were likewise interred neer his own body. The *Scythians* at the burial of their Kings used for to strangle one of his harlots, his cupbearer, his Cook, his Horse-keeper, his Messenger, and also Horses and other Cattle; and after a year they do this the second time; taking fifty of his dearest servants which were natural *Scythians* and strangled them; likewise fifty of his best Horses, out of whose bellies they pull out their bowels and guts, and filling their bellies up again with chaffe, they sow them up: then make they half an arch upon two posts standing upright, and likewise the other half upon two other posts over the Kings grave; likewise fastening in the earth divers other sharp posts upon which they put the fifty Horses, so fastening them with thick pieces of timber all along their neck and back, so that the shoulders of the Horses rest upon the fore-arch and their bellies on the hinder, their legs standing upward, then bridle they the Horses, and stretch forth the rains of their bridles unto the posts of the earth, afterwards upon every one of the dead Horses they lay a dead man, putting a stake through his back out of his neck, and the neather part of the said stake they fasten in the post, which pierceth or goeth through the Horse; and thus having compassed about the grave of their King, with such Horses and Horse-men, they depart, leaving both the one and the other to the consumption of nature, and after this manner did they bury all their Kings.

Adrian buryed his Hunting Horse, *Ennomaus* his Mares, *Partheria* and *Eripha*. Likewise *Miltiades*, *Evagoras*, and *Augustus* the Emperour. At *Agrigentum* also there are many *Pyramides* erected upon the Sepulchres of Horses. And thus much shall suffice for the burial of Horses.

We have shewed you already how Men and Women have been transformed into Horses, according to the fiction of the Poets, as of *Saturne, Jupiter, Neptune, Ceres, Hippes*, and *Ocyrrhoes* the Daughters of *Chiron*. In like sort there have been predictions or ostentations of things to come, taken from a Wolf, a Fox, a Serpent, and a Horse, which were called *Auspicia Pedestria*.

Dreams also have been declared by Horses, for *Publius Vatinius* in the *Macedonian* war, coming towards Rome in the night time, supposed be saw two young men of excellent beauty to meet him, and tell him that *Perses* the King was taken by *Paulus*, which thing he declared to the Senate, but was by them put into prison as a contemner of the Majesty and honour of that Captain, but afterwards it appeared by the letters of *Paul* that *Perses* was taken that very day; whereupon *Vatinius* was delivered out of Prison, and rewarded with land and liberty.

It also appeareth that the same day that *Castor* and *Poliux* washed away the sweat of themselves and their Horses in the lake of *Juturne*, that they watched for the safety of the *Roman* Empire, and their Temple which was joyned to the same fountain being fast locked, upon a suddain flew open without the hand of man.

Æneas also in *Virgil* saith, that he knew war would follow by the appearance of four Horses, which in a green field set upon a whole Campe, whereupon in *Virgil*, he speaketh thus to *Anchises*.

> *Quatuor hic, primum omen, Equos in gramine vidi*
> *Tondentes campum late, candore nivali.*

Hipater Anchises, Bellum O terra hospita portas;
Bello armantur equi, Bellum hæc armenta minantur.
Sed tamen iidem olim curru succedere sueti
Quadrupedes, & fræna jugo concordia ferre;
Spes est pacis, ait. ———

Lucan also speaketh to the same purpose that Horses presage war;

Primus ab æquorea percussis cuspide saxis
Thessalicus sonipes bellis feralibus omen
Exiluis. ——— ———

Alexander also writeth, that the *Germans* were wont to bring up white Horses which were never used to labour, by whose neighing they were forewarned of wars, and of other strange events. It is vulgarly known how *Darius* came to the Kingdom of *Persia*, after it was agreed amongst the seven Princes, that he whose Horse did first neigh in the morning in a place appointed, should be saluted King. *Ebores* his rider in the night, time took one of the mares which he knew his Masters Horse loved, and led her into the Suburbs, and there tied her, afterward he brought thither *Darius* his Horse, and led him about her two or three times, and at length suffered him to cover her, and so led them both away together. In the next morning the Princes met as soon as day brake, and road up and down the Suburbs, until at last they came to the place where the Mare of *Darius* was tyed the night before, whereunto the Horse of *Darius* ran neighing strongly, and presently it thundred and lightned in a clear day: whereupon the residue of the Princes alighted from their Horses, and did reverence to King *Darius*, who by divine appointment was thus advanced to the Scepter.

Although there be some that say *Ebores* by handling of a Mares genital and keeping his hand warm, untill they came to the place aforesaid, there stroking the Nostrils of his Masters Horse, caused him thus to neigh and win the Kingdom; yet I rather in cline to the former opinion which was related by *Herodotus* in his *Thalia*.

There have also been Horses of strange fashions, for as we have shewed already, that a Mare did bring forth a Hare, so also (*Livie* saith) an Ox did bring forth a Foal. *Nero* did shew certain *Hermaphrodite*

Mares, wherewithal his Chariot was drawn, which was a thing worth the sight, that the Monarch of the world should sit upon Monsters.

Julius Cæsar had a Horse which had cloven hoofs like a Mans fingers, and because he was foaled at that time when the Sooth-sayers had pronounced that he should have the government of the world, therefore he nourished him carefully, and never permitted any man to back him but himself, which afterwards he dedicated in the Temple of *Venus*, for he conceived that such a strange beast bred in his own flock, was a prediction unto him of great honour. The *Palatine* of *Vilva* had a Horse foaled with five legs, and *Henry* the *Count-Palatine* had likewise a Horse with six legs. Thus much may suffice for the monster Horses.

In the next place it is good to enquire what the *Centaures* are, who are described by the Poets to have their forepart like men, and their hinder part like Horses, the occasion whereof is thus related by *Pindarus*: that *Centaurus* the Son of *Ixion*, committed buggery with the Mares of *Magnetia*, under the mountain *Pelius*, from whence came that monstrous birth in the upper part resembling the Father and in the neather the mother. These saith he possessed the Mountains and Desert places of *Thessaly*, being given to all manner of Latrociny and Deprædation. They were called also *Hippocentauri*: And some say that they were first of all nourished by the Nymphes in the mountain *Pelius*, who afterwards being the first that tamed Horses, were thought to be half Men, and half Horses, because they were seen backward, and from hence came the fable that they were tamed by *Hercules*, which was one of his greatest labours: But yet that no man may wonder or think it impossible that such monstrous creatures should have existence in nature, these authorities following may perswade sufficiently.

Plutarch in his Banket of Wisemen, affirmeth, there was a Horse-keeper which brought into the house of *Periander* an Infant or rather a Monster which he had got upon a Mare, which had the head, neck, hands and voice of a childe, and the other parts like a Horse, *Diocles* presently judged it to be a Monster, and signified contentions and strifes in the world. But *Thales* told *Periander* he was of another opinion, namely, that it was no Monster, but a meer natural birth from such a copulation, and therefore advised *Periander*, that either he should keep no Riders, or else let them have Wives.

Claudius Cæsar also writeth, that in the time of his reign there was such a one born in *Thessaly*, which dyed the same day it was born: and *Pliny* that he afterwards saw it seasoned in hony, brought out of *Egypt* to be shewed to the Emperor. These *Centaures*, *Homer* calleth *Fera*, that is, *Feræ*, wilde persons. The *Lapithæ* and the *Centaures* are said to be very like the one to the other, and were also once very loving, but they fell afterwards to deadly war, by reason the *Centaures* in a banket being drunk, offered to ravish the females of the *Lapithæ*, for which cause the *Lapithæ* slew them in their jealousie, whereon fell a mortal war: whereby the Poets signifie how intemperancy in Men and Beasts doth not only bring with it other sins, but also causeth much slaughter. And so I conclude the story of *Centaures*, holding it possible that such should be generated by unclean and natural copulation, but unpossible that they should live long after birth, and therefore the *Centaures* of the Poets are nothing else but men sitting on Horseback, mistaken for one entire creature which were divided, and so conclude with the Verse of *Horace*:

> *Humano Capiti cervicem pictor Equinam*
> *Jungere si velit.* ———
> *Hoc monstrum puto Centaurus foret.*

OF THE STATUES AND FIGURES OF HORSES.

IT was no small dignity that the ancient *Cephalenes* did stamp their money with the picture of a Horse, for surely from them it came, that coin was first of all called currant, because of the image of a speedy Horse, wherewithal it was imprinted. *Textor* also writeth, that amongst the ancients there was a custom to make the Charcter of a Horse in the forehead of a bondslave; there was also images of Horsemen and Horses renowned in many Countries for the honour of both, such were the statues of the *Amazons* (cald *Hippiades*) who by *Lysias* the Orator are said to be the first that ever backed Horses: Such was the statue of *Clælia*, *Quintus Martius, Tremulus, Domitianus*, and many other both Men and Women: for the *Romans* had the Equestrial statues in great reverence and ceremony, no doubt in imitation of the *Grecians*, but with this difference, that they pictured none but the swift Horses, but the *Romans*, Horses and Chariots, and from hence came the custome to have Chariots in triumph.

But this custome to have six Horses in a Chariot was brought in last of all by *Augustus*. *Aristodemus* pictured the Chariots and Wagoner. *Pisicrates* the woman *Pitho*, with a Wagon. *Euthycrates*, the Son of *Lysippus* expressed the Equestrial combate at the Oracle of *Trophonium* with singular art, also many Chariots of *Medea*, the Horse and his carriage. There were also earthen Chariots at *Rome* in the porch of *Jupiters* Temple, as we have shewed before in the discourse of Chariots.

When *Constantinus* the great took a view of the City of *Rome*, and passing from place, to place, came at length to *Forum Trajani*, the most exquisite building of all the world, he stood amazed at the admirable frame of Giants, which were lineally deciphered therein, whereof despairing to imitate any part of that work, he chose only to erect the picture of such a Horse and Prince, as in the middle of the same was erected in remembrance of *Trajane*, and so much he intimated to his followers: close by him stood that Princely *Hormisda* (a *Persian*) who made the Emperour this answer, *Ante imperator stabulum tale condi jubeto si vales: Equus quem fabricare disponis ita late succedat ut iste quem videmus:* O Noble Emperour before you make such a Horse, first of all build such a stable; that your work in all parts may be correspondent to this which you propose unto your self to imitate.

Metellus the *Macedonian* raised two porches which were compassed about with two Horses, without inscription or dedication, which now are compassed with the porches of *Octavia*, and the row of Equestrial statues in the front of the said buildings, now the greatest ornament of that place, he also brought out of *Macedonia*. And it is said that *Alexander* the great caused *Lysippus* (that singular workman) to frame the pictures of all those Knights which in his company were slain at the River *Granicum*, and also to place his own picture among them.

In the City of *Rome* there are two mountains called *Equilini*, in one of them are the bathes of *Diocletian*, and the great Marble Horses, with two men half naked, holding their rains, being most singular wormanship, whereof one hath this inscription in *Latin* letters, *Opus Praxitelis*, the work of *Praxitelis*; the other *Opus Phidiæ*, the work of *Phidias*: and it is clear, that they were brought thither by *Tyridates* King of *Armenia*, for whose entertainment *Nero* caused the Theatre of *Pompey* to be covered all over with gold in the space of one day. The story of the *Trojan* Horse is vulgarly known, which is also called *Equus Durateus*, or *Dureus*, wherein the *Grecian* Princes hid themselves, when they took *Troy*, according to these Verses;

Nec cum durateus Trojanis Pergama partu
Inflammascit Equus nocturno Grajugenarum.

The truth whereof standeth thus, The *Grecians* making shew that they had vowed a vow unto *Pallas*, framed a Horse of so great bigness, that it could not be taken into *Troy*, except the gates were pulled down; and this they placed hard to the wals of *Troy*: *Sinon* (the counterfeit runnagate) being then within the wals among the *Trojans*, perswaded them to pull down their wals and pull in that wooden Horse; affirming that if they could get it, *Pallas* would stand so friendly to them that the *Grecians* should never be able to move war against them: wherefore they pull down their gates, and part of their wall, and by that means do bring the Horse into the City: while the *Trojans* were thus revelling and making merry with themselves, and not thinking of any harm might ensue upon them, the leaders of the *Grecian* Army who by deceit all this while kept themselves close hid, (ever since which time the *Grecians* are tearmed of all Nations deceitful) on a suddain rose out of their lurking places and so going forward invaded the City, being destitute of any defence, and by this means subdued it.

Others are of opinion, that the Poets fiction of the *Trojan* Horse, was no other but this, that there was a mountain neer *Troy* called *Equus*, and by advantage thereof *Troy* was taken, whereunto *Virgil* seemeth to allude, saying;

Instar montis Equum divina Palladis arte
Ædificant. —— ——

For they say that *Pallas* and *Epeus* made the Horse, and therefore I conjecture, that the *Trojan* Horse was nothing else but an engine of War, like unto that which is called *Aries*: For *Pausanias* saith, that *Epeus* was the inventer thereof. And *Higinus* saith, that the *Trojan* Horse was *Machina oppugnatoria*, a devise of war, to overthrow the wals.

Of this Horse there was a brazen image at *Athens* in *Acropolis*, with this inscription, *Chæridemus, Fuangeli filius cælenatus dicavit.* When *Alexander*, looked upon his own picture at *Ephesus* which *Apelles* had drawn with all his skill, the King did not commend it according to the worth thereof: It fortuned that a Horse was brought into the room, who presently neighed at the picture of *Alexanders* Horse, smelling unto it as to a living Morse, whereat *Apelles* spake thus to the King;

Ho men Hippos eoice sou graphicoteros cata polu.

That is to say, The Horse is a better discerner of truth then you.

There was one *Phormis* which went from *Mænalus* in *Arcadia* into *Sicilia*, to serve *Gelon* the Son of *Dinomenes*, under whom and his brother *Hiero* he arose to great estate of wealth, and therefore he gave many gifts to *Apollo* at *Delphos*, and made two brazen Horses with their riders at *Olympia*, setting *Dionisius* the *Grecian* upon one and *Simon Egineta* upon the other.

Æmilius Censorinus (a cruel Tyrant in *Sicilia*) bestowed great gifts upon such as could invent new kinde of torments; there was one *Aruntius Paterculus*, hoping to receive from him some great reward, made a brazen Horse, and presented it to the Tyrant: to include therein such as he should condemn to death: at the receipt whereof *Æmilius* which was never just before, first of all put the Author into it that he might take experience how cursed a thing it was to minister unto cruelty.

Apelles also painted *Clytus* on Horse-back hastening to war, and his Armour-bearer reaching his helmet unto him, so lively, that other dumb beasts were affraid of his Horse. And excellent was the skill of *Nealces*, who had so pictured a Horse foaming, that the beholders were wont to take their handkerchefs to wipe it from his mouth. And this much for the moral uses of Horses.

OF THE SEVERAL DISEASES OF HORSES AND THEIR CURES.

SEEING in this discourse I have principally aimed at the pleasure, delight, and profit of *Englishmen*, I have thought good to discourse of the diseases of Horses and their cures in the words of our own Countreymen, M. *Blundevile*, and M. *Markham*, whose works of these matters are to be recorded like the *Iliads* of *Homer* in many places and several Monuments, to the intent that envy of Barbarism may never be able to bury them in oblivion, or neglect to root them out of the world, without the losse of other memorable labours.

Wherefore good Reader, for the ensuing Tractate of diseases and cures compiled by them, after that I had read over the labours of *C. Gesner*, and compared it with them, finding nothing of substance in him, which is not more materially, perspicuously, profitably, and familiarly, either extracted or expressed by them, in a method most fitting this History, I have thought good to follow them in the description of the disease and the remedy; first (according to time) declaring them in the words of *M. Blund.* and afterwards in the words of *M. Markham*, methodically one after the other, in the same place: wherewithal I trust the living authors will not be displeased, that so you may with one labour examine both; and I hope, that neither they, nor any of their friends or Scholars shall receive any just cause of offence, by adding this part of their studies to our labours, neither their books imprinted, be any way disgraced or hindered, but rather revived, renobled, and honoured. To begin therefore (saith Master *Blundevile*) after the discourse of the nature of a Horse followeth those things which are against nature, the knowledge whereof is as needfully profitable as the other. Things against nature be those whereby the healthful estate of a Horses body is decayed, which are in number three; that is, the causes, the sickness, and the accidents; of the two first in order, and the other promiscuously as need requireth.

OF CAUSES AND KINDS THEREOF.

THE causes of sickness be unnatural affects, or evil dispositions preceding sickness, and provoking the same, which of themselves do not hinder the actions of the body, but by means of sickness coming betwixt. Of causes, some be called internal, and some external. Internal be those that breed within the body of the Beast, as evil juice. External be those that chance outwardly to the body, as heat, cold, or the stinging of a Serpent, and such like. In knowing the cause of every disease, consisteth the chief skill of the Farriar. For unlesse he knoweth the cause of the disease, it is impossible for him to cure it well and skilfully. And therefore I wish all Farriars to be diligent in seeking to know the causes of all diseases, as well in the parts similar, as instrumental, and to know whether such causes be simple, or compound; for as they be simple or compound, so do they engender simple or compound diseases.

OF SICKNESS, WHAT IT IS, AND HOW MANY GENERAL KINDS THERE BE; ALSO WITH WHAT ORDER THE DISEASES OF HORSES ARE HEREIN DECLARED. AND FINALLY, OF THE FOUR TIMES, BELONGING TO EVERY SICKNESS.

SICKNESS is an evill affect contrary to nature, hindering of it self, some action of the body Of sickness there be three general kinds, where of the first consisteth in the parts similar; the second in the parts instrumental; and the third in both parts together. The first kind is called of the *Latins Intemperies*, that is to say, evil temperature, which is either simple or compound. It is simple, when one quality only doth abound or exceed too much, as to be too hot, or too cold; it is compound, as when many qualities do exceed, as when the body is too hot and too dry, or too cold and too moist. The second kind is called *Mala constitutio*, that is to say, an evill state or composition, which is to be considered, either by the shape, number, quantity, or sight of the member, or part evill affected or diseased. The third kind is called *Unitatis solutio*, that is to say, the loosening or division of the unity, which as it may chance diversly, so it hath divers names accordingly; for if such solution or division be in a bone, then it is called a fracture; if it be in any fleshie part, then it is called a Wound or Ulcer; in the veins, a Rupture; in the sinews, a Convulsion or Cramp; and in the skin, an Excoriation.

Again, of diseases, some be called long, and some sharp and short, called of the *Latins, Morbi acuti*, which be perillous and do quickly kill the body. The long, do tarry longer by it. Yet moreover, there is sickness by it self, and sickness by consent: Sickness by it self, is that which being in some member, hindereth the action thereof by it self. Sickness by consent, is derived out of one member into another, through the neighbourhood and community that is betwixt them: as the pain of the head which cometh from the stomach.

Thus the learned Physitians which write of Mars body, do divide sickness. But *Absyrtus* writing of Horse-leach craft, saith of that sickness, or rather malady (for so he termeth it, using that word as a general name to all manner of diseases that be in a Horse) there be four kinds, that is to say, the moist malady, the dry malady, the malady of the joynts, and the malady betwixt the flesh and the skin. The moist malady is that which we call the Glanders. The dry malady is an incurable consumption, which some perhaps would call, the mourning of the chein, but not rightly, as shall appear unto you hereafter. The malady of the joints comprehendeth all griefs and sorentes that be in the joints. And the malady betwixt the flesh and the skin, is that which we call the Scab. Unto which four kindes of maladies, *Vegetius* addeth three others, that is, the Farcine, the pathe of the Reins or Kidnies, and the cankered Marginess, most commonly called of the old writers the Leprosie; and so maketh seven kindes of maladies, under which all other particular diseases are comprehended.

Again, *Laurentius Rusius*, useth an other kind of division of sickness. Of Horses diseases, saith he, some be natural, and some accidental. The natural be those that do come either through the excesse, or lack of engendring seed, or by error of nature, in misforming the young, or else by some defect of the dam or sire, in that perhaps they be diseased within, and have their seed corrupted.

The accidental diseases be those that come by chance, as by surfetting, of cold, heat, and such like thing. But forasmuch as none of these writers do follow their own divisions, nor handle the parts thereof accordingly: to avoid their confusion, and to teach plainly: I thought good and profitable therefore to use this my own division and order here following.

First, then, of diseases some be inward, and some be outward. The inward be those that breed within the Horses body, and are properly called maladies and diseases, whereof some do occupy all the whole body, and some particular parts or members of the body.

Of those then that occupie all the body, and not be accident to any private member, I do first treat, as of Agues, of the Pestilence, and such like, and then of those that be incident to every particular member, beginning at the head, and so proceed orderly throughout all the members, even down to the sole of the foot, observing therein so nigh as I can, the self same order that *Galen* useth in his book, *De locis male affectis*, declaring what manner of disease it is, and how it is called in *English*, and also in *Italian*, because the Kings stable is never without *Italian* Riders, of whom our Farriars borrowed divers names, as you shall perceive hereafter. Then the causes whereof it proceeds, and the signes how to know it, and finally, the cure and diet belonging to the same; and because I find not inward diseases enow to answer every part of the body, I do not let to interlace them with outward diseases incident to those parts, yea rather, I leave out no outward disease belonging to any particular member, and to the intent you may the better know to what diseases or sorances every part or member of the Horses body is most commonly subject. And note by the way, that I call those outward diseases that proceed not of any inward cause, but of some outward cause, as when a Horse is shouldered by means of some outward cause, or his back galled with the saddle, or his sides spurgalled, or his hoof cloid with a nail, which properly may be called sorances or griefs.

Thirdly, I talk of those diseases as well outward as inward, that may indifferently chance in any part of the body, as of Impostumes, Cankerous Ulcers, Wounds, Fistulaes, Burnings, Brusings, Breaking of bones, and such like.

Fourthly, because most diseases are healed either by letting of bloud, by taking up of veins, by purgation, or else by cauterisation, that is to say by giving the fire: I talk of those four necessary things severally by themselves; and finally I shew you the true order of paring and shooing all manner of hoofs, according as the diversity of hoofs require: and to the intent you may the better understand me, you have the perfect shapes of all necessary shooes, plainly set forth in figures before your eyes. Thus much touching mine order which I have hitherto observed.

Now it is necessary to know, that to every disease or malady, belongeth four several times, that is to say, the beginning, the increasing, the state, and declination, which times are diligently to be observed of the Farriar, because they require divers applying of medicine; for that medicine which was meet to be used in the beginning of the disease, perhaps is not to be used in the declination thereof: and that which is requisite, and very needful, to be applyed in the state or chiefest of the disease, may be very dangerous to be used in the beginning. And therefore the Farriar ought to be a man of judgement, and able to discern one time from another, to the intent he may apply his medicines rightly. Hither of causes and sickness in general. Now it is also meet, that we speak in general of signes whereby sickness is known.

OF THE SIGNES OF SICKNESS IN GENERAL.

SICKNESS according to the learned Physitians, is known four manner of wayes. First, by inseparable or substantial accidents, as by the shape, number, quality, and sight of the part or member diseased. For if it be otherwise formed, or more or lesse in number or quantity, or else otherwise placed then it ought to be, then it is not well. Secondly, sickness is known by alteration of the quality, as, if it be too hot, or too cold, too moist, or too dry. Thirdly, when the action of any member is hurt or letted, as when the eye-sight is not perfect, it is a manifest sign that the eye is evill affected or sick. Likewise, when there breedeth no good bloud in the body, it is an evident token that the Liver is not well. Fourthly, sickness is known by the excrements that come from the Beast, as by dung or stale; for if his dung be too strong of sent, full of whole Corns, or of Wormes, too hard, or too soft, or evill coloured, it is a token that he is not well in his body: so likewise if his stale be too thick, or too thin, too white, or too red, it betokeneth some surfet, raw digestion, or else some grief in his reins, bladder or stones. But *Vegetius* saith, that it is best known, whether a Horse be sick or not, or toward sickness, by these signes here following; for if he be more slow and heavie in his trotting, or gallopping, harder of

Spur then he was wont to be, or spreadeth his litter abroad with his feet, often tumbling in the night season, fetching his breath short and violently, loud snuffling in the Nose, and casting out vapors at his Nostrils, or lyeth down immediately after his provender, or maketh long draughts in his drinking, or in the night season is now down, and now on foot, or if in the next morning he be very hot in his pasterns, or betwixt his ears, or that his ears hang more then they are wont to do: again, if his eye sight be dim, and his eyes hollow in his head, his hairs standing right up, and his flanks hollow and empty, whensoever two or three of these signes do concur together, then it is to be thought, saith *Vegetius*, that the Horse is not well, and therefore he would have him immediately to be separated from his companions that be whole, and to be placed by himself untill his disease be perfectly known and cured, and especially if it be any contagious disease.

I have seen divers Farriars here in *England* to use that for the trial of a Horses sickness, which I never read in any Author, that is, to feel his stones, whether they be hot or cold, and to smell at his nostrils, and so by the savour thereof to judge what sickness the Horse hath. Truly I think that no evill way, if they can discern with their sense of smelling, the diversity of savours, that cometh out of his Nostrils, and then aptly apply the same to the humours whereof such savours be bred, and so orderly to seek out the originall cause of his sickness. But I fear me, that more Farriars smell without judgement, then with such judgement, and no marvell why, sith that few or none be learned, or have been brought up with skilful Masters. But from henceforth I trust that my travail will cause such Farriars as can read, and have some understanding already, to be more diligent in seeking after knowledge then they have been heretofore, whereby they shall be the better able to serve their Countrey, and also to profit themselves, with good fame, whereas now for lack of knowledge they incur much slander.

OF THE FEVER AND DIVERS KINDS THEREOF IN A HORSE.

I think it will seem strange unto some, to hear that a Horse should have an Ague or Fever, but it was not strange unto the men of old time,

611

as to *Absyrtus, Hierocles, Xenophon, Vegetius,* and such like old Souldiers, throughly experimented in Horses griefs. A Fever, according to the learned Physitians, is an unnatural and immoderate heat, which proceeding first from the heart, spreadeth it self throughout all the arteries and veins of the body, and so letteth the actions thereof.

Of Fevers there be three general kinds, whereof the first, is that which breedeth in the spirits, being inflamed or heated more then their nature requireth. The second breedeth in the humors, being also distempered by heat. The third in the firm parts of the body, being continually hot. What spirits and humors be, hath been told you before in the keepers Office. Of these three general kinds do spring many other special kinds, as Quotidians, Tertians, Quartans, Fevers Hectick, and very many others, whereunto mans body is subject, whereof none of my Authors do treat, unless *Vegetius,* who speaketh somewhat of a Fever Quotidian, of a Fever continual, and also of a Fever accidental. He speaketh also of Summer, Autumn, and Winter Fevers, without making any great difference betwixt them, more then that one is worse then another, by reason of the time and season of the year, so that in effect all is but one Fever. Wherefore according unto *Absyrtus* opinion, I will briefly shew you first the causes whereof it proceeds, and then the signes how to know it, and finally how to cure the same.

The Fever chanceth sometime by surfetting of extreme labour or exercise, as of too much travelling, and especially in hot weather, of too swift gallopping and running, and sometime by extreme heat of the Sun, and also by extreme cold of the aire, and sometime it breedeth of crudity or raw digestion, which many times happeneth by over greedy eating of sweet green corn, or of such provender as was not thoroughly dryed or cleansed: for after such greedy eating, and specially such meat, never followeth perfect digestion. The signes to know a Fever be these, The Horse doth continually hold down his head, and is not able to lift it up, his eyes are even blown so as he cannot easily open them: yea and many times they be watering, the flesh of his lips and of all his body is lush and feeble, his stones hang low, his body is hot, and his breath is very hot and strong, he standeth weakly on his legs, and in his going draweth them lasiely after him, yea he cannot go but very softly, and that staggering here and there he will lie down on his side, and is not able to turn himself, or to wallow; he forsaketh his meat both hay and provender, and is desirous of nothing but of drink, which, as *Absyrtus* saith, is an assured token of a Fever: he also sleepeth but little. The cure and diet. Let him bloud in the face and temples, and also in the palat of his mouth, and the first day give him no meat, but only warm drink, and that by little and little. Afterward give him continually grasse, or else very sweet hay wet in water, and let him be kept warm, and sometime walke him up and down fair and softly in a temperate air, and then let him rest, and when you see that he begins to amend, give him by little and little at once Barley fair sifted and well sodden, and also mundified, that is to say, the huske pulled away, like as when you blanch Almonds.

OF DIVERS SORTS OF FEVERS ACCORDING TO VEGETIUS, AND FIRST OF THAT WHICH CONTINUETH BUT ONE DAY.

THE Fever of one day called by the *Greek* name *Ephemera*, or else by the *Latin* name *Diaria*, chanceth many times through the rashness and small discretion of the keeper, or some other that letteth not to ride a Horse unmeasurably, either before or after watering, whereby the Horse afterward in the stable entreth into an extream heat, and so falleth into his Fever, which you shall know partly by his waterish and bloud-shotten eyes, and partly by his short violent and hot breathing and panting. Moreover, he will forsake his meat, and his legs will wax stiffe and feeble. The cure; Let him have rest all the next day following, and be comforted with warm meat, then let him be walked up and down fair and softly, and so by little and little brought again to his former estate.

OF THE FEVER CONTINUAL.

THE Fever continual, is that which continueth without intermission, and is called in *Italian* by the *Latin* name *Febris continua*, which springeth of some inflamation or extream heat, bred in the principal members or inward parts, about the heart, which is known in this sort. The Horse doth not take his accustomed rest, whereby his flesh doth fall away every day more and more, and sometime there doth appear hot inflations in his flanks, and above his withers. The cure; Purge his head by squirting into his Nostrils Mans urine, or the Water of an Ox that hath been rested a certain time, to the intent such water may be the stronger, and then give him the drink written in the next Chapter.

OF THE FEVER TAKEN IN THE AUTUMN, THAT IS TO SAY, AT THE FALL OF THE LEAF.

IF a Horse chance to get a Fever at the fall of the leaf, cause him immediately to be let bloud in the neck vein, and also in the third furrow of the roof of his mouth, and then give him this drink; Take of Jermander four ounces, of Gum-dragant, and of dryed Roses, of each one ounce, beat them all into fine powder, and put them into a quart of Ale, adding thereunto of Oil-olive four ounces, and of Hony as much, and give it the Horse lukewarm.

OF THE FEVER IN SUMMER SEASON.

A Fever taken in Summer season is much worse then in any other time, and especially if it be taken in the Dog days, for then the accidents be more furious. The signes be these, his arteries will beat evidently, and he will shed his seed when he staleth, and his going will be unorderly. The cure; Let him bloud in a vein that he hath in his hinder hanch, about four fingers beneath the fundament, or if you cannot finde that vein, let him bloud in the neck vein, toward the withers, and if it be needful you may also give him this drink; Take the juyce of a handful of Parslein mingled with Gum-dragant, with Ensens, and a few Damask roses, beaten all into fine powder, and then put thereunto a sufficient quantity of Ale made sweet with Hony.

OF THE FEVER IN WINTER.

FOR the Fever in Winter, it shall be good to take the powder of the drugs last mentioned, and with a quill or reed, to blow it up into his left nostril to make him to neese. It shall be good also to let him bloud in the neck vein, and in the palat of the mouth, and then give him one of these drinks here following; Take of Ireos six ounces, of round Pepper one ounce, of Bay berries, and of the seed of Smallage, of each one ounce, and let him drink them with sodden Wine. Or else take a pinte of good Milk, and put therein of Oile four ounces, of Saffron one scruple, of Myrrhe two scruples, of the seed of Smallage a spoonful, and make him drink that: or make him this drink; Take of Aristoloch, otherwise called round Hartwort, one ounce, of Gentian, of Hysop, of Worm-wood, of Sothernwood, of each one ounce, of dry fat figs six ounces, of the seed of Smallage three ounces, of Rue a handful, boil them all in a clean Vessel with River Water, untill the third part be consumed, and when you see it look black and thick, take it from the fire, strain it, and give the Horse to drink thereof lukewarm.

As touching his diet, let his water be always lukewarm, wherein would be put a little Wheat meal, and remember to give him no meat so long as his fit continueth. And because in all Agues it is good to quicken the natural heat of the Horse, by rubbing and fretting his body; it shall not be amisse in some fair day to use this Friction, called of the ancient writers *Apotorapie*, which is made in this sort, Take of Damaske Roses one pound, of old Oil a pinte, of strong Vinegar a pinte and a half, of Mints and Rue beaten into powder, of each one ounce and a half, together with one old dry Nut, beat them and mingle them together, then being strained and made lukewarm, rub and chafe all the Horses body therewith against the hair, untill he beginneth to sweat, then set him up in the warmest place of the stable, and cover him well.

OF THE FEVER WHICH COMETH OF RAW DIGESTION, OR OF REPLETION.

YOU shall know if the Fever proceedeth of any such cause, by these signes here following. The Horse will blow at the nose more then he is accustomed to do, seemeth to fetch his winde only at his nose, and his breath will be short, hot and dry, you shall see his flanks walk, and his back to beat. The cure: Cause him to be let bloud abundantly in the head and palat of his month, and by squirting warm Vinegar in the morning into his nostrils, force him to neese: and if he be costive, let his fundament be raked, or else give him a Glyster to ease the pain in his head. And as touching his diet, give him but little provender or hay, neither let him drink much nor often, but betwixt times. But in any wise let him be well rubbed and chafed, and that a good while together, and if you use the Friction declared in the last Chapter before in such sort as there is said, it shall do him very much good.

OF THE FEVER ACCIDENTAL COMING OF SOME ULCER IN THE MOUTH OR THROAT.

THE Horse not being well kept and governed, after that he hath been let bloud in the upper parts; yea, and also besides that of his own nature is subject unto the distillation in his throat, or parts thereabout, the painful swelling or Ulcer whereof, causeth the Horse to fall into a grievous Ague. Whereof, besides the former remedies apt to purge humors, it shall be necessary also, to let him bloud in the vein of the head, and in the palat of his mouth, and to be short, in all those places where the disease causeth most grief. And if the Horse be so sore pained as he cannot swallow down his meat, it shall be good to give him lukewarm water mingled with Barley meal, or Wheat meal, and beside that, to make him swallow down seven sops sopped in Wine one after another, at one time: some use at the second time to dip such sops in sweet Sallet Oil. Thus far *Vegetius*.

OF THE PESTILENT AGUE.

IT seemeth by *Laurentius Russius*, that Horses be also subject to a Pestilent Fever, which almost incurable, is called of him *Infirmitas Epidemialis*, that is to say, a Contagious and pestiferous disease, whereof there dyed in one year in *Rome* above a thousand Horses, which as I take it came by some corruption of the air, whereunto *Rome* in the chief of Summer is much subject, or else corrupt humours in the body ingendered by unkind food, by reason perhaps, that the City was then pestered with more Horse-men then there could be conveniently harbored or fed

Laurentius himself rendreth no cause thereof, but only sheweth signes how to know it, which be these, The Horse holdeth down his head, eateth little or nothing, his eyes waterish, and his flanks do continually beat. The Cure: First give him this Glyster, Take of the pulp of Coloquintida one ounce, of Dragantum one ounce and a fals, of Ceutaury and Wormwood, of each one handful, of *Castoreum* half an ounce, boil them in Water, then being strained, dissolve therein of Gerologundinum six ounces, of Salt an ounce and a half, and half a pound of Oil-olive, and minister it lukewarm with a horn, or pipe made of purpose. Make also this Plaister for his head; Take of Squilla five ounces, of Elder, of *Castoreum*, of Mustard seed and of *Eusorbium*, of each two ounces, dissolve the same in the juice of Daffodil, and of Sage, and lay it to the Temples of his head next unto his eares; or else give him any of these three drinks following, Take of the best Triacle two or three ounces, and distemper it in good Wine, and give it him with a horn; or else let him drink every morning the space of three dayes, one pound or two of the juyce of Elder roots; or else give him every morning to eat, a good quantity of *Venus* hair, called of the *Latins, Capillus Veneris*, newly and fresh gathered, but if it be old, then boil it in Water, and give him the decoction thereof to drink with a horn.

MARTINS OPINION AND EXPERIENCE TOUCHING A HORSES FEVER.

THOUGH *Martin* have not seen so many several kinds of Fevers to chance to Horses, yet he confesseth that a Horse will have a Fever, and saith, that you shall know it by these signes; For after the Horse hath been sick two or three dayes, if you look upon his tongue you shall see it almost raw and scalt, with the heat that comes out of his body, and he will shake and trembles, reel and stagger when his fit cometh, which fit will keep his due hours, both of coming and also of continuance, unlesse you prevent it by putting the Horse into a heat, which would be done so soon as you see him begin to tremble, either by riding him, or tying up his legs, and by chasing him up and down in the stable, untill he leave shaking, and then let him be kept warm, and stand on the bit the space of two houres, that done, you may give him some hay, by a little at once, and give him warm water, with a little ground malt twice a day, the space

617

of three or four dayes; and once a day wash his tongue with Alomwater, Vinegar & Sage. But if you see that all this prevaile not, then purge him with this drink, after that he hath fasted all one night; Take of Aloes one ounce, of Agarick half an ounce, of Licoras and Annis seeds, of each a dram beaten to powder, and let him drink it with a quart of white wine likewarme, and made sweet with a little hony in the morning fasting, and let him be chafed a little after it, and be kept warm, and suffered to stand on the bit meatlesse two or three hours after, and he shall recover his health again quickly.

OF SICKNESS IN GENERAL, AND THE FEVER.

IN general, sickness is an opposite foe to nature, warring against the agents of the body and mind, seeking to confound those actions which uphold and maintain the bodies strength and livelyhood. Who coveteth to have larger definition of sickness, let him read *Vegetius, Rusius*, or excellent Master *Blundevile*, who in that hath been admirably well-deserving painful. For mine one part, my intent is to write nothing more then mine own experience, and what I have approved in Horses diseases most availeable: and first of the Fever or Ague in a Horse, though it be a disease seldom or not at all noted by our Mechanical Horse Farriars, who cure many times what they know not, and kill where they might cure, knew they the cause: yet I have my self seen of late (both by the demonstrate opinions of others better learned, and by the effects of the disease) some two Horses which I dare avouch were mightily tormented with a Fever; though divers Leeches had thereof given divers opinions, one saying it was the Bots, by reason of his immoderate languishment: another affirmed him to be bewitched, by reason of great shaking, heaviness, and sweating: but I have found it and approved it to be a Fever, both in effect, nature, and quality: the cure whereof is thus; for the original cause of a Fever, is surfet, breeding putrifaction in the bloud; then when his shaking beginneth, take three new laid Egges, break them in a dish, and beat them together, then mix thereto five or six spoonfuls of excellent good *Aquavitæ*, and give it him in a horn, then bridle him, and in some Close or Court, chase him till his shaking cease, and he begin to sweat: then set him up and cloath him warm. And during the time of his sickness, give him no water to drink, but before he drink it, boil therein Mallowes, Sorrel, Purslain, of each two or three handfuls.

As for his food, let it be sodden Barly, and now and then a little Rie in the sheaf to clense and purge him, chiefly if he be dry inwardly and grow costive. This I have proved uneffectless for this disease, and also much availeable for any other inward sickness proceeding either of raw digestion, too extream riding, or other surfet. Divers have written diversly of divers Agues, and I could prescribe receipts for them, but since I have not been experimented in them all, I mean to omit them, intending not to exceed mine own knowledge in any thing.

OF THE PESTILENCE.

THE Pestilence is a contagious disease, proceeding, as *Pelagonius* saith, sometime of overmuch labour, heat, cold, hunger, and sometime of sudden running after long rest, or of the retention or holding of stale or urine; or of drinking cold water whiles the Horse is hot and sweating; for all these things do breed corrupt humors in the Horses body, whereof the Pestilence doth chiefly proceed, or else of the corruption of the air, poisoning the breath whereby the Beasts should live, which also happeneth sometime of the corruption of evill vapors and exhalations that spring out of the earth, and after great floods or earthquakes, and sometime by means of some evill distillation or influence of the Planets, corrupting sometime the plants and fruits of the earth, and sometime divers kind of Cattle, and sometime both Men, Women and Children, as we dayly see by experience. It seemeth that this evill or mischief in times past came suddenly, without giving any warning, for none of mine Authors doth declare any signes how to know whether a Horse hath this disease or not, but only affirm, that if one Horse do die of it, all his fellows that bear him company will follow after, if they be not remedied in time: so that as far as I can learn, the sudden death of one or two first, must be the only mean to know that this disease doth reign. And the remedy that they give is this; First separate the whole from the sick; yea, and have them clean out of the air of those that be dead, the bodies whereof, as *Vegetius* saith, if they be not deep buryed, will infect all the rest. And let them bloud as well in the neck, as in the mouth; and then give them this drink, Take of Gentian, of Aristoloch, of Bay berries, of Myrrhe, of the scraping of Ivory, of each like quantity, beat them into fine powder, and give as well to the sick as to the whole, whom you would preserve from this contagion, every day a spoonful or two of this powder in a pinte of good Wine, so long as you shall see it needful. This medicine before rehearsed, is called of the ancient writers *Diapente*, that is to say, a composition of five simples, and is praised to be a sovereign medicine and preservative against all inward diseases, and therefore they would have such as travell by the way, to carry of this powder alwayes about them.

There be many other medicines which I leave to write, because if I should rehearse every mans medicine, my book would be infinite; I for my part would use no other then that before expressed, or else Wine and Treacle only.

OF THE DISEASES IN THE HEAD.

THE head is subject to divers diseases according to the divers parts thereof: for in the panicles or little fine skins cleaving to the bones, and covering the brain, do most properly breed head-ach and Migram. Again, in the substance of the brain, (which in a Horse is as much in quantity as is almost the brain of a mean Hog) do breed the Frensie, madness, sleeping evill, the Palsie and forgetfulness. Finally, in the ventricles or cels of the brain, and in those conducts through which the spirits animal do give feeling and moving to the body, do breed the Turnsick or staggers, the Falling-evill, the Night-mare, the Apoplexy, the Palsie, and the Convulsion or Cramp, the Catar or Rhume, which in a Horse is called the Glaunders: but first of Head-ach.

OF HEAD-ACH.

THE Head-ach either cometh of some inward causes: as of some cholerick humor, bred in the panicles of the brain, or else of some outward cause, as of extream heat or cold, of some blow, or of some violent savour. *Eumelus* saith, that it cometh of raw digestion: but *Martin* saith most commonly of cold: the signes be these; the Horse will hang down his head, and also hang down his ears; his sight will be dim, his eyes swollen and waterish; and he will forsake his meat. The cure. Let him bloud in the palat of his mouth: also purge his head with this perfume; Take of Garlike stalks a handful, all to broken in short pieces, and a good quantity of Frankincense, and being put into a chafing-dish of fresh coals, hold the chafing-dish under the Horses nostrils, so as the fume may ascend up into his head: and in using him thus once or twice, it will make him to cast at the nose, and so purge his head of all filth. *Pelagonius* saith, that it is good to pour into his nostrils Wine, wherein hath been sodden *Euforbium*, Centaury, and Frankincense.

OF THE FRENZY AND MADNESS OF A HORSE.

THE learned Physitians do make divers kindes, as well of Frensie, as of Madness, which are not needful to be recited, sith I could never read in any Author, nor learn of any Farriar, that a Horse were subject to the one half of them. *Absyrtus, Hierocles, Eumelus, Pelagonius*, and *Hippocrates*, do write simply *de furore & rabie*: that is to say, of the madness of a Horse. But indeed, *Vegetius* in his second Book of Horse-leach-craft, seemeth to make four mad passions belonging to a Horse, intituling his Chapters in this sort, *de Appioso, de Frenetico, de Cardiacis, de Rabioso*, the effects thereof, though I fear me it will be to no great purpose, yet to content such as perhaps have read the Author as well as I my self, I will here briefly rehearse the same.

When some naughty bloud (saith he) doth strike the film or pannicle of the brain, in one part only, and maketh the same grievously to ake, then the beast becometh *Appiosum*; that is to say, as it seemeth by his own words next following, both dull of minde and of sight. This word *Appiosum* is a strange word, and not to be found again in any other Author, and because in this passion, the one side of the head is only grieved, the Horse turneth round, as though he went in a Mill. But when the poyson of such corrupt bloud doth infect the mid brain, then the Horse becometh Frantick, and will leap and fling, and will run against

621

the wals. And if such bloud filleth the veins of the stomach, or breast, then it infecteth as well the heart as the brain, and causeth alienation of minde, and the body to sweat, and this disease is called of *Vegetius*, *Passocardiaca*, which if *Equus Appiosus* chance to have, then he becometh *Rabiosus*, that is to say, stark-mad. For saith he, by overmuch heat of the liver and bloud, the veins, and arteries of the heart are choaked up, for grief and pain whereof the Horse biteth himself, and gnaweth his own flesh.

Of two sorts of mad Horses, I believe I have seen my self here in this Realm. For I saw once a black *Sweatbland* Horse (as I took him to be) in my Lord of *Hunsdons* stable at *Hunsdon*, coming thither by chance with my Lord *Morley*, which Horse would stand all day long biting of the manger, and eat little meat or none, suffering no man to approach unto him, by which his doings, and partly by his colour and complexion, I judged him to be vexed with a melancholy madness called of the Physitians *Mania*, or rather *Melancholia*, which cometh of a corrupt Melancholy, and filthy bloud or humor, sometime spread throughout all the veins of the body, and sometimes perhaps remaining only in the head, or else in the spleen, or places next adjoyning. The other mad Horse was a Roan of Master *Ashlies*, Master of the Jewel house, which with his teeth crushed his Masters right fore-finger in pieces, whilest he offered him a little Hay to eat, whereby he lost in a manner the use of his whole hand, to the great grief of all his friends, and also of all the Muses, which were wont to be much delighted with such passing sweet musick as that his fine quavering hand could sometime make upon divers Instruments, but especially upon the Virginals.

This Horse I say, though he could eat his meat, drink his drink, and sleep: yet if he were never so little offended, he would take on like a spirit, and both bite and strike at any man that came nigh him: yea and would bite himself by the shoulders most terribly, pulling away lumps of flesh, so broad as a mans hand: and whensoever he was ridden, he was fain to be musled with a muslel of iron, made of purpose to keep him from biting either of his Rider or of himself, which no doubt proceeded of some kinde of frenzy or madness, whereunto the Horse was subject; by means that hot bloud (as I take it) abounded over-much in him. But now as touching the causes, signes, and cure of Horses madness, you shall hear the opinion of old Writers: for *Martin* never took such cure in hand. *Absyrtus* and the other Authors before mentioned, say, that the madness of a Horse cometh either by means of some extream heat taken by travelling, or long standing in the hot Sun, or else by eating over many fitches, or by some hot bloud resorting to the panicles of the brain; or through abundance of choler remaining in the veins; or else by drinking of some very unwholesome water. The signes be these, he will bite the manger and his own body, and run upon every man that comes nigh him, he will continually shake his ears, and stare with his eyes, and some at the mouth: and also, as *Hippocrates* saith, he will forsake his meat, and pine himself with hunger.

The cure, Cause him to be let bloud in his legs abundantly, which is done (as I take it) to divert the bloud from his head. Notwithstanding it were not amiss, to let him bloud in the neck and brest veins. Then give him this drink: take the roots of wilde Cowcumber, and boil it in harsh red Wine, and put thereunto a little Nitre, and give it him with a horn luke-warm: or if you can get no Cowcumber, then take Rue, and Mints, and boil them in the Wine: it were not amiss also to add thereunto a handful of black *Elleborus*, for that is a very good herb against madness. *Eumelius* saith, that if you give him mans dung in Wine, to drink three mornings together, it will heal him: also to take of black *Elleborus* two or three handfuls, and boil it in a sufficient quantity of strong Vinegar, and therewith rub and chafe both his head, and all his body once or twice a day; for the oftner his head is rubbed, the better, and often exercise is very profitable to all his body. Some again would have the skin of his body to be pierced in divers places with an hot iron, to let out the evill humors: but if none of all this will prevail, then the last remedy is to geld him of both his stones, or else of one at the least; for either that will heal him, or else nothing. As touching the diet and usage of a mad Horse, the Authors do not agree; for some would have him kept in a close, dark and quiet house, void from all noise, which as *Absyrtus* saith, will either make him madder, or else kill him out of hand. His diet would be thin, that is to say, without any provender, and that day that he is let bloud, and receiveth his drink, they would have him fast untill even, and then to have a warm mash of Barley meal: yea, me thinks it were not amiss to feed him only with warm mashes and hay; and that by a little at once, untill he be somewhat recovered.

ANOTHER OF THE HEAD-ACH.

THE Head-ach, as most are opinionated, proceedeth of cold and raw digestion: the cure is; Take a Goose feather anointed with Oyl-de-bay, and thrust it up into the Horses nostrils, to make him neese; then take a wreath of Pease-straw or wet hay, and putting fire thereunto, hold it under the Horses nose, so as the smoke may ascend up into his head; then being thus perfumed, take a knife and prick him in the palat of the mouth, so that he may lick up and chaw his own bloud, which done, have great care in keeping his head warm, and doubt not his recovery.

OF THE SLEEPING-EVIL.

THIS is a disease forcing the Beast continually to sleep, whether he will or not, taking his memory and appetite clean away, and therefore is called of the Physitians *Lethargus*, it proceedeth of abundance of flegm moistning the brain overmuch. It is easie to know it, by the continual sleeping of the Horse. The cure of this disease according to *Pelagonius*, *Vegetius*, and others, is in this sort: Let him bloud in the neck, and then give him this drink: Take of Camomile and Mother-wort, of each two or three handfuls, and boil them in a sufficient quantity of water, and put thereunto a little Wheat-bran, Salt and Vinegar, and let him drink a pinte of that every day, the space of three or four days together. It is good also to perfume and chafe his head, with Thyme and Pennyroyal sodden together in Vinegar, or with Brimstone and feathers burned upon a chafingdish of coals under his nose: and to provoke him to neese, by blowing Pepper and Pyrethre beaten to powder, up into his nostrils: yea and to anoint the palate of his mouth, with Honey and Mustard mingled together, and in his drink, which would be always warm water, to put Parsley seed, and Fennel seed, to provoke urine. His legs also would be bathed, and his hoofs filled with Wheat-bran, Salt, and Vinegar, sodden together, and laid to so hot as he may endure it, and in any case suffer him not to sleep, but keep him waking and stirring, by continual crying unto him, or pricking him with some sharp thing that cannot pass through the skin, or else by beating him with a whip, and this doing he shall recover.

ANOTHER OF THE SLEEPING-EVILL.

THE Sleeping-evill in a Horse, differeth nothing from that which the Physitians call the Lethargy in men, for it provoketh the Horse to sleep continually, without desisting, robbing his memory and appetite of their qualities: the knowledge thereof is easily known by his drowsiness, and the cure in this sort: Let one stand by him, and either with fearful noise or stripes, perforce keep him waking; then let him bloud under the eyes, and in the neck, and then take a leaf or two of the best Tobacco, which being dryed and beaten to powder, with a quill blow it up into his nostrils, and give him to drink Vinegar, Salt, and Mustard mingled well together, to which if you put a little Honey, it shall not be amiss; and also when he drinketh any water, put thereto either Fennel-seeds, Aniseeds or Pepper.

OF A HORSE THAT IS TAKEN.

A Horse is said to be taken, when he is deprived of his feeling and moving, so as he is able to stir no manner of way, but remaineth in such state and form, as he was taken in; which disease is called of the Physitians by the *Greek* name *Catalepsis*, and in *Latine, Deprehensio*, or *Congelatio*; and of *Vegetius, Sideratio*; which also calleth those Beasts that have this disease *Jumenta sideratitia*. The Physitians say, that it cometh of abundance of phlegm and choler mixt together, or else of melancholy bloud, which is a cold dry humor oppressing the hinder parts of the brain. But *Vegetius* saith, that it comes of some extream outward cold, striking suddenly into the empty veins, or some extream heat or raw digestion; or else of some great hunger, caused by long fasting. It is easie to know by the description before mentioned.

As touching the cure, *Vegetius* saith, that if it come of cold, then it is good to give him to drink one ounce of *Laserpitium*, with Wine and Oyl mixt together, and made luke-warm: if of heat, then to give it him with Water and Honey: if of crudity, then to heal him by fasting: if of hunger, then by feeding him well with Pease. But *Martin* saith, that this disease is called of the *French* men *Surprins*, and it cometh (as he saith) most chiefly of cold taken after heat, and he wisheth a Horse that is thus taken, to be cured in this sort. First to be let bloud on both sides of the breast, and then to be put in a heat either by continual stirring and molesting him; or else if he will stir by no means, then to bury him all save the head in a warm dunghill, and there to let him ly untill his limbs have some feeling. And before you so bury him, it shall be good to give him this drink: Take of Malmsie three pintes, and put thereunto a quartern of Sugar, and some Cinamon and Cloves, and let him drink it good and warm, and untill he be perfectly whole, let him be kept warm, and often exercised and walked up and down in the stable, and thinly dieted, and drink nothing but warm water, wherein if you put some Fennel and Parsley seed, to provoke him to urine, it shall be the better. And if he cannot dung, let him be raked, and have a Glyster made of the broth of Mallows and fresh Butter.

ANOTHER OF A HORSE THAT IS TAKEN.

A Horse which is bereft of his feeling, moving or stirring, is said to be taken, and in sooth so he is, in that he is arrested by so villainous a disease; yet some Farryers, not well understanding the ground of the disease, conster the word taken, to be stricken by some Planet, or evill spirit, which is false; for it proceedeth of too great abundance of phlegm and choler, symbolized together: the cure is thus; Let him bloud in his spur veins, and his breast veins, and then by foulding him in abundant number of cloaths, drive him into an extream sweat, during which time of his sweating, let one chafe his legs with Oyl-de-bay; then after he hath sweat the space of two hours, abate his clothes moderately; and throughly after he is dry, anoint him all over with Oyl Petrolium, and in twice or thrice dressing him he will be found.

626

Of the Staggers.

THIS is a dizziness of the head, called in *Latine, Vertigo*; and of the *Italians*, as I remember, *Capistura*. It cometh of some corrupt bloud, or gross and tough humors oppressing the brain, from whence proceedeth a vaporous spirit, dissolved by a weak heat, which troubleth all the head. The signes be these; dimness of sight, the reeling and staggering of the Horse, who for very pain will thrust his head against the walls, and forsake his meat. The cure according to *Martin* is thus:

Let him bloud in the temple veins, and then with a knife make an hole an inch long over-thwart his fore-head, hard underneath his fore-top, and raise the skin with a Cornet, thrusting it upward towards the head-stale a good handful, and then put in a tent dipt in Turpentine and Hogs grease molten together, renewing the tent every day once untill it be whole, and do the like upon the ridge of the rump; but me thinks it were better to do the like, in the powl of his head, or nape of his neck, for so should the evill humors have both ways the easier and speedier passage: and as touching his diet, let him have continually warm drink, and mashes; and once a day be walked up and down fair and softly to exercise his body.

Of the Staggers.

THE Staggers is a dizy disease, breeding frenzy in a Horse, which if it be not instantly helped, is mortal: the cure is thus; Let him bloud in the temple veins, and then apply to his temples cloth wet in the juyce of Garlike, and *Aqua vitæ* mixt together: if you crush Garlike, and put it in his ears, it is excellent; or if you slit his fore-head, and loosening the skin from the bone, taint is with Turpentine and Sallet-oyl, it will undoubtedly help him.

Of the Falling-evil.

THIS is a kinde of Convulsion or Cramp, called of the *Latines* by the *Greek* name *Epilepsia*; in *Italian, Il morbo caduco*, depriving the Beast at certain times, and for a certain space of the use of feeling, hearing, and seeing, and of all the other senses. And although it be a disease hath been seldom seen to chance unto Horses of this Countrey, yet it appeareth by *Absyrtus*, and also by *Vegetius*, and divers others, that Horses be subject thereunto. For *Absyrtus* writing to his friend *Tiberius Claudius* saith, that unto Horses chanceth many times the Falling-sickness. The signs whereof are these; The Horse will fall down suddenly, partly through the resolution of his members, and partly through distension of his sinews, and all his body will quiver and quake, and sometime he will some at the mouth. *Vegetius* again writeth in this sort; By a certain course of the Moon Horses and other beasts many times do fall, and dy for a time as well as men. The signes whereof are these: Being fallen, their bodies will quiver and quake, and their mouths will some, and when a man would think that they would dy out of hand, they rise suddenly up and fall to their meat. And by feeling the gristle of their nostrils with your finger, you shall know whether they will fall often or not; for the more cold the gristle be, the oftner, and the less cold it be, the seldomer they will fall. The cure:

Let him bloud abundantly in the neck veins, and within five days after, let him bloud again in the temple veins, and let him stand in a warm and dark stable, and anoint all his body with comfortable Ointments, and his head and ears with Oyl of Bay, and liquid Pitch or Tar, mingled together. And also put some thereof into his ears, and then make a Biggen for him of some sort warm skin, as of a Sheeps skin, or else of Canvas stuffed underneath with Wool, and make him this purging drink. Take of Radish roots two ounces, of the root of the herb called in *Latine, Panax* or *Panaces*, and of Scammony, of each one ounce; beat all these things together, and boyl them in a quart of Honey, and at sundry times as you shall see it needful, give him a good spoonful or two of this in a quart of Ale luke-warm, whereunto would be put three or four spoonfuls of Oyl. It is good also to blow the powder of Motherwort, or of Pyrethrum, up into his nostrils; and if the disease do continue still for all this, then it shall be needful to pierce the skin of his fore-head in divers places with a hot iron, and to let out the humors oppressing his brain.

Of the Night-mare.

THIS is a disease oppressing either Man or Beast in the night season when he sleepeth, so as he cannot draw his breath, and is called of the *Latines, Incubus.* It cometh of a continual crudity or raw digestion of the stomach, from whence gross vapours ascending up into the head, do oppress the brain, and all the sensitive powers, so as they cannot do their office, in giving perfect feeling and moving to the body. And if this disease chancing often to a man, be not cured in time, it may perhaps grow to a worse mischief, as to the Falling-evil, Madness, or Apoplexy. But I could never learn that Horses were subject to this disease, neither by relation, nor yet by reading, but only in an old *English* Writer, who sheweth neither cause nor signes, how to know when a Horse hath it, but only teacheth how to cure it with a food foolish charm; which because it may perhaps make you gentle Reader to laugh, as well as it did me, for recreation sake I will here rehearse it. Take a flint stone that hath a hole of his own kinde, and bang it over him, and write in a bill,

In nomine patris, &c.
Saint George our Ladies Knight,
He walked day, so did he night,
Until he her found,
He her beat, and he her bound,
Till truly her troath she him plight,
That she would not come within the night,
There as Saint George our Ladies Knight,
Named was three times, Saint George.

And hang this Scripture over him, and let him alone: with such proper charme as this is, the false Fryars in times past were wont to charm the money out of plain folks purses.

Of the Apoplexy.

THE Apoplexy, is a disease depriving all the whole body of sense and moving. And if it deprive but part of the body, then it is called of the

Latines by the *Greek* name *Paralysis*, in our tongue a Palsie. It proceeds of cold, gross, and tough humors, oppressing the brain all at once, which may breed partly of crudities and raw digestion, and partly by means of some hurt in the head, taken by a fall, stripe, or otherwise. As touching Apoplexy, few or none writing of Horse-leach-craft, do make any mention thereof: but of the Palsie *Vegetius* writeth in this manner; A Horse (saith he) may have the Palsie as well as a man, which is known by these signes: He will go grovelling and sideling like a Crab, carrying his neck awry, as if it were broken, and goeth crookedly with his legs, beating his head against the wals, and yet forsaketh not his meat nor drink, and his provender seemeth moist and wet. The cure. Let him bloud in the temple vein, on the contrary side of the wrying of his neck, and anoint his neck with comfortable Oyntment, and splent it with splents of wood to make it stand right, and let him stand in a warm stable, and give him such drinks as are recited in the next chapter following. But if all this profiteth not, then draw his neck with a hot iron on the contrary side: that is to say, on the whole side, from the neather part of the ear down to the shoulders, and draw also a good long strike on his temple, on that side, and on the other temple make him a little star in this sort, and from his reins to his mid back, draw little lines, in manner of a ragged staffe, and that will heal him.

Of the Cramp or Convulsion of the Sinews and Muscles.

A Convulsion or Cramp, is a forcible and painful contraction or drawing together of the sinews and muscles, which do happen sometime through the whole body, and sometime but in one part or member only. And according as the body may be diversly drawn, so do the Physitians, and also mine Authors that write of Horse-leech-craft, give it divers names. For if the body be drawn forward, then they call it in *Greek, Emprosthotonos*; in *Latine, Tensio ad anteriota*. And if the body be drawn back, it is called in *Greek, Opisthotonos*; in *Latine, Tensio ad posteriora*.

But if the body he stark and strait, bowing neither forward, nor backward, then it is called simply in *Greek, Tetanos*; in *Latine, Distensio* or *Rigor*: which names also are applyed to the like Convulsions of the neck.

Notwithstanding, *Vegetius* writing of this disease, entituleth his chapters *de Roborosis*, a strange tearm, and not to be found again in any other Author: A Convulsion, as I said before, may chance as well to one part or member of the body, as to the whole body: as to the eye, to the skin of the fore head, to the roots of the tongue, to the jaws, to the lips, to the arm, hand or leg: that is to say, whensoever the sinew or muscle serving to the moving of that part, is evill affected or grieved. Of which Convulsions, though there be many divers causes: yet *Hippocrates* bringeth them all into two: that is to say, into fulness and emptiness: for when a Convulsion proceedeth either of some inflamation of superfluous eating or drinking, or for lack of due purgation, or of overmuch rest and lack of exercise, all such causes are to be referred to repletion or fulness. But if a Convulsion come by means of over-much purging or bleeding, or much watching, extream labour, long fasting; or by wounding or pricking of the sinews, then all such causes are to be referred unto emptiness. And if the Convulsion proceed of fulness, it chanceth suddenly, and all at once; but if of emptiness, then it cometh by little and little, and leisurely.

Besides these kindes of Convulsions, there is also chancing many times in a mans fingers, legs and toes, another kinde of Convulsion, which may be called a windy Convulsion, for that it proceeds of some gross or tough vapour, entred into the branches of the sinews, which maketh them to swell like a Lute string in moist weather, which though it be very painful for the time, yet it may be soon driven away; by chasing or rubbing the member grieved with a warm cloth. And this kinde of Convulsion or Cramp chanceth also many times to a Horses hinder-legs standing in the stable.

For I have seen some my self, that have had one of their hinder-legs drawn up with the Cramp almost to the belly so stiffe and hard, as no man hath been able to stir it, neither could the Horse himself set it down to the ground of a long season, which I think might be soon remedied: first by continual chasing, fretting, or rubbing his legs with a good wispe, and then by tying up the other hinder-leg, or else the foreleg on the sore side, whereby he should be forced to set down the pained leg: Thus far I have discoursed of the Convulsion of sinews, and of the causes thereof, according to the opinions of the learned Physitians. Now I will briefly shew you the causes, signes, and cure thereof, according to the doctrine of mine Authors that write of Horse-leech-craft.

Absyrtus saith, that this disease doth come, either by driving the Horse into a sweat when he halteth, or for that he hath troden upon some nail, or by taking cold after journeying and sweating in Winter season, whereby his lips are clung together, or by long lying and rest after sweating, whereby the sinews of his fore-legs be nummed, or by having some stripe of his privy members; or by long travelling in the cold Mountains, where Snow and Ice doth abound. For *Theomnestus* writeth, that coming out of *Pæonia*, with the King and his Army, and passing over the Mountains to go into *Italy* there fell such abundance of Snow, as not only many Souldiers dyed, sitting still on their Horses backs, with their Weapons in their hands, being so stark and stiffe, and cleaving so fast to their Saddles, as they could not easily be pulled out of them: but also divers Horses in their going were so nummed as they could not bow their legs: yea and some were found stark dead, standing still on their feet, and few Horses or none escaped at that time free from this Convulsion of sinews, insomuch that *Theomnestus* his own Horse which he loved dearly, was sore vexed therewith. The signes to know whether a Horse be troubled with the Convulsion in the sinews or not, be these:

His head and neck will be so stiffe and stark, as he can bow it no manner of way, his ears will stand right up, and his eyes will be hollow in his head, and the fleshy parts thereof in the great corners, will be turned backward; his lips will be clung fast together, so as he cannot open his mouth, and his tongue so nummed as he can neither eat nor drink; his back-bone and tail will be so stiffe, as he cannot move it one way nor other and his legs so stiffe, as they will not bow, and being laid he is not able to rise, and specially on his hinder-legs, but falleth down on his buttocks, like a Dog when he sitteth on the ground; and by means of the Convulsion in his back, his bladder also for neighbour-hood sake, suffereth, whereby the Horse cannot stale, but with great pain. The cure:

Put him into a sweat, either by burying him all save the head in some warm dunghill; or if he be a Horse of price, carry him into a hot house, where is no smoke, and let him sweat there. Then anoint all his body, head, neck, legs, and all, with Oyl of Cypres, and Oyl of Bay mingled together. Or else with one of these Ointments: Take of Hogs grease two pound, of Turpentine half a pound, of Pepper beaten in powder one dram, of new Wax one pound, of old Oyl two pound; boil all these together, and being made very warm, anoint all his body therewith. Or else with this Ointment: Take of new Wax one pound, of Turpentine four ounces, of Oyl-de-bay as much, of Opopanax two ounces, of Deers sewet and Oyl of Storax, of each three ounces, melt all these together, and anoint all his body therewith.

It is good also to bath his head with the decoction of Fitches, or else of Lupines, and make him this drink: Take twenty grains of long Pepper, finely beaten into powder, of Cedar two ounces, of Nitre one ounce, of *Laserpitium* as much as a Bean, and mingle all these together with a sufficient quantity of white Wine; and give him thereof to drink a quart every morning and evening, for the space of three or four days; or else this drink: Take of Opopanax two ounces, of Storax three ounces, of Gentian three ounces, of Manna Succary three ounces, of Myrrhe one scruple, of long Pepper two scruples, give him this with old Wine: or make him a drink of *Laserpitium*, Cumin, Anise seed, Fenigreek, Bay-berries, and old Oyl.

In old time they were wont to let him bloud in the Temples, which *Absyrtus* doth not allow, saying, that it will cause the sinews of his lips to dry up, so as the Horse being not able to move them, shall pine for hunger. As touching his diet, give him at the first warm mashes, and such soft meat as he may easily get down, and wet Hay, bringing him to harder food by little and little. And in any case, let him be kept very warm, and ridden or walked once a day to exercise his legs and limbs. *Theomnestus* cured his Horse, as he saith, by placing him in a warm stable, and by making a clear fire without any smoke round about him; and the Horse not being able to open his jaws of himself, he caused his mouth to be opened, and put therein sops dipt in a confection called *Emrigon conditum*, and also anointed all his body with a Medicine or Ointment called *Acopum* (the making whereof hereafter followeth) dissolved in Cypres Oyl, which made him to fall into a sweat, and being before half dead and more, brought him again to his feeling and moving, so as he did rise and eat his meat.

OF THE CRAMP OR CONVULSIONS OF THE SINEWS OR MUSCLES.

A Convulsion or Cramp, is a forcible drawing together of the sinews, sometimes universally over the whole body; as I have seen one Horse in my life time, and sometimes but in one part or member, as I have known and helpt divers. These Convulsions have two grounds, namely, either natural, or else accidental; natural, as proceeding of cold windy humors ingendered in the body, and dispersed into those parts, work there the effects of grievance. Accidental, is by wounding or pricking the sinews, of which immediately ensueth a Convulsion. If it be natural, and the disease generally dispersed; then the cure is thus: Dig a great deep hole in some old dung-hil, and there bury him all save the head, so as he may sweat there for the space of two hours at the least; then take him out, and anoint his body all over with Nerve oil, Turpentine, and Deers suet mingled together on the fire, and bath his head in the juyce of Rue and Camomile.

Then give him to drink old Ale brewd with Cinamon, Ginger, Fenigreek and long Pepper: of each three ounces. As for his diet, let it be warm mashes, sodden wheat and hay, throughly carded with a pair of Wool-cards: let him be kept very warm and aired abroad once a day at the least.

If this Convulsion be but only in one member, then it is sufficient, if every day with hard ropes of hay or straw you rub and chafe that part exceedingly, and apply there to a little quantity of the Oyl of Pepper. If the Convulsion be accidental, proceeding of some hurt, whereby the sinew is wounded or prickt; then shall you incontinently take up the sinew so wounded, searching the wound with great discretion, and cut it clean in sunder; then shall you endeavour to heal up the same with unguents, plaisters and balms, as shall be hereafter mentioned in the chapters of wounds and ulcers, of what kinde or nature soever.

OF THE COLD IN THE HEAD.

ACCORDING as the cold which the Horse hath taken, is new or old, great or small, and also according as humors do abound in his head, and as such humors be thick or thin, so is the disease more or less dangerous. For if the Horse casteth little or no matter out of his nose, or hath no very great cough, but only heavy in his head, and perhaps lightly cougheth now and then, it is a sign that he is stopped in the head, which we were wont to call the pose. But if his head be full of humors congealed by some extream cold taken of long time past; and that he casteth foul filthy matter out at the nose, and cougheth grievously; then it is a sign that he hath either the Glaunders, or the Strangullion, mourning of the chein, or Consumption of the Lungs. For all such diseases do breed for the most part of the rheume or distillation that cometh from the head. Of the cures thereof we leave to speak, until we come to talk of the diseases in the throat, minding here to shew you how to heal the pose or cold before mentioned.

Martin saith, it is good to purge his head, by perfuming him with Frankincense, and also to provoke him to neeze, by thrusting two Gouse feathers dipt in Oyl-de-bay up into his nostrils, and then to trot him up and down half an hour, for these feathers will make him to cast immediately at the nose, *Laurentius Russius* would have him to be perfumed with Wheat, Pennyroyal, and Sage sodden well together, and put into a bag so hot as may be; which bag would be so close fastened to his head, that all the savour thereof may ascend up into his nostrils, and his head also would be covered and kept warm: and to provoke him to neeze, he would have you to binde a soft clout anointed with Sope; or else with Butter and Oyl-de-bay unto a stick, and to thrust that up and down into his nostrils, so high as you may conveniently go, and let him be kept warm, and drink no cold water. Yea, it shall be good for three or four days, to boil in his water a little Fenigreek, Wheat meal, and a few Anise-seeds. And every day after that you have purged his head by perfuming him, or by making him to neeze, cause him to be trotted up and down, either in the warm Sun, or else in the house half an hour, which would be done before you water him, and give him his provender.

OF THE COLD IN THE HEAD.

THE pose or cold in a Horse, is the most general disease that hapneth, and is the easiest perceived, both by stopping, ratling in the nose, and coughing, the cure thereof is in this sort: If it be but newly taken by some-careless regard, and immediately perceived, you shall need no other remedy, but to keep him warm every morning and evening after his water, to ride him forth, and to trot him up and down very fast till his cold break, and then gently to gallop him a little, which moderate exercise with warm keeping will quickly recover him again; but if the cold hath had long residence in him, and still encreaseth, then you shall give him this drink three days together: Take of strong Ale one quart, of the best Treakle six penny-worth, of long Pepper and grains, of each as much beaten to powder, of the juyce of Garleek two spoonfuls, boyl all these together, and give it the Horse to drink; so warm as he may suffer it, and then trot him up and down by the space of an hour or more, and keep him warm, giving him to drink no cold water.

OF THE DISEASES OF THE EYES.

HORSES eyes be subject to divers griefs, as to be waterish or bloud-shotten, to be dim of sight, to have the Pin and Web, and the Haw, whereof some comes of inward causes, as of humors resorting to the eyes, and some of outward, as of cold, heat, or stripe.

OF WEEPING OR WATERING EYES.

THIS, as *Laurentius Russius* saith, may come sometime by confluence of humors, and sometime by some stripe, whose cure I leave to recite, because it doth not differ from *Martins* experience here following: Take of Pitch, Rosen and Mastick, a like quantity, melt them together. Then with a little stick, having a clout bound to the end thereof, and dipt therein, anoint the temple veins on both sides, a handful above the eyes, as broad as a Testern, and then clap unto it immediately a few flocks of like colour to the Horse, holding them close to his head with your hand, untill they stick fast unto his head, then let him bloud on both sides, (if both sides be infected) a handful under the eyes. *Russius* also thinketh it good to wash his eyes once a day with pure white wine, and then to blow therein a little of *Tartarum*, and of Pumice stone, beaten into fine powder.

OF WATERING EYES.

WATERING eyes come most commonly in some stripe or blow, and the cure is thus: Lay unto his temples a plaister of Turpentine and Pitch molten together, then wash his eyes with white Wine, and afterward blow the powder of burnt Allum into the same.

OF BLOUD-SHOTTEN EYES, ALSO FOR A BLOW OR ITCHING, AND RUBBING IN THE EYES.

MARTIN never used any other medicine, then this water here following, wherewith he did always heal the foresaid griefs: Take of pure Rose water, of Malmsie, of Fennel water, of each three spoonfuls, of Tutia as much as you can easily take with your thumb and finger, of Cloves a dozen beaten into fine powder; mingle them together, and being luke-warm, or cold if you will, wash the inward part of the eye with a feather dipt therein, twice a day untill he be whole. *Russius* saith, that to bloud-shotten eyes it is good to lay the white of an Egge, or to wash them with the juyce of Celidony.

ANOTHER OF BLOUD-SHOTTEN EYES, OR ANY OTHER SORE EYE, COMING OF RHEUME OR OTHER HUMOR.

FOR any sore eye make this water: Take of the water of Eye-bright, of Rose water, and Malmsey, of each three spoonfuls, of Cloves six or seven beaten to fine powder; of the juyce of Houseleek two spoonfuls; mix all these together, and wash the Horses eyes therewith once a day, and it will recover him.

OF DIMNESS OF SIGHT, AND ALSO FOR THE PIN AND WEB, OR ANY OTHER SPOT IN THE EYE.

IF the Horse be dim of sight, or hath any Pearl growing in his eye, or thin film covering the ball of his eye, then *Russius* would have you take of Pumice stone, of *Tartarum*, and of *sal Gemmæ,* of each like weight, and being beaten into very fine powder, to blow a little of that in his eye, continuing so to do every day once or twice, untill he be whole. *Martin* saith, that he always used to blow a little Sandivoir into the eye once a day, which simple he affirmeth to be of such force, as it will break any Pearl or Web in short space, and make the eye very clear and fair. *Russius* amongst a number of other medicines, praiseth most of all the powder of a black flint stone.

OF THE PIN AND WEB, AND OTHER DIMNESS.

FOR to cure the Pin, Web, Pearl, Film, or other dimness, use this means following: Take of Sandivoir, the powder of burnt Allum, and the powder of black Flint-stone, of each like quantity: and once a day blow a little thereof into the Horses eye, and it will wear away such imperfect matter, and make the eye clear.

OF THE HAW, CALLED OF THE ITALIANS, ILLUNGHIA DEGLI OCCHI.

THIS is a gristle covering sometime more then one half of the eye: It proceedeth of gross and tough humors, descending out of the head; which Haw, as *Martin* saith, would be cut away in this sort: First, pull both the eye-lids open with two several threds, stitched with a needle to either of the lids. Then catch hold of the Haw with another needle and thred, and pull it out so far as you may cut it round the bredth of a penny, and leave the black behinde. For by cutting away too much of the fat and black of the eye, the Horse many times becometh blear-eyed. And the Haw being clean taken away, squirt a little white Wine or Beer into his eye.

ANOTHER OF THE HAW.

A Haw is a gross gristle growing under the eye of a Horse, and covering more then one half of his sight; which if he be suffered will in short time perish the eye: the cure is thus: Lay your thumb under his eye, in the very hollow, then with your finger pull down the lid, and with a sharp needle and thred take hold of the Haw, and plucking it out, with a sharp knife, cut it away the compass of a penny, or more, that done, wash the eye with a little Beer.

OF LUNATICK EYES.

VEGETIUS writeth *De oculo Lunatico*, but he sheweth neither cause nor signes thereof, but only saith that the old men tearmed it so, because it maketh the eye sometime to look as though it were covered with white, and sometime clear.

Martin saith, that the Horse that hath this disease, is blinde at certain times of the Moon, insomuch that he seeth almost nothing at all during that time, and then his eyes will look yellowish: yea, and somewhat reddish, which disease according to *Martin*, is to be cured in this fort: First, use the plaister mentioned before in the chapter of Waterish or Weeping eyes, in such order as is there prescribed; and then with a sharp knife make two slits on both sides of his head an inch long, somewhat towards the nose, a handful beneath the eyes, not touching the vein: and with a cornet loosen the skin upward the breadth of a groat, and thrust therein a round peece of leather, as broad as a two penny peece, with a hole in the midst to keep the hole open, and look to it once a day, that the matter may not be stopped, but continually run the space of ten days, then take the leather out, and healthe wound with a little flax dipt in the salve here following: Take of Turpentine, of Honey, of Wax, of each like quantity, and boyl them together, which being a little warmed, will be liquid to serve your purpose, and take not away the plaisters from the temples untill they fall away of themselves, which being fallen, then with a small hot drawing Iron, make a star in the midst of each temple-vern where the plaister did ly. Which star would have a hole in the midst made with the button end of your drawing Iron.

ANOTHER OF LUNATICK OR MOON-EYES.

OF these Lunatick eyes, I have known divers: they are blinde at certain times of the Moon, they are very red, fiery, and full of film: they come with over-riding, and extraordinary heat and fury, the cure of them is thus: Lay upon the Temples of his head a plaister of Bitch, Rozen, and Mastick molten together very exceeding hot: then with a little round Iron made for the purpose, burn three or four holes an inch or more underneath his eyes, and anoint those holes every day with Hogs grease, then put it in his eyes every day with a little Honey, and in short time he will recover his sight.

OF THE CANKER IN THE EYE.

This cometh of a ranck and corrupt bloud descending from the head into the eye. The signes. You shall see red pimples, some small, and some great, both within and without upon the eye-lids, and all the eye will look red, and be full of corrupt matter. The cure according to *Martin* is thus: First, let him bloud on that side the neck, that the eye is grieved, the quantity of a pottle. Then take of Roch Allum, of green Copperas, of each half a pound, of white Copperas one ounce, and boil them in three pintes of running water, untill the half be consumed, then take it from the fire, and once a day wash his eye with this water being made luke-warm with a fine linnen cloth, and cleanse the eye therewith so oft as it may look raw, continuing thus to do every day untill it be whole.

OF DISEASES INCIDENT TO THE EARS, AND POLL OF THE HEAD, AND FIRST OF AN IMPOSTUME IN THE EAR.

IMPOSTUMES breed either by reason of some blow or bruising, or else of evill humors congealed in the ear by some extream cold; the signes be apparent, by the burning and painful swelling of the ear and part thereabout. The cure according to *Martin* is in this sort. First, ripe the Impostume with this plaister. Take of Linseed beaten into powder, of Wheat flowre, of each half a pinte, of Honey a pinte, of Hogs grease, or Barrows grease one pound. Warm all these things together in an earthen pot, and stir them continually with a flat stick or slice, untill they be throughly mingled and incorporated together, and then spread some of this plaister, being warm, upon a peece of linnen cloth, or soft white leather, so broad as the swelling, and no more, and lay it warm

640

unto it, and so let it remain one whole day, and then renew it with fresh Ointment, continuing so to do untill it break; then lance the sore, so that it may have passage downward, and tent it to the bottom with a tent of flax dipt in this Ointment: Take of *Mel Rosatum*, of Oyl Olive and Turpentine, of each two ounces, and mingle them together, and make him a biggen of Canvas to close in the sore, so as the tent with the Ointment may abide within, renewing the tent once a day untill it be whole. But if the Horse have pain in his ears, without any great swelling or Impostumation, then thrust in a little black Wooll dipt in Oyl of Camomile, and that will heal it.

OF THE POLL EVILL.

THIS is a disease like a Fistula growing betwixt the ears and the poll or nape of the neck, and proceedeth of evill humors gathered together in that place, or else of some blow or bruise, for that is the weakest and tenderest part of all the head, and therefore soonest offended, which rude Carters do little consider, whilest in their fury they beat their Horses upon that place of the head with their whip-stocks; and therefore no Horse is more subject to this disease then the Carthorse; and this disease cometh most in Winter season. The signes. You shall perceive it by the swelling of the place, which by continuance of time will break it self, rotting more inward then outward and therefore is more perillous if it be not cured in time; and the sooner it be taken in hand, the better. The cure according to *Martin* is thus; If it be not broken, ripe it with a plaister of Hogs grease laid unto it so hot as may be; and make a biggen for the Poll of his head to keep it from cold; which biggen would have two holes open, so as his ears may stand out; and renew the plaister every day once, untill it break, keeping the sore place as warm as may be.

And if you see that it will not break so soon as you would have it, then there as it is softest and most meetest to be opened; take a round hot Iron, as big as your little finger, and sharp at the point and two inches beneath that soft place, thrust it in a good deepness upward, so as the point of the Iron may come out at the ripest place, to the intent that the matter may descend downward, and come at the neather hole, which would be always kept open; and therefore tent it with a tent of flax dipt in Hogs grease, and lay a plaister of Hogs grease also upon the same, renewing it every day once the space of four days, which is done chiefly to kill the heat of the fire.

Then at the four days end, take of Turpentine half a pound, clean washed in nine sundry waters, and after that throughly dryed, by thrusting out the water with a slice on the dishes side, then put thereunto two yolks of Egges, and a little Saffron, and mingle them well together: that done, search the depth of the hole with a whole quill, and make a tent of a piece of spunge, so long as it may reach the bottom, and so big as it may fill the wound, and anoint the tent with the aforesaid Ointment, and thrust it into the wound, either with that quill, or else by winding it up with your finger and thumb, by little and little, untill you have thrust it home: and lay on the plaister of Hogs grease made luke-warm renuing it every day once or twice, untill it be whole. But if the swelling cease, then you need not to use the plaister, but only to tent it, and as the matter decreaseth, so make your tent every day lesser and lesser, untill the wound be perfectly whole.

OF THE VIVES.

THE Vives be certain kernels growing under the Horses ear, proceeding of some rank or corrupt bloud resorting to the place, which within are full of little white grains, like white salt kernels. The *Italians* call them *Vivole*, which if they be suffered to grow, *Laurentius Russius* saith, that they will grievously pain the Horse in his throat, so as he shall not be able to swallow his meat, nor to breath. They be easie to know, for they may be felt, and also seen: The cure according unto *Martin*, is in this sort: First draw them down in the midst with a hot iron, from the root of the ear so far as the tip of the ear will reach, being puld down: and under the root again draw two strikes on each side like a broad arrow head; then in the midst of the first line lance them with a lancet, and taking hold of the kernels with a pair of pinsons, pull them so far forward, as you may cut the kernels out without hurting the vein; that done, fill the hole with white Salt. But *Hierocles* would have them to be cured in this sort: Take a piece of Spunge sowsed well in strong Vinegar, and binde that to the sore, renewing it twice a day untill it hath rotted the kernels; that done, lance the neathermost part where the matter lyeth, and let it out, and then fill it up with Salt finely brayed, and the next day wash all the filth away with warm water, and anoint the place with Honey and Fitchflowre mingled together. But beware you touch none of the kernels with your bare finger, for fear of venoming the place, which is very apt for a Fistula to breed in.

ANOTHER OF THE VIVES.

The Vives be certain kernels, growing under the Horses ear, which come of corrupt bloud, the cure is diversly spoke and written of; but this is the best mean which I have tryed, that if you finde the kernels to enflame and grieve the Horse, take a handful of Sorrel, and lay it in a Burdock leaf, and rost it in the hot embers like a Warden; then being taken out of the fire, apply it so hot as may be to the fore part, suffering it to ly thereunto the space of a day and a night, and then renew it, till such time that it ripen and break the sore, which it will in short space do. When it is broken, and the vilde matter taken away, you shall heal up the sore place with the yolk of an Egge, half a spoonful of Honey, and as much Wheat-flower as will serve to make it thick, plaister-wise, which being bound thereunto, will in three or four days heal the same.

OF THE CANKEROUS ULCER IN THE NOSE.

THIS disease is a fretting humor, eating and consuming the flesh, and making it all raw within, and not being holpen in time will eat through the gristle of the nose. It cometh of corrupt bloud, or else of sharp humors ingendered by means of some extream cold. The signes be these: He will bleed at the nose, and all the flesh within will be raw, and filthy stinking savours, and matter will come out at the nose. The cure according to *Martin* is thus: Take of green Copperas, of Allum, of each one pound, of white Copperas one quartern, and boil these in a pottle of running water, untill a pinte be consumed, then take it off, and put thereunto half a pinte of Honey: then cause his head to be holden up with a drinking staffe, and squirt into his nostrils with a squirt of brass, or rather of Elder, some of this water being luke-warm, three or four times one after another, but betwixt every squirting, give him liberty to hold down his head, and to blow out the filthy matter, for otherwise perhaps you may choke him. And after this it shall be good also without holding up his head any more, to wash and rub his nostrils with a fine clowt bound to a white sticks end, and wet in the water aforesaid; and serve him thus once a day untill he be whole.

OF BLEEDING AT THE NOSE.

I have seen Horses my self, that have bled at the nose, which have had neither sore nor ulcer in their nose, and therefore I cannot choose, but say with the Physitians, that it cometh by means that the vein which endeth in that place, is either opened, broken or fettered. It is opened many times by means that bloud aboundeth too much, or for that it is too fine, or too subtil and so pierceth through the vein. Again, it may be broken by some violent strain, cut or blow. And finally, it may be fretted or gnawn through, by the sharpness of some bloud, or else of some other humor contained therein. As touching the cure, *Martin* saith, it is good to take a pinte of red Wine, and to put therein a quartern of Bole Armony, beaten into fine powder, and being made luke-warm, to pour the one half thereof the first day into his nostril that bleedeth, causing his head to be holden up, so as the liquor may not fall out, and the next day to give him the other half. But if this prevaileth not, then I for my part would cause him to be let bloud in the breast vein, on the same side that he bleedeth at several times: then take of Frankincense one ounce, of Aloes half an ounce, and beat them into powder, and mingle them throughly with the whites of Egges, untill it be so thick as Honey, and with soft Hares hair, thrust it up into his nostril, filling the hole so full, as it cannot fall out; or else fill his nostrils full of Asses dung, or Hogs dung, for either of them is excellent good to restrain any flux of bloud.

644

OF THE BLEEDING AT THE NOSE, OR TO STANCH FLUX OF BLOUD IN ANY SORT.

I have known many Horses in great danger by bleeding, and I have tryed divers remedies for the same, yet have I not found any more certain then this: take a spoonful or two of his bloud, and put it in a Sawcer, and set it upon a chafing dish of coals, and let it boyl till it be all dryed up into powder, then take that powder, and if he bleed at the nose, with a Cane or Quill blow the same up into his nostrils: if his bleeding come of any wound or other accident, then into the wound put the same powder, which is a present remedy. New Horse-dung, or earth, is a present remedy, applyed to the bleeding place; and so are Sage leaves bruised and put into the wound.

OF THE DISEASES IN THE MOUTH, AND FIRST OF THE BLOUDY RIFTS, OR CHOPS IN THE PALAT OF THE MOUTH.

THIS disease is called of the *Italians, Palatina*; which as *Laurentius Russius* saith, cometh by eating hay or provender that is full of pricking seeds, which by continual pricking and fretting the furrows of the mouth do cause them to ranckle, and to bleed corrupt and stinking matter, which you shall quickly remedy, as *Martin* saith, by washing first the sore places with Vinegar and Salt, and then by anointing the same with Honey.

OF THE BLADDERS IN A HORSES MOUTH, WHICH OUR OLD FARRIERS WERE WONT TO CALL THE GIGS. THE ITALIANS CALL THEM FRONCELLE.

THESE be little soft swellings, or rather pustules with black heads, growing in the inside of his lips, next unto the great jaw-teeth, which are so painful unto the Horse, as they make him to let his meat fall out of his mouth; or at the least to keep it in his mouth unchawed, whereby the Horse prospereth not: *Russius* saith, that they come either by eating too much cold grass, or else pricking, dusty, and filthy provender. The cure whereof, according to *Martin*, is in this sort: Slit them with a lancet, and thrust out all the corruption, and then wash the sore places with a little Vinegar and Salt; or else with Allum water.

OF THE BLADDERS IN A HORSES MOUTH.

SOME Horses will have bladders like paps growing in the inside of their lips, next to their great teeth, which are much painful: the cure whereof is thus: Take a sharp pair of shears, and clip them away close to the gum, and then wash the sore place with running water, Allum and Honey boiled together, till it be whole.

OF THE LAMPASS.

THE Lampass, called of the *Italians, Lampascus*, proceedeth of the abundance of bloud, resorting to the first furrow of the mouth, I mean that which is next unto the upper fore-teeth, causing the said furrow to swell so high as the Horses teeth, so as he cannot chew his meat, but is forced to let it fall out of his mouth. The remedy is to cut all the superfluous flesh away, with a crooked hot iron made of purpose, which every Smith can do.

ANOTHER OF THE LAMPASS.

THE Lampass is a thick spongy flesh, growing over a Horses upper teeth, hindering the conjunction of his chaps, in such sort that he can hardly eat: the cure is as followeth. Cut all that naughty flesh away with a hot iron, and then rub the sore well with Salt, which the most ignorant Smith can do sufficiently.

OF THE CANKER IN THE MOUTH.

THIS disease, as *Martin* saith, is a rawness of the mouth and tongue, which is full of blisters, so as he cannot eat his meat. Which proceeds of some unnatural heat, coming from the stomach. For the cure whereof, take of Allum half a pound, of Honey a quarter of a pinte, of Columbine leaves, of Sage leaves, of each a handful: boyl all these together in three pintes of water, untill a pinte be consumed, and wash the sore places therewith so as it may bleed, continuing so to do every day once untill it be whole.

ANOTHER OF THE CANKER IN THE MOUTH.

THIS disease proceedeth of divers causes, as of unnatural heat of the stomach, of foul feeding, or of the rust or venome of some bit or snaffel, indiscreetly lookt unto. The cure is thus; Wash the sore place with warm Vinegar, made thick with the powder of Allum, two or three dayes together, every time until it bleed, which will kill the poison and vigor of the exulcerated matter: then make this water; Take of running water a quart, of Allum four ounces, of Hony four or five spoonfuls, of Woodbine leaves, of Sage leaves, and of Columbine leaves, of each half a handful, boil all these together till one half he consumed, then take it off, and every day with the water warmed, wash the sore until it be whole.

OF THE HEAT IN THE MOUTH AND LIPS.

SOMETIME the heat that cometh out of the stomach breedeth no Canker, but maketh the mouth hot, and causeth the Horse to forsake his meat. The cure whereof, as *Martin* saith, is in this sort: First, turn up his upper lip, and jagge it lightly with a launcer, so as it may bleed, and then wash both that and all his mouth and tongue with Vinegar and Salt.

OF THE TONGUE BEING HURT WITH THE BIT OR OTHERWISE.

IF the tongue be cut or hurt any manner of way, *Martin* saith, it is good first to wash it with Allum water, and then to take the leaves of black Bramble, and to chop them together small with a little Lard, that done, to binde it up in a little clout, making it round like a ball, then having dipt the round end in Hony, rub the tongue therewith: continuing so to do once a day until it be whole.

647

OF THE BARBLES OR PAPS UNDERNEATH THE TONGUE.

THESE be two little paps, called of the *Italians, Barbole*, growing naturally (as I think) in every Horses mouth underneath the tongue, in the neather jawes, which if they shoot of any length, *Russius* saith, that they will hinder the Horses feeding, and therefore he and *Martin* also would have them to be clipt away with a pair of sheers, and that done, the Horses mouth to be washed with Vinegar and Salt.

OF THE PAIN IN THE TEETH AND GUMS, OF THE WOLFSTEETH, AND JAW TEETH.

A Horse may have pain in his teeth, partly by descent of humors from his head, down into his teeth and gums, which is to be perceived by the rankness and swelling of the gums, and partly having two extraordinary teeth, called the Wolfs teeth, which be two little teeth growing in the upper jawes, next unto the great grinding teeth, which are so painful to the Horse, as he cannot endure to chaw his meat, but is forced either to let it fall out of his mouth, or else to keep it still half chawed, whereby the Horse prospereth not, but waxeth lean and poor, and he will do the like also when his upper Jaw-teeth be so far grown as they overhang the neather Jaw-teeth, and therewith be so sharp, as in moving his jawes they cut and rase the insides of his cheeks, even as they were rased with a knife. And first as touching the cure of the pain in the teeth, that cometh by means of some distillation: *Vegetius* saith, it is good to rub all the outside of his gums with fine chalk and strong Vinegar mingled together, or else after that you have washed the gums with Vinegar, to strew on them of Pomegranate piles. But me thinks that besides this it were not amisse to stop the temple veins, with the plaister before mentioned, in the Chapter of weeping and waterish eyes. The cure of the Wolfs teeth, and of the Jaw-teeth, according to *Martin*, is in this sort, First cause the Horse head to be tyed up to some raster or post, and his mouth to be opened with a cord, so wide as you may easily see every part thereof; Then take a round strong iron toole, half a yard long, and made at the one end in all points like unto the Carpenters gouge, wherewith he maketh his holes to be bored with a wimble or auger, and with your left hand set the edge of your tool at the foot of the Wolfs teeth, on the outside of the jaw, turning the hollow side of the tool downward, holding your hand steadily, so as the tool may not slip from the aforesaid tooth: then having a mallet in your right hand, strike upon the head of the tool one prety blow, and therewith you shall loosen the tooth, and cause it to bend inward: then staying the midst of your tool upon the Horses neather jaw, wrinch the tooth outward, with the inside or hollow side of the tool, and thrust it clean out of his head: that done serve the other Wolfs tooth on the other side in like manner, and fill up the empty places with Sale finely brayed. But if the upper jaw teeth do also overhang the neather teeth, and so cut the inside of his mouth as is aforesaid, then keeping his mouth still open, take your tool and mallet, and pare all those teeth shorter, running along them even from the first unto the last, turning the hollow side of your tool towards the teeth, so shall not the tool cut the inside of his cheeks, and the back or round side being turned towards the foresaid cheeks, and that done wash all his mouth with Vinegar and Salt, and let him go.

WHY THE DISEASES IN THE NECK, WITHERS, AND BACK, BE DECLARED HERE BEFORE THE DISEASES IN THE THROAT.

HAVING hitherto spoken of the diseases incident to a Horses head, and to all the parts thereof, natural order requireth that we should now descend into the throat, as a part next adjacent to the mouth. But forasmuch as the diseases in the throat have not only affinity with the head, but also with the lungs and other inward parts, which are many times grieved by means of distillation coming from the head, and through the throat: I will speak of the diseases incident to the neck, withers, and back of a Horse, to the intent that when I come to talk of such diseases, as Rheumes and distillations do cause, I may discourse of them orderly without interruption.

OF THE CRICK IN THE NECK.

BECAUSE a Crick is no other thing then a kinde of Convulsion, and for that we have spoken sufficiently before of all kindes thereof in the

Chapter of Convulsion, I purpose not here therefore to trouble you with many words, but only shew you *Russius* opinion, and also *Martins* experience therein. The Crick then called of the *Italians, Scima,* or *Lucerdo* according to *Russius,* and according to *Martin* is, when the Horse cannot turn his neck any manner of way, but hold it still right forth, insomuch as he cannot take his meat from the ground but by times, and that very slowly; *Russius* saith, it cometh by means of some great weight laid on the Horses shoulders, or else by overmuch drying up of the sinews of the neck. The cure whereof, according to *Martin,* is in this sort. Draw him with a hot iron from the root of the ear on both sides of the neck, through the midst of the same even down to the brest, a straw deep, so as both ends may meet upon the breast, then make a hole in his forehead, hard under the foretop, and thrust in a Cornet upward betwixt the skin and the flesh a handful deep, then put in a Goose feather, doubled in the midst and anointed with Hogs grease to keep the hole open, to the intent the matter may run out the space of ten dayes. But every day during that time, the hole must be cleansed once, and the feather also cleansed and fresh anointed, and so put in again. And once a day let him stand upon the bit one hour or two, or be ridden two or three miles abroad, by such a one as will bear his head, and make him to bring it in. But if the Crick be such as the Horse cannot hold his neck straight, but clean awry, as I have seen divers my self: then I think it not good that the Horse be drawn with a hot iron on both sides of the neck, but only on the contrary side. As for example, if he bend his head toward the right side, then to draw him as is aforesaid only on the left side, and to use the rest of the cure as is abovesaid, and if need be, you may splent him also with handsome staves meet for the purpose to make his neck stand right.

OF WENS IN THE NECK.

A Wen is a certain kirnell like a tumor of swelling, the inside whereof is hard like a gristle, and spongious like a skin full of wrets. Of Wens, some be great, and some be small. Again, some be very painful, and some not painful at all. The Physitians say, that they proceed of grosse and vicious humors; but *Vegetius* saith, that they chance to a Horse by taking cold, or by drinking of waters that be extreme cold. The cure according to *Martin* is thus, Take of Mallowes, Sage, and red Nettles, of each one handful, boil them in running water, and put thereunto a little Butter and Honey, and when the Herbs be soft, take them out and all to bruise them, and put thereunto of oil of Bay two ounces, and two ounces of Hogs grease, and warm them together over the fire, mingling them well together; that done, plaister it upon a piece of leather so big as the Wen, and lay it to so hot as the Horse may endure it, renewing it every day in such sort, the space of eight days, and if you perceive that it will come to no head, then lance it from the midst of the Wen downward, so deep as the matter in the bottom may be discovered and let out; that done, heal it up with this Salve, Take of Turpentine a quarter, and wash it nine times in fair new water, then put thereunto the yolk of an Egge and a little *English* Saffron beaten into powder, and make a tent or rowle of Flax, and dip it in that ointment, and lay it unto the sore, renewing the same every day once untill it be whole.

OF SWELLING IN THE NECK AFTER BLOOD-LETTING.

THIS may come of the fleam being rusty, and so causing the vein to rankle, or else by means of some cold wind striking suddainly into the hole. The cure according to *Martin* is thus; First anoint it with oil of Camomile warmed, and then lay upon it a little hay wet in cold water, and bind it about with a cloth, renewing it every day the space of five dayes, to see whether it will grow to a head, or else vanish away. If it grow to a head, then give it a slit with a lancer, and open it with a Cornet that the matter may come out. Then heal it up, by tenting it with Flax dipt in Turpentine and Hogs grease molten together, dressing it so once a day untill it be whole.

HOW TO STAUNCH BLOUD.

IF a Horse be let bloud when the signe is in the neck, the vein perhaps will not leave bleeding so soon as a man would have it, which if any such thing chance, then *Russius* saith, it is good to binde thereunto a lettle new

Horse dung tempered with chalke and strong Vinegar, and not to remove it from thence the space of three dayes, or else to lay thereunto burnt silk, felt, or cloth, for all such things will staunch bloud.

OF THE FALLING OF THE CREST.

THIS cometh for the most part of poverty, and specially when a fat Horse falleth away suddainly. The cure according to *Martin* is thus; Draw his Crest the deepness a straw, on the contrary side with a hot iron, the edge of which iron, would be half an inch broad, and make your beginning and ending somewhat beyond the fall, so as the first draught may go all the way hard upon the edge of the mane, even underneath the roots of the same, bearing your hand right downward, into the neckward, then answer that with another draught beneath, and so far distant from the first as the fall is broad, compassing as it were all the fall, but still on the contrary side: and betwixt those two draughts right in the midst, draw a third draught, then with a button iron of an inch about, burn at each end a hole, and also in the spaces betwixt the draughts, make divers holes distant three fingers broad one from another: that done, to slake the fire anoint it every day once, for the space of nine dayes, with a feather dipt in fresh Butter moulten. Then take Mallows and Sage, of each one a handful, boil them well in running water, and wash the burning away untill it be raw flesh then dry it up with this powder; Take of Hony half a pinte, and so much unsleck't lime as will make that Hony thick like paste; then hold it in a fire-pan over the fire untill it be baked so hard as it may be made in powder, and sprinkle that upon the sore places.

OF THE FALLING OF THE CREST.

THE falling of the Crest is occasioned most commonly through poverty; yet sometimes I have seen it chance through the ill proportion of the Crest, which being high, thick and heavy, the neck thin and weak underneath, is not able to support or sustain it up, however it be, there is remedy for both: if it proceed of poverty, first try by good keeping to get it up again, but if it will not rise, or that the original of the disease be in the ill fashion of the Crest, then let this be the cure, First with your hand raise up the Crest as you would have it stand, or rather more to that side from which it declineth, then take up the skin between your fingers on that side from which the Crest swarveth, and with a sharp knife cut away the breadth of very near an inch, and the length of four inches; which done, stitch up the skin together again with three or four stitches, and by means of strings, weights, or other devises, keep the Crest perforce on that side, applying thereunto a plaister of Deers sewet and Turpentine, boiled together, till the sore be healed; and at the self same instant that by this manner of insition you draw together and straiten the skin on that side, you shall in this sort give liberty to the other side, whereby the Crest may the easier attain to his place; Take a hot iron made in fashion of a knife, the edge being a quarter of an inch broad, and therewith from the upper part of his Crest unto the neather part of the same extending towards his shoulder, draw three lines in this forme

$$||\,|$$

and the same anoint dayly with fresh Butter, untill such time as it be perfectly whole. By this manner of cure, you may make any lave-ear'd Horse, to be as prick-ear'd and comely, as any other Horse whatsoever.

OF THE MANGINESS OF THE MANE.

THE manginess proceedeth of rankness of bloud, or of poverty, of lowsiness, or else of rubbing where a mangy Horse hath rubbed, or of filthy dust lying in the mane for lack of good dressing. The signes be apparent by the itching and rubbing of the Horse, and the Scabs fretting both flesh and skin. The cure, according to *Martin*, is thus; Take of fresh grease one pound, of Quicksilver half an ounce, of Brimstone one ounce, of Rape oil half a pinte, mingle them together, and stir them continually in a pot with a slice, untill the Quicksilver be so wrought with the rest, as you shall perceive no Quicksilver therein. That done, take a blunt knife, or an old Horse-comb, and scratch all the mangy places therewith untill it be raw and bloudy, and then anoint it with this ointment, in the sun-shine if it may be, to the intent the ointment may sink in: or else hold before it in a fire-pan or some broad bar of iron made hot, to make the ointment to melt into the flesh. And if you see that within the space of three dayes after, with this once anointing, he leave hot rubbing, then marke in what place he rubbeth, and dresse that place again, and you shall see it heal quickly.

OF THE FALLING OF THE HAIR OF THE MANE.

IT falleth for the most part, because it is eaten with little Wormes, fretting the roots in sunder; which, according to *Martin*, you shall remedy in this sort; Anoint the mane and Crest with Sope, then make strong lie and wash all the mane and Crest withall, and that will kill the Wormes, within twice or thrice washing.

OF GRIEFS IN THE WITHERS.

TO a Horses withers and back, do chance many griefs and sorances, which, as *Russius* saith, do sometime proceed of inward causes, as of the corruption of humors; and sometime of outward causes, as through the galling and pinching of some naughty saddle, or by some heavy burthen laid on the Horses back, or such like. And of such griefs, some be but superficial blisters, swellings, lightgals or bruisings, and be easily cured. Some again do pierce to the very bone, and be dangerous, and especially if they be nigh the back bone; let us first then shew you the cure of the smaller griefs, and then of the greater.

ANOTHER OF BLISTERINGS, OR SMALL SWELLINGS IN THE WITHERS OR BACK AND GALLINGS.

Whensoever you see any swelling rise, then *Martin* would have you to binde a little hot Horse dung unto it, and that will asswage it. If not, then to prick it round about the swelling, either with a fleam, or else with a sharp pointed knife not too deep, but so as it may pierce the skin, and make the bloud to issue forth. That done, take of Mallowes or else of

Smallage, two or three handfuls, and boil them in running water untill they be so soft as pap; then strain the water from it, and bruise the herbs in a trean dish, putting thereunto a little Hogs grease, or else Sallet oil, or Sheeps sewet, or any other fresh grease, boil them and stir them together, not frying them hard, but so as it may be soft and supple, and then with a cloud lay it warm upon the sore, renewing it every day once untill the swelling be gone. For this will either drive it away, or else bring it into his head, which lightly chanceth not, unlesse there be some gristle or bone perished.

Russius biddeth you, so soon as you see any swelling rise, to shave the place with a rasor, & lay thereunto this plaister; Take a little Wheat flower and the white of an Egge beaten together, and spead it on a little clout, which being laid unto the swelling two or three dayes and not removed, will bring it to a head, and when you come to take it off, pull it away so softly as you can possible, and whereas you see the corruption gathered together, then in the lowest place thereof, pierce it upward with a sharp iron somewhat hot, that the corruption may come out, and anoint the sore place every day once with fresh Butter, or Hogs grease; but if the skin be only chafed off without any swelling, then wash the place with Water and Salt, or else with warm Wine, and sprinkle this powder thereon; Take of unsleck't Lime beaten into fine powder, and mingle it with Hony untill it be as thick as any paste, and make rols or bals theof, and bake them in a fire-pan over the fire, untill they be so hard as they may be brought to powder, for this is a very good powder to dry up any galling or sore. The powder of Myrrhe or burnt silk, felt, or cloth, or any old post, is also good for such purposes; but whensoever you use this powder of Lime and Hony, let the place be washed, as is aforesaid.

OF GREAT SWELLINGS AND INFLAMATIONS IN A HORSES WITHERS.

IF the swelling be very great, then the cure according to *Martin* is thus; First draw round about the swelling with a hot iron, and then crosse him with the same iron in manner of a checker, then take a round hot iron having a sharp point, and thrust it into the swelling place on each side up toward the point of the withers; to the intent the matter may issue downward at the holes. That done, tent both the holes with a tent dipt in Hogs grease to kill the fire, and also anoint all the other burnt places therewith, continuing so to do untill the swelling be asswaged, renewing it every day once, untill the fiery matter be clean fallen away, and then tent him again with washed Turpentine mingled with yolks of Egges and Saffron in such manner as hath been aforesaid, renewing the tent every day once untill it be whole.

If you see that the swelling for all this go not away, then it is a signe of some impostumation within, and therefore it shall be necessary to lance it, and to let out the corruption; then take of Hony half a pinte, of Verdigrease two ounces beaten to powder, and mingle it together with the Hony, then boil them in a pot untill it look red, then being lukewarm, make either a tent or plaister, according as the wound shall require, renewing the same every day once, untill it be whole. But the sore may be so vehement, that for lack of looking in time, it will pierce downward betwixt both shoulders toward the intrails, which is very dangerous: yea, and as *Russius* saith, mortal, because the corruption of the sore infecting the lungs and heart (which be the vitall parts and chief preservers of life) the body must needs decay. And therefore *Martin* would have you to fill the hole with the Salve last mentioned, and to thrust in afterward a piece of a spunge, as well to keep the hole open, as also to suck out the corruption, renewing it every day once untill it be whole.

OF THE HORNS OR HARD KNOBS GROWING UNDER THE SADDLE SIDE.

THIS is a dead skin like a piece of leather, called of the *Italians, Corno*, that is to say, a horn, for that it is hard under hand, and cometh by means of some strait Saddle, pinching the Horse more on the one side then on the other; or else on both sides equally. The cure whereof according to *Martin*, is in this sort; Anoint them with fresh Butter or Hogs grease, untill they be mollified and made so soft as you may either cut them, or pull them away, and then wash the wound with mans stale, or with white Wine, and dry it with powder of unsleck't Lime mixt with Hony.

OF WENS OR KNOBS GROWING ABOUT THE SADDLE SKIRTS.

THESE be great hard knobs growing most commonly betwixt two ribs, apparent to the eye, which by their hardness seem to come of some old bruise, and are called of the *Italians, le Curs*. The cure whereof, according to *Martin*, is thus; First mollifie them, by anointing them with Hogs grease every day once or twice, the space of eight dayes, and if you perceive that it will come to no head with this, then lance it from the middle downward, that the matter may come out: then tent it with washed Turpentine, yolks of Egges, and Saffron mingled together as is aforesaid, renewing the tent everyday once until it be whole.

OF THE NAVILL GALL.

THE Navil gall, is a bruise on the back behinde the Saddle right against the Navil of the Horse, and thereof taketh his name. It cometh either by splitting of the Saddle behinde, or for lack of stuffing, or by means of the hinder buckle fretting that place, or else by some great weight laid on his back: you shall perceive it by the puffed up and spungy flesh, looking like rotten Lights or Lungs, and therefore is called of the *Italians, Pulmone*, or *Pulmonsello*. The cure whereof, according to *Martin*, is thus; Cut it round about with a sharp knife or rasor even to the bone, leaving no rotten flesh behinde: that done, take the white of an Egge and Salt beaten together, and lay that plaisterwise to the sore upon a little towe, renewing it once a day the space of two dayes. Then take of Hony a quartern of a pinte, and of Verdigrease an ounce beat into powder, and boile them together in a pot, stirring it still untill it look red, and being lukewarm, make a plaister with towe and clap it to the wound, washing and cleansing well the wound first with a little warm Vinegar or white Wine, continuing it once a day untill it begin to heal and skin, then dry it up, by sprinkling thereon this powder following; Take of Hony a quartern, and as much of unsleck't Lime as will thicken the Hony like unto paste, and in a fire-pan over the fire, stir it still until it be hard baked, so as it may be beaten into powder, but before you throw on the powder, wash the wound first with warm Vinegar, continuing so to do untill it be perfectly skinned and whole.

OF THE SWAYING OF THE BACK.

THIS is called of the *Italians, Malferuto*, and according to *Russius* and *Martins* opinions, cometh either by some great strain, or else by heavy burthens: you shall perceive it by the reeling and rolling of the Horses hinder parts in his going, which will faster many times, and sway some-times backward, and sometime sideling, and be ready to fall even to the ground, and the Horse being laid, is scant able to get up. The cure, according to *Martin*, is thus; Cover his back with a Sheeps skin, coming hot from the Sheeps back, laying the fleshie side next unto his back, and lay a housing cloth upon the same to keep his back as warm as may be, and so let it continue until it begin to smell; then take the old skin away, and lay a new unto it, continuing so to do the space of three weeks. And if he amend not with this, then draw his back with a hot iron out on both sides of the ridge of his back, from the pitch of the Buttocks, unto a handful within the Saddle, and let every line be an inch distant one from another, and then again overthwart checker-wise, but let not such strokes be over deep, and so burned as every one look yellow, then say on this charge following; Take Pitch one pound, of Rozen half a pound, of Bole Armony half a pound made in powder, and half a pinte of Tar, and boil all these together in a pot, stirring it untill everything be molten and thoroughly mingled together, then being lukewarm, dawb all the burnning therewith very thick, and thereupon clap as many flocks of the Horses colour, as you can make to abide on, and remove it not before it fall away it self, and if it be in Summer, you may turn him to grasse.

OF THE WEAKNESS IN THE BACK.

IT doth appear by *Laurentius Russius*, that there is another kind of weakness in the back, called in *Italian, le gotte* or *morsecatura de le reni*, that is to say, the fretting or biting of the reins, which as the said *Russius* saith, proceedeth of abundance of humors resorting to that place, whereby all the hinder parts of the Horse do lose their feeling and strength, and the Horse falleth down on the ground; yea, and such humors resorting to the heart, do suffocate the same, and in two or three hours do cause the Horse to die. The remedy, according to *Russius*, is in this sort; Let him bloud abundantly in the neck, and draw his back with a hot iron, in such sort as is declared in the last Chapter. He saith also it is good to make him swim through a river, and to rowel him on his hanches nigh the huckle bones; and to make the hair to grow again, it is good, as he saith, to anoint the place with Hogs grease, and three leaved grasse stamped together.

OF HIDEBOUND.

HIDEBOUND, is when the skin cleaveth so fast to the Horses back, that a man cannot pull it from the flesh with his hand, which *Ruellius* calleth *Coriago*; it cometh for the most part of poverty, or else when the Horse after some great heat hath been suffered to stand long in the rain or wet weather, for that will cause the skin to shrink, and to cling to his ribs. It is known by the leanness of the Horse, and gantness of his belly, and by fast sticking of the skin unto the ribs when you pul at it with your hand. The cure, according to *Martin*, is thus: Let him bloud on both sides the belly in the flank veins betwix the flank and the girding place: that done, give him this drink; Take a quart of white Wine, or else of good Ale, and put thereunto three ounces of good Sallet Oil, of Cumin one ounce, of Annis seeds two ounces, of Licoras two ounces, beaten all into fine powder, and give it him lukewarm with a horn. And when he hath drunk, let one standing at his huckle bone, rub him hard with his hand along the back, and overthwart the ribs, the space of half an hour: that done, set him in a warm stable, and let him stand in litter up to the belly, and cover all his back and ribs with a sack first, throughly soaked in a tub of cold water, and then well and hard wrung, and over that cast another cloth, and gird it fast with a surcingle, stuffing him well about the back with fresh straw, continuing thus to do every day once the space of a week, during which time give him no cold water, but lukewarm, and put therein a little ground Mault. The wet sack will cause the back to gather heat it self, and the skin to loosen from the flesh, and if you will bestow more cost, you may anoint all his body with Wine and oil mingled together, according to the opinion of the old writers, which no doubt is a very comfortable thing, and must needs supple the skin, and loosen it from the flesh.

Of the diseases in the throate and lungs, and why the griefs of the shoulders and hips be not mentioned before amongst the griefs of the withers and back.

Some perhaps would look here, that for so much as I have declared the diseases of the neck, withers and back, that I should also follow on now with the griefs of the shoulders and hips. But sith that such griefs for the most part doe cause a Horse to halt, and that it requireth some skill to know when a Horse halteth, whether the fault be in his shoulder, hip, leg, joint, or foot, I think it is not good to separate those parts asunder, specially sith nature hath joyned them together, that is to say, the shoulders to the forelegs, and the hips to the hinder legs. And therefore according to natures order, I will treat of them in their proper place; that is to say, after that I have shewed all the diseases that be in the inward Horses body, not only above the midriffe, as the diseases of the throat, lungs, breast and heart, but also under the midriffe, as those of the stomach, liver, guts, and of all the rest. And first, as touching the diseases of the throat, the Glaunders, and Strangullion, to all Horses is most common.

Of the Glanders and Strangullion, so called according to the Italian name Stranguillion.

Most Farriars do take the Glanders and Strangullion to be all one disease, but it is not so, for the Glanders is that which the Physitians call *Tonsillæ*, and the Strangullion is that which they call in *Latine, Angina*, in *Greek, Cynanch*, and we commonly call it in *English* the Squinancy, or Quinsie. *Tonsillæ*, is interpreted by them to be the inflamations of the kirnels, called in *Latin, Glandes*, the *Italian, Glandulæ*, which lie on both sides of the throat, underneath the root of the tongue, nigh unto the swallowing place; of which word *Glandes*, or *Glandulæ*, I think we borrow this name Glanders; for when the Horse is troubled with this disease, he hath great kirnels underneath his jawes, easie to be seen or felt, paining him so, as he can not easily swallow down his meat, which cometh first of cold distillations out of the head: But if such kirnels be not inflamed, they will perhaps go away of themselves, or else by laying a little hot horse-dung and straw unto them, the warmth thereof will dissolve them, and make them to vanish away.

But if they be inflamed, they will not go away but encrease and wax greater and greater, and be more painful every day then other, and cause the Horse to cast continually filthy matter at his Nose. The cure whereof, according to *Martin*, is this; First ripe the kernels with this plaister; Take of bran two handfuls, or as much as will thicken a quart of Wine or Ale: then put thereunto half a pound of Hogs grease, and boyl them together, and lay it hot to the sore with a cloth, renewing it every day until it be ready to break, then lance it, and let out all the matter, and tent it with a tent of Flax dipt in this salve; Take of Turpentine, of Hogs grease, of each like quantity, and a little wax, and melt them together, and renew the tent every day until it be whole. *Laurentius Russius* saith, that this disease is very common to Colts, because in them doth abound fluxible moisture, apt to be dissolved with every little heat, and to turn to putrifaction: and therefore if the Horse be not over young, he would have you first to let him bloud in the neck vein, and then to lay unto the same sore a ripening plaister, made of Mallowes, Linseeds, Rew, Wormwood, ground Ivy, Oyl of Bayes, and Dialthea, and to anoint his throat also, and all the sore place with fresh Butter: and the sore being ripe, to lance it, or else to rowel it, that the matter may come forth.

But if the kernels will not decrease, then pull them away by the roots, and dry up the Ulcerous place with an ointment made of unsleck't Lime, Pepper, Brimstone, Nitrum, and Oyl Olive. It shall be also good to purge his head by perfuming him every day once, in such sort as hath been before declared. And let the Horse be kept warm about the head, and stand in a warm stable, and let him drink no cold water: but if you see that after you have taken away the kernels, the Horse doth not for all that leave casting filthy matter at the Nose, then it is to be feared that he hath some spice of the mourning of the Chine, for both diseases proceed of one cause, and therefore I think good to speak of it here presently.

But first I will set down a drink which I have seen proved upon a Horse that I thought could never have been recovered of the same disease, and yet it did recover him in very short space, so as he travelled immediately after many miles, without the help of any other medicine.

661

A DRINK FOR THE STRANGULLION OR GLANDERS.

TAKE of warm milk as it cometh from the Cow a quart, or in stead thereof a quart of new Beer or Ale warmed, and put thereunto of moulten Butter the quantity of an Egge; and then take one head of Garlick, first clean pilled and then stamped small, which you must put into the milk or drink being made lukewarm, and give it the Horse with a horn, and immediately after the drink be given, catch hold of his tongue with your hand, and having broken two raw Egges, either upon his foreteeth, or against the staffe wherewith his head is holden up, cast those broken Egges, shels and all into his throat, making him to swallow down the same; that done, ride him up and down till he begin to sweat, then set him up covered warm with an old coverlet and straw, not suffering him to eat nor drink for the space of two or three hours after, and let his drink for the space of two or three dayes be somewhat warm, whereunto it is good to put a handful or two of Bran or ground Malt, and in giving the said drink, it shall not be amisse to powre some thereof into either Nostril.

OF THE MOURNING OF THE CHINE.

THIS word, Mourning of the Chine, is a corrupt name borrowed of the *French* tongue, wherein it is called *Morte deschien*, that is to say, the death of the back. Because many do hold this opinion, that this disease doth consume the marrow of the back; for remedy whereof, they use strange kinds of cures. For some taking it to be a rheume, go about to stop it, by laying astrictive, or binding charges to the nape of the neck. Some again, do twine out the pith of the back with a long wire thrust up into the Horses head, and so into his neck and back, with what reason I know not. Well; I know that few Horses do recover that have this disease. Some again think that the Lungs of the Horse be rotten, and that the Horse doth cast them out at his Nose. But *Martin* saith, that he hath cut up divers Horses which have been judged to have dyed of the mourning of the Chine, but he could finde never either Back or Lungs to be perished, but only the Liver, and most commonly that side of the Liver which answereth the Nostril whereat he casteth, whereof we will talk in his proper place, when we come to speak of the diseases in the Liver. The *Italians* do call this disease *Ciamorro*, the old Authors do call it the moist malady, whereof *Theomnestus* maketh two differences. For in the one the matter which he doth cast at the Nose is white, and doth not smell at all: and in the other that which he casteth is filthy and stinking corruption. They proceed both of cold humors congealed in the head, but more abounding in the one then in the other; by reason perhaps that the Horse was not cured in time: for of cold first cometh the Pose, and the Cough, then the Glanders, and last of all the Mourning of the Chine, When the Horse casteth matter at the Nose that is not stinking; he may easily be cured by such remedies as have been before declared in the Chapter of the Pose; but if the matter be very filthy and stinking, then it is very hard to cure. Notwithstanding it shall not grieve me to write unto you here, the experience of *Theomnestus*, and of *Laurentius Russius*. *Theomnestus* cure is thus; Take of Water and Hony, called of the Physitians *Hydromel*, a quart, and put thereunto three ounces of Oyl, and powre that into his Nostril every morning the space of three dayes; and if that do not profit him, then let him drink every day, or once in two dayes, a quart of old Wine, mingled with some of the medicine, or rather the precious meat, called of the old writers *Tetrapharmacum*, and that will restore him to his former estate. *Laurentius Russius* saith, that of all diseases there is none more perillous, nor more to be suspected, then the rheume which cometh of cold, for Horses have large Conduites, and are full of moisture, and therefore if cold once enter, it findeth matter enough to work on, to breed continual distillation, as well outwardly at the Nose, as inwardly, descending down to the vitall part in such sort, as it doth not suffocate the same.

The signes, according to the said *Russius*, be these; the Horse doth cast matter continually at the Nose, sometime thin, and sometime thick, his Nostrils, Ears, and all his outward parts, will be cold to the feeling, his eyes, head, and all his body heavy, and he will cough, and have small appetite to his meat, and lesse to his drink, and sometime he will tremble and shake. His cure is in this sort; Purge his head, partly by perfuming him, & partly by making him to neeze in such sort as hath been before taught in the Chapter of the Pose, which wayes of perfuming and purging his head as they be good, so doth *Russius* praise these two here following to be most excellent; the first is this: Take of the stalks of *Vitis alba*, otherwise called *Brionie*, or wilde Vine, two or three good handfuls, and being bruised put them into a linnen bag, and fasten the bag to the Horses head, so as he may receive the sent up into his Nostrils, without touching the hearb with his mouth, and this will cause the humors to run down abundantly. The second medicine; Take of Euforbium beaten into fine powder, three ounces, of the juice of Betes one pound, of Swines bloud half a pound, boyl all these together until they be throughly mingled together, and liquid like an ointment, and then take it from the fire, and put thereunto one ounce more of Euforbium, and mingle them again throughly together, and preserve the same in a box, to use at needful times in this sort; Make two stiffe long rols or tampins of linnen clouts, or such like stuffe, sharp pointed like Sugar loaves: which tampins are called of the Physicians in *Latin*, *Pessi*, and being anointed with the ointment aforesaid, thrust them up into the Horses Nostrils, and let them abide therein a pretty while, then pull them out, and you shall see such abundance of matter come forth at his Nose, as is marvellous to behold. *Russius* also praiseth very much this medicine here following.

Take as much of the middle bark of an Elder tree, growing on the water side, as will fill a new earthen pot of a mean size, putting thereunto as much clear water as a pot will hold, and let it boyl until one half be consumed, and then to be filled up again with fresh water, continuing so to do three times one after another, and at the last time that the one half is consumed, take it from the fire, and strain it through a linnen cloth. Then take two parts of that decoction, and one part of Hogs grease, or Butter, and being warmed again together, give the Horse to drink thereof one hornful, and powre another hornful into his Nostril that casteth; and whensoever you give him this medicine, let the Horse be empty and fasting, and keep him without meat also two or three hours after, for this is a very good drink for any sickness that cometh of cold. Moreover, open the skin of his forehead, and of his temples, and also of his tail with a sharp hot iron, that the corrupt humors may issue outward. That done, take hot brickes, or else a pan of fresh burning coles, and hold it nigh unto his belly and flanks, to the intent that they may be throughly warmed, and being so warmed, anoint them all over with Oyl-de-bay, or Dialthea, to defend his body from the cold, and let his head be well covered, and all his belly kept warm. Yea, and it were good to bathe his head sometime, as *Russius* saith, with a bath made of Rew, Wormwood, Sage, Juniper, Bay leaves, and Hysop. And let his drink be warm water mingled with Wheat meal; yea, and to make it the more comfortable, it were good, as *Russius* saith, to put thereunto some Cinamon, Ginger, Galingale, and such hot pieces. And his meat in Winter season would be no other but sodden Corn, or warm Mashes, made of ground Malt and Wheat bran: in Summer season, if he went to grasse, I think it would do him most good, so that he go in a dry warm ground, for by feeding alwayes downward, he shall purge his head the better, as *Russius* saith. Thus much of the Glanders, and mourning of the Chine. Now we will speak somewhat of the Strangullion, according to the opinion of the Authors, though not to the satisfaction perhaps of our *English* Farriars.

OF THE STRANGULLION OR SQUINANCY.

THE Strangullion, called of the *Latines, Anginæ*, according to the Physitians, is an inflamation of the inward parts of the throat, and as I said before, is called of the *Greeks, Cynanche*, which is as much to say in *English* as Strangling, whereof this name Strangullion as I think is derived, for this disease doth strangle every Man or Beast, and therefore is numbred amongst the perillous and sharp diseases, called of the *Latines, Morbi acuti*; of which strangling, the Physitians in Mans body make four differences; The first and worst is, when no part within the mouth nor without, appeareth manifestly to be inflamed, and yet the patient is in great peril of strangling. The second is, when the inward parts of the throat only be inflamed. The third is, when the inward and outward parts of the throat be both inflamed. The fourth is, when the muscles of the neck are inflamed, or the inward joynts thereof so loosened, as they straiten thereby both the throat, or wesand, or wind-pipe; for short breath is incident to all the four kinds before recited, and they proceed all of one cause; that is to say, of some cholerick or bloudy fluxion, which comes out of the branches of the throat veins into those parts, and there breedeth some hot inflamation. But now to prove that a Horse is subject to this disease, you shall hear what *Absyrtus, Hierocles, Vegetius*, and others do say, *Absyrtus* writing to his friend a certain Farriar or Horse-leach, called *Aistoricus*, speaketh in this manner, When a Horse hath the Strangullion it quickly killeth him; the signes whereof be these; His temples will be hollow, his tongue will swell and hang out of his mouth, his eyes also will be swollen, and the passage of his throat stopt so as he can neither eat nor drink. All these signes be also confirmed by *Hierocles*.

Moreover, *Vegetius* rendereth the cause of this disease, affirming that it proceedeth of aboundance of subtle bloud, which after long travel will inflame the inward or outward muscles of the throat or wesand, or such affluence of bloud may come, by use of hot meate after great travel, being so alterative as they cause those parts to swell in such sort, as the Horse can neither eat nor drink nor draw his breath. The cure, according to *Vegetius*, is in this sort: First bathe his mouth and tongue in hot water, and then anoint it with the gall of a Bull; that done, give him this drink, Take of old Oyl two pound, of old Wine a quart, nine Figs, and nine Leeks heads well stamped and brayed together. And after you have boiled these a while before you strain them, put thereunto a little Nitrum Alexandrinum, and give him a quart of this every morning and evening. *Absyrtus* and *Hierocles* would have you to let him bloud in the palace of his mouth, and also to powre Wine and Oyl into his Nostrils, and also give him to drink this decoction of Figs and Nitrum sodden together, or else to anoint his throat within with Nitre, Oil, and Hony, or else with Hony and Hogs dung mingled together, which differeth not much from *Galên* his medicine, to be given unto man. For he saith, that Hony mingled with the powder of Hogs dung that is white, and swallowed down, doth remedy the Squinancy presently. *Absyrtus* also praiseth the ointment made of Bdellium, and when the inflamation beginneth somewhat to decrease, he saith it is good to purge the Horse, by giving him wilde Cucumber and Nitre to drink. Let his meat be grasse if it may be gotten, or else wet hay, and sprinkled with Nitre. Let his drink also be lukewarm water, with some Barley meal in it.

OF THE COUGH.

Of Coughs, some be outward, and some be inward. Those be outward which do come of outward causes, as by eating a feather, or by eating dusty or sharp straw, and such like things: which tickling his throat, causeth him to cough: you shall perceive it by wagging and wrying his head in his coughing, and by stamping sometime with his foot, labouring to get out the thing that grieveth him, and cannot. The cure, according to *Martin*, is thus: Take a Willow wand, rolled throughout with a fine linnen clout, and then anoint it all over with Hony, and thrust it down his throat, drawing your hand to and fro, to the intent it may either drive down the thing that grieveth him, or else bring it up, and do this twice or thrice, anointing every time the stick with fresh Hony.

OF THE INWARD AND WET COUGH.

Of inward Coughs, some be wet, and some be dry. The wet Cough is that cometh of cold, taken after some great heat given to the Horse, dissolving humors, which being afterward congealed, do cause obstruction and stopping in the Lungs. And I call it the wet Cough, because the Horse in his coughing will void moist matter at his mouth after that it is once broken. The signes be these; The Horse will be heavie, and his eyes will run with water, and he will forsake his meat; and when he cougheth, he thrusteth out his head, and reacheth with great pain at the first, as though he had a dry Cough, untill the fleam be broken, and then he will cough more hollow, which is a signe of amendment. And therefore, according to *Martins* experience, to the intent the fleam may break the sooner, it shall be necessary to keep him warm, by clothing him with a double cloth, and by littering him up to the belly with fresh straw, and then to give him this drink; Take of Barley one peck, and boyl it in two or three gallons of fair water, untill the Barley begin to burst, and boyl therewith of bruised Licoras, of Anise seeds or Raisins, of each one pound, then strain it, and to that liquor put of Hony a pinte, and a quartern of Sugarcandy, and keep it close in a pot to serve the Horse therewith four several mornings, and cast not away the sodden Barley with the rest of the strainings, but make it hot every day to perfume the Horse withal, being

667

put in a bag and tied to his head, and if the Horse will eat of it, it shall do him the more good. And this perfuming in Winter season would be used about ten of the clock in the morning, when the Sun is of some height, to the intent the Horse may be walked abroad, if the Sun shine, to exercise him moderately. And untill his Cough wear away, fail not to give him warm water, with a little ground Mault. And as his Cough breaketh more and more, so let his water every day be lesse warmed then other.

OF THE DRY COUGH.

THIS seemeth to come of some grosse and tough humor cleaving hard to the hollow places of the Lungs which stoppeth the winde-pipes, so as the Horse cannot easily draw his breath, and if it continue, it will either grow to the Pursick, or else break his winde altogether. The signs be these; He will cough both often, drily, and also vehemently, without voiding at the nose or mouth. The cure, according to *Martin*, is in this sort; Take a close earthen pot, and put therein three pintes of strong Vinegar, and four Eggs, shels and all unbroken, and four Garlick heads clean pilled and bruised, and set the pot being very close covered in some warm dunghil, and there let it stand a whole night; and the next morning with your hand take out the Egges, which will be so soft as silk, and lay them by untill you have strained the Garlick and Vinegar through a fair cloth, then put to that liquor a quartern of Hony, and half a quartern of Sugarcandy, and two ounces of Licoras, and two ounces of Anise seeds, beaten all into fine powder. And then the Horse having fasted all the night before, in the morning betwixt seven and eight of the clock, open his mouth with a cord, and whorle therein one of the Egges, so as he may swallow it down, and then immediately powre in after a hornefull of the aforesaid drink, being first made lukewarm, and cast in another Egge with another hornful of drink, and so continue to do, untill he hath swallowed up all the Egges, and drunk up all the drink; and then bridle him, and cover him with warmer clothes then he had before, and bring him into the stable, and there let him stand on the bit, at the bate rack, well littered up to the belly, the space of two hours. Then unbit him, and if it be in Winter, offer him a handfull of Wheaten straw; if in Summer, give him grasse, and let him

668

eat no hay unless it be very well dusted and sprinkled with water, and give him not much thereof. And therefore you shall need to give him the more provender, which also must be well cleansed of all filth and dust, and give him no water the space of nine dayes. And if you perceive that the Cough doth not wear away, then if it be in Winter, purge him with these pils; Take of Lard two pound laid in water two hours, then take nothing but the clean fat thereof, and stamp it in a morter, and thereto put of Licoras, of Anise seeds, of Fenegreek, of each beaten into powder three ounces, of Aloes in powder two ounces, of Agarick one ounce: Knead these together like paste, and make thereof six bals as big as an Egge. Then the Horse having fasted over night, give him the next morning these pils one after another, anointed with Hony and Oyl mingled together in a platter; and to the intent he may swallow them down whether he will or not, when you have opened his mouth, catch hold of his tongue, and hold it fast while you whirle in one of the pils; that done, thrust it into his throat with a rolling-pin, and then let his tongue go untill he hath swallowed it down; then give him in like manner all the rest of the pils, and let him stand on the bit warm clothed and littered, the space of three hours at the least, and after that give him a little wet hay, and warm water with a little ground mault in it to drink, and let him drink no other but warm water the space of a week. And now and then in a fair sunny day, it shall be good to trot him one hour abroad to breath him.

OF THE FRETIZED, BROKEN AND ROTTEN LUNGS.

THIS proceedeth, as *Absyrtus* and *Theomnestus* saith, either of an extreme Cough, or of vehement running, or leaping, or of over greedy drinking after great thirst, for the Lungs be inclosed in a very thin film or skin, and therefore easie to be broken, which if it be not cured in time, doth grow to Apostumation, and to corruption, oppressing all the Lungs, which of old Authors is called *Vomica*, and *Suppuratio*. But *Theomnestus* saith, that broken Lungs, and rotten Lungs, be two divers diseases, and have divers signes, and divers cures. The signes of broken Lungs be these; the Horse draweth his wind short, and by little at once, he will turn his head often toward the place grieved, and groaneth in his breathing, he is afraid to cough, and yet cougheth as though he had eaten small bones. The same *Theomnestus* healed a friends Horse of his, whose Lungs were fretized, or rather broken as he saith, by continual eating of Salt, with this manner of cure here following; Let the Horse have quiet and rest, and then let him bloud in the hanches, where the veins appear most: and give him to drink the space of seven dayes, Barley, or rather Oates sodden in Goats milk; or if you can get no milk, boil it in water, and put therein some thick collops of Lard and of Deers sewet, and let him drink that: and let his common drink in Winter season be the decoction of Wheat meal; and in the Summer time, the decoction of Barley; and this as he saith will bind his Lungs again together. *Vegetius* utterly disalloweth letting of bloud in any such disease as this is and all manner of sharp medicines, for fear of provoking the Cough, by means whereof the broken places can never heal perfectly. And therefore neither his medicines nor meat would be harsh, but smooth, gentle and cooling. The best medicine that may be given him at all times is this; Take of Fenegreek, and of Linseed, of each half a pound, of Gum dragant, of Mastick, of Myrrhe, of Sugar, of Fitch flowre, of each one ounce. Let all these things be beaten into fine powder, and then infused one whole night in a sufficient quantity of warm water, and the next day give him a quart of this luke-warm, putting thereunto two or three ounces of Oyl of Roses, continuing so to do many dayes together, and if the disease be new, this will heal him; yea, and it will ease him very much, although the disease be old, which is thought uncurable. And in Winter season so long as he standeth in the stable, let him drink no cold water, and let his meat be clean without dust, but in Summer season it were best to let him run to grasse; for so long as he eateth grasse, a man shall scantly perceive this disease. Thus much of broken lungs.

OF PUTRIFIED AND ROTTEN LUNGS.

THE signes to know whether a Horses lungs be putrified or rotten, according to *Theomnestus* are these; The Horse will eat and drink greedilyer then he was wont to do, he shall be oftner vexed with a

Cough, and in coughing he will cast little lumps of matter out of his mouth. The cure whereof, according to *Theomnestus*, is thus; Give him to drink every morning, the space of seven dayes, the juyce of Purslain mingled with Oil of Roses, and add thereunto a little Tragagantum that hath been layed before in steep in Goats milk, or else in Barley or Oaten milk, strained out of the Corn. When the Apostume is broken, then a very strong vile and evill savour will come out of his Nostrils, for remedy whereof it shall be good to give him the space of seven dayes this drink here following; Take of the root called Costus two ounces, and of Gasia or else of Cinnamon three ounces into fine powder, and a few Raisins, and give it him to drink with wine. But *Vegetius* would have him to be cured in this sort, and with lesse cost I assure you; Take of Frankincense and Aristoloch, of each two ounces, beaten into fine powder, and give him that with wine; or else take of unburnt Brimstone two ounces, and of Aristoloch one ounce and a half beaten into powder, and give him that with wine. And he would have you also to draw his beast with a hot iron, to the intent the humors may issue forth outwardly.

OF SHORTNESS OF BREATH.

A Horse may have shortness of breath, by hasty running after drinking, or upon a full stomach, or by the descending of humors unto his throat or lungs after some extreme heat dissolving the said humors, which so long as there is nothing broken, may in the beginning be easily holpen. The signes be these; The Horse will continually pant, and fetch his breath short, which will come very hot out at his nose, and in his breathing he will squise in the nose, and his flanks will beat thick: yea and some cannot fetch their breath unlesse they hold their necks right out and straight, which disease is called of the old writers by the *Greek* name *Orthopnœa*. The cure; Let him bloud in the neck, and give him this drink; Take of Wine and Oil, of each a pinte, of Frankincense half an ounce, and of the juice of Horehound half a pinte. It is good also to powre into his throat Hony, Butter and Hogs grease moulten together, and made lukewarm *Tiberius* saith, it is good to give him whole Egges, shels and all, steeped and made soft in Vinegar; that is to say; the first day three, the second day five, and the third day seven, and to powre Wine and oil into his nostrils. I for my part would take nothing but Annis seeds, Licoras and Sugarcandy, beaten all into fine powder, give him that to drink, with Wine and Oil mingled together.

OF THE PURSICK.

THIS is a shortness of breath, and the Horse that is so diseased is called of the *Italians, Cavallo pulsivo,* or *Bolso,* which I think is derived of the *Latin* word *Vulsus,* by changing *V.* into *B.* and I think differeth not much from him that hath broken lungs, called of *Vegetius* and other old writers *Vulsus,* for such shortness of breath comes either of the same causes, or else much like, as aboundance of grosse humors, cleaving hard to the hollow places of the Lungs, and stopping the windepipes. And the winde being kept in, doth resort downward, as *Russius* saith, into the Horses guts, and so causeth his flanks to beat continually without order; that is to say, more swiftly and higher up to the back, then the flanks of any Horse that is sound of winde. And if the disease be old, it is seldom or never cured; and though I finde many medicines, prescribed by divers Authors, few or none do content me, unless it be that of *Vegetius,* recited before in the Chapter of broken Lungs. And if that prevaileth not, then I think it were not amisse according to *Russius* to purge him with this drink here following; Take of Maiden hair, of Ireos, of Ash, of Licoras, of Fenigreek, of Raisins, of each half an ounce, of Cardanum, of Pepper, of Bitter Almonds, of Baurach, of each two ounces, of Nettle seed, and of Aristoloch, of each three ounces, boil them all together in a sufficient quantity of water, and in that decoction dissolve half an ounce of Agarick, and two ounces of Coloquintida, together with two pound of Hony, and give him of this a pinte or a quart at divers times: and if it be too thick, make it thinner, by putting thereunto water wherein Licoras hath been sodden: and if need be, you may also draw both his flanks crosse-wise with a hot iron, to restrain the beating of them, and also slit his Nostrils, to give him more air. And if it be in Summer, turn him to grasse; if in Winter, let him be kept warm, and give him now and then a little sodden wheat.

Russius would have it to be given him three dayes together, and also new sweet wine to drink, or else other good wine mingled with Licoras water.

OF A CONSUMPTION.

A Consumption is no other thing but an exulceration of the lungs, proceeding of some fretting or gnawing humor, descending out of the head into the lungs. And I take it to be that disease which the old Writers are wont to call the dry Malady; which perhaps some would rather interpret to be the mourning of the chine, with whom I intend not to strive. But thus much I must needs say, that every Horse having the mourning of the Chine, doth continually cast at the nose, but in the dry Malady it is contrary. For all the Authors that write thereof affirm, that the Horse avoideth nothing at the nose. And the signes to know the dry Malady, according to their doctrine, be these: His flesh doth clean consume away, his belly is gaunt, and the skin thereof so hard stretched, or rather shrunk up, as if you strike on him with your hand it will sound like a Taber, and he will be hollow backt, and forsake his meat, and though he eateth it, (as *Absyrtus* saith) yet he doth not digest it, nor prospereth not withal, he would cough and cannot but hickingly, as though he had eaten small bones. And this disease is judged of all the Authors to be incurable. Notwithstanding they say, that it is good to purge his head with such perfumes as have been shewed you before in the Chapter of the Glanders, and also to give him always Coleworts, chopt small with his provender. Some would have him to drink the warm bloud of sucking Pigs new slain; and some the juyce of Leeks, with Oyl and Wine mingled together. Others praise Wine and Frankincense; some, Oyl and Rue; some would have his body to be purged and set to grass.

OF THE CONSUMPTION OF THE FLESH, AND HOW TO MAKE A LEAN HORSE FAT.

MARTIN saith, that if a Horse take a great cold after a heat, it will cause his flesh to wast, and his skin to wax hard and dry, and to cleave fast to his sides, and he shall have no appetite unto his meat, and the fillets of his back will fall away, and all the flesh of his buttocks, and of his shoulders will be consumed. The cure whereof is thus: Take two Sheeps heads unflead, boyl them in three gallons of Ale, or fair running water, until the flesh be consumed from the bones, that done, strain it through a fine cloth, and then put thereunto of Sugar one pound, of Cinamon two ounces, of Conserve of Roses, of Barberries, of Cherries, of each two ounces; and mingle them together, and give the Horse every day in the morning a quart thereof luke warm, untill all be spent: and after every time he drinketh, let him be walked up and down in the stable, or else abroad if the weather be warm, and not windy, and let him neither eat nor drink in two hours after, and let him drink no cold water, but luke-warm, the space of fifteen days, and let him be fed by little and little, with such meat as the Horse hath most appetite unto. But if the Horse he nesh and tender, and so wax lean without any apparent grief or disease, then the old Writers would have him to be fed now and then with parched Wheat, and also to drink Wine with his water, and eat continually Wheat-bran mingled with his provender, untill he wax strong; and he must be often dressed and trimmed, and ly soft, without the which things his meat will do him but little good. And his meat must be fine and clean, and given often and by little at once. *Russius* saith, that if a Horse eating his meat with good appetite, doth not for all that prosper, but is still lean: then it is good to give him Sage, Savin, Bay-berries, Earth-nuts, and Boares-grease, to drink with Wine: or to give him the intrails of a Barbel or Tench, with white Wine. He saith also that sodden Beans mingled with Bran and Salt, will make a lean Horse fat in very short space.

OF GRIEF IN THE BREAST.

LAURENTIUS Russius writeth of a disease called in *Italian, Gravezza di petto*, which hath not been in experience amongst our Farriers, that I can learn. It comes, as *Russius* saith, of the superfluity of bloud, or other humors dissolved by some extream heat, and resorting down the breast, paining the Horse, so as he cannot well go. The cure whereof according to *Russius* is thus: Let him bloud on both sides of the breast in the accustomed veins, and rowel him under the breast, and twice a day turn the rowels with your hand, to move the humors that they may issue forth, and let him go so roweled the space of fifteen days.

OF THE PAIN IN THE HEART CALLED ANTICOR, THAT IS TO SAY, CONTRARY TO THE HEART.

THIS proceedeth of abundance of ranck bloud bred with good feeding and over much rest: which bloud resorting to the inward parts doth suffocate the heart, and many times causeth swellings to appear before the brest, which will grow upward to the neck, and then it killeth the Horse. The signes: The Horse will hang down his head in the manger, for saking his meat, and is not able to lift up his head. The cure according to *Martin* is thus: Let him bloud on both sides abundantly in the plat veins, and then give him this drink: Take a quart of Malmsie, and put thereunto half a quartern of Sugar, and two ounces of Cinamon, and give it him luke-warm, then keep him warm in the stable, stuffing him well about the stomach, that the wind offend him no manner of way; and give him warm water with mault always to drink, and give him such meat as he will eat. And if the swelling do appear, then besides letting him bloud, strike the swelling in divers places with your fleam, that the corruption may go forth: and anoint the place with warm Hogs grease, and that will either make it to wear away, or else to grow to a head, if it be covered and kept warm.

OF TIRED HORSES.

BECAUSE we are in hand here with the vital parts, and that when the Horses be tired with over-much labour, their vital spirits wax feeble, I think it best to speak of them even here, not with long discoursing, as *Vegetius* useth; but briefly to shew you how to refresh the poor Horse, having need thereof, which is done chiefly by giving him rest, warmth and good feeding as with warm mashes and plenty of provender. And to quicken his spirits, it shall be good to pour a little Oyl and Vinegar into his nostrils, and to give him the drink of Sheeps heads recited before in the Chapter of Consumption of the flesh; yea, and also to bath his legs with this bath: Take of Mallows, of Sage, of each two or three handfuls, and of a Rose-cake; boil these things together, and being boyled, then put unto it a good quantity of Butter, or of Sallet-oyl. Or else make him this charge: Take of Bole Armony, and of Wheat-flowre, of each half a pound, and a little Rozen beaten into powder, and a quart of strong Vinegar, and mingle them together, and cover all his legs therewith; and if it be Summer turn him to grass.

OF THE DISEASED PARTS UNDER THE MIDRIFF, AND FIRST OF THE STOMACH.

THE old Authors make mention of many diseases incident to a Horses stomach, as loathing of meat, spewing up his drink, surfeting of provender, the hungry evil, and such like, which few of our Farriers have observed: and therefore I will briefly speak of as many as I think necessary to be known; and first of the loathing of meat.

OF THE LOATHING OF MEAT.

A Horse may loath his meat through the intemperature of his stomach, as for that it is too hot or too cold. If his stomach be too hot, then most commonly it will either inflame his mouth and make it to break out in blisters, yea and perhaps cause some Cancker to breed there. The cure of all which things hath been taught before. But if he forsake his meat only for very heat, which you shall perceive by the hotness of his breath and mouth, then cool his stomach by giving him cold water, mingled with a little Vinegar and Oyl to drink, or else give him this drink: Take of Milk, and of Wine, of each one pinte, and put thereunto three ounces of *Mel Rosatum*, and wash all his mouth with Vinegar and Salt. If his stomach be too cold, then his hair will stare and stand right up, which *Absyrtus* and others were wont to cure, by giving the Horse good Wine and Oyl to drink, and some would seethe in Wine Rew, or Sage; some would adde thereunto white Pepper and Myrrhe; some would give him Onyons and Rocket-seed to drink with Wine: Again, there be other some which prescribe the bloud of a young Sow with old Wine. *Absyrtus* would have the Horse to eat the green blades of Wheat, if the time of the year will serve for it. *Columella* saith, that if a Horse, or any other Beast, do loath his meat, it is good to give him Wine, and the seed of Gith; or else Wine and stampt Garlick.

OF CASTING OUT HIS DRINK.

VEGETIUS saith, that the Horse may have such a Palsie proceeding of cold in his stomach, as he is not able to keep his drink, but many times to cast it out again at his mouth. The remedy whereof is to let him bloud in the neck, and to give him Cordial drinks, that is to say, made of hot and comfortable Spices; and also to anoint all his breast, and under his shoulders with hot Oyls, and to purge his head, by blowing up into his nostrils, powders that provoke neezing, such as have been taught you before.

OF SURFETING WITH GLUT OF PROVENDER.

THE glut of provender or other meat not digested, doth cause a Horse to have great pain in his body, so as he is not able to stand on his feet, but lyeth down, and waltereth as though he had the Bots. The cure whereof according to *Martins* experience, is in this sort: Let him bloud in the neck, then trot him up and down for the space of an hour; and if he cannot stale, draw out his yard, and wash it with a little white Wine luke-warm, and thrust into his yard either a bruised clove of Garlick, or else a little oyl of Camomile, with a wax Candle. If he cannot dung, then rake his fundament, and give him this Glyster: Take of Mallows two or three handfuls, and boil them in a pottle of fair running water; and when the Mallows be sodden, then strain it, and put thereunto a quart of fresh Butter, and half a pinte of Oyl Olive; and having received this Glyster, lead him up and down, untill he hath emptyed his belly, then set him up, and keep him hungry the space of three or four days, and the Hay that he eateth, let it be sprinkled with water, and let him drink water, wherein

677

should be put a little Bran, and when he hath drunk, give him the Bran to eat, and give him little or no provender at all, for the space of eight or ten days.

Of another kinde of surfeting with Meat or Drink, called of us, foundering in the body.

THIS disease is called of the old Writers in *Greek*; *Crithiasis*; in *Latine*, *Hordeatio*; it cometh as they say, by eating of much provender suddenly after labour, whilest the Horse is hot and panting, whereby his meat not being digested, breedeth evill humors, which by little and little do spread throughout his members, and at length do oppress all his body, and do clean take away his strength, and make him in such a case, as he can neither go, nor bow his joynts, nor being laid, he is not able to rise again; neither can he stale, but with great pain. It may come also, as they say, of drinking too much in travelling by the way when the Horse is hot, but then it is not so dangerous, as when it cometh of eating too much.

But howsoever it cometh, they say all, that the humors will immediately resort down into the Horses legs, and feet, and make him to cast his hoofs: and therefore I must needs judge it to be no other thing but a plain foundering; which word foundering is borrowed, as I take it, of the *French* word *Fundu*, that is to say, molten. For foundering is a melting or dissolution of humors, which the *Italians* call *Infusione*. *Martin* maketh divers kindes of foundering, as the foundering of the body, which the *French* men call most commonly *Morfundu*; and foundering in the legs and feet; also foundering before and behinde, which some Authors do deny, as *Magister Maurus*, and *Laurentius Russius*, affirming that there are fewer humors behinde then before, and that they cannot easily be dissolved or molten, being so far distant from the heart, and the other vital parts. Whereunto a man might answer, that the natural heat of the heart doth not cause dissolution of humors, but some unnatural and accidental heat, spred throughout all the members, which is dayly proved by good experience. For we see Horses foundered not only before or behinde, but also of all four legs at once, which most commonly chanceth either by taking cold suddenly after a great heat; as by standing still upon some cold pavement, or abroad in the cold winde; or else perhaps the Horse travelling by the way, and being in a sweat, was suffered to stand in some cold water whilest he did drink, which was worse then his drinking: for in the mean time the cold entering at his feet, ascended, upward, and congealed the humors which the heat before had dissolved, and thereby when he cometh once to rest, he waxeth stiffe and lame of his legs. But leaving to speak of foundering in the legs, as well before as behinde, untill we come to the griefs in the legs and feet; we intend to talk here only of foundering in the body, according to *Martins* experience. The signes to know if a Horse be foundered in the body, be these: His hair will stare, and he will be chill, and shrug for cold, and forsake his meat, hanging down his head, and quiver after cold water; and after two or three days he will begin to cough. The cure, according to *Martin* is thus: First, scour his belly with the Glyster last mentioned, and then give him a comfortable drink made in this sort: Take of Malmsie a quart, of Sugar half a quartern, of Honey half a quartern, of Cinnamon half an ounce, of Licoras and Anise seeds, of each two spoonfuls, beaten into fine powder, which being put into the Malmsie, warm them together at the fire, so as the Honey may be molten, and then give it him luke-warm: that done, walk him up and down in the warm stable the space of half an hour, and then let him stand on the bit two or three hours without meat; but let him be warm covered, and well littered; and give him Hay sprinkled with a little water, and clean sifted provender by a little at once; and let his water be warmed with a little ground Malt therein. And if you see him somewhat cheered, then let him bloud in the neck, and also perfume him once a day with a little Frankincense; and use to walk him abroad, when the weather is fair and not windy, or else in the house, if the weather be foul: and by thus using him you shall quickly recover him.

OF THE HUNGRY EVILL.

THIS is a very great desire to eat, following some great emptiness, or lack of meat, and it is called of the old Authors by the *Greek* name *Bulimos*, which is as much to say, as a great hunger proceeding, as the

Physitians say, at the first of some extream outward cold, taken by long travelling in cold barren places, and especially where Snow aboundeth, which outward cold causeth the stomach to be cold, and the inward powers to be feeble. The cure according to *Absyrtus* and *Hierocles*, is in the beginning to comfort the Horses stomach, by giving him Bread sopt in Wine. And if you be in a place of rest, to give him Wheat-flowre and Wine to drink; or to make him Cakes or Bals of Flowre and Wine kneaded together, and to feed him with that; or with Wine and Nuts of Pine trees. *Hierocles* saith, if any such thing chance by the way whereas no flowre is to be had, then it shall be best to give him Wine and earth wrought together, either to drink, or else to eat in Bals.

OF THE DISEASE IN THE LIVER.

ALL the old Authors speak much of the pain in the liver, but none of them do declare whereof it cometh, or by what means, saving that *Hippocrates* saith, that some Horses get it by violent running upon some stony or hard ground. I for my part think that the liver of a Horse is subject to as many diseases as the liver of a man, and therefore may be pained diversly. As sometime by the intemperateness of the same, as for that it is perhaps too hot, or too cold, too moist, or too dry: sometimes by means of evill humors, as choler, or flegm abounding in the same, according as the liver is either hot or cold: for heat breedeth choler, and cold, flegm, by means of which intemperature proceedeth all the weakness of the liver. It may be pained also sometime by obstruction and stopping, and sometime by hard knobs, inflamation, Apostume, or Ulcer bred therein, sometime by Consumption of the substance thereof. The signes of heat and hot humors, be these; loathing of meat, great thirst, and looseness of belly, voiding dung of strong sent, and leanness of body. The signes of cold, and cold humors be these: appetite to meat without thirst, a belly neither continually loose nor stiptike, but between times, no strong sent of dung, nor leanness of body, by which kinde of signes, both first and last mentioned, and such like, the weakness and grief of the liver is also to be learned and sought out. Obstruction or stopping most commonly chanceth by travelling or labouring upon a full stomach, whereby the meat not being perfectly digested, breedeth gross and tough humors, which humors by vehemency of the labour, are also driven violently into the small veins, whereby the liver should receive good nutriment, and so breedeth obstruction and stopping. The signes whereof in mans body is heaviness and distension, or swelling, with some grief in the right side under the short ribs, and especially when he laboureth immediately after meat, which things I believe if it were diligently observed, were easie enough to finde in a Horse, by his heavy going at his setting forth, and often turning his head to the side grieved: Of an old obstruction, and especially if the humors be cholerick, breedeth many times a hard knob on the liver, called of the Physitians *Schirrus*, which in mans body may be felt, if the body be not over fat: and it is more easie for him to ly on the right side than on the left, because that lying on the left side, the weight of the knob would oppress the stomach and vital parts very sore, by which signes methinks a diligent Farrier may learn, whether a Horse hath any such disease or not. The inflamation of the liver cometh by means that the bloud either through the abundance, thinness, boyling heat, or sharpness thereof; or else through the violence of some outward cause, breaketh out of the veins, and floweth into the body of the liver, and there being out of his proper vessels doth immediately putrifie and is inflamed, and therewith corrupteth so much fleshy substance of the liver as is imbrewed withall; and therefore for the most part, the hollow side of the liver is consumed: yea, and sometime the full side.

This hot bloudy matter then is properly called an Inflamation, which by natural heat is afterward turned into a plain corruption, and then it is called an Impostume, which if it break out and run, then it is called an Ulcer, or filthy sore: Thus you see, of one evill Fountain may spring divers griefs, requiring divers cures. And though none of mine Authors, nor any other Farrier that I know have waded thus far, yet I thought good by writing thus much, to give such Farriers as be wise, discreet and diligent, occasion to seek for more knowledge and understanding then is taught them; and me thinks that it is a great shame, that the Farriers of this age should not know much more than the Farriers of old time, sith that besides that the old mens knowledge is not hidden from them, they have also their own experience; and time also bringeth every day new things to light. But now to proceed in discoursing of the liver according to the Physitians doctrine as I have begun; I say then of an inflamation in the hollow side of the liver, the signes be these: loathing of meat, great thirst, looseness of belly, easie lying on the right side, and painful lying on the left. But if the inflamation be on the full side or swelling side of the liver, then the patient is troubled with difficulty of breathing, with a dry cough and grievous pain, pulling and twitching the winde-pipe, and to ly upon the right side is more painful than the left, and the swelling may be felt with a mans hand. But you must understand by the way, that all these things last mentioned be the signes of some great inflamation, for small inflamations have no such signes, but are to be judged only by grief under the short ribs and fetching of the breath.

The signes of Apostumation is painful and great heat. The signes of Ulcerations is decrease of the heat with feebleness and fainting. For the filthy matter flowing abroad with evill vapours corrupteth the heart, and many times causeth death. The signes of the Consumption of the liver, shall be declared in the next Chapter; and as for the curing of all other diseases before mentioned, experience must first teach it ere I can write it. Notwithstanding, I cannot think but that such things as are good to heal the like diseases in Mans body, are also good for a Horse, for his liver is like in substance and shape to a mans liver, differing in nothing but only in greatness. And therefore I would wish you to learn at the Physitians hands, who I am sure first, as touching, the weakness of the liver, proceeding of the untemperateness thereof, will bid you to heal every such untemperateness by his contrary; that is to say, heat by cold, and driness by moisture: and so contrary: And therefore it shall be very necessary for you to learn the qualities, natures, and vertues of hearbs, drugs, and all other simples, and how to apply them in time. And for to heal the obstruction of the liver, they will counsel you perhaps to make the Horse drinks of such simples as these be, Agrimony, Fumitory, Camomise, Wormwood, Licoras, Anise seeds, Smallage, Parsly, Spikenard, Gentian, Succory, Endive, Sperage, Lupines, the vertues whereof you shall learn in the Herbals: but amongst all simples, there is none more praised than the liver of a

Woolf beaten into powder, and mingled in any medicine that is made for any disease in the liver.

The cure of an inflamation consisteth in letting bloud, and in bathing, or fomenting the sore place with such herbs and Oyls, as may mollifie and disperse humors abroad, wherewith some simples that be astringent would be always mingled: yea, and in all other medicines that be applyed to the liver, for any manner of diseases. Simples that mollifie and disperse be these: Linseed, Fenigreek, Camomile, Anise seeds, Melliot; and such like things. Simples astringent be these: Red Rose leaves, Bramble leaves, Wormwood, Plantain, Myrrhe, Mastick, Stirax, and such like. Apostumes are to be ripened and voided. Ulcers must be cleansed, and scowred downward, either by the belly, or by urine: and therefore the use of such simples as provoke urine in such case is necessary. The old Writers of Horse-leech-craft do say, that when a Horse is grieved in his liver, he will forsake his meat, and his body will waste, his mouth will be dry, his tongue rough and harsh: yea, and it will smell, and he will refuse to ly on that side where his grief is. The cure whereof according to *Absyrtus* is in this sort: Let him drink stampt Ireos with Wine allayed with water. He praiseth also an herb much like unto Calamint; called of *Pliny, Polymoria*; or let him drink Savory with Wine and Oyl. I think that Agrimony or Liver-wort is as good as the best of them. *Absyrtus* would have his body to be chafed with Wine and Oyl mixt together; and to be well littered that he may ly soft: and his provender that should be given him to be steeped first in warm water: and now and then some *Nitrum* to be put into his drink.

OF THE CONSUMPTION IN THE LIVER.

I believe that no inward member of a Horse doth suffer so much as the lungs and liver, and that not so much by continual, as by unordinate, and untimely travail, labour, and exercise, whereby either the Horses lungs, or his liver do most commonly perish, and is consumed: yea, and some-time both. Of the Consumption of the lungs, we have talked sufficiently before: therefore let us shew you here the causes whereof the Consumption of the liver proceedeth. The Physitians say, that it may come of any humor, but chiefly and most commonly of cholerick matter, shed throughout the substance of the liver, which putrifying by little and little, and leisurely, doth at length corrupt and perish all the substance of the liver, which thing in mans body doth first proceed, as the Physitians say, either by eating corrupt meats, or else by continual drinking of sweet Wines.

But me thinks that the Consumption of a Horses liver, should come by some extreme heat, inflaming the bloud, which afterward being putrified, doth corrupt and exulcerate the substance of the liver. For after inflamation, as I said before, cometh Apostumation, and Exulceration, which is very hard to cure, because the substance of the liver is spongeous like unto the lungs. And whilest the liver is so corrupted, there can be no good digestion, for lack whereof the body receiveth no good nutriment, and therefore must needs also languish and consume. The signes according to *Martin* be these:

The Horse will forsake his meat, and will stand stretching himself in length, and never cover to ly down; and his breath will be so strong, as no man can abide it, and he will continually cast yellowish matter at the one nostril, or else at both, according as one or both sides of the liver is corrupted; and on that side that he casteth most, he will have under his jaw, even about the midst thereof, a knob or kernel as much as a Walnut, which when *Martin* findeth, he committeth his carkase to the Crows, taking him to be past cure. But if he were let bloud in time, and had such drinks given him, as are good to comfort and strengthen the liver, he thinketh that the Horse might be recovered. I never read any medicine for the wasting of the liver, as I remember, but this only diet, which I found in an old *English* Book: Let him drink for the space of three days no other thing but warm wort; and let him eat no other meat but Oats baked in an Oven, and let him stand meatless the first night before you give him the wort: But I think it were not amiss to put into the wort that he drinketh every morning some good confection of powder made of Agrimony, red Rose leaves, *Saccharum, Rosaceum, Diarchadon, Abbatis, Diasantalon,* Licoras, and of the liver of a Wolf, and such other simples as do comfort and strengthen the liver; or else to give him the same things with Goats milk luke-warm.

OF THE DISEASES IN THE GALL.

IN my opinion the gall of a Horse is subject to divers diseases, as well as the gall of a Man, as to obstruction, whereof cometh the fulness and emptiness of the bladder, and likewise the stone in the gall. But obstruction may chance two manner of ways: First, when the way, whereby the choler should proceed from the liver unto the bladder of the gall as unto his receptacle, is stopped, and thereby the bladder remaineth empty, whereof may spring divers evill accidents: as vomiting, the Lax or Bloudy flix. Secondly, when the way whereby such choler should issue forth of the bladder of the gall down into the guts is shut up, whereby the bladder is over full and aboundeth with two much choler, which causeth heaviness, suffocation, belching, heat, thirst, and disposition to angryness. The signes of both kindes of obstruction in the gall is costiveness and yellowishness of skin infected with the yellow Jaundise. The stone in the gall, which is somewhat blackish, proceedeth of the obstruction of the conduits of the bladder, whereby the choler being long kept in, waxeth dry, and turneth at length to hard gravel or stones, whereof because there is neither signes nor any grievous accident known to the Physitians, I leave to talk any farther thereof, and the rather for that none of mine Authors do make any mention of the gall at all. Notwithstanding to give some light to the learned Farriers, and that they may the better understand the inward parts of a Horse; I thought good to write thus much, thinking it no time lost while I may profit them any way.

OF THE DISEASES IN THE SPLEEN.

THE Spleen, as I have said before in many places, is the receptacle of melancholy, and of the dregs of bloud, and is subject to the like diseases that the Liver is, that is to say; to swelling, obstruction, hard knobs, and inflamation, for the substance of the Spleen is spongeous, and therefore apt to suck in all filth, and to dilate it self; wherefore being full it must needs swell, which will appear in the left side under the short ribs; and such swelling causeth also shortness of breath, and especially when the body doth labour or travel. It is painful also to ly on the right side, because the Spleen being swoln so oppresseth the midriffe, and especially when the stomach is full of meat, and the patient hath worse digestion then appetite, and is troubled with much winde, both upward and downward. Moreover the vapour of the humor doth offend the heart, making it faint, and causeth all the body to be heavy and dull; and if such swelling be suffered to go uncured, then if it be a melancholy humor, and abounding over-much, it waxeth every day thicker and thicker, causing obstruction not only in the veins & arteries, which is to be perceived by heaviness and grief on the left side, but also in the Spleen it self; whereas by vertue of the heat it is hardned every day more and more, and so by little and little waxeth to a hard knob, which doth not only occupy all the substance of the Spleen, but also many times all the left side of the womb, and thereby maketh the evill accidents or griefs before recited much more than they were.

Now as touching the inflamation of the Spleen which chanceth very seldom; for so much as every inflamation proceedeth of pure bloud, which seldom entereth into the Spleen: I shall not need to make many words, but refer you over to the Chapter of the Liver, for in such case they differ not, but proceeding of like cause, have also like signes, and do require like cure. The old Writers say, that Horses be often grieved with grief in the Spleen, and specially in Summer season with greedy eating of sweet green meats, and they call those Horses *Lienosos*; that is to say, Spleenetick. The signes whereof (say they) are these, hard swelling on the left side, short breath, often groning, and greedy appetite to meat. The remedy whereof according to *Absyrtus* is to make a Horse to sweat once a day during a certain time, by riding him, or otherwise travelling him, and to pour into his left nostril every day the juyce of Mirabolans mingled with Wine and Water, amounting in all to the quantity of a pinte. But me thinks it would do him more good, if he drank it as *Hierocles* would have him to do. *Eumelius* praiseth this drink: Take of Cummin seed and of Honey, of each six ounces, and of *Laserpitium* as much as a Bean, of Vinegar a pinte; and put all these into three quarts of water, and let it stand so all night, and the next morning give the Horse thereof to drink, being kept over night fasting. *Theomnestus* praiseth the decoction of Capers, especially if the bark of the root thereof may be gotten sodden in water to a syrup. Or else make him a drink of Garlick,

Nitrum, Hore-hound, and Wormwood, sodden in harsh Wine: and he would have the left side to be bathed in warm water, and to be hard rubbed. And if all this will not help, then to give him the fire, which *Absyrtus* doth not allow, saying the Spleen lyeth so, as it cannot easily be fired, to do him any good. But for so much as the Liver and Spleen are members much occupied in the ingendring and separating of humors, many evill accidents and griefs do take their first beginning of them, as the Jaundise, called in a Horse, the yellows, driness of body, and Consumption of the flesh, without any apparent cause why, which the Physitians call *Atrophia*; also evill habit of the body, called of them *Cachexia*, and the Dropsie. But first we will speak of the Jaundise or Yellows.

OF THE YELLOWS.

THE Physitians in a mans body do make two kindes of Jaundise: that is to say, the Yellow, proceeding of choler dispersed throughout the whole body, and dying the skin yellow; and the Black, proceeding of melancholy, dispersed likewise throughout the whole body, and making all the skin black. And as the yellow Jaundise cometh for the most part, either by obstruction or stopping of the conduits belonging to the bladder of the gall, which (as I said before) is the receptacle of choler; or by some inflamation of the Liver, whereby the bloud is converted into choler, and so spreadeth throughout the body: even so the black Jaundise cometh by mean of some obstruction in the Liver-vein, that goeth to the Spleen, not suffering the Spleen to do his office, in receiving the dregs of the bloud from the Liver, wherein they abound too much; or else for that the Spleen is already too full of dregs, and so sheddeth them back again into the veins. But as for the Black Jaundise, they have not been observed to be in Horses as in Men, by any of our Farriers in these days that I can learn. And yet the old Writers of Horse-leech-craft, do seem to make two kindes of Jaundise called of them *Cholera*, that is to say, the dry choler, and also the moist choler. The signes of the dry choler, as *Absyrtus* saith, is great heat in the body, and costiyeness of the belly, whereof it is said to be dry. Moreover, the Horse will not covet to ly down, because he is so pained in his body, and his mouth will be hot and dry.

It cometh, as he saith, by obstruction of the conduit, whereby the choler should resort into the bladder of the gall, and by obstruction also of the urine vessels, so as he cannot stale. The cure according to his experience, is to give him a Glyster made of Oyl, Water and *Nitrum*, and to give him no provender, before that you have raked his fundament, and to pour the decoction of Mallows mingled with sweet Wine into his nostrils, and let his meat be grass, or else sweet Hay sprinkled with Nitre and Water; and he must rest from labour, and be often rubbed. *Hierocles* would have him to drink the decoction of wilde Coleworts sodden in Wine. Again of the moist choler of Jaundise, these are the signes: The Horses eyes will look yellow, and his nostrils will open wide; his ears and his flancks will sweat, and his stale will be yellow and cholerick; and he will grone when he lyeth down; which disease the said *Absyrtus* was wont to heal, as he saith, by giving the Horse a drink made of Thyme and Cumin, of each like quantity stampt together, and mingled with Wine, Honey, and Water, and also by letting him bloud in the pasterns. This last disease seemeth to differ nothing at all from that which our Farriers call the Yellows. The signes whereof, according to *Martin*, be these: The Horse will be faint, and sweat as he standeth in the stable, and forsake his meat: and his eyes, and the inside of his lips and all his mouth within will be yellow. The cure whereof according to him is in this sort: Let him bloud in the neck-vein, a good quantity, and then give him this drink: Take of white Wine, of Ale a quart, and put thereunto of Saffron, Turmerick, of each half an ounce, and the juyce that is wrung out of a handful of Celandine, and being luke-warm, give it the Horse to drink, and keep him warm the space of three or four days, giving him warm water with a little Bran in it.

OF THE YELLOWS.

THE Yellows is a general disease in Horses, and differ nothing from the yellow Jaundise in men: It is mortal, and many Horses die thereof:

the signes to know it is thus; pull down the lids of the Horses eyes, and the white of the eye will be yellow, the inside of his lips will be yellow, and gums; the cure followeth: First, let him bloud in the palat of his mouth, that he may suck up the same, then give him this drink: Take of strong Ale a quart, of the green odure of Geese strained, three or four spoonfuls, of the juyce of Celandine as much, of Saffron half an ounce; mix these together, and being warm, give it the Horse to drink.

OF THE EVILL HABIT OF THE BODY, AND OF THE DROPSIE.

As touching the driness and Consumption of the flesh, without any apparent cause why, called of the Physitians as I said before *Atrophia*; I know not what to say more then I have already before in the Chapter of Consumption of the flesh, and therefore resort thither. And as for the evill habit of the body, which is to be evill coloured, heavy, dull, and of no force, strength, nor liveliness, cometh not for lack of nutriment, but for lack of good nutriment, for that the bloud is corrupted with flegm, choler, or melancholy, proceeding either from the Spleen, or else through weakness of the stomach or liver, causing evill digestion, or it may come by foul feeding: yea, and also for lack of moderate exercise. The Evill habit of the body, is next cousen to the Dropsie, whereof though our Farriers have had no experience, yet because mine old Authors writing of Horse-leechcraft do speak much thereof: I think it good here briefly to shew you their experience therein, that is to say, how to know it, and also how to cure it. But sith none of them do shew the cause whereof it proceeds; I think it meet first therefore to declare unto you the causes thereof, according to the doctrine of the learned Physitians, which in mans body do make three kindes of Dropsies, calling the first *Anasarca*, the second *Ascites*, and the third *Timpanias*. *Anasarca*, is an universal swelling of the body through the abundance of the water, lying betwixt the skin and the flesh, and differeth not from the disease last mentioned, called *Cachexia*, that is to say, Evill habit of the bloud, saving that the body is more swoln in this then in *Cachexia*, albeit they proceed both of like causes as of coldness and weakness of the liver, or by means that the heart, spleen, stomach, and other members serving to digestion, be grieved or diseased. *Ascites* is a swelling in the covering of the belly, called of the Physitians. *Abdomen*, comprehending both the skin, the fat, eight muscles, and the film, or panicle called *Peritoneum*, through the abundance of some whayish humor entred into the same, which besides the causes before alleadged, proceedeth most chiefly by means that some of the vessels, within be broken or rather cracked, out of the which, though the bloud being somewhat gross cannot issue forth, yet the whayish humor being subtil, may run out into the belly, like water distilling through a cracked pot.

Timpanias, called of us commonly the Timpany, is a swelling of the aforesaid covering of the belly, through the abundance of winde entred into the same, which winde is ingendered of crudity and evill digestion, and whilest it aboundeth in the stomach, or other intrails finding no issue out, it breaketh in violently through the small conduits among the panicles of the aforesaid covering not without great pain to the patient, and so by tossing to and fro, windeth at length into the space of the covering it self. But surely such winde cannot be altogether void of moisture.

Notwithstanding, the body swelleth not so much with this kinde of Dropsie as with the other kinde called *Ascites*. The signes of the Dropsie is shortness of breath, swelling of the body, evill colour, lothing of meat, and great desire to drink, especially in the Dropsie called *Ascites*, in which also the belly will sound like a bottle half full of water: but in the Timpany it will sound like a Taber. But now though mine Authors make not so many kindes of Dropsies, yet they say all generally, that a Horse is much subject to the Dropsie. The signes according to *Absyrtus* and *Hierocles*, be these: His belly, legs, and stones, will be swoln; but his back, buttocks, and flancks, will be dryed and shrunk up to the very bones.

Moreover the veins of his face and temples, and also the veins under his tongue will be so hidden, as you cannot see them; and if you thrust your finger hard against his body, you shall leave the print thereof behind, for the flesh lacking natural heat will not return again to his place, and when the Horse lyeth down he spreadeth himself abroad, not being able to lie round together on his belly; and the hair of his back by rubbing will fall away. *Pelagonius* in shewing the signes of the Dropsie, not much differing from the Physitians first recited, seemeth to make two kindes thereof, calling the one the *Timpany*, which for difference sake may be called in *English* the Winde Dropsie, and the other the Water Dropsie. Notwithstanding both have one cure, so far as I can perceive, which is in this sort: Let him be warm covered, and walked a good while together in the Sun to provoke sweat, and let all his body be well and often rubbed alongst the hair, and let him feed upon Coleworts, Smallage, and Elming boughs, and on all other things that may loosen the belly, or provoke urine; and let his common meat be grass if it may be gotten, if not, then Hay sprinkled with Water and *Nitrum*. It is good also to give him a kinde of Pulse called Cich, steeped a day and a night in water, and then taken out, and laid so as the water may drop away from it. *Pelagonius* would have him to drink Parsly stampt with Wine, or the root of the herb called in *Latine, Panax*, with Wine. But if the swelling of the belly will not decrease for all this, then slit a little hole under his belly a handful behinde the navil, and put into that hole a hollow reed or some other pipe, that the water or winde may go out, not all at once, but by little and little at divers times, and beware that you make not the hole over wide, lest the kall of the belly fall down thereunto; and when all the water is clean run out, then heal up the wound as you do all other wounds, and let the Horse drink as little as is possible.

OF THE EVIL HABIT OF THE STOMACH.

IF your Horse either by inward sickness, or by present surfeit, grow to a loath of his meat, or by weakness of his stomach cast up his meat and drink; this shall be the cure for the same: First, in all the drink he drinks, let him have the powder of hot Spices; as namely, of Ginger, Anise seeds, Licoras, Cinamon, and Pepper; then blow up into his nostrils the powder of Tobacco to occasion him to neese, instantly after he hath eaten any meat, for an hour together after, let one stand by him, and hold at his nose a piece of sowre leaven steept in Vinegar, then anoint all his breast over with the Oyl of Ginnuper and Pepper mixt together.

OF THE DISEASES OF THE GUTS OF A HORSE, AND FIRST OF THE COLICK.

THE guts of a Horse may be diseased with divers griefs, as with the Colick, with Costiveness, with the Lax, with the Bloudy flux and Worms. The Colick is a grievous pain in the great gut, called of the Physitians *Colon*, whereof this disease taketh his name, which gut, because it is very large and ample, and full of corners, it is apt to receive divers matters, and so becometh subject to divers griefs. For sometime it is tormented with the abundance of gross humors gotten betwixt the panicle of the said gut, and sometime with winde having no issue out, sometime with inflammation, and sometime with sharp fretting humors. But so far as I can learn; a Horse is most commonly troubled with the Colick that cometh of winde, and therefore our Farriers do tearm it the winde Colick. The signes whereof be these: The Horse will forsake his meat, and lie down and wallow and walter upon the ground, and standing on his feet he will stamp for very pain with his fore-feet, and strike on his belly with his hinder foot, and look often towards his belly, which also towards his flancks will swell, and seem greater to the eye then it was wont to be. The cure whereof according to *Martin*, is in this sort: Take a quart of Malmsie, of Cloves, Pepper, Cinamon, of each half an ounce, of Sugar half a quartern, and give it the Horse luke-warm, and anoint his flancks with Oyl of Bay, and then bridle him and trot him immediately up and down the space of an hour, until he dung, and if he will not dung, then take him; and if need be provoke him to dung, by putting into his fundament an Onyon pilled and jagged with a knife cross-wise, so as the juyce thereof may tickle his fundament; and for the space of three or four days let him drink no cold water, and let him be kept warm. *Russius* was wont to use this kinde of cure: Take a good big reed a span long or more, and being anointed with Oyl, thrust it into the Horses fundament, fastning the outward end thereof unto his tail, so as it cannot slip out, and then having first anointed and chased all the Horses belly with some hot Oyl, cause him to be ridden hastily up and down some hilly ground, and that will make him to void the winde out of his belly through the reed: which done, let him be kept warm and fed with good provender, and warm mashes made of Wheat-meal, and

Fennel seed, and let him drink no cold water until he be whole. *Absyrtus* would have you to give him a Glyster made of wilde Cowcumber, or else of Hens dung, *Nitrum*, and strong Wine.

OF COSTIVENESS, OR BELLY-BOUND.

COSTIVENESS is when a Horse is bound in the belly and cannot dung, which may come by glut of provender, or overmuch feeding and rest, whereof we have talked sufficient before, also by winde, gross humors, or cold causing obstruction, and stopping in the guts. The cure whereof, according to *Martin*, is in this sort: Take of the decoction of Mallows a quart, and put thereunto half a pinte of Oyl, or in stead thereof, half a pinte of fresh Butter, and one ounce of *Benedicte laxative*, and pour that into his fundament with a little Horn meet for the purpose, that done, clap his tail to his fundament, holding it still with your hand, whilest another doth lead him in his hand, and trot him up and down, that the medicine may work the better, and having voided all that in his belly, bring him unto the stable, and there let him stand a while on the bit well covered, and warm littered, and then give him a little Hay, and let his drink be warmed; it shall not be amiss also to give him that night a warm mash.

OF THE LAX.

The *Italians* call this disease *Ragiatura*, and the Horse that hath this disease *Cavallo Arragiato*, or *Sforato*. It may come through the abundance of cholerick humors descending from the liver or gall, down to the guts. But *Russius* saith, that it cometh most commonly by drinking overmuch cold water immediately after provender, or by sudden travelling upon a full stomach, before his meat be digested, or by hasty running, or galloping immediately after water. If this disease continue long, it will make the Horse very weak and feeble, so as he shall not be able to stand on his legs. Notwithstanding, sith nature feeling her self oppressed, endevoureth thus to ease her self by expelling those humors that grieve her, I would not wish you suddenly to stop it, lest some worse inconvenience grow thereof. But if you see that the Horse looseth his flesh, and waxeth more dull and feeble then he was wont to be; then give him this drink often experimented by *Martin*, and that shall stop him: Take of Bean-flowre, and of Bole Armony, of each a quartern; mingle these things together in a quart of red Wine, and give it him luke-warm, and let him rest and be kept warm, and let him drink no cold drink but luke-warm, and put therein a little Bean-flowre, and let him not drink but once a day, and then not over-much, for the space of three or four days.

OF THE BLOUDY FLUX.

It seemeth by the old Writers, that a Horse is also subject to the Bloudy flux. For *Absyrtus, Hierocles*, and *Democritus*, say all with one voyce, that the guts of a Horse may be so exulcerated, that he will void bloudy matter at his fundament, yea and his fundament therewith will fall out, which disease they call *Dysenteria*, which is as much to say, as a painful exulceration of the guts, under the which the old men as it seemeth by the words of *Hierocles*, and *Absyrtus*, would comprehend the disease called of the Physitians *Tenasmus*, that is to say, a desire to dung often, and to do but little, and that with great pain: And also another disease called *Procidentia ani*, that is to say, the falling out of the fundament, which the Physitians do account as several diseases. Notwithstanding, for so much as *Dysenteria*, and *Tenasmus*, do spring both of like causes: yea, and also for that the falling out of the fundament hath some affinity with them, I will follow mine Authors, in joyning them all together in this one chapter.

The Physitians make divers kindes of Bloudy flux, for sometime the fat of the slimy filth which is voided, is sprinkled with a little bloud, sometime the matter that voideth is mixt with the scraping of the guts, and sometime it is waterish bloud, like water wherein flesh hath been washed, and sometime bloud mixt with melancholy, and sometime pure bloud, and by the mixture of the matter you shall know in mans body, whether the ulceration be in the inner small guts or no; if it be, the matter and bloud will be perfectly mixt together; but if it be in the outward guts, then they be not mingled together, but come out several, the bloud most commonly following the matter. Of this kinde is that disease called before *Tenasmus*, for that is an ulcer in the right gut serving the fundament; and doth proceed even as the flux doth of some sharp humors, which being violently driven, and having to pass through many crooked and narrow ways, do cleave to the guts, and with their sharpness fret them, causing exulceration and grievous pain. The flux also may come of some extream cold, heat or moistness, or by mean of receiving some violent purgation, having therein over-much Scammony, or such like violent simple; or through weakness of the Liver, or other members serving to digestion. Now as touching the falling out of the fundament, the Physitians say, that it cometh through the resolution or weakness of the muscles, serving to draw up the fundament, which resolution may come partly by over-much straining, and partly they may be loosened by over-much moisture, for which cause children being full of moisture are more subject to this disease then men. And for the self same cause I think that Horses having very moist bodies be subject thereunto. Thus having shewed you the causes of the diseases before recited, I will shew you the cure prescribed by the old Writers. *Absyrtus* would have the fundament on the outside to be cut round about, but so as the inward ring thereof be not touched, for that were dangerous, and would kill the Horse, for so much as his fundament would never abide within his body; and that done, he would have you to give him to drink the powder of unripe Pomgranate shels, called in *Latine, Malicorium*, together with Wine and Water, which indeed because it is astringent, is not to be misliked: but as for cutting of the fundament, I assure you I cannot judge what he should mean thereby, unless it be to widen the fundament, by giving it long slits or cuts on the outside; but well I know that it may cause more pain, and greater inflamation. And therefore me thinks it were better in this case to follow the Physitians precepts, which is first to consider whether the fundament being fallen out be inflamed or not; for if it be not inflamed, then it shall be good to anoint it first with Oyl of Roses somewhat warmed, or else to wash it with warm red Wine.

But if it be inflamed, then to bathe it well, first with a spunge dipt in the decoction of Mallows, Camomile, Linseed, and Fenigreek, and also to anoint it well with Oyl of Camomile and Dill mingled together, to asswage the swelling, and then to thrust it in again fair and softly, with a soft linnen cloth. That done, it shall be good to bathe all the place about with red Wine, wherein hath been sodden *Acatium*, Galles, Acorn cups, parings of Quinces, and such like simples as be astringent, and then to throw on some astringent powder made of Bole Armony, Frankincense, *Sanguis Draconis*, Myrrhe, *Acatium*, and such like: yea, and also to give the Horse this drink, much praised of all the old Writers. Take of Saffron one ounce, of Myrrhe two ounces, of the herb called in *Latine*, *Abrotonum*, named in some of our *English* Herbals Southernwood, three ounces, of Parsly one ounce, of garden Rue, otherwise called Herb Grace three ounces, of *Piritheum*, otherwise called of some people Spittlewort, and of Hysop, of each two ounces, of *Cassia*, which is like Cinamon, one ounce. Let all these things be beaten in fine powder, and then mingled with Chalk and strong Vinegar wrought into paste, of which paste make little cakes, and dry them in the shadow, and being dryed, dissolve some of them in a sufficient quantity of Barly milk, or juyce called of the old Writers, and also of the Physitians, *Cremor Ptisanæ*, and give to the Horse to drink thereof with a horn, for the medicine, as the Authors write, doth not only heal the Bloudy-flix, and the other two diseases before recited, but also if it be given with a quart of warm water, it will heal all grief and pain in the belly, and also of the bladder, that cometh for lack of staling. And being given with sweet Wine, is will heal the biting of any Serpent or mad Dog.

OF THE WORMS.

IN a Horses guts do breed three kindes of Worms, even as there doth in Mans body, though they be not altogether like in shape. The first long and round, even like to those that children do most commonly void, and are called by the general name Worms. The second little worms having great heads, and small long tails like a needle, and be called bots. The third be short and thick like the end of a mans little finger, and therefore be cald Troncheons: and though they have divers shapes according to the diversity of the place perhaps where they breed, or else according to the figure of the putrified matter whereby they breed: yet no doubt they proceed all of one cause, that is to say, of a raw, gross and flegmatick matter apt to putrifaction, ingendered most commonly by foul feeding: and as they proceed of one self cause, so also have they like signes, and like cure. The signes be these: The Horse will forsake his meat, for the Troncheons and the Bots will covet always to the maw, and pain him sore. He will also lie down and wallow, and standing he will stamp and strike at his belly with his hinder-foot, and look often toward his belly.

The cure according to *Martin* is thus: Take of sweet Milk a quart, of Honey a quartern, and give it him luke-warm, and walk him up and down for the space of an hour, and so let him rest for that day, with as little meat or drink as may be, and suffer him not to lie down. Then the next day give him this drink: Take of Herb-grace a handful, of Savin as much, and being well stampt, put thereunto a little Brimstone, and a little Soot of a Chimney, beaten into fine powder, and put all these things together in a quart of Wort or Ale, and there let them lie steep the space of an hour or two, then strain it well through a fair cloth, and give it the Horse to drink luke-warm, then bridle him, and walk him up and down the space of an hour: that done, bring him into the stable, and let him stand on the bit two or three hours, & then give him a little Hay. *Laurentius Russius* saith, that it is good to give the Horse the warm guts of a young Hen with a Salt three days together in the morning, and not to let him drink untill it be noon. Some say that it is good to ride him, having his bit first anointed with dung coming hot from the man: some again use to give him a quantity of Brimstone, and half as much Rozen beaten into powder, and mingled together with his provender, which he must eat a good while before he drinketh.

I have found by often tryal, that if you give the Horse with a horn a good pretty dishful of Salt brine, be it flesh brine, or Cheese brine, it will kill any of the three kindes of Worms, and make the Horse to avoid them dead in short time after.

OF WORMS IN GENERAL.

BESIDES the Bots, there are other Worms, which lie in the great paunch or belly of a Horse, and they be shining, of colour like a Snake,

697

six inches in length, great in the midst and sharp at both ends, and as much as a Spindle: they cause great pain in a Horses belly, as you shall perceive by his continual striking of himself on the belly with his foot. The cure is thus: Give him two or three mornings together new Milk and Garlick boyled together, or chopt Hay in his provender, either of both will serve: it killeth the worms and maketh them to void.

OF THE PAIN IN THE KIDNEYS.

ME thinks that the Kidnies of a Horse should be subject to as many griefs as the Kidnies of a Man, as to Inflamation, Obstruction, Apostumes and Ulcers, and specially to obstruction that cometh by means of some stone or gravel gathered together in the Kidnies whereby the Horse cannot stale but with pain; for I have seen divers Horses my self that have voided much gravel in their stale, which without doubt did come from the Kidnies; but my Authors do refer such griefs to the bladder and urine, and write of no disease but only of the inflamation of the Kidnies, which is called of them *Nephritis*, and so it is cald of the Physitians. It cometh, as they say, by some great strain over some ditch; or else by bearing some great burthen. The signes whereof be these: The Horse will go rolling behinde and staggering, his stones will shrink up, and his stale will be blackish and thick. I think this disease differeth not from that which we called before the swaying of the back when we talked of the griefs in the back and loins, and therefore resort thither. The cure of this disease, according to the best of the old Writers, is in this sort: Bathe his back and loins with Wine, Oyl, and *Nitrum* warmed together, after that you have so bathed him, let him be covered with warm clothes, and stand littered up to the belly with straw, so as he may lie soft; and give him such drinks as may provoke urine, as those that be made with Dill, Fennil, Anise, Smallage, Parsley, Spikenard, Myrrhe, and *Cassia*. Some say it is good to give him a kinde of pulse called Cich with Wine. Some again do praise Ewes milk, or else Oyl and Deers sewet molten together, and given him to drink, or the root of the herb called *Asphodelus*, *Englished* by some Daffadil, sodden in Wine.

698

Of the diseases belonging to the Bladder and Urine of a Horse.

HIEROCLES saith, that a Horse is subject to three kinde of diseases incident to the Bladder or Urine, the first is called *Stranguria*; the second *Dysuria*; the third *Ischuria*. *Stranguria*, otherwise called in *Latine*, *Stillicidium*, and of our old Farriers, according to the *French* name *Chowdepis*, is, when the Horse is provoked to stale often, and voideth nothing but a few drops, which cometh, as the Physitians say, either through the sharpness of the urine, or by some exulceration of the bladder, or else by means of some Apostume in the liver or kidnies; which Apostume being broken, the matter resorteth down into the bladder, and with the sharpness thereof causeth a continual provocation of pissing.

Dysuria is when a Horse cannot piss but with great labour and pain, which for difference sake I will call from hence forth the pain-piss. It may come sometime through the weakness of the bladder and cold intemperature thereof, and sometime through the abundance of flegmatick and gross humors, stopping the neck of the bladder. *Ischuria*, is when the Horse cannot piss at all, and therefore may be called the piss-supprest, or suppression of urine, whether you will: me thinks always that the shorter and the more proper the name is, the better and more easie it is to pronounce.

It may come, as the Physitians say, by weakness of the bladder, or for that the Water conduit is stopt with gross humors, or with matter descending from the liver or kidnies, or with the stone: yea and sometimes by means of some inflamation or hard knob growing at the mouth of the conduit, or for that the sinews of the bladder is nummed, so as the bladder is without feeling: or it may come by retention, and long holding of the water, most of which causes *Hierocles* also reciteth, adding thereunto that it may chance to a Horse through over-much rest and idleness, and also by means of some extream cold, and especially in Winter season; for the which, warmth of the fire is a present remedy. But now mine Authors do not shew for every one of these three kindes of diseases several signes; but only say, that when a Horse cannot stale, he will stand as though he would stale, and thrust out his yard a little; and also for very pain, stand beating his tail betwixt his thighes.

Neither do they seem to appoint several cures, but do make a hochpoch, mingling them all together: some of them praising one thing, and some another: For some say it is good to mingle the juyce of Leeks with sweet smelling Wine and Oyl together, and to pour it into his right nostril, and then to walk him up and down upon it, and that will make him to stale. Some say it is good to give him Smallage seed, or else the root of wilde Fennil sodden with Wine to drink; or to put fine sharp Onions clean pilled, and somewhat bruised into his fundament, and to chase him immediately upon it, either by riding him or otherwise, and that shall cause him to stale presently. It is good also to bathe all his back and loins with warm water.

The scraping of the inward parts of his own hoofs beaten into powder and mingled with Wine, and poured into his right nostril, will make him to stale; if you chafe him upon it, and the rather as *Hierocles* saith, if you cary him to some Sheeps cot, or other place where Sheep are wont to stand, the smell of whose dung and piss, without any other medicine, as he saith, will provoke him to stale.

Some will give the Horse white Dogs dung dryed and mingled with Salt, Wine, and *Ammoniacum* to drink, some Hogs dung only with Wine, and some the dregs of Horse-piss with Wine, and many other medicines which I leave to rehearsed, for fear of being too tedious, and especially, sith *Martins* experience doth follow here at hand; agreeing in all points with *Laurentius Russius* cure, which is in this sort: First, draw out his yard, and wash it well in white Wine, and scour it well, because it will be many times stopped with durt and other baggage together, and hardned like a stone; and then put a little Oyl of Camomile into the conduit; with a wax Candle and a bruised clove of Garlick, and that will provoke him to stale. And if that will not help: Take of Parsley two handfuls, of Coriander one handful, stamp them and strain them with a quart of white Wine, and dissolve therein one ounce of Cake-sope, and give it luke-warm unto the Horse to drink, and keep him as warm as may be; and let him drink no cold water for the space of five or six days; and when you would have him to stale, let it be either upon plenty of straw, or upon some green plot, or else in a Sheeps cot, the savour whereof will greatly provoke him to stale, as hath been aforesaid.

PELAGONIUS saith, that if a Horse be over-much laboured, or over-charged with heavy burthen, or over fat, he will many times piss bloud, and the rather as I think, for that some vein is broken within the Horses body, and then cleer bloud will come forth many times, as the Physitians say, without any piss at all. But if the bloud be perfectly mingled together with his stale, then it is a signe that it cometh from the Kidnies, having some stone therein, which through vehement labour, doth fret the kidnies and veins thereof, and so cause them to bleed, through which while the urine passeth, most needs be infected and dyed with the bloud. It may come also by some stripe, or from the muscle that incloseth the neck of the bladder. The cure according to *Pelagonius, Absyrtus, Hierocles*, and the rest, is thus: Let the Horse bloud in the palate of the mouth, to convert the bloud the contrary way; then take of Tragagant that hath been steeped in Wine, half an ounce, and of Poppy seed one dram and one scruple, and of Stirax as much; and twelve Pine-apple-kernels: let all these things be beaten and mingled well together, and give the Horse thereof every morning, the space of seven days, the quantity of a Hasel-nut distempered in a quart of Wine: me thinks that the quantity of a Wal-nut were too little for so much Wine. Some write that it is good to make him a drink with the root of the herb *Asphodelus*, which some call Daffadil, mingled with Wheat-flowre and Sumach sodden long in water, and so to be given the Horse with some Wine added thereunto; or make him a drink of Goats milk and Oyl, straining thereunto a little Fromenty. *Anatolius* saith, that it is good to give the Horse three days together, sodden Beans clean pilled, whereunto would be added some Deers Sewet, and a little Wine.

OF THE COLT EVIL.

THIS name Colt Evil, in my judgement, doth properly signifie that disease, which the Physitians call *Pilapismus*, which is a continual standing together, with an unnatural swelling of the yard proceeding of some winde, filling the arteries and hollow sinew or pipe of the yard; or else through the abundance of seed, which do chance oftentimes to man, and I think some-time to stoned Horses. Notwithstanding *Martin* saith that the Colt Evil is a swelling of the sheath of the yard, and part of the belly thereabout, caused of corrupt seed, coming out of the yard, and remaining within the sheath where it putrifieth. And Geldings most commonly are subject to this disease, not being able for lack of natural heat, to expel their seed any further. For Horses, as *Martin* saith are seldom troubled with this disease, because of their heat, unless it be when they have been over travelled, or otherwise weakened. The cure according to him is thus: Wash the sheath clean within with luke-warm Vinegar then draw out his yard and wash that also: that done, ride him into some running stream up to the belly, tossing him therein to and fro to allay the heat of the members, and use him thus two or three days, and he shall be whole.

ANOTHER OF THE COLT EVIL.

THE Colt Evil is a disease that cometh to stoned Horses, through ranckness of nature and want of vent, it appeareth in his cod and sheath, which will swell exceedingly; the cure is nothing: for if you will but every day, twice or thrice drive him to the mid-side in some Pond or running River, the swelling will fall, and the Horse will do well. If the Horse be of years, and troubled with this grief; if you put him to a Mare, it is not amiss; for standing still in a stable without exercise, is a great occasion of this disease.

OF THE MATTERING OF THE YARD.

IT cometh at covering time, when the Horse and Mare both are over-hot, and so perhaps burn themselves. The cure according to *Martin* is thus: Take a pinte of white Wine, and boil therein a quartern of roch Allum; and squirt thereof into his Yard three or four squirtfuls, one after another, and thrust the squirt so far as the liquor may pierce to the bottom, to scour away the bloudy matter, continuing thus to do once a day untill he be whole.

OF THE SHEDDING OF SEED.

THIS disease is called of the Physitians *Gonorrhea*, which may come sometime through abundance and ranckness of seed, and sometime by the weakness of the stones and seed vessels not able to retain the seed untill it be digested and thickned. *Vegetius* saith, that this disease will make the Horse very faint and weak; and especially in Summer season. For cure whereof, the said *Vegetius* would have the Horse to be ridden into some cold water, even up to the belly, so as his stones may be covered in water; and then his fundament being first bathed with warm water and Oyl, he would have you to thrust in your hand and arm even to the very bladder; and softly to rub and claw the same, and the parts thereabouts, which be the seed vessels: that done to cover him warm that he take no cold, and every day he would have you to give the Horse Hogs dung to drink with red Wine untill he be whole. I for my part, if I thought it came of weakness, as is aforesaid, which I would judge by the waterishness of the seed and unlustiness of the Horse, would give him red Wine to drink, and put therein a little *Acatium*, the juyce of Plantain, and a little Mastick, and bath his back with red Wine and Oyl of Roses mingled together.

OF THE FALLING OF THE YARD.

IT cometh, as I take it, through the weakness of the member, by means of some resolution in the muscles and sinews serving the same, caused at the first (perhaps) by some great strain or stripe on the back. It may come also by weariness and tiring. For remedy whereof, *Absyrtus* was wont to wash the yard with salt water from the Sea, if it may be gotten; and if not, with water and salt; and if that prevailed not, he would all to prick the outmost skin of the yard with a sharp needle, but not deep, and then wash all the pricks with strong Vinegar, and that did make the Horse, as he saith, to draw up his yard again immediately: yea, and this also will remedy the falling out of the fundament. *Pelagonius* would have you to put into the pipe of his yard, Honey and Salt boyled together and made liquid, or else a quick flie; or a grain of Frankincense, or a clove of Garlick clean pilled, and somewhat bruised; and also to pour on his back Oyl, Wine, Nitre made warm and mingled together. But *Martins* experience is in this sort: First; wash the yard with warm white Wine, and then anoint it with Oyl of Roses and Honey mingled together, and put it up into the sheath, and make him a Cod-piece of Canvas to keep it still up, and dress it thus every day once until it be whole. And in any case let his back be kept warm, either with a double cloth, or else with a charge made of Bole Armony, Egges, Wheat-flowre, *Sanguis Draconis*, Turpentine, and Vinegar; or else lay on a wet sack, which being covered with another dry cloth will keep his back very warm.

OF THE SWELLING OF THE COD AND STONES.

ASSYRTUS saith, that the inflamation and swelling of the cod and stones, cometh by means of some wound, or by the stinging of some Serpent, or by fighting one Horse with another. For remedy whereof, he was wont to hathe the cod with water wherein hath been sodden the roots of wilde Cowcumber and Salt, and then to anoint it with an Ointment mde of *Gerusa* Oyl, Goats grease, and the white of an Egge. Some again would have the cod to be bathed in warm Water, *Nitrum*, and Vinegar together, and also to be anointed with an Ointment made of Chalk, or of Potters earth, Oxe dung, Cumin, Water and Vinegar, or else to be anointed with the juyce of the herb *Solanum*, called of some Night-shade, or with the juyce of Hemlock growing on dunghils: yea, and also to be let bloud in the flanks. But *Martin* saith, that the swelling of the cods cometh for the most part after some sickness or surfeting with cold, and then it is a signe of amendment. The cure according to his experience is in this sort. First let him bloud on both sides the flank veins. Then take of Oyl of Roses, of Vinegar of each half a pinte, and half a quartern of Bole Armony beaten to powder. Mingle them together in a cruse, and being luke-warm, anoint the cods therewith with two or three feathers bound together, and the next day ride him into the water, so as his cods may be within the water, giving him two or three turns therein, and so return fair and softly to the stable, and when he is dry anoint him again as before, continuing thus to do every day once until they be whole. The said *Martin* saith also, the cods may be swollen by means of some hurt or evill humors resorting into the cod, and then he would have you cover the cods with a charge made of Bole Armony and Vinegar wrought together, renewing it every day once untill the swelling go away, or that it break of it self, and if it break, then tent it with *Mel Rosatum*, and make him a breech of Canvas to keep it in, renewing the tent every day once untill it be whole.

OF INCORDING AND BRUISING.

THIS term, Incording, is borrowed of the *Italian* word *Incordato* which in plain *English* is as much to say as Bursten and might be more rightly tearmed of us uncodded. For when a Horse is Bursten, his guts falleth down into the cod making it to swell. The *Italians*, as I take it, did call it *Incordato*, because the gut follows the string of the stone; called of them *Il cordone*, or *La corda*, whereof *Incordato* seems to be derived with some reason. According to which reason we should call it rather Instringed, then Incorded; for *Corda* doth signifie a string or cord. Notwithstanding, sith that Incording is already received in the stable, I for my part am very well content therewith, minding not to contend against it. But now you have to note; that either Man or Beast may be Bursten diversly, and according to the names of the pants grieved, the Physitians do give it divers names, for you shall understand, that next unto the thick outward skin of the belly, there is also another inward thin skin covering all the muscles, the Caul, and the guts of the belly, called of the Anatomists *Peritoneum*, which skin cometh from both parts and sides of the back, and is fastened to the Midriffe above, and also to the bottom of the belly beneath, to keep in all the contents of the neather belly. And therefore if the skin be broken, or over sore strained or stretched, then either some part of the caul or guts slippeth down, sometime into the cod, sometime not so far.

If the guts slip down into the cod, then it is called of the Physitians by the *Greek* name *Enterocele*, that is to say, Gut-bursten, But if the caul falldown into the cod, then it is called of the Physitians *Epiplocole*, that is to say, Caul-bursten. But either of the diseases is most properly incident to the male kinde, for the female kinde hath no cod. Notwithstanding they may be so bursten, as either gut or caul may fall down into their natures, hanging there like a bag; but if it fell not down so low, but remaineth above nigh unto the privy members or flanks, which place is called of the *Latins, Inguen*, then of that place the Bursting is called of the Physitians *Bubonocele*, whereunto I know not what *English* name to give, unlesse I should call it flank bursten. Moreover, the cod or flank may be sometimes swollen, by means of some waterish humour gathered together in the same, which is called of the Physitians *Hydrocele*, that is to say, Water-bursten; and sometimes the cod may be swollen by means of some hard peece of flesh cleaving the thin skins or panicles of the stones, and then it is called of the Physitians *Sarcocele*, that is to say, Flesh-bursten.

But forasmuch as none of mine Authors, *Martin*, nor any other Farrier in these dayes that I know, have intermedled with any kind of Bursting, but only with that wherein the gut falleth down into the cod; leaving all the rest apart, I will only talke of this, and that according to *Martins* experience, which I assure you differeth not much from the precepts of the old writers: But first you shall understand, that the Gut-bursten, and Flank-bursten, doth proceed both of one cause, that is to say, by means that the skin, called before *Peritoneum*; is either fore strained, or else broken, either by some stripe of another Horse, or else by some strain in leaping over a hedge, ditch, or pale, or otherwise; yea, and many times in passing a career, through the carelesness of the Rider, stopping the Horse suddenly without giving warning, whereby the Horse is forced to cast his hinder legs abroad, and so straineth or bursteth the skin aforesaid, by means whereof the gut falleth down into the cod. The signs be these; The Horse will forsake his meat, and stand shoring and leaning alwayes on that side that he is hurt; and on that side if you search with your hand betwixt the stone and the thigh upward to the body, and somewhat above the stone you shall find the gut it self big and hard in the feeling, whereas on the other side you shall find no such thing. The cure, according to *Martin*, is thus; Bring the Horse into some house or place that hath over head a strong balk or beam going overthwart, and strew that place thick with straw; then put on four pasternes with four rings on his feet, and then fasten the one end of a long root to one of those rings, then thread all the other rings with the loose end of the rope, and so draw all his four feet together, and cast him on the straw. That done, cast the rope over the baulk, and hoise the Horse so as he may lie flat on his back, with his legs upward without struggling. Then bathe his stones well with warm Water and Butter molten together, and the stones being somewhat warm; and well mollified, raise them up from the body with both your hands being closed by the fingers fast together, and holding the stones in your hands in such manner, work down the gut into the body of the Horse, by striking it downward continually with your two thumbs, one labouring immediately after another, untill you perceive that side of the stone to be so small as the other, and having so discorded, that is to say returned the gut into his right place; take a list of two fingers broad throughly anointed with fresh Butter, and tie his stones both together with the same so nigh as may be, not over hard, but so as you may put your finger betwixt. That done, take the Horse quietly down, and lead him fair and softly into the stable, where he must stand warm, and not be stirred for the space of three weeks. But forget not the next day after his discording to unloosen the list, and to take it away, and as well at that time, as every day once or twice after, to cast a dish or two of cold water up into his cods, and that will cause him to shrink up his stones, and thereby restrain the gut from falling down, and at the three weeks end be sure, it were not amisse to gold the stone on that side away, so shall he never be encorded again on that side. But let him not eat much nor drink much, and let his drink be alwayes warm.

OF THE BOTCH IN THE GRAINS OF A HORSE.

IF a Horse be full of humours and then suddenly laboured, the humours will resort into the weakest parts, and there gather together and breed a Botch, and especially in the hinder parts betwixt the thighs, not far from the cods. The signes be these; The hinder legs will be all swollen, and especially from the hoofs upward, and if you feel with your hand you shall find a great kind of swelling, and if it be round and hard it will

707

gather to a head. The cure, according to *Martin*, is thus; First ripe it with a plaister; take of Wheat-flowre, of Turpentine, and of Hony, of each a like quantity, stirring it together to make a stiffe plaister, and with a cloth lay it unto the sore, renewing it every day once untill it break or wax soft, and then lance it as the matter may run downward; then tent it with Turpentine and Hogs grease molten together, renewing it every day once, untill it be whole.

OF THE DISEASES INCIDENT TO THE WOMB OF A MARE, AND SPECIALLY OF BARRENNESS.

IT seemeth by some writers, that the womb of a Mare is subject to certain diseases, though not so many as the womb of a Woman, as to ascent, descent, falling out, Convulsion, Barrenness, aborsement; yea, *Aristotle* and others do not let to write, that menstrual bloud doth naturally void from the Mare, as from the Woman, though it be so little in quantity, as it cannot be well perceived. But sith none of mine Authors have written thereof to any purpose, nor any Farrier of this time that I know, have had any experience in such matters, I will passe them all over with silence, saving barrennesse, whereof I promised before in his due place, to declare unto you the causes and such kind of cure for the same, as the old writers have taught. A Mare then may be barren through the untemperateness of the womb or matrix, as well for that it is too hot and fiery, or else too cold and moist, or too dry, or else too short, or too narrow, or having the neck thereof turned awry, or by means of some obstruction or stopping in the matrix; or for that the Mare is too fat, or too lean, and many times Mares go barren, for that they be not well Horsed. Wel, the cure of barrenness that cometh through the fault of the matrix or womb according to the old writers is thus; Take a good handful of Leeks, stamp them in a morter with half a glasse full of wine, then put thereunto twelve Flies, called of the Apothecaries *Cantharides*, of divers colours if they may be gotten, then strain all together with a sufficient quantity of water to serve the Mare therewith two dayes together, by powring the same into her nature with a horn or glyster-pipe made of purpose, and at the end of three dayes next following offer the Horse unto her that should cover her,

708

and immediately after that she is covered, wash her nature twice together with cold water.

ANOTHER RECEIPT FOR THE SAME PURPOSE.

TAKE of Nitrum, of Sparrows dung, and Turpentine, of each a like quantity well wrought together and made like a Suppository, and put that into her nature, and it will cause her to desire the Horse, and also to conceive. *Hippocrates* saith, that it is good also to put a nettle into the Horses mouth that should cover her.

OF THE ITCH, SCAB, AND MANGINESS IN THE TAIL, AND FALLING OF THE TAIL.

IN Spring time Horses many times are troubled with the Troncheons in their fundament, and then they will rub their tail, and break the hair thereof, and yet in his tail perhaps, shall be neither Itch, Scurffe nor Scab; wherefore if you rake the Horse well with your hand anointed with Sope, and search for those Troncheons and pull them clean out, you shall cause him to leave rubbing and if you see that the hair do fall away it self, then it is a sign, that it is either eaten with Worms, or that there is some Scurffe or Scab fretting the hair, and causing such an itch in his tail as the Horse is alwayes rubbing the same. As touching the wormes, Scurffe or Scab, it shall be good to anoint all the tail with Sope, and then to wash it clean even to the ground with strong lie, and that will kill the Wormes, and make the hair to grow again. And if much of the tail be worn away, in shall be needful to keep the tail continually wet with a spunge dipt in fair water, and that will make the hair to grow very fast. But if the Horses tail be mangy, then heal that like as you do the manginess of the mane before rehearsed. Again, if there breed any Canker in the tail (which will consume both flesh and bone, and as *Laurentius Russius* saith, make the joints to fall away one by one) it shall be good, as *Martin* saith, to wash all his tail with *Aqua fortis*, or strong water made in this sort: take of green Copperas of Allum, of each one pound, of white Copperas a quartern. Boyl of all these things together in three quarts of running water in a strong earthen pot, untill one half be consumed, and then with a little of this water being made lukewarm, wash his tail with a little clout, or flax bound to the end of a stick, continuing so to do every day once untill it be whole.

OF THE SCAB.

THE Scab is a foul scurffe in divers parts of a Horses body, and cometh of poverty or ill keeping, or many times by going amongst woods wherein they are infected with water boughs: it is most incident to old Horses, which will die thereof, and chiefly in the Spring time when the new bloud appears: the cure whereof I have spoken before.

HOW TO KNOW WHEN A HORSE HALTETH BEFORE IN WHAT PART HIS GRIEF IS.

BEING now come to talke of the griefs in the shoulders, legs, hips, houghes, joynts and hoofs, causing the Horse most commonly to halt: I think it good first to shew you the way how to find in what part of his legs the Horse is grieved when he halteth either before or behind. And first you have to consider that if a Horse halteth before, it must be either in his shoulders, in his legs, or in his feet. If it be in his shoulders and new hurt, the Horse will not lift that leg, but trail it nigh the ground. If it be old hurt, he will cast that leg further from him in his going then the other, and if he be turned on the foreside, then he will halt so much the more. If a Horse halteth in the leg, it is either in the knee, in the shank, or else in the pastern joynt; if it be either in the knee, or pastern joynt, he will not bow that leg in his going like the other, but go very stifly upon it. If he halteth in the shank, then it is by means of some splent, wind gal, or such apparent grief, apt to be seen or felt. If he halt in the foot, it is either in the cronet, heel, in the toe, in the quarters, or sole of the foot. If it be in the cronet, the grief will be apparent, the skin being broken or swollen some manner of way. If in the heel, as by over-reach, or otherwise, then he will tread most on the toe. If upon any of the quarters, then going on the edge of a bank or hilly ground, he will halt more then on the plain ground, and by the Horses coming toward you, and going from you upon such edge or bank, you shall easily perceive whether his grief be in the inward quarter or in the outward quarter; the quarter is to be understood, from the mid hoof to the heel.

If he halt in the toe, which is not commonly seen, then he will tread more upon the heel. If the grief be in the sole of the foot, then he will halt all after one sort upon any ground, unlesse it be upon the stones. And to be sure in what part of the foot the grief is, it shall be good first to make him go upon the plain ground, and then upon a hard and stony ground: yea, and also a bankie ground. Thus having declared unto you in general, how to know in what part a Horse is grieved when he halteth before: I think it meet first to shew you orderly all the particular griefs and sorances, whereunto the foreparts of a Horse is subject, together with the causes, signes and cure thereof. That done, I will speak of halting behind, and shew you first generally where the grief is, and then particularly declare unto you every grief incident to the hinder parts of a Horse. And lastly, I will speak of such griefs and sorances as are commonly in both parts, that is to say, as well to the fore legs and fore feet, as to the hinder legs and hinder feet.

Of the grief and pinching in the shoulder.

This cometh either by labouring and straining the Horse too young, or else by some great burthen; you shall perceive it by the narrowness of the breast, and by consuming flesh of the shoulders, insomuch as the forepart of the shoulder bone will stick out, and be a great deal higher then the flesh. And if it be of long continuance, he will be very hollow in the brisket towards the armeholes, and he will go wider beneath at the feet, then above at the knees. The cure, according to *Martin*, is thus. Give him a slit of an inch long with a sharp knife or rasor upon both sides an inch under the shoulder bones: then with a Swans quill put into the slit, blow up first the one shoulder, and then the other, as big as can possible, even up to the withers, and with your hand strike the winde equally into every place of the shoulders. And when they be full, then beat all the windy places with a good hasell wand, or with both your hands, clapping upon the places puffed up with wind, so fast as they can

711

walk one after another over all the shoulder; then with a flat slice of iron, loosen the skin within from the flesh: that done, roll the two slits or cuts with two round rols made of the upper leather of an old shooe, with a hole in the middest that the matter may issue forth, and let such rols be three inched broad, and so put in as they may lie plain and flat within the cut; then make a charge to lay upon the same in this sort; Take of Pitch, and Rosen, of each one pound, of Tar half a pinte, boyl these things all together in a pot, and when it is somewhat cooled, take a stick with a woollen clout bound fast to the end thereof, and dip it into this charge, and cover and daub all the shoulder therewith. That done, clap thereunto a pound of Flox of such colour as the Horse is, or as nigh unto the same as may be, every other day cleanse both the wounds and rols, and put them in again, continuing thus to do the space of fifteen dayes. Then take them out; and heal up the wounds with two tents of Flax dipt in Turpentine, and Hogs grease molten together, renewing the same every day once, untill the wounds be whole. But let the change lie still, untill it fall away of it self, and let the Horse run to grasse untill he hath had a frost or two.

OF THE WRINCHING OF THE SHOULDER.

THIS cometh sometime by a fall, and sometime by turning too suddenly in some uneven ground, or by rash running out of some door, or by some stripe of another Horse, or by some sudden stop in passing a Career: you shall perceive it in his going, by trailing his legs upon the ground, so close unto himself as he can possible. The cure, according to *Martin*, is thus: Let him bloud the quantity of three pintes, on the breast in the palat-vein, receiving the bloud in a pot; and thereunto put first a quart of strong Vinegar, and half a dozen broken Egges, shels and all, and so much Wheat-flowre as will thicken all that liquor. That done, put thereunto Bole Armony beaten into fine powder one pound, *Sanguis Draconis* two ounces, and mingle them all together, so as the flowre may not be perceived, and if it be too stiffe, you may make it more liquid or soft, with a little Vinegar. Then with your hand daub all the shoulder from the mane downward, and betwixt the fore-bowels, all against the hair, and let not the Horse depart out of that place, untill the charge be surely fastned unto the skin.

That done, carry him into the stable, and tie him up to the rack, and suffer him not to lie down all that day, and give him a little meat, dieting him moderately the space of fifteen days: during which time he may not stir out of his place, but only lie down, and every day once refresh the shoulder point with this charge, laying still new upon the old, and at the fifteen days end, lead him abroad to see how he goeth, and if he be somewhat amended, then let him rest without travelling, the space of one month; and that shall bring his shoulder to perfection. But if he be never the better for this that is done, then it shall be needful to rowel him with a leather rowel upon the shoulder-point, and to keep him rowelled the space of fifteen days, renewing the rowel, and cleansing the wound every other day; and then walk him up and down fair and softly, and turn him always on the contrary side to the sore; and when he goeth upright, pull out the rowel and heal the wound with a tent of flax dipt in Turpentine, and Hogs grease molten together. And if all this will not serve, then it shall be needful to draw him checker-wise with a hot iron over all the Shoulder-point; and also make him to draw in a plough every day two hours at the least, to settle his joynts for the space of three weeks or a month; and if anything will help him, these two last remedies will help him, and make him to go upright again.

OF SPLAITING IN THE SHOULDER.

THIS cometh by some dangerous sliding or slipping, whereby the shoulder parteth from the breast, and so leaves an open rift, not in the skin, but in the flesh and film next under the skin, and so he halteth and is not able to go; you shall perceive it by trailing his leg after him in his going. The cure according to *Martin* is thus: First put a pair of straight pasterns on his fore-feet, keeping him still in the stable without disquieting him: Then take of *Dialthea* one pound, of Sallet Oyl one pinte, of Oyl-de-bays half a pound, of fresh Butter half a pound; melt all these things together in a Pipkin, and anoint the grieved place therewith, and also round about the inside of the shoulder, and within two or three days after, both that place and all the shoulder besides will swell. Then either prick him with a lancet or fleam, in all the swelling places, or else with some other sharp hot Iron, the head whereof would be an inch long, to the intent that the corruption may run out, and use to anoint it still with the same Ointment. But if you see that it will not go away, but swell still, and gather to a head, then lance it where the swelling doth gather most, and is soft under the finger, and then tent it with flax dipt in this Ointment: Take of Turpentine and of Hogs grease, of each two ounces, and melt them together, renewing the tent twice a day untill it be whole.

OF THE SHOULDER PIGHT.

THIS is when the shoulder point or pitch of the shoulder is displaced, which grief is called of the *Italians, Spallato*; and it cometh by reason of some great fall forward, rush or strain. The signes be these: That shoulder-point will stick out further then his fellow, and the Horse will halt right down. The cure according to *Martin* is thus: First make him to swim in a deep water up and down a dozen turns, and that shall make the joynt to return into his place. Then make two tough pins of Ashen wood as much as your little finger, sharp at the points, each one five inches long: that done, slit the skin an inch above the point, and an inch beneath the point of the shoulder, and thrust in one of the pins from above downward, so as both ends may equally stick without the skin. And if the pin of wood will not easily pass through, you may make it way first with an Iron pin. That done, make other two holes cross to the first holes, so as the other pin may cross the first pin right in the midst with a right cross, and the first pin would be somewhat flat in the midst, to the intent that the other being round, may pass the better without stop, and close the juster together. Then take a piece of a little line somewhat bigger then a whip-cord, and at one end make a loop, which being put over one of the pins ends, winde the rest of the line good and straight about the pine ends, so as it may lie betwixt the pins ends and the skin, and fasten the last end with a pack-needle and packthread unto the rest of the cord, so as it may not slip: and to do well, both the pricks and the

714

cord would be first anointed with a little Hogs grease. Then bring him into the stable, and let him rest the space of nine days, but let him lie down as little as may be, and put on a pastern on the sore leg, so as it may be bound with a cord unto the foot of the manger, to keep that leg always whilest he standeth in the stable more forward then the other. And at the nine days end take out the pricks, and anoint the sore places with a little *Dialthea*, or with Hogs grease, and then turn him out to grass.

OF THE SWELLING OF THE FORE-LEGS AFTER GREAT LABOR.

GREAT labour and heat causeth humors to resort down into the legs making them swell. The cure whereof according to *Martin* is thus: Bathe them with buttered Beer, or else with this bath here following: Take of Mallows three handfuls, a Rose cake, Sage one handful: boil them together in a sufficient quantity of water, and when the Mallows be soft, put in half a pound of Butter, and half a pinte of Sallet Oyl, and then being somewhat warm, wash the swelling therewith every day once, the space of three or four days. And if the swelling will not go away with this; then take Wine lees, and Cumin, and boil them together, and put thereunto a little Wheat-flowre, and charge all the swelling therewith, and walk him often: and if it will not serve, then take up the great vein above the knee on the inside, suffering him not to bleed from above, but all from beneath.

OF THE FOUNDERING IN THE FORE-LEGS.

THE cause of this grief is declared before in the Chapter of foundering in the body, whereas I shewed you, that if a Horse be foundered in the body, the humors will immediately resort down into his legs, as *Martin* saith, within the space of 24 hours, and then the Horse will go crouching all upon the hinder-legs, his fore-legs being so stiffe, as he is not able to bow them. The cure whereof, according to *Martin*, is in this sort: Garter each leg immediately one handful above the knee, with a list good and hard, and then walk him or chafe him, and so put him in a heat, and being some-what warmed, let him bloud in both the breast veins, reserving the bloud to make a charge withall in this manner:

Take of that bloud two quarts, and of Wheat-flowre half a peck, and six Egges, shels and all, of Bole Armony half a pound, of *Sanguis Draconis* half a quartern, and a quart of strong Vinegar; mingle them all together, and charge all his shoulders, breast, back, loyns, and fore-legs therewith, and then walk him upon some hard ground, suffering him not to stand still; and when the charge is dry, refresh it again. And having walked him three or four hours together, lead him into the stable, and give him a little warm water with ground Mault in it, and then a little Hay and provender, and then walk him again, either in the house, or else abroad, and continue thus the space of four days: and when all the charge is spent, cover him well with a housing cloth, and let him both stand and lie warm, and eat but little meat during the four days. But if you see that at four days end he mendeth not a whit, then it is a sign that the humor lies in the foot, for the which you must search with your Butter, paring all the soles of the fore-feet so thin as you shall see the water issue through the sole. That done, with your Butter, let him bloud at both the toes, and let him bleed well. Then stop the vein with a little Hogs grease, and then tack on the shooes, and Turpentine molten together, and laid upon a little Flax; and cram the place where you did let him bloud hard with Tow, to the intent it may be surely stopt. Then fill both his feet with Hogs grease, and bran fryed together in a stopping pan, so hot as is possible. And upon the stopping clap a piece of leather, or else two splents to keep the stopping. And immediately after this, take two Egges, beat them in a dish, and put thereto Bole Armony, and Bean-flowre so much as will thicken the same, and mingle them well together, and make thereof two plaisters, such as may close each foot round about, somewhat, above the cronet, and binde it fast with a list or roller, that it may not fall away, not be removed for the space of three days, but let the sole be cleansed, and new stopped every day once, and the cronets to be removed every two days, continuing so to do untill it be whole. During which time let him rest walked, for fear of loosening his hoofs. But if you see that he begin to amend, you may walk him fair and softly once a day upon some soft ground, to exercise his legs and feet; and let him not eat much, nor drink cold water. But if this fundering break out above the hoof, which you shall perceive by the looseness of the coffin, above by the cronet; then when you pare the sole, you must take all the fore-part of the sole clean away, leaving the heels whole, to the intent the humors may have the freer passage downward, and then stop him, and dress him about the cronet as is before said.

OF FOUNDRING.

OF all other sorances, foundering is soonest got, and hardlyest cured: yet if it may be perceived in twenty four hours, and taken in hand by this means hereafter prescribed, it shall be cured in other twenty and four hours: notwithstanding, the same receit hath cured a Horse that hath been foundered a year and more, but then it was longer in bringing it to pass. Foundering cometh when a Horse is heated, being in his grease and very fat, and taketh thereon a sudden cold which striketh down into his legs, and taketh away the use and feeling thereof. The sign to know it is, the Horse cannot go, but will stand cripling with all his four legs together; if you offer to turn him, he will couch his buttocks to the ground, and some Horses have I seen sit on their buttocks to feed.

The cure is thus: Let him bloud of his two breast veins, of his two shackle veins, and of, his two veins above the cronets of his hinder hoofs; if the veins will bleed, take from them three pintes at least; if they will not bleed, then open his neck vein, and take so much from thence. Save the blood, and let one stand by and stir it as he bleeds, lest it grow into lumps; when he hath done bleeding, take as much Wheat flowre as will thicken the blood, the whites of twenty Egges, and three or four yolks; then take a good quantity of *Bolearminack*, and a pinte of strong Vinegar, incorporate all these well together, and withal charge his back, neck, head, and ears; then take two long rags of cloth and dip in the same charge, and withal garter him so strait as may be above both his knees of his forelegs; then let his keeper take him out to some stony causie, or high-way paved with stone, and there one following him with a cudgel, let him trot up and down for the space of an hour, or two, or more: that done, set him up and give him some meat; and for his drink, let him have

717

a warm mash: some three or four hours after this, take off his garters, and set him in some pond of water up to the mid-side, and so let him stand for two hours, then take him out and set him up; the next day pull off his shooes, and pare his feet very thin, and let him blood both of his heels and toes; then set on his shooes again, and stop them with Hogs grease and bran boiling hot, and splint them up, and so turn him out to run, and he shall be sound.

OF THE SPLENT AS WELL IN THE INSIDE OR OUTSIDE OF THE KNEE, AS OTHER WHERE IN THE LEGS.

THIS sorance to any mans feeling, is a very gristle, sometime as big as a Walnut, and sometime no more then a Hasel-nut, which is called of the *Italians, Spinella*, and it cometh, as *Laurentius Russius* saith, by travelling the Horse too young, or by oppressing him with heavie burthens offending his tender sinews, and so causeth him to halt. It is easie to know, because it is apparent to the eye, and if you pinch it with your thumb and finger, the Horse will shrink up his leg.

The cure whereof, according to *Martin*, is in this sort: Wash it well in warm water, and shave off the hair, and lightly scarifie all the sore places with the point of a rasor, so as the blood may issue forth. Then take of Cantharides half a spoonful, and of Euforbium as much, beaten into fine powder, and mingle them together with a spoonful of Oyl-de-bay, and then melt them in a little pan, stirring them well together, so as that they may not boil over, and being so boiled hot, take two or three feathers, and anoint all the sore place therewith. That done, let not the Horse stir from the place where you so dresse him for one hour after, to the intent he shake not off the ointment. Then carry him fair and softly into the stable, and tie him as he may not reach with his head beneath the manger, for otherwise he will covet to bite away the smarting and pricking medicine, which if it should touch his lips, would quickly fetch off the skin. And also let him stand without litter all that day and night. The next day anoint the sore place with fresh butter, continuing so to do every day once for the space of nine dayes, for this shall allay the heat of the medicine, and cause both that, and the crust to fall away of it self, and therewith either clean take away the splent, or at least remove it out of the knee into the leg, and so much diminish it, as the Horse shall go right up, and halt no more through occasion thereof. *Laurentius Russius* would have the splent to be cured by firing it longst wise and overthwart. I have seen the splent to be clean taken away thus: first having clipt away the hair growing upon the hard place, you must beat it with a good big stick of Hasel almost a foot long, in which stick somewhat distant from the one end thereof would be set fast a sharp prick of a little bit of steel, to prick the sore place therewith, once or twice to make the bloud issue out, never leaving to beat it first softly, and then harder and harder until it waxeth soft in every place to the feeling, and to thrust out the blood, partly with the stick, leaning on it with both your hands, and partly with your thumbs: that done, wind about the sore place with a piece of double red woollen cloth, holding it so as it may lie close thereunto; then sear it upon the cloth with the flat side of your searing iron, made hot, and not red-hot, but so as it may not burn through the cloth; that done, take away the cloth, and lay upon the sore a piece of Shoomakers wax, made like a little cake, so broad as is the sore place, and then sear that into his Legs with your searing iron, until the wax be throughly moulten, dryed, and sunken into the sore: that done, sear another piece of wax in like manner into the sore, until it be dryed up, and then you may travel your Horse immediately upon it if you will, for he will not halt no more.

OF THE SPLENT.

A Splent is a sorance of the least moment, unlesse it be on the knee, or else a through Splent, both which cannot be cured. A Splent is a spungy hard gristle or bone, growing Fast on the inside of the shin-bone of a Horse, where a little making stark the sinews compels a Horse somewhat to stumble. The cures are divers, and thus they be; If the Splent be young, tender, and but new in breeding, then cast the Horse, and take a spoonful of that Oyl called *Petrolium*, and with that Oyl rub the Splent till you make it soft; then take a fleam, such as you let a Horse bloud withal, and strike the Splent in two or three places, then with your

719

two thumbs thrust it hard, and you shall see crush't matter and bloud come out, which is the very Splent; then set him up and let him rest, or run at grasse for a week or more. Others for a young Splent do thus; Take a Hasell stick and cut it square, and therewithal beat the Splent till it be soft, then take a blew cloth and lay upon the Splent, and take a Taylors pressing Iron made hot and rub it up and down upon the cloth over the Splent, and it shall take it clean away. But if the Splent be old and great, and grown to the perfection of hardness, then you must cast the Horse, and with a sharp knife slit down the Splent; then take *Cantharides* and *Euforbium*, of each like quantity, and boyl them in Oyl-de-bay, and with that fill up the slit, and renew it for three dayes together, then take it away and anoint the place with Oyl-de-bay, Oyl of Roses or Tar, until it be whole.

OF A MALANDER.

A Malander is a kinde of Scab growing in the forme of lines, or strokes, overthwart the bent of the knee, and hath long hairs with stubborn roots, like the bristles of a Bore, which corrupteth and cankereth the flesh, like the roots of a childes scabbed head: and if it be great, it will make the Horse to go stiffe at the setting forth, and also to halt. This disease proceedeth some-time of corrupt bloud, but most commonly for lack of clean keeping, and good rubbing. The cure, according to *Martin*, is thus; First wash it well with warm water, then shave both hair and scab clean away, leaving nothing but the bare flesh, whereunto lay this Plaister: Take a spoonful of Sope, and as much of Lime, mingle them together, that it may be like paste, and spread as much on a clout as will cover the sore, and binde it fast on with a list, renewing it every day once the space of two or three dayes, and at the three dayes end, take away the Plaister and anoint the sore with Oyl of Roses made luke-warm, and that shall fetch away the crust-scurfe, bred by means of the Plaister, which being taken away, wash the sore place well every day once with his own stale, or else with mans urine, and then immediately strow upon it the powder of burnt Oystershels, continuing thus to do every day once until it be whole.

ANOTHER OF THE MALANDER.

A Malander is a peevish sorance, and cometh of ill keeping, it is on the fore-legs, just on the inside, at the bending of the knee, it will make a Horse go stark, and stumble much. The cure is in this sort; Cast the Horse, and with some instrument pluck off the dry scab that will stick thereon, and rub it till it bleed, then take and bind it thereto for three days, in which space you shall see a white asker on the sore, then take that off and anoint it with Oyl of Roses or fresh Butter until it be throughly cured.

OF AN UPPER ATTAINT OR OVER-REACH UPON THE BACK SINEW OF THE SHANKE, SOMEWHAT ABOVE THE JOYNT.

THE *Italians* call this sorance *Attincto*, which is a painful swelling of the master sinew, by means that the Horse doth sometimes over reach, and strike that sinew with the toe of his hinder-foot, which causeth him to halt. The signes be apparent by the swelling of the place, and by the Horses halting. The cure, according to *Martin*, is thus; Wash the place with warm water, and shave all the hair so far as the swelling goeth, and scarifie every part of the sore place lightly with the point of a Rasor, that the bloud may issue forth. Then take of *Cantharides* and of *Euforbium*, of each half an ounce, mingle them together with half a quartern of Sope, and with a slice spread some of this Ointment over all the sore, suffering him to rest there as you dresse him for one half hour after, and then you may carry him into the stable, and there let him stand without litter, and tyed as hath been said before in the Chapter of the Spleen, and the next day dresse him with the same Ointment once again, even as you did before. And the third day anoint the place with fresh Butter, continuing so to do the space of nine dayes, and at the nine dayes end, make him this bath; Take of Mallowes three handfuls, a Rose-cake, of Sage a handful; boyl them together in a sufficient quantity of water. And when the Mallowes be soft, put in half a pound of Butter, and half a pinte of Sallet Oyle; and then being somewhat warm, wash the sore place therewith every day once, the space of three or four dayes.

Of a Nether taint.

THIS is a little bladder full of jelly, much like unto a Wind-gal, not apparent to the eye, but to the feeling, growing in the midst of the pastern, somewhat above the frush. It cometh by a strain, or else by some wrench, or by any other over-reach, and maketh the Horse to halt. The signes be these; The neather-joynt toward the fewter-lock will be hot in feeling, and somewhat swollen. The cure, according to *Martin*, is in this sort; Tie him above the joynt with a list somewhat hard, and that will cause the bladder to appear to the eye. Then lance it with a sharp pointed knife, and thrust out all the jelly. That done, lay unto it the white of an Egge, and a little Salt beaten together, and laid upon flax or tow, and bind it fast unto the sore, renewing it once a day the space of four or five dayes, during which time let him rest, and then you may boldly labour him.

Of an Attaint.

AN Attaint is a grief that cometh by an over-reach, as clapping one leg upon another, or by some other Horses treading upon his heels. The cure is; Take a sharp knife and cut out the over-reach, that is, if it be never so deep like a hole, cut it plain and smooth, how broad so ever you make it, then wash it with Beer and Salt, and lay to it Hogs grease, Wax, Turpentine, and Rosen, of each like quantity, boyled and mingled together, and this will in few dayes heal him, be it never so sore.

Of an over-reach upon the heel.

THIS is a cut, so as the skin hangs down at the heel, made with the toe of the hinder foot, and is apparent to the eye, and it will cause the Horse somewhat to halt. The cure whereof, according to *Martin*, is thus; Cut away the skin that hangeth down, and bind a little flax dipt in the white of an Egge mingled with a little Bole-armony, renewing it every day once the space of three or four days, and that will heal it.

Of false quarters.

THIS is a rift sometime in the outside, but most commonly in the inside of the hoof, because the inside is ever the weaker part, which sides are commonly called quarters, and thereof this sorance taketh his name, and is called a false quarter; that is to say, a crased or unsound quarter, which name indeed is borrowed of the *Italians*, calling it in their tongue, *Falso quarto*. It cometh by evill shooing, and partly by evill paring. The signes be these: The Horse will for the most part halt, and the rift will bleed, and is apparent to the eye. The cure, according to *Martin*, is thus; If the Horse halt, then pull off the shooe, and cut so much away on that side of the shooe where the grief is, as the shooe being immediately put on again, the rift may be uncovered. Then open the rift with a Rosenet or drawer, and fill the rift with a roll of Toe dipt in Turpentine, Wax, and Sheeps sewet molten, renewing it every day once until it be whole. And the rift being closed in the top, draw him betwixt the hair and the hoof with a hot Iron overthwart that place, to the intent that the hoof may shoot all whole downward, and when the Horse goeth upright, ride him with no other shooe, until his hoof be throughly hardned again.

Of halting behind, and where the grief is.

IF a Horse halt behind, the grief must either be in the hip, in the stifle, in the hough, in the ham, in the leg, in the neather joynt, pastern or foot. If he halt in the hip of a new hurt, the Horse will go sideling, and not follow so well with that leg as with the other; but if it be old hurt, the sore hip will shrink and be lower then the other. And is best seen, when he goeth up a hill, or upon the edge of some bank, so as the worst leg may go on the higher side, for then he will halt so much more, because it is painful unto him to go so unevenly wrinching his leg. If the grief be in the stifle, then the Horse in his going will cast the stifle joynt outward, and the bone on the inside will be far bigger then the other. If the grief be in the hough, then it is by means of some Spaven, or some other hurt apparent to the eye. And the like may be said of the ham, wherein may be seen the Selander, or such like apparent sorance, causing the Horse to halt. If the grief be either in the leg, pastern or foot, then you shall finde it by such signes as have been taught you before. And therefore let us now speak of those sorances that are properly incident to the hinder legs.

OF THE STRING-HALT.

THE String-halt is a disease that maketh a Horse twitch up his leg suddenly, and so halt much, it cometh sometimes naturally, and sometimes casually, by means of some great cold whereby the sinews are strained: the best cure thereof, is to dig a pit in some dunghil, as deep as the Horse is high, and set the Horse in, and cover him with warm dung, and so let him stand the space of two hours, then take him out and make him clean, and then bathe him all over with Train-oyl made warm, and it will help him.

OF A HORSE THAT IS HIPPED, OR HURT IN THE HIPS.

THE Horse is said to be hipt, when the hip-bone is removed out of his right place, which grief is called of the *Italians, Mal del ancha*. It cometh most commonly by some great stripe or strain. slipping, sliding or falling. The signes be these: The Horse will halt, and in his going he will go sideling, and the sore hip will fall lower then the other, and the flesh in processe of time will consume clean away. And if it be suffered to run so long, it will never be restored unto his pristine estate. The best way, as *Martin* saith, to make him go upright, is to charge his hip and back with Pitch and Rosen molten together, and laid on warm, and then some flocks of his own colour to be clapped upon the same, and so let him run to grasse untill he go upright. But the sore hip will never rise again so high as the other. If the Horse be not hipped, but only hurt in the hip, and that newly, then first take of the Oyl de-bay, of *Dialthea*, of Nerval, of Swines grease, melt them all together, stirring them continually until they be throughly mingled together, and anoint the sore place against the hair with this Ointment every day once, the space of a fortnight, and make the Ointment to sink well into the flesh, by holding a hot broad bar over the place anointed, weaving your hand to and fro, until the Ointment be entred into the skin. And if at the fortnights end, you see that the Horse amendeth no whit for this, then slit a hole downward in his skin, and an inch beneath the hip-bone, making the hole so wide, as you may easily thrust in a rowel with your finger, and then with a little broad slice or iron, loosen the skin from the flesh above the bone, and round about the same, so broad as the rowel may lie flat and plain betwixt the skin and the flesh, which rowel would be made of soft Calves Leather, with a hole in the midst like a ring, having a threed tied unto it, to pull it out when you would cleanse the hole, and if the rowel be rolled about with flax fast tyed on, and anointed with the ointment under written, it will draw so much the more; and thrust in the rowel first double, and then spread it abroad with your finger. That done, tent it with a good long tent of flax or tow dipt in a little Turpentine and Hogs grease molten together and made warm, and cleanse the hole, and the rowel every day once, and also renew the tent every day for the space of a fortnight. And before you dresse him, cause him every day to be led up and down a foot pace a quarter of an hour, to make the humors come down, and at the fortnights end pull out the rowel, and heal up the wound with the same salve, making the tent every day lesser and lesser until it be whole. And so soon as it is whole, draw with a hot Iron crosse lines, of eight or nine inches long, right over the hip-bone, so as the rowelled place may be in the very midst thereof, and burn him no deeper, but so as the skin may look yellow, and then charge all that place, and over all his buttocks with this charge: Take of Pitch a pound, of Rosen half a pound, of Tar half a pinte; boyl them together, and then being good and warm, spread it on with a clout tyed in a riven stick, and then clap on a few flocks of the Horses colour. And if it be in Summer; let the Horse run to grasse a while, for the more he travelleth at his own will, the better it is for him.

OF STIFLING, AND HURTS IN THE STIFLE.

THE Horse is said to be stifled, when the stifling bone is removed from the place; but if it be not removed nor loosened, and yet the Horse halteth by means of some grief there, then we say that the Horse is hurt in the stifle, and not stifled. The stifle cometh by means of some blow, or some great strain, slipping or sliding. The signes be these; If he be stifled, the one bone will stick out farther then the other, and is apparent to the eye. *Martin* would have you to cure the stifle in all points like unto the shoulder-pight, saving that the pins need not be so long, because the stifling place is not so broad as the shoulder, and standing in the stable, let him have a pastern with a Ring on his sore-leg, and thereunto fasten a cord, which cord must go about his neck, and let it be so much strained, as it may bring his sore leg more forward then the other to keep the bone from starting out. But if the Horse be but hurt in the stifle with some stripe or strain, then the bone will not stand out, but perhaps the place may be swollen. The cure, according to *Martin*, is thus; First anoint the place with the Ointment mentioned before, every day once the space, of a fortnight; and if the Horse amend not with this, then rowel him with a hearen rowel, or else with a quill, and let the neather hole be somewhat before the sore place, and cleanse the hole every day, by turning the rowel, continuing still to anoint the place with the Ointment aforesaid, and that will make him whole.

OF FOUNDERING BEHIND.

THIS haps most commonly when a Horse is very fat, and hath his grease moulten within him, which is soon done with every little heat. You shall perceive it by his going, for he will be afraid to set his hinder-feet to the ground, and he will be so weak behind, as he will stand quivering and shaking, and covet always to lie down. The cure, according to *Martin*, is thus: First garter him about the houghes, and then force him to go a while to put him in a heat, and being some-what warm, let him bloud in the thigh veins, reserving of that bloud a pottle, to make him a charge in this sort; Put unto that bloud, of Wheat-flower and of Bean-flower, of each a quarter of a peck, of Bole-armony one pound, of *Sanguis Draconis* two ounces, six Egges, shels and all, of Turpentine half a pound, of Vinegar a quart; mingle all these things together, and therewith charge both his hinder-legs, his reins, and flanks, all against the hair. And if the Horse cannot dung, let him be raked, and give him this glyster; Take of Mallowes three handfuls, and boyl them well in fair Water from a pottle to a quart; then strain it, and put thereunto half a pound of Butter, and of Sallet Oyl a quarter of a pinte, and having emptied his belly, give him also this drink to comfort him; Take of Malmesie a quart, and put thereunto a little Cinamon, Mace, and Pepper, beaten into fine powder, and of Oyl a quarter of a pinte, and give the Horse to drink of that luke-warm with a horn. That done, let him be walked up and down a good while together if he be able to go; if not, then tie him up to the rack, and let him be hanged with Canvas and Ropes, so as he may stand upon the ground with his feet: For the lesse he lyeth, the better; and pare his hinder-feet thin, untill the dew come out, and tacking on the shooes again, stop the hoofs with Bran and Hogs grease boyled together, and let both his feet, having this geer in it, be wrapped up in a cloth even to his pasterns, and there tie the clout fast. Let his diet be thin, and let him drink no cold water, and give him in Winter wet hay, and in Summer grasse.

OF THE DRY SPAVEN.

THE dry Spaven, called of the *Italians, Spavano*, or *Sparavagno*; is a great hard knob as big as a Walnut growing in the inside of the hough; hard under the joynt, nigh unto the master vein, and causeth the Horse to halt, which sorance cometh by kinde, because the Horses Parents perhaps had the like disease at the time of his generation; and sometime by extreme labor and heat dissolving humors which do descend through the master vein, continually feeding that place with evil nutriment, and causeth that place to swell. Which swelling in continuance of time becometh so hard as a bone, and therefore is called of some the Bone Spaven. It needeth no signes or tokens to know it, because it is very much apparent to the eye, and therefore most Farriers do take it to be incurable.

Notwithstanding, *Martin* saith, that it may be made lesse with these remedies here following; Wash it with warm water, and shave off the hair so far as the swelling extendeth, and scarifie the place so as it may bleed; then take of *Cantharides* one dozen, of *Euforbium* half a spoonful, break

727

them into powder, and boyl them together with a little Oyl-de-bay, and with two or three feathers bound together, put it boyling hot upon the sore, and let his tail be tyed up for wiping away the medicine; and then within half an hour after, set him up in the stable, and tie him so as he may not lie down all the night for fear of rubbing off the medicine, and the next day anoint it with fresh butter, continuing thus to do every day once the space of five or six days, and when the hair is grown again, draw the sore place with a hot Iron; then take another hot sharp Iron like a Bodkin, somewhat bowing at the point, and thrust it in at the neather end of the middle line, and so upward betwixt the skin and the flesh to the compasse of an inch and a half. And then tent it with a little Turpentine and Hogs grease moulten together and made warm, renewing it every day once the space of nine dayes. But remember first immediately after his burning to take up the master vein, suffering him to bleed a little from above, and tie up the upper end of the vein, and leave the neather end open, to the intent that he may bleed from beneath until it cease it self, and that shall diminish the Spaven, or else nothing will do it.

OF THE SPAVEN, BOTH BONE AND BLOUD.

DOUBTLESS a Spaven is an evill sorance, and causeth a Horse to halt principally in the beginning of his grief; it appeareth on the hinder-legs within, and against the joynt, and it will be a little swoln; and some Horses have a thorough Spaven, which appeareth both within and without. Of the Spaven there are two kindes, the one hard, and the other soft; that is, a Bone-Spaven, and a Bloud-Spaven: for the Bone-Spaven, I hold it hard to cure, and therefore the lesse necessary to be dealt withal, except very great occasion urge; and thus it may be holpen.

Cast the Horse, and with a hot Iron slit the flesh that covereth the Spaven, and then lay upon the Spaven, *Cantharides* and *Euforbium* boyled together in Oyl-de-bay, and anoint his legs round about, either with the Oyl of Roses, and with *Unguentum album camphiratum*. Dresse him thus for three dayes together, then afterward take it away, and for three dayes more lay unto it only upon flax and unsleck't Lime, then afterward dresse it with Tar until it be whole.

The *Cantharides* and *Euforbium*, will eat and kill the spungy bone, the Lime will bring it clean away, and the Tar will suck out the poison, and heal all up sound: but this cure is dangerous, for if the incision be done by an unskilful man; and he either by ignorance, or by the swarving of his hand, burn in twain the great vein that runs crosse the Spaven, then the Horse is spoiled.

Now for the bloud Spaven that is easily helpt, for I have known divers which have been but newly beginning, helpt only by taking up the Spaven vein, and letting it bleed well beneath, and then stop the wound with Sage and Salt, but if it be a great bloud Spaven, then with a sharp knife, cut it as you burnt the bone Spaven, and take the Spaven away, then heal it up with Hogs grease and Turpentine only.

Of the wet Spaven, or through Spaven.

This is a soft swelling growing on both sides of the hough, and seems to go clean through the hough, and therefore may be called a through Spaven. But for the most part the swelling is on the inside, because it is continually fed of the master vein, and is greater then the swelling on the outside. The *Italians* call this sorance *Laierda*, or *Gierdone*, which seemeth to come of a more fluxible humour, and not so viscous or slimy as the other Spaven doth, and therefore this waxeth not so hard, nor groweth to the nature of a bone as the other doth, and this is more curable then the other. It needs no signes, because it is apparent to the eye, and easie to know by the description thereof before made. The cure, according to *Martin*, is thus; First wash, shave, and scarifie the place as before; then take of *Cantharides* half an ounce, of *Euforbium* an ounce broken to powder, and Oyl-de-bay one ounce, mingle them well together cold, without boyling them, and dresse the sore therewith two dayes together, and every day after, until the hair be grown again anoint it with fresh Butter. Then fire him both without and within, as before, without tenting him, and immediately take up the master vein, as before; and then for the space of nine dayes, anoint him every day once with Butter, until the fired place begin to scale, and then wash it with this bath; Take of Mallowes three handfuls, of Sage one handful, and as much of red Nettles, boyl them in water until they be soft, and put thereunto a little fresh Butter, and bathe the place every day once for the space of three or four dayes, and until the burning be whole, let the Horse come in no wet.

OF THE SELANDER.

THIS is a kinde of Scab breeding in the ham, which is the bent of the hough, and is like in all points to the Malander, proceeding of like causes, and requireth like cure, and therefore resort to the Malander.

OF THE HOUGH BONY, OR HARD KNOB.

THIS is a round swelling bony, like a *Paris* ball, growing upon the tip or elbow of the hough, and therefore I thought good to call it the hough-bony. This sorance cometh of some stripe or bruise, and as *Martin* saith, is cured thus; Take a round hot iron somewhat sharp at the end like a good big bodkin, and let it be somewhat bending at the point; then holing the sore with your left hand, pulling it somewhat from the sinews, pierce it with the iron, being first made red-hot, thrusting it beneath in the bottom, and so upward into the belly, to the intent that the same jelly may issue downward out at the hole, and having thrust out all the jelly, tent the hole with a tent of Flax dipt in Turpentine, and Hogs grease molten together, and also anoint the outside with Hogs grease made warm, renewing it every day once until the hole be ready to shut up, making the tent every day lesser and lesser; to the intent it may heal up.

OF THE CURB.

THIS is a long swelling beneath the Elbow of the hough, in the great sinew behind, and causeth the Horse to halt, after that he hath been a while laboured, and thereby somewhat heated. For the more the sinew is strained, the greater grief, which again by his rest is eased. This cometh by bearing some great weight when the Horse is young; or else by some strain or wrinch, whereby the tender, sinews are grieved, or rather bowed (as *Russius* saith) whereof it is called in *Italian, Curba, Curvando*, that is to say of bowing, for anguish whereof it doth swell, which swelling is apparent to the eye, and maketh the leg to shew bigger then the other. The cure, according to *Martin*, is thus; Take of Wine-lees a pinte, a porringer full of Wheat flowre, of Cumin half an ounce, and stir them well together, and being made warm, charge the sore three or four dayes, and when the smelling is almost gone, then draw it with a hot iron, and cover the burning with Pitch and Rosen molten together, and lay it on good and warm, and clap thereon some flocks of his own colour, or so nigh as may be gotten, and remove them not, until they fall away of themselves. And for the space of nine dayes let the Horse rest, and come in no wet.

ANOTHER OF THE CURB.

A Curb is a sorance that maketh a Horse to halt much, and it appears upon his hinder legs, straight behind upon the cumbrel place, and a little beneath the Spaven, and it will be swoln as big as half a Walnut. The cure followeth; Take a small cord and bind his legs hard above it, and beneath it, then beat it, and rub it with a heavy stick till it grow soft, then with a fleam strike it in three or four places, and with your thumbs crush out the filthy bruised matter, then loose the cord, and anoint it with Butter until it be whole.

OF THE PAINS.

THIS is a kind of Scab, called in *Italian, Crappe*, which is full of fretting matterish water, and it breedeth in the pasterns for lack of clean keeping and good rubbing after the Horse hath been journyed, by means whereof, the sand and dirt remaineth in the hair, fretteth the skin and flesh, and so breedeth a Scab. And therefore those Horses that have long hair, and are rough about the feet, are soonest troubled with this disease, if they be not the cleanlier kept. The signes be these; His legs will be swollen and hot, and water will issue out of the Scab, which water is hot and fretting, as it will scald off the hair and breed Scabs, so far as it goeth. The cure, according to *Martin*, is thus; First wash well all the pasterns with Beer and Butter warmed together, and his legs being somewhat dryed with a cloth: clip away all the hair, saving the sewter locks. Then take of Turpentine, of Hogs grease, of Hony, of each like quantity, mingle them together in a pot, and put thereto a little Bole-armony, the yolks of two Egges, and as much Wheat flowre as will thicken the things aforesaid, and make it plaister like, and for that cause it had need to be very well wrought and stirred together. Then with a slice strike some of the plaister upon such a piece of linnen cloth as will serve to go round about the pastern, and bind it fast on with a roller, renewing it once a day until it be whole, and let not the Horse be travelled nor stand wet.

ANOTHER OF THE PAINS.

PAINS is a sorance that cometh of hot ill humors of ill keeping; it appeareth in the Fetlocks, and will swell in the Winter time, and will send forth a sharp water; the hair will stare: and the cure is thus; Wash them every day twice or thrice with gunpowder and Vinegar, and they will be whole in one week at the most.

OF MULES OR KIBED HEELS, CALLED OF THE ITALIANS, MULE.

THIS is a kind of Scab breeding behind, somewhat above the neather joynt, growing overthwart the fewter lock, which cometh most commonly for being bred in cold ground, or else for lack of good dressing, after that he hath been laboured in foul mire and dirty wayes, which durt lying still in his legs, fretteth the skin, and maketh scabby rifts, which are soon bred, but not so soon gotten away. The anguish whereof maketh his legs somewhat to swell, and specially in Winter and Spring time, and then the Horse goeth very stifly, and with great pain. The sorance is apparent to the eye and is cured, according to *Martin*, in this sort; Take a piece of linnen cloth, and with the salve recited in the last Chapter, make such a plaister as may cover all the sore place, and bind it fast on that it may not fall off, renewing it every day once until the sore leave running, and beginneth to wax dry, then wash it every day once with strong water, until it be clean dryed up, but if this sorance be but in breeding, and there is no raw flesh, then it shall suffice to anoint it with Sope two or three dayes, and at the three dayes end, to wash them with a little Beef broath or dish water.

OF FRETTISHING.

FRETTISHING is a sorance that cometh of riding a Horse till he sweat, and then to set him up without litter, where he taketh suddenly cold in his feet, and chiefly before; it appears under the heel in the heart of the foot; for it will grow dun, and wax white and crumbly like a Pomys, and also in time it will show, by the wrinkles on his hoof, and the hoof will grow thick and brickle, he will not be able to tread, on stones or hard ground, nor well to travel but stumble and fall. The cure is thus: Take and pare his feet so thin as may be, then rost two or three Egges in the Embers very hard, and being extreme hot taken out of five, crush them in his foot, and then clap a piece of Leather thereon, and splint it that the Egges may not fall out, and so let him run and he will be sound.

OF SORANCES OR GRIEFS THAT BE COMMON TO ALL FORE-FEET.

HITHERTO we have declared unto you the causes, signes and cure of all such griefs as are properly incident, either to the fore-legs, or hinder-legs: now therefore we speak of those griefs that be common to them both, and first of Windgals.

OF WINDGALS.

THE Windgal called of the *Italians, Galla*; is a bladder full of corrupt jelly, whereof some be great, and some be small, and do grow on each side of the joynt, and is so painful, and especially in Summer season, when the weather is hot and the ways hard, as the Horse is not able to travel, but halteth down right. They come for the most part through extreme labour and heat, whereby the humors being dissolved, do flow and resort into the hollow places about the neather joynts, and there be congealed and covered with a thin skin like a bladder. They be apparent to the eye, and therefore need no other signes to know them. The cure whereof according to *Martin* is thus: Wash them with water, and shave off the hair, scarifie them with the point of a rasor, and dress them with Cantharides in the self same manner as the splent in the knee was taught before and anoint them afterward with Butter untill the skin be whole. And if this will not heal it, then draw them with a hot Iron like a ragged staffe. That done, slit the middle line which passeth right down through the windgal with a sharp knife, beginning beneath, and so upward the length of half an inch, to the intent you may thrust the jelly out at that hole; then lay unto it a little Pitch and Rozen molten together, and made luke-warm and put a few flocks on it, and that will heal him. And you may dry up the Windgal in such manner as here followeth: First chop off the hair so far as the Wind-gal extendeth, and having strieken it with a fleam, thrust out the jelly with your finger. Then take a piece of red wollen cloth and clap it to the place, and with a hot broad searing Iron sear it, so as the Iron may not burn through the cloth, which is done to dry up the humors.

Then having taken away the cloth, lay unto the place a piece of Shoomakers wax made like a flat cake, about the breadth of a testorn, and with your Iron not made over hot, streek softly upon it to and fro, untill the said wax be throughly melted into the sore. Whereupon lay a few flocks, and let him go. Which flock will afterward fall away of their own accord.

OF WINDGALS.

WINDGALS are easie to cure, they be little swellings like blebs or bladders, on either side the joynt next unto the fewter-locks, as well before as behinde, and they come through the occasion of great travel, in hard, gravelly, or sandy ways. The cure is: Take Pitch, Rozen, and Mastick, of each like quantity, melt them together, and with a stick lay it round about the Horses legs, and whilest it is hot lay flocks thereon: the nature of this plaister, is never to come away whilest there is any Windgal on the Horses legs; but when they are dryed up, then it will fall away of it self.

OF WRINCHING THE NEATHER JOYNT.

THIS cometh many times by treading away in some Cart root or otherwise. The signes be these: The joynt will be swollen and sore, and the Horse will halt. The cure whereof according to *Martin* is thus: Take of *Dialthea* half a pound, and as much of Nerval; mingle them together, and anoint the sore place therewith chasing it well with both your hands, that the Ointment may enter, continuing so to do every day once, until the Ointment be all spent, and let the Horse rest. But if this will not prevail, then wash it with warm water and shave away all the hair saving the fewter-lock. Scarifie it, and lay to it Cantharides, and heal it as you do each splent in the knee.

OF ENTERFERING.

BECAUSE Enterfering is to be holpen by shooing, we purpose not to speak of it, untill we come to talk of the order of paring and shooing all manner of hoofs.

ANOTHER OF ENTERFERING.

ENTERFERING is a grief that cometh by sometimes by all shooing, and sometimes naturally, when a Horse trots so narrow that he hews one leg upon another, it appeareth both before and behinde, between the feet against the set-locks, and there is no remedy but shooing him with shooes made thin and flat on the outside, and narrow and think within.

OF THE SHAKEL-GALL.

IF a Horse be galled in the pasterns, with shakel, lock pastern, or haster, anoint the sore place with a little Honey and Verdigrease boyled together, untill it look red, which is a good Ointment for all gallings on the withers, and immediately strow upon the Ointment, being first laid upon the leg, a little chopt flax or tow, and that will stick fast, continuing so to do every day once untill it be whole.

OF HURTS IN THE LEGS, THAT COMETH BY CASTING IN THE HALTER OR COLLAR.

IT chanceth many times, that a Horse having some itch under his ears; is desirous to scratch the same with his hinder-foot, which whilest he reacheth to and fro, doth fasten in the collar or halter, wherewith the more that he striveth the more he galleth his legs; and many times it chanceth for that he is tyed so long, by means whereof being laid, and the halter slack about his feet, rising perhaps or turning he snarleth himself so as he is not able to get up, but hangeth either by the neck or legs, which sometime are galled even to the hard bone.

Russius calleth such kind of galling *Capistratura*, which he was wont to heal with this Ointment here following, praising it to be excellent good for the cratches, or any scab, bruise, or wound: Take of Oyl Olive one ounce, of Turpentine two or three ounces; melt them together over the fire, and then put thereunto a little Wax, and work them well together, and anoint the sore place therewith. *Martin* saith, it is good to anoint the sore place with the white of an Egge and Sallet Oyl beaten together; and when it cometh to a scab, anoint it with Butter being molten, until it look brown.

OF THE CRATCHES, OR RATS TAILS, CALLED OF THE ITALIANS, CREPACCIE.

THIS is a kinde of long scabby rifts growing right up and down in the hinder part, from the fewter-lock up to the curb, and cometh for lack of clean keeping, and is easily seen if you take up the Horses foot, and lift up the hair. The cure according to *Martin* is thus: Take of Turpentine half a pound, of Honey a pinte, of Hogs grease a quartern, and three yolks of Egges, and of Bole-armony a quartern, beaten into fine powder, of Bean-flowre half a pinte; mingle all these well together, and make a salve thereof, and with your finger anoint all the sore places, sheading the hair as you go, to the intent you may the easier finde them, and also to make the salve enter into the skin, and let the Horse come in no wet, untill he be whole.

OF THE SCRATCHES.

SCRATCHES will cause a Horse to halt sore, and they come only by naughty keeping, and they appear in the pasterns under the Fet-locks; as if this skin were cut over-thwart, that a man may lay in a Wheat-straw. The cure is thus: Binde unto them, (the hair being cut clean away) black-Sope and Lime kned together, for three days, then lay that by, and anoint the place with Butter; and heal the sore with Bores grease and Tar mixt well together.

OF THE RING-BONE.

THIS is a hard gristle growing upon the cronet, and sometime goeth round about the cronet, and is called in *Italian, Soprosso. Laurentius Russius* saith, that it may grow in any other place of the leg; but then we call it not a Ring-bone, but a knot or knob. It cometh at the first either by some blow of another Horse, or by striking his one foot against some stub, or stone, or such like casualty. The pain whereof breedeth a viscous and slimy humor, which resorting to the bones, that are of their own nature cold and dry, waxeth hard, cleaveth to some bone, and in process of time becometh a bone. The signes be these: The Horse will halt, and the hard swelling is apparent to the eye, being higher then any place of the cronet. The cure according to *Martin* is thus: First wash it well with warm water, and shave away all the hair, so as the sore place may be all discovered. Then scarifie it lightly with the point of a rasor, so as the bloud may issue forth. Then if the sore be broad, take of *Euforbium* one ounce, of Cantharides half an ounce, broken into fine powder, and of Oyl-de-bay one ounce; and if the sore be but little; the one half of this may serve: Boyl these things together, stirring them continually, lest it run over; and with two or three feathers, lay it boiling hot unto the sore, and let not the Horse stir from that place for half an hour after, then carry him into the stable, both using and curing him for the space of nine days, in such order is hath been said before in the chapter of the splent. But when the hair beginneth to grow again, then fire the sore place with right lines from the pastern down to the could of the hoof; and let the edge of the drawing Iron be as thick as the back of a meat-knife, and burn him so deep as the skin may look yellow: that done, cover the burning with Pitch and Rozen molten together, and clap thereon flocks of the Horses own colour, or somewhat nigh the same, and about three days after lay again some of the last mentioned plaister, or Ointment; and also new flocks upon the old, and there let them remain, until they fall away of themselves.

But if these Ring-bones, or knobs, breed in any other place, then in the Cronet, you shall cure them as is before said, without firing them.

OF THE RING-BONE.

THE Ring-bone is an ill disease, and appeareth before on the foot above the hoof, as well before as behinde, and will be swoln three inches broad, and a quarter of an inch or more of height, and the hair will stare and wax thin, and will make a Horse halt much. The cure is: Cast the Horse, and with an Iron made flat and thin, burn away that gristle which annoys him; then take Wax, Turpentine, Rozen, Tar, and Hogs-grease, of each like quantity, mingle them together Plaister-wise, and with it cure the sore: This Plaister will also cure any other wound or ulcer whatsoever.

OF THE CROWN-SCAB.

THIS is a kinde of filthy and stinking Scab, breeding round about the feet upon the Cronets, and is an elvish and painful disease, called in *Italian, Crisaria*. It seemeth to come by means that the Horse hath been bred in some cold wet soil, striking corrupt humors up to his feet; and therefore the Horse that hath this grief is worse troubled in Winter then in Summer. The signes be these: The hair of the Cronets will be thin and staring like bristles, and the Cronets will be always mattering, and run on a water. The cure according to *Martin* is thus: Take of Sope, of Hogs-grease, of each half a pound, of Bole-armony a little, of Turpentine a quartern; and mingle them all together, and make a Plaister, and binde it fast on, renewing it every day once, until it leave running, and then wash it with strong Vinegar, being luke-warm, every day once, until the sore be clean dryed up; and let him come in no wet until it be whole.

OF HURTS UPON THE CRONET CROSSING ONE FOOT OVER ANOTHER, WHICH THE ITALIANS CALL SUPRAPOSTE.

MARTIN saith, wash it well with white Wine, or with a little stale, and then lay unto it the white of an Egge, mingled with a little Chimny soot and Salt, and that will dry it up in three or four days, if it be renewed every day once.

OF THE QUITTER-BONE.

THIS is a hard round swelling upon the Cronet, betwixt the heel and the quarter, and groweth most commonly on the inside of the foot, and is commonly called of the *Italians, Setula* or *Seta*. It cometh by means of gravel gathered underneath the shooe, which fretteth the heel, or else by the cloying or pricking of some nail evil driven, the anguish whereof looseneth the gristle, and so breedeth evil humors, whereof the Quitter-bone springeth. The signes be these: The Horse will halt, and the swelling is apparent to the eye, which is four or five days coming to a head, will break out with matter at a little deep hole like a *Fistula*. The cure according to *Martin* is thus: First, burn about the quitter-bone with a hot Iron, in manner of half a circle, and then with the same Iron draw another right strike through the midst thereof. Then take of Arsenick the quantity of a Bean beaten into fine powder, and put it into the hole, thrusting it down to the bottom with a quill, and stop the mouth of the hole with a little tow, and binde it so fast with a cloth, and cord, as the Horse may not come at it with his mouth, and so let it rest for that day. And the next day, if you see that the sore looketh black within, then it is a signe that the Arsenick hath wrought well and done his part. Then to allay the burning thereof, tent the hole with flax dipt in Hogs-grease, and Turpentine, molten and mingled together, and cover the tent with a bolster of Tow dipt also in the Ointment aforesaid, continuing so to do every day once, until you have gotten out the core. Then shall you see whether the loose gristle in the bottom be uncovered or not; and if it be uncovered, then feel with your finger, or with a quill, whether you be nigh it or not. And if you be, then raise the gristle with a little crooked instrument, and pull it clean out with a pair of small nippers, meet for the pupose. That done, tent it again with a full tent dipt in the aforesaid Ointment, to asswage the anguish of the last dressing, and stop it hard, to the intent that the hole may not shrink together, or close up; and the next day take out the tent, and tent it a new with the Salve or Ointment taught in the Chapter of the Shakel-gall, renewing it every day once until it be whole, keeping always the mouth of the sore as open as you may, to the intent that it heal not up too fast; and let not the Horse be in any wet, nor travel, until he be perfectly whole.

OF THE QUITTER-BONE.

QUITTER-BONE is a round hard swelling upon the Cronet of the hoof, betwixt the hoof and the quarter, and for the most part groweth on the inside of the foot: the Original effect thereof is the fretting of gravel underneath the shooe, which bruiseth the heel; or else by means of some stub, or the pricking of some nail, through the pain whereof the gristle is loosened, breeding evil humors, which be indeed the ground of the Quitter-bone: it is to be known by the Horses hasting, and by the apparent swelling to the eye of that part, which in three or four days will grow unto a head and break, evacuating great abundance of filthy matter at a little hole. The cure is thus: Take a hot Iron, made in fashion of a knife, and with it burn out the flesh, in compass of a Moon, till you come to feel the gristle, then burn it out too: Then take Verdigrease, fresh Butter, and Tar, molten together, and dip fine Tow therein, stop up the hole, then lay thereon a Sear-cloth of Deer-sewet and Wax, and so let him rest for the first day: the next day; take of *Mel rosatum*, Oyl of Roses, Wax, and Turpentine, of each like quantity, infuse them all on the fire together; and with the Salve dress the sore morning and evening, till it be whole. But if you finde any proud flesh to grow, then forget not to lay thereon some red Lead, or Verdigrease: and witall have an especial regard, that the upper part of the wound heal not faster then the bottom, for fear of Fistulating.

OF THE GRAVELLING.

THIS is a fretting under the foot, most commonly in the inside, and sometime in the outside, and sometime in both sides together of the heel.

It cometh by means of little gravel stones getting betwixt the hoof, or calking, or spunge of the shooe, which by continual labour and treading of the Horse, doth eat into the quick, and the rather, if his heel be soft and weak, or that the shooe do lie flat to his foot, so as the gravel being once gotten in, cannot get out. The signes be these: The Horse will halt, and covet to tread all upon the toe, to favour his heel. The cure according to *Martin* is thus: First pare the hoof, and get out the gravel with a corner, or drawer, leaving none behinde, for if you do, it will breed to a Quitter-bone. That done, stop him with Turpentine and Hogs-grease molten together, and laid on with tow or flax, and then clap on the shooe to keep in the stopping, renewing it every day once until it be whole. And suffer the Horse to come in no wet, until he be throughly whole. If a gravelling be not well stopt to keep down the flesh, it will rise higher then the hoof; and not only require more business in bolstering it, but also put the Horse to more pain.

OF GRAVELLING.

GRAVELLING is a hurt will make a Horse to halt, and cometh of gravel and little stones, that goeth between the shooe and the heart of the foot. The cure is: Take off the shooe, and let him be well pared; then set on the shooe again, and stop it with Pitch, Rozen, and Tallow, and this shall help.

OF SURBATING.

THIS is a beating of the hoof against the ground, called of the *Italians, Sobatitura*; it cometh sometime by means of evil shooing, lying too flat to his foot; or by going long bare foot, and sometime by the hardness of the ground, and high lifting of the Horse. And those Horses that be flat-footed, the coffins whereof are tender and weak, are most commonly subject to this sorance. The signes be these: the Horse will halt on both his fore-legs, and go stiffely and creeping, as though he were half foundered. The cure according to *Martin* is thus: Take off his shooes, pare him as little as may be; and if the shooes be not easie, that is to say, long, large, and hollow enough, then make them so, and then tack them

741

on again with four or five nails. That done, stop his feet with Bran, and Hogs-grease boyled together, so hot as may be; and also cover all the coffin round about with the same, binding all in together with a cloth, and a list fastened about the joynt, renewing it every day once, until it be whole, and give the Horse during that while warm water; and let him stand dry and warm, and not be travelled until he be whole.

OF A PRICK IN THE SOLE OF THE FOOT, BY TREADING ON A NAIL, OR ANY OTHER SHARP THING THAT DOTH ENTER INTO THE FOOT.

THE signes be these: If a man be on his back when he treadeth on any such thing, he shall feel that the Horse will lift up his foot, and covet to stand still to have help. And if it chance at any other time, the halting of the Horse, and the hurt it self will shew. The cure according to *Martin* is thus: Pull off the shooe, and pare the foot; and with a drawer uncover the hole, making the mouth so broad as a two penny piece, then tack on the shooe again. That done, stop it, by pouring into the hole Turpentine and Hogs-grease molten together, and lay some flax, or tow upon it; and then stop all the Horses foot with Horse-dung, or rather with Cow-dung, if you can get it; and splent it either with sticks, or else with an old shooe-sole, so as the stopping may abide in, renewing it every day once until it be whole, and let the Horse come in no wet. If this be not well cured, or looked to in time, it will cause the hoof to break above, and to loosen round about, and perhaps to fall clean away. But if you see that it begins to break above, then make a greater issue beneath by opening the hole wider, and taking more of the sole away, that the flesh may have the more liberty. Then take of Bole-armony half a quartern, Bean-flowre, and two Egges. Beat them, and mingle them well together, and make a plaister thereof upon Tow, and lay it round about the Cronet, binde it fast on, and so let it remain the space of two days, and then renew it again, not failing so to do every two days untill you see it wax hard and firm above. For this Plaister being restrictive, will force the humors to resort all downward, which must be drawn out with Turpentine and Hogs-grease as before, until it leave mattering, and then dry it up with burnt Allum beaten to powder, and strowed upon it, with a little flax laid again upon that, continuing so to do every day once, until it be hardned; and let not the Horse come in any wet, until he be whole.

OF ACCLOYD OR PRICKT.

ACCLOYD is a hurt that cometh of shooing, when a Smith driveth a nail in the quick, which will make him to halt. And the cure is; to take off the shooe, and to cut the hoof away, to lay the sore bare: then lay to it Wax, Turpentine, and Deer-sewet, which will heal it.

OF THE FIG.

IF a Horse having received any hurt, as before is said, by nail, bone, splent, or stone, or otherwise in the sole of his foot, and not be well dressed and perfectly cured, there will grow in that place a certain superfluous piece of flesh, like a Fig: and it will have little grains in it like a fig, and therefore is rightly called of the *Italians, Unfico*, that is to say, a fig. The cure whereof according to *Martin* is thus: Cut it clean away with a hot Iron, and keep the flesh down with Turpentine, Hogs-greese, and a little Wax laid on with Tow, or Flax, and stop the hole hard; that the flesh rise not, renewing it once a day until it be whole.

OF A RETREAT.

THIS is the pricking of a nail, not well driven in the shooing, and therefore pulled out again by the Smith, and is called of the *Italians, Tratta messa*. The cause of the pricking may be partly the rash driving of the Smith, and partly the weakness of the nail, or the hollowness of the nail in the shank. For if it be too weak, the point many times bendeth awry into the quick when it should go right forth. It flatteth and shivereth in the driving into two parts, whereof one part raseth the quick in pulling out, or else perhaps breaketh clean asunder, and so remaineth still behinde, and this kinde of pricking is worse than the cloying, because it will ranckle worse, by reason of the flaw of Iron remaining in the flesh. The signes be these: If the Smith that driveth such a nail be so lewd, as he will not look unto it before the Horse depart, then there is no way to know it, but by the halting of the Horse, and searching the hoof first with a hammer by, knocking upon every clinging. For when you knock upon that nail, where the grief is, the Horse will shrink up his foot. And if that will not serve, then pinch or gripe the hoof with a pair of pinsons round about, until you have found the place grieved. The cure according to *Martin* is thus: First, pull off the shooe, and then open the place grieved with a Butter or Drawer, so as you may perceive by feeling or seeing, whether there be any piece of nail or not; if there be, to pull it out, and to stop the hole with Turpentine, Wax, and Sheeps-sewet molten together, and so poured hot into the hole, and then lay a little Tow upon it, and clap on the shooe again renewing it thus every day, until it be whole, during which time, let not the Horse come in any wet, and it must be so stopped, though it be but prickt without any piece of nail remaining. And if for lack of looking to it in time, this retreat cause the hoof to break above, then cure it with the Plaister restrictive in such order as is mentioned in the last place saving one before this.

OF CLOYING.

CLOYING is the pricking of a whole nail, called of the *Italians, Inchiodatura*; passing through the quick, and remaining still in the same, and is clenched as other nails be, and so causeth the Horse to halt. The grieved place is known, by searching with the hammer and pinsons, as is before said: If the Horse halt immediately, then pull off his shooe, and open the hole, until it begin to bleed; and stop it with the Ointment aforesaid, in the same page of the Retreat, and clap on the shooe again; and the hoof may be so good, and the harm so little, as you may travel him immediately upon it, but if he be ranckled, then renew the stopping every day once; let him come in no wet, until it be whole.

OF LOOSENING THE HOOF.

THIS is a parting of the hoof from the cronet, called of the *Italians, Dissolatura del unghia*, which if it be round about, it cometh by means of foundering; if in part, then by the anguish caused by the pricking of the canel nail, piercing the sole of the foot, or by some Quitter-bone, Retreat, Gravelling, or. Cloying, or such like thing: The signes be these: When it is loosened by foundering, then it will break first in the fore-part of the Cronet, right against the toes, because the humor doth covet always to descend towards the toe. Again, when the pricking of a canel nail, or such like cankered thing is the cause, then the hoof will loosen round about, equally even at the first. But when it proceedeth of any of the other hurts last mentioned: then the hoof will break right above the place that is offended, and most commonly will proceed no further. The cure according to *Martin* is thus: First, of which soever of these causes it proceeds, be sure to open the hoof in the sole of the foot, so as the humor may have free passage downward, and then restrain it above with the Plaister restrictive before mentioned, and in such order as is there written, and also heal up the wound, as is before taught in the Chapter of a prick in the sole of the foot.

OF CASTING THE HOOF.

THIS is when the coffin falleth clean away from the foot, which cometh by such causes as were last rehearsed, and is so apparent to the eye, as it needeth no signes to know it. The cure according to *Martin* is thus: Take of Turpentine one pound, of Tar half a pinte, of unwrought Wax half a pinte: Boil all these things together, and stir them continually until they be throughly mingled, and compact together. Then make a Boot of Leather with a good strong sole meet for the Horses feet, to be laced or buckled about the pastern; and dress his foot with the Salve aforesaid laid upon the Flax or Tow, and bolster or stuffe his foot with soft Flax, so as the Boot may grieve him no manner of way, renewing it every day once until it be whole, and then put him to grass.

OF THE HOOF-BOUND.

THIS is a shrinking of all the whole hoof. It cometh by drought, for the hoofs perhaps are kept too dry, when the Horse standeth in the

745

stable, and sometime by means of heat, or of over-straight shooing. The *Italians* call the Horse thus grieved *Incastellado*. The signes be these: The Horse will halt, and the hoofs will be hot; and if you knock on them with a hammer, they will sound hollow like an empty bottle, and if both the feet be not hoof-bound, the sore foot will be lesser than the other indeed, and appear so to the eye. The cure according to *Martin* is thus: Pull off the shooes, and shooe him with half Moon-shooes called *Lunette*; the order and shape whereof you shall finde among the Farriers, and rase both the quarters of the hoof with a drawer, from the cronet unto the sole of the foot, so deep as you shall see the dew it self come forth. And if you make two rases on each side, it shall be so much the better, and inlarge the hoof the more. That done, anoint all the hoof about, next unto the cronet round about, with the Ointment prescribed before in the Chapter of casting the hoof, continuing so to do every day once until he begin to amend for the space of a month; and if he goeth not well at the months end, then take off the half shooes, and pare all the soles, and thrushes, and all so thin as you may see the dew come forth, and tack on a whole shooe; and stop all the foot within with Hogs-grease and Bran boiled together, and laid hot to the foot; renewing it dayly once the space of nine days, to the intent the sole may rise. But if this will do no good; then take away the sole clean, and clap on a whole shooe, and stop the foot with Nettles and Salt brayed together, renewing it once a day, but not over hard, to the intent the sole may have liberty to rise, and being grown again, let him be shod with the lunets, and sent to grass.

OF THE RUNNING FRUSH.

THE Frush is the tenderest part of the hoof towards the heel, called of the *Italians, Fettone*, and because it is fashioned like a forked head, the *French* men call it *Furchette*, which word our Farriers, either for not knowing rightly how to pronounce it; or else perhaps for easiness sake of pronuntiation, do make it a monosyllable, and pronounce it the Frush; in which Frush breedeth many times a rottenness or corruption proceeding of humors that cometh out of the leg, whereby the leg is kept clean from the Windgals, and all other humors and swellings by means that the humors have passage that way. Notwithstanding the discommodity of the sorance is greater then the commodity, because it maketh the Horses feet so weak and tender, as he is not able to tread upon any hard ground. The signes be these:

The Horse will halt, and specially when the passage of the humor is stopt with any gravel gathered in the Frush, and not being stopt it will continually run, the savour whereof will be so strong, as a man is not able to abide it, and in some places it will look raw. The cure according to *Martin* is thus. First take off the shooe and pare away all the corrupt places, and make them raw, so as you may see the water issue out of the raw places, then tack on the shooe again, being first made wide and large enough. That done, take of Soot one handful, of Salt as much; bruise them well together in a dish, and put thereunto the white of three Egges, and temper them together, and with a little Tow dipt therein, stop all the foot, and especially the Frush, and splent it so as it may not fall out, renewing it once a day the space of seven days, and then he will be whole. During which time let the Horse rest, and come in no wet, at the seven days end leave stopping him, and ride him abroad, and always when he cometh in, let his sore foot be clean washed, that no gravel remain therein, without doing any more unto him.

OF THE FRUSH.

THE Frush is the tenderest part of the sole of the foot, which by humors distilling many times down from the legs, occasion inflamations in that part, which may easily be perceived by the impostumation of the same. The cure is thus: First having taken off the shooe, pare away all the corrupted and naughty matter, until the sore look raw, then nail on a hollow shooe made for the same purpose; and take of soot a handful, of the juyce of House-leek and of Cream, with the white of an Egge or two, as much as will thicken the same: with this stop up the sore, and splint it, so as it may not fall out, renewing it until it be whole: but during the cure, have regard that the sore foot touch not any wet, for that is very much hurtful.

OF DISEASES OR GRIEFS INDIFFERENTLY INCIDENT TO ANY PART OF THE BODY, BUT FIRST OF THE LEPROSIE, OR UNIVERSAL MANGINESS, CALLED OF THE OLD WRITERS ELEPHANTIA.

THIS is a cankred Manginess, spreading over all the body, which cometh of abundance of melancholy, corrupt and filthy bloud. The signes be these: The Horse will be all mangy and scurvy, full of scabs, and raw plots about the neck, and evil favoured to look on, and always rubbing and scratching. The cure according to *Martin* is thus: Let him bloud the first day in the one side of the neck, and within two days after that, in the flanck veins; and last of all, in the vein under the tail. Then wash all the sore places with Salt brine, and rubbing them hard with a wispe of straw hard twisted, so as they may bleed well, and be all raw. That done, anoint the place with this Ointment: Take of Quick-silver one ounce, of Hogs-grease one pound, of Brimstone beaten into powder a quartern, of Rape Oyl a pinte; mingle these things well together, until the Quick-silver be throughly incorporated with the rest; and having anointed all the raw places with this Ointment, make it to sink into the flesh, by holding and weaving up and down over it a hot broad bar of Iron, and then touch him no more again the space of two or three days; during which time, if you see that he rubbeth still in any place, then rub that place again with an old Horse-combe, to make it raw, and anoint it with fresh Ointment. But if all this will not help, then with a hot Iron, and blunt at the point, so big as a mans little finger; burn all the mangy places, making round holes, passing only through the skin, and no further. For which intent it shall be needful to pull the skin first from the flesh, with your left hand, holding it still until you have thrust the hot Iron through it, and let every hole be a span off one from another, and if need be, you may anoint those holes with a little Sope, and let the Horse be thin dieted, during his curing time.

OF THE FARCIN, CALLED IN ITALIAN OF SOME IL VERME, AND OF SOME FARCINA.

THIS kinde of creeping Ulcer groweth in knots, following a long some vein, and it proceedeth of corrupt bloud ingendered in the body, or else of some outward hurt, as of spur-galling, or the biting of some other

Horse; or of biting of ticks, or of Hogs lice, or such like casualities: Or if it be in the legs, it may come by interfering. It is easily known, partly by the former description, and also it is apparent to the eye. The cure according to *Martin* is thus: Let him bloud in that vein where it cometh, as nigh the sore place as may be, and let him bleed well; then fire every knot one by one, taking the knot in your left hand, and pulling it so hard as you can from his body, to the intent you may better pierce the knot, with a blunt hot Iron, of the bigness of a mans fore-finger, without doing the body any hurt, and let out the matter, leaving none unburn'd, be it little or much. That done, anoint every knot so burned with Hogs-grease warmed every day once, until the coars be ready to fall away: and in the mean time prepare a good quantity of old Urine, and when you see the coars ready to fall, boil the Urine, and put therein a little Copperas and Salt, and a few strong Nettles, and with that water being warm, wash out all the coars, and the corruption.

That done, fill every hole immediately with the powder of fleck't lime, continuing thus to do every day once, until the holes be closed up; and if any be more ranker then other, fill those with Verdigrease; and during this cure let the Horse be thinly dieted, that is to say, with straw and water only, unless it be now and then to give him a loaf of bread: for the lower he be kept, the sooenr he will be whole. And in any wise let his neck be yoked in an old bottomless pail, or else with short staves to keep him from licking the sores, and the less rest he hath, the better. Or do thus: Take a good great Dock-root clean scraped, and cut thereof five little rundles or cakes to be used as followeth. First with a knife make a slit right down in the Horses fore-head three inches long, then with a Cornet loosen the skin within the flesh, so as you may easily put therein five rundles of Dock, that is to say, two on each side of the slit one above another, and put the fist rundle in the very midst betwixt the other four: that done, fasten to each of the slits two short Shoomakers ends, to serve as laces to tie in the foresaid rundles, so as they may not fall out, and clense the sore every day once, for the vertue of the root is such, as it will draw all the filthy matter from any part of the body; yea, though the Farcin be in the hinder-legs, which matter is to be wiped away from time to time, and new roots be thrust into the slit according as you see it needful.

OF THE FARCION.

THE Farcion is a vilde disease, ingendered of ill bloud, flegmatick matter, and unkindely feeding; it appeareth in a Horse like unto little knots in the flesh, as big as a Hasel-nut; the knots will encrease daily and inflame, Impostume, and break; and when the knots amount to threescore, they will every night after breed so many more, till they have over-run the Horses body, and with the poyson, which is mighty and also strong soon bring him to his death: This disease is very infectious and dangerous for some Horses, yet if it be taken in any time, it is easie to be holpen: The cure thereof is in this manner: Take a sharp Bodkin, and thrust it through the neather part of his nose, that he may bleed: or if you will, to let him bloud in the neck-vein shall not be amiss, then feel the knots, and as many as are soft lance them and let them run; then take strong Lye, Lime, and Allum, and with the same bathe all his sores, and it shall in short space cure him. There is also another manner of curing this disease, and that is thus: Take a sharp lance-knife, and in the top of the Horses fore-head, just between his eyes, make a long slit even to the skull: then with a blunt instrument for the purpose lose the flesh from the scalp a pretty compass: then take Carret-roots cut into little thin round pieces, and put them between the skin and the skull, as many as you can, then close up the wound, and once a day anoint it with fresh Butter: This is a most sure and approved way to cure the Farcion; for look how this wound thus made, shall rot, waste, and grow sound, so shall the Farcion break, dry up, and be healed, because all the poyson that feedeth the disease shall be altogether drawn into the fore-head, where it shall die and waste away. The only fault of this cure is, it will be somewhat long, and it is a foul eye-sore until it be whole. Some use to burn this sorance, but that is naught and dangerous, as who so proves it shall finde.

A MOST APPROVED MEDICINE TO CURE THE FARCION.

TAKE of *Aqua-vitæ* two spoonfuls, of the juyce of Herb of grace as much; mingle them together, then take of Plegants or Bals of Flax or Tow, and sleep them therein, and stop them hard into the Horses ears; then take a needle and a thread, and stitch the tips of his two ears together, by means whereof he cannot shake out the medicine, and use him thus but three several morning, and it will kill any Farcion whatsoever, for it hath been often approved.

ANOTHER MEDICINE OF THE SAME.

SLIT every hard kernel with a sharp knife, and fill the hole with an Ointment made of old Lard, Sope, and gray Salt, for that will eat out the coar, and cause it to rot, and so fall out of the own accord.

OF THE CANKER, CALLED OF THE ITALIAN, IL CANCRO.

A Canker is a filthy creeping Ulcer, fretting and gnawing the flesh in great breadth. In the beginning it is knotty, much like a Farcine, and spreadeth it self into divers places, and being exulcerated, gathereth together in length into a wound or fore. This proceedeth of a melancholy and filthy bloud ingendered in the body, which if it be mixt with Salt humors, it causeth the more painful and grievous exulceration, and sometime it cometh of some filthy wound that is not cleanly kept, the corrupt matter whereof cankereth other clean parts of the body. It is easie to be known by the description before. The cure whereof according to *Martin* is thus: First let him bloud in those veins that be next the sore, and take enough of him. Then take of Allum half a pound, of green Copperas, and of white Copperas, of each one quartern, and a good handful of Salt: boil all these things together in fair running water, from a pottle to a quart. And this water being warm, wash the sore with a cloth, and then sprinkle thereon the powder of unsleck't lime, continuing so to do every day once the space of fifteen days; and if you see that the lime do not mortifie the ranck flesh, and keep it from spreading any further; then take of black Sope half a pound, of Quick-silver half an ounce, and beat them together in a pot, until the Quick-silver be so well mingled with the Sope, as you can perceive none of the Quick-silver as it. And with an Iron slice, after that you have washed the sore with the Strong-water aforesaid, cover the wound with this Ointment, continuing thus to do every day once, until the Canker leave spreading abroad. And if it leave spreading, and that you see the ranck flesh is mortified, and that the edges begin to gather a skin, then after the washing, dress it with the lime as before, continuing so to do until it be whole. And in the dressing, suffer no filth that cometh out of the sore, to remain upon any whole place about, but wipe it clean away, or else wash it away with warm water, And let the Horse during this cure, be as thinly dieted as may be, and throughly exercised.

OF THE FISTULA, CALLED OF THE ITALIANS FISTULA.

A Fistula is a deep hollow crooking Ulcer, and for the most part springs of malign humors, ingendered in some wound, sore, or canker, not throughly healed. It is easie to know by the description before. The cure according to *Martin* is thus: First, search the depth of it with a quill, or with some other instrument of Lead, that may be bowed every way, meet for the purpose. For unless you finde the bottom of it, it will be very hard to cure: And having found the bottom, if it be in such a place as you may boldly cut, and make the way open with a lancet or rasor, then make a slit right against the bottom, so as you may thrust in your finger, to feel whether there be any bone or gristle perished, or spongy or loose flesh, which must be gotten out, and then tent it with a tent of flax dipt in this Ointment: Take of Hony a quartern; and of Verdigrease one ounce beaten into powder. Boil them together, until it look red, stirring it continually, lest it run over; and being luke-warm, dress the tent wherewith, and bolster the tent with a bolster of flax. And if it be in such a place, as the tent cannot conveniently be kept in with a band, then fasten on each side of the hole, two ends of Shoomakers thread right over the bolster to keep in the tent, which ends may hang there as two laces, to tie and untie at your pleasure, renewing the tent every day once until the sore leave mattering. And then make the tent every day lesser and lesser, until it be whole. And close it up in the end, by sprinkling thereon a little sleckt lime. But if the Fistula be in such a place as a man can neither cut right against the bottom, or nigh the same: then there is no remedy, but to pour in some Strong-water, through some quill, or such like thing, so as it may go to the very bottom, and dry up all the filthy matter, dressing him so twice a day, until the Horse be whole.

THIS is a great spungy Wart full of bloud, called of the *Italians*, *Moro*, or *Selfo*, which may grow in any place of the body, and it hath a root like a Cocks stone. The cure according to *Martin* is thus: Tie it with a thread, so hard as you can pull it, the thread will eat by little and little in such sort, as within seven or eight days it will fall away by it self. And if it be so flat as you can binde nothing about it, then take it away with a sharp hot Iron, cutting it round about, and so deep as you may leave none of the root behinde, and dry it with Verdigrease. *Russius* saith, that if it grow in a place full of sinews, so as it cannot be conveniently cut, away with a hot Iron; then it is good to eat out the core with the powder of *Resalgar*, and then to stop the hole with flax dipt in the white of an Egge for a day or two; and lastly, to dry it up with the powder of unsleck't Lime and Hony, as before is taught.

Of Wounds.

WOUNDS come by means of some stripe or prick, and they are properly called wounds, when some whole part is cut or broken. For a wound according to the Physitians, is defined to be a solution, division, or parting of the whole; for if there be no solution or parting, then me thinks it ought rather to be called a bruise then a wound. And therefore wounds are most commonly made with sharp or piercing weapons, and bruises with blunt weapons. Notwithstanding, if by such blunt weapons, any part of the whole be evidently broken, then it ought to be called a wound as well as the other: Of wounds some be shallow, and some be deep and hollow: Again, some chance in the fleshy parts, and some in the bony and sinewie places: And those that chance in the fleshy parts, though they be very deep, yet they be not so dangerous as the other; and therefore we will speak first of the most dangerous: If a Horse have a wound newly made, either in his head, or in any other place that is full of sinews, bones, or gristles: First, *Martin* would have you to wash the wound well with white Wine well warmed: That done, to search the bottom of the wound with some instrument meet for the purpose, suffering it to take as little winde in the mean while as may be.

Then having found the depth, stop the hole close with a clout, until your salve be ready: Then take of Turpentine, of *Mel Rosatum*, of Oyl of Roses, of each a quartern, and a little unwrought Wax, and melt them together; and if it be a cut, make a handsome roll of clean picked Tow, so long and so big as may fill the bottom of the wound, which for the most part is not so wide as the mouth of the wound: then make another roll greater than that, to fill up the rest of the wound, even to the hard mouth, and let both these rolls be anointed with the ointment aforesaid luke-warm. But if the hurt be like a hole made with some prick, then make a stiffe tent, such a one as may reach the bottom, anointed with the aforesaid Ointment, and bolster the same with a little Tow; And if the mouth be not wide enough, so as the matter may easily run forth, if it be in such place you may do it without hurting any sinew, then give it a pretty slit from the mouth downward, that the matter may have the freer passage, and in any wise have a special regard, that the tent may be continually kept in by one means or other, as by binding or staying the seme with the ends of Shoomakers thread as is aforesaid. And if the hole be deep, and in such place as you may not then make your tent of a Spunge, and so long as it may reach to the bottom, and the tent, being made somewhat full, with continual turning and wrying of it, you shall easily get it down, and then dress the wound with this twice a day, cleansing the wound every time with a little white Wine luke-warm. For this Spunge, anointed with the Ointment aforesaid, will both draw and suck up all the filthy matter, and make it so fair within as is possible: and as it beginneth to heal, so make your tent every day lesser and lesser, until it be ready to close up, and never leave tenting it, so long as it will receive a tent, be it never so short. For hasty healing of wounds breedeth Fistula's, which properly be old wounds, and therefore must be cured like Fistula's.

OF WOUNDS IN THE FLESHY PARTS.

USE the same Ointment and manner of proceeding as before. And if the wound be large, then to keep in the tent or rolls, you shall be fain to put two or three Shoomakers ends on each side of the sore, leaving them so long as you may tie them together, and loosen them when you will like laces.

OF OLD ULCERS OR WOUNDS.

TO cure an old Ulcer, as Fistula, Gall, or Botch, or any new received wound, these are the best Salves, and most approved in mine experience: Take of Hony half a pinte, of Deer-sewet two ounces, of Verdigrease beaten into powder as much; boil all these exceeding well upon the fire, then with the same luke-warm, tent or plaister any venemous sore, and it will recure it. If you take of Wax, Turpentine, Oyl of Roses, of Hogs-grease, of each like quantity, and half so much Tar as any one of the other simples; melt all these together, and being well incorporated together, either tent or plaister any wound, and it will heal it. Also, if you take the green leaves of Tobacco bruised, and put them into a green wound, they will heal it: the ashes of Tobacco burnt, if they be strewed upon any sore that is neer skinning, it will also skin it perfectly, and it will incarnate well, if the Ulcer be not too deep and dangerous. There be many other Salves, Plaisters, and Unguents which I could set down; but since I have experienced these for most effectual, I omit the others as superfluous.

OF AN HURT WITH AN ARROW.

IF the Horse be hurt with an Arrow, tent the hole with Hogs-grease and Turpentine molten together, renewing it every day once until it be whole.

OF PULLING OUT SHIVERS OR THORNS.

MARTIN saith, that if it be not very deep, Sope being laid unto it all night will make it to appear, so as you may pull it out with a pair of nippers. But if it be very deep, then you must open the place with a knife or lancet, and get it out, and afterward heal up the wound as hath been taught you before. *Russius* saith, that the roots of Reed being stampt and mingled with Hony, will draw out any thorn or shiver: and so will Snails, as he saith, being stampt and wrought with fresh Butter; and if the place be swoln, he saith it is good to mollifie it with Hogs-grease and Hony, which will asswage any new swelling, that cometh by stripe or otherwise.

Of Bruisings or Swellings.

MARTIN saith, First prick it with a fleam. Then take of Wine lees a pinte, as much Wheat-flowre as will thicken it, and an ounce of Cumin; boil them together, and lay this somewhat warm unto it, renewing it every day once until the swelling either depart, or else come to a head. And if it do, then lance it, and heal it up as a wound.

Of Sinews cut, prickt, or bruised.

TAKE of Tar, and Bean-flowre, and a little Oyl of Roses, and lay it hot unto the place. And if this do no good, then take Worms and Sallet Oyl fryed together, or else the Ointment of Worms, which you shall have at the Apothecaries, and one of these will knit it again, if it be not clean asunder.

How to cure a wound made with Harquebush-shot.

MARTIN saith, First seek with an instrument whether the pellet remain within or not, and if it do, you must get it out with an instrument meet for the purpose. Then to kill the fire: Take a little Vernish, and thrust it into the wound with a feather, anointing it well within with the feather, and after that, stop the mouth fair and softly with a little soft flax, to keep the winde out, and on the outside, charge all the swelling with this charge: Take of Bole-armony a quartern, of Linseed beaten into fine powder half a pound, of Bean-flowre as much, and three or four broken Egges, shels and all, and of Turpentine a quartern, and a quart of Vinegar, and mingle them well together over the fire, and being somewhat warm, charge all the sore place with part thereof, and immediately clap a cloth, or a piece of leather upon it, to keep the wound from the cold air, continuing both to anoint the hole within with Vernish, and also to charge the swelling without, the space of four or five days, and at the five days end leave anointing of it, and tent it with a tent reaching to the bottom of the wound, and dipped in Turpentine and Hogs-grease molten together, renewing it every day twice until it be throughly killed, which you shall perceive by the mattering of the wound, and by falling of the swelling: for so long as the fire hath the upper hand, no thick matter will issue out, but only a thin yellowish water, neither will the swelling asswage. And then take of Turpentine, washed in nine several waters, half a pound, and put thereon three yolks of Egges, and a little Saffron, and tent it with that Ointment, renewing it every day once until the wound be whole.

OF BURNING WITH LIME OR ANY OTHER FIERY THING.

MARTIN saith; First wash away the Lime, if there be any, with warm water. Then kill the fire with Oyl and Water beaten together, dressing him so every day until it be all raw, and then anoint it with Hogs-grease, and strew thereupon the powder of slecked lime, dressing him so every day once until it be whole.

OF THE BITING OF A MAD DOG.

IF a Horse be bitten with a mad Dog, the venom of his teeth will not only pain him extremely, but also infect all his bloud, and make him to dye mad. The cure according to the old Writers is thus: Take of Goats dung, of flesh that hath laid long in Salt, and of the herb *Ebulus*, called of some Danewort, of each half a pound, and forty Walnuts. Stamp all these things together, and lay thereof unto the sore, and this will suck out the venom, and heal the wound. It is good also to give the Horse Treacle, and Wine to drink: yea, and some would have the sore place to be fiered with a hot Iron.

OF HURTS BY TUSKS OF A BOAR.

IF a Horse be hurt with the tusk of a Boar, lay Vitriol, and Copperas thereunto; and the powder of a Dogs head being burned, but let the tongue be first pulled out and cast away.

To heal the biting or stinging of Serpents.

LAURENTIUS Russius saith; Take a good quantity of the herb called *Sanicula*, stamp it, and distemper it with the milk of a Cow, that is all of one colour, and give him that to drink, and that will heal him.

Another Medicine for the same purpose.

MAKE a plaister of Onions, Hony and Salt, stampt and mingled together, and lay that to the sore place, and give the Horse Wine and Treacle to drink. *Absyrtus* would have you to give him white Pepper, Rhue, and Thyme, to drink with the Wine.

Of drinking of Horse-leaches.

IF a Horse chance to drink Horse-leaches, they will continually suck his bloud, and kill him. The remedy, according to *Absyrtus*, is to pour Oyl into the Horses mouth, which will make them to fall away and kill them.

Of swallowing down Hens dung.

IF a Horse swallow down Hens dung in his Hay, it will fret his guts, and make him to avoid filthy matter at the fundament. For remedy whereof, *Absyrtus* would have you to give him drink made of Smallage-seed, Wine, and Hony, and to walk him throughly upon it, that he may empty his belly.

Of Lice, and how to kill them.

THEY be like Geese Lice, but somewhat bigger, they will breed most about the ears, neck, and tail, and over all the body. They come of poverty, and the Horse will be always rubbing, and scratching, and will eat his meat, and not prosper withal, and with rubbing he will break all his mane and tail. The cure, according to *Martin*, is thus; Anoint the place with Sope and Quicksilver, well mingled together, and to a pound of Sope, put half an ounce of Quicksilver.

Of Lousiness.

THERE be Horses that will be Lousie, and it cometh of poverty, cold and ill keeping, and it is oftnest amongst young Horses, and most men take little heed unto it, and yet they will die thereon. The cure is, to wash them three mornings together in Stau-aker and warm water.

How to save Horses from the stinging of flies in Summer.

ANOINT the Horses coat with Oyle, and Bay-beries, mingled together, or tie to the headstal of his collar, a sponge dipt in strong Vinegar, or sprinkle the stable with water wherein Herb-grace hath been laid in steep, or perfume the stable with Ivie, or with Calamint, or with Gith burned in a pan of coles.

Of bones being broken out of joynt.

FEW or none of our Farriers do intermeddle with any such griefs, but do refer it over to the Bonesetter, whose practised hand, I must needs confesse, to be needful in such business. Notwithstanding, for that it belongeth to the Farriers art, and also for that the old writers do make some mention thereof, I thought good not to passe it over altogether with silence. Albeit, they speak only of fractures in the legs beneath the knee. For they make little mention or none of bones above the knee, taking them to be incurable, unlesse it be a rib, or such like. If a bone then be broken in the leg, it is easie to perceive, by feeling the roughness and inequality of the place grieved, one part being higher then another. The cure whereof, according to *Absyrtus* and *Hierocles*, is in this sort:

First put the bone again into his right place: that done, wrap it about with unwash't wool, binding it fast to the leg with a small linnen roller, soaked before in Oyl and Vinegar mingled together. And let that roller be laid on as even as is possible, and upon that again lay more wool dipt in Oyl and Vinegar, and then splent it with three splents, binding them fast at both ends with a thong, and let the Horses leg be kept straight, and right out, the space of forty days, and let not the bonds be loosened above three times in twenty days, unlesse it shrink, and so require to be new drest, and bound again. But fail not every day once, to pour on the sore place, through the splents, Oyl and Vinegar mingled together. And at the forty dayes end, if you perceive that the broken place be sowdered together again with some hard knob or gristle; then loosen the bonds, so as the Horse may go fair and softly, using from that time forth to anoint the place with some soft grease or Ointment.

OF BROKEN BONES.

I have not for mine own part had any great experience in broken bones of a Horse, because it chanceth seldom, and when it doth chance, what through the Horses brutish unruliness, and the immoderate manner of the act, it is almost held incurable; yet for the little experience I have, I have not found for this purpose any thing so soverain or absolute good, as Oyl of Mandrag, which applyed, conglutinateth and bindeth together any thing, especially bones being either shivered or broken.

OF BONES OUT OF JOYNT.

IF a Horses knee or shoulder be clean out of joynt, and no bone broken, *Martin* saith the readiest way is, to bind all the four legs together, in such sort as hath been taught before in the Chapter of Incording, and then to hoise the Horse somewhat from the ground, with his heels upward, so shall the weight and poise of his body, cause the joynt to shoot in again into the right place: for by this means he pleasured not long since a friend and neighbour of his, who going with his Cart from S. *Albons*, towards his own house, his Thiller fell and put his shoulder clean out of joynt, so as he was neither able to rise, nor being holpen up, could stand on his legs: to which mischance *Martin* being called, made no more ado, but taking his friends Cart-rope, bound the Horses legs all four together, and with a lever being staid upon the Cart wheel, they putting their shoulders to the other end, hoised up the Horse clean from the ground, the poise of whose body made the bone to return into his right place, with such a loud knack or crack, as it might be heard a great way off, and the Horse immediately had the use of his leg, so as he drew in the Cart, and went also safe home without complaining thereof ever after.

CERTAIN RECEIPTS OF PLAISTERS, VERY GOOD FOR BROKEN BONES, TAKEN OUT OF THE OLD AUTHORS, RITING OF HORSE-LEACH CRAFT.

TAKE of *Spuma argenti*, of Vinegar, of each one pound, of Sallet Oyl half a pound, of *Ammoniacum*, and Turpentine, of each three ounces, of Wax, of Rosin, of each two ounces, of Bitumen, of Pitch, of Verdigrease, of each half a pound. Boyl the Vinegar, Oyl and *Spuma argenti* together, until it wax thick, then put thereunto the Pitch, which being molten, take the pot from the fire, and put in the Bitumen, without stirring it at all, and that being also molten, then put in all the rest, and set the pot again to the fire, and let them boyl all together until they be all united in one: that done, strain it, and make it in a plaister form, and this is called *Hierocles* Plaister.

ANOTHER RECEIT FOR BROKEN BONES.

TAKE of liquid Pitch one pound, of Wax two ounces, of the purest and finest part of Frankincense one ounce, of *Ammoniacum* four ounces, of dry Roses, and of *Galbanum*, of each one ounce, of Vinegar two pintes. Boyl first the Vinegar and Pitch together, then put in the *Ammoniacum*, dissolved first in Vinegar, and after that, all the rest of the aforesaid drugs, and after they have boyled together, and be united in one, strain it, and make it plaisterwise, and this is called *Emplastrum flavum*, that is to say, the Yellow plaister.

AN OINTMENT FOR BROKEN BONES.

TAKE of old Sallet Oyl a quart, and put thereunto of Hogs grease, of *Spuma nitri*, of each one pound, and let them boyl together until it begin to bubble above, and let this ointment be very warm when you use it.

761

Hitherto of all the diseases belonging to a Horse. Now therefore my promise was made unto you to speak of those things wherein the cure of all diseases do consist, that is to say, in letting of bloud, in taking up of veins, in purging, and in giving the fire; yea, and also order it self bindeth me to treat of the said things presently, and first of letting bloud.

IN HOW MANY VEINS A HORSE MAY BE LET BLOUD, AND TO WHAT END.

As touching the order, time of the year, Moon, and day, and other circumstances belonging to letting of bloud, we have sufficiently spoken already in the keepers Office, in the 22 Chapter. It resteth therefore here to shew you what veins should be opened when the Horse is sick of any disease, according to Vegetius opinion. But first I will rehearse unto you once again, in how many veins a Horse may be let bloud, and the rather for that I follow *Vegetius*. A Horse then may be let bloud in the two Temple veins. *Item*, in the two eye veins, which are easie to finde in the face of the Horse, somewhat beneath the eyes. *Item*, in the two palat veins of the mouth. In the two neck veins. *Item*, in the two palat veins which are in the breast. *Item*, in the two fore thigh veins. *Item*, in the four shakle veins before. *Item*, in the two toe veins before. *Item*, in the two side veins, which may be otherwise called flank veins. *Item*, in the tail vein. *Item*, in the two hanch veins. *Item*, in the two hough veins. *Item*, in the four shakle veins behind. *Item*, in the two toe veins behind; so that by this account, a Horse may be let bloud in 31 veins. All which veins are easie enough to know, because that every one lyeth in a little gutter, which by feeling softly with your finger, you shall finde immediately.

And *Vegetius* saith, that if any Horse be pained with any grief in his head, as with ach, heaviness, frenzy, falling-evil, or such like, then it is good to let him bloud in the two temple veins with a fleam. If his eyes be waterish, bloudshotten, or grieved with pin, web, or haw, then it is good to strike the eye vein with a fleam. If he have any heaviness or weariness of body, or be diseased in the throat with the strangullion, quinzie, or swelling of the arteries, either within or without, then it is good to let him bloud in the mouth, in the palat veins with a Cornet. If he be vexed with an Ague, or with ony other disease universally hurting the body, then let him bloud in the neck veins. If his grief be in the lungs, liver, or in any other inward member, then let him bloud in the brest veins, which we called before the palat veins. If he be grieved in the shoulder, then let him bloud in the fore-thigh veins above the knee with a lancet, and that very warily, because that place is full of sinews, and if he be grieved in his joynts, then let him bloud in the shakle veins, and that warily, because that place is also full of sinews.

And if he be foiled on his fore-feet, by foundering or otherwise, then let him bloud in the toe veins, making way first with your drawer, or Cornet in the hoof to come to the vein. If he be diseased in the kidnies, reins, back, or belly, then let him bloud in the flank veins, and in the tail. If he hath any grief in his hips, or houghs, then let him bloud in the hip or hough veins. And if his hinder-legs, joynts, or feet be grieved, then let him bloud in the shakel veins, and toe veins, as is aforesaid.

THE ORDER OF TAKING UP VEINS, AND WHEREFORE IT IS GOOD.

THE order observed by *Martin*, is in this sort; First, if the Horse be very curst and shrewd, then cast him upon a dunghil, or some straw, then having found the vein that you would take up, marke well that part of the skin which covereth the vein, and pull that somewhat aside from the vein with your left thumb, to the intent you may slit it with a Rasor, without touching the vein. And cut no deeper then only through the skin, and that longst wise, as the vein goeth, and not above an inch long. That done, take away your Thumb, and the skin will return again into his place, right over the vein, as it was before. Then with a Cornet uncover the vein and make it up, and being bare, thrust the Cornet underneath it, and raise it up, so as you may put a Shoomakers threed underneath, somewhat higher then the Cornet, to knit the vein when time is. And if your Cornet had a hole in the small end to put in the threed, it should be the easilier done. Then the Cornet standing so still, slit the vein longst wise that it may bleed, and having bled somewhat from above, then knit it up with a sure knot, somewhat above the slit, suffering it to bleed only from beneath, and having bled sufficiently, then knit up the vein also beneath the slit with a sure knot, and fill the hole of the vein with Salt, and then heal up the wound of the skin with Turpentine and Hogs grease molten together, and laid on with a little Flax. The taking up of veins is very necessary, and doth ease many griefs in the legs: for the taking up of the fore-thigh veins easeth Farcins, and swellings of the legs; the taking up of the shakel veins before, easeth the Quitter-bone and swelling of the joynts, scabs, and cratches. The taking up of the hinder veins, helpeth the Farcin, Swellings, and both the Spavens; the taking up of the shakel veins behind, helpeth swelling of the joynts, the pains, and kibed heels, and such like diseases.

OF PURGING WITH PURGATION OR GLYSTER.

PURGATIONS is defined by the Physitians, to be the emptying or voiding of superfluous humors, annoying the body with their evill quality. For such humors bring evill juyce and nutriment, called of the Physitians *Cacochymia*, which when it will not be corrected or holpen with good diet, alteration, nor by the benefit of nature and kindly heat, then it must needs be taken away by Purgation, Vomit, or Glyster. But forasmuch as Horses are not wont to be purged by Vomit, as men be, I will speak here only of Glysters and Purgations. And first because a Horse is grieved with many diseases in his guts, and that nothing can purge the guts so well as a Glyster, and especially the thick guts, I wish that our Farriers would learn to know the diversities of Glysters, to what end they serve, and with what drugs or simples they should be made, for as the disease requireth, so must the Glyster be made; some to allay griefs and sharpness of humors, some to binde, some to loosen, some to purge evill humors, some to cleanse Ulcers: but our Farriers use Glysters, only to loosen the belly, and for no other purpose; yea, few or none do that unlesse it be *Martin*, and such as he hath taught, who is not ignorant that a Glyster is the beginning of purgation. For a Glyster, by cleansing the guts, refresheth the vital parts, and prepareth the way before. And therefore whensoever a Horse is surfeited and full of evill humors, needing to be purged, and specially being pained in the guts, I would wish you to begin first with a Glyster, lest by purging him by medicine upon the sudden, you stir up a multitude of evill humors, which finding no passage downward, because the guts be stopt with winde and dregges, do strike upwards, and so perhaps put the Horse in great danger.

But now you shall understand, that Glysters be made of four things, that is to say, of Decoctions, of Drugs, of Oyls, or such like unctious matters, as Butter and soft grease, and fourthly of divers kindes of Salt to provoke the virtue expulsive. A Decoction is as much to say as the broth of certain hearbs or simples boyled together in water till the third part be consumed. And sometime in stead of such Decoction, it shall be needful perhaps to use some fat broth, as the broth of Beef, or of Sheeps heads, or Milk, or Whay, or some other such like liquor, and that perhaps mingled with Hony or Sugar, according as the disease shall require, the Glyster to be either Lenitive, that is to say, easing pain; or Glutinative, that is, joyning together; or else Abstersive, that is to say, cleansing or wiping away filthy matter, of which Decoction of broth being strained, you shall need to take three pintes or a quart at the least. And then into that, you may put such drugs as shall be needful to the weight of three or four ounces, according as the simples shall be more or lesse violent. Of Oyl at the least half a pinte, and of Salt two or three drams, and then to be ministred luke-warm with a horn or pipe made of purpose, when the Horse is not altogether full panched but rather empty, be it either in fore-noon, or after-noon. And as touching the time of keeping Glysters in the body, you shal understand, that to Glysters abstersive half an hour or lesse may suffice to Glysters Lenitive, a longer time if it may be: and to Glysters Glutinative, the longest time of all is most needful.

OF PURGATIONS.

PURGATIONS for Men may be made in divers sorts and forms; but Horses are wont to be purged only with pils, or else with purging powders put into Ale, Wine, or some other liquor. But the simples whereof such pils or powders be made, would be chosen with judgement and aptly applyed, so as you may purge away the hurtful humors, and not the good. Learn first therefore to know with what humor or humors the Horse is grieved, be it Choler, Flegm, or Melancholy, and in what part of the body such humors do abound: then what simples are best to purge such humors, and with what property, quality, and temperament they be indued. For some be violent and next cousins to poyson, as Scammony, or *Coloquintida*. Some again are gentle, and rather meat than medicines, as *Manna, Cassia*, Whay, Prunes, and such like. And some again be neither too violent, nor too gentle, but in a mean, as Rhubarb, Agarick, *Sene*, Aloes. The old men did use much to purge Horses with the pulp of *Coloquintida*, and sometime with the roots of wilde Cowcumber; and sometime with the broath of a sodden Whelp mingled with *Nitrum*, and divers other things, whereof I am sure I have made mention before in the curing of Horses diseases.

Notwithstanding I would not wish you to be rash in purging a Horse after the old mens example. For as their simples many times be very violent, so the quantities thereof by them prescribed are very much, and dangerous for any Horse to take in these days, in the which neither man nor beast, as it seemeth, is of such force or strength as they were in times past. And therefore whensoever you would purge him with such like kindes of Purgations as *Martin* useth, whereof you have example before in divers places; and whensoever you list for knowledge sake to deal with other simples, to prove them first upon such Jades as may well be spared. For whosoever mindeth to purge a Horse well, that is, to do him good and no hurt, had need to consider many things: as the nature of the Horses disease, and the Horses strength: also the nature, strength and quantity of the medicine that he ministreth: the Region, or Countrey, the time of the disease, the time of the year and day. For as the diseases and evil humors causing such diseases are divers, so do they require to be purged with divers medicines, diversly compounded, wherein consisteth a point of Art to be learned at the Physitians hands, and not at mine.

Again, weak, delicate, and tender Horses may not be purged in such sort, as those that be of a strong sturdy nature. And therefore in such cases the quality and quantity of the simples is not a little to be considered; neither is the hotness or coldness of the Region to be neglected, nor the time of the disease. For some require to be purged in the very beginning some not until the matter be throughly digested: and though the disease proceed perhaps of cold, and cold humors, yet a man may not minister such hot things in Summer, as he would do in Winter, nor in the contrary case, such cold things in Winter as he would in Summer. And therefore the time and season of the year is also to be observed: yea the day and time of the day. For the more temperate the day is, the better; not in an extreme hot day, for making the Horse to faint; nor yet when the winde bloweth in the cold North, for that will stop and hinder the working of the medicine, but rather in a temperate moist day, when the winde is in the South, if it may be; for that will further and help the working of the medicine, and make the body loose and soluble.

Again for a Horse, whether you purge him with pils or drink, it is best for him (as *Martin* saith) to take them in the morning, after that he hath fasted from meat and drink all the night before. And having received his medicine, let him be walked up and down, one hour at the least, and then set him up, and suffered to stand on the bit two or three hours without any meat, but in the mean time see that he be well littered, and warm covered: and at three hours end, offer him a little of a warm mash made with Wheat-meal, or with Bran or else with ground mault. Give him little meat, or none until he be purged: all which things have been shewed you before in divers places, and therefore I think it not good to be tedious unto you with often recital thereof.

OF CAUTERIZATION, OR GIVING THE FIRE, AS WELL ACTUAL AS POTENTIAL.

FORASMUCH as the Fire is judged of all the old Writers to be the chiefest remedy, and as it were the last refuge in all diseases almost whereunto a Horse is subject, I thought good therefore to talk of it in this place; and the rather, for that few or none of our Farriers, unless it be *Martin*, or such as have been taught, do know how to give the fire, or to what end it serveth. But first you shall understand, that according to the learned Chirurgeons, yea, also according to my old Authors, there be two kindes of Cautery, the one actual, and the other potential. The

Cautery actual is that which is done only by fiering of the grieved place with a hot Iron. The potential Cautery is done by applying unto the grieved place some medicine corrosive, putrifactive, or caustick. But we will speak first of the actual Cautery, shewing you wherefore it is good, then of what metal and fashion your instrument should be made, and finally how and when to use them.

Avicen saith, that an actual Cautery moderately used, is a noble remedy to stop corruption of members, to rectifie the complexion of the same, and also to stanch bloud. Howbeit you must beware (saith he) that you, touch not the sinews, cords, or ligaments, lest the member be weakened, or that the Cramp ensueth. *Vegetius* also writing of Horse-leach-craft, praiseth the actual Cautery very much, speaking in this sort: The actual Cautery saith he, bindeth together parts loosened, it doth attenuate parts blown and puffed up, it dryeth up superfluous moisture, it looseneth and divideth evill matter gathered together into knots, it asswageth old griefs, it rectisieth those parts of the body that are corrupted by any manner of way, reducing them to their pristine estate, and suffereth no superfluity to grow or increase, for the skin being opened with a hot iron, all kind of corruption by virtue of the fire is first digested and ripened, and then dissolved, so as the matter doth issue out at the holes, whereby the member or part before offended is now healed; and eased of all pain and grief; yea the holes being once closed and clean shut up, that place is stronger and better knit, and covered with a tougher skin then ever it was before.

Now as touching the instrument whereof, and of what fashion they should be made, you shall understand, that *Vegetius* and the other old Writers would have them to be made of Copper, praising that metal to be far better to burn with, then Iro. The Chirurgions for mans body do praise Gold and Silver; but as for the fashion of the Irons, it is to be referred to the kind of sore place and grieved, wherewith you have to deal, according to the diversity whereof, the instruments are to be made of divers fashions, as some with searing Irons with sharp edges, and some with blunt and broad edges, some like right, and some like crooked Bodkins, and some like hooks and sickles, and some with a great Button, and some with a small Button at the one end; in making whereof, the Farriers judgement is most needful, who ought to be so skilful as he may be able to make all manner of Irons that he should occupie, and to alter them according as need shall require. And therefore I thought good only here to speak of the common drawing Iron, and of the Button Iron, like in form to those that *Martin* useth, referring all the rest to your own judgement, and specially sith you have been fully instructed before of what sort they should be made meet to serve your turn in any disease.

Now as touching the use of the instruments, two things are specially to be considered, that is the heating of the Iron, and the bearing of the hand. For the back of the Iron may not be red hot, but only the edge, for fear of yeelding too much heat. And therefore though it be made red hot at the first, yet it shall be good before you occupie it, to cool the back of the instrument in water; and as touching the bearing of the hand, more evenly and lightly it is done, the better and that according as the fineness and thinness of the skin shall require, which is to be judged by the hair. For if the hair be short and fine, then it is a signe of a fine skin, if long and rough, then it betokeneth a thick skin. The fine skin requireth the lighter hand, and not to be burned so deep as the thick skin, yet both must be burned until they look yellow. But the fine skin will look yellow with lesser burning then the thick skin. For the thick skin with his long hair doth choke the fire, and therefore requireth a more heavy hand: yea, and more often heating of the instrument then the thin skin doth, and be sure to draw alwayes with the hair, and not against the hair, in what forme and in what manner of lines hath been taught you before; for those must be made either long, short, deep, shallow, right-crooked, or over-thwart, according as the disease doth require: you have learned also how to allay the heat of the fire, after such drawing. And therefore I have no more to say here, but only to admonish you according to *Vegetius* precepts, not to fire any sinewie place, nor bone that is broken or out of joynt, for fear of weakning the whole member, not to bear so heavie or uneven hand, as you should thereby deform or misfashion any part of the Horse, nor be too hasty in giving the fire, but to attempt first all other convenient remedies, and when nothing else will help to make the fire your last refuge, and yet not so much to neglect it and abhor it, like the ignorant sort, as you will not use it when need requireth, for lack whereof many Horses go lame, and uncured of divers diseases. Practise your selves therefore in giving the fire at needful times with judgement and discretion, so shall you do it to the Horses benefit, and to your own great praise and profit.

OF CAUTERIES POTENTIAL.

CAUTERIES Potential, as *Johannes Vigo* saith, are medicines Corrosive, Putrifactive and Caustick. This word Corrosive, is derived of the *Latin* word *Corrodo*, which is as much to say, as to gnaw and fret; and of such Corrosives, some be simple and some compound. The simple, as *Vigo* saith, be such as these be, Roch Alum, as well burnt as not burnt, spunge of the Sea somewhat burnt, Lime, red Coral, powder of Mercury. Compound Corrosives be these, *Unguentum Apostolorum, Unguentum Ægyptiacum, Unguentum Ceraceum*. Medicines Putrifactive, called of the learned sort, *Septica*, according to *Avicen*, be those that have strength to corrupt the complexion of the member, and to induce any scar like dead flesh, causing great pain; yea and Fevers, and therefore ought not to be ministred but to strong bodies and in strong diseases, as in Carbuncles, Cankers, Ulcers, and such like, and they be these, *Arsenicke, Sublimat, Resalgar*, and other medicines compound therewith. *Silvius* also addeth thereunto *Sandaraca, Chrysocolla*, and *Aconitum*, but he doth not agree with *Avicen* in the description of the putrifactive medicines: For he saith, that they have little pain or none, neither be they so hot and drie as those that are called *Escharotica*; that is to say, Crustive: which be hot in the fourth degree, and do breed a crust and scar, and cause great pain, as unsleck't Lime, and the burned dregs of Wine: wherefore it seemeth that *Avicens* description belongeth rather to the crustive then to the Putrifactive medicines.

Notwithstanding, I must needs say that our Chirurgions and also Farriers, do finde both *Arsenicke* and *Resalgar*, to be so sharp, hot and burning things, as when they minister the same to any part of the body, they are forced to allay the sharpness thereof: the Chirurgions with the juice of Plantain, or Daffadil, or else of House-leek, the Farriers with Hogs grease. Medicines Caustick, that is to say, Burning, are those whose operation are most strong and incline to the nature of the fire, and yet more easily allayed as *Vigo* writeth, then the medicines Putrifactive, and therefore may be more safely used. They be made as he saith, of strong lie, called *Capitelum*, or *Magistra*, of *Vitriolæ Romanæ*, *Sal Nitri*, *Aqua fortis*, of this sort be all those which *Vigo* calleth the blistering medicines, as *Apium*, *Cantharides*, *Ciclamine*, Onions, strong Garlick, *Melanacardinum*, the stones or grains of *Vitis Alba*, otherwise called Brionie. Moreover, *Vigo* maketh every one of these Cauteries Potential to excell one another, as it were by certain degrees, saying, that Corrosives be weaker then putrifactives, and Putrifactives be weaker then Causticks, and therefore Corrosives work in the upper part, and in soft flesh; Putrifactives, in hard flesh and deep. But Causticks have power to break the skin in hard flesh, and do enter most deeply. The use of the most part of which things have been taught you before in sundry places, according to *Martins* experience.

And therefore I leave to trouble you any further, wishing you that are desirous to know any more of those matters, to read *Taugantius* writing *Depiroticis*; and *Silvius de medicamentorum compositione*; and *John Vigo* writing of Surgery, *Englished* but few years since. But the old writers, so far as I can judge by the words of *Absyrtus*, and others, that write of Horse-leach craft, do apply this word Caustick, to such medicines as are astrictive, and binding, called of *Martin* and other Farriers in these dayes, binding charges, as may well appear by the composition and use here following, recited by *Vegetius* in this sort.

THE RECEIPT OF A CAUSTICK USED BY CHIRON, TO DRY UP THE SUPERFLUOUS MOISTURE, AND TO BIND PARTS LOOSENED, AND TO STRENGTHEN PARTS WEAKNED.

TAKE of *Bitumen Judaicum* two pound, of *Bitumen Apollonii* two pound, of the purest part of Frankincense six ounces, of *Bdellium Arabicum* two ounces, of Deers sewet two pound, of *Populeuni* two ounces, of *Galbanum* two ounces, of the drops of *Storax* two ounces, of common Wax two pound, of *Resin Gabial* one pound, of *Viscus Italicus* three ounces, of *Apoxima* two ounces, of the juyce of Hysop two ounces, of the drops of *Armoniack* two ounces, of Pitch one pound.

771

ANOTHER CAUSTICK USED BY PELAGONIUS, TO DRY UP SWELLINGS, BLADDERS, WIND-GALS AND SPLENTS IN THE LEGS AND JOYNTS.

TAKE Virgin Wax one pound, of Rosin two pound and a half, of *Galbanum* three ounces, of *Asphaltum Judaicum* two pound, of Mirrhe secondary two pound, of *Bitumen* one pound, of Armoniack six ounces, of *Costus* six ounces. Boyl all these things together in an earthen pot, saving the *Asphaltum*, Armoniack and Costum, which being first ground like fine flowre, must be added unto the other things, and after that they have been boyled and cooled, and then boiled all together again, and well stirred, so as they may be incorporated together, and made all one substance. These kindes of Emplaisters or Ointments ought in my judgement to be so called, as I said before, rather binding charges, then Caustick medicines, because there be no such extreme Corrosive or burning simples in these, as are before recited. Notwithstanding I refer my judgment to those that be better learned, and so end for being over tedious. For if I would, I could take very good occasion here to speak of divers other medicines, whereof some are called *Anodyna*, easing pain and grief. *Martin* calleth them Linoges, which are made of Linseed, Camomile, soft grease and such like things, as are hot in the first degree; some again are called *Narcotica*, that is to say, astonying or bringing to sleep, as those that are made of *Opium*, *Mandragora*, *Poppie*, and such like cold and grosse things. And some are called *Sarcotica*, that is, Breeding flesh, as Barly flowre and Frankincense. And many other kinds of Emplaisters, Ointments, waters and salves, which would occupy a book of no small volum, to be written hereafter by some other perhaps, if not by my self. And in the mean time, let this that I may have already written suffice.

OF THE ANTICOR.

AN Anticor cometh of superfluity of evill-bloud or spirit in the arteries, and also of inflamation in the liver, which is ingendred by means of too choise keeping, and overmuch rest, which choaketh the vital power, and occasions unnatural swellings in the brest, which if they ascend upward and come into the neck, they are instantly death. The cure whereof is in this sort; Let him bleed so as he may bleed abundantly, then with a sharp knife in divers places cut the swelling: which done, set a cupping-glasse thereon, and cup it till the glasse filled with foul water fall away it self; then give the Horse to drink three mornings together a pinte of Malmesie well stirred with Cinamon, Licoras, and a little Bezar stone, and during his sickness, let his drink be warmed, and mingled with either Bran or Malt.

OF THE CORDS.

THE Cord is a disease that maketh the Horse stumble, and many times fall, and they appear in a Horses fore-legs: this is the cure thereof; Take a sharp knife, and cut a slit even at the top of his nose, just with the point of the gristle, open the slit being made, and you shall perceive a white string, take it up with a Boars tooth, or some crooked bodkin, and cut it in sunder, then stitch up the slit and anoint it with Butter, and the Horse doubtless shall be recovered.

OF THE MILLETS.

THE Millets is a grief that appeareth in the Fetlocks behind, and causeth the hair to shed, three or four inches long, and a quarter of an inch in breadth, like as it were bare and ill to cure. But thus is the cure; First wash it well with wrong lie, and rub it till it bleed, then binde unto it Hony, unsleck't Lime, and Deers sewet, boyled and mingled together, this do for the space of a week, and it shall be whole.

OF THE SEREW.

A Serew is a foul sorance, it is like a Splent, but it is a little longer, and is most commonly on the outside of the fore-leg, as the Splent is on the inside. The cure is thus; Take two spoonfuls of strong Wine Vinegar, and one spoonful of good Sallet Oyl, mingle them together, and every morning bestow one hour in rubbing the sorance with it altogether downward till it be gone, which will not be long in going.

THE MEDICINES ARISING OUT OF HORSES.

THE *Grecians* have written nothing at all concerning wilde Horses, because in their Countrey there was none of them usually bred or gotten: yet notwithstanding the same we ought to think that all medicines or any other things, which do proceed from them, are more strong in operation, and have in them greater force and power then any common Horses have, as it falleth out in all sorts of other beasts.

The bloud of a Horse (as *Pliny* affirmeth) doth gnaw into dead flesh with a putrifactive force; the same vertue hath the blood of Mares, which have been covered by Horses: Also the bloud of a Horse (but especially of one which is a breeder) doth very much make and help against impostumes, and small bunches which do arise in the flesh. Moreover it is said that the bloud of a young Asse is very good against the Jaundies, and the over-flowing of the gall, as also the same force and effect is in the bloud of a young Horse. The Horse-leaches do use the bloud of Horses for divers diseases which are incident unto them, both by anointing or rubbing the outward parts, as also within their bodies.

Furthermore if one do cut the veins of the palat of a Horses mouth, and let it run down into his belly, it will presently destroy and consume the maw or belly-worms, which are within him. When a Horse is sick of the Pestilence, they draw bloud out of the veins in his spurring place, and mingling the same upon a stone with Salt, make him to lick it up. The bloud of a Horse is also mingled with other medicines, and being anointed upon the armes and shoulders of men or beasts, which are broken or out of joynt, doth very much help them. But a Horse which is weary or tyred, you must cure after this manner; First, draw some bloud out of his matrix or womb, and mingle it with Oyl and Wine, and then put it on the fire till it be luke-warm, and then rub the Horse all over against the hairs.

If the sinews of Horses do wax stiffe or shrink in together, it is very necessary that the sick parts should be anointed with the hot bloud which doth proceed from him, for Horses also which are fed in the field use their flesh and dung, against the biting and stinging of Serpents.

We do also finde that the flesh of Horses being well boiled is very medicinable for divers diseases. Moreover it is very usuall and common with the women of *Occitania* to take the fat or grease of Horses to anoint

774

their heads to make the hair of their heads multiply and increase; and certain later Physitians do mingle the marrow of a Horse with other Ointments for a remedy against the Cramp.

The marrow of a Horse is also very good to loosen the sinews which are knit and fastned together, but first let it be boyled in Wine, and afterwards made cold, and then anointed warmly either by the fire or Sun. If a Horse do labor in that kinde of impostume which they vulgarly call the Worm, either any where as well as in the nose, they do open the skin with a searing iron, and do sprinkle Verdigrease within the Horses mouth being brent, and being added thereunto sometimes the seed of Henbane.

The teeth of a male Horse not gelded, or by any labour made feeble, being put under the head, or over the head of him that is troubled or starteth in his dream, doth withstand and resist all unquietness which in the time of his rest might happen unto him. Pliny also doth assent that flowre doth heal the soreness of a Horses teeth and gums, and the clefts and chinks of a Horses feet.

The teeth also of a Horse is very profitable for the curing of the Chilblanes which are rotten and full of corruption when they are swollen full ripe. *Marcellus* saith, that the tooth of a Horse being beaten and crushed into very small powder, and being sprinkled upon a Mans genital doth much profit and very effectually help him: but the teeth which were first ingendred in a Horse, have this virtue in them, that if they should touch the teeth of Man or Woman who are molested and grieved with the tooth-ach, they shall presently find a final end of their pain: if in the like manner a childe do kisse the nose or snowt of a Horse, he shall never feel pain in his teeth, neither at any time shall the childe be bitten by the Horse.

The teeth which do first of all fall from Horses, being bound or fastned upon children in their infancy, do very easily procure the breeding of the teeth, but with more speed and more effectually if they have never touched the ground, wherefore the Poet doth very well apply these Verses, saying;

Collo igitur molli dentes nectentur equini,
Qui prima suerint pullo crescente caduci.

It is also said, that if the hair of a Horse be fastned unto the House of a mans enemy it will be a means that neither little flies or small gnats shall flie by his dwelling place or aboad. The tongue of a Horse being never accustomed unto wine, is a most present and expedient medicine to allay or cure the milt of a Man or Woman (as *Cæcillus Bion* reporteth unto us, that he learned it of the *Barbarians*.) But *Marcellus* saith, that the Horse tongue ought to be dryed and beaten into small powder, and put into any drink, except wine only, and forthwith it will shew the commodity which riseth thereupon, by easing either Man or Woman, of the pain of the Spleen or Milt divers also do think that a Horses tongue used after this manner, is a good means or preservative against the biting of Serpents or any other venemous creatures.

But for the curing of any sores or griefs in the inward parts, the genital of a Horse is most of all commended: for as *Pliny* supposeth, this genital of a Horse is very medicinable for the loosing of the belly, as also the bloud, marrow, or liver of a Goat, but these things do rather dry up and close the belly (as before we have taught) concerning the Goat.

In the heart of Horses there is found a bone, most like unto a Dogs tooth, it is said that this doth drive away all grief or sorrow from a mans heart, and that a tooth being pulled from the cheeks or jaw bones of a dead Horse doth shew the full and right number of the sorrowes of the party so grieved. The dust of a Horse hoof anointed with Oyl and Water, doth drive away impostumes and little bunches which rise in the flesh, in what part of the body soever they be: and the dust of the hoof of an Asse anointed with Oyl, Water and hot urine, doth utterly expell all Wens and kernels which do rise in the neck, arme-holes, or any other part of the body, of either man or woman.

The genital of a gelded Horse dryed in an Oven, beaten to powder, and given twice or thrice in a little hot broth to drink unto the party grieved, is by *Pliny* accounted an excellent and approved remedy for the seconds of a woman. The foam of a Horse, or the dust of a Horse hoof dryed, is very good to drive away shamefastness, being anointed with a certain titulation. The scrapings of the Horses hoofs being put in wine, and poured into the Horses nostris, do greatly provoke his urine. The ashes also of an Horses hoof being mingled with wine and water, doth greatly ease and help the disease called the Colick or Stone: as also by a perfume which may be made by the hoofs of Horses being dryed, a childe which is still born is cast out.

The milk of Mares is of such an excellent virtue, that it doth quite expell the poison of the Sea-hare, and all other poison whatsoever: drink also mingled with Mares milk doth make the body loose and laxable. It is also counted an excellent remedy against the falling sickness, to drink the stones of a Boar out of a Mares milk or water. If there be any filth or matter lying in the matrice of a woman, let her take Mares milk boiled and throughly strained, and presently the filth and excrements will void clean away. If so he that a Woman be barren and cannot conceive, let her then take Mares milk (not knowing what it is) and let her presently accompany with a man, and she will conceive. The milk of a Mare being drunk doth asswage the labor of the matrice, and doth cause a still childe to be cast forth. If the seed of Henbane be beaten small and mingled with Mares milk, and bound with a Harts skin, so that it may not touch the ground, and fastened or bound to a woman, they will hinder her conception.

The thinnest or latest part of the milk of a Mare, doth very easily, gently and without any danger purge the belly. Mares milk being dayly anointed with a little Hony doth without any pain or punishment take away the wounds of the eyes being new made Cheese made of Mares milk doth represse and take away all wringings or aches in the belly, whatsoever. If you anoint a comb with the foam of a Horse, wherewith, a young man or youth doth use to comb his head, it is of such force as it will cause the hair of his head neither to encrease, or any whit to appear. The foam of a Horse is also very much commended for them which have either pain or difficulty of hearing in their ears, or else the dust of Horse dung being new made and dryed, and mingled with Oyl of Roses. The grief or soreness of a mans mouth or throat, being washed or anointed with the foam of a Horse which hath been sed with Oates or Barly, doth presently expel the pain of the soreness, if so be that it be two or three times washed over with the juyce of young or green Sea-crabs beaten small together; but if you cannot get the Sea-crabs which are green, sprinkle upon the grief the small powder which doth come from dryed Crabs which are baked in an Oven made of Brasse, and afterward wash the mouth where the pain is, and you shall finde present remedy. The foam of a Horse being three or four times taken in drink, doth quite expell and drive away the Cough. But *Marcellus* doth affirm that whosoever is troubled with the Cough, or consumption of the lungs, and doth drink the foam of a Horse by it self alone without any drink, shall finde present help and remedy: but as *Sextus* saith, the Horse will presently die after it. The same also being mingled with hot water, and given to one who is troubled with the same diseases, being in manner past all cure, doth presently procure health, but the death of the Horse doth instantly ensue. The sweat of a Horse being mingled with Wine, and so drunk, doth cause a woman which it very big and in great labor, to cast a still childe.

The sweat of any Beast, (but as *Albertus* saith only of a Horse) doth breed wind in a man or womans face, being put thereupon, and besides that, doth bring the Squince or Squincy, as also a filthy stinking sweat. If Swords, Knives, or the points of Spears when they are red fire hot, be anointed with the sweat of a Horse, they will be so venemous and full of poyson, that if a man or woman be smitten or pricked therewith, they will never cease from bleeding as long as life doth last. If a Horse be wounded with an Arrow, and have the sweat of another Horse, and bread which hath been brent, being mingled in mans urine, given him to drink, and afterwards some of the same being mingled with Horse grease put into the wound, it will in short time procure him ease and help. There are some which will assure us, that if a man be troubled with the belly worms, or have a Serpent crept into his belly, if he take but the sweat of a Horse being mingled with his urine, and drink it, it will presently cause the Worms or the Serpent to issue forth.

The dung of a Horse or Asse which is fed with grasse, being dryed and afterward dipped in wine, and so drunk, is a very good remedy against the bitings and blowes of Scorpions. The same medicines they do also use, being mingled with the genital of a Hare in Vinegar, both against the Scorpion, and against the Shrew-mouse. The force is so great in the poyson of a mad Dog or Bitch, that his pargeted Urine doth much hurt, especially unto them that have a sore boil upon them; the chiefest remedy therefore against the same is the dung of a Horse mingled with Vinegar, and being warmed put into the scab or sore. The dung as well of Asses as of Horses, either raw, cold, or burned, is excellent good against the breaking forth or issues of the bloud.

The dung of Horses or Asses being new made or warm, and so clapped and put to a green wound, doth very easily and speedily stanch the bleeding. If the vein of a Horse be cut, and the bloud do issue out in too much aboundance, apply the dung of the same Horse unto the place where the vein is cut, and the bleeding will presently cease, wherefore the Poet doth very well express it i these Verses following;

> *Sive fimus manni cum testis uritur ovi,*
> *Et reprimit fluidos miro medicamine cursus.*

The same doth also very well drive away the corruption in mens body which doth cause the bloud to stinke if it be well and justly applyed unto the corrupt place. The same also being mingled with Oyl of Roses, and new made, and so applyed unto the ears, doth not only drive away the pain, but also doth very much help for hearing: There is another remedy also for the hearing, which is this, to take the dung of a Horse which is new made, and to make it hot in a furnace, and then to pour it on the middle of the head against the *Uvula*, and afterward to tie the aforesaid dung in a linnen or woollen cloth unto the top of the head in the night time.

The dung of a young Asse when he is first foaled, given in Wine to the quantity or magnitude of a Bean, is a present remedy for either man or woman who is troubled with the Jaundice or the over-flowing of the gall: and the same property hath the dung of a young Horse or Colt when he is new foaled. But the dung of an old Horse, being boiled in fair water, and afterward strained and so given to the party to drink, who is troubled with Water in his belly or stomach, doth presently make vent for the same.

There is also an excellent remedy against the Colick and Stone, which is this, to take a handfull of the dung of a Horse which hath been fed with Oates and Barly, and not with grasse, and mingle very well it with half a pinte of Wine, all which I do guesse will amount unto the weight of eighteen ounces, and then boyl them all together untill half of them be boyled or consumed away, and then drink the same by little and little until it be all drunk up, but it will be much better for the party that is troubled to drink it up all together if he be able.

There is moreover a very good and easie way by Horse dung to cure the Ague or Quartern Fever, which is thus, to burn the foresaid dung, and to mingle the very dust it self thereof in old wine, and then beat it unto small powder, and so give it unto the party who is troubled therewith, to drink or suck without any water in it, and this will very speedily procure ease and help. If that a woman supposeth her childe which is in her womb to be dead, let her drink the milt or spleen of a Horse in some sweet water, not to the smell, but to the taste, and she will presently cast the childe. The same virtue are in the persume which is made of a Horses hoof, as also in the dry dung of a Horse: There is some which do use this means against the falling sickness, or the sickness called Saint *Johns evill*, that is to mingle the water or urine which a Horse doth make with the water which cometh from the Smiths trough, and so to give it the party in a potion. There is a very good help for Cattel which do avoid bloud through their Nostrils or secret parts, which is this, to make a paste of Wheat flowre, and beat it and mingle it together with Butter and Egges in the urine of a Horse which hath lately drunk, and afterward to give that paste or poultess baked even to ashes to the beast so grieved.

To provoke urine when a mans yard is stopt, there is nothing so excellent as the dung or filth which proceedeth from the urine which a Horse hath made, being mingled with wine, and then strained, and afterwards poured into the Nostrils of the party so vexed.

There are certain Tetters or Ring-wormes in the knees of Horses, and a little above the hoofs in the bending of these parts, there are indurate and hardned thick skins, which being beaten into small powder and mingled with Vinegar, and so drunk, are an exceeding good preservative against the Falling-sickness: the same is also a very good remedy for them which are bitten with any wilde Beast whatsoever. By the Tetter or Ring-worm which groweth in a Horses knees or above the hoofs, beaten and mingled with Oyle, and so poured in the ears, the teeth of either man or woman which were weak and loose, will be made very strong and fast. The aforesaid Tetter, without any mingling with Oyl, doth also heal and cure the head-ache and Falling-sickness, in either man or woman. The same also being drunk out of Clarret Wine or Muscadel for forty dayes together, doth quite expell and drive away the Colick and Stone. If that any man do get and put up the shooe of a Horse being struck from his hoof as he travelleth in his pace (which doth many times happen) it will be an excellent remedy for him against the sobbing in the stomach called the Hicket.

OF THE HYÆNA, AND THE DIVERS KINDS THEREOF.

WE are now to discourse of a Beast whereof it is doubtful whether the names or the kinds thereof be more in number, and therefore to begin with the names, it seemeth to me in general, that it is the same Beast which is spoken of in Holy Scripture, and called *Zeeb-ereb,* and *Araboth, Zephan.* 3. *Principes urbis Hierosolymæ velut Leones-rugientes, judices ejus similes sunt lupis Vespertinis qui ossa non relinquunt ad diluculum:* Their Princes are roaring Lions, and their Judges are like to night-wolves which leave not the bones till the morning, as it is vulgarly translated. In like sort *Jer.* 5. calleth them *Zeeb-Araboath,* Wolves of the wilderness, and the Prophet *Habakkuk,* Cap. 1. useth the word *Zeeb-ereb,* Wolves of the evening. By which it is made easie to consider and discusse what kinde of Beasts this Hyæna may be deemed; for the Hyæna, as I shall shew afterward, is a *Greek* word. And first of all I utterly seclude all their opinions, which translate this word *Arabian* Wolves, for the *Hebrew* notes cannot admit such a version or exposition: But seeing we read in *Oppianus* and *Tzetzes,* that there are kinds of Wolves which are called *Harpages,* more hungry then the residue, living in Mountains, very swift of foot, and in the Winter time, coming to the gates of Cities, and devouring both flesh and bones of every living creature they can lay hold on, especially Dogs and men, and in the morning go away again from their prey, I take them to be the same Beasts which the *Grecians* call *Hyænæ,* which is also the name of a Fish much like in nature hereunto. It is also called *Glanos,* and by the *Phrygians,* and *Bythinians, Ganos,* and from one of these came the *Illyrian* or *Sclavonian* word *San,* and it seemeth that the *Grecians* have given it a name from Swine, because of the gristles growing on the back, for an Hyæna can have no better derivation then from *Hus* or *Hyn. Julius Capitolinus* calleth it *Belbus* in *Latin*, in the same place where he recordeth that there were *decem Belbi sub Gordiano*, ten *Hyænaes* in the days of *Gordianus*: And the reason of this name is not improbably derived from *Belba* a City of *Egypt. Pincianus* a learned man calleth it *Grabthier*, because it hunteth the Sepulchres of the dead. *Albertus* in stead of Hyæna, calleth it *Iona*. The *Arabians* call it *Kabo*, and *Zabo*, or *Ziba* and *Azaro*. I take it also to be the same Beast which is called *Lacta*, and *Ana*, and *Zilio*, because that which is reported of these, is true in the Hyæna; they frequent graves, having sharp teeth and long nails, being very fierce, living together in herds and flocks, and loving their own kinde most tenderly, but most pernicious and hateful to all other, being very crafty to set upon a fit prey, defending it self from the rage of stronger Beasts by their teeth and nails, or else by flight or running away. Wherefore we having thus expressed the name, we will handle the kinds, which I finde to be three, the first *Hyæna*, the second *Papio* or *Dabuh*, the third *Crocuta*, and *Leucrocuta*, whereunto by conjecture we may add a fourth, called *Mantichora*.

THE FIGURE OF THE FIRST HYÆNA.

THIS first and vulgar kinde of Hyæna, is bred in *Africk* and *Arabia*, being in quantity of body like a Wolfe, but much rougher haired, for it hath bristles like a Horses mane all along his back, and in the middle of his back it is a little crooked or dented, the colour yellowish, but bespeckled on the sides with blew spots, which make him look more terrible, as if it had so many eyes. The eyes change their colour at the pleasure of the beast, a thousand times a day, for which cause many ignorant writers have affirmed the same of the whole body, yet can he not see one quarter so perfectly in the day as in the night; and therefore he is called *Lupus vespertinus*, a Wolf of the night. The skilful *Lapidarists* of *Germany* affirm that this beast hath a stone in his eyes (or rather in his head) called *Hyæna* or *Hyænius*; but the Ancients say, that the apple or puple of the eye is turned into such a stone, and that it is indued with this admirable quality, that if a man lay it under his tongue, he shall be able to foretel and prophesie of things to come; the truth hereof I leave to the reporters. Their back-bone stretcheth it self out to the head, so as the neck cannot bend except the whole body be turned about, and therefore whensoever he hath occasion to wry his neck, he must supply that quality by removing of his whole body.

This Beast hath a very great heart, as all other Beasts have which are hurtful, by reason of their fear. The genital member is like a Dogs or Wolfs; and I marvail upon what occasion the writers have been so possessed with opinion that they change sexes, and are sometime male and another female, that is to say, male one year, and female another, according to these Verses,

> *Si tamen est aliquid miræ novitatis in istis*
> *Alternate vices, & quæ modo fœmina tergo*
> *Passa marem est, nunc esse marem miremur Hyænam.*

Both kindes have under their tails a double note or passage, in the male there is a scissure like the secrets of a female, and in the female a bunch like the stones of the male, but neither one nor other inward, but only outward; and except this hath given cause of this opinion, I cannot learn the ground thereof: only *Orus* writeth, that there is a Fish of this name which turneth sex, and peradventure some men hearing so much of the Fish, might mistake it more easily for the four-footed Beast, and apply it thereunto.

783

These engender not only among themselves, but also with Dogs, Lions, Tygers, and Wolves, for the *Ethiopian* Lion being covered with an Hyæna, beareth the *Crocuta*. The *Thoes*, of whom we shall speak more afterward, are generated betwixt this Beast and a Wolf: and indeed it is not without reason that God himself in holy Scripture calleth it by the name of a *Vespertine Wolfe*, seeing it resembleth a Wolf in the quantity, colour, in voracity and gluttoning in of flesh, in subtilty to overcome Dogs and Men, even as a Wolf doth silly Sheep. Their teeth are in both Beasts like sawes, their genitals alike, and both of them being hungry, range and prey in the night season.

This is accounted a most subtill and crafty beast, according to the allusive saying of *Mantuan*;

Est in tis Pietas Crocodili, astutia Hyænæ.

And the female is far more subtill then the male, and therefore more seldom taken, for they are afraid of their own company. It was constantly affirmed that among eleven Hyænaes, there was found but one female; it hath been believed in ancient time that there is in this beast a Magical or enchanting power, for they write, that about what creature so ever he goeth round three times, it shall stand stone-still, and not be able to move out of the place: and if Dogs do but come within the compasse of their shadow and touch it, they presently lose their voice: and that this she doth most naturally in the full moon; for although the swiftness or other opportunity of the Dogs helpeth them to flie away from her, yet if she can but cast her shadow upon them, she easily obtaineth her prey. She can also counterfeit a mans voice, vomit, cough and whistle, by which means in the night time she cometh to Houses or folds where Dogs are lodged, and so making as though she vomited or else whistling, draweth the Dogs out of doors to her, and devoureth them. Likewise her nature is, if she finde a Man or a Dog on sleep, she considereth whether she or he have the greater body, if she, then she falleth on him, and either with her weight, or some secret work of nature by stretching her body upon him killeth him, or maketh him senselesse; whereby without resistance she eateth off his hands: but if she finde her body to be shorter and lesser then his, then she taketh her heels and flyeth away.

If a Man meet with this Beast, he must not set upon it on the right hand, but on the left, for it hath been often seen, that when in haste it did run by the Hunter on the right hand, he presently fell off from his Horse senseless; and therefore they that secure themselves from this beast, must be careful to receive him on the left side, that so he may with more facility be taken, especially (saith *Pliny*) if the cords wherein he is to be ensnared be fastened with seven knots. *Ælianus* reporteth of them, that one of these coming to a Man asleep in a Sheep-cot, by laying her left hand or fore-foot to his mouth, made or cast him into a deep-sleep, and afterward digged about him such a hole like a grave, as she covered all his body over with earth, except his throat and head, whereupon she sat untill she suffocated and stifled him; yet *Philes* attributeth this to her right foot. The like is attributed to a Sea-calf, and the fish Hyæna, and therefore the old Magicians by reason of this exanimating property, did not a little glory in these beasts, as if they had been taught by them to exercise Diabolical and præstigious incantation, whereby they deprived men of sense, motion, and reason. They are great enemies to men, and for this cause *Solinus* reporteth of them, that by secret accustoming themselves to houses or yards, where Carpenters or such Mechanicks work, they learn to call their names, and so will come being an hungred and call one of them with a distinct and articulate voice, whereby he causeth the man many times to forsake his work and go to see the person calling him; but the subtile Hyæna goeth further off, and so by calling allureth him from help of company, and afterward when she seeth time devoureth him, and for this cause her proper Epithet is *Æmula vocis*, Voyce-counterfeiter.

There is also great hatred betwixt a *Pardall* and this Beast, for if after death their skins be mingled together, the hair falleth off from the *Pardals* skin, but not from the Hyænaes; and therefore when the *Egyptians* describe a superiour man overcome by an inferiour, they picture these two skins; and so greatly are they afraid of Hyænaes, that they run from all beasts, creatures and places, whereon any part of their skin is fastened. And *Ælianus* saith, that the *Ibis* bird which liveth upon Serpents, is killed by the gall of an Hyæna.

He that will go safely through the mountains or places of this beasts abode, *Rasis* and *Albertus* say, that he must carry in his hand a root of

Colloquintida. It is also believed that if a man compasse his ground about with the skin of a Crocodile, an Hyæna, or a Sea-calf, and hang it up in the gates or gaps thereof, the fruits enclosed shall not be molested with hail or lightning. And for this cause Mariners were wont to cover the tops of their sails with the skins of this Beast, or of the Sea-calf: and *Horus* saith, that a man clothed with this skin may passe without fear or danger through the middest of his enemies: for which occasion the *Egyptians* do picture the skin of an Hyæna to signifie fearless audacity. Neither have the Magicians any reason to ascribe this to any præstigious enchantment, seeing that a Fig-tree also is never oppressed with hail nor lightning.

And the true cause thereof is assigned by the Philosophers to be the bitterness of it; for the influence of the heavens hath no destructive operation upon bitter, but upon sweet things, and there is nothing sweet in a Fig tree, but only the fruit. Also *Columella* writeth, that if a man put three bushels of seed grain into the skin of this Beast, and afterward sow the same, without all controversie it will arise with much encrease. *Gentian* worn in an Hyænaes skin seven dayes in stead of an Amulet, is very soveraign against the biting of mad dogs. And likewise if a man hold the tongue of an Hyæna in his hand, there is no Dog that dareth to seize upon him. The skin of the forehead, or the bloud of this Beast, resisteth all kinde of Witchcraft and Incantation. Likewise *Pliny* writeth, that the hairs layed to Womens lips, maketh them amorous. And so great is the vanity of the Magicians, that they are not ashamed to affirm, that by the tooth of the upper jaw of this Beast on the right side bound unto a mans arme or any part thereof, he shall never be molested with Dart or Arrow.

Likewise they say, that by the genital of this beast, and the Article of the back-bone which is called *Atlantios*, with the skin cleaving unto it preserved in a House, keepeth the family in continual concord, and above all other, if a man carry about him the smallest and extreme gut of his intrails, he shall not only be delivered from the Tyrany of the higher powers, but also foreknow the successe and event of his petitions and sutes in Law.

If his left foot and nails be bound up together in a Linnen bag, and so fastened unto the right arme of a Man, he shall never forget whatsoever he hath heard or knoweth. And if he cut off the right foot with the left hand and wear the same, whosoever seeth him shall fall in love with him, besides the Beast. Also the marrow of the right foot is profitable for a Woman that loveth not her Husband, if it be put into her nostrils. And with the powder of the left claw, they which are anointed therewith, it being first of all decocted in the bloud of a Weasil, do fall into the hatred of all men. And if the nails of any beast be found in his maw after he is slain, it signifieth the death of some of his hunters. And to conclude, such is the folly of the Magitians, that they believe the transmigration of souls, not only out of one man into another, but also of man into beasts. And therefore they affirm, that their men *Symis* and religious votaries departing life send their souls into Lions, and the religious women into Hyænaes.

The excrements or bones coming out of the excrements when it is killed, are thought to have virtue in them against Magical incantations. And *Democritus* writeth, that in *Cappadocia* and *Mesia*, by the eating of the hearb *Therionarcha*, all wilde beasts fall into a deadly sleep, and cannot be recovered but by the aspersion of the urine of this beast. And thus much for the first kinde, now followeth the second.

The Second kind of Hyæna, called Papio or Dabuh.

This Beast aboundeth near *Cæsarea* in quantity resembling a Fox, but in wit and disposition a Wolf; the fashion is, being gathered together, for one of them to go before the flock singing, or howling, and all the rest, answering him with correspondent tune: In hair it resembleth a Fox and their voices are so shrill and sounding, that although they be very remote and far off, yet do men hear them as if they were hard by: And when one of them is slain, the residue flock about his carcase, howling like as they made funeral lamentation for the dead.

When they grow to be very hungry by the constraint of famine they enter into Graves of men, and eat their dead bodies, yet is their flesh in *Syria, Damascus*, and *Berutus*, eaten by men. It is called also *Randelos, Abeneum, Aldabha, Dabha, Dabah*, and *Dhoboha*, which are derived from the *Hebrew* word *Deeb*, or *Deeba*. *Dabuh* is the *Arabian* name, and the *Africans* call him *Lesoph*, his feet and legs are like to a mans, neither is it hurtful to other Beasts being a base and simple creature. The colour of it is like a Bear, and therefore I judge it to be *Arctocyon*, which is ingendered of a Bear and a Dog, and they bark only in the night time. They are exceedingly delighted with Musick, such as is used by Pipes and Timbrels, wherefore when the Hunters have found out their caves, they spread their nets and snares at the mouth thereof, and afterwards striking up their instruments, the silly beast inconsiderate of all fraud cometh out and is taken, the picture hereof is formerly expressed. And there was one of these in *Germany* in the year of our Lord 1551 at the City *Auspurg* to be seen publickly. It was brought out of the Wilderness of *India*, it did eat Apples, Pears, and other fruits of trees, and also bread, but especially it delighted in drinking of Wine: when it was an hungry, it climed up into trees, and did shake the boughs to make the fruit fall; and it is reported, that when it is in the tree, it feareth not an Elephant, but yet avoideth all other Beasts which it is not able to resist. It was of a chearful nature, but then especially when it saw a woman, whereby it was gathered that it was a lustful Beast. His four feet were divided like a mans fingers; and the female ever bringeth forth twins, a male and a female together.

It continually holdeth up his tail, shewing the hole behinde, for at every motion it turneth that, as other Beasts do their head. It hath a short tail, and but for that, I should judge it to be a kinde of Ape; I know not whether it be that kinde of little Wolf which *Bellonius* saith aboundeth in *Cilicia* and *Asia*, which in the night time raveneth and cometh to the bodies of sleeping men, taking away from them their boots, caps, or bridles: when they are shut up in the night time they bark like Dogs; but being at liberty they live two hundred in a company, so that there is no Beast so frequent as these in all *Cilicia*.

As for the golden Wolf spoken of by *Oppianus*, I defer the description of it to his due place, for they are not all of one colour: and thus much shall suffice for the second kinde of *Hyæna*.

OF THE CROCUTA.

THE third kinde of *Hyæna* is called *Crocuta*, not the *Gulon* aforesaid, but another different from that, which is said to be an *Æthiopian* four-footed beast, because it is ingendred betwixt a Lyoness and an *Hyæna*. His teeth are all of one bone, being very sharp on both sides of his mouth, and included in the flesh like as in a case, that they may not be dulled: with their teeth they break any thing. It is said also by *Solinus*, that it never winketh, and that their nature seemeth to be tempered betwixt a Dog and a Wolf, yet is it more fierce then either of both, more admirable in strength, and especially of the teeth and belly, having power to break and digest any bone: it imitateth also the voyce of a man to devour them, as is said before in the *Hyæna*.

In the Region *Dachinabades*, which is a mediterranean Country in the East, containing great and high mountains, amongst other wilde Beasts, are abundance of these *Crocutaes*; and at the marriage of *Antonius* the son of *Severus* the Emperor, to *Plautilla* the daughter of *Plautianus*, amongst the spectacles set forth for the delight of the beholders, was a combate betwixt an Elephant and this Beast, which before that time was never to be seen at *Rome* (as *Dion* reporteth). And thus much for the third kinde of *Hyæna*, except I may adde thereunto that Beast which the *Italians* call *Loupchat*, that is *Lupus Catus*, a Wolfe-cat, resembling in face a Cat with sharp and harmful claws, being betwixt a black and spotted colour, and was called an *Indian* Wolf, and this was to be publickly seen, in the Bishops Castle at *Trent*.

OF THE MANTICHORA.

THIS beast or rather Monster (as *Ctesias* writeth) is bred among the *Indians*, having a treble row of teeth beneath and above, whose greatness, roughness, and feet are like a Lyons, his face and ears like unto a mans, his eyes gray, and colour red, his tail like the tail of a Scorpion, of the earth, armed with a sting, casting forth sharp pointed quils; his voyce like the voice of a small Trumpet or Pipe, being in course as swift as a Hart; his wildeness such as can never be tamed, and his appetite is especially to the flesh of man. His body like the body of a Lyon, being very apt both to leap and to run, so as no distance or space doth hinder him; and I take it to be the same Beast which *Avicen* calleth *Marion*: and *Maricomorion*, with her tail she woundeth her Hunters, whether they come before her or behinde her, and presently when the quils are cast forth new ones grow up in their room, where withal she overcometh all the Hunters: and although *India* be full of divers ravening Beasts, yet none of them are stiled with a title of *Anthropophagi*, that is to say, Men-eaters; except only this *Mantichora*. When the *Indians* take a Whelp of this Beast, they all to bruise the buttocks and tail thereof, that so it may never be fit to Bring sharp quils, afterwards it is tamed without peril. This also is the same Beast which is called *Leucrocuta* about the bigness of a wilde Ass, being in legs and Hoofs like a Hart, having his mouth reaching on both sides to his ears, and the head and face of a female like unto a Badgers. It is called also *Martiora*, which in the *Persian* tongue signifieth a devourer of men; and thus we conclude the story of the *Hyæna* for her description, and her several kindes: Now followeth the medicines arising out of her several parts.

THE MEDICINES OF THE HYÆNA.

The Oyl in which a Fox is baked either alive or dead; doth either altogether cure and make whole those which are troubled with the Gout, if so be that the disease or sickness be green or new, or at the least not of too long continuance; it doth so cure them, that although it may happen to return again, yet it will be much more milde and gentle then before it had been. But the Oyl which proceedeth from Foxes doth nothing more drive away the forenamed disease, then that which likewise is got or prepared out of the *Hyæna*; for that hath an excellent and eminent quality of dissolving and dispersing. The flesh of the *Alzabo* is both hot and cold, and being baked with Oyl, doth very much help either men or women which have their feet Gowty, or have any pain in their joynts, which may happen or come by the occasion of cold: for it is of a slender and dissolute substance.

The vanity of the *Magi*, or Wise-men, which is witty in nothing but in circumstance of words, doth say, the best time to take *Hyæna's*, is, when the Moon passeth over the signe called *Gemini*, and that for the most part the hairs be kept and preserved. The *Magi* do also affirm, that the skin of an *Hyæna* being spread upon a sore which was bitten by a mad Dog, doth presently and without any pain cure the same. The same also being bound to that part of the head, which doth ake, will immediately drive away the pain and grief thereof.

The same doth very effectually and speedily help them which are troubled with the Gout, or swelling in the joynts. The flowre of Barley being mingled with the bloud of an *Hyæna*, and fryed or baked over the fire and so taken; doth very much asswage the wringings and wrinchings either in the guts or belly of a man or woman. If the bloud of an *Hyæna* being hot be anointed on them which are infected with the Leprosie, it will without delay very effectually cure them.

The *Hyæna's* flesh being eaten, doth much avail against the bitings of ravenous Dogs; but some are of opinion, that the liver being only eaten is of more force and power to cure or heal them. The nerves or sinews of an *Hyæna*, being beaten to small powder, and dryed and mingled with Frankincense, together, and so drunk, doth restore fertility and plenty of seed in that woman which before was barren.

There is also for the biting of a ravenous Dog another excellent remedy, which is this, first to anoint the place so bitten with the fat or grease of a Sea-calf, or else to give it in drink: and then to make the operation more effectual, mingle the marrow of an *Hyæna*, and Oyl that cometh from the Mastick tree and Wax together, and being so applyed and anointed upon the sore, it will presently cure the same. The same marrow of the *Hyæna* is very good and effectual against the pain and grief in the sinews, as also for the looseness and weakness of the reins.

The marrow which proceedeth from the Chine-bone of an *Hyæna*, being mixed with his Gall and old Oyl altogether, and so boiled until they come unto a soft temperance, and mollifying medicine, being anointed upon the sinews, doth expel and force away an pain of grief thereof whatsoever. The same marrow being bound unto the back of either man or woman, who are troubled with vain phantasies or dreams in their sleep, doth very speedily and very effectually help them. The fat or grease of an *Hyæna* being burnt, doth drive away all venemous Serpents from the place where it is so used.

The same being mingled with leaven, and so being wrought into a plaister, is a very good cure or remedy for the falling of the hair, or the disease called the Foxes evill. The left part of the brain of an *Hyæna* being either anointed upon the nostrils of either men or beasts, is of such vertue, that it will cure diseases upon them which are in a manner mortal. For the sterility or barrenness of women, the eye of an *Hyæna* being mixed with Licoras, and the herb called Dill, and so taken in drink, is of such force and power, that in three days it will make them fit for conception.

The teeth of an *Hyæna* either touched, or bound in order unto the teeth of any man or woman who are troubled with the tooth-ach, will presently ease the pain and vexation thereof. One of the great teeth of an *Hyæna*, being bound with a string unto any that are troubled in the night times with shadows and phantasies, and which are frayed out of their sleep with fearful visions, doth very speedily and effectually procure them ease and rest. The tooth of an *Hyæna* (called *Alzabo*) being bound upon the right arm of any one which is either oblivious or forgetful, and hanging down from the arm unto the middle finger or wrist, doth renew and refresh their decayed memory.

The palat of an *Hyæna* being dryed and beaten to powder, and then mingled with *Egyptian* Allum, and so made hot and mixed altogether, being three times turned in any ones mouth, which hath either sore or ulcer in it, will in small time procure them remedy and help of their vexation and trouble. The flesh which groweth upon the hinder part of the neck, being burned, and then eaten or taken in drink, doth very speedily help and cure the grief and aches of the loins.

The shoulders likewise being used in the aforesaid manner, doth profit much for the healing of any who are vexed with any anguish or pain in their shoulders or sides. The lungs being dryed and taken in drink, do ease any, either man or woman which is troubled either with Colick or Stone. But being dryed into powder, and mingled with Oyl, and so anointed upon the belly; it killeth the Worms, and expelleth all aches away from the belly. The Heart being used in the aforesaid manner and taken in drink, doth ease and help all aches, pains or griefs in the body whatsoever. The white flesh being taken from the breast of an Hyæna, and seven hairs, and the genital of a Hart, being bound all together in the skin or hide of a Buck or a Doe, and afterwards hanged about the neck of a woman which is in travel, will greatly hinder her for bringing forth her childe.

If there shall be any flesh or bones of men found in the body of a dead Hyæna, being dryed and beaten to powder, and then mixed with a certain perfume, they will be very excellent to help the Gowt, or drive away the Convulsion of the sinews. The kell or caull wherein the bowels are contained, being used in the aforesaid manner, and also mixed with Oyl, will be a present remedy against the burnings and inflamations of sores, botches, and Ulcers.

The chine bone of an Hyæna being bruised and beaten into small powder, and so dryed, and then mingled with the tongue and the right foot of a Sea-calf, the gall of an Ox being added thereunto, and all of them boyled or baked together, and anointed upon the hide or skin of an Hyæna; and so lapped about the legs or joynts of them which are troubled with the Gowt, will in short time ease the pain, and rid them altogether of the grief thereof.

The chine bone being also beaten to powder, and given in Wine to drink, is very profitable and necessary for those which are in sore travel or pain of childe-birth. The first or eighth rib of the same Beast, being beaten and mingled with a certain perfume, is very good and medicinable for sores and botches which do break through the flesh.

Their flesh also being eaten, doth quickly cure and heal the bitings or tearings of a ravenous Dog; but their liver being so used, is more effectual and speedy for the curing thereof. The liver of the aforesaid Beast is also very curable for Agues or quartern Feavers being beaten to powder, and drunk in Wine, before the augmentation or second assaults thereof. The same also is an excellent and speedy remedy for the wringings and aches of the belly, as also for that grievous and painful disease called the Colick and Stone. For the same diseases, the gall of a Sea-scorpion, and of a fish called *Hælops*, and of a Sea-crab, and of an Hyæna, being beaten to powder, and mixed together, and so drunk in Wine, is a very good and effectual cure and help. The gall of an Hyæna, by it self alone being rub'd or anointed upon the head of either man or woman whose hairs are fallen off, doth presently procure the hair to renew and grow again; it will also bring hair upon the eye-lids, being rubbed thereupon.

The gall of an Hyæna being mingled with Hony, and anointed upon the eyes; doth sharpen and clear the eye-sight, and expel and drive away all blemishes and small skins which cover the sight of the eye; as also the pain in the eyes called the Pin and the Web. But *Apollonius Pitaneus* doth say, that the gall of a Dog being used in the aforesaid manner, is better to cure the sight of the eyes then the gall of an Hyæna. But *Pliny* whom I think best to follow, and worthyest to be believed, doth best allow of the Hyæna's gall for the aforesaid purpose; and also for the expelling of certain white spots in the eye, which do hinder the sight thereof.

The gall of a Bear and of a Hyæna, being dryed and beaten to powder, and so mixed with the best Hony which is possible to be had, and then stirred up and down a long time together, doth help them unto their eye-sight which are stark blinde, if that it be daily anointed and spread upon the eyes for a reasonable space together: The gall of a Hyæna being baked in a cruse of *Athenian* Hony, and mingled with the crooked herb *Crocis*, and so anointed upon the brows or fore-head of them which are purblinde, doth speedily help them; it doth also ease them which are troubled with the water or rheume which falleth in the eyes. *Democritus* doth also affirm, that if the brow of either man or woman be anointed with the gall of an Hyæna only, it will drive away all darkenings, and blemishes in the eyes, and expel the water or rheume thereof, and also asswage the pain or grief which may come or happen in them whatsoever it be.

The marrow which proceedeth from the chine-bone of an Hyæna, being mixed with his own gall, and with old Oyl, and then baked or boiled in a cruse until it come unto a temperate and mollifying medicine, and then being laid or anointed upon the sinews or nerves, who is in those parts troubled; will throughly heal and cure any default or pain which may happen thereunto. The gall of a male Hyæna being pounded or beaten, and bound about the left thigh of any woman that is barren, doth help for conception. The gall of the same Beast being drunk in Wine, to the value of a dram, with the decoction or liquor which cometh from Spike-lavender, called Oyl of Spike, is a very good remedy and help against the Tympany or swelling of the belly. The gall also being beaten and mixed with the stone called Eat-flesh, is very good and profitable for them which are troubled with the Gowt. The milt of an Hyæna is very effectual to cure and heal any pain or grief in the milt of either man or woman. The lungs being dryed and beaten to powder, and mingled with oyl, and anointed upon the loins of any one who is grieved or troubled in those places, will speedily cure the aches or griefs thereof.

The bladder of an Hyæna being drunk in Wine, is a very good and effectual remedy against the incontinency of man or womans urine, or the running of the reins. But if there be any urine in the bladder of the Hyæna found when he is taken, let it be poured forth into some clean vessel, and mixed with Oyl which proceedeth from the pulse or corn of *India*, and so drunk up, and it will much ease and help them who are troubled in minde, and are full of care and grief. The secret parts of a female Hyæna beaten and mixed with the rinde or skin of a Pomgranate, and taken in drink, is very profitable to cure the inconveniences or pain of a womans secret parts.

The genital of a male Hyæna dryed and beaten to powder, being mingled with a certain perfume, doth cure and help those which are troubled with the Cramp, and Convulsion of the sinews. The feet of an Hyæna being taken, doth heal and cure those which are sand-blinde, and such as have botches and sores breaking through the skin and flesh; and also such as are troubled with inflamations or breedings of winde in their bodies, only by touching and rubbing them over.

The durt of dung which is found in the interior parts of an Hyæna, being burned, and dryed into powder, and so taken in drink, is very medicinable and curable, for those which are grieved with painful excoriations and wringings of the belly, and also for those which are troubled with the Bloudy-flix. And the same being mingled with Goose-grease, and anointed over all the body of either man or woman, will ease them of any pain or grief which they have upon their body whatsoever. The dung or filth of an Hyæna also, being mingled with certain other medicines, is very excellent to cure and heal the bites and stingings of Crocodiles, and other venemous Serpents. The dung it self is also very good to purge and heal rotten wounds and sores which are full of matter, and filthy corruption.

OF THE IBEX.

THIS Beast Deut. the 14. is called *Ako*, and is there rehearsed among the clean Beasts, which although the Septuagints translate *Tragelaphus*, yet we have shewed already in that story, that it cannot stand with the meaning of the holy Ghost, because that Beast is found no where but near the River *Phasis*, or in *Arabia*, (as *Pliny* and *Diodorus* write:) and besides the *Chaldee* translation hath *Jaela*; the *Persians*, *Cotziotu*; the *Arabians*, *Ohal*; all which by *Abraham Ezra*, and *Rabbi Solomon*, and many other of the learned *Jews*, are interpreted to be the *Ibex*, which of the *Germans* is called *Steinbock*; and the female of the *Helvetians* is called *Ybschen*, and *Ybschgeiss*; which words seemeth to be derived from the *Latine* word *Ibex*, and the *Cisalpine French*, which speak *Italian*, dwelling about *Millain*, retain the *German* word for the male, but the female by a proper word they call *Vesina*, and so also do the *Rhætians*. The *Transalpine French*, *Boucestane*; the *Illyrians*, *Kozoroziecz*, and some *Latine* Authors call him *Capricornus*. The *Græcians*, *Ixalos*, and *Ægoceros*: Although I have never read *Capricornus* to signifie a Beast, but only a star, excepting some Poetical *Grammarians*, who affirm this Beast to be a monster of the Sea; and that *Pan* when he fled out of *Egypt*, with other Gods from *Typhon* the Giant, their great Enemy, cast himself into the water, and was transformed into this Beast. But *Jupiter* admiring his wit, placed him among the Stars near to *Leo*, according to this verse:

Humidus Ægoceros, nec plus Leo tollitur urna.

Although there be some that affirm, this Capricorn to be placed among the Stars by *Jupiter*, because he was nursed with him. And that *Pan* hath his hinder parts like a fish, and his fore-part like a Goat, according to these verses:

Tum gelidum valido de pectore frigus anhelans,
Corpore semifero, magno capricornus in orbe.

Wherefore by the signes *Cancer* and *Capricornus*, the Ancients were wont to understand the descending and ascending of the soul: that is to say, by the Cancer or Crab which goeth backward, the souls descent, by Capricorn, (because the Goat climbeth) the souls ascent: and therefore they place it in the Zodiack, where the Sun after the short days beginneth to ascend, for no other cause then for that which I have rehearsed. The Epithets that are given unto this Capricorn, do also belong unto the Ibex, such as are these, moist, cold, swift, horn-bearer, watery, snowy, wool-bearer, tough, bristly, cared, horrible, fierce, tropick, frowning; showring, threatning, black, and such like.

To return therefore unto the Ibex, although I do not dislike the opinion of them, which take it to be a wilde Goat, yet I have reserved it

797

into this place, because of many eminent differences, as may appear by the story. First these are bred in the Alpes, and are of an admirable celerity, although their heads be loaded with such horns, as no other Beasts of their stature beareth. For I do read in *Eustathius*, that their horns are sixteen palms long, of five spans and one palm, and sometimes seaven spans; such was the horn consecrated at *Delos*, being two cubits and a span long, and six and twenty pounds in weight. This Beast (saith *Polybius*) in his neck and hair is like a Buck-goat, bearing a beard under his chin of a span long; as thick as a Colts tail, and in other parts of his body resembleth a Hart.

It seemeth that his *Hebrew* name *Jaal*, is derived of climbing, and *Isidorus* saith that *Ibices* are *quasi Avices*, that is like Birds, because like Fowls of the air, they inhabit the tops of clifts, Rocks, and Mountains, far from the view and sight of men. Their horns reach to their buttocks or hips, so that if at any time he doth chance to fall, he cowcheth his whole body betwixt his horns, to break the strong force and violence of his own weight, and also he is able to receive upon his horns the strokes of great stones which are shot or cast at him; they are knotty and sharp, and as they encrease in age, so do their horns in strongness and other qualities, until they be twenty years old.

These Beasts inhabit and keep their abode in the tops of those Mountains, where the ice never thaweth or dissolveth; for it loveth cold by nature, otherwise it would be blinde; for cold is agreeable to the eye sight and beauty. It is a noble Beast, and very fat. In the small head, and lean legs, it resembleth a Hart; the eyes are very fair and bright; the colour yellowish; his hoof cloven and sharp like wilde Goats. It far excelleth a wilde Goat in leaping; for no man will believe how far off, or what long space it will leap, except he saw it. For there is no place so steep or cragged, that if it afford him but so much space as his foot may stand on, but he will pass over it with a very few jumps or leaps. The Hunters drive them to the smooth and high Rocks, and there they by enclosing them, take them in ropes or toils, if they cannot come near them with shot or swords. When the Beast seeth his hunter which descendeth to him by some Rock, he observeth very diligently, and watcheth if he can see any distance or space betwixt him and the Rock; yea, but so much as his eye-sight can pierce through: and if he can, then he leapeth up and getteth betwixt the Hunter and the Rock, and so casteth him down head-long; and if he can espy no distance at all, then doth he keep his standing until he be killed in that place.

The hunting of this Beast were very pleasant, but that it is encumbred with much labour and many perils, and therefore in these days they kill them with guns. The Inhabitants of *Valois* (neer the River *Sedunus*) take them in their infancy when they are young; and tame them, and until they be old, they are contented to go and come with the tame Goats to pasture, but in their older and riper age they return to their former wilde nature.

Aristotle affirmeth, that they couple or engender together (not by leaping upon each other) but standing upright, upon their hinder legs: whereunto I cannot consent, because the joynts and nerves of their hinder-legs will not be stretched to such a copulation; and it may be that he or his relator had seen them playing together as Goats do, standing upright, and so took that gesture in their pastime for carnal copulation. The female hath less horns then the male, but a greater body; and her horns are very like to a wilde Goats.

When this Beast feeleth infallible tokens of her death, and perceived in that her end by some wound or course of nature approacheth, and is at hand, it is reported by the Hunters, that the ascendeth to the top of some Mountain or high Rock, and there fasteneth one of her horns in the same steep place, going round continually and never standing still, until she have worn that horn asunder, whereby she stayeth her self, and so at length at the instant or point of death, breaking her horn, falleth down and perisheth. And because they the among the Rocks, it falleth out seldom that their bodies are found, but many times when the Snow falleth from the Mountains in great and huge masses, it meeteth wish a living Ibex, and other wilde Beasts, and to oppressing them driveth them down to the foot of the Hils or Mountains, as it doth trees and small houses, which are built upon the sides of them.

In *Creet* they make bows of the horns of these Beasts. And concerning their taking it is not to be forgotten how the Hunter which persueth her from one rock to another, is forced many times for the safegard of his own life, to forsake his standing, and to observe the Beast when it maketh force at him, and to rid himself from danger of death by leaping upon his back, and taking fast hold on his horns, whereby he escapeth. In the house of *Pompey*, where the memorable Forrest of *Gordianus* was painted, there were among other Beasts, two hundred *Ibices*, which *Pompey* gave unto the people at the day of his triumph, for to make spoil thereof at their own pleasure.

THE MEDICINES OF THE IBEX.

Some do commend the bloud of the Ibex to be a very good remedy against the stone of the bladder, being used in this manner: First, they divide it in parte, and put one part of the bloud, and about some six parts of Wine *Apiat*, and Hony mixed together, and do boil them both together luke-warm, and afterwards they reserve it in a clean vessel, and the third day in the morning they give it unto the party to drink who is grieved and then they put him into a Bath about noon time, and in the evening, and this order is to be observed for three days together for it will come to pass, that in that space the Stone will be dissolved and turned into sand gravel, and so by that means will have vent together with the urine.

There is also by the dung of the aforesaid Beast, an excellent remedy against the *Sciatica* or Hipgout, by which that most excellent Physitian *Ausonius* himself was healed, and many other lying desperate of remedy, which is this; to gather the dung of this Beast in the seventeenth day of the Moon, neither is it any great matter whether you gather it in some part of the old Moon, for it will have the same operation: you shall therefore take as much or this dung as you can hold in your hand or fist at one time: so that the quantity of the dung be unlike, and you shall put it in a morter and beat it to powder, and cast twenty grains of Pepper into the same fime, being very diligently pounded or bruised, and then you shall adde nine ounces of the best Hony unro the aforesaid mixture, and four pounds of the best Wine, and mix the potion in the manner of a compound Wine, and the dung or dirt being dryed and beaten first; you shall mingle all the rest, and put them together in a vessel made of glass, that when you have any need, you may have the medicine ready prepared, to comfort him or her which is so afflicted.

OF THE ICHNEUMON.

MARCELLUS and *Solinus*, do make question of this Beast (Ichneumon) to be a kinde of Otter, or the Otter a kinde of this Ichneumon, which I find to be otherwise called *Enydros*, or *Enhydrus*, because it liveth in water; and the reason of this name I take to be fetched *ab investigando*, because like a Dog or hunting Hound, it diligently searcheth out the seats of wilde Beasts, especially the Crocodile and the Asp, whose Egs it destroyeth, And for the enmity unto Serpents, it is called *Ophiomachus*. *Istdorus* is of opinion, that the name of this Beast in the *Greek* is given unto it, because by the favour thereof, the venom and wholesomess of meates is descried. Whereof *Dracontius* writeth in this manner:

Prædicit Suillus vim cujuscunq; veneni.

The Ichneumon foretelleth the power, and presence of all poyson. And it is called *Suillus* in *Latine*, because like a Hog, it hath bristles in stead of hair; *Albertus* also doth call it Neomon, mistaking it for Ichneumon.

There be some that call it an *Indian* Mouse, because there is some proportion or similitude in the outward form between this Beast and a Mouse. But it is certain, that it is bred in no other Nation but only in *Egypt*, about the River *Nilus*; and of some it is called *Mus Pharaonis, Pharaohs* Mouse, For *Pharoah* was a common name to all the *Egyptian* Kings.

There be some that call it *Thyamon*, and *Anschycomon*, and also *Damula*, mistaking it for that Weasil which is an enemy to Serpents called by the *Italians, Donola*: yet I know no learned man but taketh these two names, to signifie two different Beasts. The quantity of it or stature is sometimes as great as a small Cat or Ferret, and the hairs of it like the hairs of a Hog; the eyes small and narrow, which signifie a malignant and crafty disposition; the tail of it very long like a Serpents, the end turning up a little, having no hairs but scales, not much unlike the tail of a Mouse *Ælianus* affirmeth, that both sexes bear young, having seed in themselves, whereby they conceive. For those that are overcome in combates one with another, are branded with a warlike mark of Villanage or subjection to their Conquerours; and on the contrary side they which are conquered and overcome in fight, do not only make vassals of them whom they overcome but in token thereof for further punishment, fill them with their seed by carnal copulation, so putting off from themselves to them, the dolours and torments of bearing young.

This first picture of the Ichneumon was taken by Bellonius except the back be too much elevated.

The second picture taken out of Oppianus Poems, as it was found in an old Manuscript.

When it is angry the hairs stand upright, and appear of a double colour, being white and yellowish by lines or rows in equal distance, entermingled, and also very hard, and sharp, like the hair of a Wolf, the body is something longer then a Cats, and better set or compacted, the beak black, and sharp at the nose like a Ferrets, and without beard; the ears short and round; the legs black, having five claws upon his hinder-feet, whereof the last or hindmost of the inner side of the foot is very short; his tail thick towards the rump: the tongue, teeth and stones are like a Cats, and this it hath peculiar, namely a large passage, compassed about with hair, on the outside of his excrement hole like the genital of a woman, which it never openeth but in extremity of heat; the place of his excrements remaining shut, only being more hollow then at other times. And it may be that the Authors aforesaid, had no other reason to affirm the mutation of feeble or common transmigration of genital power, beside the observation of this natural passage in male, and female. They bring forth as many as Cats and Dogs, and also eat them when they are young: they live both in land and water, and take the benefit of both elements; but especially in the River *Nilus*, amongst the Reeds, growing on the banks thereof, according to the saying of *Nemetian*;

————— *Et placidis Ichneumona quærere ripis,*
Inter arundineas segetes. —————

For it will dive in the water like an Otter, and seem to be utterly drowned, holding in the breath longer then any other four-footed

Beast, as appeareth by his long keeping under water, and also by living in the belly of the Crocodile, until he deliver forth himself, by eating through his bowels, as shall be shewed afterwards. It is a valiant and nimble creature, not fearing a great Dog, but setteth upon him and biting him mortally, but especially a Cat; for it killeth or strangleth her with three bites of her teeth, and because her beak or snout is very narrow or small, it cannot bite any thing, except it be less then a mans fist. The proportion of the body is much like a Badgers, and the nose hangeth over the mouth, like as it were always angry; the nature of it is, finding the Crocodile asleep, suddenly to run down into his throat and belly, and there to eat up that meat which the Crocodile hath devoured, and not returning out again the way it went in, maketh a passage for it self through the Beasts belly.

And because it is a great enemy and devourer of Serpents, the common people of that Countrey do tame them, and keep them familiarly in their houses like Cats, for they eat Mice, and likewise bewray all venemous Beasts: for which cause as is said before, they call it *Pharaohs* Mouse, by way of excellency. At *Alexandria* they sell their young ones in the Market, and nourish them for profit: It is a little Beast, and marvellously studious of purity and cleanliness.

Bellonius affirmeth that he saw one of them at *Alexandria*, amongst the ruines of an old Castle, which suddenly took a Hen and eat it up, for it loveth all manner of fowls, especially Hens and Chickens, being very wary and crafty about his prey, oftentimes standing upright upon his hinder-legs, looking about for a fit booty, and when it espyeth his prey near him, it slideth so close to the ground, as is very admirable, until it be within the reach, and then leapeth upon it with incredible celerity, flying to the throat, and like a Lion killeth all by strangling. It eateth indifferently every living thing, as Snails, Lizards, Camelions, all kindes of Serpents, Frogs, Mice, and Asps. For *Strabo* saith, when he findeth an Asp by the water side, it catcheth hold on the tail, and so draweth the Beast into the water, and receiveth help from the flouds to devour her enemy; and whereas we have said already, that the Ichneumon entreth into the belly of the Crocodile, *Ammianus Marcellinus, Strabo, Pliny,* and *Oppianus,* maketh thereof this discourse following. When the Crocodile hath filled his belly, and over-glutted himself with meat, he cometh to the land to sleep.

Now there is in *Egypt*, a certain Bird called *Crochillus*, whose nature is to wait upon the Crocodile, and with her breath and claws, gently and with a kinde of delight, to pull out the remnants of the meat sticking in the Crocodiles teeth; wherewithal the Crocodile being pleased, openeth his mouth wide, to be thus cleansed by this Bird, and so falling fast asleep gaping, watched all the while by the vigilant eye of the Ichneumon, perceiving him to be deeply plunged in a senseless security, goeth presently and walloweth in sand and dirt, and with a singular confidence entereth into the gate of death, that is, the Crocodiles mouth, and suddenly pierceth like an Arrow through the Monsters wide throat down into his belly.

The Crocodile feeling his unlooked for evil, awaketh out of sleep, and in a rage or madness, void of counsel, runneth to and fro, far and wide, plunging himself into the bottom of the river, where finding no ease, returneth to land again, and there breatheth out his untolerable poyson, beating himself with all his power, striving to be delivered from this unsufferable evil. But the Ichneumon careth not for all this, sitting close upon the liver of the Crocodile, and feeding full sweetly upon his intrails, until at last being satisfied, eateth out her own passage through the belly of her hoast. The self same thing is related by *Plutarch*: but I wonder for what cause the Beast should rowl her self in sand and dirt, to enter into the Crocodiles belly; For first of all, if after her rolling in dirt, she dry her self in the Sun, yet will not that hard crust be any sufficient armour of proof to defend her small body from the violence of the Crocodiles teeth, and besides, it encreaseth the quantity of her body, making her more unfit to slide down through the Crocodiles narrow throat: and therefore, the Authors cannot be but deceived in ascribing this quality to her, when she is to enter into the Crocodile, but rather I believe, she useth this defence against the Asp, as *Aristotle* saith, and therefore the Author seeing her so covered with mud, might easily be mistaken in her purpose. For it is true indeed that when she seeth the Asp upon the land, she calleth her fellows, who arm themselves as before said before the combate, by which means they are safely preserved from the bitings of their enemies; or if it be true that they wallow themselves in the mud, they do not dry themselves in the Sun, but while their bodies are moist, slide down more easily into the Crocodiles belly.

Concerning their fighting with Asps, and the arming of themselves as aforesaid, the *Ægyptians* make this Hieroglyphick of the Ichneumon, to signifie a weak man, that wanteth and craveth help of others; *Pliny* also saith that when the Asp fighteth with this Beast, the Ichneumon turneth to her, her tail, which the Asp taking for defiance, presently maketh force at it, whereby she is overtaken and destroyed by the Ichneumon, but in my opinion this combate is better expressed by *Oppianus*.

For saith he, the *Ichneumon* covereth her body in the sand, as it were in a grave, leaving nothing uncovered but her long Serpentine tail, and her eyes, and so expecteth her enemy. When the Aspe espyeth her threatning rage, presently turning about her tail, provoketh the Ichneumon to combate, and with an open mouth and lofty head doth enter the list, to her own perdition. For the Ichneumon being nothing afraid of this great bravado, receiveth the encounter, and taking the head of the Asp in his mouth, biteth that off, to prevent the casting out of her poyson: afterwards tearing her whole body in pieces, although gathered together wound in a circle; for the success of these two combatants, lyeth in the first blow. If the Asp first bite the Ichneumon, then doth her poyson destroy her adversary; and so on the contrary, if the Ichneumon first bite the Asp, then is the Ichneumon conquerour; and for this cause she covereth her body as aforesaid.

Furthermore, this Beast is not only enemy to the Crocodile and Asp, but also to their Egs, which she hunteth out by the sagacity of her nose, and so destroyeth them, yet doth she not eat them: whereby the merciful providence of God doth notably appear, for the safeguard of mankinde, which in those Countries where these noisome Beasts are bred, hath provided such an enemy to destroy them, both Egs, and Birds, as is friendly and tameable by the hand and wit of man.

For which cause the blinde Pagans, consecrated this Beast to *Latona*, and *Lucina*, and the *Heracleopolites* did think that they possessed all religion; the *Egyptians* themselves did worship them, because as their Countrey is above all other plagued with Serpents, so they are much eased by the help of this little Beast. And when they die, they do not only lament them, but also bury them religiously. And thus much for the description of the Ichneumon. Now followeth their medicinal vertues.

THE MEDICINES OF THE INCHEUMON.

The skin of the Ichneumon, being dryed and beaten into small powder, afterwards mingled with Wine Vinegar, and anointed upon those which are grieved with the venemous or poysonsome bites of the same Beast; doth very effectually and speedily cure them of the same. The pretious stone called by the name of *Iris*, which is very hard, as *Horus* saith, being burned, and afterward beaten or pounded into powder, is an excellent remedy against the venemous biting of the Ichneumon. It is also said, that all Beasts (but especially the Crocodile) do for the most part hate and detest the society of this Beast. There is moreover a very ranck and venemous poyson, which proceedeth from the genital or groin of this Beast.

The hairs of the Ichneumon being taken in a certain perfume, doe very much help and cure those which are troubled or grieved with the Maw-worms. The dung of a Cat, or the dung of this Beast, is very medicinable to be put in any salve, or potion, for the strengthening and confirming of the body. The urine or tail of an Ichneumon, being mixed with the milk of a black Cow, and given unto those which are troubled with that grievous disease, called the Colick and Stone, for the space of three days together in any kinde of drink, will easily and speedily cure them of their pain. The stones of an Ichneumon, being either beaten in powder, or taken raw, either in Wine or any other drink, is very medicinable, and cureable for the easing of all such as are troubled or grieved with any ach, pain, or disease in their belly: And thus much shall suffice concerning the cures, and medicines of the Ichneumon.

OF THE LAMIA.

THIS word *Lamia* hath many significations, being taken sometime for a Beast of *Lybia*, sometimes for a fish, and sometimes for a Spectre or apparition of women called *Phairies*. And from hence some have ignorantly affirmed, that either there were no such Beasts at all, or else that it was a compounded monster of a Beast and a Fish, whose opinions I will briefly set down. *Aristophanes* affirmeth, that he heard one say, that he saw a great wilde Beast having several parts resembling outwardly an Ox, and inwardly a Mule, and a beautiful Woman, which he called afterwards *Empusa*.

When *Apollonius* and his companions travelled in a bright Moon-shine-night, they saw a certain apparition of *Phairies*, in *Latine* called *Lamiæ*, and in *Greek*, *Empusæ*, changing themselves from one shape into another, being also sometimes visible, and presently vanishing out of sight again: as soon as he perceived it, he knew what it was, and did rate it with very contumelious and despiteful words, exhorting his fellows to do the like, for that is the best remedie against the invasion of Phairies. And when his companions did likewise rail at them, presently the vision departed away.

The Poets say, that *Lamia* was a beautiful woman, the daughter of *Bellus* and *Lybia*, which *Jupiter* loved, bringing out of *Lybia* into *Italy*, where he begot upon her many sons, but *Juno* jealous of her husband, destroyed them as soon as they were born, punishing *Lamia* also with a restless estate, that she should never be able to sleep, but live night and day in continual mourning, for which occasion she also stealeth away and killeth the children of others, whereupon came the fable of changing of children: *Jupiter* having pity upon her, gave her exemptile eyes that might be taken in and out at her own pleasure, and likewise power to be transformed into what shape she would: And from hence also came the faigned name of *Acho*, and *Alphito*, wherewithal women were wont to make their children afraid, according to these verses of *Lucilius*.

Terricolas Lamias, Fauni quas Pompiliiq;
Instituere Numæ, tremithas, &c.

Of these *Angelus Politianus* relateth this old wives story, in his preface upon *Aristotles* first book of *Analyticks*, that his Grand-mother told him when he was a childe, there were certain *Lamiæ* in the Wilderness, which like Bug-bears would eat up crying boys, and that there was a little Well

808

near to *Fesulanum*, being very bright, yet in continual shadow, never seeing Sun, where those Phairy women have their habitation, which are to be seen of them which come thither for water.

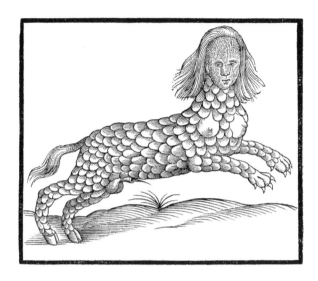

Plutarch also affirmeth, that they have exemptile eyes as aforesaid, and that as often as they go from home, they put in their eyes, wandring abroad by habitations, streets, and cross ways, entring into the assemblies of men, and prying so perfectly into every thing, that nothing can escape them, be it never so well covered: you will think (saith he) that they have the eyes of Kites, for there is no small mote but they espy it, nor any hole so secret but they finde it out, and when they come home again, at the very entrance of their house they pull out their eyes, and cast them aside, so being blinde at home, but seeing abroad. If you ask me (saith he) what they do at home, they sit singing and making of wool, and then turning his speech to the *Florentins*, speaketh in this manner: *Vidistisne oosecro Lamias istas, viri Florentini, quæ se & sua nesciunt, alios & aliena specu antur? Negatis? atqui tamen sunt in urbibus friquentes: verum personatæ incedunt, homines credas, Lamiæ sunt*: that is, to say; O ye *Florentines*, did you ever see such *Phairies*; which were busie in prying into the affairs of other men, but yet ignorant of their own? Do you deny it? yet do there commonly walk up and down the City, *Phairies* in the shapes of men.

There were two women called *Macho*, and *Lamo*, which were both foolish and mad, and from the strange behaviours of them, I came the first opinion of the *Phairies*: there was also an ancient *Lybian* woman called *Lamia*, and the opinion was, that if these *Phairies* had not whatsoever they demanded, presently they would take away live children, according to these verses of *Horace*.

> *Nec quodcunque volet, poscat sibi fabula credi,*
> *Neu pransæ Lamiæ vivum puerum extrahat alvo.*

It is reported of *Menippus* the *Lycian*, that he fell in love with a strange woman, who at that time seemed both beautiful, tender, and rich, but in truth there was no such thing, and all was but a fantastical ostentation; she was said to insinuate herself into his familiarity, after this manner: as he went upon a day alone from *Corinth* to *Conchrea*, he met with a certain phantasm or spectre like a beautiful woman, who took him by the hand, and told him that she was a *Phœnician* woman, and of long time had loved him dearly, having sought many occasions to manifest the same, but could never finde opportunity until that day, wherefore she entreated him to take knowledge of her house, which was in the Suburbs of *Corinth*, therewithal pointing unto it with her finger, and so desired his presence: The young man seeing himself thus wooed by a beautiful woman, was easily overcome by her allurements, and did oftentimes frequent her company.

There was a certain wise man, and a Philosopher, which espyed the same, and spake unto *Menippus* in this manner: *O formose, & a formosis expetite mulieribus, ophin thalpeis, cai su ophis?* that is to say, O fair *Menippus*, beloved of beautiful women, art thou a Serpent and dost nourish a Serpent? by which words he gave him his first admonition, or inkling of a mischief; but not prevailing, *Menippus* purposed to marry with this Spectre, her house to the outward shew being richly furnished with all manner of houshold goods; then said the wise man again unto *Menippus*, this gold, silver, and ornaments of house, are like to *Tantalus* Apples, who are said by *Homer* to make a fair shew, but to contain in them no substance at all: even so whatsoever you conceive of this riches, there is no matter or substance in the things which you see, for they are only inchanted Images and shadows, which that you may believe, this your neat Bride is one of the *Empusæ* called *Lamiæ* of *Mormolyciæ*, wonderful desirous of copulation with men, and loving their flesh above measure, but those whom they do entice, with their venereal marts, afterward they devoure without love or pity feeding upon their flesh: at which words, the wife man caused the gold and silver plate and houshold stuffe, Cooks and Servants, to vanish all away; Then did the Spectre like unto one that wept, entreat the wise man that he would not torment her, nor yet cause her to confess what manner of person she was; but he on the other side being inexorable, compelled her to declare the whole truth, which was, that she was a *Phairy*, and that she purposed to use the company of *Menippus*, and feed him fat with all manner of pleasures, to the intent that afterward she might eat up and devour his body; for all their kinde love was but only to feed upon beautiful young men.

These and such like stories and opinions there are of *Phairies*, which in my judgement arise from the prestigious apparitions of Devils, whose delight is to deceive and beguile the mindes of men with errour, contrary to the truth of holy Scripture, which doth no where make mention of such inchanting creatures; and therefore if any such be, we will hold them the works of the Devil, and not of God, or rather I beleeve, that as Poets call Harlots by the name of *Charybdis*, which devoureth and swalloweth whole Ships and Navies, alluding to the insatiable gulph of the Sea, so the *Lamiæ* are but Poetical allegories of beautiful Harlots, who after they have had their lust by men, do many times devour and make them away, as we read of *Diomedes* daughters; and for this cause also Harlots are called *Lupæ*, She-wolves, and *Lepores*, Hares.

To leave therefore these fables, and come to the true description of the Lamia, we have in hand. In the four and thirty chapter of Esay, we do finde this beast called *Lilith* in the *Hebrew*, and translated by the Ancients *Lamia*; which is there threatned to possess *Babel*. Likewise in the fourth chapter of the Lamentations, there it is said in our *English* translation, that the Dragons lay forth their breasts in *Hebrew* they are called *Ethannim*, which by the confession of the best Interpreters, cannot signifie Dragons, but rather Sea-calves, being a general word for strange wilde Beasts. Howbeit the matter being well examined, it shall appear that it must needs be this Lamia, because of her great breasts, which are not competible, either to the Dragon or Sea-calves; so then we will take it for granted, by the testimony of holy Scripture, that there is such a Beast as this. *Chrysostomus Dicn* also writeth that there are such Beasts in some part of *Lybia*, having a womans face, and very beautiful, also very large and comely shapes on their breasts, such as cannot be counterfeited by the art of any Painter, having a very excellent colour in their fore-parts without wings, and no other voice but hissing like Dragons: they are the swiftest of foot of all earthly Beasts, so as none can escape them by running; for by their celerity they compass their prey of Beasts, and by their fraud they overthrow men. For when as they see a man, they lay open their breasts, and by the beauty thereof, entice them to come near to conference, and so having them within their compass, they devour and kill them: unto the same things subscribe *Cœlius* and *Giraldus*; adding also, that there is a certain crooked place in *Lybia*, near the Sea-shore, full of sand like to a sandy Sea, and all the neighbour places thereunto are Deserts.

If it fortune at any time, that through shipwrack men come there on shore, these Beasts watch upon them, devouring them all, which either endevour to travel on the Land, or else to return back again to Sea, adding also that when they see a man they stand stone still, and stir not till he come unto them, looking down upon their breasts, or to the ground; whereupon some have thought, they seeing them at the first sight, have such a desire to come near them, that they are drawn into their compass, by a certain natural Magical Witch-craft: but I cannot approve their opinions, either in this or in that, wherein they describe him with Horses, feet, and hinder-parts of a Serpent; but yet I grant that he doth not only kill by biting, but also by poysoning, feeding upon the carcasse which he hath devoured: His stones are very filthy and great, and smell like a Sea-calves, for so *Aristophanes* writing of *Cleon* a Coriar, and lustful man, compareth him to a Lamia, in the greatness and filthiness of his stones; the hinder part of this Beast are like unto a Goat, his fore-legs like a Bears, his upper parts to a Woman, the body scaled all over like a Dragon, as some have affirmed by the observation of their bodies, when *Probus* the Emperour brought them forth into publick spectacle: also it is reported of them, than they devour their own young ones, and therefore they derive their name *Lamia* of *laniando*. And thus much for this Beast.

OF THE LION.

BEING now come to the discourse of the Lion (justly styled by all writers the King of Beasts) I cannot chuse but remember that pretty fable of *Esope*, concerning the society and honour due unto this beast. For (saith he) the Lyon, Asse, and the Fox entred league and friendship together, and foraged abroad to seek convenient booties, at last having found one and taken the same, the Lion commanded the Asse to make division thereof, the silly Asse regarding nothing but society and friendship, and not honor and dignity, parted the same into three equall shares; one for the Lion, an other for the Fox, and the third for himself: Whereat the Lion disdaining, because he had made him equall unto the residue, presently fell upon him and tear him in pieces; then bidding the Fox to make the division, the crafty. Fox divided the prey into two parts, assigning unto the Lion almost the whole booty, and reserving to himself a very small portion; which being allowed by the Lion, he asked him, who taught him to make such a partition, Marry (quoth the Fox) the calamity of the Asse, whom you lately toar in pieces.

In like manner, I would be loath to be so simple, in sharing out the discourse of the Lion, as to make it equall with the treatise of the Beasts, lately handled, but rather according to the dignity thereof, to expresse the whole nature, in a large and copious tractate. For such is the rage of illiterate or else envious men, that they would censure me with as great severity, if I should herein, like an Asse, forget my self (if I were in their power) as the Lion did his colleague for one foolish partition.

And therefore as when *Lysimachus*, the son of *Agathocles*, being cast by *Alexander* to a Lion to be destroyed, because he had given poison to *Calisthenes* the Philosopher, that was for the ending of his misery, who was included by the said *Alexander* in a cave to be famished to death; upon some slight displeasure the said *Lysimachus*, being so cast unto the Lion, did not like a cowardly person offer himself to his teeth, but when the Lion came gaping at him to devour him, having wrapped his arme in his linnen garment, held him fast by the tongue, untill he stopped his breath, and slew him; for which cause, he was ever afterwards the more loved and honored of *Alexander*, having at the time of his death, the command of all his treasure.

In like sort, I will not be afraid to handle this Lion, and to look into him both dead and alive, for the expressing of so much of his nature, as I can probably gather out of any good writer.

First of all therefore to begin with his several names, almost all the Nations of *Europe* do follow the *Greeks* in the nomination of this Beast, for they call him *Leon*; the *Latines, Leo*; the *Italians, Leone*; the *French* and *English, Lion*; the *Germans* and *Illyrians, Lew*; the reason of the *Greek* name *Leon*, is taken *para to leussein*, from the excellency of his sight; or from *Laoo* signifying to see, and *Alaos* signifyeth blinde; for indeed there is no creature of the quantity of a Lion, that hath such an admirable eye-sight. The Lionesse, called in *Greek, Leæna*, which word the *Latines* follow, from whence also they derive *Lea* for a Lionesse, according to this Verse of *Lucretius*;

Irritata Leæ jaciebant corpora saltu.

The *Hebrews* have for this Beast male and female, and their young ones, divers names: and first of all for the male Lion, in Deut. 33. they have *Ari*, and *Arieh*, where the *Caldeans* translate it *Ariavan*, the *Arabians, Asad*; the *Persians, Gehad*, and plurally in *Hebrew, Araiius, Araiot, Araoth*, as in the first of Zeph. *Araoth, Schojanim*, roaring Lions; and from hence comes *Ariel*, signifying valiant and strong, to be the name of a Prince: and Isai. 29. Ezek. 43. it is taken for the Altar of Burnt-offerings, because the fire that came down from heaven, did continually lie upon that Altar, like a Lion in his den: or else because the fashion of the temple was like the proportion of the Lion; the *Assyrians* call a Lionesse *Arioth*, the *Hebrews* also call the male Lion *Labi*, and the female *Lebia*, and they distinguish *Ari*, and *Labi*, making *Ari* to signifie a little Lion, and *Labi* a great one; and in Num. 23. in this verse, containing one of Gods promises to the people of *Israel* for victory against their enemies; *Behold my people shall arise like Labi, and be lifted up like Ari*: there the *Caldee* translation rendereth *Labi, Leta*, the *Arabian, Jebu*; the *Persians, Seher*; and *Munster* saith that *Labi* is an old Lion. In Job 38, *Lebaim* signifieth Lions, and in Psal. 57.

Lebaot signifieth *Lionesses*. In the Prophet *Nahum* the 2. *Laisch* is by the *Hebrews*, translated a Lion, and the same word Isa. the 30. is by the *Caldees* translated a Lions whelpe; and in the aforesaid place of the Prophet *Nahum*, you shall finde *Arieh*, for a Lion, for a Lionesse, *Cephirim* for little Lions, *Labi* and *Gur* for a Lions whelp, all contained under one period. The *Saracens* call a Lion at this day *Sebey*. And thus much for the name.

In the next place we are to consider the kinds of Lions, and those are according to *Aristotle* two, the first of a lesse and well compacted body, which have curled manes, being therefore called *Acro-Leonies*, and this is more sluggish and fearful then the other. The second kinde of Lion hath a longer body, and a deeper loose hanging mane, these are more noble, generous, and couragious against all kinds of wounds. And when I speak of manes, it must be remembred, that all the male Lions are maned, but the females are not so; neither the Leopards which are begotten by the adultery of the Lionesse; for from the Lion, there are many Beasts which receive procreation, as the *Leopard* or *Panther*.

There is a beast called *Leontophonus*, a little creature in *Syria*, and is bred no where else but where Lions are generated. Of whose flesh, if the Lion taste, he loseth that Princely power which beareth rule among four-footed beasts, and presently dyeth; for which cause, they which lie in waite to kill Lions, take the body of this *Leontophonus*, which may well be *Englished*, *Lion-queller*, and burneth it to ashes, afterwards casting those ashes upon flesh, whereof if the Lion taste she presently dyeth, so great is the poison taken out of this beast for the destruction of Lions; for which cause, the Lion doth not undeservedly hate it, and when she findeth it, although she dare not touch it with her teeth, yet she teareth it in pieces with her claws. The urine also of this beast sprinkled upon a Lion, doth wonderfully harm him, if it doth not destroy him: They are deceived that take this *Lion-queller* to be a kinde of Worm, or reptile creature, for there is none of them that render urine; but this excrement is meerly proper to four-footed living-beasts. And thus much I thought good to say of this beast in this place, which I have collected out of *Aristotle, Pliny, Solinus,* and other Authors aforesaid, although his proper place be afterward among the Lions enemies.

The *Chimæra* is also faigned to be compounded of a Lion, a Goat, and a Dragon, according to this Verse;

Prima Leo, postrema Draco, media ipsa Chimæra.

There be also many Fishes in the great Sea, about the Isle *Taprobane*, having the heads of Lions, Panthers, Rams, and other beasts. The Tygers of *Prasta* are also engendred of Lions, and are twice so big as they. There are also Lions in *India*, (called *Formicæ*) about the bigness of *Egyptian* Wolves. *Camalopardales* have their hinder parts like Lions. The *Mantichora* hath the body of a Lion. The *Leucrocuta* the neck, tail, and breast like a Lion, and there is an allogorical thing cald *Dæmonium Leoninum*, a Lion Devil, which by *Bellunensis*, is interpreted to be an allegory, signifying the mingling together reasonable understanding with malicious hurtful actions.

It is reported also by *Ælianus*, that in the Island of *Cheos*, a Sheep of the flock of *Nicippus*, contrary to the nature of those beasts, in stead of a Lamb, brought forth a Lion, which monstrous prodigy was seen and considered of many; whereof divers gave their opinions what it did portend, namely, that *Nicippus* of a private man should effect superiority and become a Tyrant: which shortly after came to passe, for he ruled all by force and violence, not with fraud or mercy; for *Fraus* (saith *Cicero*) *quasi Vulpeculæ, vis Leonis esse videtur;* that is, *Fraud is the property of a Fox, and violence of a Lion.*

It is reported that *Meles* the first King of *Sardis*, did beget of his Concubine a Lion, and the Sooth-sayers told him that on what side soever of the City he should lead that Lion, it should remain inexpugnable, and never be taken by any man; whereupon *Meles* led him about every tower and rampier of the City, which he thought was weakest, except only one tower, standing towards the River *Tmolus*, because he thought that side was invincible, and could never by any force be entred, scaled or ruinated. Afterwards in the reign of *Cresus*, the City was taken in that place by *Darius*.

There are no Lions bred in *Europe*, except in one part of *Thracia*, for the *Nemæan*, or *Celonæan* Lion is but a fable; yet in *Aristotles* time, there were more famous and valiant Lions in that part of *Europe*, lying betwixt the Rivers *Achelous* and *Nessus*, then in all *Africa* and *Asia*. For when *Xerxes* led his Army through *Pæonia* over the River *Chidorus*; the Lions came and devoured his Camels in the night time: But beyond *Nessus* towards the East, or *Achelous* towards the West, there was never man saw a Lion in *Europe*; but in the region betwixt them which was once called the Countrey of the *Abderites*, there were such store, that they wandered into *Olympus, Macedonia*, and *Thessalia*; but yet of purpose Princes in Castles and Towers for their pleasures sake, do nourish and keep Lions in *Europe*, where sometimes also they breed, as hath been seen both in *England* and *Florence*. *Peloponnesus* also hath no Lions, and therefore when *Homer* maketh mention of *Dianaes* hunting in the mountains of *Erimanthus* and *Taygetus*, he speaketh not of Lions, but of Harts and Boars.

All the Countries in the East and South, lying under the heat of the Sun, do plentifully breed Lyons, and except in hot Countries they breed seldom, and therefore the Lions of *Fesse, Temesna, Angad, Hippo,* and *Tunis*, are accounted the most noble and audacious Lions of *Africk*, because they are hot Countries. But the Lions of colder Countries have not half so much strength, stomach, and courage. These *Lybian* Lions have not half so bright hair as others, their face and neck are very horrible rough, making them to look fearfully, and the whole colour of their bodies betwixt brown and black; *Apollonius* saw Lions also beyond *Nilus, Hiphasis,* and *Ganges:* and *Strabo* affirmeth that there are Lions about *Meroe, Astapæ,* and *Astabore,* which Lions are very gentle, tame, and fearful, and when the Dog star called *Canu Sirius* doth appear, whereof cometh the Dog days, that then they are drove away by the bitings of great gnats.

Ethiopia also breedeth Lions, being black coloured, having great heads, long hair, rough feet, firy eyes, and their mouth betwixt red and yellow. *Cilicia, Armenia,* and *Parthia,* about the mouth of *Ister,* breed many fearful Lions, having great heads, thick and rough necks and cheeks, bright eyes, and eye-lids hanging down to their noses. There are also plenty of Lions in *Arabia,* so that a man cannot travel neer the City *Aden* over the mountains, with any security of life, except he have a hundred men in his company. The Lions also of *Hircania* are very bold and hurtful; and *India,* the mother of all kinde of beasts, hath most black, fierce and cruell Lions. In *Tartaria* also, and the Kingdom of *Narsinga,* and the Province of *Abasia,* are many Lions, greater then those of *Babylon* and *Syria;* of divers and sundry intermingled colours, both white, black and red. There be many Lions also in the Province of *Gingui,* so that for fear of them, men dare not sleep out of their own houses in the night time. For whomsoever they finde, they devour and tear in pieces. The ships also which go up and down the River, are not tyed to the bank side for fear of these Lions, because in the night time they come down to the waterside, and if they can finde any passage into the barks, they enter in, and destroy every living creature, wherefore they ride at Ancor in the middle of the River.

The colour of Lions is generally yellow, for these before spoken of, black, white and red, are exorbitant. Their hair some of them is curled, and some of them long, shaggy and thin, not standing upright, but falling flat, longer before, and shorter behind, and although the curling of his hair be a token of sluggish timidity, yet if the hair be long and curled at the top only, it portendeth generous animosity. So also if the hair be hard: for beasts that have soft hair, as the Hart, the Hare, and the Sheep, are timorous, but they which are harder haired, as the Boar and the Lion, are more audacious and fearless.

There is no four footed beast, that hath hairs on his neather eye-lids like a man, but in stead thereof, either their face is rough all over as in a Dog, or else they have a foretop as a Horse and an Asse, or a mane like a Lion. The Lionesse hath no mane at all, for it is proper to the male, and as long hairs are an ornament to a Horses mane, so are they to the neck and shoulders of a Lion; neither are they eminent but in their full age, and therefore *Pliny* said; *Turrigeros elephantorum miramur humeros, leonum jubas.* We wonder at the Tower-bearing shoulders of Elephants, and the long hanging manes of Lions. And *Ælianus Rationis expertibus mari præstantiam quandam natura largita est, juba Leo antecellit fœminam, serpens crista.* Nature hath honoured the Male, even in creatures without reason, to be distinguished from the female, as the mane of the male Lion, and the comb of the male Serpent do from their females. *Martial* writeth thus of the Lions mane:

O quantum per colla decus, quem sparsit honorem,
Aurea lunatæ cum stetit unda jubæ!

A Lion hath a most valiant and strong head, and for this occasion, when the Nymphes were terrified by the Lions and fled into *Carystus*, the Promontory wherein they dwelled was called *Coleon*, that is, the Lions-head, where afterwards was built a goodly City. It fortuned as *Themistocles* went thither to manage the affairs of the *Grecians, Epiries* the *Persian*, president of *Phrygia*, intended his destruction, and therefore committed the business unto one *Pisis*, with charge that he should behead *Themistocles*, who came thither to execute that murder; but it happened as *Themistocles* slept at the noon day, he heard a voice crying out unto him, *O Themistocles effuge leonum caput ne ipse in leonem incurras*; that is to say, O *Themistocles* get thee out of the Lions head, lest thou fall into the Lions teeth: whereupon he arose and saved his life.

The face of a Lion is not round as some have imagined, and therefore compared it unto the Sun, because in the compasse thereof, the hairs stand out eminent like Sunbeams, but rather it is square figured like as his forehead, which *Aristotle* saith, you may chuse whether you will call it a forehead, or *Epipedon frontis*, that is, the superficies of a forehead; for like a cloud it seemeth to hang over his eyes and nose, and therefore the *Germans* call a man that looketh with such a countenance, *Niblen* of *Nubilare*, to be cloudy, and it betokeneth either anger or sorrow; also it is called *Scythicus aspectus*, because the *Scythians* were alwayes wont to look as though they were ready to fight.

The eyes of a Lion are red, firy, and hollow, not very round nor long, looking for the most part awry; wherefore the Poets style the Lioness *Torva leæna*. The pupils or apples of the eye shine exceedingly, insomuch as beholding of them, a man would think he looked upon fire.

His upper eye-lid is exceeding great, his Nose thick, and his upper chap doth not hang over the neather, but meet it just: his mouth very great, gaping wide, his lips thin, so that the upper parts fall in the neather, which is a token of his fortitude: his teeth like a Wolves and a Dogs, like sawes, losing or changing only his canine teeth, the tongue like a Cats or Leopards, as sharp as a file, wearing through the skin of a man by licking; his neck very stiffe, because it consisteth but of one bone without joynts, like as in a Wolfe and on Hyæna; the flesh is so hard as if it were all a sinew: There are no knuckles or turning joynts in it called *Spondyli*, and therefore he cannot look backward.

The greatness and roughness of his Neck, betokeneth a magnanimous and liberal minde; Nature hath given a short Neck unto the Lion, as unto Bears and Tygers, because they have no need to put it down to the earth to feed like an Ox, but to lift it up to catch their prey. His shoulders and breasts are very strong, as also the forepart of his body, but the members of the hinder part do degenerate. For as *Pliny* saith, *Leoni vis summa in pectore*, the chiefest force of a Lion is in his breast.

The part above his throat-hole is loose and soft, and his *Metaphrenon* or part of his back against his heart (so called) betwixt his shoulder-blades, is very broad. The back bone and ribs are very strong, his ventricle narrow, and not much larger then his maw. He is most subject to wounds in his flanck, because that part is weakest, in all other parts of his body he can endure many blowes.

About his loyns and hip-bone he hath but little flesh. The lionesse hath two udders in the midest of her belly, not because she bringeth forth but two at a time, for sometimes she bringeth more, but because she aboundeth in milk, and her meat (which she getteh seldom) and is for the most part flesh, turneth all into milk. The tail of a Lion is very long, which they shake oftentimes, and by beating their sides therewith, they provoke themselves to fight. The *Grecians* call it *Alcea*: and *Alciatus* maketh this excellent emblem thereof upon wrath.

> *Alcæam veteres caudam dixere Leonis,*
> *Qua stimulante iras concipit ille graves.*
> *Lutea quum surgit bilis crudescit, & atro*
> *Felle dolor, furias excitat indomitas.*

The neather part of his tail is full of hairs and gristles; and some are of opinion, that there is therein a little sting wherewithal the Lion pricketh it self, but of this more afterwards.

The bones of Lions have no marrow in them, or else it is so small that it seemeth nothing: therefore they are the more strong, solid, and greater then any other beast of their stature, and the males have ever more harder bones then the female, for by striking them together you may beget fire, as by the percussion of Flints; and the like may be said of other beasts that live upon flesh, yet are some of the bones hollow. The legs of a Lion are very strong and full of Nerves, and in stead of an ankle-bone it hath a crooked thing in his pastern, such as children use to make for sport, and so also hath the *Lynx*.

His forefeet have five distinct toes or clawes on each foot, and the hinder feet but four. His clawes are crooked, and exceeding hard, and this seemeth a little miracle in nature, that Leopards, Tygers, Panthers, and Lions, do hide their clawes within their skin when they go or run, that so they might not be dulled, and never pull them forth except when they are to take or devour their prey: also when they are hunted, with their tails they cover their footsteps with earth, that so they may not be bewrayed.

The Epithets of this beast are many, whereby the authors have expressed their several natures, such are these, the curst kind of Lions, full of stomach, sharp, bold, greedy, blunket, flesh-eater, *Caspian*, *Cleonean*, the Lord and King of the beasts and woods, fierce, wilde, hairy, yellow, strong, fretting, teeth-gnashing, *Nemean*, thundering, raging, *Getulian*, rough, lowring, or wry-faced, impatient, quick, untamed, free, and mad, according to this saying of the Poet;

Fertur Prometheus insani Leonis
Vim stomacho opposuisse nostro.

For as the Eagle is faigned to feed upon the heart of *Prometheus*; so also is the Lion the ruler of the heart of man, according to the *Astrologians*. And from hence it cometh that a man is said to bear a stomach when he is angry, and that he should be more subject to anger when he is hungry, then when he is full of meat.

These also are the Epithets of Lions, wrathful, maned, *Lybian*, deadly, stout, great, *Mastlian, Mauritanian, Parthian, Phrygian, Molorchæan, Carthaginian*, preying, ravening, stubborn, snatching, wrinkled, cruell, bloudy, terrible, swelling, vast, violent, *Marmarican*.

These also are the Epithets of the Lionesse, *African*, bold, stony-hearted, vengible, cave-lodging, fierce, yellow, *Getulian, Hyrcanian*, ungentle, *Lybian*, cruell, frowning, and terrible. By all which the nature of this Beast, and several properties thereof, are compendiously expressed in one word.

The voice of the Lion is called *Rugitus*, that is, roaring, or bellowing; according to this Verse of the Poet;

Tigrides indomita rancant, rugiuntq; Leones.

And therefore cometh *Rugitus Leonis*, the roaring of the Lion. It is called also *Gemitus*, and *Fremitus*, as *Virgil, Fremit leo ore cruento*. And again;

Hinc exaudiri gemitus, iræq; leonum
Vincla recusantum, & sera sub nocte rudentum.

And when the young Lions have gotten a prey, in token thereof they roar like the bleating of a Calf, thereby calling their elders to participate with them. The places of their aboad are in the mountains, according to this saying; *Leo cacumina montium amat*.

Their sight and their smelling are most excellent, for they sleep with their eyes open, and because of the brightness of their eyes, they cannot endure the light of fire: for fire and fire cannot agree: also their smelling (for which cause they are called *Odorati*) is very eminent, for if the Lionesse have committed adultery with the Leopard, the male discovereth it by the sense of his Nose, and for this cause also they are tamed in *Tartaria*, and are used for hunting Boars, Bears, Hares, Roebucks, wilde Asses, as also for wilde and outlandish Oxen, and they were wont to be carryed to hunting, two Lions in a Cart together, and either of them had a little Dog following them.

There is no beast more vehement then a she or female Lion, for which cause *Semiramis* the *Babylonian* tyranness, esteemed not the slaughter of a male Lion or a Libbard; but having gotten a Lionesse, above all other she rejoyced therein. A Lion when he eateth is most fierce, and also when he is hungry, but when he is satisfied and filled he layeth aside that savage quality, and sheweth himself of a more meek and gentle nature, so that it is lesse danger to meet with him filled then hungry, for he never devoureth any till famine constraineth him.

I have heard a story of an *Englishman* in *Barbary* which turned *Moor*, and lived in the Kings Court, on a day it was said in his presence that there was a Lion within a little space of the Court, and the place was named where it lodged. The *Englishman* being more then half drunk, offered to go and kill the Lion hand to hand, and therewithal armed himself with a Musket, Sword and Dagger, and other complements, and he had also about him a long Knife; so forth went this regenerate *English Moor*, more like a mad man then an advised Champion to kill this Lion, and when he came to it, he found it a sleep, so that with no perill he might have killed her with his Musket before she saw him: but he like a fool-hardy fellow, thought it as little honour to kill a Lyon sleeping, as a stout Champion doth to strike his enemy behind the back. Therefore with his Musket top he smote the Lion to awake it, whereat the beast suddenly mounted up, and without any thankes or warning, set his forefeet on this Squires brest, and with the force of her body overthrew the Champion, and so stood upon him, keeping him down, holding her grim face and bloudy teeth over his face and eyes; a sight no doubt that made him wish himself a thousand miles from her, because to all likelihood they should be the grinders of his flesh and bones, and his first executioner to send his cursed soul to the Devill for denying Jesus Christ his Saviour. Yet it fell out otherwise, for the Lion having been lately filled with some liberal prey did not presently fall to eat him, but stood upon him for her own safegard, and meant so to stand till she was an hungry; during which time, the poor wretch had liberty to gather his wits together, and so at the last, seeing he could have no benefit by his Musket, Sword, or Dagger, and perceiving nothing before him but unavoidable death, thought for the saving of his credit, that he might not die in foolish infamy, to do some exploit upon the Lion whatsoever did betide him; and thereupon seeing the Lion did bestride him, standing over his upper parts, his hands being at some liberty, drew out his long *Barbarian* knife, and thrust the same twice or thrice into the Lions flank: which the Lion endured, never hurting the man, but supposing the wounds came some other way, and would not forsake her booty to look about for the means whereby she was harmed. At last finding her self sick, her bowels being cut asunder within her (for in all hot bodies wounds work presently) she departed away from the man above some two yards distance, and there lay down and dyed. The wretch being thus delivered from the jawes of death, you must think made no small brags thereof in the Court, notwithstanding, he was more beholding to the good nature of the Lion, which doth not kill to eat except he be hungry, then to his own wit, strength, or valour.

The Male Lion doth not feed with the female, but either of them apart by themselves. They eat raw flesh, for which cause the *Grecians* call them *Omesteres, Omoboroi,* and *Omophagoi*: the young ones themselves cannot long be fed with milke, because they are hot and dry; being at liberty they never want meat, and yet they eat nothing but that which they take in hunting, and they hunt not but once a day at the most, and eat every second day: whatsoever they leave of their meat, they return not to it again to eat it afterwards, whereof some assigned the cause to be in the meat, because they can endure nothing which is unsweet, stale, or stinking; but in my opinion they do it through the pride of their natures, resembling in all things a Princely majesty, and therefore scorn to have one dish twice presented to their own table. But tame Lions being constrained through hunger, will eat dead bodies, and also cakes made of meal and hony, as may appear by that tame Lion which came to

Apollonius, and was said to have the soul in it of *Amasis* King of *Egypt*, which story is related by *Philostratus* in this manner.

There was (saith he) a certain man which in a leam led up and down a tame Lion like a Dog, whithersoever he would, and the Lion was not only gentle to his leader, but to all other persons that met him; by which means the man got much gains, and therefore visited many Regions and Cities, not sparing to enter into the temples at the time of sacrificing, because he had never shed bloud but was clear from slaughter, neither licked up the bloud of the Beasts, nor once touched the flesh cut in pieces for the holy Altar, but did eat upon Cakes made with meal and hony; also bread, Gourds, and sod flesh, and now and then at customary times did drink wine. As *Apollonius* sat in a Temple, he came unto him in more humble manner, lying down at his feet, and looking up into his face, then ever he did to any, as if he had some special supplication unto him, and the people thought he did it for hope of some reward, at the command and for the gain of his Master: At last *Apollonius* looked upon the Lion, and told the people that the Lion did entreat him to signifie unto them what he was, and wherewithal he was possessed; namely that he had in him the soul of a man, that is to say, of *Amasis* King of *Egypt*, who raigned in the Province of *Sai*. At which words the Lion sighed deeply, and mourned forth a lamentable roaring, gnashing his teeth together, and crying with abundance of tears; whereat *Apollonius* stroked the Beast, and made much of him, telling the people that his opinion was, forasmuch as the soul of a King had entred into such a kingly Beast, he judged it altogether unfit that the Beast should go about and beg his living, and therefore they should do well to send him to *Leontopolis*, there to be nourished in the Temple. The *Egyptians* agreed thereunto, and made sacrifice to *Amasis*, adorning the Beast with Chains, Bracelets, and branches, so sending him to the inner *Egypt*, the Priests singing before him all the way, their idolatrous *Hymnes* and *Anthems*; but of the transfiguration of men into Lions, we shall say more afterward, only this story I rehearsed in this place to shew the food of tame and enclosed Lions.

The substance of such transfigurations, I hold to be either Poetical, or else Diabolical. The food therefore of Lions is most commonly of meek and gentle Beasts, for they will not eat Wolves or Bears, or such Beasts as live upon ravening, because they beget in them melancholy: they eat their meat very greedily, and devour many things whole without chewing, but then they fast afterwards two or three days together, never eating untill the former be digested; but when they fast, that day they drink, and the next day they eat, for they seldom eat and drink both in one day: and if any stick in his stomach which he cannot digest, because it is overcharged, then doth he thrust down his nails into his throat, and by straining his stomach pulleth it out again; the self same thing he doth when he is hunted upon a full belly: And also it must not be forgotten that although he come not twice to one carcasse, yet having eaten his belly full, at his departure by a wilful breathing upon the residue, he so corrupteth it, that never after any beast will taste thereof: for so great is the poison of his breath, that it putrifieth the flesh, and also in his own body after it is suddainly ripped up, the intrails stink abominably. The reasons whereof I take to be their great voracity which cannot but corrupt in their stomach, and also the seldom emptying of their belly, for they utter their excrements not above once in three days, and then also it is exceeding dry like a Dogs, stinking abominably, and sending forth much winde: and because their urine smelleth strongly, which also they render like a Dog holding up one of their legs: They never make water, but first of all they smell to the tree, I mean the male Lion. They fall upon some creatures for desire of meat, and especially when they are old, and not able to hunt they go to Towns and Villages, to the stables of Oxen; and folds of sheep, and sometimes to men and devour them, wherefore they never eat herbs but when they are sick.

Polybius affirmeth that he saw them besiege and compasse about many Cities of *Africk*, and therefore the people took and hanged them up upon crosses and gallowses by the high wayes to the terror of others. Wherefore as they excell in strength and courage, so also they do in cruelty, devouring both men and beasts, setting up troops of Horsemen, depopulating the flocks and herds of Cattel, carrying some alive to their young ones, killing five or six at one time, and whatsoever they lay hold on, they carry it away in their mouth, although it be as big as a Camel; for they love Camels flesh exceedingly.

826

And therefore the Lions that set upon the Camels of *Xerxes*, neither medled with the Men, Oxen, nor victuals, but only the Camels: so that it seemeth no meat is so acceptable unto them.

They hate above measure the wilde Asses, and hunt and kill them, according to the saying of the Wiseman, *Leonum venatio onager*; the wilde Asse is the game of Lions, Ecclus. 13. They hate also the *Thoes*, and fight with them for their meat, because both of them live upon flesh, of whom *Gratius* writeth;

> *Thoes commissos (clarissima sama) Leones*
> *Et subiere astu, & parvis domuere lacertis.*

They eat also Apes, but more for Physick then for nourishment. They set upon Oxen, using their own strength very prudently, for when they come to a stall or herd, they terrifie all, that they may take one. They eat also young Elephants, as we have shewed before in the story of Elephants: and so terrible is the roaring of the Lion, that he terrifieth all other Beasts, but being at his prey, it is said he maketh a circle with his tail, either in the snow, or in the dust, and that all Beasts included within the compasse of that circle, when they come into it presently know it, and dare not for their live passe over it (believe this who that list.)

It is also said, that when the Beasts do hear his voice, all of them do keep their standing and dare not stir a foot; which assertion wanteth not good reason, for by terrour and dread they stand amazed. And the writer of the Glosse upon the Prophet *Amos*, upon these words of the Prophet, *Nunquid rugiet Leo in saltu, nisi habuerit prædam?* Will the Lion roar except he have a prey? *Leo* (saith he) *cum famem patitur, si videt prædam dat rugitum, quo audito feræ stant fixo gradu stupefactæ*: that is to say, the Lion when he is hungry and seeth his prey roareth, and then all the wilde Beasts stand still amazed.

They drink but little, and also seldom, as we have said already, and therefore *Gyrus* praising good Souldiers in *Xenophon*, useth these words, *Vos famem habetis pro opsonio, & hydropostan de raon teon Leontoon pherete*; that is to say, hunger is your shambles, and you are more patient of thirst then Lions, although you drink water. Notwithstanding this great valiancy of Lions, yet have they their terrors, enemies, and calamities, not only by Men, but also by Beasts, over whom they claim a soveraignty. We have shewed already in the story of Dogs, that the great Dogs in *India* and *Hircania*, do kill Lions, and forsake other Beasts to combat with them. There is a *Tygre* also called *Lauzani*, which in many places is twice as big as a Lion, that killeth them, and despiseth the huge quantity of Elephants. *Martial* also writeth, that he saw a tame Tygre devour a wilde Lion. A Serpent, a Snake doth easily kill a Lion, whereof *Ambrosius* writeth very elegantly; *Eximia Leonis pulcritudo per comantes cervicis toros excutitur, cum subito a serpente os pectore tenus attollitur, itaque Coluber cervum fugit sed Leonem interficit.* The splendant beauty of a Lion in his long curled mane is quickly abated and allayed when the Serpent doth but lift up his head to his breast; for such is the ordinance of God, that the Snake which runneth from a fearful Hart, should without all fear kill a couragious Lion; and the writer of S. *Marcellus* life, *Alla O men dracon, &c.* How much more will he fear a great Dragon, against whom he hath not power to lift up his tail? And *Aristotle* writeth that the Lion is afraid of the Swine; and *Rasis* affirmeth as much of the Mouse.

The Cock also both seen and heard for his voice and comb, is a terror to the Lion and Basiliske, and the Lion runneth from him when he seeth him, especially from a white Cock; and the reason hereof, is because they are both partakers of the Suns qualities in a high degree, and therefore the greater body feareth the lesser, because there is a more eminent and predominant sunny property in the Cock, then in the Lion.

Lucretius describeth this terrour notably, affirming that in the morning when the Cock croweth the Lions betake themselves to flight, because there are certain seeds in the body of Cocks, which when they are sent and appear to the eyes of Lions, they vex their puples and apples, and make them against nature become gentle and quiet; the Verses are these;

> *Quinetiam gallum nocte explaudentibus alis*
> *Auroram clara consuetam voce vocare,*
> *Quem nequeunt rapidi contra constare Leones*
> *Inq; tucri: ita continuo meminere fugai.*
> *Nimirum quia sunt gallorum in corpore quædam*
> *Semina; quæ quum sint oculis immissa Leonum*

Pupillas intersodiunt, acremq; delorem
Præbent, ut nequeant contra durare seroces.

We have spoken already of the *Leontophonus* how she rendreth a urine which poisoneth the Lion; the noises of wheeles and chariots do also terrifie them, according to the saying of *Seneta, Leoni pavida sunt ad lovissimos strepitus pectora.* The high stomach of a Lion is afraid of a little strange noise. *Anthologius* hath an excellent Epigram of one of *Cybels* Priests, who travelling in the mountans by reason of frost, cold, and snow, was driven into a Lions den, and at night when the Lion returned, he scared him away by the sound of a Bell. The like also shall be afterwards declared of Wolves in their story.

They are also afraid of fire, *Ardentesq; faces, quas quamvis sæviat horret*; For as they are inwardly filled with natural fire (for which cause by the *Egyptians* they were dedicated to *Vulcan*) so are they the more afraid of all outward fire, and so suspicious is he of his welfare, that if he tread upon the rinde or bark of Oke or the leaves of Osyer, he trembleth and standeth amazed. And *Democritus* affirmeth that there is a certain herb growing no where but in *Armenia* and *Cappadocia* which being laid to a Lion, maketh him to fall presently upon his back and he upward without stirring, and gaping with the whole breadth of his mouth, the reason whereof (*Pliny* faith) is because it cannot be bruised.

There is no Beast more desirous of copulation then a Lioness, and for this cause the males oftentimes fall forth, for sometimes eight, ten, or twelve males follow one Lioness, like so many Dogs one salt Bitch: for indeed their natural constitution is so hot, that at all times of the year both sexes desire copulation, although *Aristotle* seemeth to be against it, because they bring forth only in the spring.

The Lioness (as we have shewed already) committeth adultery by lying with the *Libbard*, for which thing she is punished by her male if she wash not her self before she come at him; but when she is ready to be delivered, she flyeth to the lodgings of the Libbards, and there among them hideth her young ones, (which for the most part are males) for if the male Lion finde them, he knoweth them and destroyeth them, as a bastard and adulterous issue, and when she goeth to give them suck she saigneth as though she went to hunting.

By the copulation of a Lioness and an Hyæna is the *Ethiopian Crocuta* brought forth. The *Arcadian* Dogs, called *Leontomiges*, were also generated betwixt Dogs and Lions. In all her life long she beareth but once, and that but one at a time, as *Esop* seemeth to set down in that fable, where he expresseth that contention between the Lioness and the Fox, about the generosity of their young ones: the Fox objecteth to the Lioness, that she bringeth forth but one whelp at a time, but he on the contrary begetteth many cubs, wherein he taketh great delight; unto whom the Lioness maketh this answer: *Parere se quidem unum sed Leonem*; that is to say, she bringeth forth indeed but one, yet that one is a Lion; for one Lion is better then a thousand Foxes, and true generosity consisteth not in popularity, or multitude, but in the gifts of the minde joyned with honorable descent. The Lionesses of *Syria* bear five times in their life; at the first time five, afterwards but one, and lastly they remain barren. *Herodotus* speaking of other Lions, saith, they never bear but one, and that only once, whereof he giveth this reason, that when the whelp beginneth to stir in his Dams belly, the length of his claws pierce through her matrix, and so growing greater and greater, by often turning leaveth nothing whole; so that when the time of littering cometh she casteth forth her whelp and her womb both together, after which time she can never bear more: but I hold this for a fable, because *Homer, Pliny, Oppianus, Solinus, Philes*, and *Ælianus* affirm otherwise contrary, and besides experience sheweth the contrary.

When *Apollonius* travelled from *Babylon* by the way they saw a Lioness that was killed by hunters the Beast was of a wonderful bigness, such a one as was never seen: about her was a great cry of the Hunters, and of other neighbours: which had flocked thither to see the monster, not wondering so much at her quantity, as that by opening of her belly, they found within her eight whelps, whereat *Apollonius* wondring a little, told his companions that they-travelling now into *India* should be a year and eight moneths in their journey; for the one Lion signified by his skill one year, and the eight young ones eight moneths. The truth is that a Lion beareth never above thrice, that is to say, six at the first, and at the most afterwards two at a time, and lastly but one, because that one proveth greater, and fuller of stomach, then the other before him; wherefore nature having in that accomplished her perfection, giveth over to bring forth any more.

Within two moneths after the Lioness hath conceived the whelps are perfected in her womb, and at six moneths are brought forth blinde, weak, and (some are of opinion) without life, which so do remain three dayes together, untill by the roaring of the male their father, and by breathing in their face they be quickned, which also he goeth about to establish by reason; but they are not worth the relating. *Isidorus* on the other side declareth that for three dayes and three nights after their littering, they do nothing but sleep, and at last are awaked by the roaring of their father: so that it should seem without controversie, they are senseless for a certain space after their whelping: At two moneths old they begin to run and walk. They say also that the fortitude, wrath, and boldness of Lions, is conspicuous by their heat, the young one containeth much humidity contrived unto him by the temperament of his kinde, which afterwards by the driness and calidity of his complection groweth viscous and slimie like bird-lime, and through the help of the animal spirits prevaileth especially about his brain, whereby the nerves are so stopped, and the spirits excluded, that all his power is not able to move him, untill his parents partly by breathing into his face, and partly by bellowing, drive away from his brain that viscous humor; these are the words of *Physiologus*, whereby he goeth about to establish his opinion; but herein I leave every man to his own judgment, in the mean season admiring the wonderful wisdom of God, which hath so ordered the several natures of his creatures, that whereas the little Partridge can run so soon as it is out of the shell; and the duckling the first day swim in the water with his dam, yet the harmful Lions, Bears, Tygres, and their whelps are not able to see, stand or go, for many moneths; whereby they are exposed to destruction when they are young, which live upon destruction when they are old: so that in infancie, God clotheth the weaker with more honor.

There is no creature that loveth her young ones better then the Lioness, for both shepherds, and hunters, frequenting the mountains, do oftentimes see how irefully she fighteth in their defence, receiving the wounds of many Darts, and the stroaks of many stones, the one opening her bleeding body, and the other pressing the bloud out of the wounds, standing invincible, never yielding till death, yea death it self were nothing unto her, so that her young ones might never be taken out of her Den; for which cause *Homer* compareth *Ajax* to a Lioness, fighting in the defence of the carcass of *Patroclus*. It is also reported, that the male will lead abroad the young ones, but it is not likely, that the Lion which refuseth to accompany his female in hunting, will so much abase his noble spirit, as to undergoe the Lionesses duty in leading abroad the young ones. In *Pangius* a mountain of *Thracia*, there was a Lioness which had whelps in her den, the which den was observed by a Bear, the which Bear on a day finding the den unfortified, both by the absence of the Lion and the Lioness, entred into the same and slew the Lions whelps, afterward went away, and fearing a revenge, for her better security against the Lions rage, climed up into a tree, and there sat as in a sure castle of defence: at length the Lion and the Lioness returned both home, and finding their little ones dead in their own bloud, according to natural affection fell both exceeding sorrowful, to see them so slaughtered whom they both loved; but smelling out by the foot the murderer, followed with rage up and down untill they came to the tree whereinto the Bear was ascended, and seeing her, looked both of them gastly upon her, oftentimes assaying to get into the tree, but all in vain, for nature which adorned them with singular strength and nimbleness, yet had not endued them with power of climbing, so that the tree hindring them from revenge, gave unto them further occasion of mourning, and unto the Bear to rejoyce at her own cruelty, and deride their sorrow.

Then the male forsook the female, leaving her to watch the tree, and he like a mournful father for the loss of his children, wandred up and down the mountain making great moan and sorrow, till at the last he saw a Carpenter hewing wood, who seing the Lion coming towards him let fall his Axe for fear, but the Lion came very lovingly towards him, fawning gently upon his breast with his forefeet, and licking his face with his tongue; which gentleness of the Lion the man perceiving; he was much astonished, and being more and more embraced, and fawned on by the Lion, he followed him, leaving his Axe behind him which he had let fall, which the Lion perceiving went back, and made signes with his foot to the Carpenter that he should take it up: but the Lion perceiving that the man did not understand his signes, he brought it himself in his mouth and delivered it unto him, and so led him into his cave, where the young whelps lay all embrewed in their own bloud, and then led him where the Lionesse did watch the Bear, she therefore seeing them both coming, as one that knew her husbands purpose, did signifie unto the man that he should consider of the miserable slaughter of her young whelpes, and shewing him by signes, that he should look up into the tree where the Bear was, which when the man saw, he conjectured that the Bear had done some grievous injury unto them; he therefore took his Ax and hewed down the tree by the roots, which being so cut, the Bear tumbled down headlong, which the two furious Beasts seeing, they toar her all to pieces: And afterwards the Lion conducted the man unto the place and work where he first met him, and there left him, without doing the least violence or harm unto him.

Neither do the old Lions love their young ones in vain and without thanks or recompence, for in their old age they requite it again, then do the young ones both defend them from the annoyances of enemies, and also maintain and feed them by their own labor; for they take them forth to hunting, and when as their decrepit and withered estate is not able to follow the game, the younger pursueth and taketh it for him: having obtained it, roareth mightily like the voice of some warning piece, to signifie unto his elder that he should come on to dinner, and if he delay, he goeth to seek him where he left him, or else carryeth the prey unto him: at the sight whereof, in gratulation of natural kindness, and also for joy of good success, the old one first licketh and kisseth the younger, and afterward enjoy the booty in common betwixt them.

Admirable is the disposition of Lions, both in their courage, society and love, for they love their nourishers and other men with whom they are conversant: they are neither fraudulent nor suspicious, they never look awry or squint, and by their good wils they would never be looked upon.

Their clemency in that fierce and angry nature is also worthy commendation, and to be wondered at in such Beasts, for if one prostrate himself unto them as it were in petition for his life, they often spare, except in extremity of famine; and likewise they seldom destroy women or children: and if they see women, children, and men together, they take the men which are strongest, and refuse the other as weaklings

833

and unworthy their honor; and if they fortune to be harmed by a Dart or stone by any man, according to the quality of the hurt, they frame their revenge; for if it wound not, they only terrifie the hunter, but if it pinch them further, and draw bloud, they increase their punishment.

There is an excellent story of a Souldier in *Arabia*, who among other his colleagues, rode abroad on geldings to see some wilde Lions: now geldings are so fearful by nature, that where they conceive any fear, no wit or force of man is able by spur and rod to make him to come near the thing it feareth, but those which are not gelded are more bold and couragious, and are not at all afraid of Lions, but will fight and combate with them. As they road they saw three Lions together, one of the Souldiers seeing one of them stray and run away from his fellowes, cast a Dart at him, which fell on the ground neer the Lions head, whereat the Beast stood still a little and paused, and afterward went forward to his fellowes. At last the Souldier road betwixt him and his fellowes which were gone before, and run at his head with a spear, but missed it, and fell from his Horse to the earth, then the Lion came unto him and took his head in his mouth, which was armed with a Helmet, and pressing it a little did wound him, taking of him no more revenge, then might requite the wrong received, but not the wrong intended; for generally they hurt no more then they are harmed.

There is an obscure Author that attributeth such mercy and clemency to a Beast which he calleth *Melosus*, for he persecuteth with violence and open mouth stout men, and all whom he is able to resist, but yet is afraid of the crying of children. It is probable that he mistaketh it for the Lion, for besides him, I have not read of any Beast that spareth young children. *Solinus* affirmeth that many Captives having been set at liberty, have met with Lions as they returned home, weak, ragged, sick, and disarmed, safely without receiving any harm or violence.

And in *Lybia* the people believe that they understand the petitions and entreatings of them that speak to them for their lives; for there was a certain Captive woman coming home again into *Getulia* her native Countrey through many woods, was set upon by many Lions, against whom she used no other weapon but only threatnings and fair words, falling down on her knees unto them beseeching them to spare her life, telling them that she was a stranger, a captive, a wanderer, a weak, a lean and lost woman, and therefore not worthy to be devoured by such couragious and generous Beasts as they: at which words they spared her, which thing she confessed after her safe return: the name of this woman was called *Juba*. Although about this matter there be sundry opinions of men, some making question whether it be true, that the Lion will spare a prostrate suppliant, making confession unto him that he is overcome; yet the *Romans* did so generally believe it, that they caused to be inscribed so much upon the gates of the great *Roman* Palace in these two Verses;

Iratus recolas; quam nobilis ira leonis;
In sibi prostratos, se negat esse feram.

It is reported also, that if a Man and another Beast be offered at one time to a Lion to take his choise whether of both he will devoure, he spareth the Man and killeth the other Beast. These Lions are not only thus naturally affected, but are enforced thereunto by chance and accidental harmes; as may appear by these examples following; *Mentor* the *Syracusian* as he travelled in *Syria* met with a Lion, that at his first sight fell prostrate unto him, rolling himself upon the earth like some distressed creature, whereat the man was much amazed, and not understanding the meaning of this Beast, he indevoured to run away; the beast still overtook him, and met him in the face, licking his footsteps like a flatterer, shewed him his heel, wherein he did perceive a certain swelling, whereat he took a good heart, going unto the Lion, took him by the leg, and seeing a splint sticking therein, he pulled it forth, so delivering the Beast from pain; for the memory of this fact, the picture of the man and the Lion were both pictured together in *Syracusis*, untill *Plinies* time as he reporteth. The like story is reported of *Elpis*, the *Samian*, who coming into *Africk* by ship, and there going a shore, had not walked very far on the Land, but he met with a gaping Lion, at which being greatly amazed, lie climed up into a tree, forasmuch as there was no hope of any other flight, and prayed unto *Bacchus* (who in that Countrey is esteemed as chief of the Gods) to defend him, as he thought, from the jawes of death; but the Lion seeing him to climb into the tree stood still, layed himself down at the root thereof, destring him in a manner, by his heavie roaring, to take pity upon him, gaping with his mouth and shewing him a bone sticking in his teeth, which through greediness he swallowed, which did so pain him that he could eat nothing; at the last the, man perceiving his minde (moved by a miracle) said aside all fear, and came down to the dumb speaking distressed Lion, and eased him of that misery: which being performed, he not only shewed himself thankful for the present time, but like the best natured honest man, never forsook shore, but once a day came to shew himself to the man his helper, during the time that they abode in those quarters; and therefore *Elpis* did afterward dedicate a Temple unto *Bacchus* in remembrance thereof. And this seemeth to me most wonderful, that Lions should know the vertue of mens curing hands above other creatures, and also come unto them against nature and kinde, but so much is the force of evill and pain, that it altereth all courses of savage minds and creatures.

When *Androcles* a servant run away from a Senator of *Rome*, because he had committed some offence (but what his offence was I know not) and came into *Africa*, leaving the Cities and places inhabited to come into a desert region: Afterwards when *Androcles* had obtained a Master being Consull of that Province of *Africa*, he was compelled by dayly stripes to run away, that his sides might be free from the blows of his Master, and went into the solidary places of the fields, and the sandes of the wilderness; and if he should happen to stand in need of meat; he did purpose to end his life by some means or other; and there he was so schortched with the heat of the Sun, that at last finding out a cave, he did cover himself from the heat of it therein; and this cave was a Lions den. But after that the Lion had returned from hunting, (being very much pained by reason of a thorn which was fastened in the bottom of his foot) he uttered forth such great lamentation & pitiful roarings, by reason of his wound, as that is should seem, he did want some body to make his moan unto for remedy; at last coming to his cave, and finding a young man hid therein, he gently looked upon him, and began as it were to flatter him and offered him his foot, and did as well as he could pray him to pull out the piece of splint which was there fastened: But the man at the first was very sore afraid of him, and made no other reckoning but of death: but after that he saw such a huge savage beast so meek and gentle, began to think with himself, that surely there was some sore on the bottom of the Beast, because he lifted up his foot so unto him and then taking courage unto him, lifted up the Lions foot and found in the bottom of it a great piece of splint, which he plucked forth, and so by that means eased the Lion of his pains, and pressed forth the matter which was in the wound, and did very curiously without any great fear throughly dry it, and wipe away the bloud: the lyon being cased of his pain, laid himself down to rest, putting his foot into the hands of *Androcles*.

With the which cure the Lion being very well pleased, because he handled him so curteously and friendly, not only gave him for a recompence his life, but also went dayly abroad to forrage and brought home the fattest of his prey. *Androcles* whom all this while (even for the space of three years) he kept familiarly, without any note of truely or evill nature in his den, and there the Man and the Beast lived mutually at one commons, the man roasting his meat in the hot Sun, and the Lion eating his part raw, according to kind. When he had thus lived by the space of three years, and grew weary of such habitation, life, and society, he bethought himself of some means to depart; and therefore when the Lion was gone abroad to hunting, the man took his journey away from that hospitality, and after he had travelled three days (wandering up and down) he was apprehended by the legionary Souldiers; to whom he told his long life and habitation with the Lion, and how he ran away from his Master a Senator of *Rome*; which when they understood, they also sent him home again to *Rome* to the Senator.

And being received by his master, he was guilty of so great and foul faults, that he was condemned to death, and the manner of his death was, to be torn in pieces of Wild beasts. Now there were at *Rome* in those days many great, fearful, cruell, and ravening beasts, and among them many Lions: it fortuned also that shortly after the taking of the man, the aforesaid *Lybian* Lion with whom he lived long, seeking abroad for his companion and man-friend, was taken and brought to *Rome*, and there put among the residue, who was the most fierce, grim, fearful, and savage, above all other in the company, and the eyes of men were more fastened upon him then all other beside. When *Androcles* was brought forth to his execution, and cast in among these savage beasts, this Lion at the first sight looking stedfastly upon him, stood still a little, and then came toward him softly, and gently, smelling to him like a Dog, and wagging his tail: the poor examinate and forlorn man, not looking for any thing but present death, trembled and was scarce able to stand upright in the presence of such a beast; not once thinking upon the Lion that had nourished him so long, but the Beast *Accepti beneficti memore* mindful of former friendship, licked gently his hands and legs, and so went round about him touching his body, and so the man began to know him, and both of them to congratulate each other in that their imprisoned occurrence, and to signifie to all the beholders their former acquaintance and conversation, the man by stroking and kissing the Lion, and the Lion by falling down prostrate at the mans feet.

In the mean time a Pardall came with open mouth to devour the man, but the Lion rose up against her, and defended his old friend, and she being instant, the Lion toar her in pieces, to the great admiration of the beholders, as it could not otherwise chuse. Then *Cæsar* which had caused those spectacles, sent for the man, and asked him the cause of that so rare and prodigious an event, who incontinently told him the story before expressed. The rumor whereof was quickly spred abroad among the people, and tables of writing were made of the whole matter, and finally all men agreed that it was fit that both the man and the Lion should be pardoned and restored to liberty: and afterward (saith *Appion*) all the people and beholders of that comedy were isuters to the Senat for the accomplishment thereof, and so the man was pardoned, and the Lion was given unto him for a reward or suffrage, who led him up and down the streets in a leam or slip; *Androcles* receiving money, and the Lion adorned with flowers and garlands, and all men that saw or met them said, *Hic est Leo hospes hominis, hic est homo medicus leonis: Here goeth the Lion which was this Mans Host, and here is the man which was this Lions Physitian.*

Seneca also in his book *De benefictis*, out of *Gellius* writeth so much of another Lion: and indeed there is no man or other Beast more fixed and constant in their love and friendship, or more ready to revenge the breach of amity and kindeness, then is a Lion; as appeareth by this story of *Eudemus*, who writeth of a certain young man, that he nourished together many years a Dog, a Bear and a Lion, who lived in perfect peace and concord without breach, snarling, or appearance of anger. On a day as the Bear and Dog played together and biting one another gently, it happened that the Dog fastened his teeth (in sport) deeper then the Bear cold digest, and therefore presently he fell upon him, and with his claws toar out the soft part of his belly, whereof he presently dyed: the Lion sitting by, and seeing this cruelty, and breach of love, amity, and concord among them that had so long lived together, fell to be inflamed to revenge that perfidie, and like a true king of Beasts, measured the same measure to the Bear as he had done to the Dog, and served him with the same sauce, tearing him instantly in pieces.

There is also in the life of S. *Jerome*, a story of a Lion that was cured by him, as you have read before the Lion was by *Elpis*, and that the Beast in gratitude of that good turn, did ever afterward follow the Asse which brought him home his carriage and provision through the woods; till at last the Lion being asleep, the Asse was stolen away, for sorrow whereof, the Lion put himself in the Asses stead, to bear burthens as he did; within short time after he found out the Asse in the theeves stable, and brought him home again; but I am of *Erasmus* minde concerning this story, that the Author thereof took upon him to write wonders and not truth.

The Kings of *Egypt* and *Syria* did keep tame Lions, to accompany them into their wars, which were led about their own bodies for their guard and custody, against all peril and invasion.

It is also very pertinent to this place, to express the clemency of these Beasts towards the Martyrs and servants of Jesus Christ, both men and women, that so we may observe the performance and accomplishment of that Prophesie, Psal. 91. *They should walke upon the Aspe, and the Cockatrice, and softly tread upon the Lion and the Dragon:* This we are not to attribute to the nature of Lions, but rather to the over-ruling hand of our and their Creator, who in remembrance of his own promise, and advancement of his own glory, stoppeth the mouth of Lions, and restraineth all violence both of living creatures and elements; yet I will not impose any necessity of believing these stories upon the Reader, for I my self report them not for truth, but because they are written. When S. *Anthony* went about to make a grave for the interring of the carkass of *Paul* the first *Anachorite*, and wanted a shovel or spade to turn up the earth, there came two Lions, and with their claws opened the earth so wide and deep, that they performed therein the office of a good grave-maker. The Prophet *Daniel* was cast unto the Lions, to whom (according to the *Babylonian* story) was given for their diet every day, two condemned men, and two sheep, and yet by power of the Almighty whom he served, the Angel of the Lord came down and stopt the Lions mouths, so that in extremity of hunger, they never so much as made force at him, but sate quietly at his feet like so many little Dogs; by which means he escaped all peril and torments of death. *Eleutherius* being cast to the Lions at the command of *Adrian* the Emperor, and *Prisca* a Noble Virgin, at the command of *Claudius Cæsar*, both of them in their several times, tamed the untamed Beasts and escaped death.

Macarius being in the Wilderness or Mountains, it fortuned a Lioness had a den neer unto his cell, wherein she had long nourished blinde whelps, to whom the holy man (as it is reported) gave the use of their eye and sight; the Lioness requited the same with such gratification as lay in her power, for she brought him very many sheep-skins to clothe and cover him. *Primus*, and *Fœlicianus*, *Thracus*, *Vitus*, *Madestus*, and *Crescentia*, all Martyrs, being cast unto Lions received no harm by them at all, but the beasts lay down at their feet, and became came, gentle, and meek, not like themselves, but rather like Doves. When a Bear and a Lion fell upon *Tecla* the Virgin, a Martyr, a Lioness came and fought eagerly in her defence against them both. When *Martina*, the daughter of a Consul could not be terrified or drawn from the Christian faith by any imprisonment, chains, or stripes, nor allured by any fair words to sacrifice to *Apollo*, there was a Lion brought forth to her, at the commandment of *Alexander* the Emperor, to destroy her; who as soon as he saw her, he lay down at her feet wagging his tail, and fawning in a loving and fearful manner, as if he had been more in love with her presence, then desirous to lift up one of his hairs against her. The like may be said of *Daria*, a Virgin, in the days of *Numerian* the Emperor, who was defended by a Lioness; but I spare to blot much paper with the recital of those things (which if they be true) yet the Authors purpose in their allegation is most profane, unlawful and wicked, because he thereby goeth about to establish miracles in Saints, which are lone agone ceased in the Church of God.

Some Martyrs also have been devoured by Lions, as *Ignatius* Bishop of *Autioch*, *Satyrus* and *Perpetua*, he under *Trajan* the Emperor, and they under *Valerian* and *Galienus*. In holy Scripture there is mention made of many men killed by Lions. First of all it is memorable of a Prophet, 1 King. 13. that was sent by the Almighty unto *Jeroboam*, to cry out against the Altar at *Bethel*, and him that erected that Altar, with charge, that he should neither eat nor drink in that place.

Afterward an old Prophet which dwelt in that place hearing thereof, came unto the Prophet, and told him that God had commanded him to go after him, and fetch him back again to his house to eat and drink; wherewithal being deceived; he came back with him contrary to the commandment of the Lord given to himself: whereupon as they sat at meat, the Prophet that beguiled him, had a charge from God to prophesie against him, and so he did: afterward as he went homeward a Lion met him and killed him, and stood by the corps, and his Ass, not eating of them till the old Prophet came and took him away to bury him.

In the twentieth chapter of the same Book of Kings, there is another story of a Prophet, which as he went by the way he met with a man, and bade him in the name of the Lord, to wound and smite him, but he would not, preferring pity before the service of the Lord: Well (said the Prophet unto him) *seeing thou refusest to obey the voyce of the Lord, Behold as soon as thou art departed, a Lion shall meet thee and destroy thee*: and so it came to pass; for being out of the presence of the Prophet, a Lion met him and tore him in pieces.

The Idolatrous people that were placed at *Jerusalem* by the King of *Babel*, were destroyed by Lions; and unto these examples of God his judgements, I will adde other out of humane stories. *Paphages* a King of *Ambracia*, meeting a Lionese leading her whelps, was suddenly set upon by her and torn in pieces, upon whom *Ovid* made these verses:

> *Fœta tibi occurrat patrio popularis in arvo,*
> *Sitq; Paphageæ causa leæna necis.*

Hyas the brother of *Hyades*, was also slain by a Lioness. The people called *Ambraciotæ* in *Africk*, do most religiously worship a Lioness; because a notable Tyrant which did oppress them was slain by such an one. There is a Mountain neer the River *Indus* (called *Litæus*) of a Shepheard so named, which in that Mountain did most superstitiously worship the Moon, and contemned all other Gods, his sacrifices were performed in the night season; at length (saith the Author) the Gods being angry with him, sent unto him a couple of Lions who tore him in pieces, leaving no monument behinde but the name of the Mountain for the accident of his cruel death. The Inhabitans of that Mountain wear in their ears a certain rich stone (called *Clitoris*) which is very black, and bred no where else but in that place.

There is a known story of the two *Babylonian* lovers, *Pyramus* and *Thisbe*, who in the night time had covenanted to meet at a Fountain new the sepulchre of *Ninus*, and *Thisbe* coming thither first, as she sate by the Fountain, a Lioness being thirsty, came thither to drink water, (after the slaughter of an Ox:) at sight whereof, *Thisbe* ran away and let fall her mantle, which the Lioness finding tore it in pieces with her bloudy teeth. Afterward came *Pyramus*, and seeing her mantle all bloudy and torn asunder, suspecting that she that loved him, being before him at the appointed place had been killed by some wilde beast, very inconsiderately drew forth his sword, and thrust the same through his own body, and being scarce dead, *Thisbe* came again, and seeing her lover lie in that distress, as one love, one cause, one affection had drawn them into one place, and there one fear had wrought one of their destructions, she also sacrificed her self upon the point of one and the same sword.

There was also in *Scythia* a cruel Tyrant (called *Therodomas*) who was wont to cast men to Lions to be devoured of them, and for that cause did nourish privately many Lions: unto this cruelty did *Ovid* allude, saying:

Therodomantæos ut qui sensere Leones.

And again:

Non tibi Therodomas crudusq; vocabitur Atreus.

Unto this discourse of the bloud-thirsty cruelty of Lions, you may add the puissant glory of them, who both in Sacred and prophane stories are said to have destroyed Lions. When *Sampson* went down to *Timnath*, it is said,

842

that a young Lion met him roaring to destroy him, but the Spirit of the Lord came upon him, and he tore it in pieces like a Kid; wherein he was a Type of Jesus Christ, who in like sort being set upon by the roaring of the Devil and his members, did with facility (through his divine nature) utterly overthrow the malice of the Devil. Afterward *Sampson* went down to the *Philistine* woman whom be loved, and returning, found that Bees had entred into the Lions carcass, and there builded, whereupon he propounded this Riddle; *A voraci exiit cibus, & ex forti egressa est dulcedo: Out of the devourer came meat, and out of the strong came sweetness.*

Benaiah the son of *Jehoiada* one of *Davids* Worthies, did in the Winter time in the snow kill a Lion in a ditch: *David* himself feeding his fathers flock, slew a Lion and a Bear which had robbed him of a Lamb.

It is reported of *Perdiccas* (one of the Captains of *Alexander*) a valiant man, that he went alone into the Den of a Lioness, but not finding her therein, took away her whelps, and brought them forth to the admiration of all men; for the Lioness both among the *Barbarians* and *Græcians* is accounted the strongest and most unresistible beast. In the Northern parts of the World (saith *Pausanias*) near the monuments of *Alcmea* and *Hyllus*, the sons of *Hercules*, there was a Lion which slew many people, and at last also *Euippus* the only son of King *Megareus*; whereat the King grew so sorrowful and angry, thirsting after revenge, that he promised to the man that could overcome him his daughter, and the succession of his Kingdom: There was a noble and valiant young man called *Alcathus*, who undertook the action and killed the Lion, for which thing he obatained both the Wife and the Kingdom according to the promise of *Megareus*, and therefore in thankfulness of so good fortune, he builded there a famous Temple, dedicating it to *Diana Agrotera*, and *Apollo Agreus*.

We have spoken before of *Lysimachus*, unto whom we may add *Polydamas* the *Scotusæan*, who in all things he took in hand, propounded unto himself the example of *Hercules*, and did kill a Lion of monstrous stature and bigness, being unarmed, in the Mountain *Olympus*; as at another time he held a Buls leg so fast in his hand, that while the Beast strove to loose himself, he left the hoof of his foot behinde him. When *Hercules* was a boy or stripling, he slew the *Teumessian* Lion in *Teumessus* a Mountain of *Beotia*, and pulled off his skin which ever after he wore in stead of a cloke. This Lion is also called a *Nemæan* Lion, yet some are of opinion that the *Nemæan* Lion, was another called also the *Molorchæan*, because having killed the son of *Molorchus* he perswaded *Hercules* which did sojourn with him, to take revenge in his stead.

From whence the *Nemæan* Sacrifices is performed by the *Græcians* in remembrance of *Hercules*, and *Lucan* maketh mention of this *Nemæan* Lion in this verse:

Si sævum premeres Nemeæum sæva Leonem.

And upon the den of the Lion was a Temple builded and dedicated to *Jupiter Nemæus*. *Varinus* speaking of the *Nemæan* Lion, telleth this story thereupon, whereas saith he the said Lion could not be killed with any sword, dart, or other sharp instrument, *Hercules* tore him in pieces with his hands without all weapons, and afterward wore his skin in remembrance of that victory: It happened on a day, that as he travelled he met with his friend *Telamon*, who wanted children, of whom he was intreated that he would make sacrifice to *Jupiter* for him in that weed or garment, and also intreat for a son. *Hercules* yeelded, and taking the golden censor in his hand, made the sacrifice and supplication to *Jupiter*, that *Telamon* might have a son, and as he sacrificed, an Eagle flew over them, which in *Greek* is called *Aetos*, wherefore when *Hercules* saw the same, he charged *Telamon* that his son should be called *Aetos*; that is, an Eagle: and so he was, but afterward he was called *Aiax*, and wore continually that Lions skin which was given him by *Hercules*: and therefore he could not be wounded: But I take this to be but a fable: rather this was the truth; *Aiax* was a valiant souldier, and so warily carried himself in many battails, that he never received wound, but at last he flew himself with his own sword, thrusting it through his neck; and for this cause it was fabled, that he never could be wounded, by a vertue (as was imagined) conferred on him from *Hercules*. *Ovid* hath a witty fiction of one *Phyllius*, who fell so deeply in love with a little boy, that at his pleasure he took many wilde Beasts, Birds, and Lions, and tamed them to the delight of his *Amasius*: at length the insatiable Boy required him to do the like by a Bull, which he had overcome, but *Phyllius* denying that request, they Boy presently cast himself down from a Rock, and was afterward turned into a Swan; by which the Poet declareth, the unmerciful regard which wretchless and childish mindes bear towards the greatest labours and deserts of the best men; and that in such society a man is no longer beloved, then he giveth; also the denial of one small request cannot be endured, although a thousand good turns have gone before it; wherefore such mindes may well be transfused into Swans, which forsake their owners and breeders, going and swimming far from their first and proper habitation.

Having but mentioned such a story, it is not exorbitant to add in one word other fictions of Metamorphosing, and transfiguring men into Lions, which we promised in the former discourse of *Amasis* and *Apollonius*, when I discoursed of the food of Lions.

And first of all, it is not unproper to remember the caution of *Timæus* the *Pythagoræan*, who affirmeth, that the mutation of men into beasts, is but a fiction brought in for the terrour of wicked men, who seeing they cannot be restrained from vice, for the love of well doing, they may be deterred for the fear of punishment, which is meant by such beastly transfigurations.

And this thing is thought to be most consonant to the opinion of *Plato*, for in consideration of the habit, and not of the kinde; a good house-keeper, and charitable nourishing man, is said to be transmuted into a tree: He which liveth by catching and snatching, to serve his own concupiscence, into a Kite; he which for love of military discipline and Martial affairs, into a Lion; he that was a Tyrant and a devourer of men, into a Dragon: and *Empedocles* also said, that if a man depart this natural life, and be transmuted into a brute beast, it is most happiest for him if his soul go into a Lion: but if he loose his kinde and senses, and be transmuted into a plant, then is it best to be metamorphosed into a Laurel or Bay-tree. And for these causes we read of *Hippo* changed into a Lion, and *Atlas* into a Lioness, and the like I might say of *Proteus*, of the *Curetes*, and others: and generally all the Eastern wise men believed the transmigration of spirits from one into another, and insinuated so much to their symmists and disciples, making little or no difference betwixt the natures of men and brute beasts. Therefore they taught that all their Priests after death were turned into Lions, their religious Vestals or women into Hyæna's, their Servants or Ministers in the Temples, about the service of their vain Gods into Crows and Ravens; the Fathers of families, into Eagles and Hawks; but those which served the Leontick Altars, meaning *Nemeæa sacra*, instituted for the honour of *Hercules*, were transformed diversly: but of all these we have already expressed our opinion; namely, to believe and think so basely of mankinde, created after Gods Image, as once to conceive or entertain one thought of such passing of one from another, were most lewd and Diabolical; but to conceive them as allegories, by which the mindes of the wise may be instructed in divine things, and God his judgements; as it is Poetical, so is it not against any point of learning, or good Religion.

As that which hath been already expressed most notably describeth the nature of the Lion, which so that succeedeth hath the same use for the manifestation of the dignity and honour of Beast.

First of all therefore, to begin with his understanding, and to shew how neer he cometh to the nature of man. It is reported by *Ælianus*, that in *Lybia* they retain great friendship with men, enjoying many things in common with them, and drinking at the same Well or Fountain. And if at any time he being deceived in his hunting, and cannot get to satisfie hunger, then goeth he to the houses of men, and there if he finde the man at home, he will enter in and destroy, except by wit, policy, and strength, he be resisted; but if he finde no man, but only women, they by railing on him and rebukes, drive him away, which thing argueth his understanding of the *Lybian* tongue; The sum and manner of those speeches and words which she useth to affright and turn them away from entering houses, are these:

Art not thou ashamed being a Lion, the King of Beasts, to come to my poor cottage to beg meat at the hands of a woman? and like a sick man, distressed with the weakness of body, to fall into the hands of a woman, that by her mercy thou mayst attain those things which are requisite for thy own maintenance and sustentation? yea rather thou shouldst keep in the Mountains, and live in them, by hunting the Hart and other Beasts, provided in nature for the Lions food, and not after the fashion of little base Dogs, come and live in houses to take meat at the hands of men and women.

By such like words she enchanteth the minde of the Lion, so that like a reasonable person, overcome with strong arguments, notwithstanding his own want, hunger, and extremity, he casteth his eyes to the ground ashamed and afflicted, and departeth away without any enterprise: Neither ought any judicious or wise man think this thing to be incredible; for we see that Horses and Dogs which live among men, and hear their continual voyces, do discern also their tearms of threatning, chiding, and rating, and so stand in aw of them; and therefore the Lions of *Lybia*, whereof many are brought up like Dogs in houses, with whom the little children play, may well come to the knowledge and understanding of the *Maurisian* tongue.

It is also said they have understanding of the parts of men and women, and discern sexes, and are indued with a natural modesty, declining the sight of womens privy parts. And unto this may be added the notable story of a Lion in *England*, (declared by *Crantzius*) which by evident token was able to distinguish betwixt the King Nobles, and vulgar sort of people.

As the ears of Horses are a note of their generosity, so is the tail of Lions, when it standeth immoveable, it sheweth that he is pleasant, gentle, meek, unmoved, and apt to endure any thing, which falleth out very seldom, for in the sight of men he is seldom found without rage. In his anger, he first of all beateth the earth with his tail, afterwards his own sides, and lastly leapeth upon his prey or adversary. Some creatures use to wag their tails, when they see suddenly those which are of their acquaintance, as Dogs; but Lions and Buls, do it for anger and wrath. The reason both of one and other, is thus rendred by *Aphrodiseus*. The back-bone of such Beasts is hollow, and containeth in it marrow, which reacheth to the tail, and therefore there is in the tail a kinde of animal motion, and power. For which cause when the Beast seeth one of his acquaintance, he waggeth his tail by way of salutation for the same reason that men shake hands, for that part is the readiest and nimblest member of his body; but Buls and Lions are constrained to the wagging of their tails for the same reason that angry men are light fingered, and apt to strike: for when they cannot have sufficient power to revenge, they either speak if they be Men, or else bark if they be Dogs, or smite their sides with their tail if they be Lions; by that means uttering the fury of their rage to the ease of nature, which they cannot to the full desire of revenge.

But we have shewed before that the Lion striketh his sides with his tail, for the stirring up of himself against dangerous perils, for which cause *Lucan* compareth *Cæsar*, in his warlike expedition at *Pharsalia*, against his own Countrey, before his passage over *Rubicon*, (whilest he exhorted his souldiers) to a Lion beating himself with his own tail in these verses;

Inde mora solvit belli, tumidumq; per amnem,
Signa tulit propere: sicut squallentibus arvis
Æstiferæ Lybies, viso Leo cominus hoste,
Subsedit dubius, totam dum colligit iram;
Mox ubi se sævæ stimulavit verbere caudæ,
Erexitq; jubas, vasto & grave murmur hiatu,
Infremuit: tum torta levis si lancea Mauri
Hæreat, aut latum subeant venabula pectus,
Per ferrum tanti securus vulneris exit.

There are many Epigrams, both *Greek* and *Latine*, concerning the rage, force, friendship, and society of Lions with other beasts, whereof these are most memorable: the first of a Hare, which through sport crept through the mouth of a tame Lion, whereof *Martial* writeth in this sort, teaching her to flie to the Lions teeth against the rage of Dogs in these verses:

Rictibus his Tauros non eripuere magistri,
Per quos præda fugax itq; reditq, lepus.
Quodq; magis mirum, velocior exit ab hoste,
Nec nihil à tanta nobilitate refert.
Tutior in sola non est cum currit arena:
Nec caveæ tanta conditur ille fide,
Si vitare canum morsus, lepus improbe, quæris,
Ad qnæ confugias, ora Leonis habes.

There is another of the same Poets, about the society of a Ram and a Lion, wherein he wondereth, that so different natures should live together, both because the Lion forgetteth his prey in the Woods, and also the Ram, the eating of green grass, and through hunger, both of them constrained to taste of the same dishes: and yet this is no other, then that which was foretold in holy Scripture, the Lion and the Lamb should play together: the Epigram is this;

Massyli Leo fama jugi, pecorisq; maritus
Lanigeri, mirum qua posuere fide,
Ipse licet videas, cavea stabulantur in una,
Et pariter socias carpit uterq; dapes,
Nec fœtu memorum gaudent, nec mitibus herbis,
Concordem satiat sed rudis agna famem.

For we have shewed before, that a Lion in his hunger will endure nothing, but fiercely falleth upon every prey, according to these verses of *Manilius*:

Quis dubitet, vasti quæ sit natura Leonis?
Quasq; suo dictet signo nascentibus artes?
Ille novas semper pugnas, nova bella ferarum
Apparat, & pecorum vivit spolio, atq, rapinis.
Hoc habet, hoc studium postes ornare superbos
Pellibus, & captas domibus configere prædas,
Atq; parare metum sylvis, & vivere rapto.

Concerning the hunting and taking of Lions, the *Indian* Dogs, and some other strong Hunters do set upon Buls, Bores, and Lions, as we have said before in the History of Dogs: but Dogs, which are begotten of Tygers, amongst the *Indians*, and those of *Hyrcania*, especially do this thing, as it is noted by *Mantuan*, concerning the fortitude and courage of a Dog, saying:

Et truculentus Helor certare Leonibus audens.

In the Province of *Gingui*, which is subject to great *Cham* King of *Tartaria*, there are very many Lions which are very great and cruel: and in that Region the Dogs are accounted so bold and strong, as they will not fear to invade or set upon those Lions; And it oftentimes cometh to pass, that two Dogs and a hunting Atcher sitting on Horse-back do kill and destroy a Lion: for when the Dogs perceive the Lion to be near them, they set upon him with great barking, but especially when they know themselves backed with the help of a man, they do not cease to bite the

Lion in his hinder parts and tail: and although the Lion doth oftentimes threaten them with his frowning and terrible countenance, turning himself this way and that way, that he might tear them in pieces, notwithstanding the Dogs looking warily unto themselves, are not easily hurt by him, especially when the hunting Horse-man following them, doth seek the best means to fasten his Dart in the Lion, when he is bitten of the Dogs, for they are wise enough to consider their own help. But the Lion then flyeth away, fearing lest the barking and howling of the Dogs, may bring more company both of Men and Dogs unto him. And if he can he betaketh himself rightly unto some tree, that he may enjoy the same for a place of defence for his back, then turning himself with a scornful grinning, he fighteth with all his force against the Dogs. But the Hunter coming nearer upon his Horse, ceaseth not to throw Darts at the Lion until he kill him: neither doth the Lion feel the force of the Darts until he be slain, the Dogs do unto him so great hurt and trouble.

If a Lion be seen in the time of hunting, being ashamed to turn his back, he doth a little turn away himself if oppressed with a multitude: but being removed from the sight of the Hunters, he doth hastily prepare for flight, thinking that his shame is cleared by concealing himself; and therefore knoweth that the Woods cannot give testimony of his fear.

He doth want in his flight the leaping which he useth in pursuing other Beasts. He doth craftily dissemble and abolish his foot-steps to deceive the Hunters: *Pollux* affirmeth, that if a Hunter do fight against any wilde Beasts, as a Bore, he must not straddle with his legs wide abroad, but keep them together within the compass of a foot, that he may keep his ground stedfast and sure, even as the manner is in Wrestling: for there are some wilde Beasts, as Panthars and Lions, when they are hunted, and are hindred in their course by their Hunters, if they be any thing near them, do presently leap upon them. But the stroke which is given ought to be directed or levelled right against the breast, and the heart, for that being once stricken is incurable. *Xenophon* saith, in his Book concerning hunting, that Lions, Leopards, Bears, Pardals, Lynxes, and all other wilde Beasts of this sort which inhabit Desert places (without *Greece*) are taken about the *Pangean* Mountain, and the Mountain called *Cyrtus*, about *Macedony*: some in *Olympus*, *Mysius*, and *Pindus*: some in *Mysia* above

Syria, and in other Mountains which are fit for the breeding and nourishing Beasts of this kinde. But they are taken partly in the Mountains by poyson of Wolf-bane; for the sharpness of the Region (because that can admit no other kinde of hunting as by Nets and Dogs) but mingling this with that thing in which every wilde Beast delighteth; the Hunters do cast it unto them near the Waters.

There are some also which do descend down in the night time, who are taken in regard that all the ways by which they should ascend unto the Mountains are stopped with Hunts-men, and weapons, neither being so excluded, are they taken without great peril unto the Hunts-men.

There are some also which make pitfals or great ditches in the ground to catch Lions, in the midst whereof, they leave a profound stony pillar, upon which in the night time they tie a Goat; and do hedge the pitfals round about with boughs, lest that it might be seen, leaving no entrance into the same. The Lions hearing the voyce of the Goat in the night, do come unto the place and walk round about the hedge, but finding no place where they may enter, they leap over and are taken.

Oppianus doth describe three manner of ways of hunting Lions, which also *Bellisarius* doth, but he doth describe them my minde very unskilfully.

The first of them is rehearsed out of *Xenophon*; we will notwithstanding also add thereunto *Oppianus*: for he doth in vary both of them. The second is made by fire. The third by whips or scourges.

The first manner of way is therefore as *Gillius* for the most part, translate out of *Oppianus*, in this sort: Where the Hunters of *Lybia* do observe the beaten path or way of the Lion going out of his Den unto the Water, they make a broad and round Ditch near unto it, in the midst whereof they raise up a great pillar, upon this they hang a sucking Lamb; they compass the Ditch round about with a wall of stones heaped together, lest that when the wilde Beast cometh near he perceive the deceit. The Lamb being fastned upon the top of the pillar, doth incitate the hunger-starven heart of the Lion by his bleating, therefore coming near, and not being able to stay longer about the wall, he doth presently leap over and is received into the unlooked for Ditch, in which being now included, he vexeth himself in all the parts of his body, lifting himself up rather at the Lamb, then to go forth, and being again overthrown, he maketh force again. These things *Gillius* affirmeth.

The other manner of hunting by fire, is the device of the people which inhabit about the River *Euphrates*, who hunt Lions after this manner: The Hunters some upon strong Horses, and some upon gray Horses, with glasen eyes, which are most swift, and which dare only meet Lions, when other Horses dare not abide the sight of Lions being on foot do set the Nets. Three of them being placed in the snares remain to under prop the Nets, with stays and stakes: one in the middle, all the rest in both the bendings or turnings of the same, so that he which is in the middle can hear both the other at the farther ends: some setting round about in warlike manner, holding pitchy fire-brands in their right hands, and bucklers in their left, for with those they make a very great noise and clamor, and with shewing their fire brands, put the wilde Beasts in an incredible fear: Therefore when all the Horse-men being spred abroad invade the Beasts, and the Foot-men likewise do follow with a great noise: the Lions being terrified with the crying out of the Hunters, not daring to resist, give place: and aswell for fear of fire, as of the men, they run into the nets and are taken: like as fishes in the night time, by fire are compelled and driven into the nets of the fishers.

The third manner of hunting is done with lesser labour: that is, four strong men armed with shields, and fortified all over with thongs of leather, and having helmets upon their heads, that only their eyes, noses, and lips may appear, with the brandishing of their fire-brands, rustle in upon the Lion lying in his den: he not bearing this indignation, with a gaping and open wide mouth, the lightning or burning of his eyes being inflamed, breaketh forth into a great roaring, and with such celerity rustleth upon them, as if it were some storm or tempest: they with a firm and constant courage abide that brunt: and in the mean while that he coveteth to catch any of them in his teeth or claws, another of them, provoking him behinde doth smite him, and with a loud noise or clamour doth vex him: then the Lion in hast leaving the first which he had taken in his mouth, turneth back his mouth unto the hinder: each of them in several parts do vex him; but he breathing forth warlike strength, runneth here and there, this man he leaveth, that he snatcheth up on high: at the length being broken with long labour, and wearyed, foaming in his mouth, he lyeth down straight upon the ground, and now being very quiet they binde him, and take him from the earth as if he were a Ram. I do also finde that Lions are intricated in snares or traps, bound unto some post or pile, nigh unto some narrow place, by which they were wont to pass.

But *Pliny* saith, that in times past it was a very hard and difficult manner to catch Lions, and that the chiefest catching of them was in Ditches.

In the Mountain *Zaronius* in *Africk*, the strongest men do continually hunt Lions, the best of which being taken, they send them unto the King of *Fesse*: and the King ordereth his hunting in this manner; in a very spacious field there are little hutches built of that height as a man may stand upright in them: every one of these is shut with a little gate; and within standeth an armed man, the Lion being raised, and forced to that place the dores being open, then the Lion seeing the dores open, runneth with great force, which being shut again, he is provoked to anger: Afterward they bring a Bull to combate with him, where beginneth a cruel fight, in which, if the Bull shall kill the Lion, the honour of that day is finished; but if the Lion overcome him, all the armed men, which in number are almost twelve, come forth to fight against the Lion; some of them having Boar-spears of six cubits long: but if the armed men shall seem to overcome the Lion, the King commandeth the number to be diminished, and if on the contrary, the armed men be overcome, the King with his Nobles sitting in an high place to see the hunting kill the Lion with Cross-bows; but it cometh oftentimes to pass, that every one of them is slain before the Lion.

The reward of those which combate with the Lion, is ten golden Crowns, together with a new garment: neither are any admitted unto this fight, except they are of a most pregnant and valorous strength, and born in the Mountain *Zalag*, but those which do first of all provoke and give on set to the Lions, are born in the Mountain *Zaronius*.

To conclude this discourse of the hunting of Lions. If it fortune that he be followed with men and Dogs, yet in the plain fields he never mendeth his pace, as some writers affirm, oftentimes turning about and looking upon his pursuers, as it were to dare their approchment, and to give defiance unto all their pretences: yet having gotten the thickets, he looketh to his safety with his best celerity and speed, so wisely tempering his fear before his foes, that it may seem a boldness, and so politickly when he thinketh no eye seeth him, no longer dissembleth with himself, but runneth away like a fearful Hart, or Hare, laying down his ears, and striking his tall betwixt his legs, like a Cur-dog, seldome times looking behinde him, but most irefully upon those that come before him, especially if he receive from them any wound, whereunto *Horace* alluded, saying:

> *Quid ut noverca me intueris,*
> *Aut ut petiia ferro bellua?*

In his course he spareth no Beast that he meeteth, but falleth upon it like a mad Dog, (except Swine) for he is afraid of their bristles; and if a man do not attempt to wound him, he will snatch at him, and overthrow him, but do him little harm; according to these verses of *Ovid*:

> *Corpora magnanimo satis est prostrasse Leoni:*
> *Pugna suum finem, cum jacet hostis, habet.*

He observeth most vigilantly the hand that woundeth him, and laboureth to take revenge for the evil turn, and so it remaineth in his minde, till opportunity send him his adversaries head: as may appear by this story following.

When *Juba* King of *Moors* (the Father of him which when he was a childe was brought in triumph) travelled through the Wilderness with an Army of souldiers, to repress certain rebels in one part of his Dominion, which had shaken off his government, and to settle them again in their first allegiance. There was a noble young Souldier in his Train, of the race of the Nobility, and not only very strong, but also well experienced in hunting, and by the way he with other of his fellows met with a Lion, at whom he presently cast a Dart, and gave him a sore wound, but not mortal; after the wound received, the Lion went away guilty of his hurt, and the young men did not prosecute him, but went forward on their journey: After a whole year, the King returned homeward the same way, and his company that he carryed with him, among whom was this young gallant that wounded the Lion: The Lion having recovered his hurt, and having his Den near the way and place of his harm, perceiving a return of the Army, went furiously among them, and found out the man whose hand had wounded him, and could not by any help of his associates be stayed from a revenge, but tore the young souldier in pieces, and departed away safe, for the residue seeing his rage, ran all away, thinking him to be some Devil in the likeness of a Lion.

After the taking of Lions, it followeth that we should intreat of their taming, and first of all, they which are tamed in their infancy while they are whelps, are most meek and gentle, full of sport and play, especially being filled with meat; so that without danger, a stranger may meet with them: but being hungry, they return again to their own nature, for as it is true (which *Seneca* saith) *Leonibus manus magister inserit, osculatur Tigrim suus custos*, that is to say; The Master of a Lion may put his hand in his mouth, and the Keeper of a Tyger may kiss him, yet is it also to be feared, *Tigres Leonesq nunquam feritatem exuunt, aliquando submittunt, & cum minime expectaveris, torvitas maligna redibit.* Lions and Tygers do never leave off their wildeness, although sometimes they yeeld, and seem to be submiss, yet upon a sudden when a man expecteth not, their malignant wrath breaketh forth, and they are exasperated.

Wherefore after they grow to be old, it is impossible to make them utterly tame; yet we read in divers stories of tame Lions, whether made so from their littering, or else constrained by the Art of man, such are these which follow; *Hanno* had a certain Lion, which in his expeditions of war carryed his baggage, and for that cause the *Carthaginians* condemned him to banishment, for said they, *Male credi libertas et, cui in tantum cessit etiam seritas,* It is not safe to trust such a man with the government of the Common-wealth, who by wit, policy, or strength, was able to overcome, and utterly to alter the wilde nature of a Lion: for they thought he would prove a Tyrant, that could bring the Lion to such meekness, as to wait on him at Table, to lick his face with his tongue, to smooth his hand on his back, and to live in his presence like a little Dog.

The *Indians* tame Lions and Elephants, and set them to plough. *Onomarchus* the Tyrant of *Cattana*, had Lions with whom he did ordinarily converse. In the Countrey of *Elymis* there was a Temple of *Adonis*, wherein were kept many tame Lions which were so far from wildeness, and fierceness, that they would imbrace and salute the people that came in there to offer: Also if any one called them to give them meat, they would take it gently, and depart from them with quietness. Likewise in the Kingdom of *Fes*, in a plain called *Adecsen*, there are certain Forrests wherein live tame and, gentle Lions, which if a man meet, he may drive away with a small stick or wand without receiving any harm. And in another region of *Africk*, the Lions are so tame, that they come daily into Cities, and go from one street to another, gathering and eating bones; from whose presence neither women nor children run away. Likewise in many parts of *India*, they have Lions so tame, that they lead them up and down in leams, and accustom them to the hunting of Boars, Bulls, and wilde Asses, like Dogs; for their noses are as well fitted for that purpose, as the best Hounds; as we have shewed before of the King of *Tartary*.

And the best means of taming them is the rule of *Apollonius*, which he said was the precept of *Pharaotes*, which is, that they be neither handled too roughly, nor too mildely, for if they be beaten with stripes, they grow over stubborn; and if they be kept in continual flatteries, and used over kindely, they grow over proud: For they held opinion, that by an equal commixtion, of threatning, and fair speaking, or gentle usage, by which means they are more easily brought to good desired conditions; and this wisdom the Ancients did not only use in the taming of Lions, but also in restraining of Tyrants, putting it as a bridle to their mouths, and a hook in their nostrils, to restrain them from fury and madness.

Albertus saith, that the best way to tame Lions, is to bring up with them a little Dog, and oftentimes to beat the same Dog in their presence, by which discipline the Lion is made more tractable to the will of his Keeper. It is said of *Heliogabalus*, that he nourished many tame Lions, and Tygers, and other such noisome beasts, calling himself their great mother; and when he had made any of his friends drunk in the night time, he shut them up together (who quickly fell asleep) through the heaviness of their heads, who being so asleep, he turned in amongst them some of his foresaid children, both Lions, Bears, Tygers, and such like: at whose presence in the morning, his drunken friends grew so amazed, that oft-times, some of them fell dead for fear: and to conclude, there is a story in a certain Epigram, of a Lion wandering abroad in the night time, for the avoiding of frost, and cold, came into a fold of Goats: at the sight whereof the Goat-heards were much afraid, calling in question not only the lives of the flock, but also their own; because every one of them, thought himself bound to fight unto death in defence hereof: whereupon according to the manner of men in extremity, they all made their prayers, desiring God to be delivered from the Lion, and according to their wishes so it came to pass; for after the Lion had lodged in the warm fold of Goats a whole night, he departed in the morning, without doing any harm to man or beast; wherefore I take this Lion to be of the tame kinde, and as in all beasts there are differences both of natures, and inclinations, as we may see in Dogs, some of them being more apt after the manners of men, and to be ruled by them then others; so also I see no reason, but that in the fierce, and royal nature of Lions, some of them should be more inclinable to obedience, subjection, and submission; whereunto being once won, they never afterwards utterly shake off their vassasage and yoke of them which overcome them.

From hence it came, that there were so many spectacles at *Rome*; as first of all *Lucius Sylla*, in the office of his ædility, or oversight of the Temple, brought into the *Roman* circle or ring, one hundred great maned Lions loose, which always before that time, were turned in bound or muffled. And King *Bochus* sent so many valiant Archers, and Dart-casters, to fight with them and destroy them. After him *Pompey* the great, in the same place brought in a combate, consisting of six hundred great Lions, and among them there were three hundred fifty maned Lions: Also he instituted hunting of Lions at *Rome*, wherein were slain five hundred. *Cæsar* when he was Dictator, presented in spectacle four hundred Lions. *Quintus Scævola* caused Lions to fight one with another. But *Marcus Antonius* in the civil War, after the battail of *Pharsalia*, did first of all cause Lions to be yoked, and draw the Chariot of triumphs; where he himself sate, with one *Citheris* a Jester: which thing was not done, without shew and observations of a prodigious and monstrous action, and especially in those times, wherein it was interpreted, that as the noble spirits of those Lions were so much abased, and vassalaged, in stead of Horses to draw a Chariot, they being in nature the King of Beasts, so it was feared that the ancient Nobility of *Rome*, the grave Senators, and gallant Gentlemen, Commanders of the whole Commonwealth, should in time to come, through civil wars, and pride of the people, be deprived of all honour, and brought down to the basest offices of the whole State. *Antoninus Pius* nourished a hundred Lions. *Domitian* the Emperor, called for *Acillius Gabrio* the Consul, into *Albania*, about the time that the games were celebrated, for the prosperity of youth and young men, which were called *Juvenalia*, to fight with a great Lion, and *Acillius* coming wisely into the combate, did easily kill him. In ancient time when Lions could not be tamed, they did discern them by their teeth, and nails, and so taking as it were the sting and poyson from the Serpent, and the weapons wherein consisteth all their strength, they were without all peril, sent into the publick Assemblies, at the time of their general meetings, and great feasts. *Martial* hath an excellent Epigram, of the great Lion before exhibited in publick spectacle by *Domitian*, wondering that the *Massylian* and *Ausonian* shepheards were so afraid of this Lion and made as great a noise, murmur, about his presence, as if he had been a heard of Lions, and therefore he commendeth the *Lybian* Countrey for breeding such a beast, and withal expresseth the joy of the shepheards for his death, as are shown in these verses following:

> *Auditur quantum Massyla per avia murmur,*
> *Innumero quoties sylva Leone furit:*
> *Pallidus attonitos ad plena mapalia pastor*
> *Cum revocat tauros, & sine mente pecus:*
> *Tantus in Ausonia fremuit modo terror arena;*
> *Quis non esse gregem crederet? unus erat,*
> *Sed cujus tremerent ipsi quoq; jura Leenes,*
> *Cui diadema daret marmore picta Nomas.*
> *O quantum per colla decus, quem sparsit honorem*
> *Aurea lunatæ cum stetit unda jubæ!*

Grandia quam decuit lotum venabula pectus,
  Quantaq; de magna gaudia morte tulit?
Unde tuis Lybie tam felix gloria sylvis?
  A Cybeles nunquia venerat ille jugis?
An magis Hereulo Germanice misit ab astro
  Hanc tibi vel frater, vel pater ipse feram?

We have shewed already that Lions although never so well tamed, become wilde again, and that through hunger, which breaketh through stone walls, according to the common proverb, and therefore maketh them to destroy whatsoever cometh in their way, according to these verses of *Virgil*;

Impastus ceu plena Leo per ovilla turbans,
(Suadet enim vesena fames) manditq; trahitq;
Molle pecus, mutumq; metu, fremit ore cruento.

Such a one was the Lion of *Borsius* Duke of *Ferrara*, who being in his cave would devour Bulk, Bears, and Boars, but with a Hare or little Whelp he would play, and do them no harm; at last leaving all his tamable nature, he destroyed a young wench, who oftentimes came unto him to combe and stroke his mane, and also to bring him meat and flowers, upon whom *Stroza* made these two verses;

Sustulit ingratus cui quondam plurima debens
Pectendasq; jubas, & fera colla dabat.

The like unto this also, was the tame Lion that *Marital* speaketh of, who returning to his first nature, destroyed two young children, and therefore he saith justly, that his cruelty exceedeth the cruelty of war; the Epigram is this:

Verbera securi solitus Leo ferre magistri,
  Insertamq; pati blandus in ora manum,
Dedidicit pacem subito, feritate reversa,
  Quanta nec in Lybicis debuit esse jugis.
Nam duo de tenera puerilia corpora turba,
  Sanguineam rastris quæ renovabat humum,

859

Sævus & infælix furiali dente peremit,
Martia non vidit majus arena nefas.

Having thus spoken of the taming and taking Lions, it also now followeth to entreat of the length of their life, and the diseases that are incident unto them, with their several cures: first therefore, it is held that they live very long, as threescore, or fourscore years: for it hath been seen, that when a Lion hath been taken alive, and in his taking received some wound whereby he became lame, or lost some of his teeth, yet did he live many years; and also it is found that some have been taken without teeth, which were all fallen out of their head through age, and *Ælianus* saith, that a Lion and a Dolphin, do both consume away through multitude of years. The sicknesses wherewithal they are annoid, are not very many, but those which they have are continual: for the most part their intrails or inward parts, are never sound, but subject to corruption, as may appear by their spittle, and also by their biting, and scratching of their nails; for a man lightly touched by them at some times is as much poysoned, as the biting of a mad Dog; also by reason of his extreme hot nature, every each other day he suffereth one sickness or other, at which time he lyeth prostrate upon the earth, roaring not all the day long, but at certain hours, and in his wrath he is consumed through the heat inclosed in his own body. And in his best estate he is afflicted with a quartane Ague, even then when he seemeth to be in health, and except this disease did restrain his violence and malice by weakning of his body, he would be far more hurtful to mankinde then he is: and this is to be understood, in the Summer time he falleth into this disease sometime at the sight of a man, and is cured by the bloud of Dogs, according to *Albertus* and *Physiologus,* when he feeleth himself sick, through abundance of meat, he falleth a vomiting, either by the strength of nature, or else helpeth himself by eating a kinde of grass, or green corn in the blade, or else rapes; and if none of these prevail, then he fasteth, and eateth no more till he finde ease; or else if he can meet with an Ape, he devoureth and eateth his flesh, and this is the principal remedy and medicine which he receiveth against all his diseases, both in youth and age; and when he groweth old, being no more able to hunt Harts, Boars, and such beasts, he exerciseth his whole strength in the hunting and taking of Apes, whereupon he liveth totally; and for these causes, there is a

comparison betwixt the Lion and the Dolphin, in *Ælianus*. *Leoni, &*
Delphino multa sunt communia, uterq; imparat, ille terrenis, hic
aquatilibus bestiis, senectute ambo tabescunt, & cum sunt in ægritudine, illi
terrestris simia medetur, huic marina quoq; simia remedio est: that is, the
Lion and the Dolphin do agree in many things, both of them are Kings,
this ruleth over the beasts of the Earth, and that over the beasts of the Sea;
both of them consume through age, and long life; and as the Lion
recovereth by eating an Ape of the Earth, so is the Dolphin cured by eating
an Ape of the Sea; and thus much for the diseases and cures of Lion.

Unto this natural discourse of Lions belongeth the use of their parts,
both outward and inward, and also the several pictures and statues erected
for their singular monuments. First therefore with the skins of Lions were
the ancient *Moores* and *Barbarians*, inhabiting betwixt the Mountain
Caucasus and the River *Cophena*, and so they appeared to *Apollonius* and
his companions; as also in the skins of Panthers, with both which, they did
not only clothe themselves in the day time, but also slept upon them in the
night; and therefore *Hercules* is pictured wearing a Lions skin, that the
world might be admonished, what was the antient attire of their fore-
fathers. *Virgil* describeth *Aventinus* covered with a Lions skin in this sort:

> —— —— *Quem fulva Leonis*
> *Pellis obit totum præfulgens unguibus aures.*

And again:

> *Ipse pedes tegmen torquens immane Leonis,*
> *Terribili impexum seta, cum dentibus albis,*
> *Indutus capiti, &c.* ——

And *Æneas* sleeping upon a Lions skin, saying:

> —— *Fulviq; insternor pelle Leonis.*

And elsewhere,

> *Præcipuumq; toro, & villosi pelle Leonis*
> *Accipit Aeneam.* ——

Adrastus was commanded by the Oracle to marry his Daughters to a Boar and a Lion, when they came a wooing unto them. Whereupon *Tydeus* came in a Boars skin, and *Polynices* in a Lions skin, unto whom he gave his Daughters in marriage, taking it to be the meaning of the Oracle, that men clothed in those skins should be the Husbands of his Daughters. From hence came the common proverb; *Induitis me Leonis exuvium*, you put upon me a Lions skin, to signifie a man that taketh upon him more then he is able to perform, and spend more then their condition will afford, and the beginning of the proverb was taken from *Hercules*, who clothed in a Lions skin as we have said before, and bearing in one hand a Club, and in the other a Bow, in which attire he went down to Hell to fetch out *Cerberus*.

Afterwards there was one *Bacchus*, which clothed with the same weed, and armed with the same weapons in like sort, in the imitation of *Hercules*, went down to Hell, to hear the fained disputation betwixt the two Poets, *Euripides*, and *Æschylus*, at the sight whereof *Hercules* laughed, telling him, that such apparel did nothing at all become him, because he was wanton, tender, and effeminate. For it is not available to have a rich ceremony, and want the true substance; a glorious outside, and a shameful inside; the armour of a Champion, and the heart of a base Coward; the outward shews of holiness, and the inward love of profaness. Others do think that the proverb was taken from that Ass called *Asinus Cumanus*, who being weary of his servitude and bondage, slipt collar, and ran away into the wilde Woods, where finding by chance a Lions skin, he crept into it, and wore it upon his body, under colour whereof he ruffled up and down the Woods, to the terrour of all the Beasts, both with his tail and his fearful voice: and the *Cumanes* themselves, which had never seen a Lion, were not a little afraid of this counterfeit beast. In this fashion he domineer'd a good time, until at last there came a stranger to *Cumæ*, who seeing the counterfeit personate Ass-lion by the way, having oftentimes seen both Lions and Asses, knew it for an Ass in a Lions skin; for if all other conjectures failed, yet this proved true, namely the length of his ears; wherefore he beat him well, and brought him home to his Master, before whom he pulled off the Lions skin, and then his Master knew him to be his Ass. From which *Socrates* concludeth wisely, that no man ought to be afraid of outward greatness, because though the Ass was clothed with a Lions skin, yet he was but an Ass. And that the skins of Lions was used in garments, the saying of *Lysander* the *Lacedemonian* doth sufficiently prove; for when he was blamed for his outward pomp, whereby he beguiled others, therefore condemned for foolish hypocrisie, he made this answer, *Quo Leonis pervenire pellis non potest, vulpinam assuisse decuerit*, every man ought to have two sutes of apparel, one of a Fox, and another of the Lion. For whither the Lions skin cannot come, the Fox will creep, and where the Fox cannot come, the Lion can. Clothes wrapt in a Lions skin killeth moths: also a mans body anointed with the fat of a Lion mingled with Garlick, so as the savour of the Garlick may overcome the Lions grease, he shall never be molested with Wolfs. Also if the folds of Sheep be compassed about with the melted grease of Lions, there is no Wolfs, nor ravening beasts will annoy the flock. And so great is the fear of Lions to Wolfs, that if any part of a Lions grease be cast into a Fountain, the Wolves never dare to drink thereof, or to come near unto it. Also *Pliny* affirmeth, that if an Amulet be made of Lions grease, no man shall be harmed, wounded, or killed, by treachery or deceit: but you must understand, that this was an invention of the Magicians or Wise men, that by such pretences and promises of great matters, they might insinuate themselves into the favour of Princes and Noble men, and so make fools of the world; and therefore they prescribe the fat which is taken from betwixt the eye-lids, or from the right part of their mouth or teeth, and the hairs from the neather chap. It is likewise affirmed, that a man anointed all over with the bloud of a Lion, shall never be destroyed by any wilde Beast.

There is an herb which *Democritus* calleth *Helianthe*, growing in the Maritime Mountains of *Cilicia*, and *Themiscira*, wherewithal the fat of Lions decocted with Saffron, and Paulm Wine, with which all the Kings of *Persia* were anointed, to make them beautiful bodies to look upon. And above all other things, the Magitians prescribed this composition, to make a man invincible; the tail and head of a Dragon, the hairs of a Lions fore-head, and the marrow of his bones, the spume or white mouth of a conquering Horse, bound up together with a Dogs claws in a Harts skin, with the nerves of a Hart or Roe. The dung of a Lion drunk in Wine, maketh a man for ever more to abhor Wine.

It was also wont to be observed, that when Lions forsook the Mountains and Woods, to come and live in fruitful and fertil soils, it did fore-shew some great drought; and the like divination did *Agarista* the Mother of *Pericles* make upon her dream, when she was with childe, for she thought she brought forth a Lion, and so in short time after she brought forth *Pericles*, who was a valiant man, and a great Conqueror in *Græcia*. The sight also of a Lion as a man travelleth by the high ways, is very ominous, and taken for an evil signe. There was also a Prophesie given out by *Pythias*, concerning *Cypselus*, the son of *Aetion*, which said in this manner;

> *Concipit in petris aquila enixura Lecnem*
> *Robustum, sævum, genua & qui multa resolvet.*
> *Hæc bene nunc animis versate, Corinthia proles,*
> *Qui colitis pulchram Pallenem, altamq; Corinthum.*

In the year of our Lord 1274 there was a certain Noble woman in the Bishoprick of *Kostnizer*, which brought forth a childe like to a Lioness in all parts, but it had the skin of a man: Unto this discourse I may add the Images of Lions, both in Temples, and also upon shields; and first of all in the Temple where the shield of *Agamemnon* hung up; (as *Paucennius* writeth) there was the picture (*Fear*,) drawn with a Lions head, because as the Lion sleepeth little, and in his sleep his eyes be open; so is the condition of Fear; for we have shewed already, that the Lion when he sleepeth hath his eyes open, and when he waketh he shutteth them, and therefore the Ancients did symbolically picture of a Lion upon the doors of their Temples, and upon the Ships also, in the fore-part of them, they ingraved the figure of Lions, according to this saying of *Virgil*:

> ———— ——— *Aeneia puppis*
> *Prima tenet rostro, Phrygios subjecta Leones.*

It was also a usual custom to picture Lions about Fountains and Conduits, especially among the *Egyptians*, that the water might spring forth of their mouths, *Quoniam Nilus arvis Ægypti novam aquam invehit, sole transeunte Leonem; because that Nilus did overflow the fields of Egypt, at what time the Sun passed through the sign Leo.* Therefore also the River Alpheus was called *Leontios poros*, the Lions fountain, because at the heads thereof, there were dedicated the pictures of many Lions. There was a noble Harlot called *Leæna*, which was acquainted with the tyrannies of *Harmodius*, and *Aristogiton*; for which cause she was apprehended, and put to grievous torments, to the intent she should disclose them, but she endured all unto death, never bewraying any part of their counsel: After her death, the *Athenians* devising how to honour that vertue, and because she was a Harlot or common Curtizan, they were not willing to make a statue for her in the likeness of a Woman, but as her name was *Leæna*, that signifieth a Lioness, so they erected for her the picture of a Lioness; and that they might express the vertue of her secresie, they caused it to be framed without a tongue. Upon the grave of *Lais*, there was a covering containing the picture of a Lion, holding a Ram in his fore-feet by the buttocks, with an inscription that a Lion held the Ram; so do Harlots hold their lovers, which *Alciatus* turned into this Epigram:

> *Quid scalptus sibi vult aries, quem parte Leæna*
> *Unguibus apprensum posteriore tenet?*
> *Non aliter captos quod & ipsa teneret amantes,*
> *Vir gregis est aries, clune tenetur amans.*

There was also a Lion at *Delphos*, which weighed ten talents of gold; and at the entrance of *Thermopylæ* upon the Tombe of *Leonides* the Captain of the *Spartans*, there stood a Lion of stone: Upon the steps of the Capitol of *Rome*, there were two Lions of black Marble touch-stone. And the *Cyziceni* ingraved upon one side of their money the picture of a Lion, and on the other side the face of a woman. King *Solomon* built his Ivory Throne upon two Lions of Brass; and upon the steps or stairs ascending up to that Throne were placed twelve Lions, here and there. And from hence it came, that many Kings and States gave in their Arms the Lion, Rampant, Passant, and Regardant, distinguished in divers colours in the fields of Or, Argent, Azure, and

Sables, with such other terms of Art. The Earth it self was wont to be expressed by the figure of a Lion; and therefore the Image of *Atergas* was supported with Lions. *Cybele* the faigned Goddess of the Mountains was carryed upon Lions. And it is faigned that the *Curetes*, which nourished *Jupiter* in *Creet*, who was committed to them by his mother *Rhea*, by the anger of *Saturn*, were turned into Lions, who afterwards by *Jupiter* when he reigned, were made the Kings of beasts, and by him enjoyned to draw the Chariot of his Mother *Rhea*, according to this verse;

Ei junctæ currum Dominæ subiere Leonet.

There is a constellation in Heaven called the Lion, of whom *Germanicus* writeth in this sort, that he is the greatest and most notable amongst the signes of the Zodiack, containing three stars in his head and one clear one in his breast, and that when the Sun cometh to that signe which happeneth in the month of *July*, at which time the vehement heat of Summer burneth the earth, and dryeth up the Rivers. And therefore because the Lion is also of a hot nature, and seemeth to partake of the substance and quantity of the Sun, he hath that place in the Heavens. For in heat and force he excelleth all other beasts, as the Sun doth all other stars.

In his breasts and fore-part he is most strong, and in his hinder-part more weak, so is the Sun, encreasing until the noon or fore-part of the year, until the Summer, and afterwards seemeth to languish towards the setting, or later part of the year called the Winter. And the Lion also seemeth always to look up with a fiery eye, even as the Sun which is patent with the perpetual and infatigal sight upon the earth. The Lion also is a signification of the Sun, for the hairs of his mane do resemble the streaming beams of the Sun, and therefore this constellation is styled with the same Epithets that the Lion and the Sun are, as heat-bearing, æstive, ardent, arent, calent, hot, flammant, burning, *Herculean*, mad, horrible, dreadful, cruel, and terrible. It is feigned of the Poets, that this Lion was the *Nemæan* Lion slain by *Hercules*, which at the commandment of *Juno* was fostered in *Arcadia*, and that in anger against *Hercules* after his death, she placed him in the heavens.

To conclude this story of the Lions, it is reported of the Devils called *Onosceli*, that they slew themselves sometimes in the shapes of Lions and Dogs, and the Dog of *Serapis*, which was feigned to have three heads, on the left side a Wolfs, on the right side a Dogs, and in the middle a Lions. We have shewed already, that the people called *Ampraciotæ*, did worship a Lioness, because she killed a Tyrant. And the *Egyptians* builded a City to the honor of Lions, calling it *Leontopolis*, and dedicating Temples to *Vulcan* for their honor. And in the porches of *Heliopolis*, there were common stipends for the nourishing of Lions.

As in other places where they are fed daliy with Beef, and have also windowes in their lodgings, with great Parkes and spaces allotted unto them for their recreation and exercises: with an opinion that the people that came unto them to offer and worship them, should see a speedy revenge through divine judgement upon all those that had wronged them by perjury, or broken the oath of fidelity.

To conclude, in holy Scripture we finde that our Saviour Christ is called the Lion of the tribe of *Judah*; for as he is a Lamb in his innocency, so is he a Lion in his fortitude. The Devil also is called a roaring Lion, because Lions in their hunger are most of all full of fury and wrath. And so I will conclude and end this story of Lions with that Emblem of *Alciatus*, describing how little Hares did rejoyce and leap upon dead Lions:

> *Æacidæ moriens percussu cuspidis Hector,*
> *Qui toties hostes viceret ante suos;*
> *Comprimere haud potuit vocem insult antibus illis,*
> *Dum curru & pedibus nectere vincla parant.*
> *Distrahite ut libitum est: sic cossi luce leonis*
> *Convellant barbam vel timidi Lepores.*

THE MEDICINES OF THE LION.

The bloud of a Lion being rubbed or spred upon a Canker, or upon a sore which is swelled about the veins, will presently and without any pain cure and ease the grief thereof. Whosoever doth anoint his body all over with the bloud of a Lion, may safely and without any danger travel amongst any wilde beasts whatsoever

The flesh of a Lion being eaten either by a Man or Woman which is troubled with dreames and fantasies in the night time, will very speedily and effectually work him ease and quietness. The same also being boyled or baked, and given to them which are distraught of their wits to eat, doth bring them ease and comfort, and renew their wits again: it is also very good for the pains of deafness or the ears. And being taken in drink, it helpeth those which are troubled with the shaking of the joynts or the Palsie.

Whosoever shall have shooes made of the hide or skin of a Lion or Wolf, and wear them upon his feet, he shall never have any pain or ach in them. They will also defend him that useth them from the Gowt, or swelling in the feet or legs. The skin or hide of a Lion is also very good for either Man or Woman which are troubled with the piles or swelling of the veins, if they shall but at some several times sit upon it.

The fat of a Lion is reported to be contrary to poison, and venemous drinks, and being taken in Wine, it will by the sent expell all wilde Beasts from any one; and it doth also resist and drive away the sent or smell of Serpents, by which they follow men to destroy them. Whosoever doth anoint his body all over with the tallow or fewet of the reins or kidney of a Lion, shall by the sent and savour thereof expell and drive away from him all Wolves, how greedy and ravenous soever they be.

A Man being throughly anointed with the grease of a Lion being melted, doth drive away from him and put to flight any living creature whatsoever, and also venemous and poisonous Serpents themselves.

If any wilde Beast be anointed with the tallow or sewet of a Lion which is dissolved and clarified, he shall neither be troubled with the stinging of Flies or Bees. The fat or grease of a Lion being mingled with Oyl of Roses doth keep the skin of the face free from all blastings and blemishes, being annointed thereupon, and doth also preserve the whiteness thereof, and being mingled with Snow-water, doth heal any flesh which is burnt or scorched upon a man, and doth also cure the swelling of the joynts.

The sewet or fat of a Lion being mingled with other ointments, and anointed upon the places of either Man or Woman who have any blemishes in any part of their bodies, doth presently expell the same. The same virtue hath the dung or dirt of a Lion being mixed with the aforesaid unguent.

The grease of a Lion being dissolved and presently again conglutinated together, and so being anointed upon the body of those who are heavie and sad, it will speedily extirpate all sorrow and grief from their hearts. The same also being mixed with the marrow of a Hart and with Lettice, and so beaten and bruised, and afterwards mingled all together, is an excellent remedy against the shrinking of the Nerves and sinews, and the aches of the bones and knuckles about the legs, being anointed thereon.

The grease of a Lion by it self only, mixed with a certain ointment, is also very profitable to expell the Gowt. The same being mingled with Oyl of Roses, doth ease and help those which are troubled dayly with Agues and Quartern Fevers. The same also being dissolved and powred into the ears of any one which is troubled with any pain in them, will presently free him from the same.

There is also in this Lions grease, another excellent virtue which is this, that if the jawbone of any one be swelled and anointed over with this grease being melted, it will very speedily avoid the pain thereof.

The fat or sewet of a Lion being melted and mixed with certain other things, and so ministred unto any one that is troubled with the wringing of the bowels, and bloudy flux, in the same manner as a glyster is used, is commended for an excellent remedy for the same. The same also being mingled with a certain Oyl and warmed together, and anointed upon the head of any one, whose hair doth shed, or is troubled with the Foxes evill, doth immediately help and cure the same. The seed of a Hare being mixed with the fat of a Lion, and anointed upon the privie members of any one, will stir and incitate them up to lust, how chast soever they shall be.

The fat of a Lion mingled with the fat of a Bear, and melted together, being anointed upon the belly, doth allay and asswage the hardness thereof, as also any other pain or grief in the same.

The brains of a Lion as also of a Cat, being taken in drink, doth make him and unto whom it is given. The same being mingled with some small quantity of Oyl of Spike, and powred or distilled into the eares of any one which is deaf or thick of hearing, will very effectually cure the deafness.

If the eye teeth of a Lion be hung about the neck of a young childe before that he cast his teeth, and the beginning of his second or new teeth, they will keep him for ever from having any ach or pain in them. The heart of a Lion being beaten into small powder, and taken in drink, doth very speedily cure and heal those which are troubled with Agues or Quartain Fevers.

The liver of the Lion being dryed and beaten to powder, and put in the purest wine which is possible to be gotten, and so drunk, doth take away the pain and grief from any one which is troubled with his liver.

The gall of a Lion being taken in drink by any one, doth kill or poison him out of hand. But some do impute this venom to be in the gall of a Leopard. The gall of a Lion being mixed with pure water, and anointed upon the eyes of any one, will take away the blemishes thereof, and cause them to see clearly: and the fat of the Lion being added thereunto, is an excellent remedy against the Falling sickness. A very little part or dram of the gall of the Lion being put in wine and so drunk, will speedily help and cure those which are troubled with the Yellow Jaundise. The same disease is also cured by yellow Carets being stamped and put in wine, and so given in drink.

For the sores or blemishes in the eyes, the gall of a Lion being mingled with Hony, and so anointed upon them, is commended for a very special and effectual cure or healing. The gall of a Lion, a Bear, or an Ox being mixed with certain other unguents, is very much used for the extending or moving forward of conception.

The right stone of a Lion being beaten together with Roses, and so strained hard untill some liquid juyce or water doth proceed from them, and so taken in drink, doth make that party barren unto whom it is given: it hath the like effect in it, if it be eaten either roasted or broyled, or raw and bloudy.

The fat which proceedeth from the privity or secret parts of a she Lion being put in a vessell made of Ivory, and so being temperately mollified, is commended for a very effectual and speedy means to hinder conception.

The dung or dirt of a Lion being dryed into powder, and mixed with some certain soft and easie ointment, with which any one may be easily anointed over all his body, doth drive away the blemishes and spots in the skin.

The hurts or sores which are bitten either by a male or female Lion, are so full of matter and filthy corruption, that the running thereof can be stayed and repressed neither by lapping of clothes about them, nor by washing them by spunges: they are cured by the same means as the sores which are bitten by ravenous Dogs are, as I have before declared in the cures of the Hyæna.

The wounds which are made by the teeth of a Lion are very hurtful; for as much as the venome of their interior parts doth go into the wounds, and when the wounds are tied, the venome issueth from them into the things with which they are tied, and the same bindings being again bound upon the wound, doth so infect it, that it can be cured by no other means but by the afore-said medicine.

The bitings of Lions and such like Beasts are so dangerous, in regard of their strength and fierceness, for they do not only bite, but also wreath and tear the wounds which they make with their teeth or nails. And thus much shall suffice for the cures of the Lion.

OF THE LINX.

THE wilde Beast which among the *Germans* is named *Luchss*, by making a name from the Linx, or as others write *Lux*, or *Luxs*: amongst the *Italians* is at this day called *Lupo cervero*, or *Cerverio*, being engendered betwixt a Hinde and a Wolf; and likewise amongst the *Rhætians* which speak *Italian*: and the *Sabaudians*, and the *Dalmatians* or *Illyrians*, *Cerviro*. But there was a certain *Bohemian* of late, which declared that the Linx as he conjectured; was called among the *Illyrians*, *Rys*, (and that it was called *Luchss* among the *Germans*) but that amongst the *Illyrians* was lesser then the other, yet very like. The *Spaniards* do as yet call him by the *Latin* name *Lince*, even as certain *Italian* writers in their vulgar tongue, as *Alunnus* doth testifie. In certain places in *Helvetia*, and about *Sedunus*, they call him *Thierwolf*. Amongst the barbarous writers he is called by the name of an *Ounce*; which I do suppose to be a *Panther*. *Fr. Alunnus* doth say, that this Beast was called of certain *Italian* writers in the vulgar tongue, *Lonza*, some interpreting it to be a Lioness, some a *Pardal*, a *Panther*, or a *Wolf*, engendred of a *Hinde* and a *Wolf*.

The picture of a Linx once in the Tower of London, which was first described by Doctor Cay.

Ounces do commonly seem to be called rather Linxes then Panthers; but although some late writers do attribute the name to a Leopard or a lesser Panther, it seemeth notwithstanding corrupt from the Linx: for he is a creature very like him both in his craft and shape of his body, but a Linx hath his tail shorter, and his longer. *Libards-bane* doth kill Leopards and Linxes.

These Figures were taken by Olaus Magnus, wherein the Linx pursneth a wilde Cat.

The *Latins* call this beast *Lupus Cervarius*, and Lynx of the *Greek* word *Lugx*, from whence the *German, ein Luchs*: and it hath been believed, that the *Latin* name was given unto it, because they were ingendred betwixt a Wolf and Hind, but there is no wise man that will suppose or be easily induced to believe, that Beasts of such hostility, and adverse dispositions in nature, should ever ingender or suffer copulation together; and therefore I rather suppose that it is called *Cervarius*, either because it hunteth Harts and Hinds, or else because it imitateth their young ones in the outward colour and spots in the skins.

There was a Beast (saith *Pliny*) which was called *Chaus*, and by the *French, Raphlus*, brought in publick spectacle by *Pompey* the great, out of *France*, which in shape resembleth a Wolf, and in spots a Leopard; and therefore I think that *Chaus, Raphlus*, and *Lupus Cervarius*, are divers names of one and the same wilde Beast and yet by divers writers it is confounded with the *Thoes*, or with the Panther, or with the Ounce.

But I cannot agree thereunto, seeing it is written by *Pliny*, that about the River *Padus* in *Italy*, there are certain Beasts called *Lynces*, from whence cometh the *Lyncurion*, which by *Zenothomis* are called *Langæ*,

873

and by others *Languriæ*. And *Solinus* also agreeth thereunto, taking *Lupus Cervarius*, for a kind of Linx.

Some have fabled that there is a Beast called *Lynceus*, which *Suidas* and *Varinus* call *Oxurderches*: and they say, that the eyes of it are the best sighted of all the Beasts in the world. *Oppianus* maketh two kind of Linxes, one a greater, and hunteth Harts and great Beasts; the other a smaller, and hunteth wilde Cats and Hares. And first of all I will set down the description of this Beast, according as it was taken in *England* by that learned Physitian D. *Cay*, whose words I do here expresse.

There is in the Tower of *London* (saith *John Cay*) a Beast which eateth flesh, his whole body being of the greatness of a Lamb of two moneths old, having his head, mouth, feet, and nails like to a Cat. But concerning his beard and tail, his beard hangeth down on both sides, divided in the middle with sundry colours, the former being white, and the latter black; his tail is short and thick, being from the middle to the uppermost part red, and to the lower part black; his eyes being yellow, the hair of the eye-lids obscurely waxing white. His ears erected upright, as the ears of a Cat, being replenished within with white hair, without covered with white and black, but so that the upper part is black, the middle (for it is divided into three parts) be white, and the lowest black again. Neither is it content to be ended in his own course, except also that his former parts, or the farthest brinkes or edges, and also his latter may be bended on the other side, in like manner as the edges of the Priests hat of the *Grecian* Church are folded amongst the *Venetians*.

In the top of his ears there are placed some black hairs, as it were a foretop or tust. The colour of this beast in the outmost parts is red, in the innermost white, but sprinkled here with black spots, and almost by rowes; and there with spots somewhat lighter then the other, all his hair being for the most part white all over: all his body, except the aforesaid spots, as it is in certain black skins of young Conies. And on both the sides of his nose there are four spots set in order. In both his lips, as now we will declare: in his uppermost lip there are five orders or rowes, being of a very equall distance.

In the first row, and the upper, four; in the second, five; in the third, eight; in the fourth, five; in the fist, there are four; and these also every one in his order, having an equall distance. In the lower lip there are only seven more manifest and evident, being placed in two rowes. In the first, four, to the very mouth of the lip; in the second after them three others; after these, other lesser but not placed with so certain and true order as the uppermost.

In the upper lip on both sides there are certain white hairs being rougher then those in Cats and, Lions. His nose is somewhat of a pale red colour, being somewhat distinct or apart from the rest of his face on every side with a black line. Another line also doth divide the outermost part of his nose by length (as in an Ounce) but only being lightly lead by the top or highest parts, not impressed higher by the lowermost.

The skin of his feet are exceeding hard, and his nails are hid in his feet (as the nails of an Ounce and a Cats are) neither doth he put them forth at any time, unlesse in taking of his prey as they do.

He doth climb wonderfully, so that what he may be able to do in that thing (either in his cave or den) nature her self doth teach. He is a quick-moving creature, and cannot stand still in a place, so that except (by meer chance) the voice of a Wood-pecker in the basket of a certain Countrey man (who came then only to see the Lions) had made him quiet and attentive, there had been no hope of the portraiting out the picture of his body. He being present he was most quiet; but he going away, he would never stand still: wherefore I was constrained to send my man after the Countrey-man to buy the bird, which being present, he stood very still untill the business was dispatched and the work absolutely perfected.

Our Countreymen call it *Luzarne*, it is doubtful whether we should call it *Leunce*, or *Lynx*, in the affinity of the words. His skin is used by Noble men, and is sold for a great price. He is angry at none but them which offer him injury; his voice is like a Cats, when he would snatch away the food from his fellow. He is loving and gentle unto his keeper, and not cruell unto any man. *So far Doctor Cay.*

Unto this description of Doctor *Caius*, I may add another description that was taken by the sight of the skin of this Beast. The length whereof from the tip of the nose unto the very tail, was four spans and five fingers, and the length of the tail seven fingers, the breadth of the shoulder-blades of his back, and the top of his neck, was two palmes six fingers and a span;

875

the length of his forelegs, a span and five fingers; and the length of his hinder-legs, a span and three fingers; the hair was very soft, but yet thick and deep, the tips of the hair upon his back were white, but in the neathermost parts they were red, and they are most white which fall downwards on both sides from the middle of his back.

In the middle they are more red and duskie, the middle of the belly, and especially the lower part is white, but both sides of it are white and red, and every where upon his belly there are black spots, but most plentiful in the bottom of the belly, and on both sides. The uppermost part of his neck, right over against his ears, hath great black spots, his ears are small, and not bigger then a little Triangle, in the edges they are black, although with the black hairs there are mingled some white. His beard is mixed with black and white hair, which hair is great like to bristles. The teeth are most white, and the upper canine teeth hang over the neather the breadth of a finger, whereof six are small, and of those six two are the greatest, and all the residue are very small on the neather chap; and to conclude, all the teeth were like a common Weasils or Martil. His feet were very rough, being five distinct claws upon the fore-feet, and four upon the hinder, which claws were very white and sharp.

The tail was of equall bigness and thickness, but in the tip thereof it is black. These skins are sold for three Nobles a piece, and sometimes for six, and sometimes for lesse, according to the quantity of the skin and Countrey wherein it is sold. And unto this description do *Bellonius* and *Bonarus* agree. For *Bellonius* at *Constantinople* saw two *Linxes*, much like unto Cats; and *Bonarus* had oftentimes seen them hunted in *Moschovia, Lituania, Polonia, Hungaria*, and *Germany*; but he commendeth above all the Linxes of *Scotland* and *Swesia*, as most beautiful, having Triangular spots upon their skins. But the *Indian* and *African* Linxes, he saith have round spots, sharp-bristly short hair, and full of spots on all parts of their body, and therefore they are not so delicate as the Linxes of *Europe*, which with good cause he conjectureth to be the Linx that *Pliny* speaketh of, and not unlike to that which is bred in *Italy*. There are Linxes in divers Countries, as in the forenamed *Russia, Lituania, Polonia, Hungary, Germany, Scotland*, so also they are most abundant in *Scandinavia*, in *Swesia*, so also about *Hyelsus*, and *Helsyngia*: likewise in all the Regions upon the *Alpes*, and in *Sylva Martia*, they are also very plentiful in *Ethiopia*, in *France* and *Italy*, about the River *Padus*, and in the Island *Carpathus*. And thus having discoursed of their Countrey and proportion, whereby their differences and kinds may be discerned, we will leave every one of them to their particular, and proceed to the treatise and description of their general natures.

There is no great difference betwixt their outward shapes and proportion, for both the smaller and the greater have bright eyes, divers coloured skins, a little head, a nimble and chearful face, and (*Albertus* saith) that their body is longer then the body of a Wolf, but their legs shorter, mistaking the Linx for the *Thoes*. Their eyes stand forth of their heads very far, their tongue like the tongue of a Serpent, and *Textor* affirmeth that they have paps or udders in their Breasts, but surely he taketh *Lynx* for *Sphinx*.

Their meat goeth into the belly straight through the maw, without staying, and therein is a note of their insatiable voracity, for none but insatiable Beasts or Birds are so affected, as in Birds, the *Cormorant*. It hath no ankle bone, but a thing like unto it; the nails are very long, as you may see in two of the former pictures, but he hideth them within his skin till he be angry, ready to fight or climb, or otherwise affected, as you may see by the picture of the Linx taken in the Tower of *London*.

The inward proportion and anatomy of their bodies is like unto a man, and therefore *Galen* giveth this lesson to students in Physick, *Præstat simiarum homini quam simillimarun artus dissecare, cum te in exemplo exercese institues, sin ea non detur, aliquam ei proximam deligito, aut si nulla omnino Simia reperiatur, Cynocephalum, vel Satyrum, vel Lincem, summatim ea omnia, quibus artuum extrema in digitos quiuq; discreta sunt*; that is to say, It is good to dissect those bodies which are likest to a man, when one would instruct himself in Anatomy, and if he cannot finde an Ape, let him take a Baboon, a Satyr, or a Linx, and generally any creature, the extremity of whose sinews and joynts are divided into five fingers or toes.

There be some that have thought, that Panthers, Pardals, Linxes, or Tygers, had been all of the kinde of Cats, because of mutual resemblance in the greatness and strength of their nails, in the distinction of their skins, which are party coloured and fair, having also a round head, a short face, a long tail, a nimble body, a wild mind, and get their meat by hunting: but herein I leave every man to this own best liking and opinion: for when we have done our best to expresse their natures and several properties, it shall be idle to spend time about disputation to what rank or order every beast ought to be referred. For every one that readeth our story, and seeth out pictures may either be satisfied, or else amend our labour.

The Linx therefore biteth most cruelly and deep, and therefore is accounted, *Rapax animal, instar lupi, sed callidius*, a Beast as ravening as a Wolf, but more crafty; they get up into trees, and from them leap down upon very great beasts, and destroy them, being enemies Both to men and beasts, and at their pleasure, according to necessity, set upon both.

They are taken sometimes in *Germany*, in the Dutchy of *Wertinberg*, and that it was once credibly affirmed, one of them leaped down from a tree upon a Countrey man, as he passed under the same tree, but being weary, and having an Ax on his neck, received her on the sharp edge thereof, and so killed her, otherwise she would soon have killed him.

They live in the mountains also, where they are killed by poison, or else hunted by armed men on Horse-back, and included with multitudes, for their hunting is perilous, and therefore they must be inclosed with great company. Some take them with ditches, as we heard before Lions were taken; others in snares or gins laid upon the rocks, and stones, and whensoever they are hunted with Dogs, they run directly to the woods or to the next trees, wherein they are killed by gun shot.

In the Summer time they are very weak and live among the Rockes, never straying far from their own lodging, hurting no man untill the Autumn. They hunt wilde Goats, whom they follow from Rock to Rock, leaping as fast or faster then the Goats. They Hunt also wilde Cats and Hares, and some other little Beasts; but the greatest Linxes hunt Harts and Asses, and their manner is, as we have said already, to get up into trees, and there to lie in wait for their prey, untill they espy it under the boughs, and then suddenly leap into the neck thereof, whether it be a Man or a great Beast, wherein they fix their claws so last, that no violence can shake them off, but with the sharpness of their teeth, bite into the scull, and eat out the brains, to the utter destruction of the Man or Beast, whomsoever they light upon, but if it be a small Beast, they eat the whole body thereof, and not only the brains.

Yet this is a wonderful secret in their nature, that although they be long afflicted with hunger, yet when they eat their meat, if they hear any noise, or any other chance cause them to turn about from their meat, out of the sight of it, they forget their prey notwithstanding their hunger, and go to seek another booty, never remembring that which they had before them, nor yet return back again to eat thereof. The voice of this Beast is called by a speciall word in *Latin, Orcare,* or *Corcare,* which I may *English* Croaking, or Whining, for the voice thereof is not great, and therefore the Author of *Philomela* saith, *Dum Linces orcando fremunt, ursus ferus uncat;* While the Linx croaketh, the wilde bear whineth. And *Arlunus* saith, *Corcare vox lupi Cervarii;* to croak is the voice of a Linx.

It is thought that of all Beasts they see most brightly, for the Poets faign, that their eye sight pierceth through every solid body, although it be as thick as a wall: yet if you offer unto it any thing which is transparent, it is much offended, and sometimes blinded, but I cannot tell, whether the sight be attributed to the Linx truely according to nature, or fabulously in imitation of the Poetical fiction of *Lynceus,* of whom it was said in ancient time, that he saw through stone wals, of whom *Horace* writeth thus:

> *Si possis oculo, quantum contendere Lynceus,*
> *Non tamen idcirco contemnas lippus inungi.*

Marcus Tullius also saith in this manner, in the admiration of *Lynceus* eye-sight, as though darkness did not hinder it, *Quis est tam Lynceus qui in tantis tenebris nihil effendat? Apollonius* saith, that so great was the perfection of this mans eye-sight, as he was believed to see perfectly down into the earth, and what was done in Hell. *Plutarch* saith, that he could see through trees and rocks. *Pausanias* writeth, that he was a King, and raigned after *Danaovita. Pyndarus* writeth, that *Ida* and *Lynceus* were the sons of *Aphareus,* and that a contention growing betwixt *Ida,* and *Castor,* and *Pollux* at the marriage of *Helena* because they twain would have ravished *Phœbe* and *Illayra*, the wives of *Ida* and *Lynceus*; *Ida* did therefore slay *Castor*, and afterwards *Lynceus* slew *Pollux* when he spyed him lie under an Oake, from the mountain *Taygetus*. Wherefore *Jupiter* slew *Ida* with lightning, and placed *Castor* and *Pollux* in heaven among the stars. There was another *Lynceus* husband of *Hypermnestra*, Daughter of *Danaus*, which *Danaus* having commanded all his Daughters in the night time to kill their Husbands, she only spared her husband *Lynceus*. But the truth is, that *Lynceus* of whom there is so many fables of his eye-sight, was the first that found out the mines of Gold, Silver and Brasse in the earth, and therefore simple people seeing him bring Gold and Silver out of the earth, and coming now and then upon him while he was digging deep for it, using the light of Candles, which he never brought out of the pits, they foolishly imagined, that by the sight of his eyes he was first of all led to seek for those treasures, and from hence came the common proverb, *Lynceo perspicactor*, for a man of excellent eye-sight. And to conclude, others say, that *Lynceus* could see the new Moon the same day or night that she changed, and that therefore the fame of his eye-sight came so to be celebrated, because never any mortall man saw that sight, himself excepted. And from these fables of *Lynceus* came the opinion of the singular perspicacity of the Beast Linx: of whom as I said before, as the sight is very excellent, and so far excelling men (as *Galen* saith) like as is also the sight of *Eagles*, so I do not hold any such extraordinary and miraculous sense to be in this beast, after any other manner, then the Poets did faign it to be in *Lynceus*, except as before said, *Omnes imbeciliore sumus cernendi potestate, si aquilarum & Lyncis acuminibus conferamur*. And therefore the proverb before spoken of, may as well be applyed metaphysically to the Beast Linx, as Poetically to the man *Lynceus*; and so much may suffice for the sight. It is reported also that when they see themselves to be taken, they do send forth tears and weep very plentifully. Their urine they render all backwards, not only the female but the male also, wherein they differ from all other Beasts: and it is said of them, that they knowing a certain virtue in their urine, do hide it in the Sand, and that thereof cometh a certain pretious stone called *Lyncurium*, which for brightness resembleth the Amber, and yet is so congealed and hardned in the sand, that no Carbuncle is harder, shining like fire, wherewithal they make sealing Rings, which caused *Ovid* to write thus;

> *Victa racemifero Lyncas dedit India Baccho,*
> *E quibus, ut memorant, quicquid vesica remisit*
> *Vertitur in lapides, & congelat aere tacto.*

But they say that of the male cometh the fiery and yellow Amber, and of the female cometh the white and pale Amber. In *Italy* they call it *Langurium*, and the Beast *Languria*, and *Lange*. This *Lyncurium* is called of some *Electrum*, *Pterygophoron*, and they say it is the same which will draw unto it leaves, straw, and plates of Brasse and Iron, according to the opinions of *Diocles* and *Theophrastus*, and that being drunk out of water is good for the stomach, and very convenient for the flux of the belly, according to *Dioscorides*; and that it cureth the pains of the reins, and healeth the Kings evill, according to *Solinus*: And *Theophrastus* goeth about to establish this opinion by reason, and laboreth to perswade it as probable, that the urine of a Linx should congeal into a stone among sand, as well as the urine of a man, to ingender a stone in the reins or in the bladder.

And of this opinion is *Pliny, Theophrastus, Hesychius, Varinus, Zenothimis, Plutarch*, and *Aristotle*. But in my opinion it is but a fable: For *Theophrastus* himself confesseth that *Lyncurium*, which he calleth *Lyngurion*, and Amber *Hualos*, is digged out of the earth in *Lyguria*. *Sudines* and *Metrodorus* say that there is a certain tree in *Lyguria*, out of which Amber is taken, and this tree is the black Popler, and it is also very probable, that seeing this Amber was first of all brought into *Greece* out of *Lyguria*, according to the denomination of all strange things, they called it *Lyngurium* after the name of the Countrey, whereupon the ignorant *Latins* did faign an etymology of the word *Lyncurium, quasi Lyncis urinam*, and upon this weak foundation have they raised that vain building; and for further demonstration of this truth, *Dioscorides* saith in his discourse of the Popler, that it growing about the River *Eridanus*, sendeth forth a certain humor like tears, which groweth hard, whereof they make that which is called *Electrum*, being rubbed, it smelleth sweet, and for that it hath not only power to draw unto it Brasse, Iron, and such things, but also Gold, it is also called *Chrysophoton*; unto this *Lucianus* subscribeth: and whereas it was said that in *Italy* this Amber-stone is begotten, neer the River *Padus*, where stand many white Poplers; my conjecture is, that some such like humor may issue out of them, and not only by accident, but through affinity of nature, and condensate into a stone, which the people finding, covered in the sand under the trees, and through their former perswasion, might easily take it for the stone engendred by the urine of the Linx.

Hermolaus also writeth this of the *Lyncurium*, that it groweth in a certain stone, and that it is a kind of *Mushrom*, or *Padstoole* which is cut off yearly, and that another groweth in the room of it, a part of the root or foot being left in the stone, groweth as hard as a flint, and thus doth the stone encrease, with a natural secundity: which admirable thing, (saith he) I could never be brought to believe, untill I did eat thereof in mine own house.

Euax (as it is recited by *Sylvaticus*) saith that the urine of the Linx, *demi servatus, generat optimos fungos suprase quotannis*, reserved at home in ones house, bringeth forth every year the best *Mushroms*. This is also called *Lapis Litzi*, and *Lapis prasius*, which is divided into three kindes, that is, *Jaspis, Armeniacus*, and *Lapis phrygius*, called also *Belemintes*; wherewithal the Chirurgians of *Prussia* and *Pomerania*, cure green wounds, and the Physitians break the stone in the bladder. But the true *Lyncurium* which is extant at this day, and currant among the Apothecaries, is as light as the Pumice-stone, and as big as filleth a mans fist, being of a blackish colour, or of a russet; the russet is more solid, sandy, and fat, and being bruised or eaten, tasteth like earth: both kindes are covered with little white skins, and there is apparent in them, a spungy tenacious substance, and this I take to be the *Mushrom* whereof *Hermolaus* speaketh. And by the little stones and small skins, it may be conjectured to be *Corpus heterogenes, in terra coalescens*: A *Hetrogenean* body encreasing in the earth, wherewithal it hath no affinity.

There was another stone of the urine of a Linx to be seen in *Savoy*, the substance whereof was clearly crystal, the form of it was triangular, the hardness so, as you might strike fire with it, and the colour partly white, and partly like Wine mingled with water; so that I will conclude, that the urine of a Linx may engender a stone, though not in such manner as is beforesaid. For the *Arabian Jorath* affirmeth, that within seven dayes after the rendring, it turneth into a stone; but it is not the *Lyncurium* properly so called, for that is the Amber or Gum before spoken of, although catachrestically so called.

And if it be true, that there be certain *Mushroms* neer the Red-sea, which by the heat of the Sun are hardned into stones, then also it may follow very naturally, that those stones may produce *Mushroms* again, for both the dissolution and the constitution of things are thought to be grounded upon the same principles. And thus much shall suffice for the urine of the Linx, and the stone made thereof.

The skins of Linxes are most pretious, and used in the garments of the greatest estates, both Lords, Kings and Emperors, as we have shewed before, and for that cause are sold very dear. The claws of this Beast, especially of the right foot, which he useth in stead of a hand, are encluded in silver, and sold for Nobles a piece, and for Amulets to be worn against the falling sickness. The love of these beasts to their young ones is very great, like as the Pardals, Lions, and Tygers. The King of *Tartaria* hath tame Linxes which he useth in hunting, in stead of Dogs. The antient *Pagans* dedicated this Beast to *Bacchus*, feigning that when he triumphed in his chariot of Vine branches, he was drawn by Tygers, and Linxes. And therefore *Virgil* saith;

> *Quid Lynces Bacchi variæ,* ———

And *Ovid*;

> *Dicta racemisero Lyncas dedit India Baccho.*

All the nails of a Linx being burned with the skin, beaten into powder, and given in drink, will very much cohibite and restrain abominable Lechery in men: it will also restrain the lust in women being sprinkled upon them: and also very effectually and speedily take away either itch or scurf in man or womans body. The urine of this Beast is accounted very medicinable for those which are troubled with the Strangury, and running of the reins.

The same is also very good and wholesome for the curing of any pain or grief in the winde-pipe or throat; *Bonarus Baro* doth a affirm that the nails of Linxes which are in their Countrey, are had in great estimation and price amongst their Peers and Noble men: for there is a very certain opinion amongst them, that those nails being put upon the yard of either Horse or Beast whose urine is kept back or restrained, will in very short space cause them to void it without any grief at all. He reporteth also that their nails do there wax white, and that they include them all in silver, and do commend them for an excellent remedy against the Cramp, if they be worn (peradventure because they are bending and crooked) by which perswasion there are some superstitious men which hang certain roots which are crooked and knotty about them against the Cramp. There are some which do ascertain that these nails are good and ready helps for the soreness of the Uvula which is in the Horses mouthes: and for that cause there are many Horsemen which carry them continually about them.

The Linx or Wolf, which is begotten of a Wolf and a Hinde, the Musk-cat, the Weasill and all such other like Beasts, do more hurt men by their biting teeth-wounds then by poison. There was a certain Hunter, as *Collinus* reporteth, which told him that the flesh of a Linx being sod in some hot pottage or broath, and afterwards eaten, would be a very good and wholesome medicine for the expelling of the Ague, or Quartan Fever; and that the bones of the same Beast being burnt and pounded into powder, would be a very excellent remedy for the curing of wounds which are old and stale, and full of putrifaction, as also the Fistulaes which grow in the thighes or hips of men.

OF THE MARDER, MARTEL, OR MARTEN.

THIS beast is called in the *Hebrew, Oach,* or as some say *Zum*; amongst the *Arabians, Eastoz,* or rather *Kacheobeon,* or *Kachineon*; in *Latine, Martes*; the *Germans, Marder,* or *Marter,* like the *English*; the *Italians, Marta, Martore,* or *Martorello*; the *French, Mardre,* or *Foyne*; the *Spaniards, Marta*; the *Illyrians* and *Polonians, Kuna*; and some latter

Latines use the words *Marta, Martarus, Marturus,* and *Marturellus*; and the reason, or etymology of this *Latine* word is taken from *Martia*, which signifieth *Martial*, because this beast in warlike and hostile manner, destroyeth her adversaries, and liveth upon the prey of Hens, Birds, and Mice. The *Germans* divide these into two kindes, which they call by the names of *Tachmarder, Hussmarder, Steinmarder, Buochmarder, Feldmarder, Wildmarder, Thanmarder, Fiechtmarder,* that is to say, the Fir-martin, the Rock-martin, the Tame-martin, the Beech-martin, the Field-martin, the Wilde-martin, and the Wall-martin. For they live either in houses, wals, and Temples, or else in rocks, fields, and woods: And yet is not their distinction taken only from the places of their aboad, but also from the goodness of their skins.

And therefore the *French* call the word Martin by the name of *Foines*: And the skins of the Fir-martin, or House-martin, are far more beautiful to look upon, then those that live wilde in the trees or Woods. *Agricola* calleth the Wood-martin *Baummarder*, because it liveth for the most part in trees, and saith that it never forsaketh the Woods, or very seldom, and therefore in that thing differeth from the Fir-martin. But herein he seemeth to be deceived, that he ascribeth to the Beech-martin, a loamy or red throat, and also a continual abode among the Woods. For they come some-times to houses, and to Rocks; for which, as we have said already, it is called a House-marder, and Rock-marder. And all these multitude of names, do but express the two kindes afore-named, whereof the Fir-Martin is most excellent; for Princes and great Nobles are clothed therewith, every skin being worth a *French* crown, or four shillings at the least. And they are so much the better, when there are more white hairs aspersed among the yellow. For their ordinary colour is a deep brown yellow, and these that are clean white, are four times worse then the former; and therefore are not sold for above three or four groats a piece, howsoever the saying of *Martial, Venator capta Marte superbus adest.* Here cometh the proud Hunter that hath killed a Martin, may very well be applyed unto them which take any of these beasts, for they cannot chuse but be very joyful, which get a good sum of money for a little labour, as they have for a Martins skin. By inspection of the *Foins*, that is, the Martins of the beech; for the *French* men called a Beech, *Fau*, from whence cometh the word *Foines*, you may see, that their skins are more dusky, having a tail both greater and blacker then the Martins of the Firs. And therefore you must understand, that they of the Firs are by way of excellency called Martins, and the other of the woods called *Foines*. There is no great difference betwixt their bigness: and if by their skins at any time there seem any inequality, in breadth, or length, it must be attributed to their age and difference of years, and not to any proportion in nature or distinction of kinde. And as we have said that the Fir-Martins are absolutely the best, yet that is not to be understood generally. For the Martins of *Polonia* are so brown, that they are altogether disliked, and are accounted no better then the common Beech-Martins. Wherefore the bright-brown aspersed with white hairs is ever accounted more pretious without all exception, and by that colour upon the back of the skin, the skinner judgeth of the worth, and not by the yellowness of the throat.

Of these Beech-Martins there are great plenty in the *Alpes*, especially on the South-side, which look towards *Italy*, but very few of the Wal-martins. But on those parts of the *Alpes* which look towards *Germany* and the *North* there are aboundance of Fir-Martins with yellow throats, for you must remember that the wilde Martin hath a white throat, and the Fir-Martin a yellow throat.

There are also of both kinds in *Helvetia*, and the most excellent are in the vales towards the *Alpes*. In *France* there are no Martins of the wall, but the Beech-Martins live in hollow beeches. There are also woods full of the Beasts in *Brussia*, which the people there call *Gayni*. *Lanzærucca* a wood of *Scandenavia* fourscore miles long, is full of Martins. Also *Muscovy*, and *Lituania* have store of these Beasts, and *Sabels*. But they of *Lituania*, are the whitest in the world.

The people of *Sarmatia* in *Europe*, wear garments of these in Sables; and the inhabitants of *Scythia*, *Hungaria*, neer *Tanais*, do pay yearly unto the Emperor of *Russia*, once called the Duke of *Muscovia*, a certain number of *Sabels* and Martins skins. There are also store of Martins neer *Bragansa*, and generally in all parts of *Europe* except in *England*.

They are in quantity about the bigness of a Cat, having longer bodies, but shorter legs, with heads and tails like a Fox, their skins ordinarily brown, white on the throat, and more yellow on the back.

Their teeth are exceeding white, and unequal, one longer then another, being above measure sharp, and the canine teeth both above and beneath hang out very long. Amongst which on the neather chap, stand six small cutting teeth in a right line over against one another, which I think happeneth not in any other, Beast of the world. The grinding teeth are like a saw, being triangular in fashion, eight above and eight beneath. Whereof the furthermost upon the upper-most side of the mouth, are more deep and inward in the palat, then all the residue, the whole number is thirty two. The long hairs upon their upward lip doe bend clean backwards.

Notwithstanding that there be two kindes of this Beast, as already we have said, yet do the Wood-Martins, or Beech-Martins, greatly desire copulation with the other wherefore *Albertus* saith, *Miscentur inter se hæc genera, & Martesphagi, fere sequitur, Martem abietum, tanquam nobiliorem, ut fœtum ex ea nobiliorem acquirat.* The Beech-Martin followeth the Fir-Martin, und desireth her copulation as the nobler kind, that he may thereby dignifie his own issue. It should seem that they breed in *March*, and make their nests like the draies of Squirrels, and bring forth many at a time; For it was constantly affirmed by a Countrey-man of *Germany*, that he found a nest of these Martins builded like a Squirrels, having four young ones in it, in the beginning of *April*.

If they be taken when they are young, both one and other kind grow wonderful tame and familiar with Men and Dogs. And *Gesner* had one of these, which loved a little Dog wonderfully, and would follow him abroad whithersoever he went for or neer. It would also play with Dogs and Men, with teeth and nails, lying flat upon the back like a Cat, and never give any little hurt. But loosened from his chain it would wander abroad into the neighbours houses, and many times far off, but alwayes returne home again. They which tame them, because that they are easily exasperated, and bite deeply when they are angry, do break off the tops of their canine teeth, with a pair of pinsons for the preventing of that mischief. *Ruellius* affirmeth, that the excrement of this Beast smelleth like a Musk-cat, and saith the reason of it is, because they feed upon sweet fruits; but we have heard that they eat Pullen-birds, Egs, and Mices but that they eat of fruits it cannot be proved. I rather attribute it unto their own nature. For as the Martin-ape smelleth sweetly after her meat, so may this Martin-weasel render a sweet excrement. To conclude, the skins of these beasts is applyed to gowty legs, and the white hairs of the throat made into a cap, is very soverain for the head-ach. They may be taken with Dogs, or in traps, but commonly they are taken in ditches or pitfals, according to this Verse of *Calentius*, wherewithal, I will conclude;

Et laqueo vulpe, & decipe casse foinas.

OF THE MOLE OR WANT.

I do utterly dissent from all them that hold opinion that the Mole or Want is of the kind of Mice, for that all of them in general, both one and other, have two long crooked foreteeth which is not in Moles, and therefore wanting those as the inseparable propriety of kinde, we will take it for granted that it pertaineth not to that rank or order of four-footed Beasts. But concerning the *Hebrew* name thereof, there is much variance, and little certainty amongst writers. Some of them calling it *Tinschemet*, which word is found Deut. 14. which is also translated by the *Chaldees*,

888

Bota or *Baveta*, a Swan, and the *Septuagints* and *Jerom, Ibis*, and *Rabbi Solomon* in another place of the same Chapter translateth it a Bat, which the *French* call *Chaulve-souris*. But in that place of Levit. 11. where the *Stellio*, the *Lizard*, and *Tinschemet*, are reckoned unclean Beasts; *Rabbi Solomon* interprets it *Talpam*, the Mole. The *Septuagints, Aspalox*; the *Caldee, Aschuta*: the *Arabian, Lambaraz*; the *Persian, Angurbah-dedach*. There is a sentence, Isa. 2. in *Hebrew* thus, *Lachepor perot velatelephim*: which by *Munster* is thus translated, *In die projiciet homo aureos & argenteos deos, in fossuras talparum & vespertilionum. In that day shall a man cast away his goods of silver and gold into the holes of Moles and Bats.* By S. *Jerom* it is translated thus, *Projiciet homo Idola, usque ut adoraret talpas & verspertiliones. A man shall cast away his Idols to worship Moles and Bats.* Some again make but one word of *Latheporperot*, and translate it a Beast digging ditches; and the *Septuagints*, Idols or abominations, and think that they were so called, because their outward forme representeth some such reptile creature, and *Symmachus*; unprofitable things; but *Aquila, Orugas*, digging Beasts: and therefore at this day all the learned take *Perot* for Moles, so called by reason of their digging. *Avicen* calleth it *Pelagoz*, a blinde Mouse. In *Greek* it is called sometimes *Spalax*, but more often *Aspalax*: yet *Albertus* calleth it by a strange *Grecian* name *Colti* and *Koky*, which he took from *Avicen*. The *Italians* retain the *Latin* word *Talpa*; the *Spaniards, Topo*; by which word the *Italians* at this day call a Mouse. The *French* call it *Taulpe*; the *Germans, Mulwerf*, and in *Saxon, Molwurffe*, from whence is derived the *English* Mole, and Molewarp. The *Helvetians, Schær* and *Schærmouse*, and the Molehil they call *Schærusen* of digging. The *Hollanders* and the *Flemmings* call it *Mol* and *Molmuss*, in imitation of the *German* word: the *Illyrians, Krtize*. And generally the name is taken from digging and turning up the earth with her nose and back, accord to the saying of *Virgil*;

Aut oculis capti fodere cubilia Talpæ.

Some are of opinion, that it is called *Talpa*, because it is appointed to an everlasting darkness in the earth; of which sort *Isidorus* writeth thus, *Talpa dicta est eo quod perpetua cæcitate tenebris damnata, est enim absque oculis.*

It is called also in *Greek, Indouros,* and *Siphneus,* of *Siphnon* the earth, because in liveth the earth, and turneth it upward to make it hollow for passage. The like I might say of his other names, *Ixliocha,* and *Orthoponticos*; But this shall suffice for his name.

In *Bœotia* about the *Champaignes* called *Orchomenius ager,* there are the greatest store of Moles in the world: for by digging they undermine all the fields, and yet in *Lebadia* another Countrey of *Bœotia,* there are none at all, and if they be brought thither from any other place they will never dig but die. *Rodolphus, Oppianus,* and *Albertus* affirm, that they are created of themselves of wet earth and rain water, for when the earth beginneth to putrifie, the Mole beginneth to take life.

They are all for the most part of a black duskie colour, with rough, short and smooth soft hair as wooll, and those hairs which were whitest when they are yong, are most glistering and perfect black when they are old: and *Gesner* affirmeth that he saw in the end of *October,* a Mole taken which was very white, mixed with a little red, and the red was most of all upon her belly, betwixt her forelegs and the neck, and that it could not be a young one, because it was two palms in length betwixt his head and tail.

These Beasts are all blinde and want eyes, and therefore came the proverb *Talpa cæcior, Tuphloteros aspalacos,* blinder then a Mole; to signifie a man without all judgement, wit or foresight; for it is most elegantly applyed to the minde. Yet if any man look earnestly upon the places where they should grow, he shall perceive a little passage, by drawing up the membrane or little skin which is black, and therefore *Aristotle* saith of them in this manner probably;

All kindes of Moles want their sight, because they have not their eyes open and naked as other Beasts, but if a man pull up the skin of their browes about the place of their eyes, which is thick and shadoweth their sight, he shall perceive in them inward covered eyes, for they have the black circle, and the apple which is contained therein, and another part of the white circle or skin, but not apparently eminent; neither indeed can they, because nature at the time of generation is hindered, for from the brains there belong to the eyes two strong nervie passages, which are ended at the upper teeth, and therefore their nature being hindered, it leaveth an imperfect work of sight behinde her.

Yet there is in this Beast a plain and bald place of the skin where the eyes should stand, having outwardly a little black spot like a Millet or Poppey-seed, fastened to a nerve inwardly, by pressing it, there followeth a black humor or moistness, and by dissection of a Mole great with young, it is apparent (as hath been proved) that the young ones before birth have eyes, but after birth, living continually in the dark earth without light, they cease to grow to any perfection; for indeed they need them not, because being out of the earth they cannot live above an hour or two.

Esop hath a pretty fable of the Asse, Ape, and Mole, each once complaining of others natural wants; the Asse, that he had no horns, and was therefore unarmed; the Ape, that he had no tail like other Beasts of his stature and quantity, and therefore was unhandsome; to both which the Mole maketh answer, that they may well be silent, for that she wanteth eyes, and so insinuateth, that they which complain shall finde by consideration and comparison of their own wants to others, that they are happy and want nothing that were profitable for them.

Oppianus saith, that there was one *Phineus* which was first deprived of his eye-sight, and afterward turned into a Mole: It should seem he was condemned first to loose his eyes, and afterward his life.

These Moles have no ears, and yet they hear in the earth more nimbly and perfectly then men can above the same, for at every step or small noise and almost breathing, they are terrified and run away, and therfore (*Pliny* saith) that they understand all speeches spoken of themselves, and they hear much better under the earth then being above and out of the earth. And for this cause they dig about their lodging long passages, which bringeth noises and voices to them, being spoken never so low and softly, like as the voice of a man carryed in a trunk, reed or hollow thing.

Their snout is not like a Weasils, as *Suidas* saith, but rather like a Shrew-mouses, or (if it be lawful to compare small with great) like to a Hogs. Their teeth are like a Shrews and a Dogs; like a Shrews in the neather teeth and furthermost inner teeth, which are sharp pointed and low inwardly; and like a Dogs, because they are longer at the sides, although only upon the upper jaw, and therefore they are worthily called by the *Grecians, Marootatous*; that is dangerous biting teeth; for as in

Swine the under teeth stand out above the upper, and in Elephants and Moles, the upper hang over the neather, for which cause they are called *Hyperphereis*.

The tongue is no greater then the space or hollow in the neather chap, and they have in a manner as little voice as sight, and yet I marvel how the proverb came of *Loquax Talpa*, a pratling Mole, in a popular reproach against wordy and talkative persons, which *Ammianus* saith, was first of all applyed to one *Julianus Capella*, after he had so behaved himself, that he had lost the good opinion of all men.

The neck seemeth to be nothing, it is so short, standing equall with the forelegs. The lights are nothing else but distinguished and separated *Fibres*, and hang not together upon any common root or beginning, and they are placed or seated with the heart, which they enclose, much lower toward the belly then in any other Beast Their gall is yellowish, their feet like a Bears, and short legs, wherefore they move and run but slowly; their fingers or toes wherewithal they dig the earth, are armed with sharp nails, and when she feeleth any harm upon her back, presently she turneth upward and defendeth her self with her snowt and feet: with her feet she diggeth, and with her nose casteth away the earth, and therefore such earth is called in *Germany, Mal werff*, and in *England, Mole-hill*: and she loveth the fields, especially meddowes and Gardens, where the ground is soft, for it is admirable with what celerity she casteth up the earth.

They have five toes with claws upon each forefoot, and four upon each foot behind, according to *Albertus*, but by diligent inspection you shall finde five behind also, for there is one very little and recurved backward, which a man slightly and negligently looking upon, would take to be nothing. The palm of the fore feet is broad like a mans hand, and hath a hollow in it if it be put together like a fist, and the toes or fingers with the nails are greater then any other beasts of that quantity. And to the end that he might be well armed to dig, the forepart of her fore-legs consist of two solid and sound bones which are fastened to her shoulders, and her claws spread abroad, not bending downward, and this is peculiar to this Beast not competible to any other, but in her hinder legs both before and behind they are like a Mouses, except in the part beneath the knee, which consisteth but of one bone which is also forked and twisted. The tail is short and hairy. And thus much for the Anatomy and several parts.

They live as we have said in the earth, and therefore *Cardan* saith, that there is no creature which hath blood and breath that liveth so long together under the earth, and that the earth doth not hinder their expiration and inspiration; for which cause they keep it hollow above them, that at no time they may want breath, although they do not heave in two or three dayes; but I rather believe when they heave, they do it more for meat then for breath, for by digging and removing the earth they take Wormes, and hunt after victuals.

When the Wormes are followed by Moles, (for by digging and heaving, they foreknow their own perdition) they flie to the superficies and very top of the earth, the silly beast knowing that the Mole their adversary, dare not follow them into the light, so that their wit in flying their enemy is greater, then in turning again when they are troad upon. They love also to eat Toads and Frogs, for *Albertus* saith, he saw a great Toad whose leg a Mole held fast in the earth, and that the Toad made an exceeding great noise, crying out for her life, during the time that the Mole did bite her. And therefore Toads and Frogs do eat dead Moles. They eat also the root of Herbs and Plants, for which cause they are called by *Oppianus, Poiophagi Herbivoræ*, herb-eaters.

In the month of *July* they come abroad out of the earth, I think to seek meat at that time when wormes be scanty. They are hunted by Weasils, and wilde Cats, for they will follow them into their holes and take them, but the Cats do not eat them: whereas we have said already, that they have an understanding of mens speech when they hear them talk of them;

I may add thereunto a story of their understanding, thus related by *Gillius* in his own experience and knowledge. When I had (saith he) put down into the earth an earthen pot made of purpose with a narrow mouth to take Moles, it fortuned that within short space as a blind Mole came along she sell into it and could not get forth again, but lay therein whining; one of her fellowes which followed her seeing his mate taken, heaved up the earth above the pot, and with her nose cast in so much, till she had raised up her companion to the brim and was ready to come forth: by which in that blind creature confined to darkness, doth not only appear a wonderful work of Almighty God, that endoweth them with skill to defend, and wisely to provide for their own safety, but also planted in them such a natural and mutual love one to another, which is so much the more admirable, considering their beginning or creation as we have shewed already. Because by their continual hearing and laboring for meat, they do much harm to Gardens and other places of their aboad, and therefore in the husband-mans and house-wifes common-wealth, it is an acceptable labor to take and destroy them. For which cause it is good to observe their passages, and mark the times of their coming to labor, which being perceived, they are easily turned out of the earth with a spade, and this was the first and most common way.

Some have placed a board full of pikes which they fasten upon a small stick in the mole hil or passage, and when the mole cometh to heave up the earth, by touching the stick she bringeth down the pikes and sharp nailed boards upon her own body and back. Other take a Wyar of Iron, and make it to have a very sharp point, which being fastened to a staffe and put into the earth where the Moles passage is, they bend and so set up, that when the Mole cometh along, the pike runneth into her and killeth her.

The *Grecians* (saith *Palladius*) did destroy and drive away their Moles by this invention, they took a great Nut, or any other kind of fruit of that quantity, receipt and solidity, wherein they included Chaffe, Brimstone and Wax; then did they stop all the breathing places of the Moles, except one at the mouth, wherein they set this devise on fire, so as the smoak was driven inward, wherewithal they filled the hole and the place of their walks, and so stopping it, the moles were either killed or driven away.

Also *Paramus* sheweth another means to drive away and take Moles: If you take white Hellebor, and the rindes of wilde Mercury in stead of Hemlock, and dry them and beat them to powder, afterward sift them and mix them with meal and with milk-beaten with the white of an Egge, and so make it into little morsels or bals and lay them in the Mole-hole and passages, it will kill them if they eat thereof, as they will certainly do.

Many use to kill both Moles and Emmets with the froath of new Oyl. And to conclude, by setting an earthen pot in the earth and Brimstone burning therein, it will certainly drive them for ever from that place. Unto which I may add a superstitious conceit of an obscure Author, who writeth, that if you whet a mowing sythe in a field or meddow upon the feast day of Christs Nativity (commonly called Christmas day) all the Moles that are within the hearing thereof, will certainly for ever forsake that field, meddow or Garden.

With the skins of Moles are purses made, for the rough, and soft hair, and also black russet colour is very delectable. *Pliny* hath a strange saying, which is this; *Ex pellibus talparum cubicularia vidimus stragula; adeo ne religio quidem a portentis summovet delicias*; that is; We have seen the hangings of Chambers made of mole skins, so that no conscience of religion cannot avert the monstrous love of delights from the affectation of men.

For all the ancient Wise men and Magicians did hold, that this beast was capeable of Religion, *Nullis æque credunt extis, nullum Religionis capacius judicant animal, ut si quis cor ejus recens palpitansq; devoraris, divinationis & rerum efficiendarum eventus promittat*; they give not so much credit to any intrails as to theirs; for they judge that no beast is so capable of Religion, because if a man eat the heart of a Mole newly taken out of her belly and panting, he shall be able to divine and foretel infallible events. Another saith, *Veteribus monumentis traditur Gullinaceorum fibras maximè diis gratas videri: sicut Talparum viscera Magi verissima dicunt, illisq; haud secus quam solenni victima litari, hæc enim sunt exta argutissima, in quibus divina mens inesse creditut*: that is, the fibres of Cocks were wont among ancient Monuments to be accounted most acceptable to the Gods, even as the bowels of Moles (as the wise men say) and to offer these as a most solemn sacrifice grateful to the Gods, and that in those intrails it was believed that the minde and pleasure of God was seated and engraven; and a little after he saith, that the bowels of Moles and frogs do foretel many great and fortunate events.

But I will leave this paganism, and let it never enter into the heart of a reasonable man, that such beasts can love Religion, or that God hath planted in their bowels and corrupt parts, such letters of his wisdom and

895

fore-knowledge, which he hath not granted to the immortal and incorruptible soul of man. Only this I finde by experience, that before any rain and change of weather, these silly beasts heave up the earth more abundantly then at other times; and that in *Thessaly* (as *Varro* saith) a whole Town was once undermined by Moles. They were wont to sacrifice this beast to *Neptune*, because of the affinity betwixt their names, for in *Greek Asphaloos*, signifieth *Neptune*, and *Asphalax*, a Mole. *Alunnus* also writeth, that they were sacred and dedicated to Hell, because they kept continually within the bosom and bowels of the earth; and to conclude, because that Moles would not live in *Coronea* a part of *Bœotia*, before spoken of, and thereof came the common proverb, *Asphalaca eis Coronean*, a Mole is brought to *Coronea*, to signifie the hatred of a gift or ghest to him that is forced to receive him. Thus much for his natural and moral story; now followeth his medicinal.

THE MEDICINES OF THE MOLE.

There is nothing which is more profitable or medicinable for the curing of the bites of a Shrew, then a Mole being flead and clapped thereunto. The same doth also very effectually cure and heal the blows or bitings of a Scorpion. Pills being made with that which proceedeth from Moles with Hony, eaten nine days together, doth preserve the body of any one from swellings or bunches in the flesh, who shall so eat them. For the avoiding or driving away the hairs which grow in any part of mans body, that they may never return or be renewed again: Take a Mole and lay her in water to be steeped or soaked, so long as she shall not have any hairs left upon her, with this water anoint the place which is full of hairs, and afterwards wash it with lie made of ashes; and then rub it with a linnen cloth; then if you shall see the hairs to return again, wash it twice or thrice in the aforesaid manner, and they will be quite expelled away, and by no means can be made either to renew or come again. For the renewing, and bringing again of those hairs which are fallen or decayed, take a Mole, and burn her whole in the skin, and mingle the dust or powder which cometh from the same with Hony unto the thickness or fashion of an Ointment, and this being rubbed or anointed upon the bare or bald place will without doubt in some short time or space procure the hair to grow thick. For the renewing of hairs which fall from Horses; Take a Mole and boil her in Oyl, until all the flesh be consumed and quite dissolved into a liquid juyce, with this Oyl anoint the place which is bare or destitute of hairs twice every day for some short space, and it will make the hairs to grow in great abundance.

For the changing of the hairs of Horses from black to white, take a Mole and boil her in Salt water, or lye made of ashes three days together, and when the water or lie shall be quite consumed, put new water or lie thereunto this being done wash or bathe the place with the water or lie somewhat hot; presently the black hairs will fall and slide away, and in some short time there will come white. Whosoever shall take a Mole and hold her in his right hand until she die, shall have such an excellent vertue therein, that she shall ease the pain of a womans breasts only by touching them.

The dust of a Mole being burnt, mingled with the white of an Egge, and anointed upon a Sheep, is an excellent and medicinable remedy against the Leprie, which cometh oftentimes upon them. The dust of a Mole mixed with Oyl or Hony, and anointed upon the skin of either man or woman which is full of Lepry, will very speedily and effectually cure and heal the same. The same being used in the aforesaid manner, is very good for the curing of those which are troubled with the disease called the Kings Evil; as also for those which have hard bunches or kernels arising in their arm-holes, and in other parts of their body.

The whole body of a mole being taken and burned in the skin into dry dust, or powder, is an excellent remedy against the disease called the Fistula, as also for the purging of the corruption in them and healing of them, being once taken by any man. The same being also mixed with Hony, and rub'd upon the teeth of any one who hath pam in them, doth not only ease the pain and grief thereof, but also doth strengthen and make them fast. The bloud of a Mole being killed, spread or anointed upon the head of any one which is bald, will very speedily renew and bring the hairs again. The head of a mole being cut off and beaten together with the earth which is stirred up by Moles, and wrought into a paste, and rowled together liked little loaf, is very much used for the healing of all swellings, and for those things which they call Impostumes; as also for all swellings or kernels which arise in the neck; so that in the time of the curing of these things, the party which is pained and grieved, be not suffered to eat any Swines flesh.

The tooth of a living Mole taken out and tyed or bound to the teeth of any who is grieved therein, is commended by the *Magi*, or Wise-men to be an excellent remedy and cure for the same. The heart of a Mole being eaten nine days together, doth very speedily and effectually cure either him or her which shall so eat it, of that pestiferous disease call'd the Kings Evil, if it be so that it hath not been of too long continuance with them. The same is also very good and profitable for the asswaging of Wens, being used in the aforesaid manner. The liver of a Mole being beaten between the hands of him that is troubled with bunches or swellings in his back, and afterwards put upon the same, is a present help and cure. The same effect hath the right foot of a Mole for the asswaging of bunches and swellings arising in the flesh.

OF THE VULGAR LITTLE MOUSE.

As we have handled the natures, and delivered the figures of the great beasts, so also must we not disdain in a perfect History to touch the smallest: For Almighty God which hath made them all, hath disseminated in every kinde both of great and small beasts, seeds of his Wisdom, Majesty, and glory. The little Mouse therefore is justly tearmed, *Incola domus nostræ*, an inhabitant in our own houses, *Et rosor omnium rerum*, and a gnawer of all things. And therefore from the sound of her teeth which she maketh in gnawing, she is called *Sorex*.

Although we shall shew you afterwards, that *Sorex* is a special kinde, and not the name of the general. Wherefore seeing there be many kindes of Mise, and every one of them desireth a particular tractate, I thought good to begin with the Vulgar little Mouse, and so to descend to the several species and kindes of all; according to the method of the Philosopher, *A notioribus ad minus nota*, from things that are most known to them that are less known. In *Hebrew* it is called *Achar*, Levit. 11. where the *Septuagints* translate it *Muys*; the *Chaldee, Acbera*; the *Arabians, Fer*, or *Phar*; from whence cometh the *Saracen* word *Fara*. The *Persians, An Mus*; the *Latines, Mus*; the *Italians, Topo*, or *Sorice, Alsorgio, O Rato, Di casa*, although *Rato* signifieth a Rat, both among the *Germans, French*, and *English*. The *Spaniards* cal the little Mouse, *Ratt*; and the great Rat, *Ratz*; the *French* the little Mouse, *Souris*; which word seems to be derived from the *Latine, Sorex*, and the great Mouse they call *Rait*. The *Germans* the great ones *Ratz*, and the little one *Muss*; the *Illyrians* and *Polonians, Myss*, which is the *Greek* word; and the great one they call *Sczurcz*; the *Venetians* call the Rat *Pantegana*, of *Pontis* the vulgar *Greek* name, and the *Romans, Sourco*.

Now the dignity of this little beast, may appear by the name, which hath spread it self both to beasts, fishes, men, herbs, and Cities. To beasts as we have shewed before in the Ichneumon, which is vulgarly called the *Indian* Mouse, or *Pharaohs* Mouse And to fishes; for there is a little fish called *Musculus*, and in *Greek, Mystocetos*, the Whale-mouse, because it leadeth the way, and sheweth the Whale whither soever she swimmeth, for the avoiding of Rocks, (according to *Pliny*) although *Rondoletius* affirmeth otherwise, namely, that that guide of the Whale is called *Egemon*, and *Egetur*, and *Mystocetus* (he saith) is a shell-fish. Generally most kinde of Oysters are also called *Myss*, because sometimes they gape and make a noise like a Mouse, and close their shels again. The purple fishes be also called *Myss*; there is likewise a kinde of pretious stone called *Mya*, about *Bosphorus Thracius*, and many other such dignities, hath the name of this beast attained.

There was one *Mys*, the servant of that famous Philosopher *Epicurus*: likewise the name of a Champion or Challenger, in *Suidas* and *Varinus*, and there was another called *Mus*, of excelcellent skill for ingraving in

Silver, and therefore did draw upon the shield of *Minerva*, the fight betwixt the *Lapithæ*, and the *Centaurs*, and many other things. Whereupon *Martial* made this verse;

Quis labor in Phiala? decti Myos? anne Myronis?

There was a Consul of *Rome*, whose name was *Mus*, and therefore *Camerarius* made this Riddle of the Mouse; *Parva mihi domus est, sed janua semper aperta, Acciduo sumptu, furtiva vivo sagina, Quod mihi nomen inest, Romæ quoq; Consul habebat.* The *Thracians* call'd *Argilus* a Mouse, and the City which he builded *Argelus*. *Myes* was a City of *Ionia*, and a Citizen of that City was called *Myetius*. *Myon* a City of *Locri* in *Epirus*, and the people thereof are called *Myones*. *Myonesus*, a little Region betwixt *Teon* and *Lebedon*, and according to *Stephanus*, an Island near *Ephesus*; the first Port or Haven of *Egypt*, opening to the Red Sea, is called *Muos armos*, the Mouses haven, and *Mysia* also seemeth to be derived from their stem. There is an Island under the Equinoctial line, called *Injula Murium*, the Mouse Island, because of the abundance of Mice therein: and to conclude, even the herbs and plants of the earth, have received names from this little beast, as *Hordeum*, *Murinum*, *Myacantha*, *Sperage*, *Myopteton*, *Myuoos*, *Myortocon*, Mouse-ear, Mouse-foot; and such like. There have been also Comedies made of *Myss*, as that of *Carsinus*, called *Myes*, wherein the Weasil strangleth the night-wandering *Myss*. And another *Greek*, called *Galeomyomachia*, that is a fight betwixt Cats and Mice, wherein the Poet doth most pleasantly faign names of Mice, as their King he calleth *Creilius*, that is, a flesh-eater, and his eldest son *Psicarpax*, a corn-eater; and his second son *Psitodarpes*, bread-eater, and his eldest daughter, *Lyenogluphe*, candle-eater; and all his Ancestors *Carpodaptai*, that is, fruit-eaters. And then he bringeth other Mice in, as *Turolicos*, *Psicolices*, *Cholecoclophos Homer* in his *Batrachomyomachia*, that is, a fight betwixt Frogs and Mice, doth very elegantly describe divers proper names of Mice. As *Piscarpax*, whose father was *Tuoxartes*, and his mother *Lychomile*, daughter of *Pternotrocta* the King, and then other Mice, as *Lychopinax*, *Terogliphus*, *Embaschitrus*, *Lychenor*, *Troglodites*, *Artophagus*, *Ptermogliphus*, *Pternophagus*, *Cnissodioctes*, *Sitophagus*, *Artophilus*,

900

Meridarpax, and *Thulacotrox*, all which are not only out of the abundance of the Authors wit, but invented for the expressing of the Mouses nature.

The Epithets of Mice are these; short, small, fearful, peaceable, ridiculous, rustick, or Country Mouse, urbane, or City Mouse, greedy, wary, unhappy, harmful, black, obscene, little, whiner, biter, and earthly. And the *Greek* ones are expressed before in the proper names, and thus much may suffice for the names of Mice. Now to come to their several nature and significations. First of all concerning their colour. It is divers, for although *Color murinus* be a common tearm for a Mouse colour of Asses, yet notwithstanding Mice are sometimes blackish, sometimes white, sometimes yellow, sometimes brown, and sometime ash colour. There are white Mice among the people of *Savoy*, and *Dauphin* in *France* called *Allobroges*, which the Inhabitants of the Countrey do believe that they feed upon snow. But the white Mouse is above all other most lascivious and leacherous, and therefore it came into a proverb, *Mys Leucos, Mys Cacos*, the white Mouse is an ill Mouse, of whose lust *Alciatus* made this Emblem;

> *Delitias & mollitiem, Mus creditur albus,*
> *Arguere; at ratio non sat aperta mihi est*
> *An quod ei natura salax, & multa libido est?*
> *Ornat Romanas an quia pelle nurus?*
> *Sarmaticum Murem vocitant pleriq zibellum,*
> *Et celebris suavi est ungutne Muscus Arabs.*

Of all which conjectures of the Poets, the first is most probable; for the Ancients were wont to call wanton and effeminate men *Pygargoi*, and *Leucopygoi*, from their beauty and whiteness. And as there is a difference in their colours, so also there is in their quantity: For some are very great, some meanly great, and some very small. Their heart is very great, and their liver and lights increase in the Winter time. Also the fibres that are in them, do increase and decrease with the waxing and waning of the Moon. For every day of the Moons age, there is a fibre increased in their liver. And therefore *Lucilius* said well, *Luna alit ostrea, & implet echinos, & Muribus fibras auget*: that is to say, The Moon feedeth Oysters, filleth Hedgehogs, and encreaseth fibres in Mice. Some of these Mice have a gall, and some have none, as *Aristotle* and *Pliny* shew in many places.

The Mouses place of conception have many holes in it, during the time she beareth her young ones. There is no creature that heareth more perfectly then a Mouse, they dwell in houses of men, especially near supping and dining rooms, kitchins, or larders, where any meat is stirring. And they make themselves places of abode by gnawing with their teeth; if they finde not convenient lodgeings prepared to their hand, and they love the hollow places of wals, or the roofs of homes; and therefore the Walps which in *Aristophanes* are called *Drophæ*, that is gnawers of roofs, are to be understood to be Mice, because *Mys Drophia* is a Mouse in the house top. In the day time they lie still so long as they either see or hear a man, or any other beast harmful unto them, for they discern their enemies; not fearing an Ox, though they run away from a Cat.

They are very desirous of bread, and delight to all those meats which are made of fruit, for the nourishment of Men. It is a creature very diligent and exquisite, both to compass, seek out and chuse the same, so that therefore it doth often endanger and lose his own life: and finding any cubboards, wood, or such like hard matter, to withstand his purpose, and hinder his passage, it ceaseth not to weary it self with gnawing, until it obtain the purpose. All kindes of Mice love grain and corn, and prefer the hard before the soft; they love also Cheese, and if they come to many Cheeses together, they tast all, but they eat of the best. And therefore the *Egyptians* in their Hieroglyphicks do picture a Mouse, to signifie a sound Judgement and good choice. Buckmast is very acceptable to Mice, and the Mice in the Isle *Parus*, in *Tenedos*, in the Island *Gyaros*, which is one of the Islands of the *Sporads* in *Cyprus*, and in *Chalcis*, they did eat Iron, as appeareth by *Aristotle*, *Ælianus*, and *Heraclides*. And it was also found, that in a certain Island near *Chalybes*, Mice eat and devour gold, and therefore the Gold-smiths did cut them in pieces among their metals. *Plutarch*, in the life of *Marcellus* saith, that there were many prodigies and fearful signes that did precede the war of *Marius*, amongst other, he saith that Mice did eat the Gold hanging in the Temple, and that one of the Temple-keepers in a certain trap took a female Mouse alive, who littered five little Mice in that place, and devoured three of them. *Anthologius* rehearseth a witty Hexastichon of *Antiphilus*, upon a Mouse which was slit asunder alive, for certain Gold-dust, which she had devoured, whereby was signified how men procure unto themselves exquisite torments, and unavoidable mortal harms by stealing, and increasing of riches signified by Gold. Vulgar Mice do ruminate or chew the cud as well as the Pontick, and they drink by licking or lapping, although their teeth be not sawed. It is reported that the Mice of *Africk*, and especially of *Lybia*, die as soon as they drink. And the reason thereof we will shew afterwards in the taking of Mice, when we come to discourse of their poysons. And for the present it should seem their temperament, or constitution is so moist, that nature can endure no addition. Yet in the plains of *Arcadia*, there are Mice which drink of a certain Fountain without any harm.

The generation and procreation of Mice, is not only by copulation, but also nature worketh wonderfully in ingendering them by earth and small showers, as we will shew in the discourse of wilde Mice.

But the house Mouse whereof we now intreat, is engendered by copulation betwixt male and female, and they are in general most libidinous, as may appear by that saying of *Cratinus* against *Xenophon*, *Phere nun ex aithrias Katapuposunen muos astrapso Xenophontos*, go to now, for from the skies I will strike by lightning the *Murin* wantonness of *Xenophon*: and the female is much more venereous then the male, as appeareth by that fable of *Ipicrates* describing the rage of a lustful woman. *Postremo subiit me detestabilis lena, dejerans per Dionam, per puellam, per Persephattam, se esse vitulam, esse virginem, esse pullam indomitam, at illa myonia erat.* Then followed me that detestable baud, swearing by *Diana*, and *Persephatta*, that she was a Heifer never touched, a Virgin never stained, and a Colt never covered, but the truth is, she was as good a Maid as a Mouse. *Politianus* in stead of *at illa myonia erat*, hath *at illa cavus erat Murinus*, that she was a Mouses hole, signifying that her virginity was lost, and that she suffered any lovers, as a Mouse-hole doth any Mice. And from hence came that verse of *Martial*, describing the speech of a lover to his love, calling him her Mouse and her Joy;

Nam cum me Murem tu, cum mea lumina dicis.

903

So that in general all Mice, and not only the white Mouse, are most desirous of copulation. And when they are in copulation, they embrace with their tails, filling one another without all delay. By tasting of Salt, they are made very fruitful, and therefore *Aristotle*, and the Souldiers of *Alexander* the Great, do report, that Mice by licking one another, and by the licking of Salt, do ingender & conceive with young without any other copulation. But what reasons they have to lead them to that opinion, I know not; beside that wonder reported by *Pliny* and *Aristotle*, that in a certain part of *Persia*, a female Mouse being slit asunder alive, all the young females within her belly are also found pregnant conceived with young.

It is very certain, that for the time they go with young, and for the number they bring forth, they exceed all other beasts, conceiving every fourteen or sixteen days, so that it hath been found by good experience, that a female Mouse having free liberty to litter in a vessel of millet-seed, within less compass, then half a year she hath brought forth one hundred and twenty young ones.

They live very long, if they be not prevented of their natural course, and dying naturally, they perish not all at once, but by little, and little, first one member, and then another, (*Pliny* saith) *E volucirbus hirundines sunt indociles, terrestribus Mures*, among the Fowls of the air, the Swallows are undocible, and among the creatures of the earth, a Mouse: *Albertus* writeth, that he saw in upper *Germany*, a Mouse hold a burning Candle in her feet, at the commandment of her Master all the time his guests were at Supper.

Now the only cause why they grow not tame, is, their natural fear, such as is in Conies, Hares, and Deer. For how can any man or beast love or hearken unto him, who they are perswaded lyeth in wait for their life, and such is the perswasion of all them that fear: which perswasion being once removed by continual familiarity, there is no cause in nature, but that a Mouse may be docible as well as a Hare or Cony, which we have shewed heretofore in their stories.

It is also very certain that Mice which live in a House, if they perceive by the age of it, it be ready to fall down or subject to any other ruin, they foreknow it and depart out of it; as may appear by this notable story which happened in a Town called *Helice* in *Greece*, wherein the Inhabitants committed this abominable act against their neighbours the *Greeks*. For they slew them, and sacrificed them upon their Altars: Whereupon, followed the ruine of the City, which was premonstrated by this prodigious event. For five days before the destruction thereof, all the Mice, Weesils, and Serpents, and other reptile creatures, went out of the same in the presence of the Inhabitants, every one assembling to his own rank and company, whereat the people wondered much, for they could not conceive any true cause of their departure; and no marvail. For God which had appointed to take vengeance on them for their wickedness, did not give them so much knowledge, nor make them so wise as the beasts to avoid his judgement, and their own destruction; and therefore mark what followed. For these beasts were no sooner out of the City, but suddenly in the night time, came such a lamentable Earth-quake and strong tempest, that all the houses did not only fall down, and not one of them stood upright, to the slaughter of men, women, and children, contained in them; but lest any of them should escape the strokes of the timber and house tops, God sent also such a great floud of waters, by reason of the tempestuous winde which drove the waters out of the Sea upon the Town, that swept them all away, leaving no more behinde then naked and bare significations of former buildings. And not only the City and Citizens perished, but also there was ten ships of the *Lacedemonians* in their port all drowned at that instant.

The wisdom of the Mouse appeareth in the preparation of her house; for considering she hath many enemies, and therefore many means to be hunted from place to place, she committeth not her self to one lodging alone, but provideth many holes; so that when she is hunted in one place she may more safely repose her self in another. Which thing *Plautus* expresseth in these words; *Sed tamen cogitato, Mus pusillus, quam sapiens sit bestia, ætatem qui uni cubili nunquam committit suam: cum unum obsidetur, aliunde perfugium quærit:* that is to say, it is good to consider the little Mouse, how wise a beast she is, for she will not commit her life to one lodging, but provideth many harbors, that being molested in one place she may have another refuge to flie unto.

And as their wisdom is admirable in this provision, so also is their love to be commended one to another, for falling into a vessel of water or other deep thing, out of which they cannot ascend again of themselves, they help one another, by letting down their tails, and if their tails be too short, then they lengthen them by this means: they take one anothers tail in their mouth, and so hang two or three in length, until the Mouse which was fallen down take hold on the neathermost, which being performed, they all of them draw her out. Even so Wolves holding one another by their tails, do swim over great Rivers: and thus hath nature granted that to them which is denyed to many men, namely, to love, and to be wise together. But concerning their manners, they are evil, apt to steal, insidious, and deceitful; and men also which are of the same disposition with these beasts, fearing to do any thing publickly, and yet privately enterprise many deceits, are justly reproved in imitation of such beasts. For this cause was it forbidden in Gods Law unto the *Jews*, not only to eat, but to touch Mice, and the Prophet Esai. ch. 66. saith, *Comedentes carnem suillam, & abominationem, atq; murem, simul consumentur, inquit Dominus*, that is, they which eat Swines flesh, abomination, and the Mouse, shall be destroyed together, saith the Lord: wherein the Prophet threatneth a curse unto the people, that broke the first Law of God in eating flesh forbidden; and the Physitians also say, that the eating of the flesh of Mice engendereth forgetfulness, abomination, and corruption in the stomach.

The eating of bread or other meat which is bitten by Mice, doth encrease in men and children a certain disease in their face, and in the flesh, at the roots of the nails of their fingers certain hard bunches, called by the *Venetians, Spelli;* and by the *Germans, Leidspyssen;* and by the *Latines, Dentes Muris:* yet it is affirmed, that the flesh of Mice is good for Hawks, to by given them every day, or every each other day together with the skin; for it helpeth their intrails, purgeth fleam and choler; restraineth the fluxions of the belly; driveth out stones and gravel; stayeth the distillation of the head to the eyes; and finally corroborateth the stomach. Yet we have heard that in the Kingdom of *Calecut*, they do eat Mice and Fishes roasted in the Sun. And it is said by some Physitians and Magicians, that the flesh is good against melancholy, and the pain of the teeth; but the medicinal vertues we reserve it to its proper place.

Pliny affirmeth a strange wonder, worthy to be remembred and recorded, that when *Hannibal* besieged *Casselinum*, there was a man that sold a Mouse for two hundred pieces of coin, so great was the extremity of famine, that the man which sold it, dyed for hunger, and as it should seem through the want of it, but he which bought it lived by eating thereof; the which thing argueth, that necessity, hunger, and famin, maketh men for the safegard of life, to make more reckoning in extremity of the basest creatures, then in prosperity they do of the best. For that person which gave so much money for a Mouse, at another time would have scorned to have given so much for four Oxen.

And on the other side, the wretched love of gain, which causeth a man to endanger his own life for love of silver. But I rather think that it was the hand of God himself taking vengeance of such a covetous disposition, which would not suffer him to live, that like *Midas* had gotten so much gold.

The enemies of Mice are many, not only men, which by sundry artificial devices kill them, because of harm, but also beasts and wilde fowl do eat their flesh, and live upon them. And first of all Cats and Weesils do principally hunt to catch Mice, and have been therefore by the late Writers called *Murilegi*, for their taking of Mice. And the nature of the Weesil is not only more inclined to hunt after them, then the Cat, but is more terrible also unto them; for if the brains of a Weesil, the hair or rennet be sprinkled upon Cheese, or any other meat whereto Mice resort, they not only forbear to eat thereof, but also to come in that place. They are also driven away by the sprinkling of the ashes of Weesils; and as all noises make them afraid, so none so much as the skreeching or crying of a Weesil, for at the hearing thereof they all fall astonished. And besides, they have more opportunity to follow and take them then Cats, because their bodies are lesser, and their noses and snowts longer, and therefore they follow them many times into their holes, and very nimbly pull them forth when they think they are most secure. Foxes also kill Mice; and in *Italy* there is a black Snake called *Carbonario*, from his colour, resembling coals, which I think to be the same that the *Græcians* call *Myagros*, from his hunting of Mice: This Snake doth also eat and devour Mice. Hawks eat Mice, and all the night-birds, especially the night-crows and Owls. How hateful a Mouse is to the Elephant, we have shewed already in that story, how in the presence thereof he will not touch his meat, nor eat any thing over which a Mouse doth run. Nor yet eat in the cratch or manger wherein a Mouse hath been. *Ponzettus* affirmeth, that there is great love between Mice and Serpents, for sometimes they play together.

There is a hatred betwixt Bats, Frogs and Mice, as may appear by *Anthologius*, *Museus*, and others. It is said also that they are hateful to Oysters, whereof I know no reason, except it be because they love their fish. And *Alciatus* hath a pretty embleme, which he entituleth *Captivus ob gulam*, wherein he sheweth, that a Mouse watcheth an Oyster when he gapeth, and seeing it open, thrusts in his head to eat the fish; as soon as ever the Oyster felt his teeth, presently he closeth his shell again, and so crusheth the Mouses head in pieces, whereby he deciphereth the condition of those men which destroy themselves to serve their bellies. And thus much for the love and enmity betwixt Mice and other Beasts.

Now concerning the actions of men, they hunt Mice to be rid from their annoyances, because they do not only destroy the things they eat, and live upon other mens cost; and therefore Parasites are compared unto them whom the *Germans* call *Schmorotzer*, and *Tellerlecker*, that is, smell-feasts, and lick-spickets, are compared to Mice, because they live at other mens tables. But also Mice do defile and corrupt, and make unprofitable whatsoever they taste; and therefore the *Egyptians* when they would describe corruption, do picture a Mouse.

For these causes have men invented many devices, snares, and gins, the general whereof is called by the *Latines*, *Muscipula*; and by the *Græcians*, *Muspala*, and *Myagra*, the divers and several forms whereof I will not disdain to set down. For the wise Reader must consider, that it is as necessary, or rather more necessary for most men to know how to take Mice, then how to take Elephants.

And although every woman, and silly Rat-catcher can give instruction enough therein, yet their knowledge cannot excuse my negligence, if I should omit the inventions and devices of the Ancients, whereby they delivered themselves from the annoyances of these beasts. And therefore first of all to declare the manner of catching them in places where corn is kept: Let your Mouse-trap be placed to catch Mice, right against the door, but let them have room to come in, and in short time it will so fear them, that they will trouble you no more. But if Mice breed in the ground under crevices, except you fill all the crevices with Mouse-traps, you will never catch them, which the Inhabitants of the Island *Pandataria* are fain to do.

There are other kinde of Mouse-traps which do catch Mice alive: and othersome which do kill them, either being pressed down with the weight of it, or stifled with water, or otherwise, as with a strong piece of Iron being small, and hung right against the button of the trap, on the which piece of Iron they hang meat, and so by that means the Mouse is catched by putting her head through the hole to snatch at the meat; for she by stirring the Iron doth loosen the button, and so her head is shut fast in the hole. And there are other kinde of Mouse-traps which are covered all over, into the which the Mouse may run; and if you have put any water therein they are presently stifled. Of all which kinde of traps shall be severally tracted: And first of all those which do catch Mice alive.

The common kinde of this Mouse-trap is made of wood, long, and four-cornerwise, and is framed of four boards, but the hinder part is strengthened with strong wiers of Iron, that she may without danger look in to see what she may get there; and that the smell of that which she findeth there, may allure her to come to it. And the former part hath a hole in the top, through which there is put a small piece of Iron; and also there is made a trap-door in form of a Percullis, to the which the Iron is very slightly hung, that when the Mouse cometh to catch at the meat, she is suddenly taken by falling of the same; but the meat which you fasten to the neather end of this Iron hook must be fat, or the crust of cheese or bread; which if it be a little toasted at the fire, it will not be amiss, that the Mouse may smell it far off. Some do make these kinde of traps double, with one door at one end, and another door at another end. These kinde of Mouse-traps *Petrus Crescent*, doth call traps belonging to houses, which shall be spoken of hereafter.

The other kinde of Mouse-trap is made with Iron hooks hung in the round circle; in the midst of the which brim is put a great many of the same wiers, which being made sharp at every end, are after the form of the top of a crest, or helmet, or as it is made in a bow-net to catch fishes; and upon the hook let there be hung meat, by which means the Mouse coming to the meat, sticketh herself upon the hooks. The manner of making lesser Mouse-traps is with Walnut-tree, and that the middle part of it be not covered, and that there be put to the mouth or brim thereof some kinde of mettle, so that the open part may bend inward, and that the Mouse may not gnaw that which is within, except she creepeth under: which if she shall do, she shall presently be shut in by stirring the trap.

Also there is another kinde of Mouse-trap which is covered with the bark of a tree, which is cut into equal pieces, and laid cross one over another; but there is tied a Swines skin in the middle, and also an earthen pot covered with the same bark, being first sprinkled with corn, that the Mice may custom to come to it, and being dryed with lying, they break in pieces, but you must lay them together again, and fill your pot with water, by the which means as soon as ever they are upon the same, they fall into the pit, and so are stifled.

And also it is reported of those which have tryed the same, that if Mice fall into a vessel without water, and remain there a long time without meat, that then they devour one another, but if they remain there so long until one among them all be left alone, that is to say, the strongest of them all, and that he be suffered to go out, wheresoever he shall finde any Mice he will eat them up, and they shall have much ado to escape him, because he hath been so long accustomed unto them. I was told also of a certain friend of mine, that a man of *Senensis* did set a purse in a hollow place, and made it to open and shut by some devise, so that at length he took a Mouse, which Mouse he fed only with the flesh of Mice, and after he had fed it so a long time, he let it go, who killed all the Mice he did meet, and was not satisfied with them, but went into every hole that he could finde, and eat them up also. Also Mice are taken in vessels, from whence they cannot escape, upon the which vessel let there be put a small staffe, which is so cut in the middle, that she may only hold her self by the meat, and when you have so done, put the kernel of a Nut upon the middle of the staffe, to the which the Mouse coming, doth fall into the vessel with the staffe, and they will be stifled if there be any water: but if there be none she will be killed.

And again, he telleth of another manner of catching of Mice, which is as great as the first, and it is after this manner: Take two smooth boards about the length of thy arm, and in breadth half thy arm, but joyn it so together, that they may be distant from the lower part in length some four fingers or little less, with two small spindles or clefts, which must be at every end one, and fasten Paper under them, and put a piece of paste therein, being cut overthwart in the middle, but you must not fasten it nigh the middle, and let it be so bound, that it may easily be lifted up betwixt the spindles, that if by slipping it should be altered, it might be brought again to the same form. But the two spindles spoken of before, ought to be joyned together in the ends above, and beyond them another small spindle to be made, which may hold in the middle a crooked wedge or butten, upon the which may be hanged a piece of Hogs skin, so that one of them may easily be turned upsidedown with the skin, and put thereunto a little piece of earth or stick, that the Mice may easily come to it: So that how many Mice soever shall come thereto, and to the meat, shall be taken, always by rowling the Paper into his wonted place.

There is another manner also, which is to make a round piece of wood fastened on both sides with Needles, and made so that the hinder part of it weigh heavier then the former, and that it stand an inch higher then the other, and then when you have so placed it, throw some corn thereon, that the Mice may be allured thereto, and tie also a piece of flesh upon the former end of it; and so the Mouse going into the middle, by the rowling off the same, slippeth into the kettle which standeth under it, which must be half full of water, the circle presently being as it was before, that very often many Mice are catched in one night by this work, all falling into the kettle. Also there are many kindes of Mice-traps, where Mice do perish by the weight thereof, and they are made of a small piece of wood made hollow, into the which shall fall down another small piece of wood; but it must be made so, that it may fall weighty to press down the Mice going to the meat, and let the meat be tied to another little small piece of wood, which being touched, the heavy piece doth presently fall down, and so by that means the Mouse is taken.

Our Country men do make a trap which is somewhat like to this, let two pieces of boards be joyned together one foot broad, & two foot long,

911

and afterwards let there be put in them a wooden pin, which you must fasten to the lower board; so that it may not touch the uppermost; and you must set it so, that the former part may easily move backward and forward; but moreover, the former board must be fastened to the hinder, like the fashion of a Gibbet or Gallows, with two pieces of wood standing upright, one being put overthwart, or after the fashion of the *Greek* letter Π, and it must stand some nine inches high, and as broad as the board will suffer you, and let the meat be hung in the middle of it, but that board which is uppermost, must touch both the ends of the other, and notched according to the breadth, the notch being made after the form of a wedge divided into two parts; and another small piece of wood must be put to that which is uppermost, almost two fingers long, and one finger broad, and let there be put into the lower notch a piece of wood with meat at it, so that it may be slightly fastened to the brim of the uppermost, that the meat being presently touched, the other may the easiler fall.

And you may lay a stone upon the uppermost board, that it may fall the heavier. And there are some also which to the lower board do fasten iron pins, made very sharp; against the which the Mice are driven by the weight of the fall. Furthermore, there is another kinde of trap made to cover them alive, one part of it cut out of a small piece of wood, the length of the palm of thy hand, and the breadth of one finger, and let the other part of it be cut after the form of a wedge: and let this piece of wood be erected like a little pillar, and let the wedge be put into the notch of another piece of wood, which must be made equal with the other, or very little shorter: and this pillar must be so made, that the Mouse may not perish before she come to the meat: the wood where the meat must stand, ought to be a span long, and you must fasten the meat about the middle of it, but the former part of it must have a cleft, which must begin a little from the brim, and shall be made almost the length of two fingers, and you must make it with two straight corners, and take away half the breadth of the wood. These three pieces of wood being thus made ready, thou shall erect a little pillar, so that the wedge may be downward, whereby the Mouse may see the meat every where: and let the meat be hung in the former corner of the pillar, so if the

Mouse shall touch the meat, he shall be pressed down with the fall of the board. Mice also by the fall of a cleft board are taken, which is held up with a pillar, and having a little spattular of wood, whereon the meat shall lye, so made that the pillar doth not open being parted, except when the Mouse cometh to touch the meat, and so by that means she is taken.

There is also another manner of Mouse-trap used among us, which is, let there be a hole made and compassed about with a board of a foot long, and five or six fingers broad, the compass whereof must be four fingers; into this hole let there be put a vessel made of wood the length of ones fist, but round and very deep; and in the middle of each side of this vessel let there be made a hole, wherein there is put in a thread made of Iron with meat, and let it be compassed about with a small thread which must be fastened overthwart the hole: and the part of the thread which hangeth down must be crooked, that the meat may be fastened thereto, and there must be a piece of the thread without; to the which may be tied a stronger piece of wood, which is the thread whereon the meat is hanged, by the which the Mouse is taken, by putting her head into the vessel to catch at the meat.

And also Mice are taken otherwise, with a great Cane wherein there is a knot, and in the top of it let there be made a little bow with a Lute string, and there stick a great needle in the middle of the pole of the Cane, and let the pole be made just in the middle, and let there be bound a piece of flesh beneath, so prepared, that when the Mouse shall bite, and move the skin, that then the string slippeth down, and so the needle pierceth through his head, and holdeth him that he cannot run away. But among all the rest, there is an excellent piece of workmanship to catch Mice; which I will here set down: Take a piece of wood, the length of both thy fists, one fist broad, and two fingers thick, and let there be cut off about some two fingers, a little beyond the middle of half the breadth. And that breadth where it was cut, ought to be more declining and lower, after the manner of this letter A. And you must put to the side of this a piece of wood, half a circle long, bending, and in the middle part of each side holes pierced through, so that the half circle may be strait, and plainly placed to the foundation of the wood, that the trap being made,

913

it may rest upon the same half circle, and upon this half circle let there be placed Iron nails very sharp, so that the instrument by falling down may cover the Irons of the half circle as soon as ever they touch the same.

Furthermore, there is another manner of trap, when a vessel out of which they cannot escape, is filled half up with water, and upon the top thereof Oat meal is put, which will swim, and not sink, making the uppermost face of the water to seem white, and solid, whereunto when the Mouse cometh, she leapeth into the Oatmeal, and so is drowned: And the like may be done with chaffe mingled with Oatmeal: and this in all traps must be observed, wherein Mice are taken alive, that they be presently taken forth, for if they make water in the place, their fellows will for ever suspect the trap, and never come near it, till the favour of the urine be abolished.

Palladius saith, that the thick froth of Oyl, being infused into a dish or brasen Caldron, and set in the middle of the house in the night time, will draw all the Mice unto it, wherein they shall stick fast, and not be able to escape.

Pliny saith, that if a Mouse be gelded alive, and so let go, she will drive away all the residue; but this is to be understood of the Sorex. If the head of a Mouse be flead; or if a male Mouse be flead all over, or her tail cut off; or if her leg be bound to a post in the house, or a bell be hung about her neck, and so turned going, she will drive away all her fellows. And (*Pliny* saith) that the smoke of the leaves of the Ewe tree, because they are a poyson, will kill Mice, so also will Libbards-bane, and Henbane-seed, and Wolf-bane, for which cause they are severally called *Myoctonos*, and the roots of Wolf-bane, are commonly sold in *Savoy* unto the Country people for that purpose.

In *Germany* they mingle it with Oatmeal, and so lay it in balls to kill Mice. The fume of Wallwort, Calcauth, Parsely, Origanum, and Deaths-herb do also kill Mice: you may also drive them away with the fume of the stone Hæmatites, and with green Tamarisk, with the hoof of a Mule, or of Nitre, or the ashes of a Weesil, or a Cat in water, or the gall of an Ox put into bread.

The seed of Cowcumbers being sod, and sprinkled upon any thing, Mice will never touch it, likewise wilde Cowcumber and Coloquintida, kill Mice. To keep Mice from Corn, make morter of the froth of Oyl mingled together with chaff, and let them well dry, and afterwards be wrought throughly, then plaister the walls of your garnery therewith, and when they are dry cast more froth of Oyl upon them, and afterwards carry in your corn, and the Mice will never annoy it.

Wormwood laid among clothes, and skins, defend them from Mice: And also the water of Worm-wood sod, sprinkled upon clothes hath the same operation.

Ink tempered with water, wherein Wormwood hath been washed, or sod, causeth that the Parchment and Paper written therewith, shall never be eaten, or touched with Mice.

Anatolius and *Tarentinus*, in the discourse of the granery or barn, do write, that Milk thistle mingled with Hony, Water, and fine Flower, or Mil-dust, made into little balls, and laid where Mice may eat of it, doth make them blinde if they cast thereof. White Hellebore mixed with pottage, or the seeds of wilde Cowcumber, Coloquintida, and Meal, mingled with black Hellebore, and put into Cheese or Bread, or any other kinde of fat meat, killeth both Rats and Mice. So likewise a white Camelion sod in broth, mingled with water and Oyl, killeth Dogs, Swine and Mice.

The juyce of the root of the herb Camelion, mixed with Water and Oyl, draweth Mice unto it, and killeth them by tasting thereof, if they drink not presently: so also doth Henbane. The roots of the bramble Tree, mingled with Butter, Bread, or Hony, Elecampane, and Sea Onions, Scammony, wilde Sparage, Arsenick, Mug-wort, otherwise called Mouse-wort, mingled with Lard in small pieces, with Auripigment, killeth Wolfs and Mice; and in some Countries, for the better dispersing of the poyson, set drink beside the same, whereof as soon as they tast, they swell and die; but I have seen them die without drinking at all. Mice and Wolfs, if they tast of the wilde Rose, and drink after it, do not only die, but also fall into madness and bite their fellows, communicating the quality of the disease to every one they bite. Flesh cut into little pieces, and fryed with Butter in a frying pan, and afterwards when it is cold, adde half so much soft pitch thereto, and mingle it together, rowling up the flesh in the Pitch, then distribute it upon little bords, and set it in the place, and places whereunto the Mice do much resort, and water beside it, and when that they have tasted of it a little, they are so eagerly a thirst, that they drink and die.

The like I may say of Rats-bane, Quick-silver, Sublimate, and Precipitate, and divers other things; and thus much may suffice for the catching, taking, and killing of Mice, whereunto I may adde the use of their members and parts, not medicinal, but natural, although I have touched it heretofore in part.

The *Scythians* were wont to be clad with the skins of Mice and Woolfs, and it is observed, that when Mice cry and screeketh above their ordinary custom, it presageth an alteration and change of the weather; and thus much shall suffice for their natural discourse.

Having thus discoursed of the nature of the vulgar Mouse, I may also add the moral use thereof, as I finde it recorded among learned Writers, delivered either in History, or in Proverb. It is reported of *Glaucus* the son of *Minos* and *Pasiphae*, that while he followed a Mouse to take her, he fell into a vessel of Hony; but after *Polyades* the Prophet, by laying an herb on him, raised him again to life. *Hatto* an Archbishop of *Metz* in the frontiers of *Germany*, was destroyed by Mice, or as other say by Rats; but the words of *Textor* are;

Hatto Archiepiscopus Moguntinus à muribus fertur devoratus.

And the error may proceed, because that *Mus* is a general word for the Rat and Mouse; and therefore they which have thought it an unreasonable thing, that so small beasts should destroy so mighty a Prince, have rather attributed it to the Rats then to the Mice; but they ought to have remembred, that it was an extraordinary judgement of God to punish a cruel covetous wretch, and that therefore it was as easie for him to make the little Mouse his instrument, as the great Rat: for we read, that *Herod* was devoured by Worms; and other have been eaten up with Lice. *Adrian* the Pope was strangled by a Fly; and therefore *Hatto* an Archbishop might aswell perish through the afflicting hand of God by a multitude of Mice.

Heliogabalus that wretch, amongst other his monstrous desires, and Tyrannical commands, *Lampridius* affirmeth, that upon a time he commanded, that there should be brought unto him ten thousand Mice alive, a thousand Weesils, and a thousand *Sorices*, or wilde Field-mice, so base were his thoughts, that while he should have attended his Emperial calling, and hearkened to the suits and complaints of poor distressed subjects, he was busied in killing of Mice, and therefore in ancient time, a Mouse-killer was taken for an opprobrious speech, for a base, sluggish, and idle companion.

The like is reported of a *Muscovian* Emperour, who to afflict his people, and to gather mony from them, commanded the Citizens of *Musco*, to bring him a peck full of Fleas: whereunto the people answered, that if they could take so many, yet could not they keep them together from leaping away. And Mice have been brought into publick spectacle, because at *Lavinium* they gnawed asunder the shields of silver; and it was afterward judged a prodigy; for there followed the *Marsick* war. When the *Scythians* understood that *Darius* with his great Army, stood in need of victuals, they sent unto him a Provant-master with these presents or gifts, a Bird, a Mouse, a Frog, and five darts. At the receit whereof the *Persians* wondered what should be meant thereby; and demanded of the messenger the meaning of the mystery. But the Ambassador answered, he knew not any signification of his presents, but only received charge to deliver them, and make hast back again, and to bid the *Persians*, if they were wise, to lay their wits together, to know and understand the meaning thereof. When the *Persians* heard him say so, they fell to consultation. *Darius* gave his opinion, that the Mouse, signified the earth; the Frog, the waters; the Bird, Horses; and the Darts, warlike furniture and strength of forces; and that the *Scythians* by sending all these unto them, yeelded that the *Persians* should be Lords of their Land, Sea, Horses, and themselves, and that therefore they ought to be of good courage.

But one *Gobrias*, a grave Counsellor, who was one of the seven that slew the *Magi*, or Wizards, answered otherwise, for his conjecture was more true: for said he; *O Persæ, nisi effecti ut aves subvoletis in Cœlum, aut ut Mures subeatis terram, aut ut ranæ insiliatis in paludes, non remeabitis unde venistis bis sagittis confecti:* O ye *Persians*, except ye become like Birds, to flie up into heaven; or like Mice, to creep into the earth; or like Frogs, to leap into the waters, you shall not return back again unto the place from whence you came, and so indeed it came to pass. We read 1 Sam. 5. that when the Ark of God was taken by the *Philistines*, and they kept it in their Temple at *Hazzah*, the hand of the Lord fell upon their Princes, and he smote them with Emrods, in the bottom of their belly, that is, God punished them with Mice, for he afflicted their bodies, and the fruits of the earth, for which cause *cap.* 6 they advice with themselves, to send back again the Ark of the Lord with a present of Golden Mice. *Ovid, Homer,* and *Orpheus,* call *Apollo Smyntheus,* for the *Cretians* in ancient time called *Mice Smynthæ*: Now the faigned cause thereof is thus related by *Ælianus*:

There was one *Crinis* which was a Priest of *Apollo*; who neglected his daily sacrifice, for the which through abundance of Mice he was deprived of the fruits of the earth, for they devoured all. At which loss *Apollo* himself was moved; and taking pity of the misery, appeared to one *Horda* a Neat-heard, commanding him to tell *Crinis,* that all the cause of that penury was, for that he had omitted his accustomed sacrifice, and that it was his duty to offer them again diligently, or else it would be far worse afterward. *Crinis* upon the admonition amended the fault, and immediately *Apollo* killed all the devouring Mice with his darts, whereupon he was called *Smyntheus.* Others again say, that among the *Æolians,* at *Troas* and *Hamaxitus,* they worshipped Mice and *Apollo* both together, and that under his Altar they had meat and nourishment, and also holes to live in safely: and the reason was; because once many thousand of Mice invaded the corn fields of *Æolia* and *Troy,* cutting down the same before it was ripe, and also frustrating the husbandman of fruit and hope: this evil caused them to go to *Delphos,* to ask counsel at the Oracle what they should do to be delivered from that extremity; where the Oracle gave answer that they should go sacrifice to *Apollo Smyntheus*; and afterward they had sacrificed, they were delivered from the Mice, and that therefore they placed a statue or figure of a Mouse in the Temple of *Apollo.*

When the *Trojans* came out of *Creet,* to seek a habitation for themselves, they received an Oracle, that they should there dwell, where the Inhabitants that were born of the earth should set upon them; the accomplishing whereof fell out about *Hamaxitus*; for in the night time a great company of wilde Mice set upon their bows, quivers, and strings, leathers of their bucklers, and all such soft instruments, whereby the people knew, that that was the place, wherein the Oracle had assigned them to build the City; and therefore there they builded *Ida*, so called after the name of *Ida* in *Creet*: and to conclude, we do read that Mice have been sacrificed, for the *Arcadians* are said first of all to have sacrificed to their Gods a Mouse; and secondly a white Horse; and lastly the leaves of an Oak.

And to conclude, *Ælianus* telleth one strange story of Mice in *Heraclea*, that there is not one of them which toucheth any thing that is consecrated to Religion, or to the service of their Gods. Insomuch, that they touch not their Vines which are sacred to religious uses, but suffer them to come to their natural maturity, but depart out of the Island, to the intent that neither hunger nor folly cause them to touch that which is dedicated to divine uses. And thus much for the natural and moral hory of Mice; now followeth the medicinal.

THE MEDICINES OF THE MOUSE.

The flesh of a Mouse is hot and soft, and very little or nothing fat, and doth expel black and melancholy choler. A Mouse being flead or having his skin pulled off, and afterwards cut through the middle, and put unto a wound or sore wherein there is the head of a Dart or Arrow, or any other thing whatsoever within the wound, will presently and very easily exhale and draw them out of the same. Mice being cut and placed unto wounds which have been bitten by Serpents, or put to places which are stinged by them, do very effectually, and in short space of time cure and perfectly heal them. Mice which do lurk and inhabit in Houses, being cut in twain, and put unto the wounds which are new made by Scorpions, doth very speedily heal them.

A young Mouse being mingled with Salt is an excellent remedy against the biting of the Mouse called a Shrew, which biting Horses and labouring Cattel, it doth venome until it come unto the heart, and then they die, except the aforesaid remedy be used. The Shrew also himself being bruised and laid unto the place which was bitten, is an excellent and very profitable remedy against the same.

919

A Mouse being divided and put or laid upon Warts, will heal them and quite abolish them, of what kinde soever they shall be. The fat which is distilled from Mice, being mixed with a little Goose-grease and boyled together, is an excellent and medicinable cure for the asswaging and mollifying of swellings and hard lumps or knots which do usually arise in the flesh. Young Mice being beaten into small bits or pieces, and mixed with old Wine, and so boyled or baked, until they come unto a temperate and mollifying medicine; if it be anointed upon the eye-lids, it will very easily procure hair to grow thereon. The same being unbeaten and roasted, and so given to little children to eat, will quickly dry up the froath or spittle which aboundeth in their mouth. There are certain of the wise men or *Magi*, who think it good that a Mouse should be flead, and given to those which are troubled with the Tooth-ach, twice in a month to be eaten. The water wherein a Mouse hath been sod or boyled, is very wholesome and profitable for those to drink who are troubled with the inflammation of the jaws or the disease called the Squincy. Mice, but especially those of *Africk*, having their skin pull'd off, and well steeped in Oyl, and rubbed with Salt, and so boiled, and afterwards taken in drink, are very medicinable for those which have any pain or trouble in their lights and lungs. The same medicine used in the aforesaid manner is very profitable for those which are troubled with a filthy, mattery, and bloudy spitting out with retching.

Sodden Mice are exceeding good to restrain and hold in the urine of Infants or children being too abundant, if they be given in some pleasant or delightsome drink. Mice also being cut in twain, and laid unto the feet or legs of those which are gowty is an excellent remedy and cure for them. Mice being dryed and beaten to powder, doe very effectually heal and cure those which are scalded or burned with hot water, or fire. Cypres nuts being burned and pounded, or beaten into dust, and mixed with the dust of the hoof of a male or female Mule, being dryed or stamped small, and the Oyl of Myrtle added unto the same, with the dirt or dung of Mice being also beaten; and with the dung of a Hedge-hog new made, and with red Arsenick: and all mingled together with Vinegar, and moist or liquid Pitch and put unto the head of any one who is troubled with the abundance and loose hanging down or overgrowning of his hair, it will very speedily and without any difficulty ease him of the same.

The dust of a Mouse pounded and beaten to powder, and mingled with a certain Oyl, is very good and wholesome, for those which are grieved with a Tetter, or scab, which may over-run their whole body. The brains or tail of a Mouse being dryed and beaten to powder, is very medicinable for those which are troubled with the casting and shedding of their hair; as also for the disease called the Foxes evill; but this operation will work more effectally, if the shedding of the hair doth happen by any venom or poyson. The same in operation hath the whole body of the Mouse being used in the aforesaid manner.

There is also another excellent remedy to cure and heal the aforesaid disease, which is this; To take Mice which inhabit in houses, and to burn or dry them in a pot, and then beat them; and being so used, to mix them with Oyl of Lawrel, and to rub the hairs which are like to fall or shed with Garlick; and to put them all together into a Frontlet or fore-head cloth, and daily to keep the same medicine or plaister unto them, until the hair do grow fast, and they be rid of that disease. There is also another remedy for the same disease, which is this: To burn a Mouse, and beat him into powder, and then to mingle the same with Hony, and the grease of a Bear, and so to anoint the head, and this is accounted for a very speedy and effectual cure.

The dust or powder of Mice being mixed with Hony and Oyl of Roses, and so baked, or boiled together, and afterward distilled into a clear water, and so poured into the ears of any one which is deaf, or troubled with any pain in his ears, and it will quickly bring him help and remedy. The dust of a dryed Mouse being also mingled with Hony, and rubbed upon the teeth of any one which is troubled with a stinking breath, will presently take away the savour thereof. If the urine of a man or woman be too fluent and abundant, let them take the dust or powder of a dryed Mouse, being beaten and stamped, and mix it with Wine, or with Goats milk, and so drink it up, and he shall speedily have remedy. The grievous and violent inflammation or turning of the eye-lids, is cured after this manner: First, they take the flesh of the Mice, as soon as ever it is beaten small, and mingle it with the yolk of an Egge, and mollifie it into a salve or plaister like unto wax, and then put it into a linnen cloth, and so wrap it upon the eye-lids in the time of sleep, and it will easily bring help and remedy.

There is an excellent remedy for the over-spreading of the eyes, or to cure the disease in them, called the Pin and the Web; or to help them which are altogether blinde, which is this: To take the bloud of a Mouse, the gall of a Cock, and some part or quantity of womans milk, and to take of each of them alike, and then to mingle or mix them together, and being well wrought or kneaded until it come to an ointment, to rub or spread it upon the eyes: and this will in very short space help them unto their sight; for it hath been tryed; and hath helped many.

The skin of a Mouse being burned or dryed, and beaten into powder, and so mingled with Vinegar, and then anointed upon the head of any one who is pained or troubled with the Head-ach, it will presently ease and help him. The head of a Mouse being also born or carryed in a linnen cloth, doth cure the same disease: The heads of Mice being burned, and beaten into small powder, and then mixed or mingled with Hony, and so anointed upon the legs or feet of them which are troubled with the Gowt, are excellent good and wholesome for the curing of that grievous disease. The same vertue hath the tails or bodies of Mice, being used in the aforesaid manner in them. Some do think, that the aforesaid disease is more speedily and effectually cured after this manner: First, to take a Beetle or Horse-fly, and stamp it all to pieces, and then to mingle it with soft and liquid Pitch, the skin being prepared or made ready with Nitre: but there must be great care taken, that it eat not too far in the flesh: then to take the head of a Mouse, and the gall and dung of a Mouse, and mingle them together with Ling-wort and Pepper, and so to anoint them, and spread them upon the aforesaid eaten or lanced wounds: and this is very much commended for a very good and medicinable cure for the aforesaid disease.

The heads of Mice dryed and beaten into powder or dust, and then mixed with Hony, and so anointed upon the eyes for the space of ten days together, will clarifie the eyes, and expel all pain or blemishes from them. Of the heads of Mice being burned, is made that excellent powder, for the scowring and clensing of the teeth called Tooth-soap: unto which if

Spikenard be added or mingled, it will take away any filthy sent or strong savour in the mouth. The brains of a Mouse being taken and put or steeped in Wine, and stamped, and beaten small, and anointed upon the brow or fore-head of any one who is troubled with a pain or ach in the head, and the shall soon finde ease and remedy. If any man shall but touch or kiss with his mouth the snowt or nostrils of a Mouse, and be troubled with the disease called the Rhume, which falleth down and stuffeth the nostrils, he shall in very short space be eased of the same. The *Magi* or wise men do very much commend this medicine for the expelling of a quartain Ague or Fever, which is thus; To take the nose or snowt of a Mouse, as also the very tops of the ears, and bruise them together, and afterward tie them in a linnen cloth, which hath had Roses or Rose-leaves in the same, and then binde them unto the arms or wrists of him which is so troubled, and they will very effectually and speedily cure and heal him. For the rottenness and deminishing of the teeth, the best remedy is to take a living Mouse, and to take out one of her teeth, whether the greatest or the least it is no great matter, and hang it by the teeth of the party grieved: but first kill the Mouse from whom you had the tooth, and he shall presently have ease and help of his pain. The heart of a living Mouse being taken out, and hanged upon the left arm of any woman, is of such force and power, as it will cause her never to conceive. The laps or fillets of the liver of a Mouse, being beaten small and mingled with four drams of sowre and unpleasant Wine, is an excellent remedy for those which are troubled with quakings in their joynts; as also for Fevers and shaking Agues. A Mouse being cut or parted in the conjunction of the Sun and the Moon, and the liver pulled out and roasted or boiled, and given to one which is troubled with the aforesaid disease to eat, will very speedily and without any difficulty or pain cure and heal him of the same. The gall of a Mouse being beaten very small, and steeped or washed in Vinegar, and so poured or distilled into the ears of any one who is deaf or thick of hearing, or hath any ach or pain in the same, is counted for the chiefest, and most singular and chiefest remedy or cure which is used for the same.

The dung or dirt of a Mouse being new made, is very profitable for those which are troubled with the disease called the *Sciatica*, or Hip-gowt, anointed or rubbed upon the same. Mouse-dung being also mingled with

Vinegar and Oyl of Roses, and so anointed or spread upon the fore-head or temples of any one who is troubled with the head-ach, will presently ease and help him of the same. The gum called Benzoin being mixed with Wine and Safron, and Pepper; as also with the dirt or dung of Mice being new made, and mixed with Vinegar, and mingled all in one medicine, and so strained and given to one to drink, which is spare and lean, in some short space or time it will make him grow very fat.

The dung or dirt of a Mouse being mingled with certain other medicines, is very good and wholesome for those which are troubled with Tetters, and dry scabs which over-run the whole Body.

The dung of Mice being mingled with the dust or powder of Frankincense, with a little red Arsenick added thereunto, is a very profitable and wholesome medicine for those to use which are troubled with little hard red bunches and swellings arising in divers and several parts of the body. Seven pills being taken out of the dung of a Mouse, and mingled with Vinegar, and anointed upon the fore-head and temples, of those which are grieved therein, will very speedily help and cure him.

The inward parts of earth mixed with Mouse-dung, white Pepper, and Myrrhe, being of each of them half an ounce, and afterwards mingled with Vinegar all together; and so anointed upon the head of any one which is troubled with the Megrim, will very effectually and speedily ease and rid him of the same. The herb called *Strumus* beaten together with Mouse-dung, and afterwards mixed with Vinegar, is an excellent remedy against the swellings in the head, or little bunches which arising therein become sores, and are full of matter and filthy corruption. The dung or dirt of Mice being melted, dissolved, and mingled with Vinegar, and then rubbed upon the head of any one who is troubled with the scurf or skaules thereon in a bathe or stove, will presently expell and drive them quite away.

The dung of Mice being mingled with Frankincense, and so beaten or tempered together until they come unto the likeness or thickness of Hony, and then anointed upon the legs or feet of any one that is troubled with the Gowt, he shall finde present help and remedy. The same disease also is very effectually cured by the dung of a Mouse, and burned or scorched Barley mingled together, of each being the same weight or quantity, and afterwards mixed with Vinegar all together, and so spread or anointed upon the diseased parts. There is also another excellent remedy for curing of the aforesaid disease, which is thus: To take Cantharides, and bruise them all to pieces, and mingle them with soft or liquid Pitch, and also with Nitre, and so anoint or rub them upon the skin being prepared for the purpose; but there must be great care had, that the skin be not rubbed or lanced too far. Afterwards unto the wound so made, there must be taken the heads, galls, and dung of Mice, being mixed with the herb Lingwort, and Pepper; and so beaten all together until they come unto a temperate salve or medicine, and then anointed upon the said wounds, and they will in very short space cure the same.

The hairs and dung of a Mouse, parched or dryed by the fire, and anointed upon the eye-lids of any one which are pield or bare, will presently procure hair to grow thereon.

Mouse-dung being dryed in the shade is an excellent remedy against the voiding or spitting of bloud which floweth from some parts of the body, but especially from the belly. The same is also very good to stanch the bloud which issueth from wounds being new made. White Sceny-seed, and the dung of a Mouse or Hare being put into broth, with the stem or stalk of Fennil, and so boyled together, and afterwards given unto a woman to drink who is destitute of milk in her breasts, will presently and very speedily procure her milk in great abundance.

The dung of Mice being steeped or washed in rain water, doth ease and refresh the swelling of womens dugs in their time of delivery. The dung of a Mouse being given in any drink or liquor to one that is troubled with the disease called the Colick and stone to drink, will in very short space or time cure him of the same. Mouse-dung being also taken in drink, doth loose the body of either man or woman, how fast soever they be bound. There is an excellent remedy arising from Mouse-dung against the *Sciatica*, or Hip-gowt, which is this: To take nine grains of a Mouses dung mixed or mingled with half a pinte of Wine, and given to the party grieved upon a bench or foot-stool to drink, so that he drink it standing upon that foot only which paineth him, even at the Sun rising; and having so drunk it, let him leap down, and afterwards let him leap three times, and let him do this but three days together, and he shall have present help and remedy of his disease.

Mouse-dung mixed with Frankincense and sweet Wine, and so drunk by any one which is troubled with the Colick and Stone, will presently ease him of the same. But the dung of Mice mingled with Frankincense, Water, and Hony, and so boyled together, and drunk, doth not only drive away the pain of the aforesaid disease, but also doth break and quite dissolve the Stone. Mouse-dung also being taken in drink by it self alone, doth dissolve and melt the Stone in the Bladder. The same being also boyled in water, is very good and profitable for those which cannot make water. The same being new made and anointed upon the belly of any one who is troubled with the Colick or Stone, shall finde present ease and remedy thereby.

There is yet moreover another excellent medicine proceeding from this dung, whereby the fruit in a womans womb may be brought forth either dead or putrified, without any hurt or prejudice unto the woman, which is thus; First to take *Egyptian* Salt, Mouse-dung, and Gourds which are sowen in Woods; and afterwards to pour in half a pinte of Hony, being half boyled, and to cast one dram of Rozen into the Hony, the Gourds, and the Mouse-dung, and beat them well and throughly together, and then rowl them up, and fashion them in the manner of Acorns, and put them to the belly of the party so grieved as often as you shall think it meet and convenient, and in using this some short space or time, you shall see the aforesaid putrified fruit to proceed and issue forth.

Mouse-dung being parched or burned, and mingled with Hony, is very good and medicinable aswell for those which are troubled with the swellings in their legs and feet; as also for those whose eye-lids are pilled and bald, to make hair to grow again upon them, being spread or anointed there-upon. The dung of Mice being dryed and beaten into small dust or powder, and put into the teeth of any one which are hollow, will presently expel away all pain from them, and also confirm and make the teeth strong. The dust or powder which proceedeth from Mouse-dung, is also very good to cure any disease in the fundament of either man or woman.

The urine of a Mouse is of such strong force, that if it shall but touch any part of a mans body, it will eat unto the very bones. The bitings of Mice are healed by no other means but by green Figs and Garlick being mixed or mingled together, and so anointed thereupon.

OF THE RAT.

THERE is no doubt that this Beast belongeth also to the rank of Mice, and the name thereof we have shewed already, is common both to the *French, Spanish, Italian*, and *English*, and it may seem to be derived from the *Greek* word *Rastes*, or *Heurex*, or *Riscos*, for the *Græcians* use all those words. And this beast is four times so big as the common Mouse, being of a blackish dusky colour, more white on the belly, having a long head, not much unlike the head of the Martin; short and round ears, a reasonable rough skin, short legs, and long claws, and exceeding great eyes, such as can see very perfectly in the dark night, and more perfectly then by candle, light; with their nails they climbe up steep and hard walls, their tail is very long, and almost naked, void of hair, by reason whereof it is not unworthily counted venomous; for it seemeth to partake with the nature of Serpents. The quantity of their body is much like a Weesils; and sometime you shall see a Rat exceeding the common stature, which the *Germans* call *Ratzen Kunig*, the King of Rats, because of his larger and greater body; and they say that the lesser bring him meat, and he lyeth idle. But my opinion is, that as we read of the Dor-mouse, she nourisheth her patent when she is old; so likewise the younger Rats bring food unto the elder, because through their age, they are not able to hunt for themselves, and are also grown to a great and unweeldy stature of body. Sometimes you shall see white Rats, as was once seen in *Germany*, taken in the middle of *April*; having very red eyes standing forth of their head, and a rough and long beard. And at *Auspurg* in *Germany*, about the Temple called the Church of S. *Huldric*, they abound in greater number then in other places. They do not lie in the earth like Mice, except in the vally of *Ioachim*, where for the Summer time they forsake houses, and go into Cony holes, but in the Winter time they return to the houses again. They are more noysome then the little Mouse, for they live by stealth, and feed

927

upon the same meat that they feed upon, and therefore as they exceed in quantity, so they devour more, and do far more harm. They are killed by the same poysons and meats that the common Mice are killed, except Wolf-bane; for if they eat thereof, they vomit it up again, and are safe. They are also taken in the same traps, but three or four times so big: Their flesh is far more hot and sharp then the flesh of the vulgar Mouse, as we have gathered by the dissection of it, and therefore in operation it is very like that it expelleth and dryeth more then the other.

The excrements are also of the same vertue; and with the dung of Rats the Physitians cure the falling off the hair. And it is said also that when they rage in lust, and follow their copulation, they are more venemous and dangerous then at other times. For if the urine do fall upon the bare place of a man, it maketh the flesh rot unto the bones, neither will it suffer any scar to be made upon the ulcer; and thus much of the vulgar Rat.

OF THE WATER-RAT.

SEEING there are two kindes of Rats, one of the earth called *Rattus terrestris*, and the other of the water called *Rattus Fluviatilis*, of which we are now to entreat, being also called of the *Latines, Mus aquaticus*; by the *Germans, Twassermaus*, and *Wafferrat*; by the *Italians, Sorgomogange*; by the *French, Rat d'eau*. This beast hunteth fishes in the Winter, and have certain caves in the water sides, and banks of the Rivers or Ponds: For which occasion it being seen in the waters, deceiveth their expectation which look for the return of it to the land. And this beast hath been forgotten by the Ancients, for they have left of it no description nor story, because it liveth partly in the water, and partly on the land, and therefore he said true, that spake of the habitation and place of abode of this beast, in this sort; *Ego non in fluviis, nec aliis aquis magnis, sed parvis tantum rivis atq; herbosis omnium ripis, hoc antmal frequentissimum versari audio.* That is to say; That this beast doth not keep in great Waters of Rivers, but in small and little currents and Ponds, where abundance of grass and other weeds do grow on the sides and banks: *Pliny* attributeth that to the Water-rat, which is proper to the Tortoise; for indeed there is some similitude of natures bewixt these beasts, with this exception, that the females in this kinde have three visible passages for their excrements, one for their urine, another for the dung, and the third for the young ones, that is a peculiar place for the littering of their young ones; and this Water-rat over and beside her common nature with other Rats, doth swim over Rivers, and feed upon herbs; and if at any time she be hunted from her native biding and accustomed lodging, then also she goeth among vulgar and common Rats and Mice, and feedeth upon such as they eat: and (*Bellonius* saith) that there are great store of these in *Nilus* and *Strymen*, and that in calm nights when there are no windes, they walk to the shores, & get up upon the banks, eating and gnawing such plants as grow near the waters; and if they hear any noise, they suddenly leap into the waters again. He expresseth also the figure of this Rat, which we have omitted because it resembleth in all parts the common Rat, excepting the snowt or beak which is rounder or blunter. Among some of the Ancients also, there is mention made of this beast, and no more. Therefore *Aristotle* saith in the *Arcadian Lusæ*, which is a City so called, (as *Stephanus* writeth,) where *Malampus* did wash the daughters of *Prœtus*, and delivered them from their madness: There is a certain Fountain, wherein do live Rats of the Earth, (they should say Rats of the Water,) for hereunto agree both *Pliny* and *Theophrastus*. Likewise in a River of *Cassinus*, the ancient Wise-men, which were followers of *Zoroastres*, made great account of the Hedgehog, but hated deadly the Water-rats, and said, that he that could kill most of them, was most dear and acceptable to God. And further more they said, that Dogs, Hens, and Hedgehogs, did proceed, and were attended from and by good Angels, and Water-rats by evill. And thus much shall suffice for the discourse of the Rat. The story which ensueth is of strange and less known Mice; and therefore I will distribute them after an alphabetical order, according to their several names.

OF THE ALPINE MOUSE.

THE *Alpine* Mouse taketh her name from the *Alpes*, wherein she is bred, and although there be many other kindes of Mice bred in the *Alpes*, yet this being the principal thereof, receiveth denomination from the Mountains, because they are bred in the very tops of the Mountains, and seldom or never come down to the roots. The *Italians* call it *Marmota*, and *Murmont*, and according to *Matheolus*, *Marmontana*; the *Rhætians*, *Montanella*; and in some part of *Italy*, *Varrosa*; in *France*, *Marmote*; although *Marmot* be also a word among them for a Munkey. The *Germans*, and especially the *Helvetians*, by a corrupt word drawn from a Mouse of the Mountain, *Murmelthier*, and *Murmentle*, and some *Mistbellerle*, by reason of his sharp whining voyce like a little Dogs. In *Latine* it is called also *Emptra*, which seemeth to be compounded of *Embdor*, and this is the least kinde of *Alpine* Mice, which is found in all the *German* Regions; of which we will speak in the end of this story. Some take this to be called *Taxus*, amongst, whom *Brassavolus* is one; yet it hath no property with the *Alpine* Mouse, except lying in a Cave; for it doth not sleep in the Winter, nor hath no outward resemblance with Mice, neither can have any affinity in disposition or manner of living, and therefore I cannot assent thereto. *Grapaldus & Alunnus*, both learned *Italians*, say, that the *Armelins* are called *Alpine* Mice, whereunto they are led, because they sleep all the Winter long, like the *Alpine* Mouse; but we shall shew in their due place, that these belong to the Weesils, and not to the Mice, which living in cold Countries, grow white in the Winter time: the *Hebrew* word is *Saphan*, according to some Authors, and is translated *Arcktonim*, but we will shew in due place, that the *Arktomys* is the *Crycetus*, or *Grycet* Mouse, and the *Saphan* we have shewed already to be the Cony.

These *Alpine* Mice are in the tops of the *Apennine* hills, and none of the Ancients except *Pliny* make mention thereof, and it is doubtful whether he doth describe it or no. For his words are, *Sunt his Muribus*

930

Alpinis pares & in Ægypto, similiterq; residunt in clunibus & binis pedibus gradiuntur, prioribusq; ut manibus utuntur, that is to say, there are Mice in *Egypt* like to the *Alpine* Mice; for they sit upon their buttocks, and go with their fore-most two feet, which also they use in stead of hands, by which we collect, that they are not the same, but like the *Alpine* Mice.

The *Alpine* Mouse is in quantity like a Hare, or at the least betwixt a Hare and a Cony, being more fat, and of a thicker body then a Cat, but shorter legs, in outward appearance most like a Mouse, and therefore it is called an *Alpine* Mouse. The back of it is very broad, and the hair harder and harsher then a Conies. The colour for the most part is yellow, which in some is more clear, and in others more obscure and brown. Their eyes of a reasonable quantity, standing far out of their heads. Their ears very short like cropt ears. The head like a Hares, and their feet with long nails; his fore-teeth like a Squirrels, two above, and two beneath, but long and sharp like a Beavers, in colour yellow; about the nose and upper lips he hath long black bristle hairs like a Cat. The tail is half a cubit long, according to *Stumpsius,* but two palms according to *Agricola.* His legs very short and thick, covered with long deep thick hair, like to the bottom of his belly. The toes of his feet are like a Bears, and his claws long and black, wherewithall he diggeth the earth to make his den; he goeth upon his hinder-feet like a Bear, or like an Ape, by jumps, and with his fore-feet he taketh his meat like a Squirrel and an Ape, sitting in the mean time upon his buttocks. His back is also very fat, although all the other parts of his body be lean, and yet that on his back cannot be said to be fat, but rather like a Cows udder, neither fat nor flesh, and they encrease or grow more in breadth then in length.

Scaliger describeth them in this manner, a *Marmot* (saith he, for so he tearmeth an *Alpine* Mouse in *French*) is a Beast about the bigness of a Badger, having hair and tail much like it; and after the same manner short legs, and little or no ears, long, sharp, firm, crooked, strong and black claws, which is numbred amongst the kindes of Mice, with whom it holdeth little correspondence, except that like a Squirel it taketh his meat in the fore-feet as with hands, and eateth sitting upon his tail. They agree also with the Dor-mouse in their sleep, for they pass over Winter sleeping.

Their teeth are like to the teeth of Hares and Mice; after that they are made tame, they are not hurtful to men or children, except they be provoked. Being kept in houses, they will eat and gnaw all linnen and woollen cloth; thus far *Scaliger*. But we have shewed already, that the outward appearance of it is like a Mouse, and that therefore it is safer to follow *Pliny, Albertus, Mathæolus, Stumpsius*, and others, then his sole and singular opinion; they keep as we have said already, in the tops of the Mountains, wherein they make their cave with wonderful art and circumspection, making two different passages into their Den, one above another a poles length, which meet in the middle like a fork, or the conjunction of two Rivers or Path-ways, making the seat of their rest to be very deep in the Mountain, and therein they remain five, seven, nine, or eleven of them together.

They play many times before the mouth of their Den together, and in their sport or pastime, bark like little Dogs. When they go out of their cave into the Mountains to gather food, or to play, or to fetch in grass; always one of them remaineth like a Watch-man near the mouth of the cave upon some high place, looking most diligently and vigilantly, both far and near; and if he see either a man or wilde beast coming towards them, then he suddenly cryeth out, and with his voyce giveth the warning word, whining like the whisling of a pipe, if his fellows be far off; or else barking like a Dog, if they be near at hand. When the residue hear it, they presently repair home, and he which kept the watch, entereth into the Den last of all. And it is reported by a certain *Greek* Writer, that if their speculator do not give them the watch-word, but that they are endangered by any man or beast through his negligence, they tear him in pieces with their teeth. There is no beast so strong as this, considering the quantity; for it hath been seen, that when a lusty young man took one of them by the hinder-leg as it ran into the Den, he could not with all his might pluck it back again. The claws of it are exceeding sharp, and fit to dig; so that it is thought if a man finde them in the earth, and seek to take them by digging unto them, he shall labour in vain, because the Beast diggeth faster from him then he can follow her; they cannot run very fast in the plain ground, but are easily killed by a man, except they get into the earth: with their teeth they bite deep, for they can sheer asunder wood with them like Beavers, they eat or live upon fruits, and especially being tamed when they are young; they refuse not bread, flesh, fish, or pottage, and above all they desire milk, butter, and cheese; for in the *Alpes* they will break into the little Cottages where milk is kept, and are oftentimes taken in the manner sucking up the milk, for they make a noise in sucking of milk like the pig. In the moneth of *May* they are much delighted to eat Hornets, or Horse-flies, also they feed upon wilde Sagapen of the meddow, and seeded Cabages, and while they are wilde in the Mountains, they never drink; the reason is, as I suppose, because in the Summer time they eat moist green herbs, and in all the Winter time they sleep.

Towards the feast of Saint *Michael* the Archangel, and of *Gallus*, they enter into their Caves; and as *Pliny* saith, they first of all carry provision of Hay, and green Herbs into their Den to rest upon, wherein their wit and understanding is to be admired; for like Beavers one of them falleth on the back, and the residue load his belly with the carriage, and when they have laid upon him sufficient, he girteth it fast by taking his tail in his mouth, and so the residue draw him to the Cave; but I cannot affirm certainly, whether this be a truth or a falsehood. For there is no reason that leadeth the Author thereunto, but that some of them have been found bald on the back. But this is certain, when the Snow begins to cover the Mountains, then do they enter into their Dens, and shut up close the passages, with sticks, grass, and earth, both so hard and so thick, that it is easier to break the solid ground, then the mouths of their Caves, and so being safely included both from the fear of the Hunters, from rain, snow, and cold, there they live until the Spring, without all manner of meat and drink, gathered round together like a Hedgehog, sleeping continually; and therefore the people inhabiting the *Alpes* have a common proverb, to express a drowsie and sleepy fellow in the *German* tongue thus; *Er musse syuzyt geschlaffen haben wie ein murmelthier:* in *Latine* thus; *Necesse habet certum, dormiendo, tempus consumere, instar muris Alpini.* He must needs sleep a little, like the Mouse of the *Alpes.* They sleep also when they be tamed, but it hath been found by experience, that when a tame one hath been taken a sleep, and laid in a warm barrel upon Hay, the mouth being shut and closed to keep out rain and snow, at the opening thereof it was found dead; and the reason was, because it lacked breath, and therefore this is most wonderful, that in the Mountains, notwithstanding the close stopping of the mouth of their Caves, yet they should not be deprived of refrigeration, that is, fresh air, for expiration, and respiration.

But this is to be considered, that after they have been long tamed, they sleep not so much as when they are wilde; for I think that their continual eating of raw and green herbs, ingendereth in them so many humors as cannot be dispersed without a long continuing sleep; but afterwards when they are dieted with such meat as is provided for the nourishment of man, they are eased of the cause, and so the effect ceaseth. During the time that they sleep, they grow very fat, and they are not awaked very easily, except with the heat of the Sun or fire, or a Hot-house. Now the manner of their taking while they are wilde, is thus;

In the Summer time when they go in and out of their Caves, they are taken with snares set at the mouth thereof; but in the Winter time, when they go not abroad, then also are Inhabitants forced to another devise, for then in the Summer time, they set up certain pillars or perches near the mouth of their Den, whereby they may be directed, when the snow doth cover the Mountains. For the pillars or poles stand up above the snow, although the snow be very deep. Then come the Inhabitants upon round pieces of wood in the midst of the Winter, fastned to their shooe-soles over the deep snow with their pyoners and diggers, and cast away the snow from the den, and so dig up the earth, and not only take the beasts, but carry them away sleeping, and while they dig, they diligently observe the frame and manner of the stopping of the Mouses den. For if it be long and deep, if is a sign of a long and a hard Winter, but if they be shallow and thin, of the contrary: so coming upon them as we have said, they take them and carry them away asleep, finding always an odd number among them;

and they diligently observe, that whilest they dig, there be no great noise, or that they bring not their fire too near them. For as *Stumpsius* saith, *Experrecti enim capi non possunt, nam utcunq; strenue fodiat venator, ipsi fodiendo sumul & retrocedunt & pedibus quam effoderint, terram rejiciendo fossorem impediunt.* That is to say, If they be once awaked, they can never be taken, for howsoever the Hunter dig never so manfully, yet they together with him, dig inward into the Mountains, and cast the earth backward with their feet to hinder his work.

Being taken as we have said, they grow very tame, and especially in the presence of their keepers, before whom they will play and sport, and take lice out of their heads with their fore-feet like an Ape. Insomuch as there is no beast that was ever wilde in this part of the world, that becometh so tame and familiar to man as they; yet do they always live in the hatred of Dogs, and oftentimes bite them deeply, having them at any advantage, especially in the presence of men, where the Dogs dare not resist nor defend themselves. When they are wilde, they are also killed asleep; by putting of a knife into their throat, whereat their fore-feet stir a little, but they die before they can be awaked.

Their bloud is saved in a vessel, and afterwards the Mouse it self is dressed in hot scalding water like a Pig, and the hair thereof plucked off, and then do they appear bald and white; next to that they bowel them, and take out their intrails: afterwards put in the bloud again into their bellies, and so seethe them, or else salt them, and hang them up in smoke, and being dressed after they are dryed, they are commonly eaten in the *Alpine* Regions with Rapes and Cabbages, and their flesh is very fat, not a fluxible or loose fat like the fat of Lambs, but a solid fat, like the fat of Hogs and Oxen. And the flesh hereof is commended to be profitable for Women with childe; and also for all windiness and gripings in the belly, not only the flesh to be eaten in meat, but also the fat to be anointed upon the belly or navil: And for this cause it is used to procure sleep, and to strengthen decayed and weak sinews: the flesh is always better salted then fresh, because the salt drieth up the overmuch humidity, and also amendeth the gravity and ranckness of the savour: but whether it be salt, or whether fresh, it is always hard to be digested, oppressing the stomach, and heating the body overmuch.

The ventricle or maw of the Mouse *Alpine*, is prescribed to be laid upon the belly against the Colick. If the hands of a man be anointed with the fat of this beast, it is said he shall be the better able to endure cold all that day after: Also the same fat being drunk up in warm broth by a woman in travail, are believed to accelerate and hasten her delivery.

Certain Horse-leeches, in the cure of that disease which they call the Worms, which are certain ulcers rising in the body, do mingle this fat with other medicines which are very drying or stiptick. And *Mathæolus* doth prescribe it for the softning and mollifying of contracted nerves and joynts in the body.

By the discourse aforesaid, it doth appear, that of these *Alpine* Mice there are two kindes, one great like a Badger, and the other in stature of a Hare or Cony: This lesser seemeth to be proper to *Germany*, which there they call *Embdor*, of the *Latine* word *Emptra*, a Mouse of the Mountain.

The story whereof I thought good to express, being short, out of *Stumpsius* and *Agricola*. The males and females say they of this kinde, do gather together wilde corn which groweth among the Rocks in the Summer time against the Winter, and carry the same into the holes of the earth, where their lodging is.

Now the female in this kinde is crafty, and more apt to devour; the male on the other side more thrifty and sparing, wherefore he driveth his female out of the Den in the Winter time, and stoppeth the mouth of his Cave, to forbid her entrance, but she getteth behinde the same, and diggeth a secret hole, whilest the male lyeth at the mouth asleep, she consumeth the whole store behinde him; wherefore in the Spring time she cometh forth very fat and comely, and he very lean. And therefore in my opinion, the makers of emblems may very well describe an unthrifty Wife, that consumeth her Husbands wealth, by the picture of this female, as by the picture of the Ass behinde *Ocnus*, biting asunder the cord that he weaveth, as we have shewed before in the History of the Ass. These beasts give themselves much to sleep, and when they are awake they are never idle, but always carrying into their Den straw, hay, sticks, rags, or pieces of cloth, wherewith they fill their mouth so full, that it may receive no more, and if they meet with any thing which is too big for their mouth, by the help of their feet they draw and rowl it to their own Den.

936

Whereas they are nourished tame in houses, it is observed, that they are a neat and cleanly kinde of beast, for they never defile their lodgings with their excrements, but seek out some secret corner, wherein they both render urine, and empty their bellies. With their teeth the gnaw wood, and make holes in bords, so large as their bodies may pass through; and while they live, they have a very ranck and strong savour like a Mouse, especially in the Summer time while they are lean, and before they grow fat; for such is the nature of this beast, that in the Summer time they labour and grow lean; but in the Winter time they sleep and grow fat. And thus much for the *Alpine* Mouse.

OF THE DORMOUSE.

THE Dormouse is called in *Latin*, *Glis*; and in *Greek*, *Myoxos*; the reason of the *Latine* name *Glis*, is taken from *gliscere*, which signifieth to grow fat, according to the saying of *Columella*, *Paleis vero quibus fere omnes regiones abundant Asinus gliscit*; that is to say, an Ass groweth fat by eating chaffe which aboundeth in all Countries. This word *Glis*, signifieth not only a beast, but a piece of fat earth, and also a Thistle; whereupon *Sylvaticus* made this verse:

Glis animal, glis terra tenax, glis lappavocatur.

The *Italians* call it *Lo Galero*, *Lo Gliero*, or *Giero*; the *Spaniards*, *Liron*; the *French* likewise *Liron*, and *Rat, Liron*, and *Ungloyer*, and *Ungratvel*; the *Germans*, *Ein greul*; the *Helvetians*, *Ein rell*, or *Rel mus*, or *Gros haselmus*; but our *English*, Dormouse, seemeth to be a compounded word of *Dormiens mus*, that is, a sleeping Mouse. The *Polonians* call him *Scurez*. But concerning his name *Myoxus*, there is some question among the Authors. For Saint *Jerom* writing upon the eleventh chapter of Leviticus, and the 66. Chapter of Esay, translateth *Akbar* the *Hebrew* word for a Mouse, *Glirem*, a Dormouse, and he giveth this reason, because all the Countries of the East, meaning *Græcia*, do say, that *Myoxus* is a Dormouse. And this *Myoxus* by *Epiphanius* in his Anchoret is alleadged to prove the resurrection. *Myoxus*, saith he, *Animal semestre moritur, &*

rursus post tempore suo reviviscit. The Dormouse at half a year old dyeth, and after her full time reviveth again: And in his Book against Heresies, he speaketh thus to *Origen; Tradunt naturæ rerum experti, Myoxum latitare, & fœtus suo simul in eodem loco multos parere; quinque, & amplius: Viperas autem hos venari, & si invenerit totum latibulum ipsa Vipera, quum non posset omnes devorare pro una ulce ad sacietatem edit unum aut duos, reliquorum vero oculos expungit, & cibos affert, excæatosque enutrit, donec voluerit unumquemq; eorum devorare. Si vero contigerit, ut aliqui inexperti in hos incidant, ipsosq; in cibum sumant, venenum sibi ipsis sumunt, eos qui à Viperæ veneno sunt enutriti. Sic etiam ô tu Origenes à Græca doctrina mente excæcatus, venenum his qui tibi crediderunt, evomuisti, & factus es ipsis in edulium venenatum, ita ut per quæ ipse injuria affectus es, per ea plus injuria afficeris.*

The Philosophers which are cunning in the nature of things do write, that the Dormouse doth lie hid, and bring forth many young ones in the same place where he lyeth, five or more at a time, and the Vipers do hunt these to destroy them: now if the Viper finde their nest, because she cannot eat them all at one time at the first, she filleth her self with one or two, and putteth out the eyes of the residue, and afterwards bringeth them meat and nourisheth them, being blinde, until the time that her stomach serveth her to eat them every one. But if it happen that in the mean time, any man chance to light upon these Viper-nourished-blinde-Dormice, and to kill and eat them, they poyson themselves through the venom which the Viper hath left in them: so fareth it with thee *O Origen*, for thou art blinded with the *Græcians* doctrine, and dost vomit out that poyson into their hearts which do believe thee, that thou art made unto them a venemous meat, whereby thou dost wrong others, as thou hast been wronged thy self.

By which it is manifest, that *Myoxus* is neither a Toad nor a Frog, but the Dormouse. And the charm which is made for the Asses urine, as we have shewed already in his story, *Gallus bibit, & non meiit, Myoxus meiit, & non bibit.* The Cock drinketh, and maketh not water, the Dormouse maketh water, and never drinketh. But whether it be true or no that she never drinketh, I dare not affirm: But this is certain, that she drinketh but very seldom; and it ought to be no wonder that she should make water, for tame Conies, as long as they can feed upon green herbs, do render abundance of urine, and yet never drink.

The *Græcians* also do call this Beast *Elayos*, although that word do likewise signifie a Squirrel. In *Mæsia* a Wood of *Italy*, there is never found Dormouse, except at the time of their littering.

They are bigger in quantity then a Squirrel, the colour variable, sometimes black, sometimes grisled, sometimes yellow on the back, but alwayes a white belly, having a short hair, and a thinner skin then the Pontique Mouse. They are also to be found in *Helvetia*, about *Clarona*. It is a biting and an angry Beast, and therefore seldom taken alive. The beak or snowt is long; the ears short and pricked; the tail short, and not very hairy at the end; the middle of the belly swelleth down betwixt the breast and the loins, which are more narrow and trussed up together, they are always very fat, and for that cause they are called *Lardironi*.

Buck-mast is very acceptable meat unto them, and doth greatly fatten them, they are much delighted with Walnuts, they climbe trees, and eat Apples, according to some: but *Albertus* saith more truly, that they are more delighted with the juyce then with the Apple. For it hath been oftentimes found, that under Apple-trees, they have opened much fruit, and taken out of it nothing but the kernels, for such is their wit and policy, that having gathered an Apple, they presently put it in the twist of a tree betwixt boughs, and so by sitting upon the uppermost bough press it asunder. They also grow fat by this means.

In ancient time they were wont to keep them in coops or tuns, and also in Gardens paled about with board; where there are Beeches or Walnut trees growing, and in some places they have a kinde of earthen pot, wherein they put them with Walnuts, Buckmast, and Chesnuts. And furthermore it must be observed, that they must be placed in rooms convenient for them to breed young ones; their water must be very thin, because they use not to drink much, and they also love dry places.

Titus Pompeius (as *Varro* saith) did nourish a great many of them enclosed, and so also *Herpinus* in his Park in *Gallia*. It is a Beast well said to be *Animal Semiferum*, a creature half wilde, for if you set for them hutches, and nourish them in Warrens together, it is observed, that they never assemble, but such as are bred in those places: And if strangers come among them which are separated from them, either by a Mountain, or by a River, they descry them, and fight with them to death.

They nourish their parents in their old age, with singular piety. We have shewed already, how they are destroyed by the Viper, and it is certain, that all Serpents lie in wait for them. Their old age doth end every Winter. They are exceeding sleepy, and therefore *Martial* saith:

Somniculosos illi porrigit glires.

They grow fat by sleeping, and therefore *Ausonius* hath an elegant verse;

Dic, cessante cibo, somno quis opimior est? glis.

Because it draweth the hinder-legs after it like a Hare, it is called *Animal tractile*, for it goeth by jumps and little leaps. In the Winter time they are taken in deep ditches that are made in the Woods, covered over with small sticks, straw, and earth, which the Countreymen devise to take them when they are asleep. At other times they leap from tree to tree like Squirrels, and that they are killed with Arrows as they go from bough to bough, especially in hollow trees: for when the Hunters finde their haunt wherein they lodge, they stop the hole in the absence of the Dormouse, and watch her turn back again; the silly Beast finding her passage closed, is busied hand and foot to open it for entrance, and in the mean season cometh the Hunter behinde her, and killeth her. In *Tellina* they are taken by this means: The Countrey men going into the fields, carry in their hands burning Torches in the right time, which when the silly Beast perceiveth, with admiration thereof flocketh to the lights, whereunto when they were come, they were so dazled with the brightness that they were stark blinde, and might so be taken with mens hands.

The use of them, being taken, was to eat their flesh, for in *Rhetia* at this day they salt it and eat it, because it is sweet and fat like Swines flesh. *Ammianus Marcellinus* wondereth at the delicacy of his age, because when they were at their Tables, they called for ballances to weigh their fish, and the members of the Dormouse, which was not done (saith he) without any dislike of some present, and things not heretofore used, are now commended daily. *Apitius* also prescribeth the muscles and flesh inclosed in them, taken out of every member of a Dormouse, beaten with Pepper, Nut-kernels, Parsenips, and Butter, stuffed all together into the belly of a Dormouse, and sewed up with thread, and so baked in an Oven, or sod in a Kettle, to be an excellent and delicate dish. And in *Italy* at this day, they eat Dormice (saith *Cælius*,) yet there were ancient laws among the *Romans*; called *Leges censoriæ*, whereby they were forbidden to eat Dormice, strange birds, Shel-fish, the necks of Beasts, and divers such other things. And thus much shall suffice for the description of the Dormouse.

THE MEDICINES OF THE DORMOUSE.

Dormice being taken in meat, do much profit against the Bulimon; The powder of Dormice mixed with Oyl, doth heal those which are scalded with any hot liquor. A live Dormouse doth presently take away all Warts being bound thereupon. Dormice, and Field mice being burnt, and their dust mingled with Hony, will profit those which desire the clearness of the eyes, if they do take thereof some small quantity every morning. The powder of a Dormouse, or field Mouse rubbed upon the eyes helpeth the aforesaid disease. A Dormouse being flead, roasted and anointed with Oyl and Salt, being given in meat, is an excellent cure for those that are short winded. The same also doth very effectually heal those that spit out filthy matter or corruption. Powder of Dormice or field Mice, or young Worms, being mixed with Oyl doth heal those that have Kibes on their heels, or Chilblains on their hands. The fat of a Dormouse, the fat of a Hen, and the marrow of an Ox melted together, and being not infused into the Ears, doth very much profit both the pains and deafness thereof.

The fat of Dormice being boiled, as also of field-mice, are delivered to be most profitable for the eschewing of the Palsie. The fat of a Dormouse is also very excellent for those which are troubled with a Palsie, or shaking of the joints. The skins and inward part of a Dormouse being taken forth, and boiled with Hony in a new vessel, and afterwards poured into another vessel, will very effectually heal all diseases which are incident to the ears, being anointed thereupon. The skin of a Dormouse, or a Silkworm being pulled off, and the inward parts thereof being boiled in a new brasen vessel with Hony, from the quantity of twenty seven ounces, even to three, and so kept, that when there is need of a certain bathing vessel, the medicine being made warm and poured into the ears, doth help all pains, deafness, or inflammation of the ears. The fat of a Dormouse is commended to be very medicinable for the aforenamed diseases. The same is profitable for all pains, aches, or griefs in the belly. The urine of a Dormouse is an excellent remedy against the Palsie. And thus much shall suffice concerning the medicinal vertues of the Dormouse.

OF THE HAMSTER OR CRICETUS.

THIS Beast is called in *Latine*, *Cricetus*, and in the *German* tongue *Hamester*, *Traner*, and *Kornfaerle*, that is, Pigs of the corn. It is a little Beast, not much bigger then a Rat, dwelling in the earth of the roots of corn, she is not drawn against her will out of her Cave at any time, but by pouring hot water or some other liquor. The head of it is of divers colour, the back red, the belly white, and the hair sticketh so fast to the skin, that it is easier to pull the skin from the flesh, then any part of the hair from the skin. It is but a little Beast as we have said, but very apt to bite and fight, and full of courage, and therefore hath received from nature this ornament and defence, that it hath a bony helmet, covering the head and the brain when it standeth up upon the hinder-legs: It resembleth both in colour and proportion a Bear. And for this cause some Writers have interpreted it to be the Beast called *Arctomys*, thus described by Saint *Jerom*. It is a creature (saith he) abounding in the Regions of *Palestina*, dwelling always in the holes of Rocks and Caves of the earth, not exceeding the quantity of a Hedgehog, and of a compounded fashion, betwixt a Mouse and a Bear.

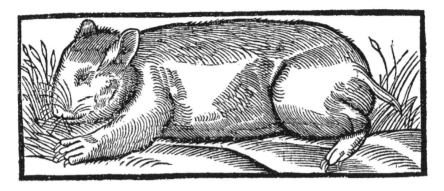

The first figure taken by Michael Horus.

The second picture taken by John Kentmant, and it is her fashion and protracture to lie thus when she is angry, for so doth her colour appear both on the back and belly.

But we have shewed already, that this is the *Alpine* Mouse, and therefore we will not stand to confute it here. The name *Cricetus* seems to be derived from the *Illyrian* word, which we read in *Gelenius* to be *Skuzetziek*: this Beast, saith he, is common in the Northern parts of the world, and also in other places, in figure and shape it resembleth a Bear, in quantity it never exceedeth a great Sorex. It hath a short tail, almost like no tail, it goeth upon two legs, especially when it is moved to wrath. It useth the fore-feet in stead of hands, and if it had as much strength, as it hath courage, it would be as fierceful as any Bear. For this little Beast is not afraid to leap into the Hunters face, although it can do no great harm either with teeth or nails. It is an argument that it is exceeding hot, because it is so bold and eager. In the uppermost chap it hath long and sharp teeth, growing two by two. It hath large and wide cheeks, which they always fill, both carrying in, and carrying out, they eat with both, whereupon a devouring fellow, such a one as *Stasimus* a servant to *Plautus* was, is called *Cricetus*, a Hamster, because he filleth his mouth well, and is no pingler at his meat.

The fore-feet are like a Moulds, so short, but not altogether so broad, with them he diggeth the earth, and maketh his holes to his den, but when he diggeth so far as he cannot cast the earth out of the hole with them, then he carryeth it forth in his mouth. His Den within he maketh large, to receive corn, and provision of fruit for his sustentation, whereinto he diggeth many holes, winding and turning every way, that so he may be safe both against Beasts that hunt him, and never be killed in his Den: And also if a man dig the earth, he may finde his lodging with more difficulty. In the harvest time he carryeth in grain of all sorts, and my Author saith, *Neque minus in colligendo industrius, quam in eligendo, conservandoque est astutus, optima enim reponit.* He is no less industrious in the gathering of his provision, then crafty and politick in the choise, and keeping it, for it lays up the best; and lest that it should rot under the earth, it biteth off the fibres and tail of the grain, laying up the residue amongst grass and stubble.

It lies gaping over his gathered grain, even as the covetous man is described in the Satyre sleeping upon his mony bags. It groweth fat with steep like Dormice, and Conies. The holes into the Cave are very narrow, so that with sliding out and in, they wear their hair. The earth which cometh out of their holes doth not lie on heaps like Mole-hils, but is dispersed abroad, and that is fittest for the multitude of the holes, and all the holes and passages are covered with earth: but that hole which for the most part he goeth out at, is known by a foot path, and hath no hinderance in it, the other places at which she goeth out are more obscure and hid, and she goeth out of them backwards. The male and female do both inhabit in one Cave, and their young ones being brought forth, they leave their old Den and seek them out some new habitation. In the male there is this perfidity, that when they have prepared all their sustenance, and brought it in, he doth shut out the female, and suffereth her not to approach nigh it, who revengeth his perfidiousness by deceit. For going into some adjoyning Cave, she doth likewise partake of the fruits which were laid up in store by some other secret hole in the Cave, the male never perceiving it.

So that nature hath wonderfully, fore-seen the poverty of all creatures: neither is it otherwise amongst men, for that which they cannot do by equity, they perform by fraud. This also cometh in the speech of the common people against one that will thrive. The young Country wenches concerning this matter, do chant out a verse not unpleasant, which I am contented to express in Iambicks, consisting of four feet:

Hamester ipse cum sua
    Prudens catusq; conjuge,
    Stipat profundum pluribus
    Per tempus antrum frugibus,
Possitque solus ut frui,
    Lectis acervis hordei
    Avarus antro credulam
    Extrudit arte conjugem.
Serva, inquit, exiens foras,
    Cœli serena & pluvias.
    Sed fœminis quis insitam,
    Vincant dolis astutiam?

Nevum parans cuniculum,
    Furatur omne triticum.
    Egens maritus perfidam
    Quærit per antra conjugem,
Nec se repellat blandulis
    Demulcet inventam sunis,
    Ille esse jam communia
    Servata dum sinit bona.
At perfidus multiplices
    Opponit intus obices.
    Rursus fruuntur mutuis
    Antris, cibis, amplexibus.

This Beast doth devour all kinde of fruit, and if he be nourished in a house he eateth bread and flesh: he also hunteth the field Mice. When he taketh his meat, he raiseth himself upon his fore-feet: he is also wont with his fore-feet to stroke his head, ears, and mouth, which thing the Squirrel and the Cat do also, and as the Beaver amongst those creatures which live as well by water as by land: but although in his body he seemeth but small, notwithstanding he is by nature apt to fight, and very furious being provoked, with his carriage in his mouth: he beateth away with both his feet that which resisteth him, directly invading his enemy: In the spirit and assaulting of his mouth he is wayward and threatning, from whence our Country men were accustomed to say of any one which was angry; he breatheth his wrath out of his mouth like a Hamster: *Du spruest vuie ein Hamster*: neither is he easily affrighted, although he be far unequal unto those in strength with whom he is in combate.

Wherefore some do give it in the place of a Proverb, that our Countrymen do call a man which is madly rash, *Ein tollen Hamster*, as *fool-hardy* as a *Hamster*. He flieth from any one that doth sharply resist him, and doth greedily follow after them that flie from him. I my self saw one of these, who by assaulting a Horse gat him by the nose, and would never leave his hold until he was killed with a sword: He is taken by divers means, for he is expelled either by hot water poured into his den, or is choaked within; or being digged up with a mattock or spade he is killed; or by Dogs. He is some-times pulled out by the Fox, or hurt: or oppressed by some snare, a great weight being put about it: or to conclude, he is taken by Art alive, and that in the night time, when he goeth to seek his prey, for in the day time for the most part he lyeth hid.

Before his usual Cave (as I have said) he is taken by the path which is worn, by a pot which is put into the earth, and afterward made plain about it like other places of the field; there is earth cast into the bottom of the pot to the deepness of two fingers, above every where covering the pot there is placed a stone, which is held up by a piece of wood, to which there is bound below a fragment of bread: In the space between the Cave and the pot there are crums of bread scattered, which he following and leaping into the pot, the wood falling, he is taken. Being taken after the manner of other beasts, he toucheth no food. If a broad stone, such an one with which they cover pavements, or of which they make roof tiles, shall be joyned unto the pot, and the beast be taken, he will be very hardly known in the morning; for the spirit of the beast being shut in, and waxing wroth, piercing for thinness doth moisten the stone. The skins of Hamsters are very durable, of which there are certain long coats which come down unto the heels, and divers coloured cloaks made, which the women of *Misena* and *Silesia* do use, and account them very honorable, of a black and red colour, with broad guards or edges of the skins of Otters: the same coats are for the most part valued at the price of fifteen or twenty *Renensian* crowns: for it doth out-wear in length three or four garments made either of linnen or woollen cloath.

In *Turingia* and *Misena* this beast is frequent, notwithstanding not in all places, for in *Turingia* his chiefest abode is about *Efurdanus*, and *Salcensis* in *Misena*, about *Lipsia*, and the field *Pegensis*, the plentifullest and most fertilest places of both those Regions. In *Lusatia* about *Radeburge*, he is digged out of those places where Painick groweth. At *Mulberge* and *Albis*, he is found in the Vineyards, for he is also fed with ripe Grapes. Our Country men are wont to burn a living Hamster in a pot, being shut, for the medicines of Horses. It hath been seen that one of these hath leaped up and caught a Horse by the nose, never letting go his hold until she was cut off with a sword. The skin is of three or four different colours, besides the spotted sides, and therefore the skin is very pretious. They abound in *Turingia* where the soil is good, and there is also great store of grain.

OF THE NORICIAN MOUSE.

THE *Norician* Mouse is called in *Latine, Citellus*, and it keepeth like the wilde Mice in the caves and dens of the earth. The body is like to a domestical Weesils, long and slender, the tail very short, the colour of the hair like to a gray Conies, but more bright. It wanteth ears like a Mole, but it hath open passages in stead of ears, wherewithal it heareth the sound, as you shall see in many birds. The teeth are like the teeth of Mice, and of their skins (although they be not very precious) they use to make garments. In *Germany* they call it *Pile* and *Zisel*, and of this *German* word was the *Latine Citellus* feigned; and it appeareth by *Agricola*, that there are two kindes of these; one greater, which are call'd *Zysell* and

Zeiseile, and another lesser (called *Pile*) which may be the same that is also called *Bilchmuss*, and differeth from other, because it is used for meat. These are bred in *Croatia*, and in the Country about *Venice*. They have a strange smell or savour, which is said to be hurtful to the head: They eat both salted and hung in the smoke, and also fresh and new killed. With their skins they edge the skirts of garments, for it is as soft as the skin of a Hare: and beside the common nature of Mice they are tamed. They also have very large cheeks, whereinto they gather an innumerable quantity of grain, and carry it into their den, as it were in bags against the Winter. They live thirty and forty together in a Cave, and are not driven forth but by infusion of hot water. They gather great store of Nuts into their Caves, and therefore as well as for their flesh do men hunt and seek after them.

OF THE MOUSE PONTIQUE.

THE name of this Mouse is given unto it from the Island out of which it was first brought, named *Pontus*, and for this cause it is also called *Venetus*, because it was first of all brought into *Germany* from *Venice*. It is called also *Varius* by *Idorus*, from whence cometh the *German* word *Vutrck*, from the diversity of the colour *Grau vuerck*. It is called also *Pundtmuss*, as it were *Ponticusmus*, or rather of *Bundi*, because they were wont to be brought in bundles to be sold fifty together, and they were sold for twenty groats, *Volaterranus*, and *Hermolaus* are of this opinion, that the white one in this kinde, be called of the *Italians, Armelline*, and the *Germans, Hermelin*, but we have promised already to prove that *Hermelin* is a kinde of Weesil, which in the Winter time is white, by reason of extremity of cold, and in the Summer returneth into her colour again, like as do the Hares of the *Alpes*. This *Pontique* Mouse differeth from others only in colour, for the white is mingled with ash colour, or else it is sandy and black, and in *Polonia* at this day they are found red and ash coloured. Their two lowermost teeth before are very long, and when it goeth, it draweth the tail after it like Mice; when it eateth it useth the fore-feet in stead of hands, and feedeth upon Walnuts, Chesnuts, Filbeards, small Nuts, Apples, and such like fruits. In the

Winter time they take sleep in stead of meat; And it is to be remembred, that the *Polonians* have four kindes of pretious skins of Mice which they use in their garments, distinguished by four several names. The first of grisel colour, called *Popieliza*. The second is called *Gronosthaii*, a very white Beast all over, except the tip of the tail which is all black, and this is the *Hermelin*.

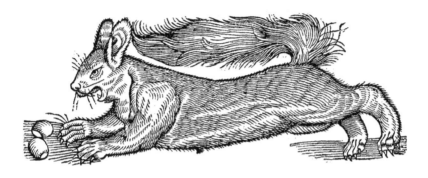

The third is called *Novogrodela*, from the name of a Town, and this is white mingled with grisel, and this is also a kinde of *Pontique* Mouse. The fourth *Uvieuvorka*, of a bright Chesnut colour, and this is the Squirrel, for they call Squirrels, Weesils, and Hermelins all by the name of Mice. These *Pontique* Mice have teeth on both sides, and chew the cud. In the Winter time as we have said they lie and sleep, especially the white ones, and their sense of taste doth excel all other, (as *Pliny* writeth) they build their nests and breed like common Squirrels.

Their skins are sold by ten together, the two best are called *Litzschna*; the third, a little worse, are called *Crasna*, and the fourth next to them *Pocrasna*, and the last and vilest of all *Moloischna*: with these skins they hem and edge garments; and in some places they make Canonical garments of them for Priests, unto which they sew their tails to hang down on the skirts of their garments; of which custom *Hermolaus* writeth very excellently in these words. *Instruxit, & ex muribus, luxuriam suam vita, alios magnis frigoribus, alios medio anni tempore, a septentrionibus petendo, armamus corpora, & debellamus animos.* That is to say; The life of man hath learned to be prodigal, even out of the skins of Mice, for some they use against extremity of cold, and they fetch others out of the farthest Northern parts, for the middle part of the year:

Thus do we arm and adorn our bodies, but put down and spoil our mindes.

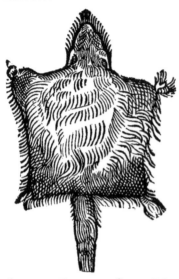

Beside, there is a flying *Pontique* or *Scythian* Mouse, which we may call the broad Squirrel Mouse, whose skin is here expressed as you may see, and for the description thereof, I have thought good to add an Epistle of *Antonius Schnebergerus* the *Lituanian* of *Vilna* unto *Gesner*, in these words following:

I send unto thee a little skin, the upper place of the hairs thereof being of a white ash colour, but the root of the hair or inner part thereof is a black brown. They call it *Popyelycza Lataacza*, that is, a *Pontique* flying Mouse: It is always so moist, that it can never be dressed by the Skinner, or Lether-dresser.

The people use it to wipe sore running eyes, having a perswasion that there is in it a singular vertue for the easing and mitigating of those pains: but I think that the softness was the first cause which brought in the first use thereof, but if the hairs do not cleave hard to the skin, it cannot be done without danger. Also the hairs hanging as it were in a round circle against or above the two former feet, they call wings, wherewithal they are thought to flie from tree to tree. Thus far *Antonius*. *Gesner* after the receit of these skins, being willing to preserve them from moths, because they were raw, for experience sake gave them to a leather dresser, who presently dressed them with Vinegar, and the Lees of Wine, so that it appeareth the Skinners of *Lituania* had not the skill how to dress it.

After they were dressed they were so soft, that they stretched above measure, so that every one of them were square, that is to say, their length and breadth were equal, for they were two palms or eight fingers broad: and no more in length, the head and tail excepted: wherefore it may well be called a square Mouse, or *Sciurus quadratus*, because we are sure of the former, but not of the flying; the tail was as long as four or five fingers are broad, being rough like the tail of other Squirrels, but beset with black and white hairs, the whole colour both of the belly and upper part was whitish, as we have said, but black underneath, the hair is so soft as any silk, and therefore fit for the use of the eyes. The ears shorter and rounder then a Squirrels, the feet did not appear by the skin: the neather part was distinguished from the upper part, by a certain visible line, wherein did hang certain long hairs, which by their roughness and solidity under the thin and broad frame of their body, might much help them to flie; even as broad fishes swim by the breadth of their bodies, rather then by the help of their fins. The *Helvetians* wear these skins in their garments. It is reported by *Ælianus*, that the Inhabitants of *Pontus*, by making supplication to their Gods, did avert and turn away the rage of Mice from their Corn-fields, as the *Egyptians* did, as we have said before in the story of the vulgar Mouse.

OF THE MOUSE CALLED THE SHREW, OR THE ERD SHREW.

THE word *Hanaka* of the *Hebrews* remembred in the 11. chapter of Leviticus, is diversly interpreted by the translators, some call it a reptile beast which always cryeth: some a reptile flying beast; some a Horse-leach, or bloud-sucker; some a Hedgehog; and some a Beaver, as we have shewed before in the Hedgehog. But the *Septuagints* translate it *Mygale*; and S. *Jerom, Mus araneus*, that is, a Shrew. *Dioscorides* calleth it *Miogale*; the *Germans* and *Helvetians*; call it *Mutzer*; in some parts of *Germany*, from the figure of the snowt it is called *Spitzmus*, by some *Zissmuss*, from the fiction of his voice; and some *Gross Zissmuss*; the *Hollanders* call it *Moll Musse*, because it resembleth a Mole. *Mathæolus* for the *Italians* call it *Toporagno*; that is, a Mole-shrew. The *Helvetians* call it *Bisemmuss*, that is, a Musk-mouse, because it being dryed in a furnace smelleth like Musk. The skin pulled from the flesh, smelleth best by it self, and yet the flesh smelleth well also, and so do the excrements. But to return to the *Greek* name, why it should be call'd *Mygale*, there is not one opinion amongst the learned: but I do most willingly condescend to the opinion of *Aetius*, who writeth that it is called *Mygale*, because in quantity it exceedeth not a Mouse, and yet in colour it resembleth a Weesil, and therefore it is compounded of two words, *Mys*, a Mouse, and *Galee*, a Weesil.

Amyntas is of opinion, that it is so called, because it is begot betwixt a Mouse and a Weesil, but this is neither true nor probable. For is it likely that Weesils and Mice will couple together in carnal copulation, whose natures are so contrary, the one living upon the death of another, that is, the Weesil upon the Mouse? And beside the difference of quantity betwixt them, maketh it impossible to have such a generation. The other derivation of *Mygale*, which is made by *Rodolphus* writing upon Leviticus, fetching *Mygale* from *Mus gulosus*, that is, a devouring Mouse, it is against the order of all good Linguists, to derive *Greek* words from *Latine*, but rather consonant to learning, to fetch the *Latine* from the *Greek*.

There is no less inquiry about the *Latine* name, why it should be called *Mus araneus*, seeing *Aranea* signifieth a Spider. This Mouse saith *Albertus*, is a red kinde of Mouse having a small tail, a sharp voice, and is full of poyson, or venom: For which cause Cats do kill them, but do not eat them. *Sipontinus* writeth thus, of this Shrew; *Mus araneus, exiguum animal, atqu; levissimum est, quod araneæ modo tenuissimum filum, & gladil aciem conscendit.* That is to say, this Shrew-mouse is a little and light creature, which like a Spider climeth up upon any small thread, or upon the edge of a sword: and therefore you see, they derive the *Latine* name from his climing like a Spider.

But in my opinion it is more reasonable, to derive it from the venom and poyson which it containeth in it like a Spider. For which cause *Silvaticus* writeth thus; *Mugali id est, draco marinus, & animal venenosum, pusillum muri simile: nam & araneum piscem, propter venenum pungentibus insitum spinis, veteres ophim, id est, serpentem nominarunt, & hodie quam vulgo draconem vel dracænam.* That is to say; There is a fish of the Sea, and a little Beast on the Earth like a Mouse, which by a general word are called *Mugale*, and the Spider-fish called at this day a Dragon, or Dragonist, was in ancient time called a Serpent, because by his prickly fins, he did poyson those which were strucken by him. And concerning the description of this beast, it may be taken from the words of an ancient *English* Physitian, called Doctor *William Turner*.

I have seen (saith he) in *England*, the Shrew-mouse of colour black, having a tail very short, and her snowt very long and sharp, and from the venemous biting of this Beast, we have an *English* Proverb or Imprecation, I beshrow thee, when we curse or wish harm unto any man, that is, that some such evil as the biting of this Mouse may come unto him. The *Spaniards* call this Beast *Raton Pequenno*; the *Illyians*, *Viemed kamys*; and the *Polonians*, *Kerit*. They were wont to abound in *Britany*, as *Hermolaus* writeth.

They are also plentiful in *Italy* beyond the Mountains *Apennine*, but not on this side (as *Pliny* writeth) yet in the hither parts of *Italy* and *Germany*, there are many found, especially in the Country neer *Trent*, in the Valley *Anania*, where this is admirable, that by reason of the coldness of that Country their bitings are not venemous. For the Scorpions there are not venemous, although in other places of *Italy* they poyson deeply. This Beast is much less then a Weesil, and of an ash colour, in most places like a Mouse, although the colour be not always constant.

The eyes are so small, and beneath the proportion of her body, that it hath not been unjustly doubted of the Ancients, whether they were blinde or no, but in their best estate their sight is very dull. And for this cause the ancient *Egyptians* did worship it: for as they held opinion, that darkness was before light, so they deemed that the blinde creatures were better then the seeing. And they also believed, that in the wane of the Moon the liver of this beast consumed. It hath a long and sharp snowt like a Mole, that so it may be apt to dig. The teeth are very small, but so as they stand double in their mouth, for they have four rows of teeth, two beneath, and two above, which are not only apparent by their dissection or Anatomy, but also, by their bitings, for their wounds are Quadruple, wheresoever they fasten their teeth. Their tail is slender and short. But the description of this Beast was better apprehended by *Gesner*, at the sight of one of them, which he relateth on this manner:

The colour (saith he) was partly red, and partly yellow, mingled both together, but the belly white. The hinder-feet seemeth to cleave to the body or loins. It smelleth strongly, and the savour did bewray or signifie some secret poyson. The tail about three fingers long, beset with little short hairs. The residue of the body was three fingers long. The eyes very small and black, not much greater then Moles, so that next to the Mole they may justly be called, the least sighted creature among all four footed Beasts; so that in old age they are utterly blinde by the Providence of God, abridging their malice, that when their teeth are grown to be most sharp, and they most full of poyson, then they should not see whom nor where to vent it.

They differ as we have said in place and number, from all four-footed Beasts, so that they seem to be compounded and framed of the teeth of Serpents and Mice. The two fore-teeth are very long, and they do not grow single as in vulgar Mice; but have within them two other smal and sharp teeth. And also those two long teeth grow not by themselves, as they do in other Mice, but are conjoyned in the residue, in one continued rank. They are sharp like a saw, having sharp points like needles, such as could not be seen by man, except the tips of them were yellow. Of either side they have eight teeth, whereas the vulgar Mice have but four, beside the two long fore-teeth, which also seem divided into two or three, which except one mark diligently, he would think them to be all one.

It is a ravening Beast, feigning it self gentle and tame, but being touched, it biteth deep, and poysoneth deadly. It beareth a cruel minde, desiring to hurt any thing, neither is there any creature that it loveth, or it loveth him, because it is feared of all. The Cats, as we have said, do hunt it and kill it, but they eat not them, for if they do, they consume away in time. They annoy Vines, and are seldom taken, except in cold; they frequent Ox-dung, and in the Winter time repair to houses, gardens, and stables, where they are taken and killed.

If they fall into a Cart-road, they die and cannot get forth again, as *Marcellus*, *Nicander*, and *Pliny* affirm. And the reason is given by *Philes*, for being in the same, it is so amazed, and trembleth, as if it were in bands. And for this cause some of the Ancients have prescribed the earth of a Cart-road, to be laid to the biting of this Mouse for a remedy thereof. They go very slowly, they are fraudulent, and take their prey by deceit. Many times they gnaw the Oxes hoofs in the stable. They love the rotten flesh of Ravens; and therefore in *France*, when they have killed a Raven, they keep it till it stinketh, and then cast it in the places where the Shrew-mice haunt, whereunto they gather in so great number, that you may kill them with shovels. The *Egyptians* upon the former opinion of holiness, do bury them when they die. And thus much for the description of this Beast. The succeeding discourse toucheth the medicines arising out of this Beast; also the cure of her venemous bitings.

THE MEDICINES OF THE SHREW.

The Shrew, which falling by chance into a Cart-rode or track, doth die upon the same, being burned, and afterwards beaten or dissolved into dust, and mingled with Goose grease, being rubbed or anointed upon those which are troubled with the swelling in the fundament coming by the cause of some inflammation, doth bring unto them a wonderful and most admirable cure and remedy. The Shrew being slain or killed, hanging so that neither then nor afterwards she may touch the ground, doth help those which are grieved and pained in their bodies, with sores called fellons, or biles, which doth pain them with a great inflammation, so that it be three times invironed or compassed about the party so troubled. The Shrew which dyeth in the furrow of a Cart-wheel, being found and rowled in Potters clay or a linnen cloth, or in Crimson, or Scarlet woollen cloth, and three times marked about the Impostumes, which will suddenly swell in any mans body, will very speedily and effectually help and cure the same.

The tail of a Shrew being cut off and burned, and afterwards beaten into dust, and applyed or anointed upon the sore of any man, which came by the biting of a greedy and ravenous Dog, will in very short space make them both whole and sound, so that the tail be cut from the Shrew when she is alive, not when she is dead, for then it hath neither good operation, nor efficacy in it. The former hoofs of a Horse being scraped, and the same fragments or scantlings thereof being beaten in the dust or earth, which hath been digged up by a Shrew, in four measures of water, poured down the mouth of a Horse which is troubled with any pain or wringing in his bowels, will soon give him both help and remedy. The Shrew being either applyed in drink, or put in the manner and form of a plaister, or hanged upon the sore which he hath bitten, is the most excellentest, and most medicinable cure for the helping and healing thereof. A preservative against poyson, would be an excellent remedy, that neither man nor any other living creature, should be bitten if they should leave or would want that superstition called an enchantment against poyson, being hanged about the neck, whereof we will speak more in the curing of the bites of this Beast.

That the biting of a Shrew is venomous, and of the reason of healing in this kinde.

In *Italy* the biting of a Shrew is accounted for a very strong poyson, and that except there be some medicine very speedily applyed for the curing and healing thereof, the party so bitten will die. These Shrews are truly so venemous and full of poyson, that being slain or killed by Cats, whose nature is to kill whatsoever Mice they take, they will not offer to touch or eat the least part of them.

But the biting of a female Shrew is most obnoxious and hurtful when she is great with young, but most dangerous of all when she biteth any one which is great with young, either a woman or any other Beast whatsoever, her self being also with young, for then it will hardly be cured.

If a Shrew shall bite any creature while she is great with young, the pushes or biles will in time be broke which they make, and will come unto a very great and malignant wound and sore. If the Shrew do also bite any creature during the time she is with young, she will presently leap off, notwithstanding she biteth more dangerous. There is nothing which do more apparently explain and shew the biting of a Shrew then a certain vehement pain and grief in the creature which is so bitten, as also a pricking over the whole body; with an inflammation or burning heat going round about the place, and a fiery redness therein, in which a black push or like swelling with a watery matter, and filthy corruption doth arise, and all the parts of the body which do joyn unto it seem black and blew with the marvellous great pain, anguish, and grief, which ariseth and proceedeth from the same.

When the push or bile which cometh by the occasion of a Shrew cleaveth or is broken, there proceedeth and issueth forth a kinde of white flesh, having a certain rinde or skin upon it, and some-time there appeareth in them a certain burning, and sometimes the same is eaten in and falleth out, but in the beginning there is a most filthy green corruption and matter which floweth in the same, afterward it is putrefied, and eaten in, and then the flesh falleth forth: the wringings also of the inward parts, the difficulty of voiding the urine, and a corrupted sweat doth follow and accompany the same.

But *Avicenna* affirmeth, that in what place soever this Beast shall bite, the sores thereof with great anguish will pant or beat, and that in every hole wherein his venemous teeth have entred, there will a certain fiery redness appear, the skin whereof being broken there will come a very white and mattery sore, which will breed much pain and trouble in all the parts of the body for the most part. The sores or wounds which are made also by this Beast are very manifestly known by the marks of the fore-teeth standing all in a row together, as also by the bloud which issueth from the wound, being at the first pure, clear, and exceeding red, but afterwards corrupt, blackish, and full of putrefaction.

There do also divers bunches arise in the flesh usually after the biting of this Beast, which if any man shall break, he shall see the flesh which lyeth under them corrupted, and divided with certain clefts or rifts in the same. Moreover the nature of this Beast is such, that for the most part he doth covet to bite those whom he can come unto by the stones or genital, not only men, but also all other brute Beasts whatsoever: and thus much shall suffice concerning the biting of this Beast.

Wormwood being beaten or bruised small, strained in a fine linnen cloth, and mingled in Wine, given to the party, either man or woman, in Wine to drink, who is bitten by a Shrew, will procure him present ease and remedy. The same also is an excellent remedy for the bitings or stingings of a Sea-dragon. Vinegar is very medicinable for the bitings of the Shrew, and of Dogs, as also for the fish called by the *Latines*, *Scolopendra*, (which voideth all her bowels out until the hook come forth, wherewith she is taken, and then sucketh them up again) the Scorpion and all other venomous Serpents.

But the *Græcian* Physitians affirm, that the same ought to be mingled with other medicines for the helping of the aforesaid diseases, as to take the ashes of the Shrew being burnt, the gum or liquor of the Herb called Fennil-giant, dryed Barly beaten into small powder, Mustard-seed pounded small with the Herb called Purple, or Mothmullein, and mingle them all together with Vinegar, and being so applyed they will presently cure the aforesaid stings or bitings.

Garlick being bruised, and the juyce thereof anointed upon the place which was bitten by a Shrew, will presently expel the pain, and wholly cure the sore. For the expelling of the superfluities of the parings of the dead flesh, growing round about the sore, being not cast away but remaining thereon. Take Cummin and cover the wound or biting therewith, then apply Garlick being beaten into Oyl thereunto, and anoint the places about the sore, as also the sore it self very diligently, and in very short space of time it will cause the same to fall away of it own accord. For the healing also of the bites of this Beast: Take Garlick, the leaves of a Fig-tree, and Cummin, mingle them very well all together, till they come to a mollifying or temperate substance; then take the same, and fashion it in the form or manner of a plaister, and it will very speedily and effectually cure the sore.

The seed or leaves of Coleworts, being beaten together with Vinegar, and the herb call'd *Assa fœ ida*, is very good and profitable to be applyed either to the bites of this Beast, or a ravening Dog. The dung of a Dog being taken and anointed upon either Man or Horse which hath been bitten by a Shrew, will be an excellent remedy both for the curing and healing them of the same. The hoof of a Ram being dryed, beaten into powder & afterwards mixed with Hony, will be likewise very good for those which are bitten with the same Beast, so that they be first tempered and fashioned in the manner of a plaister, and then applyed thereunto. The little white stalks which proceed from a black Fig, being beaten with the leaves of the herb called Moth-mullein, Wax, and Vinegar, until they come unto a mollifying juyce or salve, will be an excellent remedy against the biting of the Shrew, being anointed thereupon.

958

The young or tender stalks of a wilde Fig-tree, be they never so few or small, being first steeped in Wine, then lapped in a leaf of the same Tree, and so applyed unto the stings and bites of Scorpions, and the Shrew, will in very short time cure and heal the same. Provided always that the wound be well and diligently bathed or washed, before any thing be put or applyed thereunto.

Dioscorides, Avicenna, and *Actuarus*, do affirm, that the excellentest, and medicinablest cure for the bites of a Shrew is this: To take the Spleen of the same Beast, and beat it together with Vinegar, and the Gum called *Galbanum*, then to anoint it or rub it upon the sore, and it will presently expel away all pain, and in some short space altogether heal it. If the red bunches or ulcers which do usually grow about the bites of a Shrew, do fortune to break; take very sharp and strong brine or pickle, and rub it both about, and within the sore, and afterwards apply Barly being burned and beaten into small dust or powder thereunto, which medicine although it seem somewhat grievous and painful, yet it is very good and profitable for the expelling either of the stings of Scorpions, or the bites of the Shrew or ravenous Dog.

The genital of a Hare being beaten into powder mingled with Vinegar, and anointed upon the bites of a Shrew, doth speedily cure them. Wilde Mallows being mingled with those Mallows that grow in the Garden, have in them a very effectual force and power to cure all stings or venomous bitings, especially of Scorpions, Shrews, Wasps, and such like stinging creatures.

The Shrew being cut and applyed in the manner of a plaister, doth effectually cure her own bites. The Shrew being killed and anointed all over with Oyl, and dirt or mire, applyed unto the Ulcers or red swellings which come by her venomous teeth, will very speedily procure them to break. The Shrew being cut or beaten into small pieces, dryed into powder, mixed with Vinegar, and fashioned in the form of a plaister, will very speedily and effectually cure the bites of a Shrew, whether she be great with young or not, so that they be well applyed thereunto.

But there are some which do think it nothing convenient to mingle the Shrew with any other thing whatsoever, but that it is only after this manner to be applyed by it self, as to take it burned or dry it, and then to pound it in powder, and so to sprinkle it in the wound or sore, which in very short time will easily heal it. The Shrew falling into the furrow of a Cart wheel doth presently die: the dust thereof in the passage by which she went, being taken and sprinkled into the wounds which were made by her poysonsome teeth, is a very excellent and present remedy for the curing of the same. *Maithæolus* alleadgeth out of *Nicander*, that the dirt which cleaveth unto the wheels of a Chariot being scraped off and sprinkled into the bites of a Shrew, will be very medicinable for the healing of them, which thing he himself thinketh a meer fable, and not to be believed. If the pimples or bladders which arise in the bites of a Shrew shall be thought convenient to be broken, for the performing of the same, take the skin of a baked or roasted Pomgranate, and spread it upon the aforesaid red pimples, as hot as possible may be suffered for some small time, and it will cause the ulcers to break, and all the corruption to issue forth.

If it grow unto an Impostume, take the little berries or pellets which are within the Pomgranate, being very well baked, and apply them unto the sore some short time and they will very easily cure the same. Mustard-seed being mingled with Vinegar, anointed upon the bites of a Shrew, doth very effectually heal them. A Moul being bruised into small pieces, and applyed unto the bites of a Shrew in the form of a plaister, is a very excellent remedy for the curing of them. Pitch and Trifoly being baked, and rubbed very hot upon the bites of a Shrew, is accounted a very medicinable cure: but it is requisite that this fomentation be given unto none but such as are of a strong and powerful body, and are also able to endure pain. The liquor of the Herb called Southern-wood being given in Wine to drink doth very much profit those which are troubled, and painted in their limbs with the bites of Shrews. Wormwood being used in the like manner, will cure those which are bitten by a Shrew.

The genital of a Lamb or Kid being mingled with four drams of the Herb called *Aristolochia*, or Hart-wort, and six drams of the sweetest Myrrh, is very good and medicinable for curing of those which are bitten or stung with Shrews, Scorpions, and such like venemous Beasts. The leaves of Coleworts being dryed, mingled with flower, and tempered together, until they come into the form of a plaister, will very much help against the venemous bites of the Shrew. The seeds of Coleworts, and the leaves of the same herb being mingled with Vinegar, and the herb called *Assa fœtida* beat or pounded together, do very well and speedily cure the bites of the Shrews, as also of a ravenous Dog, if the same in due time be applyed thereunto. The liquor also of the leaves of Coleworts being given in any kinde of drink, is good and wholesome for the curing of the aforesaid bites or wounds. The Nuts of a young Cypres tree being mixed with a certain syrup or potion made of Hony, Water, and Vinegar, and afterwards drunk, doth very speedily procure ease and help for those which are bitten by a Shrew.

The root of a white or black Thistle, being beaten or bruised and given in drink, doth very effectually help or cure those which are bitten by a Shrew. The like vertue hath the herb called Rocket in it, and also the seed thereof being given in any kinde of drink. The gum or liquor which proceedeth from a kinde of Ferula, being given in Wine to drink, doth very much help and cure those which are bitten by a Shrew. The same vertue also in it hath the root of the herb called Gentian or Bitterwort, being given in Wine to drink. One or two drams of the youngest or tendrest leaves of the Laurel tree, being beaten small and given in Wine to drink, doth speedily cure the sores or wounds which are bitten by a Shrew: the same being also used in the said manner, and given in some certain portion unto Horses to drink, doth quickly help and heel them: But there are some which before all other medicines do commend this for the best, and chiefest; that is, to take the juyce which proceedeth from the leaves of the Lawrel tree, and the leaves themselves, being moist and new growing, and to boil them in Wine, and being once cooled, to give it to any which is bitten by a Shrew, and this will in very short space altogether help them. A young Weesil being given in Wine to drink, is accounted very medicinable for those which are bitten by a Shrew, or stung by a Scorpion or any other venemous creature. The herb called Baltsamint or Costmary, the herb called Bartram, or wilde Pellito, the herb called Betony, the herb called Water-mint, or Water-cresses; the sweet and delicious gum called Storax, as also the herb called Vervin, being each of them severally by themselves, either given in Wine to drink, or applyed in the manner of a plaister or anointed upon the bites or wounds which come by the venemous teeth of a Shrew, will very effectually cure the pain thereof: The biting of a field Mouse or Shrew, is very troublesome or grievous to all labouring Beasts; for instantly after her bitings there do little red Pimples arise, and there is most danger of death in those Beasts which she biteth when she is great with young; for the aforesaid pimples will then presently break, after which the Beast so bitten will instantly die. The Shrew doth also kill some labouring Beasts with poyson, as chiefly Horses and Mules, but especially and for the most part Mares, which are great with young. There are some which do affirm, that if Horses, or any other labouring creature do feed in that pasture or grass in which a Shrew shall put forth her venome or poyson in, they will presently die. In what place soever a Shrew shall bite in any creature, it will be compassed with an exceeding hard swelling, the Beast also being so bitten, doth express his grief or sorrow with much pain, and straining his body doth likewise swell all over, his eyes do in a manner weep, the swelling in his body doth squize out matter, or filthy putrifaction, he voideth poyson out of his belly; and doth vomit all sustenance up as soon as ever he receiveth it. If an Ass being great with young be bitten by this Beast, it is a very great chance if she scape death.

But if the Shrew do bite any Beast when she is great with young, it is known by these signes, or marks, there will certain red pimples compass the sore round about, and also spread themselves over all the body of the bitten Beast, and will in short space destroy him, except there be procured some present remedy. The *Normans* in *France*, do suppose the Shrew to be a Beast so full of venom, and poyson, that if he shall but pass over either an Ox, or a Horse lying down along upon the ground, it will bring such a dangerous disease upon them, that the Beast over which she shall pass, shall be lame about the loins, or shall seem as if he were immoveable, and that he can be cured by no other means but by the same Shrew, who either of his own accord, or by compulsion must pass over the contrary side of the Beast, and that then he will be cured; which thing I do hold to be very vain and not to be believed.

For the curing of Beasts which are bitten by a Shrew, thou shalt boil the seed of Parsly together with Wine and Oyl, and thou shalt cut the place which swelleth with a Pen-knife, by which the poyson may issue forth, and the wound being pointingly pulled or torn may wax raw: if by these the inflammation do wax more servent and hot, thou shalt eat the sore with Iron instruments burning with fire, taking away some part of that which is whole and sound: then shalt thou renew the wound with the Iron instruments being governed rightly, by which the corruption may issue forth: but if that part do chance to swell by the exculceration, thou shalt sprinkle Barley being burned and dryed therein; but before you do this, it is meet to joyn the old fat.

There is also another excellent medicine for the curing of the Shrew, which *Startonicus* himself doth much commend, which is this: To lance or scarifie the wound as soon as it is bitten, but especially if it be compassed with an inflammation, afterwards to sprinkle Salt and Vinegar upon it, then to encourage or provoke the Beast the next day following by some sweet water or liquor to run or go some little journey, first having anointed the sore with Fullers-earth, being beaten small and mixed with Vinegar, and then daily to nourish or bathe it with water which cometh from bathes where some have washed themselves, and this in very short time being so used, will very well and altogether cure the Beast. Against the biting of a Shrew Garlick is accounted for an excellent remedy being mingled with Nitre; but if there shall be no Nitre to be had, mix it with Salt and Cumin, then to dry and beat them al together into powder, and with the same to rub the places which are infected with the biting: but if the venemous wounds do chance to break; then to take Barly being scorched or burned, and pound it into small powder, and steep it in Vinegar, and afterwards to sprinkle it into the wound: This medicine *Pelagon* affirmeth, will only heal the bites of a Shrew, and that the grief of the sore, by the use of any other medicines doth rather encrease, then decrease.

The flowre which is made of red Wheat, the herb called Dill, the liquor or Rozen which runneth out of the great Cedar, and two pound of the best Wine, being mingled all together, given in a potion, and poured down the throat of any labouring Beast which is bitten by a Shrew, will presently ease and cure him of his pain.

There is also another potion for the curing of the bites of this Beast; which is this; To take cloves of Garlick being bruised small, Salt, Cumin, and Wine, of each the like quantity; these being given to any Beast to drink, doth presently cure him; as also any man being anointed upon the wound, but not given to drink. The herb called Nard or Pepper-wort, being beaten to the quantity of two ounces and a half, and mingled with some sweet smelling Wine, will presently help any Beast which is bitten by the Shrew, being poured through his Nose, and his sore being at that instant time anointed with Dogs dung: the same is also very medicinable or wholesome for men which are troubled with the said biting.

The bites of a Shrew being pricked with an Aul, and anointed with dust which is found in the furrows of Carts under the marks or signes of the Wheel, being mingled with sharp Vinegar, doth presently asswage the pain, and heal the sore. The earth of the track of a Cart also mingled with stale or urine, being applyed unto the bites of a Shrew, will very speedily cure them either upon Men or Beasts. A Shrew being new killed and rubbed over with Salt, applyed unto the wounds which she shall bite in any Beasts, will instantly cure them: This vertue also hath the gall of a Rere-mouse or Bat, being mixed with Vinegar.

There is a very good remedy against the bitings of Shrews, or to preserve Cattle from them, which is this; to compass the hole wherein she lyeth round about, and get her out alive, and keep her so till she dye, and wax stiffe, then hang her about the neck of the Beast which you would preserve, and there will not any Shrew come near them; and this is accounted to be most certain. And thus much shall suffice concerning the bitings of the Shrews, and of the cures thereof.

OF WILDE FIELD-MICE.

THIS wilde Mouse called by the *Latines, Mus agrestis, Mus Sylvestris, Sylvaticus, Subterraneus,* and some say *Nitedula,* (although I rather take that word to signifie a Glare-worm.) It is called also *Exiguus Mus,* and *Rusticus.* The *Græcians* call it *Myss Arourayos*; the *Germans*; Field-mouse, and Erd-mouse, that is, a Mouse of the Earth, and *Nuelmus, Nualmuss, Schorrmuss, Schoermowss, Stissmuss,* and *Luckmuss,* by reason of her digging in the earth like a Mole. The *French* call it *Mullott.* There is of these Mice two kindes, a greater and a lesser. The picture of the greater we have described here, for bearing the lesser, because in all parts it resembleth this, except in the quantity.

This greater kinde is not much lesser then a Rat, having a long broad tail like it. The ears of it are round; the head round and great; and the showt or chaps do not stand out long. They are of two colours in both kindes, some red and some black. They have a beard betwixt their mouth and their eyes; and the lesser Mice have a short tail. A Physitian taking occasion of the writings of *Bassianus Landus*, to dissect one of these Mice, found it to be true which he saith, that their maw and guts lie all straight and upright. We have shewed already, that all kinde of Mice are generated out of the earth, although also they suffer copulation. And in *Egypt* it is very common about *Thebais*, and the places where *Nilus* overfloweth, that in the decrease and falling away of the Waters, the Sun engendereth many Mice upon the slime of the earth; so that it is ordinary to see at one time their fore-parts to have life, flesh, and motion, and the hinder-parts deformed, and nothing but earth.

And about this matter there is some disputation among the Authors, for there be Philosophers which affirm, that every creature as well perfect as unperfect, may be made both by seed and of putrified matter; and from hence came the opinion in the Poets, of the sons and daughters of the earth, and so they say, that things grow by generation *in infinitum*: Some say, that perfect creatures cannot be generated in that manner, but the imperfect ones, such as Mice are, may be ingendered by seed and putrified matter, and afterwards beget more of his one kinde.

But *Aristotle* confesseth the first generation, and denyeth the second, and saith; although they do generate by copulation, yet it is not *Idem sed animal specie diversum, à quo nihil amplius gigni possit*; And therefore *Jeronimus Gabucinus* endeth this controversie, saying; *Mures ex putredine nati, generant quidem & ipsi, sed quod ex eis generatur, nec Mus est, nec sœmina, nec amplius generat*: that is; Mice engendered of putrified matter do also engender, but that which is begotten of them is neither male nor female, neither can it engender any more, that it may not proceed in infinitum, like a Mouse engendered by copulation. But concerning the beginning of these wilde Field-mice, and their encrease, *Aristotle* speaketh in this manner: We have received (saith he) the wonderful generation of wilde Field-mice, abounding in every place, and especally in corn-fields, which by their multitude, do instantly eat up and devour a great deal of grain, insomuch as it hath been seen, that divers poor Husbandmen, which have determined to day, to reap their corn on the morrow, in the mean season it was so destroyed by Mice, that when the Reapers came in the morning, they have found no corn at all.

And as the encrease of these Mice was extraordinary, so also was the destruction, for men could not drive them away, as in former times, by smoking them, or else by turning in Swine to root out their nests from the earth, or by sending Foxes, or wilde Cats among them, but their multitude did always prevail; and yet after a few days, the showers of the clouds destroyed them. And *Pliny* saith, that this ought to be no marvail, that there should be so great a harvest and store of these Mice, seeing that men yet never knew how to hinder their generation, or to kill them, being engendered, and yet for all that they are seldom found in the Winter time either alive or dead. And seeing that we have entred into the mention of the damage of these wilde Field-mice, it is profitable to set down some stories out of Authors, recording the place and persons, whom they have very much annoyed.

Pliny writeth, as we have shewed in our former discourse, that the Inhabitants of *Troas*, were driven from their habitation by these Field-mice; because they devoured all their fruits, and when they dyed, there was a worm engendered in their heads. *Diodorus Siculus* in his fourth Book of ancient Monuments recordeth, that there were certain people of *Italy*, which by incursion of Field-mice were driven to flight, and to forsake their patrimonies, for they destroyed the roots of the corn, like some horrible drought, or some unresistible cold frost. *Cossa* a Town of *Umbria*, in the days of *Pliny*, which at this day is called *Orbi tellus*, was destroyed by Field-mice, (as *Volaterranus* writeth.) *Niphus* also saith, that he saw in one night, all the Corn-fields at *Calenum* destroyed by the Mice.

There are such a number of these Mice in *Spain*, that many times their destruction caused pestilent diseases, and this thing hapned amongst the *Romans* when they were in *Cantabria*, for they were constrained to hire men by stipends to kill the Mice, and those which did kill them, scarse escaped with life. The Inhabitants of *Gyarus*, an Island of the *Cyclades*, after they had long resisted the violence of these Mice, yet at length they were fain to yeeld unto them, and forsake their Territory; and the Mice after their departure, through hunger did gnaw the Iron. We have shewed already how the *Philistines* were punished with Mice, before they sent away the Ark of the Lord, and how the *Aeolians* and *Trojans* were annoyed with them, until they had sacrificed to *Apollo Smintheus*, and how the Mice of *Heraclea*, at the time of Grape-gathering, do go out of the Countrey and return again in the Autumn. When *Senacharib*, King of the *Arabians* and *Egyptians*, invaded *Egypt*, it is said by *Herodotus*, that *Vulcan* in the night time sent upon his Army such an innumerable swarm of wilde Mice, that before morning they had eaten asunder their Quivers, Arrows, Bows, and all warlike instruments, so that the next day, for the want of weapons, and fear of their enemies, they were constrained to take their heels and run away. And to conclude, by the same means the *Chalcidensians* were driven out of *Elymnium*, a City of the Mountain *Athos*; and thus much shall suffice for the harm of these Mice. They make their dwellings and habitation in the earth, according to this saying of *Virgil*:

> —— *Sæpe exiguus mus*
> *Sub terra posuitq; domos, atq; horrea fecit.*

Yet now and then they come out of the earth, although it be but seldom. They heave up hills like Moles, and they eat and devour the roots of corn and herbs. They make not very deep holes, but dig under the turfs and upper face of the earth; so that when a man walketh upon

967

it, he may perceive it by the sinking in of his foot-steps: if the hole be opened with a Spade, they close it again as a Mole doth, but not so speedily, for they defer it two or three days together; and therefore if it be watched, they may kill her at her return by treading upon her; concerning the manner of taking them, these observations following may be put in practise.

These kinde of Mice are driven or chased away with the ashes of a Weesil, or of a Cat mingled with water, and by sprinkling or scattering seed or corn abroad, or by some things well sodden in water: but the poysoning of those Mice is in the scent or savour of bread: and therefore they think it more profitable to touch the seed or corn lightly with the gall of an Ox. *Apuleius* doth affirm, that to soke the grain or corn in the gall of an Ox before you sprinkle it abroad, is very good against these Field-mice: also (as it is read in *Geopon Græc.*) it doth very much commend the gall of Oxen, wherewith as he saith, if the seed or corn be touched, they shall be freed from the molestation or trouble of these Field-mice.

Notwithstanding in the Dog-days Hemlock-seed with the herb Hellebore is better, or with wilde Cowcumber, or with Hen-bane, or being beaten with bitter Almonds, and Bears-foot, and to mingle with them just as much meal or corn, and beat and stamp them in Oyl, and when you have so done, put it into the hollow places of these Field-mice: and they will die as soon as ever they shall tast of it. *Avicen* doth affirm also, that Hen-bane-seed doth kill these kinde of Mice, without the mixture of any other thing. Very many do stop the passages of them with the leaves of Rhododaphne, who do perish in the time they are labouring to make their passage, by the gnawing of them.

Apuleius also saith, that the people of *Bithynia* have had much experience of these things, who stopped the passages of these Mice with these Rhododaphne leaves, so that they desire to come forth by touching the same often with their teeth: which truly so soon as they shall touch or come unto, they shall presently die. But they use a kinde of incantation which is this that followeth; I do adjure all ye Mice, which do remain or abide here, that ye do not offer me wrong, or suffer me to be wronged of any other. For I do assign and appoint you this field (then he nameth the field) in which if I should surprize you hereafter, I call *Luna* to witness, I will tear every one of you into seven pieces: When as thou hast writ this charm, binde paper fast to the place wherein the Mice haunt, and that before the rising of the Sun: so that the characters or marks may appear on the outside cleaving to a natural stone of that place. I have written this (saith the Author) lest any thing should seem to be overskipped: neither do I allow or prove such things can be done, but I rather counsel all men that they do not set their minde to any of these, which are more worthy of derision then imitation. If thou shalt fill the passages of these rustical or Field-mice with the ashes of an Oak, he shall be possessed with a fervent desire to it, often touching it, and so shall die.

These Countrey Mice, that is to say, those Mice which are found in the fields, being bruised and burned to ashes, and mingled with fresh Hony, doth comfort or restore the sight of the eyes by diminishing the darkness or dimness thereof, in what field soever you shall finde any thing, dig them up by the roots with a little stake or post.

OF THE WOOD-MOUSE.

PLINY doth oftentimes make mention of this Wood-mouse, or rather a Mouse belonging to the Wood, but he doth it only in medicines; but that it doth differ from this Countrey or Field-mouse we have shewen in the chapter going before, because it doth not inhabit or dwell in the Countries or tilled places, as the Countrey or Field-mice do, but doth inhabit in Woods and Forrests. The Wood-mouse is called in *Greek* as the Countrey-mouse: but I think it to be a kinde of Dormouse, which proceedeth from the kinde of Wood-mouse. *Pliny* truly doth make the same remedy or medicines of a Dormouse, as he doth of a Wood-mouse, as I will a little after rehearse or recite unto you. Also I should have thought that a Sorex had been the same, because it is a Wood-mouse, but that, that one place of *Pliny* did hinder me, where he commendeth the ashes of a Wood-mouse to be very good for the clearness of the eyes, and by and by after did shew or declare that the ashes of the Sorex were good also in the same use, as I will recite or rehearse below in the medicines or remedies of the Wood-mouse. *Agricola,* a man of great learning, doth interpret or judge the Wood-mouse to be that Mouse, to the which they do appoint the name derived from *Avellana*: but he doth account that to be the Sorex, which I will shew or declare beneath to be the Shrew. I do understand that there are properly two kindes of the Wood-mouse spoken of before. The one of them that which *Albertus* doth write, saying that there is a certain kinde of Mouse which doth build or make her habitation in trees, and of a brown or swart colour, and having also black spots in her face, which only is called by the universal name of a Wood-mouse. Of the same kinde *Pliny* doth mean, (if I be not deceived) when he writeth, that the mast of a Beech-tree is very acceptable to Mice, and therefore they have good success with their young ones. The other which is peculiarly named the Sorex, which (saith *Pliny*) doth sleep all the Winter time, and hath a tail full of hair: whose shape or form we propose and set evidently before you. But that I may more distinctly handle those things which *Pliny* hath shewed to us concerning the Wood-mouse; I will write her down separately, or by it self, and afterwards concerning the Mouse which hath her name derived from Fil-birds, which the *Germans* have left in writing, and which I my self have considered or observed; and last of all I will write concerning the Sorex peculiarly and severally from the Ancient Writers.

The ashes of a Wood-mouse being mingled with Hony, doth cure all fractures of bones, the brains also spread upon a little piece of cloth, and covered with wooll is good also; but you must now and then spread it over the wound, and it doth almost make it whole and strong within the space of three or four days: neither must you mingle the ashes of the Wood-mouse with Hony too late: Hony also being mingled with the ashes of Earth-worms, doth draw forth broken bones. Also the fat of these Beasts, being put to Kibes is very good; but if the Ulcers are corrupt and rotten, by adding Wax to the former things doth bring them to cicatrising. The Oyl of a burned Locust is also very good; and also the Oyl of a Wood-mouse with Hony, is as effectual as the other. They say also that the heads and tails of Mice mixed with the ashes of them, and anointed with Hony, doth restore the clearness of the sight, but more effectually being mingled with the ashes of a Dor-mouse or a Wood-mouse.

OF THE NUT-MOUSE, HASEL-MOUSE, OR FILBIRD-MOUSE.

THIS Beast is a kinde of Sorex, and may be that which the *Germans* tearm *Ein gross Haselmus*, a great Hasel-mouse, so called because they seed upon Hasel-nuts, and Filbirds. The *Flemings* call it *Ein Slaperat*, that is, a sleeping Rat; and therefore the *French* call it by the name *Lerot*, whereby also we have shewed already, they understand a Dormouse.

For this sleepeth like that, and yet the flesh thereof is not good to be eaten. The colour of this Mouse is red like the Hasel, and the quantity full as great as a Squirrel, or as a great Rat: upon the back and sides it is more like a Mouse, and upon the head more red. His ears very great, and pilled without hair. The belly white, so also are his legs. The neathermost of his tail towards the tip white. His nostrils and feet reddish. The tail wholly rough, but most at the end with white hairs.

The eyes very great hanging out of his head, and all black, so that there is not in them any appearance of white. The beard partly white, and partly black, both above and beneath his ears, and about his eyes, and the upper part of his tail next his body all black. Upon his forefeet he hath four claws or distinct toes, for he wanteth a thumb. But upon his hinder-feet he hath five, I mean upon each severally. The outside of his hinder-legs, from the bending to the tip of his nails is altogether bald without hair. And the savour of all this kinde is like the smell of the vulgar Mice. They live not only in the earth, but also in trees which they climbe like Squirrels, and therefore make provision of nuts and meat against the Winter, which they lodge in the earth.

The Countreymen finding in the Summer their caves and dens, do wisely forbear to destroy them, knowing that they will bring into them the best Nuts and Fil-birds can be gotten, and therefore at one side they stick up a certain long rod, by direction whereof in the Winter time they come and dig out the den, justly taking from them both their life and store, because they have unjustly gathered it together: Some have eaten it, but they were deceived, taking it for the Dormouse.

OF THE LASCITT MOUSE.

THIS Mouse is called by the *Germans, Lascitts,* and also *Harnebal,* because of the similitude it holdeth with the *Ermeline* Weesil. The skin of it is very pretious, being shorter then the *Ermeline* two fingers breadth. And forasmuch as else, there is no difference between the *Lascitt* Mouse, and the *Lascitt* Weesil, except in the quantity: My opinion is, that they are all one, and differ only in age.

And I am rather led to affirm thus much, because there are skins annually brought to the Mart of *Franckford,* out of *Polonia* (cal'd *Lascet*) which are no other then the Weesils of *Novo grodela,* whose white skins are intermixed with grisseld; And thus much shall suffice to have said of this Mouse.

OF THE SOREX.

I am of opinion, that this kinde of Mouse belongeth to the Hasel Mouse before spoken of, because it is wilde, hath a hairy tail, and sleepeth in the Winter, all which things are by *Pliny* ascribed to the Sorex; only this hindereth, that he maketh the Sorex to have rough hairy ears, and the Sorex of *Germany* hath bald ears. For answer whereof this shall suffice, that the other three notes being so great and pregnant, there is no cause why the want of one, and that so little as the hairs on the ears, should deprive it of his naturall due and kinde. The *Italians* and the *French* use this word Sorex, for a domestical vulgar Mouse, and so peradventure did the Antients before them; but it is greater then the domestical Mouse, although *Plinies* Sorex be neither greater nor lesser. The *Spaniards* call a Sorex, *Sorace*, or *Raton Pequenno*. The *Illyrians*, *Viemegka Myss*, by which word also they understand a Shrew-mouse. The fibres of the intrails of the Sorex do encrease and decrease with the Moon, so that the number of them, do always answer the number of the days of her age.

Her ears as we have said are full of hairs, but in the lowest part or tip thereof. The reason of her name is taken from the skreeching voice she maketh in gnawing. For it is a very harmful biting Beast, cutting asunder with her teeth like a saw. Some do derive the *Greek* word from *Huras*, which anciently did signifie a Mouse, and therefore they call this *Syrax*, and *Saurex*, but I lift not to stand any longer upon the name, seeing the Beast it self affordeth little worthy matter to entreat of.

It is reported by *Varro*, that in *Arcadia* there was a Hog so fat, that a Sorex did eat into her flesh, and made her nest and brought forth young ones therein, which may very well be; for such is the nature of a fat Swine, that he will hardly rise to eat his meat, or ease himself of his excrements: And besides, fatness stoppeth sense, burying both the Nerves and Arteries very deep: so that in the body of a man, his fattest part is least sensible. *Lycinius* the Emperor going about to restrain the insolency of the Eunuches and Courtiers, called them *Tineas, Soricesq; palatinos*, that is moths and Sorices of the Court.

There was an ancient garment (as *Pliny* writeth) called *Vestis Soriculata*, and this was very pretious in my opinion, because it was garded or fringed with the skins of the Sorex. If this Beast fall into any Wine or Oyl, she corrupteth the same, and it is to be recovered by the same means, as we have formerly described in the vulgar Mouse. It should seem there was great store of them in the days of *Heliogabalus*, for he commanded (as *Lampridius* writeth) to be brought unto him, not only a thousand of these Beasts, but also a thousand Weesils, and ten thousand vulgar Mice, as we have shewed before in the story of the vulgar Mouse.

When the Sooth-sayers were about their divinations, *Pliny* writeth, that if they heard the squeaking of the Sorex, they brake off, and gave over their labour, holding it unprofitable to go any further therein: and it is also reported, that the voyce of this Mouse gave occasion to *Fabius Maximus*, to give over his Dictatorship, and unto *Caius Flaminius*, to give over the Mastership of the Horse-men, such fear of silly Beasts, was begotten in the mindes of gallant and magnanimous spirits, by the unprofitable and foolish behaviour and doctrines of the Magitians.

It is said by *Nigidius*, that these Sorices do sleep all the Winter and hide themselves like the Dor-mouse. They also when they eat any corn, do screetch and make a greater noise then other Mice, whereby they bewray themselves in the dark unto their enemies, and are killed, which was the occasion of that proverbial speech of *Parmeno* in Terence, *Egomet meo indicio miser, quasi Sorex perii.* Saint *Austine*, and Saint *Origen*, do also make use of this proverb, the one in his Book of Order, the other in a Homily upon Genesis, which caused *Erasmus* to write in this manner, *Sed videbor ipse meis indiciis captus*, that is, I have overthrown my self with my own tale. These Sorices do make hollow the trees wherein Emets or Ants breed, and there is perpetual hatred betwixt the Bittors, and these, one lying in wait to destroy the others young.

The Medicines of the Sorex.

Serenus and *Pliny* say, that if a woman with childe do eat the sinews of a Sorex, if her eyes be black, so shall the Infants be likewise;

Si prægnans artus captivi Soricis edit,
Dicuntur fœtus nigrantia lumina fingi.

The fat of these Beasts or of Dormice, is very profitable against the Palsie. The powder of the heads and tails anointed with Hony upon the eyes, restoreth the clearness of sight, and with Hony Attick, the powder and fat of a Sorex burned, helpeth running eyes; and the same powder mingled with Oyl, cureth bunches in the flesh.

There is another Mouse called by *Mathæolus, Mus Napelli*, that is, a Wolf-bane-mouse: so called, because it feedeth upon the roots of that Herb; although there be some of opinion, that it is not a creature, but another little Herb growing near unto it for a counter-poyson.

And *Marcellus* also maketh mention of *Napellus*, and *Antinapellus*, whereunto I should easily condescend, but that the eyesight of *Mathæolus* leadeth me to the contrary. For he writeth that he took one of them in the top of a high Mountain in *Italy*. And *Sylvaticus* calleth this Mouse *Mus Suring*, or *Sucsinus*, and calleth it a Counter-poyson to Wolf-bane, and that God might shew thus much unto men, he causeth it to live upon the roots, in testimony of his natural vertue destroying poyson and venemous herbs.

THE INDIAN MOUSE, AND DIVERS OTHER KINDES OF MICE, ACCORDING TO THEIR COUNTRIES.

I do finde that divers times Mice do take their names from Regions wherein they inhabite, which happeneth two manner of ways: one, because the form of their bodies will somewhat vary: the other, because not only in shape, but also in wit they have some things in them common to Mice, over and above the Mice of our Countries; therefore we will briefly comprehend all their surnames of whatsoever regions they are in one order or Alphabet. In the Oriental parts of the world, there are great Mice, (as *Alexander* writeth) of the quantity of Foxes who do harm both men and Beasts, and although they cannot by their biting kill any man, yet do they much grieve and molest them.

Americus Vespucius writeth, that he found in an Island of the Sea being distant from *Ulisbona* a thousand leagues, very great Mice. The hair of the *Egyptian* Mice is very hard, and for the most part like a Hedge-hogs: and there are also some which walk bolt upright upon two feet, for they have the hinder-legs longer, and their fore-legs shorter, their procreation is also manifold; and they do likewise sit upon their buttocks, and they use their fore-feet as hands. But *Herodotus* affirmeth these Mice to be of *Africk*, and not of *Egypt*; amongst the *African* or *Carthaginian* pastures (saith he) in *Africk* towards the Orient, there are three kindes of Mice, of the which some are called *Bipedal* or two-footed, some in the *Carthaginian* language *Zetzeries*, which is as much in our language as hills, some Hedge-hogs.

There are more kindes of Mice in the *Cyrenaican* region: some which have broad fore-heads, some sharp, some which have pricking hair in the manner of Hedge-hogs. It is reported that in *Cyrene* there are divers kindes of Mice both in colour and shape, and that some of them have as broad a countenance as a Cat; some have sharp bristles, and bear the form and countenance of a Viper, which the Inhabitants call *Echenetæ*, but improperly, as it appeareth by the words of *Aristotle* in his book of Wonders.

Herodotus also affirmeth the like of those Mice, to be in shape and colour like Vipers: but *Pliny* and *Aristotle* do both disallow it, and say that in those juice there is nothing common to Vipers, but only to Hedge hogs, as concerning their sharp bristles.

There are also some Mice in *Egypt*, which do violently rush upon pastures and corn: of which things *Ælianus* speaketh, saying in this manner; When it beginneth first to rain in *Egypt*, the Mice are wont to be born in very small bubbles, which wandering far and near through all the fields, do affect the corn with great calamity, by gnawing and cutting asunder with their teeth the blades thereof, and wasting the heaps of that which is made in bundles, do bring great pains and business unto the *Egyptians*: by which it comes to pass, that they endure all manner of ways to make snares for them, by setting of Mice-traps, and to repel them from their inclosures, and by ditches, and burning fires to drive them quite away: but the Mice as they will not come unto the traps, for as much as they are apt to leap, they both go over the hedges, and leap over the ditches. But the *Egyptians* being frustrated of all hope by their labours, all subtil inventions and policies, being left as it were of no efficacy, they betake themselves humbly to pray to their Gods to remove that calamity from them. Whereat the Mice by some fear of a divine anger, even as it were in battel aray of observing a squadron order, do depart into a certain Mountain: The least of all these in age do stand in the first order, but the greatest and eldest do lead the last troups, compelling those which are weary to follow them.

But if in their journey the least or youngest do chance through travail to wax weary, all those which follow (as the manner is in Wars) do likewise stand still, and when the first begin to go forward, the rest do continually follow them. It is also reported, that the Mice which inhabit the Sea, do observe the same order and custom.

The *African* Mice do usually die as soon as ever they take any drink: but this is commonly proper unto all Mice, (as *Ephesius* affirmeth) where it is written above concerning the poysoning of Mice. Mice, (but especially those of *Africk*) having their skins pulled off, boiled with Oyl and Salt, and then taken in meat, doth very effectually cure those which are troubled with any pains or diseases in the lungs or lights. The same doth also easily help those which are molested with corrupt and bloudy spettings with retchings.

The kindes of *African* Mice are divers; some are two footed; some have hair like unto Hedge-hogs; some faces of the breadth of a Weesil: but some call these Mice *Cirenacian*; some *Egyptian*, as I have before declared. In *Arabia* there are certain Mice much bigger then Dormice, whose former legs are of the quantity of a hand breadth, and the hinder of the quantity of the joynt to the end of the finger: I do understand them to be so short, that nothing thereof may seem to appear without the body, except the space of the joints of the finger, as it is in Martinets.

It is said, that the garments of the *Armenians* are usually woven with Mice which are bred in the same Countrey, or diversly docked with the shape of the same creature. The Author writeth, that *Pliny* maketh mention of the *Armenian* Mouse, but I have read no such thing: therefore he doth perchance take the *Armenian* Mouse for the Shrew. In *Cappadocia* there is a kinde of Mouse which some call a Squirrel. *Ælianus* writing of the *Caspian* Mice; *Amyntas* (saith he) in his Book entituled *De*

Mansionibus, which he doth so inscribe, saith that in *Caspia*, there do come an infinite multitude of Mice, which without any fear do swim in the flouds, which have great and violent currents, and holding one another by their tails in their mouths, (as it is likewise reported of Wolves) have a sure and stable passage over the water.

But when they pass over any tillage of the earth they fell the corn, and climing up into trees, do eat the fruit thereof, and break the boughs: which when the *Caspians* cannot resist, they do by this means endevour to restrain their turbulent incursions; for they remove all things which may hurt birds having crooked talons, who come presently so flying in such great flocks, or companies, that may seem to be clouds to expel the Mice from their borders, and by a proper gift incident unto them by nature, do drive away hunger from the *Caspians*. Neither in quantity are these Mice inferiour to the *Egyptian* Ichneumons: they are also ungentle, and they do no less devour with the strength of their teeth, then the Mice of *Teredon* in *Babylon* do Iron, whose soft skins the Merchants carry to the *Persians*. The *Indian* Mouse, or *Pharaohs* Mouse (as some learned later Writers do write) is no other then the Ichneumon. *Antonius musa Brasavolus*, took the before expressed figure of an *Indian* Mouse, (for so he did call it) which before that time was shewn by *Bellonius*, and I guessed it to be an Ichneumon; and truly in the snowt (if you take away the beard) and in the ears it doth agree, but in the tail it doth differ, which doth rather resemble a Cats: and in many other things, which by conferring them are easie to be marked, and as I conceived it, I have set it down.